History of Civilization

The History and Literature of Christianity from Tertullian to Boethius

The History of Civilization

In the Section of this Series devoted to PRE-HISTORY AND ANTIQUITY *are included the following volumes:—*

I. Introduction and Pre-History

II. The Early Empires

In the Section of this Series devoted to CHRISTIANITY AND THE MIDDLE AGES *are included the following volumes:—*

I. The Origins of Christianity

* An asterisk indicates that the volume does not form part of the French collection "L'Evolution de l'Humanité".

A full list of the SERIES *will be found at the end of this volume.*

History and Literature of Christianity

from

Tertullian to Boethius

By

PIERRE DE LABRIOLLE

Professor at the *Faculté des Lettres*, Poitiers

Translated from the French by
HERBERT WILSON

With Introductory Foreword by
HIS EMINENCE CARDINAL GASQUET

COUNTY COUNCIL OF DURHAM
COUNTY LIBRARY

LONDON
KEGAN PAUL, TRENCH, TRUBNER & CO., LTD.
NEW YORK: ALFRED A. KNOPF
1924

UNIVERSITY LIBRARY
OC 5 1951
NOTTINGHAM

27659

ACCESSIONS No. ....

CLASS No. 270.1

STAMPED ....

ACCESSIO ....

SHELF LIST ....

CATALOGUED ....

PRINTED IN GREAT BRITAIN

FOREWORD

I have been asked to write a brief *Foreword* to this excellent translation of this important and scholarly work, the *Histoire de la Littérature Latine Chrétienne*. I gladly accepted the task, if only to testify my personal appreciation of the volume and to record my thanks to the author, M. Pierre de Labriolle, for having given us a work that has long been wanted by scholars and students of Latin literature.

M. de Labriolle is well-known from his numerous essays upon special points and persons connected with this subject. Here in England, it is to be feared, the study of the influence of Early Christian literature upon European thought and culture has been much neglected, and it would hardly be an exaggeration to suggest that many who have been educated upon the works of the Pagan classical authors would hardly know the names, and still less the works, of the great Christian writers of the early centuries. In France and in Germany the importance of this side of general literature is being more and more recognized, and its influence is clearly seen in the literary output of the last century. In France, for instance, Chateaubriand was deeply read in the Early Christian Latin literature. This is evidenced in his *Les Martyrs* and others of his works. So, too, to name only one other case: M. Gaston Boissier has given us many charming studies of Christian Latin authors in his always suggestive *Fin du Paganisme*.

At the present time in England there is, I believe, a distinct tendency to recognize the importance of the study of the Latin writers of the Early Christian ages. The late Dr Mayor of Cambridge lectured on Tertullian, and made a profound study of the text of the *Apologeticum*, and his notes were published with an introduction and translation by Professor Souter at the Cambridge University Press in 1917. In this the eminent scholar Dr Souter fully recognizes the importance of Early Christian literature. It is well to note here that in the very useful Tables printed at the end of M. de Labriolle's volume full justice is not done to the many excellent studies and translations of the Christian classics which have been made by English scholars. To judge from these tables only, a reader would suppose that very little indeed had been done by English scholars in this field of work. There are very many such studies and translations in existence. For example, to name but a few: We have the *Ante-Nicene Christian Library* (published by T. & T. Clark), the *Library of the Fathers of the Holy Church* (Newman and other scholars), *A Select Library of Nicene and Post-Nicene Fathers* (Wace and Schaff), various translations among the S.P.C.K.'s publications, etc. This is not said by way of criticism or to detract in any way from the great value of this work of our author, but to assist any student who may desire to profit by this volume and, taking up the study of the

Christian classics, would wish to know what English editions to consult.

M. de Labriolle's volume begins with a long Introduction of some thirty pages, in which, having pointed out the relatively recent interest taken by scholars in the study of Early Christian Latin writers, he examines the attitude of Christianity, both theoretically and practically, towards the old Pagan models, and the influence of these upon the formation of the literature of the Christian ages. The Introduction should be read in its entirety; it will repay a careful study. It concludes by introducing the reader to the chief collections of Latin texts contained in the *Patrologia Latina* of Migne and the Vienna *Corpus* still in progress.

The volume itself, after this Introduction, is divided into five books, which contain notices of the chief Christian writers from the beginning till what is known as the "Middle Ages," that is, from the great Tertullian at the end of the first century of the Christian era to St Isidore of Seville at the close of the sixth. The books are divided into Chapters, prefaced by bibliographical notices and enriched by notes of anything which could serve to inform the reader on the subject-matter treated of. The lives of the various writers are brief, but are complete, and contain the important historical settings which gave occasion to the writing of the various pieces. Only an examination of the volume itself can give an adequate idea of the rich material which the author has gathered together and here offers to the student of Christian literature.

No better idea can be given of the scope and purpose of this work than a quotation from the passage

with which M. de Labriolle concludes the volume.
He writes:

"After Boethius, Cassiodorus, and Isidore of Seville,
the frame-work of the intellectual life of the Middle
Ages was established for a long time. A natural line
of demarcation at this point closes the history of Latin
Christian literature.

"I believe I have not over-estimated its merits. I
have not concealed the fact that really finished literary
authors are rare. . . . But let us guard ourselves against
a certain rather rigid type of 'humanism,' which would
only judge the Christian writings from the point of
view of the classic ideal. . . . Whatever be its defects,
this vivid Latin Christian literature deserves to be
more carefully studied than appears to be generally the
case, and whoever is interested in the history of ideals
will not regret having made the effort. There are
numerous historical and literary problems which can
only be grasped fully after we have seen their factors
coming to light during the period we have just
traversed [in this volume]. And, again, how many
strong personalities are revealed, how many magnificent
minds and pathetic souls anxious for the destiny of
mankind, each one preserving, in spite of the community of their faith and the identity of its theoretic
solutions, their original action upon this eternal enigma!
On the day when our Higher Course of Studies shall
have taken a more generous interest in some of their
masterpieces, scholarly research will again turn in the
direction of patristic study."

With these words of M. de Labriolle we may
well leave the volume to speak for itself, in the con-

fidence that in this English version it will find many readers, who will be grateful to the author and his very competent translator for having given them so valuable a help to the study of the Christian classics.

AIDAN CARD. GASQUET.

July 21st, 1924.

b

AUTHOR'S PREFACE

THIS History of Latin Christian Literature is the outcome of over twelve years spent as Professor at the University of Fribourg-en-Suisse. Thanks to the entire liberty allowed to me in the arrangement of the course of studies I was able to combine with my lectures on classic Latin literature a profound study of the Christian authors and thereby to follow the destinies of the Old Learning through their vicissitudes up to the threshold of the Middle Ages.

We do not possess in France any similar work. *L'Histoire Générale de la Littérature du Moyen Age en Occident* (Paris ; E. Leroux), the French translation from Ad. Ebert, was made as long ago as 1883, and is only of value for its sufficiently conscientious analyses. Bardenhewer's *Patrology*, translated in 1905 (Paris ; Bloud, 2nd ed.) is little more than a bibliographical repertory. The recent contribution by M. Tixeront (Paris ; Gabalda) is an elementary *précis* in which Latin literature only obtains its bare share. It seemed to me that I might be performing a useful service in providing for the first time an ample survey wherein I might endeavour to bring again to life the leading figures in Western Christianity, and to define the present stage of matters still in dispute.

I trust I have not been too prodigal of information that might be easily obtained. Those desirous only of a general view can pass over the technical remarks and the notes. The latter, together with the Tables which I have grouped at the end of the volume, will assist the serious reader to find his way rapidly over the expanse of this vast Christian literature, still inadequately explored, wherein so many problems solicit his studious inquiry. I have pointed out numerous questions still to be studied; any manual giving the impression that our knowledge is complete would be wanting in scientific value.

P. de L.

BIOGRAPHICAL NOTE BY THE TRANSLATOR

PROFESSOR PIERRE DE LABRIOLLE, the distinguished Author of this painstaking, eloquent and authoritative work, has made the study of classic literature and of patristic Christian literature the solid foundation for the high esteem in which he is held among French *savants*. As he states in his preface, it is the fruit of nearly thirteen years spent as Professor of Classic Latin Literature at the University of Fribourg - en - Suisse, during which period he was able to make a profound study of the early Latin Christian authors.

Born at Asnières, near Paris, on the 18th June 1874, he became *Agrégé de Lettres* in 1895, and was chosen to be Professor of the *Faculté des Arts* in the University of Montreal, where he remained from 1898 to 1901. He was afterwards Head Professor at the Collège Stanislas (1901-3), and at the Lycée at Rennes (1903-4). From 1904 to 1918 he was Professor of Latin Literature of the *Faculté de Philosophie* at the University of Fribourg-en-Suisse, and at present fills the chair of Latin Literature and Roman Institutions at the *Faculté des Lettres* at the University of Poitiers. He attained the distinction of *Docteur es-Lettres* in January 1914, and in February 1923 was awarded very honourable mention as *Associé Correspondant de la Société des Antiquaires de France*.

During the War he was mobilised at Belfort on the 2nd August 1914, and in 1917 at the request of the French Ambassador at Berne was chosen to direct the course of studies for the students interned at Fribourg.

Professor Pierre de Labriolle is at present engaged on a French Translation of the Confessions of St Augustine, with critical text, for the *Collection des Universités de France* under the auspices of the *Société des Belles Lettres*, who are performing a most scholarly and admirable service by their series of critical editions and translations into French of the leading examples of classic Greek and Latin Literature. From the wide learning and sympathetic appreciation of the life and writings of St Augustine, shown in the following pages, further understanding and enlightenment on the mind of that great Doctor of the Church may be confidently expected.

Amongst his other works may be mentioned *Vincent of Lérins;* the *De Paenitentia*, the *De Pudicitia* and the *De Praescriptione Hereticorum* of Tertullian ; *La Vie de Paul de Thèbes et la Vie d'Hilarion, par Saint Ambroise ; Saint Ambroise ; La Correspondance d'Ausone et de Paulin de Nole ; La Crise Montaniste,* which was crowned by the *Académie des Inscriptions et Belles Lettres; Les Sources de l'Histoire du Montanisme,* crowned by the French Academy, and the *Satires of Juvenal*, in collaboration with M. Villeneuve.

HERBERT WILSON.

May 1924.

TABLE OF CONTENTS

INTRODUCTION.

LATIN CHRISTIAN LITERATURE AND THE OLD LEARNING.

BOOK I.

THE SOURCES OF ORIGIN.

CHAPTER I. THE FIRST LATIN VERSIONS OF THE BIBLE.

CONTENTS

BOOK III.

THE GOLDEN AGE OF LATIN CHRISTIAN LITERATURE.

CHAPTER I. THE MORROW OF THE VICTORY.

CHAPTER II. ST AMBROSE, BISHOP AND DIPLOMAT.

CHAPTER III. THE THEOLOGIANS OF THE SECOND ORDER.

CONTENTS

BOOK IV.

THE BREAK UP OF THE EMPIRE.

CONTENTS

EXPLANATION OF THE SIGNS[1]

A.B. = *Analecta Bollandiana*, Brussels, 1882 et s.

** A.C.L. = A. HARNACK : *Geschichte der altchristlichen Literatur*, I. *Die Ueberlieferung und der Bestand*, Leipzig, 1893.

** A.K.L. = O. BARDENHEWER, *Geschichte der altkirchlichen Literatur*, Freiburg i. B., Vol. I (1913) ; Vol. II (1912) ; Vol. III (1914).

A.L. = *Anthologia latina*, sive poesis latinæ supplementum ediderunt Fr. BUECHELER et ALEX. RIESE, 2 parts 4 fasc. Leipzig, 1894-1906— *Anthologia latinæ supplementa*. Vol. I (1895), IHM's Edition.

A.L.L. = *Archiv für lateinische Lexicographie und Grammatik*, Leipzig, 1884 et s.

A.M. = *Anecdota Maredsolana*, Maredsous (Belgium).

A.S.C. = *Analecta sacra et classica*, ed. by dom PITRA, Paris, 1888.

B.A.L.A.C. = *Bulletin d'ancienne Littérature et d'Archéologie chrétiennes*, edited by P. DE LABRIOLLE, Paris, 1911 et s.

B.A.P. = *Briefe, Abhandlungen und Predigten aus den zwei letzten Iahrhunderten des kirchlichen Altertums und dem Anfang des Mittelalters*, hsg. von C. P. CASPARI, Christiania, 1890.

** *Bibliotheca scriptorum classicorum et græcorum et latinorum*, hsg. von Rudolf Klussmann. Zweiter Band, *Scriptores latini*. Erster Theil, Leipzig, 1912 ; zweiter Theil, 1913. (Supplementband au *Jahresbericht über die Forschritte der Klass. Altertumswissenschaft*).

B.K. = *Bibliothek der Kirchenväter*, eine Auswahl patristicher Werke in deutscher Uebersetzung hsg. von O. BARDENHEWER, TH. SCHERMANN und K. WEYMAN, Kempten et München, 1912 et s.

B.L.E. = *Bulletin de littérature ecclésiastique*, Toulouse.

B.ph.W. = *Berliner philologische Wochenschrift*, Leipzig, 1881 et s.

B.P.M. = *Beiträge zur Geschichte der Philosophie des Mittelalters*, Münster, 1891 et s.

* B.T. = *Bibliotheca Teubneriana*, Leipzig.

* C.B. = *Corpus* de Berlin : *die Griechischen christlichen Schriftsteller der ersten drei Jahrhunderte, hsg. von den Kirchenväter - Kommission der Kön. preussischen Ak. der Wiss.*, Leipzig, 1897 et s.

** Chron. = A. HARNACK, *Geschichte der altchristlichen Literatur, die Chronologie*, Vol. I (1897), Vol. II (1904).

[1] The most important collections and works are marked with one asterisk. Two asterisks give the best informed Bibliographies.

C.I.L. = *Corpus inscriptionum latinarum.*

* C.P.T. = *Cambridge Patristic Texts,* Cambridge, 1899 et s.

* C.V. = *Corpus Scriptorum ecclesiasticorum latinorum,* editum consilio et impensis Academiae Litterarum Cæsareæ Vindobonensis, Vienna, 1866 et s.

C.V.S. = MAI, *Scriptorum veterum nova Collectio,* Rome, 1825-1838, 10 vol.

* D.C.B. = *A Dictionary of Christian Biography,* ed. by W. SMITH and H. WACE, London, Vol. I (1877), Vol. II (1880), Vol. III (1882), Vol. IV (1887).

DUCHESNE = *Histoire ancienne de l'Église,* LOUIS DUCHESNE, Paris, 1906-1910, 3 vol.

* F.P. = *Florilegium patristicum,* digessit, vertit, adnotavit, G. RAUSCHEN, Bonn, 1904 et s.

G.L. = *Grammatici latini,* H. KEIL's Ed. Leipzig, 1857-1879.

* H.L. = *Textes et documents pour l'étude historique du Christianisme,* published under the direction of H. HEMMER and PAUL LEJAY, Paris, 1904 et s.

HURTER = *SS. Patrum opuscula selecta,* Hurter's Ed. Œnip., 1868-1885, 48 vol.

JORDAN = HERM. JORDAN, *Geschichte der altchristlichen Literatur,* Leipzig, 1911.

J.T.S. = *Journal of Theological Studies,* Oxford.

K.A. = CARL PAUL CASPARI, *Kirchenhistorische Anecdota,* Christiania, 1883.

K.T. = *Kleine Texte für theologische Vorlesungen und Uebungen,* hsg. H. LIETZMANN, Bonn, 1902 et s.

* MANITIUS = *Gesch. der lateinschen Literatur des Mittelalters,* by MAX MANITIUS, Münich, 1911, in I. VON MÜLLER's *Handbuch.*

MANSI = *Sanctorum conciliorum amplissima collectio,* re-edited by WELTER, Paris, 1901 et s.

* M.G.H. = *Monumenta Germaniae historica. Auctores antiquissimi,* Berlin, 1877-1898, 13 vol.

* MONCEAUX = PAUL MONCEAUX. *Histoire littéraire de l'Afrique chrétienne depuis les origines jusqu'à l'invasion arabe.* Paris, 4 vol. 1901 et s.

N.P.B. = A. MAI, *Nova Patrum Bibliotheca,* 2 vol. Rome, 1852-1854.

** p = BARDENHEWER (O), *Patrologie,* 3rd ed., Freiburg i. B., 1910.

P.C. = Collection *la Pensée chrétienne,* Paris, Bloud et Cie.

* P.G. = *Patrologie grecque,* by J. P. MIGNE.

* P.L. = *Patrologie latine,* by J. P. MIGNE.

P.L.M. = *Poetae latini minores* recensuit et emendavit ÆMILIUS BAEHRENS. Leipzig, 1879-1886 (Bibl. Teubner), 6 vol.—Vol. VI is entitled *Fragmenta poetarum romanorum.*—The collection is continued under the same title by FR. VOLLMER, 1910 et s.

** P.W. = PAULY-WISSOWA, *Real-Encyclopädie der class. Altertumswissenschaft,* neue Bearb., Stuttgart, 1893 et s.

R. Bén. = *Revue Bénédictine,* Maredsous (Belgium), 1884 et s.

R.C. = *Revue Critique,* Paris, 1866 et s.

** R.E. = *Realencyclopedie für protestantische Theologie und Kirche*, 3rd ed., Leipzig, 1896 et s.

R.E.A. = *Revue des Etudes Anciennes* (formerly *Annales de la Faculté des Lettres de Bordeaux*).

Rh.M. = *Rheinisches Museum*, Frankfort, 1827 et s.

R.H.L.R. = *Revue d'histoire et de littérature religieuses*, Paris, 1896 et s.

R.L.M. = HALM, *Rhetores latini minores*, Leipzig, 1863.

R.Q.H. = *Revue des Questions historiques*, Paris, 1866 et s.

R.S. = M. J. ROUTH, *Reliquiae Sacrae*, 2nd ed. Oxford, 1846-1848, 5 vol.

R.S.R. = *Recherches de Science religieuse*, Paris, 1909 et s.

S.B.B. = *Sitzungsberichte der Kgl. preuss. Akad. der Wiss. zu Berlin.*

S.B.M. = *Sitzungsberichte der Kön Bayerischen Akademie der Wissenschaften zu München*. Philos.-phil.-histor. Klasse.

S.B.W. = *Sitzungsberichte der Kais. Akademie der Wissenschaften*, Wien. Philos.-histor. Klasse.

** SCHANZ = SCHANZ (M.), *Geschichte der römischen Litteratur*, in I. VON MÜLLER's *Handbuch*, Vol. III (1905); Vol. IV (1914).

S.Q. = *Sammlung ausgewählter Kirchen-und dogmengeschichtlicher Quellenschriften*, hsg. by KRÜGER, Freiburg i. B., 1891-1896. Second series, 1901 et s.

S.S. = *Spicilegium Solesmense*, ed. by DOM J. B. PITRA, Paris, 1852-1856, 4 vol.

** TEUFFEL = *Geschichte der röm Litteratur*, 6th ed., revised by KROLL et SKUTSCH, Vol. III (1913), Leipzig.

* TILLEMONT = L. S. LE NAIN DE TILLEMONT, *Mémoires pour servir à l'histoire ecclésiastique des six premiers siècles*, Paris, 1693-1712, 16 vol.

T.L.Z. = *Theologische Literaturzeitung*, Leipzig, 1876 et s.

T.Q. = *Theologische Quartalschrift*, Tübingen, 1819 et s.

* T.S. = *Texts and Studies*, Contributions to Biblical and Patristic Literature, ed. by J. ARMITAGE ROBINSON, Cambridge, 1891 et s.

* T.U. = *Texte und Untersuchungen zur Geschichte der altchristlichen Literatur*, hsg. by O. v. GEBHARDT and A. HARNACK, Leipzig, 1882-1897, 15 vol. New series, 1897-1906, 15 vol. Third series, hsg. by A. HARNACK and C. SCHMIDT, 1907 et s.

V.M. = *Veröffentlichungen aus dem Kirchenhistor. Seminar München*, 1899 et s. (three series).

Z.K.T. = *Zeitschrift für Katholische Theologie*, Innsbrück.

Z.N.W. = *Zeitschrift für die neutestamentliche Wissenschaft*, Giessen, 1900 et s.

ABBREVIATIONS OF NAMES OF PLACES

B. = Berlin
Br. = Brussels
C. = Cambridge
L. = Leipsig
Lo. = London
O. = Oxford
P. = Paris

INTRODUCTION

LATIN CHRISTIAN LITERATURE AND THE OLD LEARNING

SUMMARY

I. Latin Christian Literature and Modern Criticism.—II. The Æsthetic interest which this literature offers.—III. The intellectual formation of the Christian writers.—IV. The added Dignity received from them by Roman literature.—V. The Old Learning and Christianity : the Nature of the Problem stated. The dream of St Jerome.—VI. Christian hostility to this learning—VII. The compromises necessitated.—VIII. The middle course which finally ensued.—IX. The handing on of the old literary culture by Christianity.—X. To what extent profane learning has penetrated Christian thought.—XI. Bibliographical notes. Migne's *Patrology.* The *Corpus Scriptorum Ecclesiasticorum Latinorum.*

I

IF we compare the histories and manuals concerned with Latin literature which have appeared during these last years with those which formerly were most in favour, we notice the increasingly important place occupied by Latin Christian Literature.

In the classic works of Pierron (1852), of Paul Albert (1871), and of Talbot (1883), this literature is not touched upon (with the exception of one short page devoted to the Christian hymns by Talbot). Out of 544 pages, Nageotte (1885) gives 32 to the Christian authors, but his appreciations are weak and inconspicuous. With the appearance of the short *Histoire de la Littérature latine* by Jeanroy and Puech (1891) some little progress can be seen, thanks to the personal ability of M. Puech, whose labours on Prudentius (1887) had made him familiar with a category of writers who had been systematically held in oblivion. It reached a decisive point in the hands of M. René Pichon, who out of 935 pages devoted 155 to strictly Christian literature—nearly a sixth of the total work—in the

1

A

first edition of his manual which is to-day so widely known :
" It is as living, as interesting, as profane literature," affirms
M. Pichon : " It is also almost Roman and much more
modern."

In Germany, since 1837, Baehr has added an appendix on
Latin Christian Literature to his *Histoire de la Littérature
latine.* However, Munk (*Geschichte der röm. Lit. für Gymnasien,*
Berlin, 1858–1861 ; review by Seyffert, 1875–1877) has only
a few words to say on the Christian authors. The same may
be said of Rudolf Nicolai (*Gesch. der röm. Lit.,* Magdebourg,
1881–1882). And it was only grudgingly and from time to
time that the *Jahresbericht* of Bursian and Muller condescended
to grant a short notice to detailed works relating to the period
following after the Antonines. Nevertheless, Teuffel had given
it a place in his system (1st ed. 1870). But so long-lived was
the prejudice that when Martin Schanz, who had been commissioned to write the History of Roman literature in Ivan
von Muller's *Handbuch,* thought it necessary to analyse at
some length the contents of the ecclesiastical works of the
first century, he drew down on himself lively criticism for
having encroached upon a domain reserved, as they said,
to other distinguishing features.[1]

From a historical point of view, this incurious spirit explains
itself fairly reasonably. From the time of the Renaissance,
a large number of humanists, altogether taken up with Cicero,
Horace and Virgil, made open profession of extending to the
early Christian writings and to the Latin Bible itself their
contempt for " scholastic " and " monastic " Latin.[2] With
the divine charm of the classic masterpieces they contrasted
its rustic and unadorned style. It was an easy matter for
them to take advantage of certain declared views, more or less
sincere, on the part of the Christian authors. Although
initiated, and for the most part on close terms with profane
learning, these Christian authors affected to hold them cheaply
and to contrast with their childish prodigality the noble
simplicity of the Scriptures. All that they were concerned
with was to take off the edge of the criticisms with which the
pagans loaded the language of the Holy Books from the

---

[1] Cf. Aly, in Bursian's *Jahresbericht,* t. XCVIII (1898), pp. 8–9.
[2] The humanist, Pietro Bembo, disdainfully applied the term *epistolaccie* to the
Epistles of St Paul.

literary point of view; and they thought they could do no better than to disqualify any principle pertaining to the art of style, try how they might to conform to it. They were taken at their word. And thus the text in which they wrote appeared to possess no more importance than so many documents on dogma, the liturgy, ecclesiastical history, etc. The philologists abandoned them to the theologians with a disdain in which prudence also found a place : for to touch upon them conduced to perilous disputes in which it was better worth their while not to get out of their depth. The transformation of the Latin tongue, brought about under the influence of Christianity, was considered in the light of a lamentable decadence. And right up to our times we have seen critics speaking with despair and disgust at the decline of Latin in Christian lands !

We are getting the better of an ostracism so wanting in intelligence, which explains but does not at all excuse the remarkable ignorance of the period condemned wholesale by these fastidious individuals. During the last fifty years philology has begun to turn its attention towards the Christian epoch. Undertakings such as the *Corpus Scriptorum Ecclesiasticorum Latinorum*, the programme of which was drawn up in 1864,[1] have greatly contributed to bring the philologists and theologians closer together; and little by little the philologists have recognised the impossibility of forming a correct idea of the development of Latin literature if the Christian writings are excluded therefrom *a priori*.[2]

Upon this increasing attention which so many sound minds are giving to Latin Christian Literature, it will not be without purpose to bestow a brief justification, not for the pleasure of branching out into ambitious generalities, but in order to make some fundamental observations, which, once established, will serve in some sort as a substructure to our special studies.

---

[1] Cf. S.B.W., 1864, p. 385, et s.

[2] Max Bonnet, *La Philologie Classique*, Paris, 1892, pp. 172–174 ; Paul Lejay, R.H.L.R., 1900, p. 174 (" La science de l'antiquité n'est complète qu'à condition d'y faire entrer les monuments du Christianisme ") ; Heinze, *Die gegenwärtigen Aufgaben der röm. Literaturgeschichte*, in the Neue Jahrb. f.d. kl. Alt., 1907, p. 162. For Greek Christian literature, see A. Puech's interesting observations in *Atti del Congresso internazionale delle science storiche*, vol. II : *Atti della Sezione I, Storia Antica e filologica classica*, 1905, pp. 205–212, " *L'ancienne littérature chrétienne et la philologie classique*."

II

At the outset, I will remark that for those who love to find
in the works they are studying the qualities of composition
and art which are characteristic of the classic writers, the
reading of the Christian authors—especially the Latin authors
—has some happy surprises in store. I repeat, especially the
Latin authors. As a matter of fact, if it were our task to
describe the development of Christian Greek literature, we
should first of all have to extend our examination over a series
of works, which are extremely interesting from the moral and
religious point of view, but very feeble from a proper æsthetic
standpoint. Letters, "revelations," simple and bare paraphrases from the Sacred Books—these are the channels
through which this literature took its rise. Read the Διδαχή,
the *Pastor* of Hermas, the *Epistles* ascribed to Barnabas or
Clement of Rome ; these are writings in quite popular language, for the purpose of calling to the minds of people of
manifestly very humble conditions and culture, whether
in a direct or allegorical form, the principles of fraternity
(ἀγαπή) and the subduing of evil instincts (ἐγκρατεία), which
they were too much given to forget. No literary care, no
anxiety for the arrangement of ideas and phrases, is there
betrayed.

It was only with prudence and circumspection that the
Church, little by little, assumed the forms of profane literature
in order to adapt them to her own ends. When the Canon of
the New Testament had been closed up and placed outside all
dispute, she recognised her right to draw upon them more
largely. In the case of the first Greek apologists, Tatian,
Athenagoras, Justin, etc., who addressed themselves to the
Emperors or to the great pagan public, in order to refute the
deadly accusations brought against them and to turn them
against their accusers, the tone becomes more personal, more
intense, the turn of phrase more polished, the arguments more
closely rendered and philosophic. Notwithstanding, the
diction is still incomplete, the composition flows haphazard :
" What they borrow from Greek tradition is the Greek mode of
thought," M. Maurice Croiset remarks,[1] " but they are as

---

[1] *Hist. de la Litt. grecque*, V, 326.

emancipated as may well be from a desire to satisfy the taste, or to charm or strike the imagination, without which there can be no literary creation properly so called." It was only gradually that the Greek Christian writers came to understand that to write well was not simple frivolity, and that the expression of ideas required that beauty of form which had for so long appeared to be an inconvenient and pretentious pursuit.

The Latin writers had been spared this long labour of accommodation, and that is explained at first by a chronological reason. The first Latin Christian works of which we shall have to speak are not of a date anterior to the end of the IInd century. Up to then, Greek was the language probably in use among the Christians of the West, especially in Rome. The only Christian writings in Latin were very literal, but very illiterate translations from the Greek Bible for the use of those of the faithful who had little acquaintance with Greek. Now towards the end of the IInd century, when Latin Christian Literature came to birth in Africa under the powerful impulse of Tertullian, a portion of the educated *élite* had been conquered. Some polished intellects, who had graduated under the best mental discipline, had given their adhesion to the new faith. These were destined to bring to it the powerful prestige of good diction in which they were past-masters and in which they would continue to excel, even while pluming themselves (doubtless in imitation of their Greek forerunners) in esteeming it as of slight value, and possibly experiencing some secret remorse at taking any further pleasure in it. Their skill in giving evidence of this facility will soon reveal itself to us in the *Apologeticum* of Tertullian and the *Octavius* of Minucius Felix. There is no dialogue of Cicero which surpasses in elegant grace the *Octavius*. Right from the dawn of its beginnings, Latin Christian Literature presents to us the same appearance as it will continue to present throughout its course, eager not only to spread abroad its ideas, but also to suggest them in polished language, and, after the simile of Lucretius, to spread honey on the brim of the cup in order to correct the sometimes bitter draught of truth :

Pocula circum
Contingunt mellis dulci flavoque liquore (IV, 13).

III

THERE has thus not been that divorce between Latin profane, and Christian, literature which for long separated Christian and pagan Hellenism. I will even go so far as to say that it is not possible for anyone to understand Tertullian, Cyprian, or Arnobius if he has not some little acquaintance with the purely secular literature of their time. They had been formed under the same system of education as all educated Romans under the Empire, and there is no need to suppose that when they embraced Christianity they had very profoundly altered their intellectual methods.

And what kind of education was this ? It is well to have a correct idea in order to understand the writers with whom the scholar's robe remained always so well marked a feature.

It was a hierarchy in two degrees : first in grammar, then in rhetoric. The grammarian took the child in hand when still very young, and his task consisted in teaching him to speak and write correctly either in Latin or Greek ; from this arose the study of grammar whether for the morphology or for the syntax. Then he read and commented upon the poets, Homer, Menander, Terence, Horace and Virgil, and it was only in connection with these explanations that he gave his pupils ideas in versification, philosophy, history, music, astronomy, etc. Education in general subjects was thus acquired by the accident of this literary exegesis, whether or not the texts paraphrased presented opportunity for it. Later on, the youth was entrusted to the rhetorician, whose principal ambition went no further than to make him able to speak correctly. He first of all rendered his faculties supple by written exercises, discourses, refutations, panegyrics and the development of matters of common knowledge. He then employed him on declamation proper, the pupil delivering a reasoning on some given subject, such as a case of conscience or a fictitious suit, etc.

This method was in conformity with the plan of studies which Quintilian had traced in his *Institutiones Oratoriae* which the Roman tutor continued faithfully to observe. For my part, I should not like to be too severe on it. If the prime virtue in a system of education is to interest the pupil, to shake him from his sluggishness, to force his imagination into a certain activity, it was not altogether bad.   It obliged the young man to pay in his own person, to draw from his mind, barren or fruitful as it might be, all that he could, under pain of remaining awkward and mute under the eyes of his comrades.   This presented a field for his emotions which he was not likely to forget, and success was as intoxicating as the humiliation was poignant.   St Jerome relates, when he was about sixty, that it happened to him to see himself in a dream once more before the rhetorician in the act of declaiming his *controversy*, and that he experienced a profound relief, on awaking, at feeling himself delivered of his anguish.[1]

But on the other hand, from a practical point of view, how empty, how puerile !   One cannot imagine a course of instruction less *positive* than that given by the rhetors.   Philosophy, history, law, all the sciences known at that time, had no further value in their eyes than in how far they enabled them to embellish fair phrases, impressive examples, arguments more or less juridical, and their eternal developments. Phrases, always phrases !   And if only they had drawn them from their own vat !   But the great thing was to ingeniously embody in them echoes of the classics, some hemistich from Virgil, some mocking satire from Horace, some sonorous grandeur from Cicero.   All this kind of thing lacked virility and seriousness.

Thus, if we encounter in the writings of certain ecclesiastical scribes some rather puerile reasoning, such as that in which Tertullian, under the pretext of proving that the regeneration of man by water is a matter neither ridiculous nor impossible, delivers a panegyric on water and its virtues ;[2] or again an excessive propensity to take up and develop as of common interrelation the ideas and arguments already used by their predecessors ; if our taste is sometimes shocked by a profusion of shrill tones, by figures of style twenty times repeated, and by a certain lack of proportion, tact, and discretion, it is to the rhetoric class that we must go for the cause. And if we remember that this influence is always present with them it will enable us to avoid some occasional misconstruction.   For instance, Villemain waxes very indignant over a passage in the famous letter of St Jerome to Heliodorus :

[1] *Contra Rufinum*, I, xxx.   [2] *De Baptismo*, III.

" If (in opposition to thy vocation) thy father were to lie
on the threshold of thy door to hold thee back, pass over the
body of thy father " (*Per calcatum perge patrem*).   " What
religious ferocity ! " cries Villemain.[1]   Pure rhetoric, will be
our reply.   We have only to go back to the *Controversiae* of
Seneca the rhetorician, to establish the fact that St Jerome
had in mind a trait of character much admired in this school of
thought.   A father was supposed to be desirous of keeping
back at all costs his son from going out to fight, and the
rhetorician Latro, puts into his mouth this final objurgation :
" If thou art determined to go, trample thy father's body
under thy feet." [2]   *Ut ad hostem pervenias, patrem calca*
(I. viii. 15).   Jerome had not forgotten this *sententia*—at an
unseasonable moment, we must believe, since he has given
scandal to posterity.

They preserved from their early training (which in the case
of many—St Cyprian, Arnobius, Lactantius, and even St
Augustine—had sunk into them long before from their profession as rhetoricians), a too self-satisfied virtuosity which
somewhat wearies the modern reader.   They also owed to it
their greater consideration for elegance of form and the
literary charm of their writings.

IV

BUT the real interest which they offer us does not reside
solely, nor even principally, in their technical ingenuity.
Before all else it rests on this, that by the very fact of their
being Christians, their works were nurtured on a more virile
and sterner substance and one which speaks rather to our souls.

In order to estimate what gain in depth and sincerity
Christianity brought to them, consider the most noteworthy
of their contemporaries on the pagan side.[3]   Frontonius, the
tutor of Marcus Aurelius, who passed his life in the pursuit of
elegant reasonings on futile subjects and in gathering the

---

[1] *Tableau de l'éloquence chrétienne au IV siècle*, p. 329.
[2] One will note that to contravene a father's wishes when they were in opposition
to a real vocation, is also one of the precepts of Epictetus.   Cf. Colardeau, *Étude sur
Epictète*, Paris, 1903, p. 93.
[3] Put on one side once for all the great jurisconsults.

flowers of rhetoric ; the foremost man of his time to extract from a paradox all the jests, and burlesque sequences gravely drawn out, which it was capable of producing ; who wrote a panegyric on smoke, on dust, on carelessness, and sends to his pupil rules of gender, and has the simplicity to feel disappointed when he perceived that Marcus Aurelius would have none of these impassioned exercises and, withdrawing from him more and more, was turning his mind to philosophy. Apuleius, a man of doubtless finer intelligence who penetrates us in quite another way, but in whose case (even in his most beautiful passages, even in the eleventh book of the *Metamorphoses*, wherein he has come in touch with mystic accents almost Christian in their bearing) we experience so much *dilettantism* and touching complaisance for his own special talent. Again, examine such learned writers as Aulus Gellius, and further on the inept compilers of the history of Augustus, the correct and ceremonious Symmachus, and the poet Claudian—in all these it is not art which is wanting, but depth. When they are no longer borne up by the facts which they are relating, they have nothing, or next to nothing, to say.

In face of this verbose sterility, we are able to better estimate the merit belonging to the Christian authors. They alone have some certain intention ; they alone have passion, an ideal. In the case of one of them, Tertullian, his great aim is to bring about the triumph, at all costs, of his conception of the faith and of life—a conception which is caustic, intemperate, violently hostile to nature, and drawing from his own paradoxes an indescribable, savage joy which incites him to go still further along a path deliberately narrow whither the Church is destined to refuse to follow him. In the case of St Cyprian, the organiser and administrator of genius, his efforts are directed to establishing so firmly the idea and *prestige* of the Church and of Episcopal authority that all the efforts of heretics should not be able to make a breach in the unbreakable solidarity of the faithful in union with their pastors. Lactantius is otherwise concerned ; his purpose was to win over the men of letters, stubbornly unconvinced as yet, whose intellectual contempt caused him so much suffering ; he inaugurated a method of apologetics which was more objective and more scientific, and, in full view of the doctrines of the philosophers, he arrayed a real *summa* of Christian doctrine. A few years later, St Jerome was to realise the type of *savant*, and of philologist, at once studious and impassioned. And we know further from what experiences, from what a mediocre and blemished life St Augustine drew forth his profound conception of human nature, of his own inner corruption, of that indispensable aid which must come to him from above.

What characterises the Christian writers, however vexatious their ready compliance with the tastes of their time, and however fatiguing we sometimes find the too unrelieved oratorical trend of their style, or the subtilties of their exegesis, is that literature was not for them solely a play of the mind, an agreeable diversion, or a means of doing the honours to their talent. They believed in what they said ; it was their soul which spoke ; all their moral being was engaged in their writings. I can hardly see in profane literature any single writer, who showed in his work any particle of this lively sense of conviction, save only Lucretius. But Lucretius is an altogether exceptional case. With the Romans, the art of writing always remained a little like what it had always been from quite the beginning—a simple relaxation from serious duties. They lent themselves to it for their pleasure without giving themselves up to it entirely.

With the Christian writers, on the contrary, it was a means of action, a lever to bring to bear on souls, to turn them away from error and to impel them to the truth. Their faith touched them in the bottom of their soul, and in their turn they were willing to acquiesce in the tastes of their readers just so far as that secret sanctuary where resolutions are born and acts take their rise.

We see what increase of dignity and interest Roman literature has received from their hands. From the end of the Ist century, it began to decline visibly : Greek was threatening to drive out Latin in the estimation and practice of lettered men. In order to bring it back to life, the proselytism of the new faith was required—the emotions, the mourning, the victories, which this faith aroused ; and thereby an influx of fresh ideas circulated anew under forms which were passing into decline, which by this means were rejuvenated and renewed once more.

V

THIS question of the literary quality of the Latin Christian works brings us to another which can be discussed here, once for all, with the amplitude which it deserves.   It concerns the relations existing between the classic learning and Christianity, looked at from the historical point of view.

St Jerome relates in one of his letters a curious episode of his youth.[1]   Having decided to embrace the ascetic life, he was bending his steps towards Jerusalem with the view of burying himself in the desert of Chalcis to the south-east of Antioch.   With his passion for study, he had brought with him his books, procured in Rome " at the cost of much trouble and labour," which under no pretext whatever could he do without.[2]   Here we must listen to him evolving in his own words the strange account which he related afterwards to one of the Roman patrician ladies to whom he had become the spiritual director :

" Miserable man that I am !   I was fasting and then I began to read Cicero ;   after many nights spent in watching, after many tears, which the remembrance of my faults of not so long ago drew forth from the depths of my heart, I took Plautus in my hands.   If by chance, on recollecting myself, I started reading the Prophets, their unadorned style awoke in me feelings of repulsion. My eyes, blinded, saw no longer the light, and it was not on my eyes that I laid the blame, it was on heaven.

" While the old serpent thus misused me, a violent fever penetrated the marrow of my worn-out body towards the middle of Lent, and, without any respite, in an incredible manner, it so consumed my poor members that I had scarcely any flesh left on my bones.   Already people were thinking of my funeral.   My body felt quite frozen ;   a remnant of vital heat no longer palpitated save in the lukewarmness of my poor breast.

" Suddenly, I felt myself ravished away in ecstasy and transported before the tribunal of the Judge.   Such a

---

[1] *Ep.* xxii, 30, to Eustochium (Hilberg, in C.V., lib. 189).
[2] . . . bibliotheca . . . carere non poteram.

dazzling light emanated from those present that, crouched on the ground, I dared not lift up my eyes. On being asked my profession, I replied, 'I am a Christian.' Whereupon, he who presided said, 'Thou dost lie; thou art a Ciceronian and no Christian; where thy treasure is, there is thy heart also.'

" I forthwith held my peace, and under the stripes (for he had commanded that they should beat me), I felt myself tortured still more by the burning of my conscience. . . . At last, those present, casting themselves on their knees before the President, implored him to pardon my youth and to grant to my fault the time for repentance and freedom to carry out at a future date the penalty if ever I again read profane literature. And I, who in a moment so critical was ready to promise even more, made this oath : ' Lord, if ever it happens to me to possess or to read profane books, I shall have denied Thee ! ' On this undertaking, I was dismissed and came up to the earth again. To the great astonishment of all, I opened my eyes suffused with tears, and my grief convinced the most incredulous.

" This was not a case of deep sleep, one of those unreal dreams of which we are often the dupes. I call to witness the tribunal before which I lay prostrate; I call to witness the awful sentence, the occasion of my terror ! May I never again be submitted to such an examination ! My shoulders were bruised; on awaking, I still felt the blows. From that moment, I betook myself to the reading of the divine books with as much passion as I had given to reading the books of men."

That there is in this famous " dream " of St Jerome, a large portion of fiction I have not much difficulty in admitting ; and by pressing home certain details,[1] as also certain half-admissions subsequently made by St Jerome,[2] one feels inclined to think so.[3]

[1] Cf. the observations of E. Ch. Babut, *St Martin de Tours*, Paris, Champion, s.d., p. 99, et. s. Nevertheless, I do not get the impression that St Jerome wished to make people believe in a real death followed by a resurrection, as Babut suspected.

[2] *Apol. c. Rufinum*, I, xxx (P.L., xxiii, 441).

[3] A critical study of the *Dream of St Jerome* by P. de Labriolle, will appear in the *Mélanges* which will shortly be published in Rome for the centenary of St Jerome.

But what is open to no doubt is that the scruple which he thus vividly portrayed was for him as for so many other lettered Christians of the first centuries, the cause of very real and very grievous anguish. In how far had a Christian, who was desirous of preserving in his intellectual and moral life an entirely logical attitude, the right to take pleasure in the reading of pagan books and in making of them his favourite mental diet ? Here is a problem the interest of which seems to us rather remote. However, it has excited, even in the modern world, burning controversies, at the time of the Renaissance,[1] in the XVIIth century,[2] above all in the XIXth century.[3] In its initial form, it implied consequences of great historical importance : for instance, the future of Greco-Latin learning, firstly in the bosom of Christianity itself, and then in European civilisation. At the given moment, the Church became practically the united mistress of this precious legacy. If she had rejected it decidedly, it would have been lost to us without hope of recall, and modern thought could not have rejuvenated and renewed itself from the sources of antiquity to the large extent which it has done.

VI

Let us try to begin by an effort of historical understanding to grasp the state of mind of the generations of Christians who lived in full and direct contact with the pagan world.

One must acknowledge that, in their case, there were not

1 Cf. for instance, the Lucula Noctis by Fra Giovanni Dominici, published in 1908 by Remi Coulon, Paris, Picard, from two MSS., one in the Laurentian Library at Florence, the other in the Royal Library, Berlin. The *Lucula* supplies most interesting information on the history of humanism in Florence at the beginning of the IVth century. For the middle ages, consult G. Robert in his *Les Ecoles et l'enseignement de la théologie pendant la première moitié du XII siècle*, Paris, Gabalda, 1909, pp. 76–92.

2 We should remember the debate between Mabillon and Le Bouthillier de Rancé. Cf. E. de Broglie, *Mabillon et la Soc. de l'Abbaye de Saint-Germain-des-Prés*, Paris, 1888, vol. II, pp. 97–196.

3 Cf. L'Abbé J. Gaume's truculent work, *Le ver rongeur des sociétés modernes ou le paganisme dans l'éducation*, Paris, 1851 ; and again Daniels, S.J., *Les études classiques de la société chrétienne*, Paris, 1853 ; Krabinger, *Die klass. Studien und ihre Gegner*, Munich, 1855. The Holy See has on several occasions uttered her opinion on the question (Encyl. of Pius IX, 21st March, 1853, to the Bishops of France ; Brief to Mgr. Gaume, 22nd April, 1874 ; Brief to Mgr. D'Avanzo, of the same date ; Letter of Leo XIII to Cardinal Parocchi, 20th May, 1885 ; to Mgr. Heylen, Bishop of Namur, 20th May, 1901).

wanting objects of scandal. At the circus, at the theatre, in the public exhibitions, in the institutions, in the daily scenes of their life, how many features recalled to them idolatry or breathed forth sensuality ! And these detested vices they found in nearly all the works in which were expressed the soul of antiquity. What crude coarseness in the tales of mythology, what obscenities in its symbols ! One could have no knowledge of even the prurient extracts from Greco-Latin literature over which the young men of the future toiled or slumbered, to deny that the sexual life, with its fires, its effeminacies, its enervating delicacies, sometimes even its most cynical perversities, held therein a considerable place. More than one amongst the educated Christians had learnt to beware of this profane fire from having in former days felt its scorch. Does not St Augustine go so far as to reproach himself in his *Confessions* [1] that he wept when still a child over the relatively extremely innocent pages wherein Virgil has recounted the sad love story of Dido ! We might say that in this emotional tenderness of his boyhood he proved thus early the even then somewhat morbid initial stages of that sensibility whereof in later life his whole ardent desire was summed up in these two words *amare et amari*.[2]

Yes, Christian asceticism, or in other terms the distrust felt by Christians in regard to pleasure, could not fail to be bruised in the most painful manner by the licence of the pictures or allusions with which a large number of Greek and Roman writers, devout admirers of nature only and impervious to even the notion of sin, amused themselves.[3]

[1] I, xiii.

[2] Cf. II, 11 : " Et quid erat, quod me delectabat, nisi amare et amari." Here are some modern evidences which corroborate in an interesting manner that of St Augustine. Chateaubriand relates in his *Mémoires d'Outre-Tombe* (vol. I, p. 92, ed. Biré) that as a child he owed to an unexpurgated Horace, to the IX Book of the Aeneid, to Tibullus and to Lucretius, his first revelations of the world of the senses, and of his own voluptuous and melancholy nature : " One day I translated from the open book *Æneadum genitrix, hominum divumque voluptas* from Lucretius with so much vivacity," he states, " that M. Egault (his Latin master at the College of Dol) took the poem away from me and thrust me among the Greek roots." And again, Jules Lemaitre, in his *Les Comtemporains*, vol. VI (1896), p. 38 : " . . . If I consult my own experience, I know very well what the classics of antiquity have insinuated and left in me, and that is in short, the taste for a kind of voluptuous naturalism, the principles of an epicureanism and of a stoicism, alike full of pride, and possibly the germs of some virtues, but virtues totally wanting in humility." Cf. Ad. Boschot, *Une vie romantique, Hector Berlioz*, Paris, 1919, p. 5.

[3] For the misunderstandings which sometimes arise in connection with the *pecces* of Horace, *Satires*, I, II, 63, cf. P. Lejay, *Œuvres d'Horace, Satires*, Paris, Hachette, 1911, p. 32.

The old philosophy aroused prejudices of another kind. It contained within itself a principle of intellectual independence, of unrestrained and ironic criticism, which spared neither the traditional pagan religion—in this regard the Christians had passed condemnation—nor even (and that conveyed something quite different) the idea of God, the idea of a Providence, the belief in posthumous rewards.[1] How could they maintain, in the face of such an audacious standard, the sovereign completeness of the *regula fidei?* The danger was no imaginary one. Events had demonstrated its reality. One of the most formidable intellectual movements amongst Christians which the Church at its birth had to combat, was Gnosticism, of which we see the traces at the end of the first century and which in the course of the second century developed an incredible growth. Now there was an opinion current,[2] which was justified in part, that these speculative conceits passing all limits were closely related on more than one point to certain systems of profane philosophy—a compromising joint-interest which scarcely encouraged the faithful to sympathise with it.

Finally, it was not because of literary art in itself or because of its technique of style, which had been perfected to an astonishing degree in the course of centuries, that the awakening in them of a distaste very like to aversion was due. We must recollect to what a degree of virtuosity, to what specious inventions, to what dialectical boastfulness had eloquence of speech and written literature arrived in the first centuries of the Empire. By reason of the pleasure taken in frivolous mental acrobatics, in the inexhaustible niceties of their oratorical developments, Greco-Roman literature had lost in great part a sense of reality and the taste for truth. It was the day of triumph of rhetoric and of Neo-Sophism, the strange seduction

---

[1] References in *La critique des traditions religieuses chez les Grecs*, Paris, A. Picard, 1904, by Paul Decharme. See the index in this work at the words Athéisme, Impiété, Religion, Providence, Enfer.

[2] Tertullian associates Marcion with Epicurus (adv. Marc., V, xix; Kroymann, in C.V., vol. XLVII, p. 645, line 11). In connection with this he notes that " omnes (haereses) ex subtiloquentiae viribus et philosophiae regulis constant." Cf. *de Anima*, xxiii (Reifferscheid-Wissowa, in C.V., vol. XX, p. 336, line 16) : " Doleo bona fide Platonem omnium haereticorum condimentarium factum." Hippolytus of Rome in his *Philosoph.*, associates Valentine, the Gnostic, sometimes with the Pythagoreans (VI, xxix), sometimes with the Academicians or the Peripatetics (VI, xxii), Marcus with the Pythagorean (VI, lii), Marcion with Empedocles (VI, xxix). E. de Faye admits certain affiliation of ideas between Greek philosophy and Gnosticism (*Gnostiques et Gnosticisme*, Paris, Leroux, 1913, pp. 28, 30, 41, 51, 97, 193, 419).

of which penetrated all the domains of thought, and assigned to intelligent minds as their supreme end skilfully deduced paradoxes, scholarly themes richly developed, and conceits of style. In a society intoxicated with literature, and become unaccustomed to truth, Christianity appeared to be entirely turned towards the interior life, and to be passionately convinced of the seriousness of human existence and of the tragedy of destiny, and to be *so far* removed from considering ideas as just simple incentives for dialectics ! How could the intellectual exercises in which this society placed its rapturous delight and pride fail to be accounted absurd and even pernicious !

It felt itself all the more drawn to this view by reason of the fact that the literary form of the Bible was a subject for astonishment in the eyes of lettered pagans, and became the pretext for scornful jestings without end. The Greek Bible, with its Hebraisms, its simplicity so closely related to the everyday language spoken, turned these people away in disgust, in whose eyes all was barbarian which was outside their own habits.[1] Matters became much worse when the Greek Bible had been translated into Latin by hands who, though well intentioned, had but moderate skill. These transpositions, very literal since the principal object was to render the Word of God in its exact tenor, very popular too in their language in as much as they were to be understood by the most ignorant, afforded some of the most scurrilous banter to the enemies of Christianity.[2] And, by an inevitable

---

[1] Celsus, ap. Origen, *Contra Celsum*, I, lxii (Koetschau, in C.V., *Origenes*, I, 113) ; Clement of Alex., *Protrepticus*, viii, 77. Origèn, *Hom.*, viii, i : "Deprecamur vos, o auditores sacrorum voluminum, non cum taedio vel fastidio ea, quae leguntur, audire, pro eo quod minus delectabilis eorum videtur esse narratio " ; Saint John Chrysost., *Hom. in Ioannem*, II, 2 (P.G., lix, 31) ; Saint Basil, Ep. cccxxxix ad Libanios (P.G., xxxii, 1085) ; *Hexam.*, 3 Homily (P.G., xxix, 120 D), in connection with the word φαῦσις in Genesis XVI : "Let not the singularity of the word cause you to laugh ; do not mock at us if we conform not to your choice of words, and if we seek not to arrange them in harmonious fashion, etc."

[2] Lactance, *Hist. div.*, V, i (Brandt, in C.V., vol. XIX, p. 400 ; P.L., vi, 500) : "Haec imprimis causa est, cur apud sapientes et doctos et principes huius saeculi Scriptura sancta fide careat, quod prophetae *communi ac simplici sermone, ut ad populum*, sunt locuti. Contemnuntur itaque ab iis qui nihil audire vel legere nisi expolitum ac disertum volunt, nec quicquam inhaerere animis eorum potest, nisi quod aures blandiori sono permulcet." See also *ibid.*, vi, 21 (Brandt, p. 562).—Arnob., *Adv. Nationes*, I, xlv (Reifferscheid, in C.V., vol. IV, p. 29, l. 20) ; I, lviii (ibid., p. 39, l. 8) ; I, lix, he cites a pagan objection ; "*Barbarismis, soloecismis* obsitae sunt res vestrae et vitiorum deformitate pollutae." Saint Jerome, Ep. liii, 10 (Hilberg, in C.V., vol. LIV, p. 463) : "Nolo offendaris in scripturis sanctis *simplicitate et quasi vilitate verborum*, quae vel vitio interpretum vel de industria sic prolatae sunt, ut rusticam contionem facilius instruerent et in una eademque sententia aliter doctus, aliter audiret indoctus." Cf. Ep. xxii, 30, 2.

reaction, the Christians were drawn to conceive an animosity against even the principle of art in style as being a deformity from the truth, and the leaven of vanity.

Greco-Roman civilisation, therefore, harboured for the supporters of the new faith more than one germ of bitterness and enmity. What still further poisoned this instinctive antipathy was the fact of the State becoming their persecutor, and employing against the Christians its gaols, its executioners, its tortures, and all the gamut of the atrocious Roman penalties.

It is necessary to give a complete representation of these data in order to obtain the full and impartial comprehension of a state of mind which I am now going to describe.

It has been proved that during the first centuries of our era,—in the East as well as in the West, contrary to what has been sometimes stated—there was a large number of Christians who were enemies of the old learning and who, contenting themselves with their faith alone, and with one book, the Bible, had of their own free will, without distinction or examination, rejected the intellectual heritage of the old world. Clement of Alexandria, a man of distinguished intellect and a profoundly convinced Christian, but whose enlightened eclecticism would fain have allowed him to breathe freely the air of Greek thought which he admired, reveals to us that these *intransigeants* formed the majority around him towards the end of the IIIrd century ; [1] and this in a city in which the highest forms of scholarship were traditional, the city of erudition, of the museum, of libraries ! " The common herd," he declares not without melancholy, " fear the Greek philosophy, just as children fear goblins." [2] They went so far as to contest with Clement the lawfulness of his writing at all, or at least, to be much concerned that he should use his time on a task such as that. Clement was obliged to defend himself against these strange susceptibilities which readily were turned into matter of suspicion.[3] Even still later, in the IVth and Vth centuries, in Rome, in Cappadocia, in Cyrenäica up to Constantinople, the same misgivings were evident, not alone on the part of a few isolated protesting voices, but

[1] *Stromates*, VI, xi, 89 ; *ibid.*, VII, i.
[2] *Strom.*, VI, lxxx, 5.
[3] * * *Strom.*, I, 11–14. Cf. E. de Faye, *Clément of Alexandria*, 2nd ed., p. 139 et s.

B

throughout the Christian body.[1] Men like St Jerome,[2] St Gregory of Nazianzen,[3] Synesius of Cyrene,[4] and Socrates the historian,[5] were driven to give battle to the malevolence of which ἡ ἔξωθεν παίδευσις that is, profane education, was the object.

They introduced sometimes a little spite and bad temper; but more often they displayed a longanimity which is astonishing; there are justifications, adjustments of points of view, and even concessions, whereof the tone on certain pages nearly resembles that of the *intransigeants* which they were hoping to appease.

There emerges, therefore, the fact that we can state that during the first centuries of the Empire there is hardly a Christian writer in whose case there does not intrude, or show itself more or less sincerely, more or less diplomatically, a hostility in regard to the different forms of profane learning.

With some of them it was a mania and, we might almost say, a moral certainty. For example, Tertullian—in other respects the incomparable champion, the most original writer in Latin under the Empire—scarcely ever passes over an opportunity to dig still deeper the ditch separating the world from the Church. He proclaims that all the *doctrina saecularis litteraturae* is foolishness in the eyes of God, and that the Christian must reject it.[6] He treats the philosophers as " huxters of wisdom and eloquence," [7] as " animals of self-glorification," [8] and sees in the art of dialectic, invented by that " pitiable Aristotle," the mother of heresy. " What is there in common," he cries,[9] " between Athens and Jerusalem, between the Academe and the Church ? . . . So much the worse for those who have displayed a Christianity of the Stoic, of the Platonist, of the Dialectician ! For us, we have no need for curiosity,

---

1 Οἱ πολλοὶ χριστιανῶν, said Gregory of Nazianzen (*Funeral Oration of St Basil*, xi, i; P.G., xxxvi, 508).

2 Ep. lxx (Hilberg, in C.V., vol. LIV, p. 700). A certain Magnus whom Jerome treats in the capacity of *Orator Urbis*, had asked him at the end of a letter " why he strewed here and there in his writings examples taken from profane literature, thus soiling the whiteness of the Church with pagan horrors." An insidious question wherein Jerome could suspect some snare contrived by the untiring hostility of his enemies in Rome. Cf. § 6 ; Hilberg, p. 708, l. 8 et s.

3 *Op. cit.*

4 *Ep.* cliii (P.G., xlvi, 1553).

5 *Hist. eccl.*, III, xvi (P.G., lxvii, 420).

6 *De Spectac.*, xviii.

7 *De Anima*, III (Reifferscheid-Wissowa, p. 302, l. 32).

8 *Ibid.*, I (p. 299, l. 10). Cf. Adv. Marc., I. xiii.

9 *De Praescr.*, vii.

after Jesus Christ, nor for investigation, after the Gospel ! "
" The writings of philosophers, historians and poets, appear
to be worthy of credence because of their ornaments of style,"
declared Theophilus, the Bishop of Antioch, in the second half
of the IInd century, " but at bottom they are void and insen-
sate." [1]   In the case of certain polemical writers,[2] these attacks
take the form of a systematic disparagement whose heavy
irony borders close upon the most overwhelming ineptitude.
Even the moderate minded, a Justin, an Athenagoras, a
Clement of Alexandria, an Origen, or a Lactantius, who in
their hearts could not bring themselves to admit that pagan
thought was altogether in error throughout, did not dare any
more than others to extend their feelings of goodwill and
equity to the length of depriving themselves of discharging
many criticisms.[3]   Further, with a view to redeem their sympathies and their secret respect in this regard, they took refuge
on occasion in an unlikely hypothesis which had been invented
by the Alexandrine Jews previous to Christianity, according
to which the wisdom of the Greeks could have been no other
than a by-product of Hebrew wisdom, the philosophers having
taken toll of Moses and the Bible.[4]

In endeavouring to counteract the ironical strictures of the
pagans on the simplicity of the language of Holy Scripture,
they went so far as to dispute absolutely the importance of
style and of grammar, and to reduce those laws of language,
to which literary tradition attached so high a price, to mere
conventions or to simple prejudices. This paradox found
sometimes unexpected upholders. Of such a kind was the old
rhetorician, Arnobius, whose wordy eloquence, lacking discretion and fine distinctions, lingers over developing the idea
that the faith had no need of vain *technique*, and that, in

---

[1] *Ad. Autol.*, II, xii (P.G., vi, 1069) ; cf. III, II.
[2] E. G. Tatian, *Hermias*.
[3] Very numerous references : see K. Werner, *Gesch. der apol. u. polem. Liter.*,
Schaffhausen, 1861, etc., vol. I, pp. 316–335. For Clement of Alex., cf. W. Wagner,
in the Z. fur wiss. Theol., XLV (1902), p. 220, etc. For Origen, cf. J. Denis, *La
philosophie* d'Origène, Paris, 1884, p. 17, etc. Christian opinion in regard to divers
philosophies is well reviewed in the *Dict. of Christian Biography*, by Smith and
Wace, vol. I (1877), p. 143, etc.
[4] References equally numerous. See Harnack, *Gesch. d. altchr. Liter.*, erster
Teil, p. 877, etc. This theory of which St Augustine finally conceived some doubts
(Civitas Dei, VIII, xi), was transmitted to the middle ages by Cassiodorus (cf.
Inst. Div., I, xvii). We find some traces of this in the *Discours sur l'Histoire Univ.*,
by Bossuet (part II, chap. xv at the end). Bossuet's allusion is otherwise very
prudent.

accordance with every other form of speech, there was no such thing, *per se*, as a correct or a vicious form.[1]

In this way, the sentiment of intellectual Christians, whether sincere or not, joined hands over more than one article held by the exclusive *simpliciores :* such care for uniformity of thought is very much at the heart of Catholicism. Under this train of reasoning more or less unfavourable to the Greco-Latin learning, there lay an element of rough but formidable logic. What good to make any endeavour at conciliation, or pretence of coquetting with a civilisation wherein the true faith found so few points of contact, and so many occasions for becoming impaired or broken up ? To live uprightly, to expiate one's faults, to keep oneself on the road to the eternal fatherland without too many deviations—was not this the essential duty of a Christian ? Why aggravate a task already so difficult by mingling with it the study of writers brought up on polytheism, with no care for any moral law, who welcomed all undisciplined curiosities of the spirit, all carnal weaknesses, and whose contradictory speculations disclosed uncertainties deadly to the stability of the established faith ? By reading the Scriptures, were there not revealed therein more than one counsel susceptible of justifying the energetic prejudices already suggested by experience and even by good sense ? The question then was no other than resolutely to take no account of that " wisdom of the world," which the Apostle Paul had called " foolishness," [2] in order to attach oneself to that which was the whole duty of man during his terrestrial pilgrimage.

VII

THIS psychological reconstitution which I have just sketched is not a fantastic one, nor one put together on any *a priori* principle. It rests on an immense number of texts, in which there breathes the same asceticism, incurious of all that in life appeared to be but a superfluous decking and a useless gratification of the mind. Nay more, in old compilations of ecclesiastical law, and in decisions of Councils, there are to be found

[1] *Adv. Nationes*, I. lix (Reifferscheid in C.V., vol. IV, p. 40). " . . . Si verum spectes, nullus sermo natura est integer, vitiosus similiter nullus, etc."
[2] I *Cor.*, i, 20 ; cf. *Rom.*, i, 22 ; II *Cor.*, x, 5 ; *Coloss.*, ii, 8.

formal prohibitions against reading pagan books extended to the faithful and even to the Bishops.[1] These injunctions never possessed any but a local value, and, it would appear, only an uncertain efficaciousness.   We see, however, the danger : the survival of the ancient patrimony of science and literature was directly menaced.

But for such a result the absolute principles of the *intransigeants* would have had to be pressed to their utmost limits and applied in all their rigour.   Now life has its necessary requirements and reactions, wherein our preconceived notions, however ardently held they may have been, are brought up against their own limitations, with which they are constrained to make some attempt at composition.   To have entirely rejected Greco-Latin learning might have been a bold and imposing attitude to have taken, but can we truly imagine that it could have brought about and realised its work of making a complete breach and destroying it ?

Let us consider what this Hellenic patrimony represented in power of research and creation, still further enriched as it was by Roman genius after the latter had appropriated it, and which in its decadence, already clearly visible, remained yet almost intact.

In the first place, it was the fruit of a long series of admirable strivings to explain the world to man, and man to himself. The Greek philosophers and critics had revealed, by their essays at a rational interpretation of the sum of human affairs, by their psychological intuitions, by their acute analyses of the human mind and its creations, the might of reason when applied by rule and method to its object.   Then this field of humanity in which they had exercised their profound thought had become a delight to the imagination in other hands, those of their poets and artists, by virtue of their gift of sympathy, their instinct for the beautiful and graceful, sometimes sad, sometimes full of lightness, which were the marks of the Greek spirit.   In all the domains of expression, especially of literary expression, the researches of the theorists aided by the grand creations of art, had revealed how all the delicate shades of sensibility and all the wealth of the intelligence

---

[1] *Const. apost.*, I, vi (Funk, 1 (1905), p. 13).   (Text very curious.)   Cf. IVth Council of Carthage (398), c. xvi, in Gratian, c. i. dict. xxxvii : " . . . ut episcopus gentilium libros non legat, haereticorum autem pro necessitate et tempore ".

might translate itself ; how the taste, at first instinctive, takes knowledge of itself and creates its own methods, how words acquire a power at once significant and suggestive, while the written phrase comes together duly ordered, balances itself, amplifies itself, and passes into rhythm, harmony and beauty.

Was Christianity, therefore, to sacrifice these lessons in lofty reasoning, this positive knowledge, this compelling art at once touching and refined, and these wise systems of *technique ?* Such a clean cut would have affected not only the virtuosities of art to which the serious-minded Christian had the right to remain a stranger. It would have suppressed, or paralysed for long, astronomy, music, rhetoric, dialectic, grammar and all the mental disciplines which at that time went to the make-up of a man of culture.[1] At one stroke Christianity would have condemned itself to intellectual indigence ; it closed up for itself the great avenues of thought, and with insurmountable difficulties complicated its mission of conquest and propaganda.

Had the Christian phalanxes been recruited indefinitely among the " wool-carders, cobblers and fullers," according to the sarcastic insinuation of the pagan philosopher, Celsus,[2] it would have been easy to make cheap of the intellectual treasures accumulated through the antecedent centuries. No one would have felt the loss due to such a holocaust. But quite early lettered men, and minds broken in to the traditional methods of teaching, had allowed themselves to be drawn to the new faith, and once they had become included amongst the faithful, they wished, in the proselytising of their new found certainty, to constitute themselves its apologists. How then, from that moment, could they have failed to intro- duce the necessary methods proper to their feelings as men of culture and self-respect ? For in their case it was a lively source of moral suffering, a real *cross*, to feel the overwhelming contempt which the learned among the pagans laid heavily on " this miscellaneous collection of ignorant people and credulous women gathered in from the offscourings of the populace," as

---

[1] " Orbis ille doctrinae quam Graeci ἐγκύκλιον παιδέιαν vocant " (Quin- tilian, *Inst.* Or., I, x, i).
[2] Ap. Orig. C. *Celsum*, III, lv.

one of them said in speaking of the sect,[1] and of the Book wherein they read the divine word. They accused them of lowering their intelligence, and of sacrificing the exigencies of criticism and of intellectual refinement to an irrational faith.[2] They formed the passionate desire to oblige these disdainful spirits to hold their peace, by proving to their adversaries the beauty and truth of the Christian doctrine by means of arguments which they could not challenge *a priori*, and by becoming their equals through the perfecting of their literary art and by their concern for correct language.[3]

It was the desire to raise themselves from the intellectual point of view which probably gave check to the rather fanatical tendency of which, however, some vestiges remained here and there even among those most open to reason. They reflected that St Paul had no fear in quoting profane authors in his Epistles, such as Epimenides, Euripides and Aratus. Here was ready to hand a precedent worthy of respect. Tertullian

[1] Caecilius, in the *Octavius* of Minucius Felix, viii, 4. This intellectual embarrassment was all the more grievous to them in that certain amongst their number recalled that they had been hindered in their own conversion by the form of the Biblical Latin. Cf. St Augustine, *Conf.* III, v, 9 : "Visa est mihi indigna (scriptura) quam Tullianae dignitati compararem." See also St Jerome, *Ep.*, xxii, 30.

[2] Caecilius, *ibid.*, v, 4 : Celsus, *ap.* Origen, I, ix ; xxvii ; III, xviii ; III, xliv (" Here are some of their maxims : far from us be any man who possesses any knowledge, any learning, or any light. But if it is a question of the unwise, of the ignorant and unlettered, let them come to us with confidence. . . ."); Porphyry, the Neo-Platonist philosopher, comments in these words on the passage in St Matthew, xi, 25 (" I confess to thee, O Father, Lord of heaven and earth, because thou hast hid these things from the wise and prudent, and hast revealed them to little ones.") : " On this count he should have rendered clearer and less enigmatic what he was writing for children and for those still deprived of the light of reason. If it is from the wise that the mysteries are hidden, and to children of tender years and still at the breast that, contrary to all good sense, they are allowed to be seen, all the more reason then is there to seek after unreason and ignorance with ardour. The great work of Christ on this earth was to have concealed the rays of knowledge from the wise in order to unveil them to those who were bereft of sense and to sucklings " (*Ap.* Macarius Magnetes, Apocr., IV, ix).

The Emperor Julian used to say to the Christians : " *Believe in Him only* is the sum-total of your wisdom. Your portion is ignorance and boorishness " (quoted by Gregory of Nazianzen, Or. c. *Julianum*, IV, cii (P.G., xxxv, 637)). See also Lucian, *Peregrinus*, XIII. The epithet *stulti* was commonly awarded to them (Lactant., *Inst. div.*, V, I ; Ps.—Augustine, *Quaest. in Vet. et Nov. Test.*, cxiv) ; Augustine, *Enarr*, in Ps., XXXIV, viii (P.L., xxxvi, 338) : " Ubicumque invenerunt christianum, solent insultare, exagitare, irridere, vocare insulsum, hebetem, nullius cordis, nullius peritiae."

[3] *Octavius*, xxxix ; Origen, fragm. quoted in the *Philocalia*, V ; Lactant. Inst. div., V, i–ii, and also I, i, 10 ; II, xix, i ; III, i, i ; St Jerome, Preface to the *De Vir, illustr.* The apocryphal collection of letters exchanged between Seneca and St Paul had been forged in order to combat by indirect means in the minds of the lettered pagans their repugnance to the form of the *Epistles ;* the forger represents the admiration of Seneca for the basic matter of these *Epistles*, in order to entice the scrupulous to pierce beneath the outer covering which displeased them.

himself, although by temperament inexorable, recognised that to forbid Christians to become acquainted with profane learning was to reduce them to an intellectual and practical helplessness well nigh complete.[1] There were some who went so far as to admit that very nearly all of the truth was scattered throughout the pagan philosophical systems, but that no thoughtful mind had embraced it in its integrity, because none of them knew of the master idea which dominates life and which gives it its sense and end. It was only necessary then to reconstitute again by the light of revelation these scattered morsels of truth and to bring them back to unity.[2] Clement of Alexandria notes that a knowledge of historical methods, of geometry, of astronomy, and above all of dialectics is capable of rendering great service in the interpretation of the truths of the faith and in the defence of these truths against those who misunderstood them.[3] St Gregory of Nazianzen considered that whoever developed in himself either piety or learning, and the one to the exclusion of the other, resembled a one-eyed man, but that the combination is truly complete when a man disposes of both these forces.[4]

We here have declarations which possess their value. We must not exaggerate their importance, nor believe that this apparent liberalism was not frequently contradicted, even amongst those who lent themselves to it, by observations inspired by a totally different spirit. I have already underlined these fluctuations and have given their origin. We have no right to impose on facts and on written texts a uniform tendency which is by no means reflected therein, and which might be only an opinion or an assumption of our own mind. It is best to accept them as the evidence history offers, with their incoherencies and their contributions.

---

[1] " . . . cum instrumentum sit ad omnem vitam litteratura " (de Idolol., x ; they were objecting to this, but he welcomes this objection) ; cf. de Cor., viii (Œhler, I, 436) : " (Litteras) necessarias confitebor et commerciis rerum et nostris erga Deum studiis."

[2] This is the theory of Lactantius who in this respect is in line with Justin, Athenagoras, Clement of Alexandria and Minucius Felix.

[3] Detailed references in Wagner, Zeitsch. f. wiss. Theol., xlv (1902), p. 245, etc.

[4] Panegyric of Basil, xii (P.G., xxxvi, 509 C).

VIII

TOWARDS the end of the IVth century, after all, a *via media* between these confused disputations emerged, and, thanks to the illustrious names of those who were in favour of it, it acquired for later ages not indeed the force of a law, but a real power of influence and suggestion.

There is a celebrated tract, erroneously classed amongst the sermons of St Basil,[1] wherein the Bishop of Caesarea explains to some young people, his nephews, " the right way of drawing profit from the profane authors " ; this is really the title of the treatise which has often been reprinted since the Renaissance, and which has always been dear to lovers of the literature of antiquity. Truth to tell, we do not see the subject developed with the fulness and precision which we might have hoped from it. Basil brings to his discussion less of method than of agreeable *bonhomie* and abounding humanism. Nevertheless, some important principles disengage themselves. Basil considers that all was not tainted from the moral point of view in even this profane literature so much decried at the time ; that the poets, orators and historians knew how to give praise to what is good and that they provide an abundance of precepts and examples capable of bringing an ennobling influence into the soul of a young man. Only he insists on a proper selection in order that the suspect portions may be eliminated. Under reserve of this preliminary expurgation, Basil is of opinion that there is great advantage in young people having dealings with profane letters ; they will supply them with the beginnings of a formation of character which they will later on complete by the study of the Holy Books ; they will accustom their eyes, when still young, the better to support the dazzling splendour of the teachings of Scripture. They are, in short, for the young Christian of the IVth century, what had been in former days the learning of the Egyptians to Moses, and to Daniel, that of the Chaldeans. Their value consists in being a preparation and setting out on a still higher task which is, in its special bearing, the understanding of the Old and New Testament.

[1] P.G., xxxi, 563–590.

The point of view of St Basil is thus a special one and hardly escapes the reproach of narrowness. But when one calls to mind with what distrustful susceptibilities on such a subject he had to deal one feels more inclined to render homage to the generosity of his intentions.

Some years later, towards 400, St Jerome in his turn had occasion to define his ideas on the same problem. One of his correspondents in Rome had expressed to him his astonishment at seeing him intermingling his works with quotations borrowed from profane authors.[1] Jerome replied to him, and his justification amounts to no less than a vindication of his absolute right to make use of the Greco-Latin literature in the interests and honour of the faith. He reminds him that a long tradition going back beyond St Paul right to Moses himself, authorises this kind of quotation ; that polemical requirements obliged the defenders of Christianity to have recourse to them, and that anyone amongst them would have missed his mark had he felt bound to abstain from them. He sums up his own view in a comparison : just as in the Book of Deuteronomy (xxi, 12) God ordains that before marriage with a captive her head and eyebrows must be shaved and her nails cut in order to render her worthy of the bed of her husband, so likewise the Christian who has been seduced by the beauty of the *sapientia saecularis* must make a beginning by cleansing it of all that it holds of death, idolatry, voluptuousness, error, and passion, and, when thus purified and suitably prepared, it will become worthy for the service of God.

If we are perplexed to know how St Jerome reconciled in his mind this doctrine with the somewhat formal obligations whereof his dream of Cicero has furnished the testimony, St Jerome himself removes this difficulty when he retorts that after all a dream is only a dream and engages us to nothing, in answer to a similar charge made by his old friend, Rufinus who had become the most perfidious of his adversaries.[2] However this may be, let us bear in mind the compromise which he defends.

The opinion arrived at by St Augustine in his *De Doctrina Christiana*,[3] begun in 397 and finished only in 427, is somewhat analogous.

[1] See above p. 18, n. 2.
[2] *Apol. c. Rufinum*, I, xxx (P.L., xxiii, 441).
[3] P.L., xxxiv, 15–121.

St Augustine had a perfect knowledge of profane Latin literature. He had taught it at Thagaste, his native city, afterwards at Carthage, in Rome and at Milan. He could never forget—his *Confessions* bear witness to it—that to the *Hortensius* of Cicero, a noble and eloquent exhortation to the study of philosophy, he owed his first intellectual stirrings and that *there* was kindled his passion for wisdom and truth.[1] On the other hand, the further he advanced in life the more rigorous, the more exclusive, became his Christianity : to such a degree that in his *Retractations*, written when he had reached his seventy-second year, he felt it an obligation on him to disavow—among other imperfections—all that might savour in his former writings, whether in the matter of form or expression, of any complaisance he may have felt for the *liberales disciplinae*.[2]

This twofold trend, that of the man of letters and of the Christian rigorist, betrays itself in his *De Doctrina Christiana*, but the second preponderates, as might be expected, in a tract which is nothing but a treatise on sacred rhetoric, or a manual for the interpretation of the Scriptures for the use of clerics. According to St Augustine, in profane learning there are elements so evidently sullied by superstition that no upright man should think of making experiments in it : astrology, for example. There are others, such as history, natural history, astronomy, dialectics, rhetoric, etc. . . . which, provided that they guarded against the depravities and abuses to which they give rise, are worthy of study and should render the greatest service in connection with exegesis and oral comment- ary on the Scriptures. Augustine, like Jerome, breaks into an allegorical simile wherein he sums up his views. In imitation of the Jewish people in their flight from Egypt, Christianity must carry away the gold and silver vessels of her enemies and employ them for her own uses.[3]

Under cover of such authorities and of such reasonings the old learning was enabled to be preserved. We experience some surprise in realising that its defenders had never conceived for it any more convincing apology than to represent it as a kind of preliminary preparation to the profound study of the Bible.

---

[1] *Conf.*, III, iv.
[2] See the special points noted by Harnack, *Sitz.-Ber.* of the Berlin Acad., 1905, ii, p. 1106.
[3] *De Doctr.* chr., II, xl (P.L., xxxiv, 63).

Such is however the fact.   Every age has its special reasons
for loving the past, for attaching itself to it and for giving to it
some breath of life, without which it would be nothing but
dust and ashes.   It is well then to commend the courage and
good sense of those who, resisting the pressure of the zealots
of pious ignorance, finally maintained the duty, or at least the
lawfulness, of learning the art of thinking and writing in that
school wherein this art had been pre-eminently brought to
perfection.

IX

Now come the invasions of the barbarians—those great disasters of the Vth century.   When Latin civilisation came to be
broken down on all sides, the public schools to be closed,
the whole framework of her intellectual life to be swept away,
the Church of the West, in the complete overthrow of all
regular institutions, was to appear as the one sole power able
to preserve the old order now on its path to destruction.   Will
she make it binding on the conscience to safeguard the works
of antiquity ?   Will she exercise a *rôle* of official guardianship
and prudent protection over this treasure already half fallen
into ruin ?   In order to sustain this thesis, we should have to
resort to some special pleading in regard to the texts, or to
exercise an arbitrary choice in their selection.   In reality,
according to time and place, they reveal such marked differences of attitude in regard to profane learning, that the idea of
any systematic plan in their preservation must be scouted.

But what is not open to doubt is, that in the bosom of the
Church, various initiatives were manifested which saved from
disaster a large portion of what remained at that time to be
preserved.   In this connection, a decisive impulse was given by
Cassiodorus.   A former Consul, sometime *magister officiorum*
at the court of King Theodoric, the Goth, Cassiodorus, renouncing the world, founded about the year 540, his convent of
Vivarium not far from Squillace on the South-east coast of
Italy, and resolved to establish there some means to the
intellectual life which, according to his intention, might provide some stimulus to the religious calling.   He explained to
his monks the usefulness of the " liberal arts " for the *lectio*

divina, and how secular literature, vain indeed if they were to seek their proper end in itself, might, on the other hand, receive its full reward in the case of those who regarded it not as an end, but as a means.[1]   It must not then be desired for its own sake, but only as a path whereby to approach to true wisdom. There is always the same traditional idea, whose progressive formation I have noted with a growing tendency to increasing harshness.   I ought rather to say the traditional illusion ; for the method of conceiving of a study which, based on works of the intellect, should neglect the real foundation in order to attach itself only to the form, would be to reject the thoughts conveyed and to pretend to retain only the positive facts acquired and the mechanism of their expression.   To realise this prudent, but rather chimerical distinction, would have necessitated the clerics under Cassiodorus to have killed in themselves all imagination, all curiosity, all secret pleasure in regard to the genius of Roman civilisation, whose *chefs-d'œuvres* their abbot was placing at their disposal.   Cassiodorus had got together in reality a fairly considerable library at his monastery of Vivarium.[2]   Certain recent researches might lead us to think that this library was collected at a later date, at least partially, at the famous monastery of Bobbio, founded in 612 by St Colomban.[3]   I think we may conclude that Cassiodorus, in spite of his precautionary restrictions, rendered eminent services to the old learning far superior to those to which some ill-informed minds give the honour in the Rule of his contemporary, St Benedict.[4]

There followed the Irish and British monks who gathered together and maintained the light of learning.   At what period did the Church in Ireland and Great Britain receive the first seeds of classic culture ?   The question is disputed. What is sure is that in the scattered regions of *Romania,* such as Britain, or in those which had never formed a part of it, such as Ireland (the Greco-Roman paganism, representing as it did nothing concrete, and consequently nothing very formidable), the study of classic literature was accepted as part of their instruction with rather more sereneness than else-

---

[1] *Inst. div.,* I, *Praef.* (P.L., lxx, 1108) ; I, xxvii–xxviii (P.L., lxx, 1140).
[2] *Inst. div.,* I, viii.
[3] Cf. Paul Lejay, in the B.A.L.A.C., 1913, pp. 265–269.
[4] The *Regula* is in Migne, P.L., lxvi, 215–932.   The best edition is that of G. Butler, Fr. i. B. 1912, a French translation from Dom Guéranger, 1868.

where.[1]   In the monasteries scattered in swarms throughout the West by the monk Colomban, or by his disciples,—Bobbio, in the province of Pavia, Luxeuil, near Belfort in 590, St Gall in 614—more than one *chef-d'œuvre* of antiquity found a protecting resting place which saved it from disappearing.   And when the Anglo-Saxons had felt the influence of the Irish, other asylums, such as Fulda in Prussia, Gorze near Metz, etc., opened also their portals to the relics of the past.

In this way, while these centuries of the sword and of barbarity were unfolding their course, the handing down of the old learning was effected in the West up to the time of the bursting into flower of the Carlovingian period.[2]   During the forty-five years of his reign, Charlemagne in company with Alcuin, gave strong support to the culture of the classics. The greater part of the manuscripts which we now possess date from the IXth and Xth centuries, or trace their descent to the originals transcribed during this period.[3]

X

I will not further extend this general view of the relationship that existed between the old learning and Christianity.   Whatever precaution one should take before hazarding any general statements concerning so vast a domain, I feel that there is one factor that must be insisted upon at this stage.   Received with distrust and even with a certain amount of aversion by the Christian, this culture was only in the last resort safeguarded

[1] See on this point M. Roger's fine work, *L'enseignement des lettres classiques d'Ausone à Alcuin*, Paris, Picard, 1905.

[2] As regards the East, the question is more obscure.   According to one tradition, the Greek clergy are stated to have burnt a large quantity of works in verse, of a more or less erotic character, more particularly those of Menander, Diphilis, Philemon, Sappho, Mimnermus, etc.   Krumbacher (*Byzant. Literaturgesch.*, p. 505) agrees with Bernhardy in thinking this fact very unlikely and not proven.   He states that at Constantinople in the IXth century, Greek profane literature was hardly any more abundant than it is now, save in the matter of the later historians and in works of the specialists.   He attributes the disappearance of a large portion of this literature to the intellectual decadence which marked the Byzantine Empire during the period enclosed between the years 650 and 850.   The fires lighted on the occasion of the taking of Constantinople by the Crusaders in 1204 caused fresh disasters.   Then the *débâcle* of the Empire in the XVth century brought to the West learned Byzantines whose manuscripts played a certain *rôle* (the value of which has been somewhat over-estimated) in the expansion of the Italian Renaissance.   See Ph. Monnier, *Le Quattrocento*, Paris, 1901, vol. II, p. 21.

[3] Cf. Louis Havet, *Manuel de critique verbale*, Paris, 1911, p. 3 et s.

as the servant of theology, and as an auxiliary to the interpretation of the Bible.

Here we see the somewhat humiliating *rôle* to which it must have been reduced, if we had only the declarations which the best accredited spokesmen of Christianity have uttered in this connection to go upon. "*Non discere debemus ista, sed didicisse.*" This saying of Seneca might serve as the leading characteristic of the divers Christian tracts wherein the problem of the right to use the Greco-Roman patrimony was theoretically considered. Mere exercises for giving suppleness to the mind, practised just so long as was necessary for the resulting benefit to be acquired—herein, they maintained, consisted the sole office which all the labour of mankind anterior to the new faith had any right to serve.

That was the thesis, that the official principle; that also, we may suspect, was the expedient of people driven this way and that between the urgent insistence of their own good sense and that of the iconoclasts of the old world of thought and of art.

But, taking the facts as they are, this art, this thought penetrated Christianity much more profoundly and intimately than one would have any reason to doubt if we took as current coin the opportunist professions of a Basil, a Jerome, or a Cassiodorus. I here am broaching a question the magnitude of which should at once deter me. We must however take note of certain features which will make us understand its bearing.

When in the second half of the IVth century, the great Bishop of Milan, St Ambrose, the counsellor of the Emperors Gratian, Valentinian, and Theodosius, undertook to furnish a synthesis of Christian morality worthy to take its place in opposition to the great pagan syntheses, did he endeavour to base it on the Gospel alone? No; but it was from the *De Officiis* of Cicero that he borrowed the general framework and even the title of his treatise. He likewise took a whole host of ideas from the Stoic morality of which Cicero had been the eloquent interpreter, such as the distinction between reason and the passions, the consideration of the "sovereign good," the classification of the virtues (wisdom, justice, courage, temperance), the division of duties into perfect duties and duties less binding, the value to be given to the judgment of the conscience, etc. It is true that he fathoms these ideas in a far different spirit, that he justifies them by reasons which Cicero could not have thought of, and that he gives them finally a sense, a bearing and effectiveness entirely new. However, with Ambrose, while the Christian morality affirms its originality, at the same time it resolutely assimilates all that is excellent which pagan morality could offer.

The resulting action was analogous in all domains— theological speculation, scriptural exegesis, Christian art, the liturgy, the different classes of literature and forms of style : The influence of profane ideas and customs made itself felt throughout. This phenomenon of infiltration or co-pene- tration is one of those questions in which for several years religious critical ingenuity has played a special part. It has sometimes happened that it has lost its way amid comparisons which are open to doubt. Ascertained facts show that nowhere has there been any *hiatus*, breach or complete rupture, but throughout a correspondence and continuity. In spite of the anathemas more than once pronounced against it, the genius of the ancient civilisation survived in the civilisation born of the Christian idea and largely contributed to form it. Thus through force of circumstances, the two great spiritual powers, which seemed to be wholly antagonistic, came together. Christianity had sufficient vitality to escape any deformations in essentials by the fact of this accession of ideas. And it is due to this fusion that even men who are strangers to the Christian faith, are nevertheless willing to accept the fundamental notions of morality which she proposes, since therein is also included the legacy of the past. " If we are Christians," M. Camille Jullian once declared, " if we must hold to this designation as to a formula of salvation, it is because it represents, together with all the visions which the Man of Galilee gave to the consciousness of mankind, all the lessons which the philosophers of antiquity had left there ; it is because, far from being in opposition to the past, Christianity has completed and crowned it."[1]

---

[1] *Revue historique*, vol. LX (1896), p. 342.

XI

NEARLY all the texts which will form the subject of our study will be found in the *Patrologie Latine* by Abbé Migne (Paris, 1844–1855, 221 vol., des Origines à 1216). Among these texts a fairly large number have been reproduced already in the *Corpus Scriptorum ecclesiasticorum latinorum*, now in course of publication. Some information on these two collections will not be out of place.

" Among the French clergy of the XIXth century," wrote Dom Cabrol,[1] "there were few of a more original type than that of the young priest arriving in Paris without money or special recommendation, of very moderate education, but active, enterprising, very well versed in wordly matters, fruitful in resources, and by no means averse to the desirability of self-advertisement, but placing it at the service of good causes : his imagination always busily at work over gigantic under-takings, possessing in a high degree the art of discovering hidden talent, and of cleverly extracting therefrom some portion, and of making it auxiliary to his own end ; endowed with a patience which no opposition could fatigue and with a strength of will which made all bend before it, creating work after work with no other capital than his confidence in himself and his energy, and realising the final achievement of one of the most distinguished undertakings of our century."

The Greek and Latin *Patrologies* were only one amongst many others published by Migne ; but it is in this that he showed the extent of his talent as an organiser.[2]

To bring to life again on a still vaster plan the great collec-tions of ecclesiastical writers inherited from the XVIth, XVIIth and XVIIIth centuries ; to incorporate therein the recent discoveries ; to open to all access to the monuments of Catholic thought—this was the aim he pursued.

We may ask ourselves what might have been the fate of this inordinate task if Migne had allowed himself to be guided only by his own lights. He had the happy thought to write to Dom Guéranger, who gave him the name of Dom J. B. Pitra, at

---

[1] *Histoire de Cardinal Pitra*, Paris, 1893, p. 108.
[2] For further details, cf. P. de Labriolle, in B.A.L.A.C., vol. III (1910), p. 203 et s.

that time Prior in Paris. Pitra who, though still very young (at this time he was 30 years old), was already profoundly versed in patristic literature, understood that there could be no question of getting together a new edition for each author after collating the manuscripts, but that they must choose among already existing editions those which were most worthy to form a part of the projected library. He suggested to Migne that they should have recourse to Benedictine works to supply the greater part of their material.

" The Benedictines had a less rigorous method than that demanded to-day," M. Paul Lejay states;[1] " they were guided by their predilections and their acquaintance with the authors, and by the antiquity of the manuscripts. That was the method in vogue at that time, and it gave some good results. It is clear that no very minute comparisons in detail could be founded on texts established in this manner. But the principal fault does not consist in the nature of the text; it is rather in the lack of certainty and in the insufficiency of the information on the contents of the manuscripts. The modern expert demands less a text than the materials wherewith to compile one. . . . Nevertheless," M. Lejay adds, " no one can reproach Migne with not having made a better attempt than the Benedictines. He was no philologist, and we must not forget that in France in 1844, and elsewhere, it would have been hard to discover men who were familiar with the method which was only to bear fruit some years later: if Lachmann had already published the greater part of his editions, his *Lucretius* nevertheless did not appear before 1850; Ritschl began the publication of his *Plautus* in 1848. We must not ask more of Migne than he could, or desired to, accomplish."

The *Patrologie Latine* began to appear in 1844. The printing press at Petit-Montrouge issued about 20 volumes yearly, an enormous output and superior to all expectations: in 1855, the 217 promised volumes were ready for the subscribers. From 1862 to 1864, Migne published four further volumes of *Indices*. The 162 volumes of the *Patrologie Grecque* were printed during the period between 1857 and 1866 at the rate of 18 volumes yearly. We can get some idea of the immensity of the undertaking, if we realise that the Latin

[1] R.H.L.R., I (1896), p. 98.

series represented 297,567 pages, and the Greek 235,724 pages, or a total of 533,291 pages, which were all stereotyped, that is reproduced on tin plates which permitted of successive re-impressions with no fresh corrections.

From the first moment, criticism was busy on this work and, beginning, as was natural, by taking exception to the most patent defects, went on to take note of the numerous typographical mistakes which marred certain volumes of the *Patrologie Latine*. Next, judges possessing the requisite authority, pointed out the confusion, the blunders and the unsatisfactory selection shown in some of the editions ; but at the same time, they rendered homage to the prodigious skill of the editor and signalised the immense debt which ecclesiastical studies henceforward owed to him.

In fact, Migne had grudged neither his time, his labour, nor his money. He had secured for his work the scientific aid of those most qualified to give it. He had also conceived the very happy idea of incorporating in his compilation the dissertations of the commentators of old. From a scientific point of view, was it not a real advantage to group together, as he did, the scattered works of the Ballerini, Basnage, Baronius, Dodwell, Constant, Garnier, Mabillon, Muratori, Ruinart, etc. ? If the *Patrologie* still remains indispensable to-day, even in the case of the volumes which have their *replica* in the *Corpus Scriptorum ecclesiasticorum latinorum*, it is due to the notes and learned studies which are helpfully embodied therein.

The Imperial Academy of Sciences of Vienna has been responsible for the appearance of the *Corpus*, volume after volume since 1866. The scheme of the collection embraces the accurate establishment of the text after an examination as complete as possible on the authenticity of the manuscript ; no exegetical notes (on principle), except to indicate the sources of the author ; and detailed *Indices*. Its scope was to include all the Latin ecclesiastical writers up to the VIIth century inclusively. Broadly speaking, these editions are of important value. Some portions have succeeded less well.[1] From the bibliographical point of view, we have to regret the incon-

---

[1] e.g. Hartel's *St Cyprian* ; certain portions of St Augustine's writings edited by Knoll and Zycha (cf. T.L.Z., 1892, p. 130 et s. ; 412 et s. ; 1895, p. 364 et s. ; 1898, p. 136 et s. ; R.C., 1894, 2, 277 ; 1896, 2, 104 ; 1898, 1, 227).

venient and illogical system of numbering the volumes in the collection.

Some Christian authors have also been published, in part or in their entirety, in other collections of which a list will be found further on. But the two which we have been discussing are of fundamental weight.

BOOK I

THE SOURCES OF ORIGIN

CHAPTER I

THE FIRST LATIN VERSIONS OF THE BIBLE

BIBLIOGRAPHY

For a reconstruction of the Latin versions of the Bible anterior to the Vulgate of St Jerome, we have the following sources at our disposition:—
1. An important store of manuscripts scattered among the European libraries ; 2. Quotations from ecclesiastical writers ; 3. A few rather rare quotations in the inscriptions on tombs ; 4. Portions of the Vulgate wherein St Jerome has been contented to reproduce pre-existing texts (see lib. III, chap. v). Sabatier, the Benedictine, has collected the manuscripts known in his time in an important work called *Bibliorum sacrorum latinae versiones antiquae*, etc. . . . Paris, 1749-1751. Since Sabatier, many discoveries have been made in the libraries: see Schanz, III, 486 ; art. *Latin Versions* in the *Dict. of the Bible* ; art *Bibelübersetzungen*, in R.E., vol. III, 28 ; art. *Itala* in the Index of *Thesaurus linguae lat.* Whence arose the idea of a "new Sabatier". This idea, adumbrated by Wölfflin, A.L.L., VIII (1893), p. 311, and defined by C. Weyman, *Hist. pol. Blätter* 144 (1909), pp. 897-905, was in process of being realised before the war by Joseph Denk (*der neue Sabatier*, L. 1914) who announced in 1915 three ample volumes of 1000 pages each, then a volume of *Prolegomena* and *Indices* (at a subscription of 400 marks). Denk's plan has had objections made to it elsewhere: cf. Jülicher, T.L.Z. 1917, n. 2.

For the language of these versions, see H. Rönsch, *Itala und Vulgata*, Marburg and Leipsic, 2 edit. 1875 ; ID. *Collectanea philol.*, Bremen, 1891 ; Goelzer, *Etude lexicog. et gramm. de la latinité de saint Jérôme*, thèse, Paris, 1884 ; G. Koffmane, *Gesch. des Kirchenlateins*, Breslau, I, 1879 ; II, 1881 (unfinished and otherwise mediocre) ; Burkitt, *The old Latin and the Itala*, in T.S., iv, 3 (1896): cf. C. Weyman, in B. ph. W., 1897, pp. 11-16, Heer ; *die Versio Latina des Barnabasbriefes und ihr Verh. zur altlat. Bibel*, Frib. i. B., 1908 ; L. Wohleb, *die latein. Uebers. der Didache*, Paderborn, 1913 (in the *St. zur Gesch. u. Kultur des Alt.* hsg. von. Drerup, Grimme and Kirsch. VII, 1) ; numerous indications scattered throughout the *Archiv. f. lat. Lexic.*, of Wölfflin (2 tables, one for volumes I-X (1898), the other for volumes XI-XV (1909)).

SUMMARY

I. The tardy coming into bearing of Latin Christian Literature. Greek the dialect of the Mediterranean.—II. The first Latin translations of the Bible. Their literary and grammatical character. Their influence on the Latin tongue.

I

Latin Christian Literature offers no landmark of any importance before the end of the second century. At that time,

Greek Christian literature had already produced a number of conspicuous works, in particular all that brilliant crop of apologies destined to plead the cause of Christianity before the authorities of the State and public opinion itself.

Such a tardy appearance is at first a matter of astonishment. Very simple reasons can explain this. Greece had made such a thorough conquest of the Roman world that there was hardly any town of importance in the West in which the Greek tongue was not in everyday use. During the period of the Emperors, the West was linked with the East by extensive commercial intercourse. From Greece, from the Euxine Sea, from Syria, and from Egypt, merchandise of every kind, directed in the first case to Brindisi, to Ostia or Pozzuoli, was then sent by road to Rome, the centre of the world's traffic, who then re-distributed a large part over Gaul, Spain and Africa. The *pax Romana* rendered easy these transactions : " Sed et mundus pacem habet per eos (sc. Romanos) "—wrote St Irenaeus about 180—" et nos sine timore in viis ambulamus et navigamus quocumque voluerimus." At the same time, the Levantine merchants, together with their importations brought with them their ideas, their beliefs, their religions— and their tongue. In his discourse *Pro Archia* (X, 23) Cicero had said before : " *Graeca leguntur in omnibus fere gentibus ; latina suis finibus, exiguis sane, continentur.*" In an increasing degree since his time Greek had become, during the first centuries of the Empire, a Mediterranean dialect.

Even in Rome, popular epigrams, satirical catchwords and puns at the expense of the Emperors, were current in Greek, and Suetonius has preserved for us a fairly rich collection.[1] These sayings were evidently understood by a very large public. One could readily find equally significant facts in Northern Africa. It would seem exaggerated to speak of a kind of elimination with which the Latin tongue was being threatened, as Mommsen suggests, if Rome had not made it the official language.[2] But in the towns along the coast, Adrumyttium, Carthage, Oea, Leptis Major, etc., Greek was very much in use as is evidenced by the inscriptions on the tombs.[3]

[1] They will be found collected in A. Macé's *Essai sur Suétone*, Paris, 1900, p. 274 et s.

[2] *Rom. Gesch.*, V, 643 : French translation, XI, 284.

[3] Toutain, *Les Cités rom. de la Tunisie*, Paris, 1896, p. 200 ; Audollent, *Carthage romaine*, Paris, 1904, p. 701 ; and especially Thieling, *der Hellenismus in Kleinafrica*,

The men of letters liked to make use of it.   The work on the eternity of matter, which the painter, Hermogenes, had written at Carthage and which Tertullian was to refute, appears to have been composed in Greek.[1]   Tertullian himself oscillated for some time between the two languages : he had given a first rendering in Greek to his *Virginibus Velandis*, to his *De Spectaculis* and to his *De Baptismo*.   Similarly with the *De Ecstasi*, which was never subsequently rendered in Latin.[2] The same conditions are noticeable if we pass on to Gaul. The use of Greek had been prevalent for a long time in the South.[3]   Varro had already noted the fact.[4]   The infusion of Greek elements was continually replenishing this linguistic foundation.   " The traces left by the Phocaeans," as E. Renan remarks,[5] " had not been entirely effaced.   People from Asia and from Syria, much given to emigrating towards the West, were in the habit of ascending the Rhône and the Saône, carrying with them a portable bazaar of varied merchandise, or rather of remaining on the banks of these large rivers in places which offered to them some hope of subsistence."

Furthermore, the fashion in literature from which no one can completely escape, exercised its influence.   Claudius,[6] Nero, and then Hadrian,[7] had a taste, a passion and a mania for Hellenism, and had encouraged its general use.   Favorinus the Gaul, who was born at Arles between the years 70 and 80 of our era, gave conferences in Rome in Greek just as a little later did Apuleius at Carthage,[8] and his numerous works in Greek won for him the highest honours.   From Suetonius we learn

Leipsic and Berlin, 1911, p. 30 et s. (inscriptions) ; p. 43 et s. (*tabulae defixionis*) ; p. 48 et s. (*amulets*). Out of 90 African *tabulae defixionis* of the second and third centuries after Christ, Thieling enumerates (following the collection made by Audollent) a total of 20 Greek, 29 Greco-Latin, and 41 Latin, with here and there some Greek letters.

[1] Zahn, Gesch. *d. neut. Kanons*, I, i, 49.

[2] Note also the number of Greek expressions in the *Passion of Perpetua and Felicitas*, xii : Audivimus vocem unitam dicentem : Agios, agios, agios. § x : in oromate ; § iv : machera ; § v–vi : catasta ; § vii : diastema ; § viii : fiala ; § x : afa ; § xv : cataracterius, etc.

[3] Ch. Lecrivain, *Les Grecs dans le Sud de la Gaule*, Bull. de la Soc. archéol. du Midi de la France, 1907, pp. 30–34.

[4] " Quod et Graece loquantur et Latine et Gallice," quoted by St Jerome, *Comm. in Ep. ad Gal.*, ii, pref.

[5] *L'Eglise Chrétienne*, p. 468.

[6] Suetonius, *Claudius*, xlii.

[7] Cf. Renan, *Origines de Chr.*, vi, 34 et s. We possess some Greek poetry by Hadrian : *Anth. Pal.*, vi, 332 ; vii, 674 ; ix, 17 ; ix, 137 ; ix, 387 ; Kaibel, *Epigr. gr.* n. 811 ; 888 ; 1089.

[8] *Florides*, IV, xviii. Some indications of the use of Greek in Africa among cultivated circles, *Apologia*, X ; LXXXVII ; XCVIII.

the titles of a dozen Greek *opuscula* on divers historical subjects, on archæology and literature. We see Elienus who was born at Preneste quite close to Rome and had never left Italy, rendering his books in Greek; in speaking the Attic tongue he even passed as a native-born Athenian.[1] The Stoic philosopher, Cornutus, a native of Leptis in Africa, who, even in Rome numbered amongst his pupils Persius and Lucanius, composed his writings on grammar in Latin, but made use of Greek exclusively for his philosophic essays. And many others could be quoted. It was only during the second half of the IIIrd century that the set-back from Greek became noticeable in the West. This set-back was accentuated in the IVth century and it is at this latter date that men like Rufinus and St Jerome were to undertake the useful mission of translating the most notable productions of Greek Christian thought for the use of the Western world.

But Christian propaganda, having found its *points d'appui* and obtained its first recruits principally among the Jewish or pagan element speaking the Greek tongue, had quite naturally made use of Greek as its vehicle. Even in Rome, at the heart of the Empire, Greek had for long been familiar to the communities of Christians.[2] It was in this language that the author of the Epistle to the Romans exhorted them. Rossi is of opinion that Divine Service was celebrated in Greek up to the end of the IIIrd century. The principal Christian *opuscula* written in Rome during the IInd century, such as the letter sent by St Clement to the Church in Corinth in the name of the Roman community, the *Pastor* of Hermas, and the *Dialogue* of Caius with Proclus, the Montanist, were written in Greek. St Justin, who, though born in the East, had made several sojourns in Rome, where he had founded a school and was destined later to undergo his martyrdom, does not appear to have experienced any temptation to use any other dialect than Greek for his *Apologia*. When, in about the year 177, "the servants of Christ dwelling in Vienne and Lyons" wrote "to their brethren of Asia and Phrygia having the same faith and the same hope of redemption"—(it is in these terms that they began their famous letter containing the

---

[1] Philostratus, *Vita Sophist.*, II, xxxi, i (p. 123, 3 Kayser). We may compare the testimony of Aurelius Victor, *Epist.* x, on Septimus Severus (born at Leptis).

[2] The principal facts are gathered together by Caspari, *Quellen zur Gesch. des Taufsymbols*, Christiania, 1875, vol. III, p. 267–466.

detailed account of the martyrdom and heroic sufferings of Sanctus, Blandinus and their companions), the writer (possibly St Irenæus who was to be elected Bishop in place of St Pothinus who died beneath the blows received when he was arrested) made use of the Greek tongue in inditing his message of victory and of peace.[1] At the beginning of the IIIrd century, St Hippolytus, a Roman priest, wrote his mediocre works in the same language. We do not come to any inscriptions which were not worded in Greek until those engraved on the tombs of Popes Fabianus († 250), Lucius († 254), and Eutychianus († 283).[2]

These facts are significant; they make us understand why Christian literature in the Latin tongue did not take its birth until a century and a half after the preaching of Christ.

II

As with Latin profane literature, Latin Christian literature had its beginning in translations.

" The manner in which the Hebrew Bible penetrated the Western world through the vehicle of the Latin tongue is an event which, with good reason, invites the curiosity of the learned and the reflection of the philosopher," says Gaston Paris.[3] " It is not through the agency of the Jews that it was introduced there : the translation of the Hebrew books into Greek at Alexandria, a truly memorable act, which had been one of the most remarkable consequences of the Hellenisation of the East, had no counterpart in Latin. The Jews, so numerous in Rome from the time of Augustus, were Hellenised Jews : if they read the law and the prophets, it was in Greek, and the converts which they made belonged to this Greek or semi-Greek world, which was as numerous perhaps in Rome as the purely Latin population. It was in a world of this kind that Christianity issuing from the Hellenistic synagogues, also made its first conquests. . . . Soon, however, it recruited in Rome and in the provinces proselytes who did not understand Greek or understood it very badly. For their use the New

---

[1] One of the martyrs, Sanctus, is shown nevertheless as replying in Latin to the Governor (Eusebius, H.E., V, i, 20 ; note also *ibid.*, V, i, 44).

[2] De Rossi, *Rom. Sot.*, II (1867), p. 236.

[3] *Mélanges linguist.*, I, 60.

Testament was without doubt the first to be translated, and then, when the doctrine had become established that the Old Testament was the introduction and the symbol of it, the Jewish books followed."

It was to little purpose that Greek was the cosmopolitan and international language *par excellence*, for, according to the just observation of Gaston Paris, there were certain elements in the Christian Churches of the West, who, varying in importance according to time and place, had only a slight acquaintance with Greek, or none at all. How could they have allowed the written text of the Bible, which played so important a *rôle* in the life of the Christians and which was read privately and in public,[1] to remain a dead letter to a more or less considerable portion of the faithful ? The same necessity, which was at different times to occasion the appearance of Syriac, Coptic, Armenian, and Arabian, etc., translations of the Bible, in good time made imperative the translation of versions in Latin.[2] The origins of the Latin Bible are in most respects very obscure. St Augustine himself was not at all sure of the exact date of their first appearance. " We can count those who have translated the Scriptures from the Hebrew into Greek ": he wrote in his *De Doctrina Christiana* (II, xi) : " in the case of the Latin translators that is quite impossible. In fact, in the earliest days of the faith, the first comer, if there happened to fall into his hands a manuscript, and he thought himself to have some knowledge of the two languages, considered himself at liberty to translate it." " Qui scripturas ex Hebraea lingua in Graecam verterunt numerari possunt, Latini autem interpretes nullo modo. Ut enim cuique *primis fidei temporibus* in manus venit codex Graecus et aliquantulum facultatis sibi utriusque linguae habere videbatur, ausus est interpretari." This *primis fidei temporibus*

---

[1] L. Duchesne, *Orig. du culte chrétien*, Paris, 1898, p. 106 ; Harnack, *Ueber den privaten Gebrauch der hl Schriften in der alten Kirche* (*Beitr. z. Einl. in d. Neue Test.*, VIII [1912]).

[2] Sundry *opuscula* outside the Old and the New Testament, but specially dear to the piety of the faithful, were quite early transposed into Latin : for example, the *Didache* (ed. J. Shlecht, F.R. i. B., 1900 and 1901), the first *Letter* of Clement of Rome *to the Corinthians* (Dom Morin, in A.M. II [1894]), the *Pastor* of Hermas (*versio vulgata*, Hilgenfeld, L. 1873 ; the version called *Palatina* is at the end of the IVth century [ed. Gebhardt and Harnack, *Patr. apostol. op.*, fasc. 3, L. 1877]), the *Epistle of Barnabas* (Heer, Fr. i. B., 1908), certain apocryphal writings such as the *Acta Pauli* (T.U. xxii, 2 [1902]), etc. . . . a compact review of what remains of the literature of the early days of Christianity in translation would be welcome. See the list drawn up by Harnack, A.C.L., 883–884.

is rather vague as a chronological indication. Many critics still hesitate to admit, or even expressly deny, that Tertullian had at his disposal at the end of the IInd century one or more Latin versions of the Bible either in part or complete. In reality we find in Tertullian passages which are sufficiently explicit to enable us to have the right to uphold a contrary opinion.[1] These passages show (1) that Tertullian himself habitually translated his quotations from the original Greek ; (2) that he had before his eyes Latin versions ; not that they were indispensable to him but for the satisfaction of his curiosity which was always on the alert.

The first translations must have been made in the course of the IInd century. Under what conditions, in what country, and by whose hands ? These are so many questions which cannot be solved at the present time.[2] The hypothesis of an African origin is that which would most commend itself. However this may be, these Latin versions were to multiply themselves throughout the West up to the time of the great revision by St Jerome, who has preserved them in part in his own translation of the Holy Books. More ancient than the most ancient Greek manuscripts of the Bible which have been preserved to us, they offer great interest to theologians.[3] From the literary point of view likewise their importance is considerable. They have largely contributed to shape the imagination, language, and style of the Christian writers. They have been the starting point of a mighty work in the creation and adaptation of words which has had its repercussion throughout Christian literature. We can even trace its influence much further. " The pre-Hieronymic versions," to again quote G. Paris, " have left their traces down to much later centuries : the Middle Ages without exception quoted with complaisance so-called Messianic prophecies which are found neither in the Hebrew text nor in the Vulgate, and which owe their existence only to misinterpretations of the Septuagint diffused by their old Latin translators ; and even in our days the infant Jesus is pictured between an ox and an ass

---

[1] I have quoted and discussed them, B.A.L.A.C., IV (1914), pp. 210–213.

[2] It will not be possible to classify and give the genealogy of these versions until after the completion of a series of studies of which Heer (*Rom. Quartalsch.* XXIII (1909), p. 218) has very happily outlined the salient features.

[3] " Even the most literal version," remarks Burkitt, " is also in a certain sense a commentary. Many of our current theological conceptions have come to us through this Latin channel." *The old Latin and the Itala*, p. 4.

because of a passage from Habacuc (III, 2) which, when translated by the Septuagint (between two animals), signifies in reality quite another thing."

And how many words, how many biblical expressions preserved by St Jerome in his translation has our language accepted, whether through imitation by our own writers or the intermediary of translations from the Middle Ages! [1] The Latin Bible has been " one of the elements of the alloy out of which was made the solid metal of our French tongue " [2] and one of the principal factors of our Western civilisation.

The philological character of these Latin versions was in strict correspondence with the principles which the faith of their translators could not fail to impose on them. The respect felt by the primitive Church for the Greek of the Septuagint equalled that which the Greek of the Gospels inspired in her. To be valued as authentic in all controversy connected with morals or doctrine, the texts from Scripture required that the Greek of the Old and New Testament should be transposed with the utmost exactitude and literalness.[3] On the other hand, there could be no question of delaying over the scruples of the fastidious, or the exclusive and condescending rules of the purists in their choice of words and expressions. The determining reason for these undertakings was to render the sacred texts accessible to those who could not understand them under their Greek form : it would have been scarcely reasonable to frighten them away by a too aristocratic style of Latin (always admitting that the translators had it at their disposal), or by a quantity of fine distinctions which would have escaped their notice.

Here we come upon quite a new conception of the qualities requisite in a translation. As a means of comparison, let us take the example of Cicero. He was fond of this exercise. Beginning in his early youth, he translated the *Phenomena* of Aratos into Latin hexameters ; after that came Xenophon's *Economics*, Plato's *Protagoras* and *Timaeus*, without counting

---

[1] First French *Psalters* about 1100 ; Bible of the University of Paris, between 1225 and 1250.

[2] Trénel, *L'Ancien Testament et la langue française du moyen-âge*, Paris, 1904, p. 58.

[3] *Adv. Marc.*, II, ix, Tertullian points out the mistake of certain translators who, simply by the maladroit substitution of the word *spiritus* for the word *afflatus* in Genesis ii, 7, afforded a pretext to heretics for attributing the sins of mankind to the " Spirit " of God.

the numerous passages from Greek authors (Homer, the
Tragedies, etc.) which he translated here and there in order to
embellish his own reasonings. In his treatises on philosophy
and rhetoric he had to cope with the technical formulae
employed by his models. When one studies his method, we
realise that, if he sometimes attempts to render the Greek
word for word (*infinitio* for ἀπειρία ; *anticipatio* for πρόληψις ;
mulierositas for φιλογύνεια, etc. . . .), he more often re-
duplicates his Latin equivalent (*intelligentia et ratio* for νόησις ;
genitorem et effectorem for δημιουργόν ; *fluens et tractus* for
εἰρομένη [λέξις], etc.), or rather he has recourse to some
ample periphrase conveying the equivalent with irreproachable
exactness (*qui animo cernuntur et ratione intelliguntur ani-
mantes* for τὰ νοητὰ ζῷα ; *quod est ad cultum deorum aptis-
simum* for τὸ Θεοσεβέστατον ; *genus quod in laudandis
aut vituperandis hominibus ponitur* for ἐπιδεικτικόν γένος,
etc.).[1] Such redundancies were in conformity with his customary play of style, and perhaps he thereby saw a means of
demonstrating his favourite and perhaps rather paradoxical
theory on the richness of the Latin *verborum copia*.

These literary prepossessions remained a sealed book to the
translators of the Latin versions of the Bible. Their purpose
was to make a faithful copy as accurately as possible of the
inspired Greek, while remaining intelligible : this is the ideal
which they approached more or less closely.[2] From this have
resulted consequences of grave bearing from the point of view
of the history of the Latin language. Already very receptive
of Hellenisms on the part of the profane authors of the
Empire,[3] this tongue thus incorporated a quantity of new
words formed on the Greek,[4] and her syntax itself underwent

[1] There are numerous examples of these different processes in Causeret, *Etude
sur la langue de la rhét. et de la crit. litt. dans Cicéron*, treatise, Paris, 1886, p. 13
et s. ; V. Clavel, *de M. Tullio Cic. Graecorum interprete*, treatise, Paris, 1868, p. 292 ;
Atzert, *de Cic. interprete Graecorum*, Diss, Göttingen, 1908, p. 6 et s. ; 19 et s. ; Leo,
in *Hermes*, 1914, p. 192.

[2] In this connection, St Augustine points out differences between the Latin
versions with which he was acquainted (*De Doctr. christ.*, II, xv). St Jerome remarks that only a very literal translation is admissible where Scripture is concerned, "*ubi et verborum ordo mysterium est*" (Ep. LVII, 5). A similar scruple
obtained in the bosom of Judaism : from the point of view of literalness, the
versions of Aquila and Symmachus went beyond the Septuagint. See also Gaston
Paris, *Mél. ling.*, I, 75.

[3] Cf. Goelzer, *op. cit.*, p. 221 et s. ; *id.*, *Revue intern. de l'Enseignement* 1908,
p. 105.

[4] Acedia, agonia, aporiari, apostata, apostolus, baptisma, blasphemia, catholicus, diabolus, diaconus, ecstasis, eremus, episcopus, eleemosyna, homilia, laicus,
martyr, monachus, parabolari, scisma, etc.

the same process as the Greek Bible.[1] Certain terms or Hebraic idiosyncrasies (much more restricted in number than has been sometimes stated) filtered into the Latin across the Septuagint and the Gospels.[2] Vulgarisms, such as the devotees of *elegantia* would have proscribed, crept in likewise.[3] A quantity of old words authentically Latin were called upon

[1] For example, a case of the genitive absolute, " et cogitantium omnium (διαλογιζομένων πάντων, Luke III, 15) " ; " omnium autem mirantium (πάντων δὲ θαυμαζόντων, Luke IX, 43) ". (It is quite likely that this turn of phrase was already current in the popular language, for we come across it in the *de Bello Hisp.*, xiv, i, and xxiii, 6) ; the comparative genitive : " major ejus est (μείζων αὐτοῦ ἐστίν) " (there are some examples in profane Latin which are frequently met with after Apuleius) ; *adjuvare* used with the dative ; also *adorare, decet ; benedicere, nocere* with the accusative ; expressions such as " cum esset in loco quodam orantem " (. . . ἐν τῷ εἶναι αὐτὸν ἐν τόπῳ τινὶ προσευχόμενον, Luke xi, i), etc.—We notice also that the faithful imitation of the Greek caused the translators to multiply the forms of the participle. The abundance of participles is one of the *traits* of " Church Latin." As Latin was very poorly provided with forms of this kind, ecclesiastical writers were led to a more or less abusive extension of the sense of existing forms, giving to the present participle, for instance, the value of an aorist. The prose of the classics already offered a few rare examples of this extension.

[2] Cherubim, Rabbi, Hosanna, alleluia, gehenna, Pascha, Sabaoth, etc. . . . The influence on the Greek of the Bible, previously attributed to the Hebrew, diminishes in importance in proportion as the knowledge of popular Greek became more pronounced. And more than one turn of phrase supposed to be of Hebraic origin attaches to even Latin of good style. The expression *vanitas vanitatum* usually considered as a Hebraism, is foreign neither to classic Greek nor even to Latin : Sophocles, *Œd. Col.* 1238, κακὰ κακῶν, *Œd. R.* 465, ἄρρητ' ἀρρήτων ; *Anth. Pal.*, vii, 45, Ἑλλάδος Ἑλλάς 'Αθῆναι ; cf. Varro, L. I., vii, 27, divum deus ; Plautus, *Trin.* 309 : victor victorum ; *Capt.* 825 : rex regum (also Horace, *Ep.* I, i, 107) ; Petronius, *Trimalch.*, nummos nummorum. According to Pfister, this practice would seem to have gone back as far as Gorgias and Prodicos (B. ph. W., 1914, 1449). The qualifying genitive (judex iniquitatis, filius caritatis, abominatio desolationis) unaccompanied by an adjective appeared in profane prose since the time of Apuleius. For the genitive of apposition (of the type *aevitas temporis, cupiditates libidinum* [numerous examples in Sittl, *Die lok. Verschied., d. lat. sprache,* Erl. 1882, p. 92 et s.]), compare such Greek classical expressions as πῆμα κακοῖο, εὐνῆς λέχος. In his work on the *Mathesis*, Firmicus Maternus wrote when he was not yet a Christian : *temporis aetas, erroris confusio, artis disciplina, malitiae improbitas*. Cf. Kroll, Rh. M. vol. LII (1897), 584 and Wölfflin, A.L.L., X (1898), 538.— Against the theory that the ablative of comparison accompanied by *a (major ab illo)* was of Semitic origin, the *Thesaurus ling. lat.* is of opinion that this is not true (I, 39). It quotes examples from Pliny the Elder, A.N., xviii, 126 : " alius usus praestantior *ab* iis non est " ; xxxv, 198 : " saxum utilius a sulphure." Sittl *(die lokalen Verschiedenh.)* and Wölfflin (A.L.L., vii [1892], p. 471) thought they saw in this use an imitation of the Hebrew preposition *min*. *Benedixisti benedictionem* has also analogies in archaic Latin : *cenam cenare*, Plautus (*Rud.* 507) ; *messem metere* (*Epid.* 701) ; *noxam nocere*, Titus Livius (quoting an ancient expression [IX, x, 9]). For the use *morte moriemini*, we may compare *luce lucebit*, Plautus (*Cure.*, I, iii, 26) ; *curriculo currere* (*Most.* 349) ; Cicero, *occidione occidere* (*Phil.*, XIV, xxxvi) ; *morte mori*, Sallust (*Hist.*, III, xxv) : we have already in Homer, *Odyss.*, xi, 410 : ὥς θάνον οἰκτίστῳ θανάτῳ·

[3] Some critics, such as Ronsch, have grossly exaggerated the importance of this. Cf. Corssen in Bursian's *Jahresb.*, vol. CI (1899), p. 82. Nevertheless, the repeated declarations of ecclesiastical writers do not permit us to unduly minimise it.

to render new meanings [1]—moral ideas which up till then had not been developed, and liturgical ceremonies. Others were coined in a manner sufficiently conformable to the rules governing their Latin derivation. Has not Cicero himself claimed the right to impose new names on new ideas, *imponenda nova novis rebus nomina?* [2] How could the translators have refused new formations and the adaptations of which they felt the necessity ? The Roman vocabulary the poverty of which has been deplored by Lucretius (" *propter egestatem linguae* . . ."), and which Seneca himself found to be wanting,[3] enriched itself by superabundant additions whose composite variety completely disconcerted those lettered men who had been formed on the prudent eclecticism of the traditional discipline.

[1] Devotio, aedificatio, transgressio, praevaricatio, remissio, vocatio, conversio, praedicatio, paenitentia, virtutes (miracles), tentator (the devil) ; tingere (baptize), absolvere (absolve), etc. The development of the Judaisms of certain of these words has lent itself to some interesting studies. Much still remains to be done in this connection.

[2] *De Finibus*, III, i. St Jerome was to learn later how to avail himself of this and similar passages to justify his own verbal creations which be it said were very discreet. *Comm. in Gal.*, I, 12 (P.L., xxvi, 323) : " Si itaque hi qui disertos saeculi legere consueverunt, coeperint nobis de novitate et vilitate sermonis illudere, mittamus eos ad Ciceronis libros qui de quaestionibus philosophiae praenotantur, et videant quanta ibi necessitate compulsus sit, tanta verborum portenta proferre quae nunquam latini hominis auris audivit, etc. . . ." " And," adds Jerome, " nevertheless, although I have been translating not from the Greek but from the Hebrew, I have ventured upon fewer novelties in my ample transpositions than did Cicero in works of far lesser dimensions."

[3] *Ep.* LVIII : " . . . quanta verborum novis paupertas, immo egestas sit."

CHAPTER II

THE FIRST CHRISTIAN WRITERS IN THE LATIN TONGUE: TERTULLIAN

BIBLIOGRAPHY

I. Tertullian : The question of the manuscripts of Tertullian demands a careful examination. These manuscripts fall into two families :—

A. The *Agobardinus*, so called from the name of its owner, Agobard, Bishop of Lyons, who died in 840. He had it transcribed, and bequeathed it to the Church of St Etienne at Lyons. This manuscript is to be found in the Bibliothèque Nationale in Paris (*Parisinus*, No. 1622, saec. IX). At the present time it contains no more than thirteen treatises, namely : the *Ad Nationes*, the *de Praescriptione*, the *Scorpiace*, the *de Testimonio Animae*, the *de Corona*, the *de Spectaculis*, the *de Idolotria*, the *de Censu animae* (*de Anima*), the *de Oratione*, the *de Cultu feminarum*, the *Ad Uxorem*, the *de Exhort. Castitatis*, and the half of the *de Carne Christi* (up to § x, to the words *sed animae nostrae*). In its original make-up it contained many others as is proved by a very precious index which can be read on page 2. This index enumerates twenty-one works as belonging to Tertullian. The second part of the manuscript having been torn out, eight of them have disappeared —a mutilation all the more to be regretted as out of these eight treatises, five have never been found reproduced in any other manuscript and are totally lost, namely, the *de Spe Fidelium*, the *de Paradiso*, the *de Carne et Anima*, the *de Animae Submissione*, and the *de Superstitione saeculi*.

B. The second family falls into two groups of manuscripts, the one older and the other of more recent date.

(*a*) The *oldest group* is represented by the *Montepessulanus* (biblioth. municipale de Montpellier), XIth century, which includes seven treatises, and by the *Paterniacensis* (MS. *de Payerne*), now at Schlettstadt, of near kinship with the *Montepessulanus*, and which traces its descent from the same archetype. The *Paterniacensis* comprises nine treatises.

Two other manuscripts, the *Hirsaugiensis* (from the monastery of Hirschau in Wurtemberg) and the *Gorziensis* (from the monastery of Gorze near Metz), belonged to the same group. Both of them have been lost and we only know of them through the works of Beatus Rhenanus (Bâle, 1521 ; 1528 ; 1539).

(*b*) The more recent group is made up of manuscripts of the XVth century, Italian for the most part ; Kroymann traces them to two archetypes now at Florence. Several treatises, such as the *ad Martyras*, the *de Pallio* and the *de Fuga*, are only found in the manuscripts of this group. Of these two archetypes, one traces to the *Montepessulanus*, either directly or rather through an intervening one ; the other to the *Hirsaugiensis* through an intervening one which has been likewise lost.

Kroymann is of opinion that the archetype of the *Montepessulanus*, the *Paterniacensis* and the *Hirsaugiensis* ought to be found at the Abbey of Cluny. An old catalogue (XIIth century) of the library of Cluny has led him to this hypothesis. He supposes that a *Corpus* of the works of Tertullian must have been put together independently of that which we find in the *Agobardinus*. And it is from this *Corpus*, in two volumes, preserved at Cluny, that our manuscripts should come.

Such is the state of the text of the manuscripts of the second family that there are no grounds to hope for a completely accurate edition of the treatises which have not come to us through the *Agobardinus*. That is the essential point to bear in mind. We shall also note that three treatises, the *de Baptismo*, the *de Jejuniis* and the *de Pudicitia* are only known to us in Cagny and Mesnart's edition, Paris, 1545 (Gangneius). They are not extant in any manuscript.

The *Apologeticum*, by reason of its great historical importance, has enjoyed an exceptional handing down in manuscript. It figures by itself in nineteen MSS. Montfaucon quotes three more in addition in his *Bibliothèque des Bibliothèques*. By successive eliminations, the critics have established that the only one which ought really to count is the *Parisinus lat.* 1623, of the Xth century (P).

Its rival is a certain *Fuldensis* (F). This manuscript, formerly preserved in the library of Fulda, has been lost. The first editors of Tertullian were ignorant of it. A learned Belgian, François de Maulde, a Canon of Bruges (the Latinised form of his name is "Modius"), had noted in 1585 the different readings from his copy of the edition, which had appeared shortly before in 1580 through the instrumentality of De la Barre. These very numerous readings (more than 900), were communicated to Fr. Dujon (Junius), who published them as an appendix in his edition of 1597. It is through Junius that we come to know of them. A copy collated by Modius as far as chap. xv, 8, was discovered by Hoppe in the library of the town of Bremen. In some respects it is more carefully done than the transcription by Junius. M. Waltzing published it in the *Musée Belge* in 1912.

The attention of critics was not drawn to the *Fuldensis* in any decisive manner until after it had been aroused by C. Callewaert in an article in the *Revue d'Hist. et de Litt. religieuses*, vol. VII (1902), pp. 322-353. Confining his examination to the seven first chapters of the *Apologeticum*, Callewaert came to the conclusion that the *Fuldensis* derives from a source independent of the other manuscripts of this treatise, and represents in itself a tradition which has disappeared, the traces of which can be followed in the Greek translation of the *Apologeticum* up to the IIIrd century. He signalised the excellence of several of the variants provided by the *Fuldensis*. Since then, he has brought fresh proofs to support his theory, in the *Mélanges Ch. Moeller*, in 1914.

Lively discussions have been aroused during all these latter years on the value of P. and of F. I have dealt with these in the B.A.L.A.C. 1914, 4 fasc. (published in 1917), pp. 315-316. Since then, an *Etude sur le Codex Fuldensis* by M. Waltzing has appeared (*Bibl. de la Fac. de Philos, et Lettres de l'Univ. de Liége*, fasc. 21, 1917). M. Waltzing concludes that an authorised edition of the *Apologeticum* should be based on the *Fuldensis*, but that caution must be used with even the *Fuldensis*. See also Rauschen, *Emendationes et adnotationes ad Tertulliani Apologeticum*, F.P., XII (1920).

BIBLIOGRAPHY of Tertullian in *La Crise Montaniste*, 1913, pp. vii-xx, by P. de Labriolle.

LIST OF WORKS : See Table No. 2.

II. The Fragment of Muratori.—Text in P.L., III, 173-194 ; Preuschen, S.Q., Heft. 8 (1893), p. 129 ; Rauschen, in F.P., III (1905) ; Jacquier, *le Nouveau Testament dans l'Eglise Chrétienne*, vol. I (1911), p. 189 et s. (with commentary and bibliogr.).

III. The Martyrdom of Perpetua and Felicitas. — Text in P.L., III,
13-58 ; Robinson, T.S. 1, 2 (1891) ; Franchi de Cavalieri, in *Röm. Quartal-schrift*, Suppl. Heft. 5 (Rome, 1896).—French translation by Dom Leclercq,
The Martyrs, I, pp. 120-139 ; translation of the Prologue and the Conclusion
in the *Sources de l'Hist. du Montanisme*, by P. de Labriolle, p. 9 et s.—For
a general view of the Martyrdom, cf. the excellent analysis by P. Monceaux,
I, p. 70 et s. H. Delehaye, *les Origines du Culte des Martyrs*, Brussels,
1912, p. 430, gives proofs of the long popularity of Perpetua and her
companions in Africa.

SUMMARY

I. Pope Victor. Apollonius, the " Senator ". The Fragment of Muratori.—
II. The Origins of the Church in Africa. Tertullian. — III. The
Christian view of Tertullian. The intellectual equipment of Tertullian.
—IV. His life. His transition to Montanism. Tertullian, Head of
a Sect. V. His Apologetic Works.—VI. Tertullian in his relations
to the Pagans.—VII. Tertullian and Gnosticism.—VIII. Tertullian
and Montanism.—IX. Tertullian as Writer.—X. The *Martyrdom* of
Saints Perpetua and Felicitas. Was Tertullian the author of the
account?

I

IF we take away the translators of the Bible, were there any
Christian writers before Tertullian who wrote in Latin ?
Certain hints given by St Jerome in his *de Viris Illustribus*
permit us to believe that there were. In § liii he wrote :
*Tertullianus presbyter nunc demum primus post Victorem et
Apollonium ponitur.* In another place, in Epistle LXX, 5,
while giving a list of the principal Christian authors, he places
Tertullian first. He does not mention Victor and does not
breathe a word of Apollonius, whom he quoted some lines
previously, it is true (§ 4), but amongst the Greek authors.

As regards Victor, the indication given in the *De Viris
Illustribus*, LIII, may be completed by another offered in a
very short paragraph, § xxxiv : " Victor, thirteenth Bishop
of Rome, wrote on the subject of Easter, and certain other
opuscula. . . ." In the *Chronicle*,[1] Saint Jerome qualifies
these *opuscula* (called *volumina* in this work) as *mediocria*. It
appears probable that he was simply dealing with the letters of
Pope Victor at the time of the lively disputes with the Bishops
of Asia over the controversy about Easter ; [2] Jerome was also
in a position to know of other writings analogous to those of
Victor, as for example concerning the Montanist affair.[3]

[1] *Ad ann.*, 193 (Helm, p. 210).
[2] Cf. Eusèbe, H.E., V, xxiii et s. The letters given by Migne, P.L., V, 1483,
are not authentic.
[3] P. de Labriolle, *La Crise Montaniste*, p. 271 et s.

Some of these *quasi* official documents were perhaps rendered in Latin, or in Latin and Greek. St Jerome, who was very zealous in swelling as far as possible his catalogue of the writers of the Church, did not forget to make much of it however meagre was its literary importance.

As regards Apollonius, Jerome mentions in his *de Viris Illustribus*, § xlii, an *insigne volumen* which, in the reign of Commodus, he had read before the Senate " in order to give an account of his faith " which was imputed to him as a crime. He attributes to him the rank of *Romanae urbis senator*. This mention was taken from Eusebius with certain fanciful additions with which Jerome supplements it. Eusebius relates in his *History of the Church*, V, xxi, that Apollonius when denounced for being a Christian was invited by the judge, Perennius, who knew him to be a very cultivated man, to justify himself before the Senate (Eusebius does not say that Apollonius was himself a Senator) ; that in front of all he made " a very eloquent apology of the faith for which he was bearing witness," and that after that his head was cut off. The words of Apollonius had been inserted by Eusebius in his *Relatio* of the early martyrs, which has unhappily been lost. The *acta* of Apollonius as we now possess them in Greek and in Armenian, do not give any *apologia* properly so called, but only the replies of Apollonius to the judge. The matter rests very obscure. Jerome himself, who knew no more than Eusebius, could not have been sure that this alleged apology had been written in Latin and it is from this uncertainty that his hesitating attitude without doubt proceeds.

All this is therefore of little account and doubtful, and we must pass on to more solid ground.

We will only mention, lest we forget it, the explanatory list of the New Testament, known under the name of the *Fragment of Muratori*. This index in eighty-five lines, mutilated at the beginning and possibly at the end also, was discovered by Lodovico Antonio Muratori, the learned librarian of Milan, in a manuscript of the VIIIth century in the Ambrosian Library, and published by him in 1740.[1] This manuscript, which is the only one to contain the text, came from the Monastery of Bobbio in Lombardy. The Fragment is of interest, especially to philologists, on account of its faulty Latin

---

[1] *Antiquitates Ital. medii aevi*, III, 851.

from which several critics (Hilgenfeld, Zahn, Chapman) suspect a translation from a Greek original, and to the historians of the Canon of Scripture who find therein much information of great value. The anonymous author begins by laying down what he knows of the origin of the Gospels of Luke and John, and then lays stress on the fundamental agreement of the Gospels ; he passes on to the Acts of the Apostles, to the Epistles of St Paul, of St Jude and St John (to which he joins in a quite unexpected manner the Book of Wisdom), to the Apocalypses of John and of Peter, to the *Pastor* of Hermas of which he recommends the reading in private and discountenances its public or liturgical reading. Then at the end come some very obscure lines [1] from which we may gather the opinion that we must explicitly exclude from the Canon certain heterodox books which aspired fraudulently to creep in to it, and which amongst certain sects passed for divinely inspired works. We cannot be far out in placing the writing of this fragment about the year 200. Th. Zahn [2] thinks that it must have been compiled in Rome or in some neighbouring community. But his own method of proving this somewhat impairs the conclusion at which he arrives. In fact, he notes himself that the expression *urbi* (lines 38 and 74–76) were used throughout the Empire—not only in the capital—to mean Rome ; that *sedente cathedra urbis Romae ecclesiae Pio episcopo* (I, 15–76) is a well recognised phrase on the lips of a Roman speaking to Romans ; finally, that the author shows no special *pietas* for the Church in Rome nor claims for her any exceptional privilege in the matter of deciding what was the authentic Canon. We may here add an observation which has been developed by Dom Chapman.[3] The author of the *Muratorianum* declares (I, 71) : " We also accept, and these only, the Apocalypses of John and of Peter." Now there exists no proof that the Roman Church in the IInd century admitted the Apocalpyse of Peter, which, on the other hand is quoted just like a canonical book by Clement of Alexandria.[4]

---

[1] Cf. P. de Labriolle, *La Crise Montaniste*, p. 288.
[2] *Gesch. d. neut. Kanons*, II, 14.
[3] R. Bén. XXI (1904), p. 240 et s.
[4] *Eclogae ex scriptis proph.*, § 41, 48, 49.

II

It was Northern Africa which gave to Christian literature the greater part of the writers who shed their lustre on it for the space of nearly three centuries. Up to the IVth century, Africa was the home of Western Christian thought. We know that during the same period her contribution to profane litera-ture was by no means insignificant. Here is the right place to give an account of the " genius " of Africa, her tendencies and her special characteristics. We must guard against any complete synthesis of these attributes, however brilliant the partial glimpses we may obtain : as a matter of fact, it is as embarrassing to note down the specific *nuances* of the African temperament as to define with exactitude the " Africanisms " in the vocabulary and syntax around which the school of Ed. Wölfflin made so great a stir some while back.[1]

We know nothing of the beginnings of the Church in Africa. Towards the end of the IVth century, there were noteworthy Christians in that country who were hardly better informed than ourselves. One would gladly consider her as an off-shoot of the Church in Rome. This is a plausible hypothesis but one which goes further than the texts we have to prove it.[2] She emerged on a sudden from the twilight in 180. On the 17th July, 180, twelve Christians [3] of the town of Scillium (possibly in the Pro-Consulate of Numidia, but the exact spot has not been located), seven men and five women appeared before the Pro-Consul Vigellius Saturninus. They remained steadfast in their wish to continue Christians ; they even refused the reprieve of thirty days which the Pro-Consul offered them for the purpose of thinking over the matter again, and heard their sentence to perish by the sword. We possess both in Latin and in Greek several specimens of the *Acta* of their martyrdom. These *Acta* were originally composed in Latin. The passage, which is very short, bears the sobriety of language of a lawyer's statement wherein no rhetoric mars the stern truth of their words and attitude.

[1] Cf. Wölfflin in the *Sitz.-Ber.* of the Academy of Bavaria, 1880, p. 333, and in several articles in A.L.L. ; Sittl, die lokalen Verchiedenheiten der Latein Sprache, etc., Erlangen, 1882.
[2] Paul Lejay, *les Origines de l'Eglise d'Afrique et l'Eglise romaine*, in the *Mélanges Godefroid Kurth*, Liége, 1908.
[3] It appears to be probable that out of the twelve names, six were added after the event and do not belong to the group of martyrs of the 17th July. Cf. Saltet, in B.L.E., 1914, p. 108–125.

Some days previously, the same Pro-Consul had struck down four other martyrs at Madaurus. A period of calm seems to have followed this short persecution [1] and during this respite the Christian communities swelled rapidly in Africa, especially at Carthage. " If we are willing to offer to die," Tertullian was to say to the Pro-Consul Scapula [2] about the year 212, " what would you do with so many thousand people, with these men and women, these living beings of every sex and age, and of every condition, who would come forward to hand themselves over to you ? How many butchers, how many swords would you need ? What would happen to Carthage thus decimated by you when everyone would recognise there his near relations, his neighbours, perhaps men and women of your own rank, the leading citizens and the parents, or the friends of your friends ? " In short, towards the end of the IInd century, the Church in Carthage was provided with all the organisation which assured its vitality : it counted a considerable number of the faithful, and the disputations on moral and doctrine excited there an interest which betrayed the ardour of her faith. Such was the *milieu* wherein was born the father of Latin Christian Literature, Quintus Septimius Florens Tertullianus. [3]

III

TERTULLIAN became for the early ages of Christianity a famous example of the lamentable falling away to which men of rare intelligence are exposed. If a man like him fell into the snares offered by the wild speculations of Montanism, who could dare to feel sure of himself ? They gave expression to words of grave pity in his regard not altogether lacking in bitterness. And they took advantage of his unsound reputation to copy from his writings abundantly—without giving his name !

[1] Tertullian, *ad Scap.*, IV.
[2] *Ad. Scap.*, V (Œhler, I, 550). Cf. *ibid.*, II : " cum tanta hominum multitudo, *pars paene major civitatis cujusque*, in silentio et modestia agimus."
[3] These names are vouched for by testimony of differing value. Tertullian called himself *Tertullianus* (*de Bapt.*, XX ; *de Exhort. cast.*, XIII : this last passage besides being very much spoiled is not found in the better manuscript, the *Agobardinus*) and *Septimius Tertullianus* (*de Virg. vel.*, XVII). Lactantius calls him likewise *Septimius Tertullianus* (Inst. Div., V, 1, 23). *Quintus* and *Florens* are only provided by a subsequent tradition, gathered in the XVth century by the humanist J. Trithemius (John of Trittenheim) and Politianus (Angelo Poliziano).

However, admiration found its way through censures and scandalised looks.   And it was for Tertullian's knowledge that it was especially felt.   His style is sometimes accounted obscure and not sufficiently polished.   But what prodigious erudition !   St Jerome, whose competence no one will deny, exclaims in one of his letters :   " *Quid Tertulliano eruditius, quid acutius ; Apologeticus ejus et contra Gentes libri cunctam saeculi continent disciplinam.*" [1]   Vincent of Lerins went still further than these flattering terms in his famous *Commonitorium.*[2]   In his view, Tertullian was to the Latins what Origen was to the Greeks : " Who was more learned than this man ? who as competent as he in things divine and human ? So much so, that all philosophy, all the different sects of the philosophers, their founders, their adherents, and the systems defended by the latter, history and science under their multiple forms—all these, the wonderful extent of his intellect embraced. . . ."   His praise of him goes on increasing in ample measure, to end, it is true, in regret that a man so eminent made so bad an ending and could become " a great temptation " in the Church.

Tertullian's scholarship is really remarkable.   It will appear still more so if we compare it to that of the most learned pagans of his time.   Nowadays we have become more scrupulous and harder to please, and are sometimes tempted to find it superficial, unreliable and second-hand.   But we should be wrong in minimising its solid parts and especially its amplitude. Tertullian wrote with equal facility in Latin and Greek : many of his treatises were composed in both these languages.   He was familiar with the greater part of the great systems of Greco-Roman philosophy, and, however incapable he was of following with impartiality and sympathy the ideas of others, he knew how to extract from them their leading characteristics for the purpose of refuting them, or compelling them to coincide with his contention.   He borrowed much from profane philosophy especially from Stoicism.   He was no stranger even to physiology : in an age when all development of an argument was evolved in the abstract by a simple chain of interlinked reasonings, or by texts placed together one after the other, Tertullian had the merit of enlarging the habitual field of the logicians and psychologues, his pre-

[1] *Ep.* LXX, 5.   [2] § xxiv.

decessors or his contemporaries ; he interested himself in the
results arrived at from natural sciences ; he foresaw what the
thinker might draw from them in the pursuit of his own
speculations ; and of all the Greek and Latin writers for whom
he gave evidence of the greatest consideration and even of
respect, men of science held the first place.[1]   To this we must
add his vast knowledge of law, which in a large measure gives
to his work its general tone and individual colouring.   It is
easy to see that in this respect he is a past-master.   When
he touches on law, he is not like some amateur who ventures on
ground which is not his own, but, if not quite like a consulting
lawyer, at least like a *causidicus* who knows all its secrets,
all its machinery, all its tricks, I was going to say, and who
makes them cleverly serve his own purpose.[2]   If subtilty,
strength of logic, the art of following without losing the
thread of a fundamental axiom in its application to a multitude of different cases are the essential marks of the legal
mind, Tertullian possessed them all in a high degree.   We
must also consider the great number of texts from Scripture
which he has quoted, interpreted, and paraphrased with so
much aptness and stubborn desire to convince.   It is quite
easy to see that he had at his service every *instrumentum fidei*,
and his wonderfully accurate memory, whatever else one may
say of it, provided him on each occasion with the deciding
points of which he had need.[3]

Neither the primitive Christian literature, nor that of the
IInd century even though heterodox, were strangers to him.
He had read the *Pastor* of Hermas, which for long he treated
with respect, then with fury and hatred when he saw the party
view which his anti-Montanist adversaries drew from it ; the

---

[1] This is what I have tried to demonstrate in an article in the *Archives générales
de Médecine*, 1906, pp. 1317–1328.
[2] Cf. P. de Labriolle.   *Tertullien jurisconsulte,* in the *Nouv. Revue histor. de
Droit français et étanger,* Jan.–Feb. 1906 ; and Schlossmann, *Tertullian in Lichte
der Jurisprudenz,* in Z. *fur Kirchengesch.*, XXVII (1906), 251–275, 407–430.
Schlossmann emphasises the exaggerations which tend to identify Tertullian with
the lawyer of the same name whose five fragments are quoted in the *Digeste* (I, iii,
27 : Mommsen, Berlin, 1908, p. 34 ; XLI, ii, 28 : p. 701 ; XXIX, i, 23 and 33 :
p. 437, and XLIX, xvii, 4 : p. 890).
[3] He possessed the Old Testament in the text of the Alexandrine Canon, and
of the twenty-seven books of which the New Testament is composed, he omits in
his quotations only the IInd Epistle of Peter, the IInd and IIIrd Epistles of John,
and the Epistle of James (a passage in the *Scorpiace,* XII, proves that he was not
acquainted with the latter)   He attributed to Barnabas the Epistle to the Hebrews.
His blunders in quotations from the Bible are rare ; thus, in the *de Fuga,* II, he
confuses the heretics of I Tim., i, 20, with those of II Tim., i, 15.

Acta Pauli on the origin of which he gives in the *de Baptismo*, XVII, much careful information ; perhaps also the *Acta Pilati* (cf. *Apol.* XXI).

Among the Montanist *opuscula*, a collection of oracles of the Phrygian soothsayers came into his hands. In the *de Anima*, he quotes the *Acta* of Perpetua and Felicitas, certain portions of which are penetrated with the Montanist spirit. Further he examined the work of the anti-Montanist Apollonius, which appeared in about the year 212, next he was to add almost at once a seventh book directed against this polemist to the six books of his *de Ecstasi*. With regard to the Greek apologists, he did not perhaps testify all the gratitude which was their due. He only mentions Justin, and even then only on the score of his being an opponent of Gnosticism, not in his capacity of apologist. He is content to sum up *en bloc* and in a somewhat scornful manner at the beginning of his *de Testimonio Animae* the methods of his forerunners, their unfruitful efforts at conciliation between the wisdom of the pagans, and the truths of Christianity. Two of them, nevertheless, he has laid under large contribution, namely, St Justin, whose *Apologies* and his *Dialogue* with Tryphon he exploited, and Tatian, who provided him with some important notions on the theory of the Logos and on Christology. He also stripped bare, in pursuing his polemics against individuals, the writings of the Gnostics and anti-Gnostics. The longest of his treatises, the *Adversus Marcionem*, rests on an analysis of different documents emanating from Marcion himself, in particular the New Testament retouched by the heresiarch, and his *Antitheses*, in which he placed in strong relief the contradictions between the Gospel and the Law. While taking toll of the refutations previous to his own, Tertullian had read with his own eyes the *Phaneroseis* of Apelles, the work by Hermogenes on the eternity of matter, and several other *opuscula* which were circulating amongst the Gnostics, for example, a treatise on the lawfulness of flight in face of martyrdom. He made extracts from a large portion of the orthodox disputations, such as those of Irenæus and Theophilus of Antioch, but in more than one case he went in quest of first-hand documents and thoroughly explored the prolific output of the Gnostics. He was equally familiar with the work of Melitos of Sardis whose mental equipment was not without analogy to his own. As regards Clement of Alexandria, his contemporary, it seems that he did not know him and that Clement also was equally unaware of Tertullian.

This is but a very rapid inventory. It will suffice however to reveal the amplitude of the breadth of his intellect. And what gives a correct estimate of its trend from this point of view, is to recognise that the cast of his mind was not purely speculative. There was nothing about him of the learned recluse, nor of the mystic absorbed in his dreams. He was admirably cognizant of the pagan and Christian world in the midst of which he was living. We find in his writings, interspersed in the midst of discussions and polemics, a host of features which make Carthage his native city, with its exterior and picturesque aspects, live again before our eyes, as well as its moral and religious life.[1] And all this precise information extended far beyond the horizon of Africa, as far as the most distant regions of scattered Christianity.

Endowed with a mind fundamentally positive and practical, with a talent tempered to a superior fineness, which knew how to bind together in vigorous systems, theology, moral, and discipline, without mentioning the Latin tongue itself which he constrained with so much learning to new uses, this original and powerful personality inaugurated Latin Christian Literature in the West in a manner which was most resplendent.

IV

A SHORT notice in St Jerome's *de Viris Illustribus*, § liii, and a few rare confidences of Tertullian about himself, offer us almost the only data at our disposal for relating his life.

He was born probably between the years 150 and 160 : in any case, he had reached the full maturity of his talent by 197 when he wrote the *Apologeticum*. He was a native of Carthage. According to St Jerome, his father fulfilled the duties of " proconsular centurion," which may mean either a centurion of the town cohort stationed at Carthage, or an official

---

[1] I would especially mention the *ad Scap.*, III–V ; *de Res. carnis*, XLII ; *Apol.*, XVI ; *ad Nat.*, I, xiv ; *Scorp.*, VI ; *de Idol.*, XV ; *de Pallio*, I ; *adv. Val.*, VIII, etc. Tertullian is an authority of the first order on the times of the Emperors.

personage bearing the title of centurion, not officially but one in use by common parlance.[1] His family was pagan. He himself deplores his errors of former days, and his sarcastic observations in regard to Christian beliefs : " *Haec et nos risimus aliquando : de vestris sumus. Fiunt, non nascuntur Christiani.*" [2] He confesses that he was a sinner, that he frequented the public shows,[3] that he committed adultery.[4] He may possibly have had himself initiated into the mysteries of Mithra.[5] He gives no very clear explanation of the reasons which influenced his turning to Christianity. The spectacle of the heroism of the Christians must have produced in his mind a lively impression : " Everyone, in the face of such prodigious endurance feels himself as it were struck by some doubt, and ardently desires to find out what there is at the bottom of this matter : from the moment that he understands the truth, he forthwith embraces it himself." [6] He also energetically extols the evidence that existed of the power of exorcism possessed by the Christians : " What proof can be more certain ? Here we see the truth displayed in its simplicity under the eyes of all, and strong in its own virtue. It is impossible to suspect any trickery." [7] Reading the Scriptures does the rest.[8] Tertullian therefore was a convert who exchanged a very free manner of living for the rigours of Christian discipline. His horror of paganism, even where it was least open to blame, might have proceeded from his hatred of a past whereof he felt in himself the re-awakenings.

He was married. In his *Ad Uxorem*, he addresses himself to his wife and asks of her not to contract a second marriage. Was this jealousy for himself after he should be dead ? Certainly not, since Christ predicted the altogether spiritual conditions of the Resurrection. But a salutary counsel of which every Christian will know how to draw profit.

He was a priest. St Jerome gives us formal testimony on

[1] M. René Cagnat courteously communicates the following : This information of Jerome is confirmed by a passage in the *Apolog.*, IX, 2, if we can admit the reading *patris nostri* which the *Fuldensis* alone gives. On this text, see Dessau in *Hermes*, XV (1880), 473, n. 2 ; Tissot, *Fastes* , . . , p. 8 ; Pallu de Lessert, *Fastes des Prov.* Afr., 1 (1896), p. 296 ; Audollent, *Carthage Rom.*, pp. 399 and 720.

[2] *Apol.*, XVIII, 4. Cf. *de Paen*, 1.

[3] *De Spect.*, XIX.

[4] *De Res. Carnis*, LIX.

[5] A rather enigmatic allusion in the *de Praescr.*, XL, 4.

[6] *Ad Scap.*, V ; cf. *Apol.*, L, 15.

[7] *Apol.*, XXIII, 7.

[8] Cf. *Apol.*, XVIII, 1.

this point. This testimony is in opposition to the false interpretation of critics by which they have sought to invalidate it. How can one believe, after all, that Tertullian, a layman, could constitute himself without opposition the apologist, the polemist, the Doctor, which he was, and that he could have dared to give rules to a whole community in the intimate relations of their life with so much authoritative minuteness? Such a case would have been too exceptional in the early days of Christianity for no one to have stigmatised it as unusual. After the deceptions inflicted on the Church by Tertullian, there would not have been wanting people to diminish their importance or to give some explanations of their cause by reminding themselves that he had assumed the responsibilities of a teacher to which no official charge had appointed him, and that such a usurpation had intoxicated him with pride and finally ruined him. Now these considerations—so natural from the pen of writers in the Church—are nowhere apparent, and this silence completes our conviction that the information given by St Jerome can be and should be accepted as authentic.[1]

The great event in his life as a Christian was his going over to Montanism. How could such a man, with a mind so positive, so staunch a promotor of organised regulations, in full possession of his intellectual maturity and his *prestige* amongst his brethren, have allowed himself to become mixed up with an Oriental sect whose more or less frenzied external aspects were so little calculated to attract him? This is a somewhat confusing problem the solution of which, however, as we shall see, is not beyond attainment.

This sect had its birth in Phrygia, probably about the year 172, under the impulse of Montanus, a "Prophet," in which apostolate, two women, Maximilla and Priscilla, were associated. Far from separating themselves from the "rule of faith," the Phrygian prophets formulated no proposition which was of a nature to stand in its way, and allowed themselves no rash speculations. It was not in this field that they directed their special efforts. Penetrated with the feeling that the world was shortly coming to an end (we know that this belief was common among the first generations of Christians, but these appeared to have sensed it with a quite special

[1] Cf. P. de Labriolle, B.A.L.A.C., 1913, 161–177.

intensity of apprehension), they desired above all to awaken souls from the moral lethargy under which they seemed to them to lie numbed, to arouse them by the fear of judgment to come, and to prepare them for this dread event through the agency of ascetic rules of a very precise nature. With a view to this, Montanus prescribed fastings, the carefully regulated programme of which left nothing to individual caprice ; he advocated the joyful acceptation of martyrdom ; he refused on principle all pardon to sinners convicted of grave delinquencies, in order not to encourage their weakness by any too accommodating amnesties.

This rigorousness, however formidable, did not go however to the excessive lengths to which asceticism is sometimes tempted to carry itself. Montanus possessed a certain sense of the practical, the impress of which he had shown in the clever organisation of his propaganda. Thus, he counselled that people should suffer martyrdom patiently, but not that they should go to meet it without necessity. Similarly, though distinctly hostile to re-marriage—and on this matter he had on his side a large part of the prevalent Christian opinion—he avoided any condemnation of the conjugal union in itself. He intuitively realised what human nature was capable of, but he had no hesitation in claiming from nature the most painful detachment in view of the imminent catastrophy.

Montanism might seem at first sight to have no other aim than to draw to itself, in order to carry them to the highest degree of exaltation and enthusiasm, the several strains of belief issuing from the purest vigour of Christianity. Notwithstanding, even in his native country, he soon awakened mistrust, and the Bishops of Asia were not lenient with him. The reason was that Montanus and his wives by no means gave themselves out as ordinary preachers of asceticism and virtue, as single-minded zealots seeking to communicate to others the flame by which they were animated. They considered themselves as the habitation of the Holy Spirit, or rather that they were identical with the Holy Spirit, the state of ecstasy being considered to have annihilated in them all that appertained to their own personality. Further still, the adherents of Montanus regarded him, and he regarded himself, as the living incarnation of this Consoler, this Intercessor, this

Paraclete, the coming of whom Christ had announced to his disciples according to the IVth Gospel (xvi), and who, in accordance with the promise of Jesus, was to lead them to the truth in its entirety. Thenceforward the oracles of Montanus became, as it were, a new Testament which in no way rendered void the Gospels, but completed them by filling up the gaps which Christ had left therein of His own will.

Montanism was not merely a movement, a simple guidance in the moral order, an aspiration towards a more rigid and purer life : it was belief in the mission of the Paraclete incarnate in the person of Montanus and in a lesser degree in that of his prophetesses, and in the absolute character of his precepts.

Such were the fundamental conceptions of the sect to which Tertullian gave his intellectual adhesion and the support of his rugged talent. He was not long in separating himself from the community at Carthage, and also in practically cutting off himself and his partisans from those whose lukewarmness he judged to be an offence. A passage from the *de Anima*, IX, proves that he celebrated the ritual ceremonies apart.[1]

However, the Montanist group at Carthage could never have been very numerous. People are not in the habit of giving themselves airs for loving the truth backed up by an *élite*, nor of mocking at the " vainglorious *crowd* of Psychics " ;[2] nor do they haughtily quote the *multi vocati, pauci electi* (Matth., xxii, 14), when they have the consolation of numbering around them close ranks of adherents.

The little we know of the later history of this group in Africa comes from St Augustine who informs us in chapter lxxxvi of his *de Haeresibus*. He tells us : (1) that Tertullian did not hesitate to embroil himself with the Montanist sect, and from that moment established " his own conventicles " ; (2) that the " Tertullianists "—by this name people distinguished his followers—lasted at Carthage up to the time of Augustine ; that they there possessed a basilica ; (3) that Augustine held a conference with the last adherents of the party, with the

---

[1] See P. de Labriolle, *La Crise Montaniste*, p. 461 et s.

[2] Gross, carnal beings. It was by this expression, borrowed from the vocabulary of St Paul, that the Montanists described those of the Catholics who had no desire to know anything about their apocalypses. See P. de Labriolle, *La Crise Mont.*, p. 139 et s.

result that they reconciled themselves to the Church and handed back their basilica to the Catholics.

Why should we question such precise and authoritative testimony ? A man of intractable character, always prone to find fault with others, embittered further by disputes in which no mercy was shown, by the loss of his former authority, by the dull remorse due to his own inconsistencies, it is not to be wondered at that Tertullian did not succeed in keeping under his rod all his adepts in their first fervour, and that he withdrew himself from them with a handful of irreconcilables. Besides, Augustine, having come into contact with the " Tertullianists " of his time, was able and must have questioned them on their origin. We must also note that he speaks of their reconciliation with orthodoxy as a matter of common notoriety (*basilicam, quae nunc etiam notissima est . . . ; quod etiam te* (he is writing to Quodvultdeus), *meminisse arbitror*). Neither any psychological likelihood nor any reasons of history invalidate the deliberate testimony which he gives.

When did Tertullian die ? We do not know. A. Réville [1] supposed that he entered again " within the pale of the common Mother." " It is evident," he declares, " that a man of such ecclesiastical character, so episcopal as Cyprian, would not have made the writings of a Doctor, who had formed a separate sect, his favourite reading " (cf. St Jerome, *de Vir. Ill.*, LIII). Réville's mistake is clear, and springs from the following considerations : (1) St Cyprian did, in fact, study Tertullian much. He closely imitated him in several of his treatises. But he never named him one single time, not even in the controversy around the baptism of heretics in which, however, he might well have availed himself of his opinion. (2) In addition, the tone in which ecclesiastical writers have spoken of Tertullian excludes the hypothesis of a tardy repentance. What cries of victory would have been heard had he finally recognised his error ! Now, from no quarter whatever did these hosannas resound.

Many of the details, which it would have been interesting to know, elude us in the life of this tempestuous genius. It seems probable that he made one or several sojourns in Rome.[2]

---

[1] *Nouv. Revue de Théol.*, 1858, I, p. 100.
[2] P. de Labriolle, *op. cit.*, p. 355.

E

The supposition of a journey to Greece rests on a false interpretation of *de Jejunio*, XIII.[1] However, the general line of
his biography may be approximately sketched, and the
examination of his works will render more precise its various
stages.

V

It is necessary to consider the books *ad Nationes* and the
Apologeticum together. These two treatises were written in
the year 197 at a few months' interval:[2] precise allusions to the
revolt of Albinus against Septimus Severus and to the reprisals which followed the defeat sustained by Albinus near
Lyons on the 19th February, 197, enable us to give the priority
to the *ad Nationes*. Besides, the *ad Nationes*, in more than
one place, indicates the developments in the *Apologeticum*;
and in places where the same arguments are arrayed in both,
it is in the *Apologeticum* that they are clothed in a more
finished form. The difference between the two *opuscula* is
shown in the aim which the author pursues in them : the
principal objective of the *ad Nationes* is to attack the pagan
morals and beliefs ; that of the *Apologeticum* is to defend the
morals and beliefs of the Christians. Again, the *ad Nationes*
is addressed to the " nations," that is to say, to the pagans,
to the unbelievers without ; the *Apologeticum* was destined
not for the Roman Senate, as the historian Eusebius of
Caesarea has wrongly supposed, but for the *praesides provin-
ciarum*, the Governors of the Provinces—that is to say, for the
Pro-Consul of Africa, and beyond Africa, for the entire body of
those high magistrates on whom depended practically the
fate of the Christians. Tertullian wrote his *Apologeticum* in
the form of a speech by counsel. As a matter of fact, no
defence whatever was allowed to a Christian accused before
the tribunal. It is just this lack of legal fairness that Tertullian takes for his text in developing his plea in writing,
which endeavours to anticipate the judgment of the *praesides*
whom he pretends to harangue.

[1] By the words *quibus tunc praesens patrocinatus est sermo*, the word *sermo*
does not mean the speech of Tertullian taking part personally in the Council
meetings which he mentions as taking place in Greece, but the word of God.
[2] *Ad Nat.*, I, xvii ; *Apol.*, xxxv, 9.

What were the occasions offered to Tertullian for lifting up his voice in protest ? For some fifteen years past, the Pro-Consuls of Africa had shown a certain tolerance in regard to the Christians. But unequivocal indications revealed the virulence of the popular hatred, to which a few years later in 202, the edict of Septimus Severus was to give free licence. " Day by day the people beset us," Tertullian affirms ; [1] " day by day they betray us, and very often they come to do us violence while at our meetings and assemblies." And again,[2] " how often, without consulting you (the *praesides*), on their own initiative do not the people who hate us, attack us, with stones and torches in their hands ? In their Bacchanalian fury they spare not even Christians who are dead ; from their repose in the grave, from the resting place of death, they snatch their bodies rotting in corruption, they tear them in pieces and scatter their poor remains." To violence, they added derisive mockery. An apostate Jew had devised a representation of the God of the Christians under the form of a two-footed ass and had circulated this caricature in Carthage.

" Here," relates Tertullian,[3] " is a new blasphemy against our God which the people pass from mouth to mouth. Not long ago, in this very town, an unmitigated scoundrel—a renegade from his own religion and who is only a Jew through the hurt which his own skin has undergone (we note the allusion to circumcision), exhibited a cartoon against us with this inscription : Onochoetes. It represented a personage with the ears of an ass, a cloak, a book, a cloven foot. And the crowd of people who believe this rascally Jew ! . . . There is only talk of Onochoetes throughout the town."

It was necessary at all costs to create a reaction against popular prejudices partaking of a more educated state of mind. Tertullian on the whole did no more than yield to the pressure of the same circumstances which had brought forth the Greek Apologists. These apologetic works he exploited : but he placed his characteristic mark, so vigorous and easily recognisable to all, on what he borrowed from them. It is by

[1] *Apol.*, vii, 4.
[2] *Ibid.*, xxxvii, 2.
[3] *Ad Nat.*, I, xiv. Cf. *Apol.*, xvi. The meaning of *onochoetes* has not yet been fixed (*asinarius sacerdos :* Œhler, Rauschen ; " He who lies amongst the asses " : Audollent : " engendré par accouplement avec un âne " : Dom Leclercq, etc.).

comparing Justin with Tertullian that we are able to form a better estimate of the masterful literary talent and of the strength of mind of the inexorable dialectician. Whether it was from scorn of vain *technique* or from an incapability of setting forth his ideas in order, Justin did not bind himself down to any settled plan of reasoning. When he wished to present a picture of the life of the Christians, he scattered their principal features in chapters xii, xiv, xv, xxix, lxii, of his first *Apology* and in chapter x of the second. He strikes some happy developments, but does not carry them to a point or extract the pith. The *Apologeticum,* on the other hand, is a compactly written and powerful composition. This has been sometimes contested : it could only have been otherwise without a very attentive consideration of the landmarks which Tertullian himself took pains to establish throughout the plan of his work.[1] First there is an introduction (i–vi) in which he lays down, in the first place, the *iniquitas odii erga nomen christianorum* (I, 4), and secondly, the uncertain character of those human laws which were put in force against the Christians as though they were irrevocable. In § iv the general line of his argument is indicated : " I am going to demonstrate positively the innocence of the Christians. And I shall not only refute the accusations brought against us, but I shall return them against their authors (such is, as a matter of fact, his method throughout this work) . . . ; I shall reply to each category of complaints which refers to the clandestine crimes which they bring against us (this point will be studied from § vi, 11 to § ix, 19), and to those which we perpetrate (as they say) within the knowledge of all (such as the *crimen laesae divinitatis,* examined from § ix, 20, to § xxviii, 2 ; and the *crimen* — or *titulus* — *laesae maiestatis* which is the subject of § xxviii, 3, to xlv), — crimes on account of which we are held to be abominable, mad, worthy of punishment and meet subjects for derision, *in quibus scelesti, in quibus vani, in quibus damnandi, in quibus inridendi deputamur.*"[2] A summing up in five chapters (xlvi to l)

---

[1] These points to note are marked in the following passages : i, 4 ; iv, 1–2, 3 ; vi, 11 ; ix, 1, 20 ; x, 1 ; xv, 8 ; xvii, 1 ; xxviii, 3 ; xxxix, 1 ; xl, 1 ; xlii ; xlvi, 1, 2 ; L.

[2] These last qualifications are too vague to my mind to allow one to connect them, as Callewaert would have it, with the separated parts of the development of his thesis from § vii to § xlix.

opposes the Christian doctrine to the doctrines of the philosophers and appeals to the justice of God against the ridiculous justice of man.

All this possesses a connected order as rigorously followed
as the texture of the *Apologies* of St Justin is indecisive and
wavering. It is especially in the passages dealing with law
that the superiority of Tertullian declares itself. Thus, in
chapter iv of his Ist *Apology*, Justin briefly criticised the
illegality of the procedure practised against the Christians.
Tertullian again takes up this point, but with a force, a
sequence, and technical precision, which only a long practice
in Roman law could have permitted him. The arguments
which fill the first chapters of the *Apologeticum* are irresistible
in logic and eloquence. They concentrate themselves into
well hammered formulae, they narrow themselves down into
irreducible dilemmas in which are shown the stupidity, and
the entire lack of logic of a procedure which was opposed to
all traditional forms of administering justice. In face of a
contest conducted in this manner, the Romans were to learn
that the issue was not with any haphazard attorney with more
zeal than knowledge, but rather with a man of law, broken in
to all the *finesse* of the bar, familiar with history and with law,
and whose wrongs were worthy to move (if not to convince)
their chief magistrates.[1]

The general tone of the work has an imperious and ironical
ruggedness very different from the conciliatory amenities of
Justin. Even when pleading for the sacred cause, Tertullian
is not the man to have recourse to concerted accommodation
or to diplomatic prudence. His keen wit takes his fill of
mythology, and revives those discussions inherited from
Greek apologists which likewise had received their full
measure of Jewish apologetics and Hellenic philosophy.
More respectful towards public authority, as the precepts
of St Paul enjoin as a duty, he claims however for his brethren
the right to shun the orgies for which the name-days of the
Emperors provided occasion, and to avoid all deification
of the Caesars. Where philosophers are concerned, there
must be no concession, no coquetting with them : where he

---

[1] M. Monceaux has, however, conceived with much subtilty what the Roman
magistrates could have opposed to the arguments of Tertullian, and to the reflections which his juridical thesis might have suggested to them. *Hist. litt. de l'Afrique
chr.*, i, p. 249 et s.

desires to place in relief the humility, the purity and dignity of the Christians, it is to the pride of Plato and of Diogenes, to the depravity of Socrates and Speusippus, to the base flatteries of Aristotle that he marshals them in opposition. He only slightly unbends when describing the altogether simple and correct life of the believers : yet he mingles with this more moving picture some mordant shafts which he knows not how to forgo.

He is almost completely himself in this work, with his powerful logic, the virtuosity of which is sometimes near neighbour to sophistry, with his incisive and haughty ruggedness which, one may say, seeks to humiliate his adversaries rather than to convince them, and with his nervous vigour of style.

It sometimes happens to writers to put their best selves into their first works. Tertullian has thrown into his *Apologeticum* a quantity of reflections which he is to resume later on in order to develop and make a profound study of them, and they were to form the substance of several of his treatises. Nearly all the thesis *de Testimonio Animae* is to be found in chapter xvii. He only had to accentuate in his *ad Scapulam* his proud declarations on liberty of conscience taken from chapter xxvii. In chapter xxxviii, he makes a preliminary flourish with vigorous invective against the theatre, which he is to thunder forth in the *de Spectaculis*. The leading motive of the *de Praescriptione* is already sketched out in chapter xlvii, 9 et s. And chapter xxi traces the outlines of the theory of the Word, which is to re-appear completed in the *Adversus Praxean*. All these questions, touched on *en passant* which he had neither the leisure nor the wish to study exhaustively at the time, he had in mind to take up again, when the right moment came, in order to clearly elucidate them and to extract therefrom their full measure.

The *Apologeticum* is one of those works which survive the circumstances which gave them birth and which enter into the common treasury of civilised nations. Nowhere shall we listen to more fervid demands for justice, tolerance, or the rights of an accused man ; to more vivid protestations against the tyranny of unjust laws assumed to be irrevocable ; lastly, to a more eloquent defence of Christianity, of its moral nobility, of the heroism of its martyrs. If there be in this admirable special pleading forms which are worn out, arguments which have perished with time, the contrary would have been the more wonderful. Taken as a whole, his work holds good, it still lives. " Tertullian," said Chateaubriand, " speaks like a modern ; the *motives of his eloquence have their roots in the circle of the eternal verities.* One part of his plea in favour of religion might still serve the same cause to-day " (*Génie du Christian.*, III, iv, 2).

The educated Christians immediately felt this startling superiority. The *Apologeticum* was translated into Greek a few years after its appearance, it seems. Tertullian himself did not trouble to do this, for some fragments preserved by Eusebius betray slight errors of interpretation.[1] At a time when translations of Latin works into Greek were so rare,[2] it was to the advantage of the faith to encourage these exchanges between West and East, in disregard of the national susceptibilities of Hellenism.

Compared with this masterpiece of passion and eloquence, the *De Testimonio Animae* appears a little weak. In it we see Tertullian endeavouring to establish an original method for gaining access to the heart of non-Christians. He states that the tactics of the Apologists, his predecessors, had not succeeded. They had attempted to prove through the instrumentality of a quantity of extracts drawn from the profane philosophers and poets that there were agreements more pronounced than disagreements between the new doctrine and the old pagan wisdom. These attempts at conciliation had resulted in no good : the enemies of the faith had contented themselves with rejecting their most admired masters in places where they seemed to offer support to the truth of Christianity. It was useless to have recourse to this vain pursuit of learning ; useless too, to eulogise the Holy Books, since in order to believe in them one must first be a Christian (*ad quas [litteras] nemo venit, nisi iam Christianus*). For the faith, the real point of contact must be sought for

---

[1] For example, compare Eusebius, *Hist. Eccl.*, II, ii, 4, with *Apol.*, v, 1–2 ; E. II, xxv, 4, with *Ap.* v, 3 ; E. III, xx, 7, with *Ap.* v, 4 ; E. III, xxxiii, 3, with *Ap.* ii, 6–7 ; E. V, v, 5, with *Ap.* v, 6–7. For inexactitudes in translation, see especially Eusebius, II, xxv, 4.

[2] Cf. E. Egger, *Mémoires d'Hist. anc. et de Philologie*, Paris, 1865, p. 266 et s. One might quote the *Georgics* translated by a certain Arrienus (who must be distinguished from the disciple of Epictetus) under Hadrian : The *Historiae* of Sallust, translated by Zenobius the sophist, likewise at the time of Hadrian.

in the human soul before it had undergone deformation through any learning : *te simplicem et rudem et impolitam et idioticam compello.* If we listen to the testimony of this yet whole-hearted soul, we shall realise the Christianity latent therein (*testimonium animae naturaliter christianae*). In the spontaneity of his language, of his entreaties, and of his exclamations even, his soul proclaims the unity and goodness of God, the existence of demons, a future survival and a reality of rewards beyond the grave. These are the truths which nature herself, nature pure and simple, had confided to him. And we must beware of seeing in these self-revealing phrases mere stereotypes, void of all thoughtful reflection, of the vicious forms and formalities to the use of which his familiarity with letters must have contributed. From what had literature herself borrowed these *eruptiones animae*, if not from the very soul itself ? Let the sincere-minded pagan offer an attentive ear to this truth which he carries enshrined in himself, whose accents he knows not how to comprehend !

There is nothing more curious than the divergences of criticism over this *opusculum.* Moehler and Neander admired it. Viala, a Protestant theologian, wrote : [1] " Of all the works of Tertullian this one seems to me to be the deepest, most universal, and possibly also the only one which will last out." Others, on the other hand, consider it as " one of the most feeble " by this author, and remark " that it is made up entirely of studies in Sophism and of conventional phrases in the current language of the day." [2]

Perhaps in the *De Testimonio Animae* there may be something to justify in a certain measure this enthusiasm and these slighting references. Tertullian promises more than he gives ; he traces out the main lines of a method further than he has succeeded in applying it : he sketches the theory of an agreement between the supernatural and the human soul, without establishing it by adequately defined facts. He possessed an intuition which is full of interest and he seems to have owed this to the Stoic philosophy,[3] but not sufficient psycho-

---

[1] *Tertullien considéré comme Apologiste,* Strasbourg, 1868, p. 29.

[2] Guignebert, *Tertullian* . . . , p. 252.

[3] The idea of " universal consent " is a stoic idea. See Diog. Laert., VII, LIV. We even find in stoicism whispers of a similar kind in the vulgar tongue, as revealing certain truths : Chrysippus, *Fragm. Stoic. Veterum*, fragm. 892 (Arnim, II, 243) ; Seneca, *De Benef.*, V, vii, 2 ; *Marc. Aurelius*, v, 8 ; x, 21.

logical penetration to enable anything vital it might contain to emerge, and his prescience has only approximately arrived at results.

The *Ad Scapulam* is a short " caution " in five chapters addressed to Scapula, the Pro-Consul of Africa, who, breaking away from the relative longanimity of some of his predecessors, in the year 212–13 began to persecute the Christians with hate, and did not hesitate to extend to them the penalty of burning which the worst criminals were generally able to avoid. The soldiery profited by this official rigour to despoil suspects likewise menaced by their own private enemies who denounced them freely. Right from the outset of this work, Tertullian lays down with perfect dignity the position which he intends to take up and maintain ; it was not pity he demanded for the Christians,—in becoming Christian they made the sacrifice of their life ; but it was to the self-interest of their enemies that he determines to appeal. He takes himself to task : " What am I saying ? Of their enemies ? rather of their friends, for ' to love those who love us ' is a sentiment natural to all ; it belongs only to the Christians to love their enemies (*amicos enim diligere omnium est, inimicos autem solorum Christianorum*)." He recalls certain fundamental principles : firstly, liberty of conscience (this he affirms in such formal terms that Pamelius, one of the editors of his works in the XVIIth century, cannot conceal his anxiety and observes that in the beginning of the *Scorpiace* there are precepts of quite a contrary kind) : [1] " Every man receives by natural law liberty to worship what seems good to him. . . . It is no part of religion to exercise restraint upon religion which should be embraced of one's own free will and not by force (*nec religionis est cogere religionem quae sponte suscipi debet, non vi*)." From this ensues the perfect loyalty of the Christians : " The Christian is no man's enemy, least of all the Emperor's. Inasmuch as he knows that he (the Emperor) is established by his God, he necessarily must cherish him, must respect and honour him and must desire his welfare, as well as that of the whole Roman Empire so long as the world shall last, for the Empire will last so long as the world. We therefore honour the Emperor as we are permitted to honour him, as it is fitting for him to be honoured, that is to say, as

[1] *Ap.* Migne, P.L., I, 777, note 2.

a man who is second after God. . . ." What subjects are more pacific than the Christians ?—yet nevertheless if we had a mind. . . . A muffled threat here rumbles. Already a hint of this might have been discerned in chapter xxxvii, 3, of the *Apologeticum*. In other respects, the *Apologeticum* supplied the greater part of the reasonings which are developed in the *Ad Scapulam*. There is one however which is new and which gives to this work its particular intention. Tertullian enumerates a certain number of recent facts wherein Scapula should read the portending signs of divine anger : devastating rains, balls of fire suspended over the walls of Carthage, and an eclipse of the sun.[1] We here recognise a development to which Roman historians were partial. We must note that Tertullian hits back in a very spirited manner against the pagans, and lays to their charge the common complaint, which imputed all public calamities to the Christians as despisers of the national gods. Then joining issue directly with Scapula he draws up for his consideration the warning spectacle of the punishments by which certain persecuting magistrates had been overtaken : one, Vigellius Saturninus, had lost his eyesight ; another, Claudius Herminianus, was attacked by gruesome sores festering with maggots : he recognised his mistake and died almost a Christian. Was not Scapula himself, even at this moment, bowed down by illness ? Now when had this illness begun ? Just after he had delivered up to the wild beasts the martyr, Mauilus of Adrumyttium.

The idea that Providence manifests in the world below the effects of its rigour by the chastisement whereby it strikes the impious in their bodies and in their life had for long brought to the Christians (as to the Jews of old) its avenging consolations. Josephus[2] had shown Herod falling into putrefaction, consumed while living by worms, maddened with suffering, and putting an end to his unspeakable woes by suicide. Herod Agrippa, the persecutor of the Apostles had expired, he too devoured by worms.[3] Pilate was reputed to have fallen under the yoke of such misfortunes that he was " compelled

---

[1] This eclipse took place, according to the calculations of modern astronomers, on the 14th June, 212. This allusion enables us to give a more or less authentic date to this treatise.

[2] Quoted in Eusebius, H.E., I, viii, 3–14.

[3] *Acts*, xii, 23 ; cf. Eusebius, I, x.

to become his own murderer and his own hangman."[1] Lactantius was to trumpet forth an ample score to the same strain in his *De Mortibus Persecutorum*. Tertullian already draws from these events their powerful effect in his *Ad Scapulam*; but he has sufficient moral and literary tact not to swell them to excess. The work possesses a noble and vigorous energy whose pathos becomes still more insistent towards the end where Tertullian supplicates the Pro-Consul one last time " not to fight against God " (μὴ θεομαχεῖι ; the expression, borrowed from the Acts of the Apostles, xxiii, 9, is quoted in its Greek form).

It was not only against the hostility of the public powers and the ill-usage of the crowd that the Christians had to defend themselves ; it was also against the Jews. Born of Judaism, long confounded with it by common opinion, Christianity did not have long to wait before undergoing the effects of the hostility of Israel for whom it cherished itself a profound antipathy. " *Nam et nunc adventum eius (Christi) expectant (Judaei), nec alia magis inter nos et illos compulsatio est, quam quod jam venisse non credunt* " : " The Jews are still expecting the coming of Christ and between them and us no subject of disagreement is stronger than their refusal to believe that He has already come." [2] This in reality was the cardinal point of dispute between Jews and Christians. But many other secondary subjects of strife had arisen to add to this fundamental grievance.[3]

Very numerous in Africa,[4] the Jews did their best to stir up the hatred of the pagans. *Synagogas Judaeorum, fontes persecutionum* is another phrase of Tertullian's.[5] A recent disputation in public which had resulted in failure on account of the bad behaviour of some of the audience, was to suggest to Tertullian the idea of putting in writing the arguments which it had not been possible to deliver orally. From this incident

---

[1] H.E., II, vii.

[2] *Apol.*, xxi, 15.

[3] Regarding this question, which deserves to be treated to its fullest extent, see the documents collected by Jean Juster, *les Juifs dans l'Empire Romain*, Paris, 1914, vol. I, pp. 35–76. A good general aspect is given in *Disc. et Conf.*, by Renan, p. 311 et s. ; Harnack, *Mission u. Ausb. des Christentums*, I, pp. 39, 50, 399 ; II, p. 77.

[4] Monceaux, *les Colonies juives de l'Afrique romaine* (*Rev. des Etudes juives*, XLV [1902], pp. 1–28) ; *Dict. d'Archéol. chr. et de Lit.*, I, 745 ; Audollent, *Carthage romaine*, p. 705.

[5] *Scorpiace*, X.

arose the *Adversus Judaeos*. The general purpose of this treatise is quite clear. Tertullian sets out to show the Jews that the general idea of revelation does not allow us to attribute to the Law of Moses any but a temporary value and that they were wrong in clinging to it, since the New Law had almost entirely taken the place of the ancient rites which had been abolished. An examination of the Prophecies proved that the expected Messiah had brought to mankind his message of salvation. From the time of Adam up to Christ, the divine ordinances had been evolved continuously, but from henceforth their end had been attained : " *Non potes futurum contendere, quod vides fieri.*" In matters of detail the discussion suffers from some confusion. The last chapters (ix–xiv) are borrowed for the greater part from the IIIrd book of the *Adversus Marcionem ;* [1] and this, together with instances of clumsiness, make us doubt whether it was Tertullian himself who made this unskilful transcription.[2]

VI

THE apologetic writings of Tertullian form the most generous, the most vibrating portion of his works, but not perhaps the most curious to whosoever would seek to penetrate within this soul of wrath and passion. From this point of view, far more significant are the treatises wherein he undertakes to define the attitude of the Christians in Africa as regards pagan society, and the various forms of the civilisation of his day. Here we shall learn to know him through and through with all the fierce ardour and rage of his temperament.

"Christianity and the Empire," Ernest Renan [3] stated, " regarded each other like two animals who would like to devour each other. . . . When a society of men . . . be-

---

[1] We may compare *Adv. Jud.*, ix with *Adv. Marc.*, III, xii, xiii, xiv, xvi, xvii ; *Adv. Jud.*, x with *Adv. Marc.*, III, xviii–xix ; *Adv. Jud.*, xi–xii with *Adv. Marc.*, III, xx ; *Adv. Jud.*, xiii with *Adv. Marc.*, III, xxiii ; *Adv. Jud.*, xiv with *Adv. Marc.*, III, xx–xxi.

[2] This problem in criticism can be studied anew in Monceaux, *Hist. litt. de l' Afr. chr.*, I, 295 et s., and Harnack, *Chron.*, II, 290, who both hold to its authenticity. Likewise Akerman, *Ueber die Echtheit der letzteren Haelfte von T. adv. Judaeos*, Lund, 1918, but Einsiedler, *De Tert. adv. Judaeos libro*, Diss., Augsbourg, 1897, and Kruger, *Gott. Gel. Anz.*, 1905, p. 31 et s., raise very strong objections.

[3] *Marc. Aurèle*, p. 428. A very similar argument occurs in E. Schuerer's *die aeltesten Christengemeinden in roemischen Reiche*, Kiel, 1894, p. 9.

comes a republic apart in the State, it is a scourge even though it be composed of angels. It was not without reason that they hated these men so gentle and benevolent to outward appearance. In very truth they were rending asunder the Roman Empire. They sapped her power. It was no good saying that a man is a good citizen because he pays his taxes, because he is an alms-giver and orderly, when in reality he is a citizen of heaven and only accounts his native land on earth as a prison in which he lives enchained side by side with the outcast." There are many who represent the first generations of Christians in the same light as did E. Renan; they imagined them as voluntary exiles from social life, and as stubbornly opposed to the temptations which it presented to them. We must not take too literally the somewhat emphatic declarations of certain apologists and the chiding unreasonableness of certain moralists. The reality appears to be very different. It is enough to read attentively the *opuscula* wherein Tertullian regulates matters dealing with questions of their interior economy to see how various were the leanings of the faithful in Carthage and Africa. There were the simple-minded, incapable and careless of speculative theories, who contented themselves with the quiet possession of their faith, but by reason of their simplicity were exposed to enervating sophisms;[1] there were the intellectuals, who prided themselves on broaching the most abstruse questions in religious metaphysics;[2] there were the weak, "the Christians fickle as air,"[3] who, far from savouring of martyrdom,[4] persecution,[5] and repentance,[6] before all else showed themselves desirous of their own tranquillity,[7] and pretended to contrive here below as comfortable a life as possible; even though at the

---

[1] " Qui simpliciter credidisse contenti non exploratis rationibus traditionum intentam probabilem fidem per imperitiam portant " (*De Bapt.*, I); " rudes animas " (*Adv. Marc.*, I, ix); " Nam et multi rudes et plerique sua fide dubii, et simplices plures quos instrui, dirigi, muniri oportebit " (*De Res. C.*, 11); " Simplices enim quique, ne dixerim imprudentes et idiotae, quae major semper credentium pars est " (*Adv. Pr.*, ii; cf. *ibid.*, i).

[2] Cf. *De Praesc.*, ix; *Adv. Marc.*, I, ii.

[3] " . . . Plerosque in ventum et si placuerit Christianos . . ." (*Scorp.*, i).

[4] Cf. *ibid.*, i: " sauciatam fidem vel in haeresin vel in saeculum exspirat (infirmitas)." See Harnack, *Mission*, I, 404, note 2.

[5] Arguments advanced by the partisans of flight in times of persecution are given in the *De Fuga* in § v, vi, vii, viii, x; note in § vi (Œ., i, 471) the words: " Sic enim voluit quidam, sed et ipse fugitivus, *argumentari*. . . ."

[6] *De Paen.*, v, 10–12.

[7] " Mussitant denique tam bonam et longam sibi pacem periclitari " (*De Cor.*, i).

price of the most grievous compromises ; [1] there were the " liberals ", who dreamed of reconciling Christianity with the world, or at least set themselves against all useless provocation ; [2] lastly, there were the rigorists, like-minded with himself. Tertullian assumed the task of herding this fluctuating and diversified human flotsam and jetsam willy nilly into the narrow paths which formed for him the only way permitted to a Christian.[3]

What in reality did Christianity mean for him ? A faith with no doubts, a *regula fidei*, in other words, a conglomerate compounded of precepts laid as of obligation upon the intelligence, whose authenticity was guaranteed by the unanimous voice of the Churches ; but before all else, a discipline, that is a rule of life, and a check upon the will. His legal mind approved of the idea of a doctrine which throws upon human life in all its different activities, in the infinite multiplicity of its acts, a closely circumscribed network of regulations, with the promise of eternal recompense for those who shall accept its enchaining hold, and the threat of eternal punishment against whomsoever shall set himself in opposition with a view to escape from it. The God whom he cherishes is the inflexible and jealous Judge who has established *timor* as the solid base of man's salvation, who scatters temptations in this world in order to prove His faithful ones, and who holds His vengeance ever ready. From this arose the strictures of Tertullian against the heretic, Marcion, who was given to making much of the anthropomorphic attributes of the God of the Old Testament.

" Hearken, ye sinners," cries Tertullian, " and you who are not yet sinners, in order that you may learn how you may become so. People have invented a God who doth not take offence, who neither groweth angry

---

[1] A goodly number of Christians were not at all disposed to deprive themselves of the theatre. Tertullian enumerates their excuses in the *De Spectac.*, i, ii, iii, xx, xxix. We may compare the distress of the author of the *De Spect.* (generally attributed to Novatian) in regard to certain analogous sophisms (Hartel, *Opera Cypriani*, III, p. 3). Mixed marriages had likewise their partisans (*Ad Ux.*, II). We shall notice, without wishing in any way to confuse these very distinct categories, that Tertullian admits that Christians could render themselves guilty of offences in common law (*Apol.*, xliv, 3, and xlvi, 17) and of crimes against nature (*De Pud.*, iv, 5).

[2] See especially the *De Idololatria*. It is easy to mark off the position taken up by his adversaries by following each refutation on Tertullian's side.

[3] *De Fuga*, xiv (Œ., i, 491).

nor taketh vengeance ; a God in a hell wherein no flames bubble forth, and which hath no outer darkness, no terrors to make you tremble, no gnashings of teeth. He is all good, I tell you, He forbiddeth sin surely, but only on paper. He holdeth you in regard, if you are kind enough to grant Him your obedience, for making some show of honouring Him. As for Fear, He will have none of it." [1]

A conception such as this enabled Tertullian to logically deduce for himself the necessity of a mortified life, entirely co-ordinated and hanging upon the thought of his own individual salvation. But he was not the kind of man to confine his efforts to the pursuit of a perfection purely egoistical. In addition to his duty as priest obliging him to exterior action, he was too combative, too passionate, too bent on winning over souls, and infusing into them his ideas, affections and hates, not to strive to impress on others his own ideal in so far as a perfect resemblance was possible.

To come to facts : see him busied in defining certain rules of conduct for the use of his brethren in cases of doubt or controversy. For example : in what measure was it lawful for a Christian to take part in the life of the pagans (*De Idololatria*), for a Christian woman to adorn herself (*De Cultu Feminarum*) ? Must young girls wear the veil (*De Virginibus Velandis*) ? When and how was it becoming to pray (*De Oratione*) ? He is never content with stating general principles. He enters into particular facts, in every little detail which makes up the thread of day to day. The *De Idololatria* is a kind of treatise in moral theology wherein, after having laid down the gravity of the crime of idolatry, Tertullian passes in review the different phases of life in the world, its callings, ceremonies, even its language, and sets himself to define in each case how far the Christian, who should be the enemy of indolence, might take part therein. And with what minuteness does he determine the conditions of prayer, the tone, the gestures and the attitude to observe (*De Oratione*) ! With what scrupulosity does he measure the length of the veil suitable for virgins, showing how it should be disposed before and behind, and just how long it should fall, and the exact age at which they should

[1] *Adv. Marc.*, I, xxvii.

begin to wear it! He is not one of those moralists who suppose that the spirit alone is sufficient to vivify everything. He likes to foresee, so as to give rules for everything, because he is aware of the feebleness, the perversity of man, and fears that he may escape by some side issue wherein he had omitted to trace the road he should follow or to erect warning notices. Rigidly defined explanations must therefore adapt the injunctions of the law to everyday realities.

This is the spirit, at once authoritative and punctilious, in which he treats of the problems sustaining the development of Catholic life in a heterogeneous *milieu*. Not that he was incapable of a kind of grave gentleness, even of a certain unction. Let us run hastily through the *De Paenitentia* : it is not a didactic treatise on penance as an ecclesiastical institution, but far more a kind of sermon wherein Tertullian addresses himself especially to the catechumens still only slightly familiar with the demands of Christian life, or too ready to elude them. One is struck by a certain soothing solicitude and benevolence in the tone which he adopts. Harshness, in very truth, is not wanting. He is prompt to anger against the " hearer of the word " who, while confessing to the purifying virtue of baptism, has thoroughly made up his mind, at the moment of receiving the rite, not to give up the sins which he loves (cf. § vi) ; against the sinner who grows weak with alarm at the thought that he will have to live " without taking the baths, sordidly deprived of all joy, in the coarse garb of sackcloth, under the unsightliness of ashes, with countenance disfigured by fasting " (XI). But in several places we are able to notice a gentle and compassionate mysticism, and accents of pious and tender charity : for instance, when in order to re-assure the sinner against every temptation to despair, he insists on the fatherhood of God (VIII).

The *De Patientia* and the *De Oratione* breathe the same relative serenity. In like manner, a virile emotion, with nothing insipid about it, permeates the entire *Ad Martyres* with a vein of consolation, the sustaining influence of which Tertullian brings to the *benedicti martyres designati*, who were awaiting the ordeal of torture and death in prison at Carthage. Here again, however, under an outward show of humility (*nec tantus sum, ut vos alloquar* . . .), together with respectful entreaties to accept their glorious destiny, the rigour of his asceticism pierces through, which would quickly make itself pitilessly felt before even the shadow of any weakness.[1]

This asceticism is the foundation and leading principle of Tertullian's nature. Even before he had given his full and entire adhesion to Montanism, he never ceased combating faint-heartedness, falling away, and weakness, whose deadly languor in his view weighed down the atmosphere. Formal refusal to allow the Christians to take part in the public shows under whatever form (the circus, theatre, athletic contests, gladiatorial encounters)—for all these reminded them of idolatry or exhaled pleasure (*De Spectaculis*); formal injunctions against exercising any calling which, from near or far, might give any colour to the worship of false gods; against the teaching of profane literature; express reservations in connection with engaging in commerce which thrives by cupidity and fraud and is often near neighbour to idolatry; the forbidding of any participation in any feast-day, in any ceremony, in any custom inspired by the worship of false gods; a formal interdict against accepting any public office; the incompatibility existing between military service and one's duty as a Christian; a proscription of every kind of verbal expression savouring of paganism (*De Idololatria*); the forbidding of the re-marriage of widows; of Christians to contract mixed marriages (*Ad Uxorum*). These are some of the stern limitations which he exalts, and with what merciless harshness, with what resolute, brutal acceptance of all the consequences involved in the principles which he sets forth!

There are pages, on the other hand, admirable for their dialectic, their subtil vigour and their ardent desire to convince. The curious thing is that in this fiery inquisitor there smoulders one lingering weakness: he has preserved some kindly feeling for rhetoric, its refinements and its tricks of style. Amid so much rugged exhortation, certain passages of a refined and delicate turn give a singular effect. This is how at the end of the *De Culta Feminarum*, he enumerates the virtues with which alone it becomes Christian women to embellish themselves:—

"Show yourselves adorned with the cosmetics and ornaments imitated from the prophets and the apostles.

[1] Cf. § ii and iv.

F

Derive your white vesture from simplicity, from modesty your red, paint your eyes with reserve, your lips with silence, hang on your ears the words of God, bind on your neck the yoke of Christ . . . , array yourselves in the silk of probity, the fine linen of sanctity, and the purple of chastity, and, decked out in this manner, you will have God for your lover ! "

He once gave free rein to this hidden disposition. It is in the prodigious *De Pallio* which, of a surety, is the most difficult from its Latinity, and in regard to which Claude de Saumaise, that incomparable exegetist of the XVIIth century expended large stores of ingenuity without succeeding in unravelling all its hard sayings. Under colour of justifying himself for having exchanged the toga for the rough cloak, Tertullian lets himself go (on a subject otherwise well-defined in Christian tradition) [1] in the most astounding developments, as if he were desirous of proving to the lettered men of his age what an unrivalled rhetorician he might have been if it had pleased him to have made a profession of *belles-lettres*. Such purposely trifling virtuosity in the author of the *De Idololatria* and the *Apologeticum* scandalised the good Tillemont : " We find in the *De Pallio*," he says,[2] " great erudition, but I do not think that we find in it all the wisdom and gravity which we might expect from a man with Tertullian's reputation." Malebranche,[3] for his part, in whose opinion Tertullian is a type of those " strong imaginations " whom he dislikes because " they throw passion over everything," declares that there is no excuse for " this foolish idea of making himself obscure and incomprehensible." And we must confess that it is strange that a man so penetrated with the seriousness of human life and so quivering with expectation of the eternal fatherland, should have indulged in these distilled literary conceits. A contradiction like this reveals how far Tertullian remained a man of his time, and how profoundly its profane

---

[1] Cf. Varro in his satire entitled *Modius*, fr. 314 ; Apollonius de Tyana, *Philostr*, p. 307, 19 Kayser ; Dion Chrys, *Or.*, lxxii ; Apuleius, *Apol.*, xxii. Geffcken, *Kynika und Verwandtes*, Heidelberg, 1909, has well studied the question of its sources. He refers the *De Pallio* to the " Diatribe " class and suspects Tertullian to have made extended use of Varro. The Christian note is discernible especially in § ii, iv, v and towards the end of the *opusculum*.

[2] *Mémoires pour servir a l'Hist. Eccl.*, Paris, vol. II (1701), p. 227.

[3] *De la Recherche de la Vérité*, Book II, part 3, chap. iii.

learning, which in all other respects he affects to hold in distrust, had set its mark on him.

VII

It is not only in the practical order, but also in the intellectual, that Tertullian practised his magisterial scolding. The Gnostics had no more formidable enemy.

The unbridled imagery of these pseudo-Christian intellectuals, deeply infected with individualism, and eager to promulgate new doctrines, who turned topsy-turvy the theory of creation, distinguished between the true God, and God the Creator and Legislator of the Old Testament, and placed between this supreme God and the visible universe their married Aeons, their *syzygies*, their *pleromata*, their *ogdoads* and their *archons ;* who made light of the reality of the events recorded in the Gospels and whittled down the historic Christ into a phantom Jesus who had neither suffered nor risen again, who enclosed in straitly circumscribed categories the benefits of a redemption reduced to absurdity, from which the greater part of mankind was excluded ; who distorted the idea of the Church which they personified in one of the Aeons of their grotesque cosmogonies ; of whom some ended by proclaiming that " it is quite lawful for gold to drag itself in the mud without soiling itself,"[1] that the destinies of the soul are in no wise solidly compact with the weaknesses of the flesh— acts not being able to change the spiritual nature of the human being—and that no one is obliged to suffer for an unreal Christ whose Passion was entirely fictitious : this unrestrained criticism, this pride which refused to bow before the beliefs common among the faithful inspired in Tertullian the most furious opposition.   All the more so that the Gnostics excelled in awakening doubt in the hearts of those who had the weakness or presumption to hold discourse with them,[2] and that many souls felt themselves discouraged by certain desertions which had just afflicted the Church.

In the *De Praescriptione Haereticorum*, Tertullian applied himself energetically to counter this formidable contagion of

---

[1] *St Irenæus*, I, vi, 2 (P.G., VII, 508).
[2] Cf. *de Praescr.*, VIII, i.

scandal. After an out-and-out indictment of profane philosophy, of Aristotelian dialectics,—that past mistress of
subtilty, contradiction, and of vain curiosities of the mind,—
he raises the juridical argument of " prescription " as a
supreme counter-stroke against this heresy. The true bearing
of this can only be appreciated through the practice of Roman
Law, and some explanations are here necessary.

The Law of the Twelve Tables established that whosoever
shall have enjoyed for the space of two years the use of any
property in land, and for the space of one year any other form
of property, shall become the legitimate owner thereof (with
the exception of certain cases reserved).[1] This form of acquiring property was called *usucapio*. But it was reserved only to
those possessing citizenship.[2] A different procedure was
needed for property in the provinces which did not carry with
it legal (Quiritian) ownership, and for aliens who, lacking the
title of citizens, were not qualified to obtain the *dominium*.[3]
" It was permitted to anyone who had obtained possession
of any property in the provinces in a regular manner, and had
been in possession thereof for at least ten years, to rebut
all claim on the part of the former possessor by means of a plea
in demurrer, *longae possessionis praescriptio*." [4] Supposing
a claimant came forward to claim any such property as
belonging to him. The Praetor then handed to him a written
form in which were defined the points on which the judge
designate would have to pronounce. But at the head of this
written statement he drew up, on the prayer of the defendant,
a conditional restraint setting forth that, if the defendant had
in reality possessed the property for the legal space of time,
the plaint brought against him would be non-suited *a priori*.
The *praescriptio*, therefore, was an exception enabling the
possessor to render void the action which was being brought
against him for the recovery of the property.[5]

Such was the method of procedure which Tertullian introduced into the domain of theology. The heretics arrogated to

---

[1] Cf. Cuq, *Les Institutions Juridiques des Romains*, vol. I, 2 ed. (1904), p. 85 ;
May, *Eléments de Droit Romain*, 3 ed. (1894), p. 168 et s.

[2] May, *op. cit.*, p. 143.

[3] For further details, see Cuq, II, p. 249 et s.

[4] Cuq, II, p. 249. The author adds, " This exception of which Gaius is unaware
and which is mentioned for the first time in a rescript of 29th Dec. 199, was very
likely embodied in certain provincial edicts before being made of general application
by the emperors."

[5] May, *op. cit.*, p. 170.

themselves the right to make dissertations on the Scriptures ; they interpreted them arbitrarily ; sometimes even they corrected and mutilated them. Now the whole question resolved itself into this : had they the right to touch them ? To whom did the Scriptures belong ? This point, once decided, would render unnecessary any plea on the question of principle.

It was historically indubitable, affirmed Tertullian, that they are the property of the Catholic Church who is heir to them through the channel of legitimate transmission. It was a fact that Christ charged the Apostles to preach His doctrine and made them its depositaries ; this fact they had transmitted in their turn to the Churches called Apostolic ; and, by the intermediary of these Churches, they had passed to other centres of Christianity in proportion as they became enlightened throughout the world. And what proved this uninterrupted succession still more was the identity of the traditions which perpetuated themselves among the different groups of Catholics.

This is the leading idea of this treatise, which is one of the most vigorous and most strongly put together of the writings of Tertullian and the one which modern theologians have most admired.[1] Strict logic would have demanded that, after it had been thus firmly supported upon law and upon history, any further disputation with the heterodox should have been refused. But it was too much to ask of this game fighter to obey the dictates of logic. It was above all for the use of the Catholic masses that he had hammered out his system. Once the bulk of his following had been placed in safety in the stronghold handed down to them, he did not hesitate to make on his own account the most brilliant *sorties* against the enemy as much to give additional assurance to his own people as to throw into confusion the opposite camp. The *De Baptismo*, which gives a complete theory of Christian baptism, is directed against a " viper " of the Cainite heresy. In the *Contra Hermogenem*, he joins issue with the painter of that name, " that heretic and mischief-maker who confounds eloquence with loquacity and impudence with stability." Hermogenes maintained that matter is eternal,

---

[1] I have made a study of the protracted fortunes of the argument from " prescription ", R.H.L.R., xi (1908), 408–428 ; 497–514.

and that God made everything from it. Against him Tertullian opposes a certain number of difficulties, in addition to copious abuse. In giving to matter eternity—an attribute belonging to God—Hermogenes, in his opinion, made matter the equal of God. Further, he raised it above God by reducing God to the necessity of having need of it in order to accomplish His work of creation. God, therefore, did not certainly make use of it *ut dominus*. He could only make use of it *precario*, for if He had used it *ex dominio*, it would be necessary to make Him responsible for the existence of evil in the world, since He would not have permitted matter, an attribute of Himself, to spread abroad the evil which it holds within itself. Not having possessed it *ex dominio*, He could not on that account have made use of it except as of a property outside Himself,—*aut precario* because He had need of it, *aut ex injuria*, because He was the more powerful. Let Hermogenes choose ! Thus, in each detail of the discussion, the argument from law crops up every moment. The *Adversus Valentinianos* is little more than a compilation of passages drawn from the great work of St Irenæus, *Irenæus omnium doctrinarum curiosissimus explorator*, as Tertullian calls him (§ v). He makes a point of bringing in some jesting and a rather amusing satire on the mystery in which the sect of Valentinus, the Gnostic, was presuming to involve itself. The five books of the *Adversus Marcionem* represent an original effort in quite another way.[1] I will only mention here the essence of the Marcionist thesis. Marcion had been keenly struck by the differences existing between the idea of God as revealed in the Old Testament, and that which appears in the Gospels. On the one hand, a severe and even cruel God, in whom some of the passions belonging to man live and boil over, who loves, hates, takes vengeance, and is subject to indecision and repentance ; on the other hand, a God of clemency and goodness, the celestial Father of all creatures. Marcion started from this opposition in order to accommodate to his liking the ideas contained in Revelation. In his view, the true God, the supreme God, had been in very truth and for the first time manifested in Christ ; as for the God of the Old Testament, in his eyes He was a simple Demiurge, a

[1] The beginning of the *Adversus Marcionem* is very curious in the history of the book in days of antiquity. The author explains there how this work had three editions the third of which he intended should cancel the two others.

secondary God, responsible for the creation of the ὕλη, of matter evil in itself. Of course the Catholics could not accept these views. By denying Judaism, Marcion committed not only a " colossal historical error " ; [1] he robbed Christianity of the majesty which the long vista of the centuries, previously preparing for the event, had added to the new religion. So Tertullian waged against this heresiarch a particularly implacable warfare. Each one of the five books of his treatise taken separately is longer than his other works. And what a mine of information (still indifferently well explored) for theology, history, exegesis, and the forms of Christian polemics !

However grateful the Catholics might be for such a champion, it is evident that with his mania for domineering over his fellow-Christians, Tertullian could not fail to excite around him the most lively opposition. People did not suffer themselves to be kept under as docilely as he could have wished. A coalition was set up against him, consisting not only of the " laxists," but also of the moderate minded who, pained at seeing the evangelic yoke weighted to excess, took occasion to entrench themselves behind the Scriptures and to oppose any exaction which did not find sure support in them. It is probable that the Bishops, whose actions Tertullian did not hesitate on occasion to criticise, were in favour of this reaction. How could the Bishops have supported this *intransigeant* to whom *quieta non movere* would have appeared the worst form of abdication, and who were constantly required to resolve questions on principle instead of leaving them to be cleared up by the exigencies of life itself ?

Tertullian was well aware of this spirit of opposition ; and he was the more exasperated thereby because the Scriptures, even when appealed to by the most accomplished of advocates and twisted by the most dexterous of tormentors into making the most convincing texts speak on his behalf, left him sometimes defenceless in the face of particular cases which the Holy Spirit (as they would have said) had not foreseen. [2]

In order to fill these terrible gaps, he essayed a fresh expedient. He made appeal to his studies as a man of law. He reminded himself that custom (*mos, mores majorum,*

---

[1] E. Renan, *L'Eglise chrét.*, p. 359.
[2] For instance, as regards the question of the public shows : *De Spect.*, III. From the point of view of the prohibition of flight in times of persecution, the text from *Matth.*, x, 23 caused him a great deal of worry.

consuetudo), was one of the sources whence flowed *jus civile*.
Custom was considered by the Roman jurists as expressing
the tacit consent of the people, the source of all law. Having
been proved by long use, " it was equally binding on the judge
as was the law," [1] and although its original influence was
becoming progressively feebler, none the less in principle
it remained one of the modes whereby law was fashioned. In
certain instances therefore in which the Scriptures were
either mute or ambiguous, and a certain tradition seemed to
favour his views, Tertullian bade people note that custom,
by the very fact that it is a custom, enshrines its justification
in itself.[2] *Consuetudo* evidently proceeds from *traditio*. But
in order to render valid this *traditio*, was a written origin
necessary as the " liberal " party pretended ? Not the least
in the world. Tradition, even without this *point d'appui*
of origin, was perfectly admissible. Did not a thousand
examples drawn from Christian practice prove this super-
abundantly ? Had Christ anywhere ordained the pro-
nouncing at the moment of baptism the words : " I renounce
Satan, his pomps and his angels " ? Where is it written
that we must sign ourselves with the sign of the Cross on so
many occasions ? etc. . . . All these practices have no other
authority than that of custom : *traditio auctrix, consuetudo
confirmatrix, fides observatrix*. And, as a final deduction,
it is reason which brings her support to tradition itself :
*Rationem traditioni et consuetudini et fidei patrocinaturam aut
ipse perspicies aut ab aliquo qui perspexerit disces*. From this
follows, concludes Tertullian, that in default of a definite law
it is custom which provides the law—just as in civil law—and
this law has sufficient justification in the authority of reason.

Has he made an end of it ? By no means. He hastens to
exclude a portion of this last consideration in order to guard
himself against " customs " which are too beneficent to prevent any objections which might by chance be brought against
him. If reason is a legitimate authority, why should she not
pass judgment on a tradition whenever the latter should be
found not to have explicit connection with a precept of our

---

[1] E. Cuq, *les Instit. Jurid. des Romains*, vol. I, p. 20–21 ; 168 et s. ; vol. II,
p. 17, and the article *Mores* by the same author in the *Dict. des Antiq.* (III, 2,
2001) ; Ihering, *Esprit du Droit Romain*, trans. Meulenaere, Ghent and Paris
2 ed. 1880, vol. II, p. 28 et s.

[2] *De Cor.*, ii et s.

Lord or of the Apostles ?   Better still, why not reduce to law all that reason prescribes ?   Why should it not be lawful to each believer (*omni fideli*) to do this, provided that the rule established be in conformity with the designs of God and that it be profitable in the matter of discipline and contribute to salvation ?   Has not God said : " Judge not of yourselves that which is just " ?   And did St Paul do anything else when he gave counsels in his own name under the patronage of divine reason ?

Here we can well discern the real character of Tertullian : a passionate attachment to his own private judgment which, instead of frankly avowing it, seeks to justify his craving for making rules by a complete, complicated, and abstruse system.   Tertullian would have liked to rigidly define every single thing by authority.   But his Catholic sense of tradition, of things to be respected on account of their long continuity, or of the source whence they derived, restrained this individualistic craving.   And it was a question with him how to reconcile more nearly these contradictory tendencies through the instrumentality of stratagems and sophisms.

Moreover, this kind of artifice, though useful in masking the weak spots in a line of argument carried to its last extremity, could not satisfy his own sense of logic nor long deceive those whom he had for a moment dazzled.   He was in the position of a judge firmly convinced of the necessity of repressing certain evils for whom the " arsenal " of the law provided no suitable weapon.   A living and divinely inspired message alone would have been capable of supplementing the insufficiencies of the *Sancti Commentarii*, or the silences and lack of rigour of tradition.   But where could this voice be found to make itself heard in warning the *frivola et frigida fides* of the mass of Christians and in supplying a remedy against their weakness of character ?

Such was the moral condition of the inexorable *intransigeant* when he came into touch with Montanism, or at any rate when he decided to make a profound study of it.

VIII

How did he come to know about it ?   We cannot tell.   It is certain that he had in his hands a collection of Montanist oracles, thanks to which he was put into direct contact with the thought and manner of life of the Phrygian prophets. Many things therein must have shocked him : for instance, the *rôle* that devolved upon women in the sect, and the leaven of anarchy that was contained in this doctrine wherein the " Holy Spirit " was everything. But side by side with these displeasing features, what seductive ideas he there met with ! It will suffice to record his confessions thereon.

What struck him first was the respect in which doctrine was held by Montanus, and his disdain for purely theoretical questions.

Montanism accepted the Christian revelation as an accomplished fact, as a venerable tradition, and as a heritage on which no man might lay hands. Far from endeavouring (as was the case with Gnosticism) to dissolve by analysis its elements in order to put them together again with the aid of speculation, he reverently sought from them the means of justifying his own task and advertised no other ambition than to realise an expressed promise of Christ. There was nothing among those who propagated his doctrine to render them open to the charge of spiritual pride.

In addition, this doctrine appeared to have no other object in view than how to live. The ideal which it proposed to itself was altogether moral, and its object was not at all *knowledge* so much as *practice*. With its face set entirely on the future of mankind, whose destiny it assumed henceforward to be tottering to its fall, it took care not to go in search of any justifications which might favour dereliction from ordinary duties, which might serve as a cloak to laxities of the senses, or to secret infamies of the flesh. What could be more appetising to the soul of Tertullian ? What more reassuring to the rigour of his puritanism ?

Then, what a delightful surprise to see blossoming again in the bosom of Montanism all those religious phenomena whose signification the Scriptures, and especially the Epistles of St Paul, had revealed to him—predictions about the future, the reading of hearts, improvised psalms, visions, spiritual utterances spoken in ecstasy ! As more and more fully he gave credence to the Phrygian seers, a twofold feeling came over him : first he felt better, purer, and had the impression of a moral renovation in which his *ego* was lifted up;[1] then, thanks to their clear teaching on the Paraclete, a host of problems on which hitherto his explanations had had an uncertain note through lack of explicit and unequivocal texts, received the most luminous solution, and one too which was least tolerant of the lack of firmness shown by so many Catholics.[2]

Tertullian was in search of a Code, and here he had found one which at once supplied him with a moral rule conformable to his secret desires, and an authority able to impose it by referring it to a divine source. How could he refuse to make it his own ? It was the mind of the ardent lawyer that was first conquered and fixed his choice when it came to having to decide between Montanism and the Church.

It was not sufficient for him to be personally convinced that he had made this choice with discernment and wisdom : he felt bound in addition to impose it upon others and to discover arguments which would be likely to make them become its adherents. His whole personality was formed upon opposition, and had grown great thereby. From the first awakening of his curiosity in Montanism up to his complete submission, a long and burning series of meditations took place in him, stirred up by the attacks or the replies of his enemies. It is probable that influences came from without to spur him on and to precipitate the rupture. St Jerome mentions one of them definitely : " *Invidia posthac et contumeliis clericorum romanae ecclesiae ad Montani dogma delapsus.* . . ."[3] It was therefore jealousy and the insults of the Roman clergy that drove Tertullian to the point. We do not know the details of this quarrel. But to make up for this we can clearly distinguish the fundamental questions around which the dispute turned whether at Carthage, or perhaps at Rome. These were : (A) Ecstasy ; (B) Flight during Persecution ; (C) Re-marriage ; (D) The Fasts ; (E) Penance.

A.—Ecstasy

In default of the *De Ecstasi*, which has been unhappily lost, several passages scattered through the works of Tertullian

---

[1] *De Pudic.* I, ii.
[2] *De Resurr. Carnis*, lxiii ; *De Fuga*, i ; *Adv. Pr.*, xiii.
[3] *De Vir. Ill.*, liii.

allow us to piece together approximately the thesis he there
defends so far as it touches upon the lawfulness of ecstatic
revelations.

Were they bound not to accept these "*charismata*" as
authentic ? This was certainly not the only question for
him, but it was the point round which centred the disagreement between the Catholics and Montanists. He has too
often stated this to allow of any doubt in the matter. It
was important therefore to justify the form in which these
"*charismata*" manifested themselves in the Montanists, since
their adversaries drew therefrom a pretext for declaring them
diabolic.[1] In the eyes of Tertullian *ecstasis* was a state
produced in a normal manner during sleep. The soul lost
in that state its sense of its surroundings ; its faculties of
sense were suspended ; the power of conscious reflection
became stupefied ; images, which it ceased to direct of its free
will, assailed it. However, it preserved the memory of what
it had thought it had seen and heard. God permitted this
mode of special activity sometimes to take on a religious
character and signification. Whether in sleep *or even apart
from sleep*, the state of ecstasy, *amentia*, was the modification
through which of necessity the human reason passes at the
moment when it enters into direct relation with God. Visions
and prophecies therefore postulated it of necessity.

This is the essence of Tertullian's doctrine, under reserve of
supplementary proofs on which he had to support it.

We note how wise, serious, how little revolutionary it is.
Of the "frenzy" with which in the course of their vaticina-
tions the heralds of the new prophetic spirit were animated,
not a word. He eliminates this element from his definition,
although it was of capital import as an historical reality,
and had excited so much distrust. Avoiding in this manner
all confusion with the pagan *mantique*, he retains only the
theory of the occasional loss of personality by the seer in
order to give it strenuous support.

---

[1] See especially the *De Anima*, xliii et s., and P. de Labriolle, *La Crise Montaniste*, p. 365 et s. This treatise *De Anima* is extremely rich in the matter of
psychological and even physiological observations ; it is one of those which best
shows the variety of Tertullian's learning.

B.—FLIGHT DURING PERSECUTION

To be prepared for martyrdom was, in those uncertain times, one of the objects with which every fervent Christian was concerned. But the Church did not impose upon the faithful the absolute duty of steadfastly waiting for arrest, torture, and perhaps death. Polycarp, the Bishop of Smyrna, yielding to the entreaties of his friends, had taken refuge in a small house in the country in the outskirts of the town. A similar attitude had been, or might have been, that of Clement of Alexandria, Origen, St Cyprian and of many other personages of incontestable courage. In Africa, not only the laics, but also the pastors themselves did not hesitate, when the occasion arose, to place themselves beyond the reach of their persecutors. Not long before, Tertullian had taken no scandal at this : " Etiam in persecutionibus," he had written in his *Ad Uxorem* (I, iii), " *melius est ex permissu fugere* quam comprehensum et distortum negare." And again, in the *De Patientia* (xiii) : " *Si fuga urgeat*, incommoda fugae caro militat."

The teaching of the Paraclete forced him to withdraw this concession. " Nearly all the utterances " of the Paraclete were an exhortation to martyrdom ; two of the *oracles* quoted by Tertullian expressly requested this of the faithful Christian. As for those who ran away, the Paraclete did not hesitate to " brand " them ; to make up for this, he promised his assistance to whosoever should not shrink from its terrors and torments.

There is nothing to equal the easy assurance with which Tertullian executed the necessary *volte-face*. Without troubling to excuse his inconsistency, he and his new associates set themselves to denounce as unlawful every attempt to elude persecution.

In his *De Fuga*, he laid down a principle destined to make clear all that followed. Did persecution come from God or from the devil ? Of a surety it comes from God since it exalts the faith and makes the servants of God " better." The devil is only its instrument ; it is God who is its author, and who unchains it when it pleases Him in order to prove or to chastise the just. Therefore, however evil it may appear to man's fallible judgment, persecution was a good thing in itself : *nullo modo fugiendum erit quod a Deo evenit* (§ iv). It was likewise unworthy to buy oneself off at the price of money, to treat with informers, soldiers or the judges. These negotiations were a disguised form of apostasy, a crafty method of "flight" : *Pedibus stetisti, cucurristi nummis. . . . Negatio est etiam martyrii recusatio. . . . Non quaeritur qui latam viam sequi paratus sit, sed qui angustam.*

C.—Re-Marriage

Was it, aye or no, lawful from the religious point of view to re-marry ? To-day the problem appears to be without much interest ; it is curious to have to state that during several centuries eminent minds were preoccupied—and doubtless as many souls were tortured—with moral difficulties which are nothing more than a matter of individual delicacy.

But if discussions on re-marriage have lost almost all value at the present time, at least they retain an historical importance : they clearly show the strength of the principle of asceticism held towards the beginning of the IIIrd century ; on this question also Tertullian betrays some of his most secret *arrière-pensées*, and, in the opinion of St Augustine,[1] it was the unbending attitude which he took up on this question which made him a "heretic," by the very fact that he assumed a position contrary to that maintained by the Apostle St Paul.

St Paul[2] had nowhere concealed his very clear preference for the celibate ; but, preserved by superior good sense from all excessive severity, he had contended on principle that the change from celibacy to marriage was in no wise sinful, and he had even gone so far to admit the lawfulness of re-marriage.

Such approximately are the *nuances* of the Pauline view. It was to interpret these *nuances*, to press them to an undue point, or even to force them against their real tenor, that

[1] *Haer.*, lxxxvi ; *Ep. ad Julianam Viduam*, iv, 6 (P.L., XL, 433).
[2] Cf. Ist Ep. to the Corinthians, vii.

Tertullian applied the infinite resources of his sophistic reasoning in three treatises.

The order of succession of the *Ad Uxorem*, of the *De Exhortatione Castitatis* and of the *De Monogamia*, is easy to determine. We do not notice in the *Ad Uxorem* any declaration relating to Montanism. Further, Tertullian expressly recognises in it that a Christian may take flight from persecution, which he was to deny in the *De Fuga*. In the *De Exhortatione Castitatis*, the ditch had been leapt over, for Tertullian there quotes an oracle of the " holy prophetess Prisca " ; but, besides this being the only mention of her, the fact that he abstains from all savage allusions to the Catholics, gives colour to the idea that, though he had already been conquered by Montanism, he had nevertheless not yet entirely effected his breach with the Church. On the other hand, no doubt is possible in regard to the *De Monogamia*. It is an aggressive and violent work in which he no longer extends any compromise.

In one work after another, therefore, further advances are made manifest, and we can follow the development of Tertullian's opinions on re-marriage from entire orthodoxy to declared Montanism.

It becomes evident that Montanism had scarcely modified his ideas radically. The *Ad Uxorem* contains, at least in germ, the greater part of the arguments developed in the two subsequent treatises. From the time when he wrote it, the antipathies in his mind gained in strength. Nevertheless, he represented perseverance in widowhood as being eminently profitable to the moral life rather than as a positive obligation : " *Nam etsi non delinquas renubendo. . . .*" [1] Once he had become attached to the Phrygian doctrine, he changed a counsel into a precept, and such a formal precept that all derogation therefrom was likened by him to *stuprum*. The tone of his discussion changes also. In the *De Monogamia*, he affects to consider his adversaries as beings wholly in servitude to their senses, and whose reasonings had nothing intellectual about them. He takes them to task even in their persons, their secret vices, and the shamelessness of their party. He makes no hesitation in alluding to an ignominious scandal in which, it appears, he had included the Bishop of

[1] *Ad Ux.*, I, vii.

Uthina, one of the Roman colonies in Africa. He fights for his cause with all his heart and soul by crushing these sensual-minded people who disguise their passions under principles.

His attitude towards marriage in itself is fairly ambiguous. On several occasions he repeats that he has no wish to proscribe it, but only to apply thereto the rule of temperance. But looking at it closely, however, what contradictions, what malevolent insinuations, what morose lectures ! If he does not go quite to extremes, if he is content to cast over marriage a sour discredit, instead of simply disapproving of it, the reason is that at first Montanus himself had not gone to that length, and secondly because he feared to be mixed up on this account with the ranks of his detested enemies, the Marcionists, who themselves condemned without restriction the union of the sexes. He had eloquently fought Marcion on this point ; he did not dare, however much he might have wished, to appear to justify subsequently the heresiarch and his deep-rooted asceticism.

D.—FASTING

With regard to fasting, his principal effort seems to have aimed at setting up in Carthage the practices enjoined by Montanus, which consisted either in complete obligatory fasting, or in prolonging, of obligation, certain fasts far beyond the usual limits of the " xerophagies." [1]

We can imagine how these rigorous and precise Montanist rules must have pleased Tertullian : all the postulates of his reason and all the instincts of his authoritative temperament there encountered their absolute satisfaction and blossomed forth in combative activity.

What seemed to be outrageous to the non-Montanist Catholics was this arrogant attempt to render nugatory, in the name of the *prophetia nova*, all individual initiative, and the substitution of a series of heavy mortifications *ex imperio* for mortifications which were *ex arbitrio*. Herein lay an encroachment whose lack of moderation threatened

---

[1] For the nature of the xerophagic *régime*, see *De Jej.*, I. Cf. P. de Labriolle, *op. cit.*, p. 399–400, for a picture of the Montanist fasts as compared with the Catholic.

the daily independence of everyone much more than his prohibition relating to re-marriage. Hence arose a general revolt against the pseudo-Paraclete, author of these dangerous concepts, whom the Catholics identified with the " devil " and " Anti-Christ," and against the band of " false prophets." The safest refuge offered for their defence seemed to the Catholics to lie in the Scriptures and in tradition, that is to say, the customs hitherto in force. All non-scriptural and non-traditional rules were proclaimed as a foolish novelty and a suspicious imitation of Judaic devotions, or the rites of Apis, Cybele and Isis.[1]

Tertullian could not fail to defend the authority of the Paraclete thus diminished.

His discussion is one of most rare insolence. The word *gula* occurs a dozen times in the *De Jejunio*. Guzzlers, greedy to fill their bellies, who covered their disgusting appetites under respectable terms—these are some of the features under which he depicts his adversaries. Further, gluttons were voluptuous: gluttony with them resolved itself into lasciviousness, *per edacitatem salacitas transit*. And Tertullian develops the picture and defines its leading characteristics with entire lack of modesty. The whole of chapter I is full of obscenities. There is nothing in his language more unchaste than this raving preacher of chastity.

E.—Penance

There remains the question of penance. Of all those we have found space to study in regard to Tertullian, this question is the most important. Not that Tertullian had approached it with any new dispositions : he shows himself in the *De Pudicitia*, which is especially devoted to this subject, such as we have seen him in the *De Monogamia* and the *De Jejunio*,—just as violent, just as sternly decided to *oblige* men to become better, and to transform the Church so far as it depended upon him, into a community of saints. But this time the dispute between Catholics and Montanists was not concerned solely with discipline : *a problem of a dogmatic order, the problem of the " Power of the Keys," was*

---

[1] *De Jej.*, xi ; xiv ; xvi.

G

involved in it. Tertullian was bound to take up a position ; and thus he was forced to modify, not only his old treatises on penance, but also some portions of his conceptions of the Church and of the prerogatives attaching to the clerical hierarchy.

To begin with the *De Paenitentia.* I have mentioned the comparatively temperate and benignant character of this work. In it Tertullian admitted that the sinner who had fallen after baptism into one or more grave sins, had still the right to be pardoned *once.* How different appears the spirit animating the *De Pudicitia,* even from the most superficial study !

From the very first pages, Tertullian allows his wrath to break forth. The adversary to whom he takes exception is a Bishop, a Roman Bishop without doubt. The identification of this Bishop is a problem to which very different solutions have been given. It is commonly enough admitted to-day (but without decisive proofs), that it was Callistus who was aimed at.[1] Now at that time, Callistus, by a public act, by a ruling read in the assemblies of the faithful, had just made known that he authorised fornicators and adulterers to re-enter the Church after due penance. With what abusive irony does Tertullian turn into ridicule the proud language of the Pontiff and (to him) the cunning hypocrisy of his allocution ! And it is not only by this sectarian mood that his Montanism declares itself, but also by a notable change in his ideas as regards penance and to all purposes by an appreciable evolution in doctrine. " The marks of shame borne by the flesh which has been soiled subsequently to baptism cannot be washed away by penance " (XII, I), is the new principle with which he is inspired. There are some sins which a Christian must no longer commit : the Church, the spotless virgin, cannot countenance a stain. For sins like these there is no pity ; and the guilty one need look no further to her ! He disavows without hesitation the restrained conception which he had developed in the *De Paenitentia.* In chapter xxi, he even goes so far as to take away her power of pardoning from the Church of the " psychics " (in these words he describes the Catholic Church constituted

---

[1] For recent discussions however, cf. K. Adam, *das sogen. Bussedikt des Papstes Kallistus,* Munich, 1917 (*Veroff. aus dem Kirchenhist. Seminar Munchen,* iv, 5).

with her Hierarchy) in order to transfer it into the hands of the truly "spiritual" Church, the Montanist Church which at any rate will not make use of it except in altogether exceptional cases. And he is by no means sure that in this he has not exceeded the hardihood of Montanus himself in order to satisfy the demand of his own personal views and of his controversial attitude.

Taken as a whole, a careful examination of the Montanist treatises of Tertullian proves that we should be wrong in rigorously identifying the original Montanism with that bearing the mark of Tertullian's works. At the time when he fell under the influence of the doctrine of the Phrygian prophets, he was in the full maturity of his thought and in full exercise of his talents. From that moment it was inevitable that in giving in his adherence he should put his impress on it and should adapt it in some degree to his own conception. In his theory of ecstasy, as we have seen, he guards against legitimatising the physical excesses whereof the protagonists of the sect had given a rather scandalous exhibition in the East; with knowing hand he shaded off all that savoured of irregularity, incoherency, and morbidity in the Phrygian cult of prophesying. He also endeavoured (it is one of the *leit-motifs* of his discussions) to link it up with the past, and to persuade his readers that these so-called innovations of the "Paraclete" had nothing revolutionary in them, and that they might be found outlined or in germ if one only read the Scriptures carefully. On the somewhat frail theological web of primitive Montanism, he wove his fantastic theory of successive revelations explaining the necessary outcome of the plan inaugurated by God from the beginning of Creation by the operation of the Paraclete— a gradual development in discipline, in the sense of an ever-increasing rigour, and not as an evolution of the rule of faith which, according to him, was not susceptible of any further progress in matter of doctrine.

In his heart of hearts, he would have passionately liked to have the Montanist cult of prophecy "recognised" and authorised. Feeling at last that the Church—an organism founded on a Hierarchy and containing the great majority of the faithful—would be irreducible, he took the step of separating himself from her. In other respects, he preserved intact his symbol of faith, his respect for the Scriptures, and his theory of prescription and the apostolic character of the Churches. Against dissentients, he continued to write vigorous treatises wherein, on more than one occasion, he has given to certain dogmatic formulae their almost definitive expression, as in the *Adversus Praxean*, the *De Resurrectione Carnis*, the *Scorpiace*, the *De Carne Christi*, etc.

Hampered by a past which he was not willing totally to disavow, he arrived at strange compromises and disastrous combinations, whereof no one better than he could appreciate the weak points. From the psychological and religious point of view, his case is one of extreme interest, in which there mingles some pity in regard to this strong mind struggling on incoherently and without succeeding, in spite of so much sophistry, in getting away from himself.

IX

FROM the literary point of view, Tertullian may perhaps be compared with the most striking representatives of Latin literature in the time of the emperors. This is a truth which is sometimes overlooked but of which anyone who shall have held any close commune with his works will be irresistibly convinced. It is distressing to see with what ill-natured incompetence his language and style have been sometimes appreciated : we have David Ruhnken, the German philologist of the XVIIIth century,[1] pedantically declaring : " Tertullianum latinitatis certe pessimum auctorem esse aio et confirmo " ; and Auguste Matthiae [2] branding him on account of his " barbarous " language ; Courdaveaux [3] deplores " that such a man, as great from the qualities of his heart as from the courage of his views, should only have as a vehicle for his ideas *a poor provincial patois* even more unsuited than the real Latin tongue for abstract discussions, and which he wrote in so obscure a style that his thought is even more difficult to disentangle than that of St Paul."

[1] Ruhnken passed a portion of his life at Leyden, but he was a native of Pomerania. Ruhnken's opinion is quoted at length by E. F. Leopold in the *Zeitsch. f. hist. Theol.* VIII (1838), p. 33.
[2] *Grundriss der Gesch. d. griech. und rom. Litt.*, 3rd ed., Iena, 1834, p. 221.
[3] *Revue de l'Hist. des Relig.*, XIII (1891), p. 1.

The truth is that Tertullian adhered strictly to the literary tradition of his age. He knew the methods of "artistic prose" as they had been formed among the Greeks under the influence of Gorgias, Isocrates, Theophrastus of Eresos and of the rhetoricians of Asia, which Cicero had permitted himself to appropriate, adapting them to the genius of the Latin tongue. Anaphora, alliterations, and symmetrical divisions by κῶλα, etc.—all this *technique* of rhetoric was familiar to him ; and his works present numerous examples. It was not a question of the metrical rules governing the cadence of a sentence, which he generally observed in his terminations.[1] This was the common ground of the Roman tradition which the schools had preserved and transmitted from one generation to another. In addition, Tertullian was contemporary with Apuleius whose works he had certainly read.[2] A taste for variety in his vocabulary, a love of "uncommon" forms of expression, certain affectations in style, and certain obscurities of thought may have come to him from that source. We shall never know all the richness of his vocabulary until a complete inventory, which does not exist at present, shall have been drawn up of it. He has been called "the real creator of the Latin of the Church."[3] This opinion is perhaps not absolutely exact, for we must reckon the part which belongs to the anonymous translators of the Bible. But it is clear that he largely contributed to that collective work by which the appearance of the Latin tongue was renovated. His creations of new words are innumerable : the specialists hold that they appear to be conformable after a general fashion to the rules governing their Latin derivation.[4] Likewise his syntax, with the exception of slight peculiarities, remains in line with that used by his contemporaries.[5] But he coined words and phrases such as no writer since Tacitus had had the ability to do, because his genius animated, vivified and inflamed all he wrote.

[1] Out of 852 terminations to chapters, one can count only 43, or 5 per cent. in which the closing words are not certainly of a rhythmic cadence.

[2] Cf. Kellner, *Ueber die. sprachl. Eigentumlichkeiten Tert.*, in *Theol. Quart.*, lviii (1876), p. 229 ; C. Weyman, *St zu Apuleius u. seinen Nachahmern*, in the *Sitz.-Ber. d. Bayer. Ak.* 1893, II, p. 340-343 and 352 : Van Der Vliet, *Studia eccles.*, Leyden, 1891, I, p. 9 et s. ; E. Norden, *die Antike Kunstprosa*, p. 614-615.

[3] Harnack, A.C.L., I, 667 ; cf. Norden, *op. cit.*, p. 607.

[4] Hoppe, *Synt. u. Stit. des T.*, L. 1903, p. 115.

[5] *Ibid.*, p. 114.

Formed on the discipline of juridical learning, he illuminated his theological discussions with clear-cut forms which the West was to appropriate (*una substantia, tres personae ; duae substantiae, una persona ;* and, for the distinction between the Divine persons, *distinctio, non divisio, discreti, non separati ;* for the distinction between the two natures in Christ, *conjunctio, non confusio,* etc.). Then, although marked by a hereditary culture, his dominating and original personality exercised a sovereign mastery of the forms he used. Unlike Minucius Felix or Lactantius and so many other Christian writers, we hardly ever surprise him practising the art of stealing his turns of phrase and similies from the classics. He disdained these lawful pilferings. It is in very truth his own vigour which circulates through so many sturdy and subtile pages. Far from impairing his literary gifts, Montanism gave them their full scope. Here and there there may be found a certain fastidious oppressiveness in his treatises at the beginning, in the *De Baptismo* and the *De Paenitentia,* for example. Montanism put his temperament at ease, long held in check by the fear of saying too much, and by certain scruples which were henceforth to vanish. And this wrathful and passionate soul breathed itself forth still more freely in that he believed that he was representing the true religious ideal in face of the lapses which dishonoured it in bringing it down to their level. His last treatises are brimful of sophistry, yet, notwithstanding, Tertullian was never so keen, so vibrating, so urgent and at the same time so pathetic.

When one has tasted the pleasure produced by his combative prose, one experiences some difficulty in not finding a certain insipidity in the purer and more sugary style recommended by classic " good taste." It has some strange condensations which in places render it formidable ; but it is a triumph of mind to have succeeded in piercing through some of its obscurities.

X

A CONSIDERATION of the *Passion* of Saints Perpetua and Felicitas should be taken in connection with Tertullian. We shall see a little further on the reason for this. On reading this celebrated little account, instinct with such ardent and pure exaltation and with such touching and graceful simplicity, hardly spoilt here and there by a suspicion of rhetoric, we can easily understand it. Chapter I forms a prologue which we owe to the compiler who has pieced together the different portions of the account. In Chapter II, this compiler relates in a few words the simultaneous arrest of Vibia Perpetua, a young woman of twenty-two, educated and of good family, of two young people, Saturninus and Secundulus, and of two slaves, Revocatus and Felicitas—all catechumens. (Shortly after, a certain Saturus, who had instructed them, was to give himself up of his own free will : § iv.) He then states that he will leave Perpetua to continue the narrative, who drew up in her own hand the account of their sufferings. We then have the narrative of Perpetua herself beginning at § iii : she brought it to a close at the end of § x remarking that she stopped on the eve of the combat, and that it must be left to another to relate, if he will, what was to take place in the amphitheatre. At the beginning of § xi, the compiler takes up his pen again, but only for an instant : he merely adds the description given by Saturus himself of the visions which were vouchsafed to the martyr in his prison. All the last part of the *Acta* from § xiv is by the compiler who, in carrying out his own wish or rather as he says, the *fideicommissum* of Perpetua, traces a picture of the wonderful struggle of the martyrs and their bloody death, and in a peroration whose spirit is altogether analogous to that which is breathed in the prologue, accentuates the lesson which comes forth from these examples.

We must therefore represent to ourselves the incidents very much as follows : Perpetua and Saturus found leisure in their dungeon to draw up a short account of the sufferings they were enduring, and especially of the " graces " which God sent to them.[1] These notes fell into the hands of a witness of their torment who takes information therefrom complementary to what he had not been able to see with his own eyes,[2] completes the narrative given by the martyrs and, out of these diverse elements, forms a complete story which he encloses in a moral and religious exhortation. There are

[1] § ii : " sicut conscriptum manu sua et suo sensu reliquit " ; § xi : " visionem, quam ipse conscripsit ". Cf. § xiv.

[2] E.G. § xv.

thus two portions to distinguish in these *Acta :* the portion of the compiler and that of the martyrs themselves.

Some traces of Montanism have sometimes been thought to emerge from the passages explicitly attributed to Perpetua and Saturus. Thus, a point has been made of the four *visions* of Perpetua and that related also by Saturus. But how were these visions a Montanist phenomenon in a special degree ? There were very few in ancient times (I will say pagan as well as Christian) who had any doubts as to the religious signification of such warnings.

The case of the compiler is very different. I think we may boldly identify him with Tertullian, and for reasons of an entirely philological order. It is *his* style, *his* language, *his* phraseology.[1] His Montanism, which had not yet been declared but was already in full religious effervescence, is likewise betrayed (the text must have been written shortly after the years 202–3, the date of the martyrdom).

What was his aim in the twofold dedication with which the *Passion* begins and closes ? He desired to show that the activity of the Holy Spirit has in no way diminished ; that its " virtue " remains permanent ; that God continues to fulfil his promises in " invisible proofs for infidels, favours for believers." Only a weak faith, a faith at its last gasp (*imbecillitas aut desperatio fidei*) could imagine that the Divine grace only dwelt within " the men of old time " and that the present age was excluded from it. It was thus a pious duty and a sure means to edification to put on record in writing (*digerere*) the graces recently given, just as it had been at the birth of Christianity in the case of the " old examples of faith." No preoccupation could be more correct.

But there is something else in this prologue. In the opinion of the author, the flood of grace had never been so abundant : there was an *exuperatio gratiae* and that was because the end of the world was quite near, and because God, by the mouth of his prophet Joel, had promised an " outpouring " of His Spirit " on all flesh " during the last days.

What is still more startling is that the compiler (let us say, Tertullian) takes upon himself to include in the *instrumentum Ecclesiae* the recent visions and also the " new prophecies." *Instrumentum* in legal language meant every

[1] Cf. P. de Labriolle, *la Crise Montaniste*, pp. 345–351.

document claiming credence, and all written proof. It is evidently in this sense that he here uses this word. But if we are to believe that by *instrumentum* Tertullian means merely the *Corpus* of Scripture, we must note an ambiguity, under cover of which some vexatious confusion might arise.

The *Passion*, which is very attractive of itself, becomes still more so in so far as it reveals to us the state of mind of Tertullian in the first phase of his adhesion to Montanism.

BOOK II

THE IIIᴿᴰ CENTURY

DOWN TO THE PEACE OF THE CHURCH (313)

CHAPTER I

THE *OCTAVIUS* OF MINUCIUS FELIX

BIBLIOGRAPHY

THE manuscript numbered 1661, IXth century, in the Bibliothèque Nationale in Paris, which contains the seven books of Arnobius, *Adversus Nationes*, holds also an eighth book which is no other than the *Octavius*. The difference in tone and style between the *Adversus Nationes* and the *Octavius* is striking. However, the title *Octavius*, without doubt, read incorrectly as *Octavus* (the eighth), conducted in the Middle Ages to a confusion which the first editors of Arnobius did not perceive. It was only in 1560 that the oversight was rectified by François Beaudoin (Balduinus) in his Heidelberg edition.

The text of the *Parisinus*, transcribed by a copyist who was clearly very ignorant, swarms with mistakes. There is in Brussels a manuscript of the XIth-XIIth century, which is only a copy of the *Parisinus*.

Editions : P.L., III, 239-376 ; C.V., II (1867), by Halm ; H. Boenig, in B.T. (1903) ; J. P. Waltzing, Louvain, 1903 ; Bruges, 1909, B.T. (1912) : there is important documentation in these three editions ; G. Rauschen, F.P. fasc. VIII (1913).

French translations : J. P. Waltzing, Louvain, 1902 ; Bruges, 1909 ; Louvain, 1914.

Consult : J. P. Waltzing, *Lexicon Minucianum*, Liége and Paris, 1909 ; Monceaux, I, 462-508 ; B. ph. W. 1914, 1452 (*coup d'œil* of collective bibliography relating to the *Octavius*); C. Synnerberg, *Die neuesten Beitraege zur Minutius-Literatur*, Helsingfors, 1914 ; *Hermes*, 1915, 456-463 and 609-623 ; *Bursian*, vol. 170/173 (1916), p. 57.

SUMMARY

I. Minucius Felix.—II. The *Octavius* analysed.—III. The religious bearing of the *Octavius*.—IV. Literary art in the *Octavius*.—V. The priority of the *Apologeticum* over the *Octavius*.

I

" THE pearl of apologetic literature " is what Ernest Renan called the *Octavius*.[1] To this judgment it is difficult not to subscribe after reading this well-ordered dialogue, so happily written, in which is revealed such agreeable goodwill to convince without offending anyone.

Lactantius wrote of the author in his *Inst. Div.*, V, 1, 21 :

[1] *Marc. Aurèle*, p. 389.

" Among the defenders of our cause known to me, Minucius Felix occupied a very distinguished rank at the bar. His book entitled *Octavius* shows what an excellent champion of the truth he could have been had he devoted himself entirely to this kind of study." St Jerome mentions him in various places, notably in the *De Viris Illustribus*, LVIII : " *Minucius Felix, Romae insignis causidicus, scripsit dialogum christiani et ethnici disputantis, qui Octavius inscribitur.*" He tells us that Minucius had also composed a *De Fato*.

The information given by Lactantius and Jerome is corroborated by the work itself from which doubtless Lactantius and Jerome obtained it. As a matter of fact, it comes out in § ii, 3, and xxviii, 3, that Minucius was practising the calling of an advocate. He calls himself Marcus Minucius Felix (cf. III, 1 ; V, 1). From his own testimony (I, 4 ; V, 1), he had been a pagan for a long time, and then he was converted.

Jerome tells us that he exercised his profession in Rome, and this is confirmed by § ii. It is thought that he must have been of African origin. The name of a Minucius Felix has been discovered on a column at Tebessa [1] and on a dedication found at Carthage.[2] Certain very strong expressions on the Roman sway (xxv, 4–5), surprising from the lips of a Roman of the old stock, are more comprehensible in the case of a provincial. In another respect points of style reveal the familiarity of the author with African writers such as Frontonius, Flaurus, Apuleius and Tertullian.

The other characters taking part in the dialogue are not necessarily imaginary, which does not imply nevertheless that the conversation which Minucius is supposed to be describing really took place. It was the ordinary practice of Cicero, the model favoured by the author, to represent characters he had known or whose name was familiar to the Roman public in discussion, in order to convey his views in a more or less fictitious setting.

About Octavius Januarius (cf. XV, 2), who gives the name to the work, we know nothing more than what is contained in it. A married man and father of a family (II, 1), he was converted at the same time as Minucius or even a little before

---

[1] C.I.L., viii, 1964.
[2] *Ibid.*, Suppl. 12, 499.

him (I, 4). The name of one Octavius Januarius figures in an inscription found at Bougie (C.I.L., viii, 1962).

As regards the third interlocutor, Caecilius Natalis, some lively discussions have been provoked by certain epigraphic discoveries made between the years 1853 and 1859. In two places in the course of the dialogue, allusion is made to Frontonius who was born at Cirta. In § ix, 6, Caecilius says : "*id etiam Cirtensis nostri testatur oratio*" ; and Octavius goes on to refute the alleged calumny by employing these words : *Fronto tuus* (xxxi, 2). From merely reading the dialogue there is then some temptation to suppose that Caecilius was a native of Cirta. Now five inscriptions have been recovered at Cirta of the years 212–217, which come from a triumphal arch erected by M. Caecilius Natalus as a mark of appreciation for his election to the dignity of quin-quennial triumvir.[1] This coincidence is interesting. How-ever there are some difficulties which render the identification uncertain and we have no reason to insist too much on it.

II

THE dialogue opens with the author confiding to us his ardent affection for Octavius now no longer living. The memory of this dear friend and the perfect community of their senti-ments had recently returned to him with singular force. From being both pagans had they not together passed " to the light of wisdom and of truth " ? And his thoughts thus wandering over those happy years dwell on the conversations in which Octavius succeeded in bringing in Caecilius to the true religion.

Minucius Felix details in a leisurely manner the circum-stances which surrounded the incident which he is going to relate (II–IV).

Taking advantage of the Courts being in vacation, Octavius, Minucius Felix, and Caecilius his intimate friend, have betaken themselves to Ostia, a country resort favoured by the Romans. One morning they direct their footsteps towards the sea, with the breeze blowing in their faces, when Caecilius, per-ceiving a statue of Serapis, brings his hand to his mouth

---

[1] C.I.L., viii, 1, 7094–7098 ; cf. 6996.

after the pagan rite, and imprints on it a kiss. His friends notice the action, and in a few ironical words Octavius reproaches Minucius Felix for allowing his dear Caecilius to fall into such childish practices. These stinging words are not noticed at first. The three friends continue their walk and amuse themselves with looking at the different objects which meet their eye. But the taciturn and wounded expression of Caecilius at last strikes his companions. On being questioned, Caecilius confesses that the shaft levelled by Octavius just now has wounded him keenly and that he wishes to have a thorough explanation with him. The three friends take up a position on a dyke going out some distance into the sea ; Minucius Felix is to preside over the debate. All is ready : Caecilius opens the discussion and begins to plead his cause.

This prelude written in a soothing cadence and refined elegance, discloses a skilful art and one fully master of its own resources.

The speech of Caecilius (V–XIII) is appreciably shorter than the reply which Octavius is going to give. However, in making the " Devil's advocate " speak, the author has not thought it necessary to put in his mouth futile arguments which might be refuted with ease. No intentioned arrangement weakens the expression of the pagan's complaint.

Caecilius begins with a formal declaration of agnosticism. Mystery envelops us. For us the universe is a riddle which passes our understanding, and it is at once wiser and more religious to leave it in peace. The Christians pretend to solve it—they, unlettered people ! How ridiculous ! It was a fact that nowhere have we been able to discern in action any Divine intervention, a Providence, an intelligent will anxious to counteract chance and to regulate the course of events for the betterment of good people.

After such an avowal, we may ask how Caecilius is going to defend the pagan religion. Will he content himself with insinuating that, in the universal ignorance, the Christians at least should acknowledge that they have not been wise much longer than the rest ? By no means. He concludes that, since everything evades man's grasp, he ought to cling with all the more tenacious energy to those fixed points which are open to him. Now the religion of Rome is seen as a body of venerable traditions with which her greatness has always been bound up. Here the tone of Caecilius becomes warm and he is moved in recalling the beneficent action of those gods to whose solicitude the great festivals in the history of Rome bear witness. He who but now was relegating Divine intervention to the ranks of unverified hypotheses, now gets near to the approaches of a real faith; and his Roman nationality comes to his aid in getting over this difficult step.

After having thus exalted " this religion of such antiquity, so practical and so salutary ", Caecilius hits back angrily against those who would like to destroy it. The speech for the prosecution, to give it its true name, now begins. He first loads with contempt the Christian sect which is recruited among the dregs of the people and " forms a coalition of impiousness out of this rabble." The chief points of his accusation define themselves : their disdain for things that are holy, their iniquitous mysteries which, with these wretched people, bind them together in infamous intercourse at their nocturnal meetings. He then attacks the conception of the God of the Christians, whose inquisitorial ubiquity appears to him to be a marvel of presumptuousness and madness, and the Christian eschatology, especially the doctrine of the Resurrection, for which he reserves his most mordant irony. The speech ends with an appeal to humility and to that prudent doubt which the new Academe had enjoined, and which is the safest attitude of mind to adopt.

From a historical and moral point of view, these few pages are of exceptional richness. Caecilius is an admirable representative of those lettered pagans who were very sceptical as regards the foundation of things, but who, from civic *pietas* and from respect for the *mos majorum*, thought it to be their duty to energetically defend the religion of tradition—an essential element in the prosperity and greatness of Rome. The author must have possessed a rare openness of mind to lend so eloquent and so persuasive an accent to the cause which he detested.

After a short respite (XIV–XV), Octavius takes his turn to speak (XV–XXXVIII). His method is as follows : to pursue his adversary step by step in order to refute all his complaints without omitting one, then to turn them the moment he can against the pagans; to select his examples

H

and his *points d'appui* from among the pagan thinkers in
order not to lead Caecilius astray and to prove to him that
these *semi-nudi*, whom he despises, are not so far removed
from him as he appears to think.

As against the transcendental scepticism of Caecilius,
Octavius first defines the notion of Providence. In a broad
and full development in which his talent and his Ciceronian
recollections have full play, he describes the splendour of the
heavens, the ordered course of the seasons, etc. All reveals
the highest intelligence which has an eye to details as well
as to the whole. Must we believe from these manifestations
that there is one God or many ? It is enough to behold what
passes on the earth, which is the image of the heavens : every
kingdom which is divided perishes. God is therefore one.
Reason attests it, and the mind of the philosopher so near to
Christian thought recognises it equally.

After having established these fundamental truths, Providence and the oneness of God, Octavius makes a point against
the pagan religion. On this question the arguments of
Christian apologetics were already fixed—namely, the entirely
human origin of the gods, the scandal of mythology and of
the rites consecrated by law. Octavius does not parti-
cularise them except by the allusions he makes to the
very words which Caecilius had employed. He points out in
particular the danger of an education, which corrupts by all
these untruths the minds of children, and renders them
impermeable to the truth. He seeks to loosen the bonds of
solidarity which Caecilius wished to establish between the
glories of Rome and the pagan religion. He does not dare
to deny outright the prodigies vaunted by the pagans, but he
attributes them to demons, wandering and impure spirits
who have fallen from heaven, and who console themselves
for their misfortunes by deceiving and destroying souls.

He next approaches the charges brought by Caecilius
against the Christians. Here his line of argument becomes
more solid : reasons of heart and also reasons of Reason.
He declares to his friend that he pardons him his mistake for
he remembers that he himself had likewise shared the same.
But let him give up believing in these miserable fables !
Only those give credence to such shameful things who are
capable of perpetrating them themselves. Then step by

step Octavius justifies the different conceptions of Christianity over which Caecilius had been scandalised—the watchfulness exercised by God over his creatures, the catastrophe of the end of the world, the resurrection and punishments beyond the grave.

In these latter pages and in those which follow, there are all the constituents of a picture of Christian life : virtue under suffering piously accepted, the heroism of the martyrs, the purity of heart which refuses consent to everything that might soil it. And these things are said with a fire of enthusiasm which throws its final brightness over the warm and vibrating peroration.

The three friends remain for a moment silent (XXXIX). It was then Minucius' part to give judgment. But Caecilius anticipates him, declaring himself to be convinced on the principal points discussed. A few further interchanges of views will do the rest.

" We then separated," the author concludes, " happy and enraptured, Caecilius at having found belief and Octavius at having won the day, and myself at the faith of the one and the victory of the other."

III

A PERFECT naturalness in the setting of the work or, if you will, in the setting of the scene ; a remarkable attempt at impartiality in exposing the charges brought by pagans ; much warmth and conviction in the reply of the Christian, Octavius ; an extremely supple style of many lights and shades, wherein the elegance of the Ciceronian age is heightened by a freshness of quick and picturesque expressions—such are the merits which all agree to recognise in this work by Minucius Felix. Nevertheless even those who most gladly render homage to the literary beauty and seduction of this dialogue, are astonished at only finding such fugitive examples of Christian doctrine in it. Octavius claims to convert the pagan Caecilius and appears to have succeeded in doing so : but is it not true that Caecilius at the close of the discussion is almost as ignorant of the faith to which he gives his willing adherence as at the beginning ? Octavius gives proof of a very strange discretion and, what is more serious, certain of his words only give very imperfect expression to Christian doctrine which he appears to shrink from explaining completely.

This complaint may be readily brought against the *Octavius*. Let us examine more precisely what failings from an intrinsically Christian point of view can be justly brought against it :

(*a*) In the first place, the conception which Octavius, the mouthpiece of the author, makes to himself of God is, in the opinion of certain critics, of Gaston Boissier [1] among others, " far more abstract and philosophic than intrinsically Christian." " We must not," says Octavius, " seek out a name for God : His name is—God. We only require names when we have to distinguish by some special appellation each individual among a multitude : to God, who is alone of His kind, the name of ' God ' belongs in every respect. If I call Him ' Father,' people might believe He is of flesh ; if ' King,' people might suppose that He is of earth ; if ' Master,' people might certainly understand that He is mortal. Put aside all these accessory names and you will perceive it in all its clearness." [2] Certainly we have not here quite the God of the Christians. True, but the intrinsically Christian idea comes out elsewhere. G. Boissier himself perceived this for he brings back his reader to chapter xxxv, 4, in which God is called *parentem omnium et omnium dominum*. He could have chosen a far more significant passage (xxxi, 8). " What is troubling you," says Octavius to his interlocutor, " is that we love each other with mutual affection because we know not hate ; again (and that makes you envious) we call each other ' brethren ' as being the sons of one God our Father (*ut unius Dei parentis homines*), as being participators in the same faith, as being heirs to the same hope."

There is thus no reason to insist on this point.

(*b*) A second charge of more weight is the roundabout, ambiguous, almost equivocal manner in which Octavius makes allusion to Christ : " You attribute," he says, " to our religion the worship of a malefactor and his cross ; but you err very far from the truth in supposing that a malefactor has deserved to pass for a God, or that a being of earth could have passed for such. Assuredly that would be

[1] *Fin du paganisme*, I, 284. [2] *Otavius*, xviii, 10.

worthy of pity if all our hope should rest on a man subject to death : for all our support in him would cease in the death of this man, etc." [1] Baehrens,[2] one of the editors of the *Octavius*, has thought to see in this passage a manifest negation of the Divinity of Christ.   The idea which seems to me to emerge from it, on the contrary, is this : you may make quite certain that we are not the people to adore a man and especially a malefactor ; our hope rests on something else than what is ephemeral and perishable.   In transposing the expression in a positive sense, we can almost draw from it an affirmation of the virtue and of the Divine immortality of Christ.   But we must readily agree with M. Boissier that we might expect something else " than a brief and obscure phrase " [3] on such a subject : " What is he doing," M. Boissier exclaims, " that in an apology of Christianity he has been unwilling to pronounce the name of Christ ? " In fact, this *is* surprising : we should however remember— a fact which is too often ignored—that amongst the apologists of the IInd century, Aristides, St Justin and Tertullian are the only ones who have uttered the name of Jesus Christ.

(*c*) We likewise find that in several places in the *Octavius*, the doctrine of grace seems either to be ignored or contradicted. Hear again what G. Boissier says : [4] " In order to give an answer to the jeers of his opponent, who makes fun of these ignorant people, of these worthless nobodies who dare to discuss God and the world, Octavius says to him : Know that all men, without distinction of age, sex or position, are capable of reason and of good sense, and that of themselves they can arrive at wisdom." If nature alone leads them thither, if they have no need of God's aid in obtaining it, what becomes of the necessity of grace ?   He adds a little further on that in order to know God, instead of listening to the errors of those by whom we are surrounded, it is enough to interrogate ourselves and to believe in ourselves, *sibi credere*. This is just how Seneca expresses himself (*Ep.* 31, 3) ; but Athenagoras the apologist, a contemporary of Minucius, speaks very differently. He attacks those wise men of the world who pretend that reason unaided can lead them to the truth and who flatter themselves that they

---

[1] xxix, 2 ; cf. ix, 4.
[3] *Fin du Paganisme*, I, 280.
[2] Ed. Teubner, 1886, p. xi.
[4] *Op. cit.*, p. 280–281.

can know God by their own lights. " Unlike them," he says, " in our search for what we should believe, we place our trust in the testimony of the prophets who, being inspired of God, speak to us of Him in His name." Here we have language which is truly Christian and which appears to be a direct reply to the words of Minucius.

And G. Boissier adds in a note : " See also the following passage in which the necessity of grace, in order to arrive at the truth, appears to be not admitted : *Cum sit veritas obvia, sed requirentibus,* 23, 2." [1]

I do not know if these criticisms ought to be accepted in their entirety. G. Boissier first tells us : " The doctrine of grace is nowhere mentioned." As a matter of fact, it is nowhere expounded didactically ; but more or less enveloped allusions to it are made. See XXVII, 7, in regard to the power of exorcizing demons possessed by the Christians : " In spite of themselves," Octavius says, " the wretches (he is speaking of impure spirits) tremble with fright in the body and take flight at once, or rather disappear little by little according to the aid which the faith of the sufferer is able to provide, or according to the succour which the grace proceeding from the deliverer lends to him (*prout fides patientis adjuvat aut gratia curantis adspirat*)." Compare again XXXVII, 5–6, concerning the martyrs : " Our children, our weak women laugh at crosses and tortures, at ferocious beasts and all the terrors of their sufferings, with a patience which comes to them from on high (*et omnes suppliciorum terriculas inspirata patientia doloris inludunt*). And do you not understand, unhappy man that you are, that there is no one . . . who could support these tortures *without help from God ?* " Finally, can we not see an allusion to grace, fully or slightly comprehended, in this reproach of the pagan Caecilius : " *You attribute to God all our actions,* just as others attribute them to fate : thus, it is not from a spontaneous act that people adhere to your sect but because they are chosen by God." [2] Boissier's assertion appears therefore to be a little rash. As for the arguments which he brings forward in order to show that Octavius speaks as a Stoic rather than as a Christian, possibly they too have not all the weight which he deduces from them. If Octavius affirms that all men,

---

[1] The correct reference is xxiii, 8.　　　　　　[2] xi, 6.

without distinction of age and social position, are capable of arriving by nature at wisdom, *natura insitos esse sapientiam*, it is because he desires to offer a protest against the aristocratic disdain of Caecilius who, in his estimate of these bare-footed Christians appeared to believe that, in order to be a thinker, a man must be well clothed. Octavius aims at making him understand that reason is the most freely distributed thing in the world, and that it is of little importance what rank a disputant holds if he argues well. It would have been altogether without purpose to confuse the question by making the doctrine of grace intervene, and we ought to be thankful to the author for not having done so. The same may be said for the other passages to which Boissier takes exception. Let us put back into its context the *sibi credere* in which he perceives an echo of Seneca. Octavius has just been speaking at length on the deplorable credulity of their ancestors and of the mass of errors with which tradition, reinforced by education, encumbered the spirit, and adds : " You fear them (these contemptible gods) . . . : this is because you foolishly strive to follow your parents, and because you prefer to fall into the mistakes of others *rather than to place confidence in yourselves*." [1] One can easily catch the sense of these words. The following lines from Renan might serve as a commentary to them : " Se convertir au christianisme n'était pas un acte de crédulité ; c'était presque un acte de bon sens relatif. Même au point de vue du rationalisme, le christianisme pouvait être envisagé comme un progrès ; *ce fut l'homme religieusement éclairé qui l'adopta*." [2] As for the last passage brought forward : " Truth offers herself of her own accord but on condition that men seek for her," the idea that truth is before all else a conquest of the soul is such an elementary factor in psychology [3] that we ought not to wonder that Minucius Felix advanced it as a fact without further widening the debate.

(*d*) Another criticism : Minucius Felix has allowed imprudent expressions to escape which he never would have ventured to make if he had been a sincere Christian. For example the following, on pagan prodigies : " *Quae si essent*

---

[1] xxiv, 2.
[2] Marc. Aurèle, p. 582.
[3] Especially for a mind brought up on the writings of Plato.

facta, fierent ; quia fieri non possunt, ideo non sunt.'' [1] Baehrens cannot believe that Minucius Felix did not perceive how
easily the argument could be turned against the Christian
miracles. G. Boissier himself makes a *piquant* [2] analogy
between the above reflection and the following one of Renan :
" Nous repoussons le surnaturel par la même raison qui
nous fait repousser l'existence des centaures et des hippo-
griffes : c'est qu'on n'en a jamais vu."

In reality, Minucius Felix would only have thought of
applying to his own faith the reasoning by which he claimed
to destroy belief in the pagan miracles if he had himself been
a hesitating Christian, which is just the point debated.
Let us rest assured that he believed in the reality of supernatural " graces " whose favours the Christian communities
received with so much happiness and pride. If the argument
which he used has been retorted against Christianity, what
does this prove ? Any phrase isolated from the context
may cut both ways. At that rate we ought to suspect
Arnobius, for he has cast ridicule on mythology by methods
very analogous to those which Voltaire was to employ
against the Bible ; and it would be prudent to be mistrustful
of Lactantius, who has one quite " Protestant " passage
on the right of everyone to make his own religion.[3] If we
are to see in the incriminated words some sceptical insinuation,
we must be in the state of mind of Baehrens who, without
blinking, calls Minucius Felix " a forerunner of Strauss and
Renan " !

(*e*) G. Boissier is also amazed at the antipathy displayed
by Minucius Felix against the externals of worship, against
temples, statues and every representation or, if I may dare
to say so, any definition of what is divine. In the mind of
Octavius there was only one good way of praying to God,
and that was the offering to Him of a pure heart : " Here
we have doubtless a fine profession of faith," G. Boissier
remarks ; " but Seneca could have subscribed to that as well

[1] xx, 4.
[2] *Fin du Paganisme*, I, 277.
[3] *Instit. Div.*, II, viii. " Everyone should trust to himself in what is the most
important affair in his life, and should use his own judgment and his own sense in
seeking after and weighing up the truth ; our predecessors in time have not necessarily been before us in the paths of wisdom, etc." A Jesuit of the XVIIIth century, Father de Laubrussel, remarks, not without a tinge of spite, that " critics
have always made use of this maxim of Lactantius which is little understood."
Traité des Abus de la Critique en Matière de Religion, 1711, p. 70, note.

as Minucius.   If that is all the doctrine held by the Christians, they were nothing more than a sect of philosophers just like others." [1]   G. Boissier's surprise is quite legitimate ; but it is not only in the case of the *Octavius* that he has a right to show it.   Among the apologists of the first centuries and up to the time of Lactantius, there was a marked disdain for all ceremonial in matters of religion.   They feared even the shadow of idolatry and shrank from it ; and besides there were texts from Scripture like those from Isaias, i, 11 ; lxvi, 1 ; from the Acts, xvii, 24 ; vii, 48–50, which urged them to oppose to all the exterior forms of religion the far more preferable holocaust of piety and virtue.   The question only arose little by little under pressure of the requirements of public worship.   It is not then surprising that Minucius Felix seems to be here and there very intemperate, and he a Catholic, in his hostility against certain outward manifestations of religious sentiment.

(*f*) We come lastly to the principal charge which we should specially notice.   The most disconcerting thing in the *Octavius* is not its contradiction of Christian doctrine— it is nowhere proved that this exists in reality—it is the silence on Christian doctrines preserved by the author.

Octavius deliberately keeps himself to the domain of the most general philosophic truths—the need for a Providence who organises and rules the universe, the oneness of God, the discussion and reprobation of the scandalous fables put to the account of the gods, and of the rites by which the pagans pretended to honour them, and an apology of the life of the Christians.   These are the principal points which the champion of Christianity successively touches upon.   It is impossible not to be struck by so many gaps.   In his pleading there are some things which remind one of the Scriptures ; [2] but nowhere does he explain what are the sacred sources of the faith.   He completely neglects the proof from the accom-

---

[1] *Fin du Paganisme*, I, 281.   Similar declarations by Seneca are, as a matter of fact, pointed out by Fr. X. Burger, *Minucius Felix und Seneca*, Munich, 1904, p. 28.

[2] A few in number : compare *Octavius*, XXXIII, 3, and *Josue*, X, 11 ; *Oct.*, XXIX, 3, and *Jeremias*, XVII, 5.   Some expressions are taken from St Paul : *spei coheredes* (xxxi, 8), cf. *Ep. to Titus*, III, 7 ; *Ep. to the Romans*, viii, 17 ; *unum bonum sapimus* (xxxi, 6) and *Ep. to the Romans*, xv, 5 et s.   In many places we may ask whether he has drawn from St Paul or from Seneca ; very probably from Seneca to judge from the analogy of certain of his expressions.   (See *Oct.*, xxxvi, 8, and Seneca, *De Prov.*, ii, 2.)

plishment of the prophecies, which had appeared so decisive to St Justin.[1] We have here a very paltry, a very incomplete account which gives an entirely inadequate idea of the economy of the Christian revelation.

On this point the fact is indubitable and it would be idle to try and elude it. We must therefore give some explanation. Let us see what has been put forward.

At first people had recourse to an interpretation which was formerly in favour, but which has since lost much of its credit. Minucius Felix was bound to silence by that " discipline of the secret," which it is alleged obliged the faithful " never to speak openly of the faith and of their worship before catechumens and unbelievers." But why should he have been more mysterious than St Justin who, in his first apology, unfolds all the mystery of the Eucharist,[2] or than the author of the *Cohortatio ad Graecos*, who, however little explicit he is on dogma, nevertheless is able to explain in a few words the doctrine of the Word ?[3] What is this obligation which must have weighed on him (Minucius Felix), from which St Irenæus and Tertullian escaped ? As a matter of fact, it has been shown that the " discipline of the secret " was enclosed in far more rigorous bounds than people for a long time believed.[4]

Roeren, who suggested the above hypothesis in 1859, relied principally on this phrase in the *Octavius :* " We never speak of God in public unless it be that anyone interrogates us."[5] This is a too brief indication in which we can hardly seriously see any hint of the *disciplina arcani*.

Another critic, Keim,[6] thought that Minucius Felix was a catechumen still little versed in matters of faith and who could only say what his zeal as a neophyte had already taught him. But does he reflect that Minucius Felix wrote long after his conversion when his friend, Octavius, was already dead ?[7] Unless we are to suppose that all is fictitious in the dialogue and that the confidences of the author, as well

---

[1] See the *Apol.*, xlv–lv et s.
[2] 1 *Ap.*, lxvi et s.
[3] Ch. xxxviii.
[4] Cf. Batiffol, *Etudes d'Histoire et de Théol. Positive*, Paris, 1902.
[5] xix, 15.
[6] *Rom. und das Christenthum*, Berlin, 1881, p. 472.
[7] Cf. Chap. i.

as the characters that he puts in it, are imaginary, Keim's hypothesis falls to the ground of itself.

It has been upheld, on a better foundation, that if Minucius Felix showed himself so reserved, it was simply because he did not wish to go further than his own particular conviction. In that case, he must have been an altogether soft-spoken and prudent heretic. The most moderate expression of this interpretation is found in Kuehn.[1] According to Kuehn, Minucius Felix, an eclectic philosopher, must have *chosen* among the Christian doctrines those which best suited his cast of mind and thus he must have advanced his " personal doctrine," buoyed up on beliefs which could not have been accepted. Baehrens [2] took up the same idea but pushed it to extremes. In his eyes, the reticences of Minucius Felix, as well as his unskilful arguments, are explained by the excellent reason that he was not a believer. It was the case of a philosopher and man of letters who had seen an excellent rule of discipline in Christianity nearly approaching the wisdom of the Greeks, but one better adapted to the daily wear and tear of life. He connected himself therefore with it thinking to show his brethren a highly refined interpretation of it ; and to the untrained crowd he abandoned chimeras which were repugnant to reason.

This is an evident paradox the falseness of which cries aloud. If Lactantius and St Jerome recognised him as one of themselves, without doubt this was because they did not find in him any trace of " rationalism."

Ernest Renan too advanced his own explanation which is much more elaborate. He thought to see in the gaps of the *Octavius* the concerted dissimulation of a " skilful lawyer " passing over the points in his belief that he found difficult in order the more easily to win the adhesion of his uninformed hearers. Once more yielding to his mania for comparisons he likens Minucius Felix to the preacher at Notre Dame [3] " addressing people of the world who are easy to satisfy, making himself all things to all men, studying the weaknesses and passions of the persons he desires to convince, affecting under his heavy cope the gestures of the man of open mind

1 *Der Octavius des M.F.*, Leipsic, 1882.
2 See the Preface to his edition.
3 *Marc. Aurèle*, p. 403.

and falsifying his office in order to render it acceptable. Become a Christian on the faith of this pious sophist—nothing can be better; but remember that all this is a bait. . . ."

Here indeed is a lively thrust: should we accept these severe words in all their rigour? Would not Minucius be an unctuous Tartuffe and a juggling devotee in that case? In order to establish the exact shade of the truth (at least this is how it seems to me), I think we must put before our eyes the end which Minucius Felix is pursuing in his work. It is the indispensable condition to thoroughly appreciate the method which he used in order to attain to it.

Minucius Felix clearly did not write the *Octavius* for the popular eye: he wrote it for men of the world, for educated men. His characters have a high distinction and an evidently very refined culture if we consider the number of allusions and quotations which they grasp without the least effort. Minucius Felix was not a Christian after the manner of Tertullian; he was living amongst his people, he numbered excellent friends in pagan circles and he was well aware of the anti-Christian prejudices with which his caste was especially imbued.

It was just because he was well aware of them and possible because some work, some discourse of Frontonius, the rhetorician, had shown him once more all their virulence, that he wished to endeavour to dissipate them.

In order to prove to his pagan hearers that he was by no means unmindful of the force of their reasons, he gave logical sequence to the leading speech of Caecilius and employed the most closely-reasoned eloquence; his refutation must consequently assume all the greater authority.

What was the spirit in which he drew up this refutation? A very characteristic passage in which Minucius, the arbiter in the debate, reviews his impression of the discourse of Octavius, will show us:[1] "As for me, my admiration was so great that I was quite beside myself; I marvelled that he should have proved all those things which it is easier to feel than to speak, by arguments, by examples and by authorities derived from what he had read; that he should have vanquished the perverse with these same weapons from philosophy which he employed, finally, that he should have demonstrated

[1] XXXIX, 1.

the truth to be not only easy to understand, but congenial "
(to reason).   According to this confession, which is without
any doubt the view of the author, it was for him first of all
to give a form to his belief, to make it emerge from the limbo
of sentiment, and to explain it in the light of day to minds
accustomed by long practice to the art of disputation—
assuredly a task needing tact.   Next, to support his apology
by arguments which the pagans could not refuse *a priori*.
From that arose the necessity of so many reflections from
good authors and his satisfaction in backing up his argument
by profane philosophy.   Finally, it was desirable to give his
doctrine a happy turn, to render it pleasing and to incline
their hearts to make it their own.

But it remained an understood thing that the general
orientation of his detailed apology must not deviate from the
line which the opening speech of Caecilius had previously
traced out for him.   Octavius says so in so many words at
the beginning of his reply.   He wishes " to blot out the
defilement proceeding from these bitter insults in the living
water of the words of truth."   That is why he takes the
allegations of his adversary one by one, in order to endeavour
to demonstrate their nothingness.   Apart from the oneness
of God, and Providence, he only lays down two dogmas,
the dogma of the resurrection and that of future punishments :
these are just those which Caecilius had attacked.   He
attempts to purge the mind of his friend of his false ideas
and erroneous judgments.   Caecilius little by little is won
over by the warm conviction of this antagonist, who, besides,
is so dear to him.   His prejudices fall to the ground, he confesses himself beaten ; but it is not quite the *Je vois, je sais,
je crois, je suis désabusée* of Pauline in *Polyeucte*.   He gives his
adhesion to the points laid down, which have been the subject
of the discussion, and to those alone.[1]   Difficulties remain to
him, but the solution is put off to the morrow.

Octavius avoided adding any debatable matter pro-
visionally beside the mark, which, by turning him from his
object, might have caused him to overlook the refutation of
any charge already definitely brought : and he followed this
line not only on the question of religion but also on the ques-

---

[1] " *Itaque quod pertinet ad summam quaestionis, et de providentia fateor et de
Deo cedo et de sectae jam nostrae sinceritate confido.*"   (xl, 2.)

tion of purely natural order. That is why he only makes a hasty allusion to the special methods in vogue against the Christians.[1] Similarly, he makes no defence of the loyalty of the Christians or of their respect for the heads of the State : Caecilius had made no charge against them in these respects. He sets before himself the establishment of a common ground of agreement, a perfect symmetry between attack and defence, and eliminates every question which does not enter into his plan.

But after all, he was the designer of this plan. Why did he not enlarge it sufficiently to admit the principal doctrines of his faith ?

Without doubt, the reason is that he wished to reach by his work, a veritable propagandist pamphlet, a definite class of readers, men like Caecilius, rather sceptical as to the real foundation of things, and rather inquisitive on metaphysical questions, but whose agnosticism was compatible with a very sensitive and a very ardent Roman piety ; men who for these reasons despised the Christians for their dogmatic intrepidity which seemed all the more outrageous coming from inferior people ; men who feared them owing to the evil reports current about them and vowed to destruction these despisers of Rome and of the gods.

In order to find points of contact with minds thus fashioned, would it have been suitable to lay down at the outset, from a kind of somewhat fanatical bravado, incomprehensible positive statements on the Word, the prophecies, and the relationship existing between the Father and the Son, etc. ? Clearly not. It was necessary to discuss their charges dispassionately, to compel them to recognise their lack of foundation, to bring them to more right-minded views, and, since to remain on the defensive is always a rather awkward attitude, to drive home a few vigorous points.

This is just what Minucius Felix has done. Of the three elements of which the first apologies are composed, namely, the justification of the Christians, the criticism of the pagan beliefs, and the dogmatic explanation of Christianity, he developed the two former and passed over or adjourned the third. These are the tactics of an advocate, if you will (Minucius Felix quite clearly was versed in the artifices of the

[1] xxviii, 3.

bar and we can find evidences of it here and there), but legitimate tactics on the whole if we consider that there is a proper way of giving instruction in belief and that this proper way presupposes gradual exercises and a progressive advancement towards an initiation by definition.[1]

Certainly the work is not perfect and we agree that from motives of prudence and policy, Minucius Felix has *minimised* doctrine to an excessive degree.[2]   But in conclusion, many omissions in which some people wish to see ignorance, dissimulation, and equivocal *ruses*, explain and almost justify themselves if we consider that the *Octavius* is not a *summa*, but simply a kind of introduction to Christian doctrine written for the use of cultivated men of the world.

IV

JUST as Minucius Felix brings forward no fresh view of the pagan religion, and no original synthesis of the truths of his own faith, so his inspiration needs to be constantly urged on and supported by the help of others. He does not possess that power of reflection which permeates a style, giving a personality and a life-like form. It is enough to consult one or other of the recent editions giving his sources to realise that the *Octavius* is, according to the expression of M. Paul Monceaux, " a mosaic of ideas, scenes and details taken from all quarters." [3] He borrowed from Cicero the general plan of the dialogue,[4] and that tone of perfect urbanity which the interlocutors maintain face to face with each other in the most burning parts of the discussion. The choice of an arbiter to settle the debate came to him perhaps from Tacitus.[5] Cicero also furnished him with the refined and delicate opening, and the greater part of the " motifs " of the eloquent leading speech of Caecilius. To Seneca he is

---

[1] See Lactantius, *De Ira Dei*, 2. " *Nam cum sint gradus multi, per quos ad domicilium veritatis ascenditur, non est facile cuilibet evehi ad summum . . .*" and the whole passage. Cf. Orig., c. *Cels.*, III, liii.

[2] His successors appear to have felt what was wanting in him. See Lactantius, *Div. Inst.*, i, ix, 22.

[3] *Hist. Litt.*, I, 490.

[4] Previous examples of the use of dialogue in apologetics are to be found in Ariston of Pella, Justin Martyr, and Caius of Rome. Lucian of Samosata, on the pagan side, had given to this class of writing a veritable second spring.

[5] *Dial. Or.*, IV. Cf. Plato, *Protag.*, 337 E ; *Symp.*, 175 E.

indebted for a quantity of pointed expressions and nearly all the developments in chapters xxxvi and xxxvii where Octavius, replying to the disdainful charges of Caecilius, exalts the poverty of the Christians and opposes to the dangers of wealth and honours the sovereign good of a pure heart. Seneca had said of the "wise" Stoic:[1] "Ecce spectaculum dignum ad quod respiciat intentus operi suo Deus, ecce par Deo dignum, vir fortis cum fortuna male compositus, etc." And Octavius repeats concerning the Christian martyr: "Quam pulchrum spectaculum Deo, cum Christianus cum dolore congreditur, cum adversum minas et supplicia et tormenta componitur. . . ." Philosophers, historians, poets—from all of them Minucius Felix takes his toll. His work is a fabric of recollections, but so cleverly interlaced and so finely adjusted that the joints do not appear. In this treatise, made up of different bits and pieces, all presents one single whole, all is ordered with the same enthusiasm. This ingenious art of adaptation (with at least some degree of originality) is that of a Ronsard, a Chénier. Minucius Felix was of the same family as these humanist experts. He was the most learned and the most delicately tempered of lettered men.

V

THE characteristics of his talent themselves furnish us with a valuable indication for taking up a position in the so much controverted question of the priority of Tertullian's *Apologeticum* as regards the *Octavius*. It is not open to doubt that between these two works there are analogies of foundation and of form. "There are long or short developments, but of a cast which is characteristic, quotations, reflections, special features, and bursts of eloquence, of bitter or ironical ridicule and of mere raillery."[2] This fact is not disputed by anyone; but the reasons given are so contradictory as to form one of the most remarkable collections of cacophony that modern criticism offers. Up to 1868, with the exception of a few rare dissidents, it was believed that the *Apologeticum*

---

[1] *De Provid.*, II, ix.
[2] Massebieau, *Rev. de l'Hist. des Relig.*, vol. XV (1887), p. 325. For a detailed account of these resemblances, see the editions of Boenig and Waltzing.

had the priority.   The *Octavius* had been printed half a
century after the *Apologeticum* (1484 ; 1543) and Tertullian's
chef-d'œuvre, already held in universal admiration, continued
to be regarded as anterior to all Latin writings of a similar
kind.   Ad. Ebert shook the prevailing opinion in a memoir
which appeared in 1868.[1] Since then, a host of articles,
dissertations, and treatises have appeared on this much
debated problem.   Three theories emerge from all this printed
matter.   One, upheld principally by Hartel, advances a
source common to Tertullian and to Minucius Felix.   According to this, they both made use of a Latin apologist who
must have drawn upon Varro, Cicero and Seneca.   But
who was the apologist ?   Here the difficulty commences.
And then, which of the two was the first to exploit him ?
The question debated would still remain even if this
mysterious source could be marked down.   The second
theory, that of Ebert, which places the *Octavius* before the
Apologeticum, has recruited a number of " authorities "
(Schanz, Boenig, Ehrhard, Geffcken, etc.).   Lastly, the third,
which is the traditional idea, was taken up in 1887 by a French
scholar, M. Massebieau, in a remarkable article in the *Revue
de l'Histoire des Religions*, which more than any later discussion
strikes at the real root of the question debated.   Massebieau
states the numerous resemblances in detail between the
Apologeticum and the *Octavius*, and asks this question : if
Tertullian really borrowed from Minucius Felix, would he
have utilised him by taking his words and his expressions
but without ever mentioning him by name ?   Such a proceeding is unlike his methods.   Tertullian likes to quote his
authors by name.   In addition, he takes from them their
ideas and the facts which they cite, but he preserves his own
style and marks with his own impress all that has come to
him from other sources.   Minucius Felix on the contrary has
no scruples in making his own the turns of phrase which he
meets with in other authors.   Does it not seem fairly reasonable from this that he would have made use of Tertullian for
the Christian part of his treatise just as he used Cicero and
Seneca for that portion which was essentially philosophic ?
In other words, that he largely drew upon the *Apologeticum*

---

[1] *Tert. Verh. zu Minucius Felix* reprinted in the *Abh. d. saechs Ges. d. Wiss.*,
XII (*Phil. Hist. Kl.*, V), 1870, pp. 319–386.

I

(and also upon other treatises of Tertullian, such as the *De Paenitentia*, the *De Resurrectione Carnis*, the *De Testimonio Animae*, the *De Corona*) to extract from them what he found suitable to his purpose ?

Another observation which has its value is the following :[1] supposing that the *Octavius* had in reality begun the series of works by Latin apologetics, would not this treatise have enjoyed among Christian antiquity (however confused the literary tradition of the first two centuries soon became) a renown superior to what he seems to have attained ? Minucius Felix would have justly been held as a pioneer of great merit. Now we do not find that this homage was anywhere meted out to him, and it is a new reason of quite a general order to give the first place to a meagre comparison of texts in which criticism has vainly exhausted itself during the last fifty years.

[1] Harnack, *Chron.*, II, 329. The not uniformly conclusive arguments of Harnack have been keenly criticised by G. Kruger in the *Gott. Gel. Anz.*, January 1905, p. 36 et s. These will be found analysed by A. d'Alès, in his *Etudes des PP. Jésuites*, vol. CIV (1905), pp. 289–317.

CHAPTER II

SAINT CYPRIAN AND HIS TIMES

BIBLIOGRAPHY

WE are able to check the manner in which the collected works of Cyprian have been got together. With his methodical habits, St Cyprian kept by him a copy of his letters. To these *dossiers* he added the letters which he himself had received on such and such religious question ; and he was glad to be able to communicate them on occasion in order to justify his conduct or to give authority to his opinion. Around these documents, thus grouped together, other letters must have come to be annexed after his death. Side by side with a division into subjects, we find in the manuscripts traces of a division into persons to whom they were sent. It does not appear that there was any general collection of the letters of Cyprian before modern times. This explains how a certain number of documents, attested by the explicit witness of the Bishop, have gone astray [1] in the course of this more or less capricious juxtaposition. As for the writings themselves, a list drawn up by the deacon Pontius in § vii of his *Vita Cypriani*, or rather a series of transparent allusions of an oratorical kind, permit us to affirm that even in the lifetime of Cyprian a first collection of eleven treatises had been established. Mommsen [2] discovered in a manuscript of the Xth century belonging to the library of Philip de Cheltenham a stichometric catalogue drawn up in 359, about a hundred years after the death of Cyprian, which nearly coincides with the list of Pontius, but some writings and some letters are added. Dom Morin [3] lastly has noted another *index* in an unpublished sermon of St Augustine : the *Quod Idola Dii non sint* only figures in this last document. It is through the aid of these three lists, checked by the text of the quotations from the Bible, that we can circumscribe those writings of St Cyprian which are certainly authentic. [4]

The authority enjoyed by the Bishop was such that certain sects made a selection of his works for their own particular use. Reitzenstein [5] has made a study of one of this series included in two manuscripts, one at Wurzbourg and the other at Munich, whose Donatist origin is not disputed.

---

[1] Harnack (in T.U., xxiii, 2 [1902]) enumerates eleven properly belonging to Cyprian.

[2] Cf. *Hermes*, XXI (1886), p. 142, *Gesamm. Schriften*, VII (1909), p. 282.

[3] B.A.L.A.C., IV (1914), p. 16 et s.

[4] K. Mengis has recently drawn attention to the index which is found on f. 43 of the manuscript of Wurzbourg Theol. 145 (W. in Hartel). He considers it to be an important document which should represent a tradition anterior to that of the manuscript of Cheltenham, and near to the time of Cyprian. Cf. B. ph. W., 1918, pp. 326-336.

[5] *Sitz.-Ber. d. Heid. Akad. d. Wiss.*, 1913, n° 14, p. 34 et s. ; *Nachr. von der Kon. Ges. d. Wiss. zu Gottingen, Phil.-Hist. Kl.* 1914, Heft I. These two manuscripts are the *Cod. Wirceburgensis theol.*, fol. 33, and the *Cod. Monacensis*, 37–39, both dating from the beginning of the IXth century. Cf. Mengis, *Ein donatistiches Corpus Cyprianischer Briefe*, Diss. Freib.-i.-B., 1916.

The most complete modern edition is that of G. von Hartel, in vol. III of the *Corpus Script. Eccl. Latinorum.*

Hartel established his text after comparing fifty manuscripts. Taken as a whole, the classification given by him is correct, although he has not valued at its true importance such a manuscript as the *Veronensis;* his edition marks a real improvement on those of Pamelus (Antwerp, 1568), of Rigaut (Paris, 1648), and of Baluze-Maran (Paris, 1718). Since Hartel, the inventory of the manuscripts of St Cyprian has been pursued. Hans Frhr von Soden in his *die Cyprianische Briefsammlung* (T.U., xxv, 3 [1904]), has counted 157 which make up a *Corpus Cyprianicum;* in addition, 274 which furnish writings or isolated pieces. Among these manuscripts, some go back to a very early date, back to the VIth and VIIth centuries. This abundant material is an almost unique occurrence in Latin Christian literature. The labours of von Soden have shown the necessity for a fresh edition of the works of Cyprian. Particularly scrupulous attention will have to be given to the quotations from Scripture, which are so important in the history of the Latin Bible. Moreover, another publication by H. von Soden, *das latein. Neue Testament in Afrika zur Zeit. Cyprians* (T.U., xxxiii [1909]), has appreciably cleared the way.

Works. See TABLE III.

The fundamental work on Cyprian is that by Paul Monceaux, *Saint Cyprien et son Temps* (*Hist. litt. de l'Afr. chr.,* vol. II, 1902). Other recent works will be pointed out in the notes.

SUMMARY

1. Tertullian and St Cyprian.—II. The life of St Cyprian.—III. The ideas which dominated him. Influences which determined them.— IV. How he realised them in practice. The matter of the *lapsi.*— V. The writings of St Cyprian.—VI. The prestige of St Cyprian The Apocryphal writings assigned to his name.

I

ST CYPRIAN called Tertullian his master. He used to like to say " *Da magistrum* " when he wished to have in his hand some work of his vigorous predecessor for his daily reading.[1] He was profoundly under the impress of that dominating genius. What a difference however between the intemperate ascetic, the crafty sophist Tertullian, and this essentially loyal and true, though very experienced soul! Cyprian had those qualities of heart which attract, which draw sympathy ; I mean charity, prudence, and love of order, of harmony and of peace. Quite from the beginning these gifts clearly belonged to his cast of mind : he was made like that. But they proceeded also from the exercise of his function. At a very early age he had the charge of souls, having been appointed scarcely two or three years after his conversion to direct the group of Christians at Carthage.

[1] St Jerome, *de Vir. Ill.,* liii.

There is nothing to equal a responsibility of this kind in making a man wise, in helping him to discern those limits where what is possible ends and what is chimerical begins. When a man knows that the opinion which he is defending, that the measure which he is putting in force will affect a whole body of people who trust in him and who consider him as the mouthpiece of the Holy Spirit, he is readily inclined to keep himself from all exaggeration and to remain carefully within the bounds of what is reasonable. Tertullian succeeded in pressing his ideas to their extreme limits, and in treating as timid and perverse those who did not range themselves on his side : this intemperance only compromised himself. Perhaps if he had assumed the hard task undertaken by Cyprian we should have seen him softening down his fine *intransigeance*, like certain politicians, who are terrible busybodies so long as they are in opposition, but become relatively prudent, conservative, and pacific when they are in power.

However this may be, what attracts us in Cyprian is the quality of just balance, the lack of which did most harm to Tertullian. He was face to face with grave trials, the persecution under Decius which was the most formidable that had yet laid its heavy hand on the Christians ; the schisms and bickerings of insubordinate priests ; disagreements with the Roman Episcopate, etc. . . . When we make a study of his conduct in each separate case, we realise that he always maintained a certain rigidity, that he was keenly alive to his own prerogatives and that he entertained the conviction that God Himself, in more than one case, had dictated his conduct by direct command.[1] But this somewhat exalted faith in his mission and this rigidity of principles did not exclude a very skilful diplomacy in their application because he had the advantage of that considered wisdom which gives a profound knowledge of men and matter.

From the strictly literary point of view, Cyprian is far inferior to Tertullian. Apart from the Bible, the principal

---

[1] The *visions* or revelations to which he appeals in justifying such and such an act or in bringing support to such and such a decision, are numerous : *Ep.*, xi, 3, 4, 5, 6 (Hartel, II, p. 497 et s.) ; *Ep.*, xl, 1 (H., 585) ; lxvi, 10 (H., 734) ; *Ep.*, lxiii, 1 (H., 701) ; *Ep.*, lxxiii, 21 (H., 799). Other allusions to phenomena of the same kind, which had not been vouchsafed to him personally, *Ep.*, xvi, 4 (H., 520) : ecstasy in children ; *Ep.*, lvii, 5 (H., 655) ; *de Mortal.*, xix (H., 138), etc. . . There had only been the Montanists who believed in the permanent outpouring of the Holy Spirit in the Church, but here it is the Catholic Church, the Bishop who proclaims its privilege, and no longer those " spiritually " without the pale.

food of his mind and of his faith, and apart from Tertullian
his constant model, the suspicion attaching to whose name he
moreover killed, he does not appear to have been acquainted
with any writings of the old Christian literature. His reading
is strictly limited and his philosophy is very brief. He was
a man to rule rather than a man of doctrine. The tradition
of cultivated intellectual curiosity of which Tertullian had
given such a brilliant example, was to be renewed only in the
second half of the IVth century by St Hilary, Marius Victorinus, St Ambrose, St Jerome, St Augustine and Rufinus.
Once more Greek Christian erudition, richer still than Tertullian had the opportunity of becoming acquainted with,
was to be incorporated by these masters of Latin thought.
The horizon of St Cyprian was much more limited.

He had received a classic education and faithfully applied
the methods of style which he had been taught—the balancing
of the parts of a sentence, *homoioteleuton*, cadenced terminations [1] (more strictly followed than by Cicero himself),
etc. . . . But it is enough to read through some of his letters
and one or two of his treatises to realise that he had none of
the biting satire, intellect, or eloquence of his predecessor.
Neither too has he the same variety in the subjects treated,
nor in the manner in which he treats them. When we read
Tertullian, we are ceaselessly spurred on by the pointed
characteristics and the passion which he betrays and by his
keenness to convince. The works of Cyprian are unrolled in
a more uniform and more tranquil movement of speech. [2]
Interest in him arises from the root matter of the subjects
and practical problems which he discusses and solves. This
is due to the fact that all that Cyprian wrote was in strict
relation to his office as a Bishop, and to the actual circumstances in which he was engaged. It was not enough for him
to enlighten his flock by word of mouth : he desired also to
reach those who could not hear him. Then on several occasions he found himself obliged to leave his flock. This is
why he writes without literary vanity, although never losing

[1] See de Jonghe, *Rec. des Travaux de l'Univ. de Louvain*, 14 fasc. (1905).
[2] " Erat ingenio *facili, copioso, suavi* . . .", Lactantius says (*Inst. Div.*, V, 1,
25). And St Jerome (*Ep.*, lviii, 10) : " Beatus Cyprianus *instar fontis purissimi
dulcis* incedit et placidus." And Cassiodorus (*Inst.*, I, xix) : " . . . *velut oleum*
decurrens in omnem suavitatem ". All three had a just impression of this mellow
prodigality spreading out over a wide surface. On the language of Cyprian, see
the conscientious work of L. Bayard, *Le Latin de Saint Cyprien*, thèse, Paris, 1903.

proper regard for and even the niceties of form in order to convince, exhort, and lead back the unruly, and confirm the faithful. We can reproach him with a certain contempt for speculation, with a lack of interest in purely theoretical questions : he hardly had the time to delay over such things. Moreover, he amply makes up for these omissions by a very penetrating intuition of soul, by an ardent mysticism which in no wise impairs his energy, lastly by all those qualities of a man of action, who, in making himself a man of letters, still continues to be a man of action. " A whole people lived on his word ; each one of his sermons, each one of his discourses was a real act, right up to that last hour in which, for reply to the Pro-Consul, he discovered a still more eloquent silence, and placed in a resolute ' No ! ' his soul which up to that moment he had laid bare by his spoken words." [1]

II

THE sources from which we can trace the life of St Cyprian are fairly abundant. (1) A few months after the martyrdom of St Cyprian a clerk in his *entourage*, named Pontius, took in hand to preserve in writing a portrait of the great Bishop. Persuaded in his inmost heart that no such remarkable figure had appeared in the Church since the days of the Apostles, he desired to make posterity share his admiration by relating the *opera ac merita* of Cyprian from the time of his conversion to his martyrdom. This *Vita Cypriani* [2] of which 23 manuscripts are known to exist at the present time, is the first Christian biography, the first specimen of a class which was to enjoy such a remarkable *prestige*. (We know that the *Life of Antony*, by St Athanasius, and the *Life of St Martin*, by Sulpicius Severus [to only mention two] obtained perhaps the most remarkable circulation in Christian antiquity.) It is far from being a *chef-d'œuvre*, and it does not appear a matter of doubt that Harnack has overrated

---

[1] Ernest Havet in the *Revue des deux Mondes*, 15 Sept. 1885, p. 311.

[2] The name of Pontius does not figure in it, but it is furnished by St Jerome in his *De Vir. Ill.*, § lxviii. His name is found on an inscription at Corubis of the IIIrd century (C.I.L., VIII, 980), a little town on the North-west coast of the Roman province of Africa, where St Cyprian found shelter during his exile. Cf. Dessau, *Hermes*, LI (1916), p. 70 et s.

its merits.[1] In the first place, it suffers from the defect
common to the greater part of the early Christian *Lives ;*
the author having no other concern than to exhibit the
exceptional action of the Holy Spirit on his hero, the psychological and really human interest is too much relegated to the
second place. Then its rhetorical grandiloquence hardly
conceals the scarcity of positive information. The recital of
facts offers disconcerting bare patches (which it is true the
contemporary reader could supplement). Pontius does not
even mention by name the two Pro-Consuls before whom the
Bishop appeared. He is aware that everyone was acquainted
with the life of Cyprian (§ i), that the *Acta* of his martyr
will provide many details which he omits (§ xi), and almost
his entire interest is given up to edifying.—(2) The *Acta
Proconsularia Cypriani*, which have been excellently analysed
by Paul Monceaux,[2] are made up of three parts : (*a*) The
report of the examination of Cyprian before the Pro-Consul
Aspasius Paternus, and his exile to Curubis, on the 30th of
August 257 ; (*b*) The report of his second examination
before the Pro-Consul Galerius Maximus and his condemnation
to death on September 258 ; (*c*) The account of his execution
on the 18th of the Kalends of October 258 at Villa Sexti near
Carthage. The document is remarkably precise. It must
have been the work of a contemporary who had seen everything with his own eyes, had heard everything with his own
ears and who at once consigned to writing what he had seen
and heard.—(3) St Jerome only devotes to Cyprian a short
notice in his *De Viris Illustribus*, § lxvii. Not that he holds
the saint in mediocre literary esteem, but on the contrary,
because his works were, as he states, " *luce clariora.*" We
owe to him a few details which we do not find elsewhere.—
(4) Lastly, Cyprian's letters provide a precious source of
information for the period of his episcopate. Taken as
a whole, this correspondence has a *quasi*-official character.
Whether he writes under his own name, or whether he is

---

[1] *Das Leben Cyprians von Pontius, die erste christliche Biographie, unters,* von
Adolf Harnack, Leipsic, 1913 (T.U., xxxix, 3). Compare with this Reitzenstein's
appreciations in the *Sitz.-Ber. der Heidelb. Ak., phil. Hist. Kl.* 1913, Abh, n° 14,
p. 46 et s. ; those of Corssen, in Z.N.W., xv (1914), 221 et s. ; 285 et s. ; xvi (1915),
54 et s. ; and that of C. Weyman, in B. ph. W., 1915, p. 1271 et s.

[2] II, 179–190. Adverse criticisms of Reitzenstein, ill-founded, are to be found
in the *Sitz.-Ber. der Heidelb. Ak. d. Wiss.*, quoted above. See also Corssen, Z.N.W.,
1916–1917.

acting as interpreter to the Synods over which he is presiding, it is always in his character as a Bishop that Cyprian shows himself. He had occasion to deliver an apology for his action in answer to certain false imputations, as we find in letter lxvi. But as a rule, he leaves himself out, and effaces himself behind the problem with which he is dealing, and does not speak of what concerns himself personally except when he is forced to. The correspondence of St Jerome was to be of quite another order. This is because Jerome was somewhat of a *franc-tireur* in the great army of the Church. St Cyprian, not requiring to express himself freely and frankly, as was to be the case with Jerome, was ruled entirely by the interests of which he was the guardian.

Cyprian was born in Africa. The date and place of his birth are not known. His family was pagan. Like all the young men of a certain position he passed through the usual course of studies and learned rhetoric, which later on, according to the testimony of St Jerome, he was to teach before his conversion. On his own confession, his youth was by no means chaste.[1] A priest, Caecilius,[2] or Caecilianus[3] by name, made him decide to change his mode of life. Cyprian adds the name of his spiritual instructor to that of his own : from that date, as it seems, he called himself C. Caecilius Cyprianus, *qui et Thascius* (the meaning of this sobriquet, *qui et Thascius*,[4] is unknown). He made a gift to the poor of part of his fortune, was baptised, became a priest, and shortly afterwards his talents caused him to be elected Bishop of Carthage at the end of the year 248 or at the beginning of 249, notwithstanding the opposition of certain members of the clergy.[5] A few months later, the persecution under Decius broke out. Cyprian did not feel it to be his duty to wait for martyrdom : he hid himself during the first month of the year 250 till April or May 251 : " He judged, and with reason, that with a Church it is the same as with an army, in which the death of a leader, however heroic this may be thought, may become the signal of defeat." [6] His flight however provoked hostile comments in Carthage and even in Rome. Cyprian felt the

[1] Cf. *Ad Donatum*, iii–iv. [2] *De Vir. Ill.*, l. c. [3] *Vita*, § lv.
[4] Monceaux, *op. cit.*, II, 202. For this form *qui et* cf. *Glotta*, IV (1912), n° 1–2.
[5] *Ep.*, lix, 6.
[6] Freppel, *Saint Cyprien*, Paris, 1890, p. 164.

need to justify himself.[1] But he gives the best apology for his conduct in the admirable solicitude which he extended from a distance over the interests of his Church. When he came back to Carthage a series of difficult cases offered themselves for his decision. It was necessary to regulate the question of the *lapsi*, that is to say, of Christians who had " fallen away " during the recent persecution, and who were seeking to re-enter the Church or even to slink back into it by very equivocal methods. He had to combat a body of rebellious priests who, with Novatus and Felicissimus at their head, were setting themselves up against the authority of the Bishop. While the Pontifical See of Rome was vacant (from the 21st of January 250 to the beginning of March 251), he energetically supported Cornelius after he had been elected a candidate together with Novatian. His influence among the Christians in Africa continued to grow, and the Churches from all parts solicited his directions. The edict of Gallus and Volusianus in the year 252 did not bring about the general persecution which at first had been feared. But other trials came upon the Christians in Africa, and Cyprian extended to them the full measure of his devotion ; these were raids on the Christians of Numidia for whose ransom it was necessary to open a public subscription, and a devastating plague which was accompanied by a real weakening in public morality and brought down on the Christians, who were made responsible for this scourge, fresh ill-usage. His last years were preoccupied by the question of the validity of baptism conferred by heretics. Cyprian entered into conflict on this subject with Pope Stephen (254–257), and the dispute soon became bitter on both sides, even to serious danger. But soon the edict of Valerian, promulgated in August 257, caused the first summons of Cyprian before the tribunal of the Pro-Consul, who banished him to Curubis. A year later, an order came to bring him back ; this time it was for his martyrdom, to which he submitted on the 14th September 258.

---

[1] *Ep.*, vii ; xiv, 1 ; xx, 1. Cf. *Ep.*, viii, written from Rome by the clergy in Rome to the clergy in Carthage.

III

LET us begin with taking a glance at the ideas which really dominated the views and conduct of St Cyprian. By this means we shall lay hold of the thread which will help us to find our position when we follow him through one or other of the crises in which he took part.

We find a conception of the Church, a conception of the *rôle*, the prerogatives, and the duties of a Bishop diffused throughout the entire writings of Cyprian, which clearly explains his permanent attitude. I will endeavour to set it out in relief principally with the aid of the celebrated treatise *De Catholicae Ecclesiae Unitate* and his letters.

A firmly convinced apology of oneness,—considered as the leaven, the unifying link and the mark of the true Church —forms the foundation of the *De Catholicae Ecclesiae Unitate* and of all the pages in which Cyprian dealt with the same question. The worst enemy which the Christians had to fear was not that which let loose persecution ; for against persecution it was sufficient to arm oneself with courage.[1] It was that which cunningly, by intrigues hatched under cover, *per pacis imaginem* [2] prepared the way for schism and heresy. There was no greater crime than to sow hatred among the faithful, than to separate them from their shepherds. At most the apostate only destroyed himself ; but the instigator of dissension applied himself to efface the fundamental and pacific character of the Church—namely, oneness. Words which come unceasingly from the pen of Cyprian are these : *unanimitas, concors, consensio.*[3] He multiplies mystical symbols borrowed from Scripture prefiguring this " unanimity " of will, this unbreakable cohesion of the faithful with their pastors : it was the seamless garment of Christ, the dove of the Canticle of Canticles (the faithful bird bringing peace, *par excellence*), the bread and wine of the Holy Sacrifice formed, the one of a handful of grains of wheat, the other of many clusters of grapes, etc. Certain of Cyprian's adversaries

[1] Cf. *de Unitate*, 1 et s.
[2] *Ibid.* (Hartel, I, 209, line 13).
[3] See Hartel's *Index*, or better still, the list drawn up by Chapman in the *R. Bén.*, 1902, pp. 365–367.

exploited the words of Christ : " Wheresoever two or three shall be gathered in My name there will I be in the midst of them," and drew from them a reason for justifying their desire for schism. Cyprian turns against them the text which they make a false use of, and proves to them that this maxim, far from justifying, condemns them. In uttering these words, the intention of Christ had been to testify His love of concord and union, since He allows it to be understood that He will be *more willingly* present with two or three persons animated by the same sentiment than with a great number of men whose hearts are beating out of unison.[1]

From such premisses, Cyprian could only draw conclusions of total exclusion against those who seceded from, or remained outside, a society so closely bound up in the spirit of obedience and charity. He did not at all recoil from the consequences, or rather insisted on them with determination. The most laudable actions, in his view, lose their merit outside the Church : martyrdom was fruitless, graces were without value, and salvation became impossible.[2]

His attitude in the matter of the baptism of heretics [3] is logically explained by the view which he held. Was it necessary to rebaptise converts who, abandoning the different sects which flourished on the outskirts of the Church, asked to be admitted within her pale ? Was the imposition of hands and anointing with oil according to the Roman practice, or *consignatio*, sufficient ? When the question was put to Cyprian by certain bishops of Mauretania, he seems to have nowhere experienced the scruples over which these latter were hesitating. Moreover, he had already expressed his opinion in the *De Catholicae Ecclesiae Unitate* (§ 11). The definitions by which he affirms it anew are of a preciseness which lends itself to no equivocation. " Baptism is one, just as the Holy Spirit is one, just as the Church is one." [4] " There can be no baptism outside the Church." [5] " We do not re-baptise ; we baptise those who come to us from among the heretics : they could not have received anything from the heretics, since these latter are of no account." [6] He added another reason which was not that of a psychologist of

---

[1] *De Unit.*, § 12.   [2] § 14–15.
[3] The most important items in the *dossier* are letters lxix to lxxv and the Acts of the Councils held on this matter.
[4] *Ep.*, lxx, 3.   [5] *Ep.*, lxxi, 1.   [6] *Ibid.*

mediocre intuition:[1] "Do not think that the heretics,
scandalised at our opposition to their baptism, in which they
see a second baptism, will be the less disposed to come back
to the Church. Very much the contrary; this public declaration of our faith will convince them the more profoundly
of the necessity in which they are placed of embracing the
truth. If they see that our decisions make their baptism
valid and legitimate, they will believe that they are in legal
possession of the Church and of its privileges. Hence they
will have no further motive to come back to us. Make
plain to them on the contrary that outside the Church baptism
is without virtue . . . you will see them very quickly im-
ploring the favours and gifts of the Mother Church." We
know with what inflexibility Cyprian opposed this absolute
theory to that of Pope Stephen. The dispute grew keener
almost to the point of a rupture. The letter of Firmilian of
Caesarea to Cyprian (*Ep.*, lxxv)[2] reveals to what a pitch the
dispute had reached. The death of Stephen, which took
place on the 2nd of August 257, somewhat calmed down
the nervous tension of the controversy. On the whole, it
was through his passion for the unity and integrity of the
Church that Cyprian had been drawn, in agreement with his
colleagues in Africa[3], to maintain so vehemently a doctrine
which the future was to decide in a contrary sense.

We can see without difficulty the *rôle* which the Bishop
played in the organisation of the Church. He was the
essential part of that collectivity of which the Church is composed, and it was on him as the successor of the Apostles that
in a special degree was laid the charge of maintaining its
entire unity.[4] Without doubt, it was the suffrage of the
people which elected him (nowhere does Cyprian protest
against this altogether democratic method of election);[5]
but it was God who conferred on him his sacred character.

[1] *Ep.*, lxxiii, 24.
[2] P.L., iii, 1154; Hartel, II, 810–827.
[3] On the Councils relating to this matter, cf. Monceaux, ii, chap. ii. See also
H. von Soden, *Sententiae* lxxxvii *Episcoporum. Das Protokoll der Synode von Kar-
thago am 1 Sept. 256 textkritisch. dargestellt und uberliefe-rungsgeschichtlich unters.*,
in the *Nachrichten* of Gottingen, 1909, 3, pp. 247–307; Id., *die Prosopographie des
afrikanischen Episkopats zur Zeit Cyprians*, extract from *Quellen und Forsch. aus
ital. Archiven u. Bibliotheken*, 1909.
[4] Cf. *Ep.*, xlv, 3 (Hartel, II, 602).
[5] He seems even to have had full confidence in the wisdom of popular choice.
Cf. *Ep.*, lxvii, 4–5 (Hartel, II, 738).

And, once provided with this twofold human and divine investiture, the Bishop enjoyed the widest prerogatives. He was the director, and the administrator of his flock, and God will punish those who revolt against his authority.[1] The price paid for this pre-eminence was the devotion, moral integrity, and constant zeal of which he ought to give proof. The rights of Bishops corresponded to their duties which were much more formidable than those which weighed on the faithful : it was by these that they were justified.[2] In other respects, even and above all for a Bishop, union with the body of the faithful, with the Church, was the mark of orthodoxy. If he compromised this unity, however regular his promotion may have been, he loses his title.[3]

Such, shortly reviewed, is Cyprian's theory of the Church and of the Episcopate. There is still a point nevertheless on which it is necessary to touch. Did Cyprian admit that there was somewhere a head of this great body of the Church ? Did he accept a centralisation in this ecclesiastical unity of which he was so ardent a defender ? In other words, did he bow before the Roman Primacy, before the magistracy of the successor of Peter ? Here is a problem which has been very often discussed [4] and to which even at this day divergent solutions are brought. Hugo Koch, an old pupil of F. X. Funk, the celebrated professor of the Faculty of Catholic Theology of Tubingen, devoted to it in 1910 quite a collection of *Texte und Untersuchungen* (xxxv, 1), as a first token of the evolution in doctrine which he had just accomplished outside the ranks of Catholicism. " Cyprian did not recognise popery either as of doctrine or as of right " (p. iv). His fundamental contention may be summed up as follows. In order to demonstrate it, Koch could have endeavoured to follow the evolution of the views of Cyprian in the course of his works,— the chronological order of his treatises and his letters being sufficiently established in spite of a few doubtful points. He preferred another plan in which his method of dialectics suited him better. He goes straight to the *De Catholicae*

---

[1] *Ep.*, iii, 1 (Hartel, II, 470, I, 1) ; *Ep.*, lxix, 4 (Hartel, II, 670, I, 16).
[2] He did not hesitate to counsel the people of Léon and Asturias to no longer " be in community with " two unworthy Bishops (*Ep.*, lxvii).
[3] *Ep.*, lv, 24 (Hartel, II, p. 643, I, 4) ; *Ep.*, lxv, 4 (Hartel, II, p. 724, I, 18).
[4] In J. Turmel's *Histoire de la Théologie Positive*, vol. II (Paris, 1902), p. 216 et s., 269 et s., we can see in what warm controversy Catholic and Protestant polemists have engaged around the disputed texts of Cyprian.

Ecclesiae Unitate and chooses two short chapters for his treatise —the ivth and the vth. From a very minute analysis, he deduces the following conclusion : If Christ first established the Church on Peter alone (cf. Mt. xvi, 18 et s.), this was solely, in the opinion of Cyprian, in order to render tangible and as it were visible by means of that unity among its members, the moral unity which was to reign in His Church. But such a priority in point of time did not at all confer on Peter any pre-eminence in authority or honour : it had a purely symbolical bearing, and the other Apostles continued to be the equals of Peter, *pari consortio praediti et honoris et potestatis.* St Cyprian too considered the Episcopate as the heir of the Apostolic College, as forming one whole, in which each Bishop, jointly and severally, held a portion of the whole (*cuius a singulis in solidum pars tenetur*), in full equality with his colleagues.

It is in the light of these fundamental principles thus deduced from the *De Cath. Eccles. Unitate,* that Koch proceeds to examine each of the declarations scattered through the writings of Cyprian, in which people have sometimes read a confession of the exceptional preponderance of the *Cathedra Petri.* He finds nothing in them which goes beyond or which contradicts them, but only the reiterated affirmation of the independence of each Bishop in his diocese. Cyprian's attitude in face of Pope Stephen over the question of the baptism of heretics, the rather curt style which he makes use of in regard to the Roman Pontiff, his manner of acting in certain ecclesiastical matters in which Rome was interested, for example, the deposition of Basilides and of Martial (*Ep.,* lxvii), the excommunication of Marcian, Bishop of Arles (*Ep.,* lxviii),—all confirm Koch in the justness of his interpretation.

His reasoning has such stern force and his putting together evinces so much logic, that on reading it for the first time we may ask how we can draw any other conclusion than he has, basing ourselves on the same texts. However, we have not to draw attention solely to his religious prejudices. Koch himself, in his introduction, partitions off the critics, his predecessors, into three groups : those who think that Cyprian explicitly admitted the primacy of jurisdiction of the Bishop of Rome ; those who make him the representative of an " episcopalism " with special characteristics, excluding any kind of primacy ; lastly, those who, taking up an intermediate position, believe that Cyprian recognised in the Roman Church, if not a primacy of jurisdiction, at least the authority belonging to a real centre of unity for the universal Church. Now Otto Ritschl is in company with Dom Chapman in the first category ; Ehrhard and Tixeront rub shoulders with Loofs and Benson in the second ; and we are surprised to see associated, in the third, Harnack, Funk and Batiffol.

The real fact of the matter is that a certain number of points are obscure, and remain so even after Koch's penetrating study. That the interpretation given by Koch to § iv of the *De Cath. Eccl. Unit.* is the only likely, the only legitimate one, and that every other does violence to the words of Cyprian or introduces into them arbitrary shades of thought, we must not hesitate to recognise. The investiture specially conferred on St Peter is very rarely taken into consideration by Cyprian in this chapter under the aspect of a symbolic prefiguration. But before adhering fully to the consequences which Koch deduces from it, one would like to rest secure on one or two preliminary certitudes whereof the correctness is in doubt. In this treatise, in which Cyprian had in fact no other object than by an energetic appeal for union and " unity " to baffle the intrigues incessantly being hatched against him by the group of restless Christian spirits, has he given us a formal and full instruction on his theory of the organisation and the hierarchy of the Church, or rather was he not at pains to demonstrate the heterogeneous nature of the spirit of schism as contrasted with the spirit of Christianity, by a series of illustrations which are not at all equivalent to considered and complete theological formulæ ? Then does Cyprian himself count for nothing in the famous " interpolation " (which is appreciably more favourable to the *primatus Petri*) of § iv in that other reading of the text in which Dom Chapman,[1] who has the support of Harnack,[2]

<hr/>

[1] Louis Saltet (B.L.E., 1920, 170–206), as against Dom Chapman, recognises a real contradiction in doctrine between the two recensions of the famous passage in the *De Unit. Eccl. Cath.*, iv. He does not think that St Cyprian retracted it, and admits unreservedly the hypothesis of an interpolation.

[2] T.L.Z., 1903, col. 262. Cf. *R. Bén.*, 1902–1903. Ernest Havet wrote in 1885 (*Rev. des Deux Mondes*, 1st Sept., p. 67) : " I do not see in it anything which formally contradicts Cyprian's ideas, and instead of supposing that additions were made to the text in the interests of the Church at Rome, we can equally well suppose on the contrary that people who were in opposition to the pretensions of that Church may have suppressed certain portions ; or further, perhaps Cyprian himself as a consequence of his quarrel with Stephen ".

recognises his style and handiwork, while Laurand even perceives in it indications of his favourite way of ending his sentences ?[1] Even if this twofold difficulty be definitely decided in the sense favoured by Koch, we should still have to ask ourselves if he does not, by despoiling them of their essence and fulness, press to an extreme limit certain of the expressions which Cyprian uses to indicate the Church in Rome (v.g. " navigare audent et ad Petri cathedram atque ad *ecclesiam principalem unde unitas sacerdotalis exorta est* " in *Ep*. LIX, 14 : Pope Cornelius, to whom the letter is addressed, must at any rate have understood it in a rather less narrow sense than Koch makes of it) ; or if, on the other hand, he does not too much exaggerate the importance of the *rôle* played by Cyprian, however ample this *rôle* may have been, when he represents the Bishop of Carthage as being the " conscience " of the whole Western Church. A man who held such personal ideas on the Episcopate and on baptism might well have formed (keenly jealous as he was of his own authority) a particular conception of the precedence of Rome.

It still remains none the less clear that the inner core of his theological system was the imperious need for co-ordination and discipline. This principle, so firmly established in his mind, served him as a criterion in all doubtful cases which it was his duty to decide.

It is worth our while to examine the influences which fixed in him this zeal for close solidarity.[2] There is no doubt that the scenes of political life which he had witnessed in his youth partly contributed to this result. We know to what prolonged anarchy the Roman Empire had been a prey during the period following the death of Marcus Aurelius. In the space of forty-three years (192–235), the Praetorians and the Legionaries brought about no less than six military *coups d'état*. The world saw itself governed by madmen or profligates, such as Commodus and Heliogabalus. The rivalry between candidates for power drenched many provinces in blood. How was the Empire able to withstand such shocks ? It was due to Roman administration, to their

---

[1] B. ph. W., 1909, col. 1016.

[2] On this point, see some interesting ideas which have had their influence on me in an article in the *Revue de théologie et de philosophie*, 1893, p. 105 et s., *Saint Cyprien et les Influences qui l'ont formé*, by Eug. de Faye.

K

system of municipal government and to the army. Thanks to their well-geared machinery, these great organisations upheld the framework of the national life and prevented it from breaking up in disorder and chaos. A mind so keenly observant as that of Cyprian could not fail to have been struck by the conservating force of the principle of order and hierarchy whose effects he could see all around him. Had he remained a pagan he would have made an excellent Pro-Consul : as a Christian, he was an admirable Bishop.

I will add that the incidents which marked his Episcopate without doubt accentuated in him this passion for moral union and some sort of material cohesion. In the very bosom of the Christian body, to his perpetual vexation, he had to deal with restless spirits who did not cease to hatch intrigues and to work against him in an underhand manner. Dom Chapman has very ably demonstrated that the *De Catholicae Ecclesiae Unitate*, in which the views of Cyprian are summed up, was composed at the time of his differences with Felicissimus.[1] This Felicissimus had been made a deacon, without the consent of the Bishop, by Novatus, one of the five priests who were implacable adversaries of Cyprian, and after the departure of Novatus he had become the head of the small hostile *clique*. Harassed as he was by schism within at a time when all Christians should have faced the enemy hand in hand, how could Cyprian have failed to feel keenly the value of a unity which his enemies were struggling hard to relax, in proportion as he himself was strengthening their bonds ?

Lastly, we may add that Cyprian's theory of the Church and of the *rôle* of the Episcopate was in some ways the outcome of a long series of facts which had prepared it beforehand. Throughout the crises which one after the other had failed to weaken the Church—the intellectual crisis connected with Gnosticism, and the moral crisis arising from Montanism, the Episcopate had become more and more strengthened as the guardian of the rule of faith, and as the authorised interpreter of the Spirit. It was thus natural that Cyprian, improving on St Irenæus and Tertullian (I am speaking of the Tertullian of the *De Praescriptione*), should accentuate this idea of the preponderating authority of the

1 *R. Bén.*, 1903, p. 26 et s.

Bishops, who were the sole organs of doctrine and the representatives of living tradition in the Church.

Such views, held by a man of such high intelligence and of such an upright heart, could not but reinforce his zeal for doing well and his ambition to be equal to his task however heavy it might be. We will now see how he put them into practical application.

IV

ONE of the first difficulties to present themselves to Cyprian when he became a Bishop was the famous question of the *lapsi*,[1] which followed on the edict of the Emperor Decius which was put in force at the end of the year 249 or at the beginning of 250. The complete text of this edict has not come down to us; but we know fairly well the manner in which it was applied. The procedure had been perfectly set out with administrative precision. On a fixed day throughout the Roman Empire in the towns and villages, the inhabitants were obliged to present themselves before a local commission composed of magistrates and notabilities.[2] On his name being called out, each one came forward and found himself under the necessity of proving by an act, or some sort of idolatrous gesture, that he had never been a Christian, or if he had been that he renounced it. The commissioners gave him in exchange a certificate, *libellus*, duly signed and dated.[3]

These well-devised dispositions threw the Christians into panic. At Carthage, where the ceremony took place at the Capitol, there was a rush to apostatise : " There were those," Cyprian tells us,[4] " who did not wait to be apprehended before mounting to the Capitol, nor to be questioned in order to apostatise. Defeated before the battle, laid low before

---

[1] These are the principal relevant documents in the *dossier :* the treatise *De Lapsis ;* letters xv, xvi, xvii, xviii, xix, xxv, xxvii, xxx, xxxiii, xxxv, xxxvi, xxxix, lv, lvi.

[2] As regards Carthage, cf. *Ep.* xliii, 3 (Hartel, 592) : " . . . quinque primores illi qui edicto nuper magistratibus fuerant copulati, ut fidem nostram subruerent."

[3] See P. Foucart, *Les certificats de sacrifice pendant la persécution de Decius,* in the *Journal des Savants,* 1908, p. 177 et s. ; Dom Leclercq, *Les certificats de sacrifice paien sous Déce en 250,* in B.A.L.A.C., vol. IV (1914), p. 52 et s. ; 188 et s. (Dom Leclercq gives the text and the translation of 25 *libelli* coming from different localities in Egypt) ; Faulhaber, in Z.K.T., 1919, p. 439 et s., 617 et s.

[4] *De Lapsis,* viii.

being assaulted, many did not even stay to make the excuse of appearing to sacrifice to idols by constraint. These people ran to the Forum and freely hastened to (spiritual) death, as if they had for long desired to do so, as if they took advantage of an opportunity long cherished in the depths of their heart. How many of them did not the magistrates, in view of the late hour, put off till the following day ! How many of them begged that their death might not be deferred ![1] . . . And to fill up the measure of these crimes, there were seen children being brought forward and led by the hand of their parents, to lose still so young the divine mark which they had received at the very threshold of their lives."

A certain number of the faithful, shrinking from a heroism the refusal of which would have been the inevitable punishment of incarceration or death, and from a formal apostasy, bethought themselves of an ingenious expedient. Thanks to the interested good-nature of minor functionaries, they secured, for a sum of money, the *libellus* which it was enough to show in order to remain henceforth unmolested.

Hence arose two categories of *lapsi :* the *sacrificati* and the *libellatici*, culpable in an unequal degree without doubt, but both reprobated by the consciences of those who had not given way.

What had been the former attitude of the Churches relative to failures of this kind ? The procedure of doing penance was not probably the same in all communities.[2] But it would appear that thirty years before Cyprian, apostasy counted as one of those crimes to which most of the Churches accorded no forgiveness.[3] Without doubt the sinner was bound to do penance ; but pardon was reserved to God, whose decision the Bishop did not recognise in himself any right to anticipate.

Such sternness seemed discouraging to those who had fallen away. Before even the rigours of the Government had ceased, several were trying how to be reinstated in the Church, from which their desertion had excluded them. Some zealots presented themselves anew before the tribunal recanting their recent weakness.[4] Others subjected themselves

---

[1] This relates, of course, to the death of *the soul*, as above.
[2] We may conclude this from St Cyprian, *Ep.* lv, 20–21.
[3] Cf. P. de Labriolle, *La Crise Montaniste*, p. 425 et s.
[4] *Ep.* xxiv.

to expiations which they might expect would last as long as
their lives.   But for the great majority such a method appeared
extremely severe and they looked about for some less stony
path whereby to re-enter the fold.

From the time of Tertullian, and doubtless even before
that, it was admitted that those who had suffered for the
faith disposed of a certain right of intercession on behalf of
sinners.   Pope Callixtus had even, as it seems, officially
sanctioned this right, without our being able to know exactly
in what way he had fixed its limitations.   The greater part of
the *lapsi* very soon conceived the idea of utilising for their
benefit the merits accumulated by the heroism of the confessors.[1]   In this they were encouraged by the group of
priests who detested Cyprian and who were not at all indis-
posed to favour in his absence—for the Bishop, as we have
said, had left Carthage when the storm broke out—any
moves of a nature to diminish his authority.[2]

However praiseworthy had been the firmness shown by
them in the face of the Roman power, the confessors were
not all of them of irreproachable moral eminence.   Some of
them were of the kind to feel flattered at playing the *rôle* of
liberator in regard to their less staunch brethren.   By an act
of generosity which cost little, and without requiring any
guarantee of repentance or of doing penance,[3] they granted
permits of reconciliation to those who solicited them.   People
succeeded in obtaining these under fictitious names for the
benefit of their friends.   A traffic arose in them.[4]   Certain
permits were issued in these terms : *Communicet ille cum suis*,
an elastic formula which under the pretext of kinship more or
less authentic allowed a host of people to obtain pardon
en bloc.[5]

We may imagine the feelings of Cyprian when he became
aware of such regrettable abuses.   These unauthorised and
unrestrained proceedings, this total forgetfulness of the just
prerogatives of the Bishop and of the methods in use up till
then for the pardon of faults committed, and all this lack of
order must have shocked in the highest degree his instincts

---

[1] Several of them had perished under torture or in prison, cf. *Ep.* xxii, 2 (Hartel,
534).   But the trial which the majority had to undergo was prolonged incarceration
under very painful conditions.
[2] Cf. *Ep.* xv, 2 (Hartel, 513).
[3] *Ibid.*   [4] xv, 3.   [5] xv, 4.

as a conscientious administrator. His *rôle*, however, was a most delicate one. To restore in its entirety the old discipline was (and this he knew well) to range against him quite a large portion of public opinion which found these cheap pardons to their advantage. Had there not been in certain towns open sedition against their Bishop in order to compel him to authorise these premature reconciliations ?[1] And in face of these outbreaks many had yielded.

However, Cyprian did not hesitate. Any weakness would have meant the abdication of the rights with which he considered himself to be invested. He entered into the struggle without resorting to fruitless strong measures, or to impulsive violence, but consistently imbued with certain very clear-cut principles : (1) By personally inaugurating the measures necessary, but taking care to inform his colleagues of the other Episcopal Sees, his clergy, and the clergy in Rome (at that time without a Bishop), so as to clearly assure himself at each step that he had been approved and followed by all those whose moral collaboration he desired ; (2) By straining longanimity as far as possible, but without permitting any encroachment on his authority as a Bishop. In the case of open and persistent rebellion, by acting with energy and cutting into the quick.

Moreover, he understood perfectly well the complexity of the problem offered to him, and did not flatter himself to be able to resolve it by himself. He realised that it would be inhuman to impose a life expiation on the " fallen," who had undergone the pressure of such difficult circumstances and of the example given by a movement that was well-nigh general. But, on the other hand, was it lawful that they should be exonerated from all penalty when, for far less grave offences, other sinners must go through the series of trials by " exhomologesis " ?[2] The difficulty did not only arise at Carthage, but in all the Churches over which the storm had passed : *Non paucorum, nec ecclesiae unius, nec unius provinciae, sed totius orbis haec causa est.*[3] Only a general Council would have the authority to adjudicate definitely on the question once tranquillity had returned.[4] But pending this

---

[1] *Ep.* xxvii, 3.   [2] Cf. *Ep.* xv, 2.   [3] *Ep.* xix, 2. Cf. xxx, 5.
[4] *Ep.* lv, 4, etc. Such was likewise the opinion of the Roman clergy : cf. *Ep.* xxx, 5.

authoritative decision which would without doubt assure uniformity of procedure, Cyprian felt it to be his right and his duty to pronounce on facts which seemed to him to admit of no hesitation. And this, shortly reviewed, was his line of theological reasoning :

With regard to those *lapsi*, who insolently demanded their reconciliation as a right and appeared to be determined to carry it by assault, he showed himself unbending and without pity. He told them that if they were in such a hurry they had at their disposal a very simple means of curtailing the delays : the field was still open to them ; why did they not hasten to suffer martyrdom ? With one blow the taint of apostasy would be wiped out.[1] He likewise blamed without hesitation those priests who, obligingly facilitating demands which were inadmissible, had communicated with *lapsi* before they had received any official absolution.[2] As regards the confessors his position was more embarrassing, for he could not diminish the claim to consideration which their courage had won for them. He was anxious when the question arose to give evidence of the real value which he attached to their intervention. Thus he decided that when one who had fallen away had received a permit of reconciliation from a martyr and found himself in danger of death, it should be lawful to him to obtain peace by the ministry of a priest or, in case of urgency, of a simple deacon without waiting for the decision of the Bishop.[3] But this concession was to be exceptional. He formally invited confessors to refrain from giving out plenary and summary immunities. Let them be content to designate by name in their *libelli* those sinners whom they thought worthy to be absolved and fitting recipients of the benefits pertaining to the right of intercession which they desired to exercise. As soon as security should return, the Bishop would submit these requests to the assembled Church, and with their advice, would give his decision with full knowledge of what he was doing.[4]

Their prerogative thus remained subordinated to due examination by the *Ecclesia* and to the decision of the Bishop. This was the principle firmly established in the mind of Cyprian : hence his indignation on receiving some such kind

---

[1] *Ep.* xviii, 2.
[3] *Ep.* xviii, 1.   Cf. *Ep.* xviii, 2
[2] *Ep.* xv, 2.
[4] *Ep.* xvii, 1.

of permit [1] in which martyrs notified to him in a peremptory tone the pardon which they were granting to all those whose conduct posterior to their apostasy should be judged to have been irreproachable.

Further, when he perceived sincere repentance and a wish to expiate the failure of the past, he leaned at once towards indulgence. Thus, in *Epistle* LVI,[2] he examines the case of three Christians who, after having victoriously emerged from a first trial, had ended by giving way before their atrocious tortures. Since then,—three years had already intervened,—they had not ceased doing penance. While reserving the decision for an approaching Council, Cyprian clearly expresses his own personal view : the circumstances of their " fall " and their present goodwill gave them the most legitimate claim to a pardon.

In the first days of April, 251, a Council was convened at Carthage to regulate these distressing questions.[3] Without doubt it was to this assembly that Cyprian read his admirable treatise *De Lapsis* in which he made as it were an examination of conscience of the Church in Africa on the morrow of the formidable crisis through which it had just passed. The work begins with an utterance of joy at peace having at last come back to the Church, and with a pious testimony of admiration in regard to those confessors who had proved stronger than their tortures. Then he enters upon the painful problem offered by the numerous desertions which the Church in Africa had witnessed. He shows that if God had been thus pleased to test His followers, it was because the weakness of their faith called for a chastisement which should reinvigorate them.[4] It was the previous attachment of nearly all to the goods of this world which by enervating their souls had led to the basest abdication. The last part of the treatise is a long exhortation to penance conceived in the most pathetic terms, but which evolves a very precise definition as to the rights of confessors, rights too often widened to excessive limits by pardons giving scandal.

This work is of surprising unction, profundity of sentiment,

[1] Cf. *Ep.* xxiii and *Ep.* xxvii, 2.
[2] Hartel, 648.
[3] It is not impossible that there may have been two Councils in 251. Cf. Monceaux, II, 43.
[4] *De Lapsis*, vi.

and tact. All that he had to say is said, but with dispositions full of a most attentive regard for charity.

Finally, the Council came to the following decisions (these are known to us, not by the acts of the Council, which we no longer have, but by Cyprian's letters, *Epistle* LV, in particular) : (1) All hope of making peace with the Church was not taken from the guilty, but a long penance was imposed upon them with the obligation to solicit the indulgence of the Bishop who would have to pronounce on particular cases ; [1] (2) Different treatment was given to the *libellatici* and the *lapsi*. The former, as being less blameworthy, would be authorised to re-enter into communion after due enquiry. [2] The *lapsi* could only obtain their pardon *in articulo mortis*. [2] On this last point, therefore, the Council showed itself more rigorous than Cyprian himself was disposed to be ; (3) Those *lapsi* who should refuse the *exhomologesis* could not be reconciled even *in articulo mortis*. [3]

In the spring of the following year, a fresh Council consisting of 42 Bishops accorded a general amnesty to those *lapsi* who should submit to the requisite penance, but all hope of recovering their priesthood was denied to Bishops, priests and deacons who had yielded during the struggle. [4]

The question of the *lapsi* was not definitely closed. It had too profoundly shaken the conscience of the Christians not to entail lengthy consequences. In Rome, the rigorist party who were grouped around the priest Novatian protested against the lenient treatment which the Councils thought to be legitimate and necessary. However, the lenient party under Cyprian won the day. It was he who had thought out in advance the most equitable solution, and the most practical at that time. These words sum up his consistent moderation and firmness : " *Conscientiae nostrae convenit,*" he wrote to Pope Cornelius, " *dare operam ne quis culpa nostra de Ecclesia pereat.*" He had suffered deeply from the thought that too much severity would plunge so many souls into despair ; but equally, his goodness of heart had been restrained by reasonable anxiety for the prerogatives of a Bishop and for the " sacrament " of union. [5]

---

[1] *Ep.* lv, 6.   [2] *Ep.* lv, 2, 6, 17 ; lviii, 1 ; lix, 13.
[3] *Ep.* lv, 23.   [4] *Ep.* lvii, 1 and 5.
[5] The expression *sacramentum unitatis* occurs frequently in his works (Hartel) : pp. 213, 11 ; 215, 11 ; 600, 4 ; 668, 8 ; 754, 15 ; 786, 13 ; 808, 3 ; 809, 9 ; 820, 1.

V

WE now have a grasp of the principles governing St Cyprian and the methods he followed in adjusting them to realities. A brief appreciation of his treatises and his *libelli* will be sufficient : this latter expression he frequently employs to designate them.

The *Ad Donatum* must be placed very shortly after the passing of Cyprian to Christianity. It is the outburst of a new convert who recalls his moral blindness before baptism, and the weight of the chains which his passions had riveted on him, and who feels himself delivered and flooded with light. He makes his friend Donatus, also a Christian but a little less ardent as it seems, his confidant in the marvellous work which the revivifying faith has operated in him.

Some have desired to transform this enthusiastic mono-logue into a dialogue :[1] to do this, it is enough to place at the beginning certain very commonplace lines which have been relegated by Hartel[2] to the category of apocryphal documents, in which Donatus clumsily asserts the community of thought which has always linked him with Cyprian, and appears to remind him of a promise : the *Ad Donatum* begins merely with these words : " Bene admones, Donate carissime ; nam et *promisisse me memini*, etc. . . ." But this con-jecture hardly appears to be a happy one. Why should this tag have been eliminated from most of the manuscripts ? Does it not destroy the parallelisms at the beginning and the end of the work between the two descriptions with which he opens and closes it ? The epithet " *sanctissime* Cypriane " is also very strange at this date. Then, there is no allusion in the rest of the work permitting us to think that the author really made use of the form of a dialogue.

Cyprian represents Donatus as climbing with him a high mountain from which they see the wide perspective of human life : on all sides reign corruption and unrest, at the games, at the theatre, in the homes, in the law courts and public life, and even in the palace of the Emperor. In contradistinction, the Holy Spirit brings equilibrium and peace to whosoever shall take God for his sole support.

A tone of strong sincerity animates the *Ad Donatum*

---

[1] Goetz in T.U., xix, 1 (1899). [2] Hartel, III. 272.

and yet its form is wordy and verbose, and void of all simplicity. St Augustine tactfully noted [1] the service which serious and " sane " Christian doctrine had rendered to Cyprian's style by gradually diverting it from these conceits : ". . . ut sciretur a posteris, quam linguam doctrinae christianae sanitas ab ista redundantia revocaverit et ad eloquentiam graviorem modestioremque restrinxerit. . . ." When Cyprian wrote the *Ad Donatum* the rhetorician still survived in him. He was never quite to renounce the niceties and affectations of his former school, but he was to become far more sparing of them than such a beginning would have allowed us to suppose.

The *Ad Demetrianum* is an eloquent denunciation of a certain Demetrianus, without doubt a magistrate,[2] or possibly merely a rhetorician, in any case an implacable enemy of the Christians, who had spread abroad the rumour that certain recent calamities—war, pestilence, famine and drought —must be put to the account of their impiousness. We are acquainted with this complaint which was for a long time yet to be revived : Tertullian had already drawn attention to it ; [3] it is mentioned at the beginning of the *Adversus Nationes* by Arnobius ; Lactantius makes allusion to it in his *Institutiones Divinae ;* [4] St Augustine examines it fully in his *Civitas Dei*. It was St Cyprian who pinned down the fundamental points of the Christian refutation. He did not concern himself to question the acts of Providence, but to demonstrate the anger of Heaven called down against the vices of the pagans, who were alone responsible, which furnished to the Christians themselves the opportunity of trials which they accepted with resignation and confidence, whereas the pagans had nothing to oppose to the sufferings which fall upon them. In § viii, we note a curious passage on slavery : here the Christian is assuming the accents of Stoicism : [5]

" From thy slave thou dost exact absolute submission. Thou art man and dost oblige a man to obey thee. You

[1] *De doct. Christ.*, iv, 14.

[2] Cf. § viii (Hartel, p. 356), x, xii, xiii. Some have objected to the tone of this work as lacking respect. Was Tertullian much more deferent in regard to the Pro-Consul Scapula ?

[3] *Apol.*, lx ; *ad Nat.*, I, ix ; *ad Scap.*, iii.

[4] V, iv, 3.

[5] Cf. Seneca, *Ep.* xlvii, 6 : " Vis tu cogitare istum, quem servum tuum vocas, ex iisdem seminibus ortum, eodem frui caelo, aeque spirare, aeque vivere, aeque mori ? "

are both called to birth by the same chance, subjected
to death by the same condition, formed of the same
matter, endowed with the same soul ; by the same law
by which you enter into this world, you go out from it.
In spite of this, if he serve thee not according to thy
wish, if he bend not to thy least desire, imperiously
and without pity thou dost make him pay the penalty
of his servitude : stripes, hunger, nakedness, even the
sword or the dungeon are the punishments which thy
cruelty exercises against him."

The tone is harsher and more biting in places than even
that of the *Ad Scapulam*. Cyprian had to deal with a dangerous fanatic whom he made it his business to unmask.
In the first pages he still lingers over a fastidious rhetorical
development on the growing decrepitude of the universe.
The rest of the pamphlet is of a fine, passionate vigour.

The authenticity of the *Quod Idola Dii non Sint* is not
absolutely certain. St Jerome,[1] however, and St Augustine [2]
attributed it to Cyprian, and such testimony should not
lightly be set aside. This mediocre *opusculum*, borrowed
almost entirely, not only in its ideas, but even sometimes in
its expressions, from Tertullian and Minucius Felix, is divided
into three parts : a criticism of mythology from the Evhemerist
point of view (§ i–vii) ; the attributes of God, among which
unity is placed first (§ viii–ix) ; an outline of a Christology
(§ x–xv). Without doubt, this is a work which came soon
after the conversion of Cyprian, who in his zeal as a neophyte
thought he could not do better than review the ideas which
he had come across in the most well-known apologies of that
period.

The three books of the *Testimonia ad Quirinum* are no
longer in dispute as being by Cyprian. At most, we can
admit that certain interpolations have crept into the third
book. When Cyprian put together this compilation—this
is the most suitable description—he must already have been
a priest, perhaps a Bishop : he calls Quirinus " *Fili carissime.*"

" The plan of this treatise," he explains to Quirinus,
" conforms to your desire : it is a *compendium*, an

[1] *Ep.* lxx, 5, *ad Magnum.*
[2] *De Bapt.*, VI, xliv, 87 ; *de Unico Bapt. c. Petie.*, iv, 6.

epitome. I did not wish to present any developments, but to group and bind together extracts so far as my poor memory can supply them. See in this, not a formal treatise, but material for the use of those who might wish to write one. This brevity has great advantages for the reader. Without confusing his mind over too long an explanation, it supplies useful summaries to his memory which it can faithfully preserve."

Each chapter opens by setting forth a thesis : thus, in the first book, the failure of the Jews and the call of the Gentiles is demonstrated in twenty-four theses ; in the second book, the divinity and the mission of Christ are developed in thirty theses ; in the third book (added afterwards, for the introduction only announced two books), the duties of a Christian in the moral and disciplinary order are given in detail in 120 theses. Under each of these theses, a certain number of quotations capable of illustrating them are given. Thanks to the *Testimonia*, we have a very good knowledge of the Latin text of the Bible as it was read in Carthage towards the middle of the IIIrd century. From this time there was something like an " official " Bible in Africa. Cyprian does not give to his quotations the variety of readings which Tertullian used. He makes his references from an almost uniform text. Thus, out of 886 verses from the New Testament quoted in the *Testimonia* and in his other works, there are 382 which are found repeated twice or several times with only insignificant variations.

For the polemists of the IIIrd and IVth centuries, the *Testimonia* became an arsenal to which they came to equip themselves. This collection of relevant and classified passages placed at their disposal appropriate weapons, and the value of such convenient resources was keenly appreciated.

The *Ad Fortunatum de Exhortatione Martyrii* has much analogy to the *Testimonia*. It is a collection of exhortations borrowed from Scripture with the view of preparing the *milites Christi* for the struggles which they might have to face. Cyprian explains his plan in a preface addressed to Fortunatus (possibly the Bishop of Thuccabori) : [1] " military " metaphors abound in accordance with the practice of Chris-

[1] This Fortunatus of Thuccabori is mentioned in the *Sententiae episcoporum* (Hartel, I, 444).

tians in the first centuries. Certain fundamental principles, such as the vanity of idols, the warning of Heaven against those who offer sacrifice to them, Jesus Christ to be preferred in everything, and the hatred of the world to Christianity, serve as a peg for quotations from the Bible with which Cyprian mingles his own observations. A fine peroration on the signal honour of martyrdom brings to an end this manual of heroism through which blows the breath of combats.

It has been remarked that all this *apologia* draws its arguments not from juridical demonstrations, nor from philosophic principles nor from " adverse " witnesses, but only from the lights derived from the Christian revelation. Such exclusiveness was to draw upon Cyprian the criticisms of some of his successors, the partisans of a more eclectic method.[1] It is difficult to decide whether Cyprian's method was better adapted than the other to his aim of defence and conquest. In any case, it is just what we should expect from a profoundly Christian mind like his, which paid little attention to methods from outside, and felt that he could do no better than offer to others the reasons which had appeared to him to be of decisive importance in the work of his own conversion.[2]

Another group of St Cyprian's writings bears a more strictly " homiletic " character. As is almost always the case with men of action, eloquence constituted one of the forces of Cyprian. " Such was his passion for speaking," Pontius[3] tells us, " that he wished, when the hoped-for day of his martyrdom should come, to meet his end while he should be speaking of God." He often preached both at Carthage and outside his Episcopal city.[4] The admirable vigour of his exhortations during the pestilence re-established order and the exercise of charity among the demoralised Christian community. Some of the treatises enable us, though imperfectly, to obtain an idea of what a " sermon " meant to Cyprian.

The *De Habitu Virginum* must belong to the beginning of his episcopate. This eulogium of virginity, specially

---

[1] Lactantius, *Inst. Div.*, V, vi, 4. " . . . Non enim Scripturae testimoniis, quam ille (Demetrianus) utique vanam, fictam, commenticiam putabat *sed argumentis et ratione* fuerat refellendus." St Jerome, *Ep.* lxx, 3, *ad Magnum*.

[2] *Vita Cypriani*, § xiv (Hartel, III, 3, p. cvi).

[3] Cf. *Ep.* lviii, 1 ; lxxvi, 1.

[4] *Vita Cypriani*, ix–x.

written for those young girls who had offered themselves to
Christ, is for the greater part based on ideas borrowed from
Tertullian's *De Pudicitia*, *De Virginibus Velandis* and *De
Cultu Feminarum*. He forbids them to adorn themselves,
to dye their hair, to take part in marriage banquets which
were so often immodest, to frequent public baths common to
both sexes, and, in a word, to court sensual temptations or
expose others to them. More clearly than Tertullian,
nevertheless, he points out that continence is not an absolute
duty or a necessity imposed by God, but that it remains
a matter of choice as free as it is meritorious.[1]

In his *De Dominica Oratione*, Cyprian likewise had before
his eyes Tertullian's *De Oratione*.[2] But he followed it with
a certain amount of independence. His plan is very different
from that adopted by Tertullian. The work is important
for its Christian conception of prayer, especially as regards
its *social* character, which does not exclude but broadens our
individual concerns :[3]

> " We do not say : *My* father, who art in heaven . . . ,
> give *me* this day *my* daily bread . . . ; forgive *me my*
> trespasses. . . .   No, prayer is general, collective (*pub-
> lica est nobis et communis oratio*). When we pray, it is
> not for one person alone but for all the people, because
> all the people form but one single body. . . ."

The *De Mortalitate* is an admirable " instruction " on
suffering and death considered from the Christian point of
view. Cyprian makes more than one maxim of the Stoics
his own ; but the resignation which he recommends is not
only the stiffening of a proud soul against destiny ; the
promises of immortality are also opened wide to it. The
disasters entailed by a scourge almost without precedent—
that terrible pestilence which towards the middle of the
IIIrd century ravaged the Roman Empire—had brought in
its train an incredible falling away of souls. Many Christians
revolted against the injustice of seeing their brethren struck
down without distinction together with the pagans themselves, and, what was more, baulked of the hope of a glorious

---

[1] § xxiii (Hartel, I, 203, l. 26 et s.).
[2] See E. Frhr. von der Goltz, *das Gebet in d. aeltesten Christenheit*, L., 1902,
pp. 279–287.
[3] § viii (Hartel, I, 271).

martyrdom.   Cyprian endeavours to inspire these dis-
heartened people with his vivifying energy.   What was life,
and what was death ?   The first was a battle to which the
second puts an end, bringing to us, if we have triumphed,
the eternal reward.   To grieve so much over the death of our
near relations was to betray the lack of vitality of our faith.
People were complaining that Christians had not been
spared.   Was then faith a guarantee against misfortune ?
Why should the Christian expect to break through for his own
benefit that solidarity which united the whole human race ?
The sole privilege which he ought to claim was that of suffering.   It was only idolatry that despaired ; the Christian
acquired new strength through trials.   Martyrdom, it was
true, escaped us if we were struck down (by the pestilence).
Let them therefore replace this loss by entire resignation to
the Divine Will, which we daily pray " may be done."
Whosoever believed in a morrow that shall make amends,
should dry his tears.   We may regret those whom we have
lost, but we must not weep for them.   Let us rather look
forward to the celestial country where we shall find again our
dear ones, reassured henceforward of their destiny, but still
solicitous for our own, who hold out their arms and ardently
call to us to come and partake of their happiness.

In the *De Opere et Eleemosynis*, he develops the idea that
good works and the giving of alms are for the Christian a duty,
and also an advantage as a principle to sanctification and
a leaven of divine favour.   He supports himself by examples
and declarations drawn from Holy Scripture, and brushes
aside the maxims current on the inconveniences of a too
great liberality.   The ideal which he invites the faithful to
approach is the disinterested life of the first community of
Christians wherein (according to the account in the Acts
of the Apostles) each one made his brethren share in what he
possessed, or rather desired to possess nothing but what was
in common with them.

The *De Bono Patientiae* is inspired by Tertullian's *De
Patientia*,[1] but Cyprian adapts his counsels to the circumstances of which he is speaking and to his constant purpose
of entire " unity."   Against the Stoic philosophy, he extols
patience,—that is to say, the ability to bear that which is

---

[1] See the comparison in Benson's *Cyprian*, 1897, p. 443 et s.

contrary to nature,—as a specially Christian virtue, of which
God himself, Christ, and the Just, have defined the marks
and furnished the model. It is that which preserved the
Christian in temptations and trials. Lack of patience, on
the contrary, had always brought with it a train of evils,
from the original fall, to schisms and heresies. He ends by
appealing to Christians not to call down vengeance from
on high so *impatiently* on those who persecute them, and to
reverently wait for the infallible day of divine punishment.

His constant preoccupation, continually kept alive by the
ill will of certain people, can easily be seen too in the *De
Zelo et Livore* (concerning envy and jealousy). It represents
this twofold fault as a pitfall, most formidable from being
hidden, into which the devil endeavoured to precipitate the
Christian.

We might fairly state that these treatises are all the
more attractive in that they are more closely connected with
the actual questions which pressed upon the mind of Cyprian.
When he merely develops ideas or general precepts with the
aid of abundant quotations from the Bible, the interest
languishes a little. It revives, on the other hand, the moment
that Cyprian comes into contact with contemporary reality.
Then his accents become more keen and more impassioned ;
his mysticism stands out more alluring and persuasive in
arriving at the relative value of the diverse attractions making
their call on the soul. Cyprian's talent grows, we should say,
in proportion as he uses it in collaboration with his work
as a Bishop and his daily struggles.

VI

ST CYPRIAN'S prestige was great in Christian antiquity.[1]
Those who had known him were penetrated with admiration,
and the biography compiled by Pontius is a proof of this.
His life so fruitful in results, his compelling eloquence, his
absolute devotion to his flock, lastly his heroic death coming
as the crown to such exceptional virtues, possessed material
whereby to pass on to posterity a figure more glorious than

[1] Evidence of this is collected in A.C.L., I, 701–717. His guidance was asked
for from Gaul, Cappadocia, and Rome. People learned his letters by heart (*Ep.*
lxxv, 4).

L

any other. Especially in Africa was his memory exalted :
" Carthage raised three basilicas in his honour, one on the
spot where he met his martyrdom, signalised by the *mensa
Cypriani*, another over his tomb at Mappalia, and a third
not far from the port." [1]   The anniversary of the saint, the
κυπριανά, was celebrated on the 14th September, not only
in his Episcopal city, but throughout entire Africa,[2] in Rome,[3]
in Constantinople [4] and in Spain.[5]   His renown radiated over
the whole Christian world.   He was read with ardour.[6]   The
reservations of Lactantius on his methods in apologetics,[7]
and those of St Augustine on his theories regarding baptism,[8]
detract in no wise from the respect which both of them have
dedicated to the Doctor and martyr.   Prudentius rises to
enthusiasm in his *Peristephanon :* [9]

> "Dum genus esse hominum Christus sinet et vigere mundum,
> Dum liber ullus erit, dum scrinia sacra litterarum,
> Te leget omnis amans Christum, tua, Cypriane, discet."

At the Council of Ephesus in 431, Cyprian was one of the
ten Fathers on whose testimony the Council based its condemnation of Nestorius.[10]   He had become one of the
accredited representatives of the mind of the Church.   When
St Augustine had to discuss any opinion of his, he found
himself obliged to remind his own adversaries that the works
of the great Bishop must nevertheless be distinguished from
writings that were properly canonical to which universal
respect had wellnigh raised them.[11]

From all this we need not be astonished that so many
opuscula to which he had not put his hand, have been placed

---

[1] H. Delehaye, *les Origines du Culte des Martyrs*, Brussels, 1912, p. 433.   Cf.
Monceaux, II, 375 et s.

[2] Saint Augustine, *Sermo* cccx, 1.

[3] *Depos. martyrum*, xviii kal. Oct.

[4] St Gregory of Nazianzen, *Or.* xxiv.

[5] Prudentius, *Peristeph.*, xi, 237.

[6] " Quae enim regio in terris inveniri potest, ubi non ejus eloquium legitur ",
doctrina laudatur, caritas amatur, vita praedicatur, mors veneratur, passionis
festivitas celebratur ? . . ." (*Tractatus* of St Augustine, edited by Dom Morin,
Munich, 1917, p. 103.)

[7] *Div. Inst.*, V, 1, 24.

[8] Cf. *De bapt. contra Donatistas.*

[9] *Perist.*, xiii, v, 6 et s.

[10] Hefele-Leclercq, *Conc.* II, i, p. 302.

[11] *Contra Cresconium*, II, xxxi, 39 ; *Ep.* xciii, 35.   See also Batiffol, in R.B.
1917, 29 et s.—In connection with the confusion between Cyprian of Carthage and
Cyprian of Antioch, a converted magician, cf. R. Reitzenstein, *Nachr. Gottingen,
Ph.-Histor. kl.*, 1917, pp. 38–79 : I have made an analysis of this study in the *Revue
de Philol. (Rev. des Revues)*, 1918.

to his account. The list of the *apocrypha*, attributed to him will be found elsewhere. Among the works which have been erroneously ascribed to him there are several reflecting the questions and disputes of his period and must have been written at about his time. For instance, the *Ad Novatianum*,[1] a kind of pastoral instruction in which Novatian is taken to task in a very sharp tone, and which brings forward the efficaciousness of penance and the salutary effect of the divine pity in opposition to the excessive rigours which he (Novatian), promulgated in regard to the *lapsi*. The *Liber de Rebaptismate*, the text of which, much spoilt, has been unfortunately preserved in only two late manuscripts which are not even independent, gives in a curiously paradoxical form the thesis maintained by certain of the adversaries of Cyprian on the question of the baptism of heretics.

The *Exhortatio de Paenitentia* is a collection of quotations from the Bible of the kind that Cyprian had drawn up in his *Testimonia*, and inspired by a similar spirit on the question of penance.

Other *apocrypha* give us several interesting ideas in connection with the history of customs. Thus we can gather in reading the *De Spectaculis* some of the excuses, which are at times *bizarre*, brought forward by Christians fond of the public shows, to give a theological justification for their taste : [2]

> "Where has this been forbidden in the Scriptures?" they asked (§ ii). "Moreover, was not Elias the ' charioteer (*auriga*) of Israel'? Did not David dance before the Ark? We find mentioned therein harps, stringed instruments, brazen instruments, drums, flutes, zithers and choirs. In the conflicts which we have to sustain against evil spirits, the Apostle offers us the model of the contest with the *cestus*. In another place, borrowing his example from the *stadium*, he promises a crown as the reward. Why then should a faithful

[1] The attribution to Pope Sixtus IInd of this tract, suggested by Harnack in 1895 (T.U., xiii, 1) is taken up by D'Alès, R.S.R. 1919, 320 et s., who likewise assigns the *Adversus Judaeos* to Sixtus.

[2] The *De Spectaculis* is claimed for Cyprian by Hartel, A.L.L., 1892, 1–22. A certain number of critics assign it to Novatian, see D'Alès, *art. cit.*, p. 298 et s., who holds the same opinion. The similarities in style do not appear to me to be very significant.

Christian be forbidden to see what Holy Scripture does not fear to mention by name ? "

A line of argument similar to that upon which Tertullian had already laid stress is developed against these complaisant advocates of vice (*vitiorum assertores blandi et indulgentes patroni*) ; and they find themselves invited to substitute the contemplation of the splendours of nature and the reading of the marvellous narrative of the Bible for an altogether idolatrous amusement. . . .

The author of the *Adversus Aleatores*, who is a Bishop, takes the gamblers to task, and declares to them that he considers it as one of the first duties of his charge to make known to them the perils of that passion to which they abandon themselves. Their " sedentary and idle perversity " (*sedentaria et pigra nequitia*, § vi) was the sure means taken by Satan to lead them on the road to mad passion, perfidy, ruin and debauchery ; for prostitutes prowl round the gambling table. Gambling was of the devil ; it was the unforgivable sin against the Holy Spirit, and a violation of the temple of God, which every Christian was.

These inexorable anathemas are expressed in language whose incorrectness almost rivals its vehemence. Solecisms and even barbarisms abound in it, especially in those manuscripts which have suffered the least amount of retouching.[1] Philologists find in the *Adversus Aleatores* (with which, from the point of view of form, we may compare certain letters coming either from the Roman clergy or from different correspondents of Cyprian),[2] precious lights on " vulgar " Latin. Harnack[3] thought he saw in it a work by Pope Victor. At the same stroke the *Adversus Aleatores* was promoted to the dignity of being the first work of Latin Christian Literature. But the hypothesis has not been able to withstand the investigations of which it has been the starting-point, and Harnack has had to abandon it.[4] All that remains to be said is that the author of the *Adversus Aleatores* makes a great point of his privileges as a Bishop,

---

[1] *Monacensis* 208, IXth century; *Trecensis* 581, VIIIth – IXth century; *Reginensis* 118, Xth century. There is also the *Parisinus* 13047, IXth century, to which Hartel and Harnack give the preference.

[2] *Ep.* viii, xxi, xxii, xxiii, xxiv, in the series of St Cyprian's letters.

[3] T.U. Bd. V.H. I (1888).

[4] A.C.L., II, 2, p. 379.

which, in his eyes, corresponded to imperative duties.[1] We may think of him either as an " African Bishop of Cyprian's school "[2] (who is frequently imitated in the treatise as regards language and the form of its Biblical quotations), or as some anti-Pope from the camp of Novatian.

The *De Singularitate Clericorum* reminds clerics in a long " instruction " in 46 chapters of the duty which is incumbent upon them of not living in the same house with women. For centuries the Church was to fulminate against this abuse without eradicating it. We already find traces of it in Hermas and St Irenæus in the IInd century. St Cyprian denounces it with great vigour. St Jerome uses harsh and outspoken terms to brand it. The author of this doctrinal letter is not known. He was certainly a Bishop,[3] and it appears a Bishop in charge of a schismatic community.[4] The manner in which he speaks of martyrdom and supposes the clerics whom he is reprimanding speak of it,[5] hardly enables us to place its appearance further back than just after peace had come to the Church.

The *De Singularitate Clericorum* provides a curious abstract of the more or less specious arguments with which the delinquents endeavoured to palliate their lively appreciation of a woman's presence, or simply their lusts. What mattered the opinion of men, they said (§ viii) ; we seek a meritorious opportunity of overcoming ourselves (ix) ; did not St Paul write : " Bear ye one another's burdens and thus ye shall fulfil the law of Christ " (x), and in another place : " Everyone of us shall render an account of himself unto God " (xiii) ? If scandal on both sides was to be feared to such an extent, how may the faithful dare to mingle the sexes when they meet together in Church (xiii) ? we are practising in our own way the duty of *caritas* (xxix), etc. The list of sophistries is further lengthened and these are refuted one by one with a perspicacity which does not allow any doubt as to their real meaning.

[1] 1 : " In nobis divina et paterna pietas apostolatus ducatum contulit et vicariam Domini sedem cælesti dignatione ordinavit et originem authentici apostolatus super quem Christus fundavit (et) Ecclesiam in superiore nostra portamus, accepta simul potestate solvendi et ligandi. . . ."

[2] Monceaux, II, 115.

[3] See Hartel's edition, p. 173, I, 5–10 ; 174, 4–12 ; 219, 6.

[4] *Ibid.*, § xxxiv (p. 210, 6) and § 1 (174, 7). For the attempts to attribute it to Novatian, cf. D'Alès, R.S.R., 1919, 312 et s.

[5] § xxxiv et s. (p. 210). § iv (p. 177, i, 27) is less convincing.

We must also mention the *De Bono Pudicitiae*, a kind of pastoral letter in imitation of Tertullian's *De Pudicitia* and of St Cyprian's *De Habitu Virginum*, on the virtue of modesty, which " locum primum in virginibus tenet, secundum in continentibus, tertium in matrimoniis " (§ iv). The critics who admit the assignment of the *De Spectaculis* to Novatian likewise attribute to him the *De Bono Pudicitiae*,[1] which is closely allied to it in language, style, and the models whom the authors follow in it. The *De Laude Martyrii* and the *Adversus Judaeos* hold a special position among the *apocrypha* attributed to St Cyprian. They figure in Cheltenham's list. The principal reason which prevents us from believing that the *De Laude Martyrii* was written by Cyprian is the preponderance of an ambitious rhetorical effect which displays itself from the first chapter and hardly squares with the gravity of the circumstances under which the work was written, when pestilence was raging and a persecution had quite recently broken out (§ viii). This reason did not appear decisive to Baronius, Bellarmine or Tillemont. However the study of this treatise gains in importance if one only compares with it the serious concern customary with the Bishop when he felt the sufferings of his flock. Harnack wishes to saddle it on Novatian, the convenient beneficiary of any works whose authorship is unknown. He advances the same solution for the *Adversus Judaeos*, one of the numerous homilies of the first centuries against the Jews. In any case, the work is not by Cyprian for the text of the Scriptural quotations differs from that which Cyprian followed. The *De Pascha Computus*, according to the author's own testimony was written in the fifth year of the reign of Gordian in the Consulate of Arrianus and Papus (§ xxii), and therefore before Easter in the year 243. The question of Easter had much exercised the Christian Churches since they had emancipated themselves from the Jewish reckoning. Already Hippolytus of Rome, about the year 222, had applied himself to deep calculations. The author of the *Pascha Computus* was inspired by Hippolytus or some source common to him. Animated with a lively enthusiasm for his dry subject (cf. § i ; xxiii), he first gives an explanation of his system, and

---

[1] Paul Lejay in the *Bull. des Humanistes franc.*, IV (1895), p. 54, has drawn attention to an interesting manuscript of the *De Bono Pud.*, Bibl. Nat. *lat.* 1658, which Hartel has wrongly made light of.

then draws up a Paschal table as Hippolytus himself had done, perhaps with the intention of correcting the latter on diverse points. The *De Montibus Sina et Sion* need not hold our attention except as a written document illustrating the history of allegorical exegesis and its fantasies. The author commits some strange mistakes of history : he places Sinai in Palestine (§ iii) ; he confuses the first temple with the second (§ iv) ; he relates things concerning the death of Christ which he could not have read either in the Synoptics or in the Gospel of St John (§ viii). The style is poor, without skill and full of gross solecisms.[1] The *De Duodecim Abusivis Saeculi* belongs to a period far removed from Cyprian, and was probably written in Ireland in the VIIth century. This enumeration of the " abuses " of the world consists in superficial commonplaces and transpositions in imitation of the style of certain rhetorical methods practised by antiquity. The *Caena Cypriani*, " more worthy of a Turk than of a Christian," declared Tillemont, who was scandalised by the ineptitudes and the incongruities of this *bizarre* production, is a kind of mnemonical *resumé* of the Bible in the form of a " banquet " at which appear the personages in the Bible with the marks and the particularities which characterise them. The second part of the work is taken up by a lawsuit which Joel, who presides over the said banquet, brings against the guests suspected of having committed larcenies to the prejudice of the royal furniture ! It is painful to think that this depressing buffoonery should have found a host of admirers if we are to judge by the manuscripts which have come down to us. As to the date of its composition, we can only form guesses (end of IVth century ?[2] or beginning of Vth ?).[3] The *Acta Pauli* are used therein as a *quasi* canonical book.

R. Reitzenstein published in 1914 in the *Zeitsch. fur die neutest. Wiss.*, p. 60 et s., following the *Codex Wirceburgensis theol.*, f. 33, s. ix, and the *Codex Monacensis* 3739, IXth century, a rather curious treatise, which may be mentioned here, on the " three kinds of wages that human life offers "

---

[1] See Corssen, Z.N.W., 1911, pp. 7–8.

[2] Brewer, in Z.K.T., 1904, p. 105 et s.

[3] Harnack (T.U., n.f. iv, 3b, p. 21 et s.), who attributes the *Caena* to Cyprian, a poet of Gaul. A. Lapôtre's attempt (R.S.R., 1912, p. 497 et s.) to transform the *Caena* into a satire by Julian the Apostate is purely fanciful.

(cf. St Matth. xiii, 8), that is to say, on the varying quality of the rewards which await the just, according to whether they had been martyrs, ascetics or ordinary Christians. This work is related in many details to the *De Habitu Virginum* of St Cyprian ; to admit that Cyprian had been influenced by it, as Reitzenstein supposes, we must have cogent reasons which this critic does not furnish ; it is the opposite which is without doubt true.   The traces of Gnosticism, which he discovers in it, only appear to be very feebly marked.[1]

[1] See Harnack in T.L.Z., 1914, 220 et s.   Observations on the syntax in B. ph. W., 1915, n 16, by Schmalz.

CHAPTER III

NOVATIAN—COMMODIAN

BIBLIOGRAPHY

I. Novatian—P.L., III, 861-970; *de Trinitate*, ed. by W. Yorke Fausset, Cambridge, 1909 (including a study); *de Cibis Judaicis*, ed. by Landgraf and C. Weyman, in A.L.L., XI. (1898), pp. 221-249.—Consult: A. d'Alès, *le Corpus de Novatien*, in R.S.R., 1919, 293-323.

II. Commodian—P.L., V., 201-282 (the *Instructiones* only); Ludwig, L., 1877 (B.T.); B. Dombart in C.V., vol. XV (1887).—Consult: Monceaux, III, 451-489.   Recent Bibliog. on the question of the date of Commodian analysed by P. de Labriolle, in B.A.L.A.C., 1912, pp. 79-80; Monti, *Bibliographia di Commodiano*, extract from the *Athenaeum* III, 2 (1915): completed in B. ph. W., 1915, 1304; Lindsay, *The MSS. of Commodian*, in B. ph. W., 1914, 509; J. Martin, in S.B.W., 181, 6 (1917) (I have reviewed Martin's study in the *Rev. de Philologie* [*Rev. des Revues*], 1918).   For the language and style of Commodian, see also Durel, *Commodien, Rech. sur la doctr.*, *la langue et le vocab. du poète*, Paris, 1912 (mediocre); Sisto Cucco, *La grammatica di Commodiano*, in the *Didaskaleion*, 1913, p. 307, et s.; Vrow, *de Commodiani metris et syntaxi*, Utrecht, 1917.

FRENCH TRANSLATION of the *Instructiones* by J. Durel, Paris, 1912.   The *Carmen Apologeticum* of Commodian is only known through a single manuscript, the *Cod. Cheltenhamensis*, n° 12261, VIIIth century.

For the *Instructiones*, the *Berolinensis*, 167, VIIIth/IXth century, formerly at Cheltenham, must be placed first.   Lindsay suspects, from certain abbreviations of a special type, that the *Cheltenhamensis*, n° 12261 and the *Berolinensis* 167 formed originally one and the same manuscript coming from Verona.

The *Cod. Berolinensis* very probably represents the Angers manuscript (*Andecavensis*) which J. Sirmond had used, and which was given up as lost.

We may also mention for the *Instructiones*, the *Cod. Cheltenhamensis*, n° 1825, XIth century and the *Cod. Parisinus*, n° 8304, XVIIth century (B) (whence derives a Leidensis Vossianus 49 (A), of the same period).   A and B furnish readings which are only conjectures by Sirmond and to which Dombart has attached too much importance.   This is one of the faults of his edition.   In addition, Dombart made the mistake of relying upon Sedlmayer and Knœll for the collating of the Cheltenham MSS., who did not bring to this task all the care that might have been desired.   More than one erudite question must remain in suspense until a fresh edition has been established, which is more correct.

SUMMARY

I. The rôle of Novatian.—II. The *De Trinitate*.—III. The *De Cibis Judaicis*.—
  IV. The works of Commodian.—V. The *Instructiones* and the *Carmen Apologeticum*.—VI. His language and metre.—VII. The riddle enveloping his personality.

I

AMONG the correspondence of St Cyprian, we come across two letters, the XXXth and the XXXVIth, coming from the clergy in Rome and addressed to the Bishop of Carthage in connection with the question of the *lapsi*. In reply to a communication from Cyprian, who was anxious to assure himself whether he was in full agreement with the clergy of that city, Letter XXX insists on the duty imposed upon the Church of maintaining a rigorous discipline with regard to the apostates under whom were included the *libellatici ;* it thanks the Bishop in warm terms for the encouraging words he had addressed to the confessors who were in prison, and concludes by declaring that the Church of Rome did not feel that it had the right to decide definitely the question of the *lapsi* before the Bishop of Rome, who had recently died, had been replaced ; that in the meantime, the *lapsi* could only do penance without trying to extort a premature amnesty, it being understood that in case of peril of death, he should take into consideration the merits which they shall individually have acquired, with a view to their reconciliation with the Church.   Letter XXXVI relates to the same discussion. It is in reply to Letter XXXV, in which Cyprian had drawn the attention of the clergy in Rome to the reprehensible obstinacy with which certain *lapsi* had refused to enter upon the way of penance, under the pretext that they had already received their pardon from the martyr Paulus. In it, Cyprian's attitude is fully commended while the inconsistency of certain martyrs, and the rebellion of certain sinners, receives a strong reprimand.

These two letters had been written by the Roman priest, Novatian. Cyprian indicates this as regards Letter XXX (*Ep.* lv, 5) ; the general contents and style of Letter XXXVI scarcely leave any doubt that it was from the same pen.

One happy result of modern criticism is to have brought to light the vigorous personality of Novatian. We have little knowledge of his origin.   According to a rather doubtful piece of evidence given by the historian Philostorgius, he was a Phrygian (H.E., viii, xv).   In one letter, part of which Eusebius has translated,[1] Pope Cornelius depicts him in the

---

[1] H.E., VI, xliii.

blackest colours. He brands his mischievousness, his falsehoods, his perjuries, his unsociable temperament and cunning
hypocrisy, and is not disposed to see anything else in him
than an ": astute and evil monster," long possessed of the
devil, and one who had received baptism under very equivocal
conditions of validity. But certain expressions used by
Cornelius to describe him, in spite of their sarcastic turn,[1]
enable us to obtain a glimpse of the important place which
Novatian held among the clergy in Rome, and of his intellectual worth which encouraged his ambitions. We may
gather the same from the significant criticism whereby St
Cyprian shows him as pluming himself on his eloquence, and
deplores his regrettable familiarity with profane philosophy.[2]

Novatian had hoped to secure his own election as Bishop
of Rome. Cornelius was chosen. His disappointment must
have been poignant. A certain Novatus (with whom he
has been on more than one occasion wrongly confused),[3]
a priest of Carthage of a very mischief-making temperament,
incited him to break with Cornelius. Novatian found the
means to exact his own ordination as a Bishop from three
Italian Bishops, who were very simple-minded people, and
whose understanding, if we are to believe Cornelius, had been
obscured with the fumes of wine. This was schism (251).
In addition, his personal rivalry was complicated by divergent
ideas. Novatian had set himself to protest against any
reconciliation of the *lapsi*. He reserved their pardon to God,
and denied to the Church the right to anticipate the Divine
verdict.[4] The *clique* on which he leant for support was too
limited to cause this rigour to prevail. He was excom-
municated both in Rome and in Carthage. His party was
numerous throughout the Roman world,[5] and it appears
that his theories later on went to the length of refusing
absolution for mortal sins whatever they were.[6] According

---

[1] ὁ δογματιστής, ὁ τῆς ἐκκλησιαστικῆς ἐπιστήμης ὑπερασπιστής. ὁ ενδικητὴς τοῦ
εὐαγγελίου.

[2] *Ep.* xliv, 3 ; lv, 16 and 24 ; lx, 3.

[3] The error has been favoured by the defective form of the name by which,
even in Rome, his partisans called themselves : *Novatiani* (instead of *Novatianani*).
See note 28 in P.G., xxxix, 420. In the East, he is usually called Νοουάτος.

[4] Cf. Cyprian, Ep. lv, 27–28 ; lvii, 4.

[5] To the West as far as Spain, to the East as far as Syria. In the East, his
disciples called themselves the "Pure" (καθαροί (Katharoi): cf. Eusebius, H.E.,
VI, xliii, 1).

[6] St Ambrose, *De Paen.*, I, x (P.L., xvi, 489).

to information given by Socrates, which is suspect, Novatian died a martyr during the persecution of Valerian.

He wrote much. In his *De Viris Illustribus* (§ lxx), St Jerome cites the following works : *De Pascha, De Sabbato, De Circumcisione, De Sacerdote, De Oratione, De Cibis Judaicis, De Instantia* (concerning Perseverance), *De Attalo, De Trinitate ;* he adds " *et multa alia*," which has encouraged his critics to impute to Novatian more than one work whose authorship is doubtful. We have seen that the *De Spectaculis* and the *De Bono Pudicitiae* should possibly be retained among the writings placed hypothetically to his account. For the *De Trinitate* and the *De Cibis Judaicis*, the literary tradition is much more solid. It will be noticed that Novatian is the first Roman writer who wrote exclusively in Latin. We have here an indication of the decline of Greek in the Christian community at Rome.

II

THE *De Trinitate* was published in 1545 by Gagny-Mesnart among the works of Tertullian. Jacques de Pamèle (*Pamelius*) restored it to Novatian in 1579. This confusion of the authors goes back to antiquity. Rufinus had already made that mistake and St Jerome had to rectify his error : " Nec Tertulliani liber est nec Cypriani dicitur (he declares) sed Novatiani, cujus et inscribitur titulo, et auctoris eloquium stili proprietas demonstrat." [1] Without doubt, the title was not due to Novatian himself, for the word *Trinitas* does not appear in the treatise. Still less is a complete theory of the Trinity developed therein ; it is rather an essay on the relationship of the Son to the Father. The plan is clear and comprises four parts : God the Father (i–viii) ; Jesus Christ distinct from the Father, true God and true Man (ix–xxviii) ; the Holy Spirit (xxix) : an appendix on the method of reconciling the Divinity of the Son with the Oneness of God (xxx–xxxi). The Christology of the author is based in essentials on that of Tertullian. Nevertheless, St Jerome has gone a little far in making the *De Trinitate* a simple *resumé* of Tertullian's " whole work " (he is doubtless thinking of the *Adversus Praxean*) : Novatian has his own

---

[1] *Contra Rufinum*, II, xix (P.L., xxiii, 444).

personal ideas, which he freely expresses in a form limited
to the syllogism,[1] sometimes with an amplitude which one
might have wished had been more discreet.[2]

III

UP to 1893, the *De Cibis Judaicis* as also the *De Trinitate*
were only known in the old edition of Gagny-Mesnart, reproduced and more or less made correct by those of Ghelen,
Pamèle, Jackson, Gallandi, etc.   At that time, a manuscript
containing in addition to the *De Cibis*, Latin versions of the
Epistle of St James and of the Epistle of Barnabas, and the
works of Filaster, the heresiologist, was discovered in the
library of St Petersburg.   This manuscript, of the IXth
century, had originally belonged to the Monastery of St
Pierre de Corbie.   It was taken to Paris in 1638, and during
the French Revolution it fell into the hands of P. Dubrowski,
a secretary in the Russian Embassy.   It served as the material
for Landgraf's and Weyman's recension.

The *De Cibis Judaicis* is in the form of a letter which
Novatian, who at the moment was separated from his flock,
addresses " to the people steadfast in the gospel " (plebi in
Evangelio perstanti).   In two previous instructions, he had
already pointed out to them how defective was the understanding of the Jews of their own Law.   They were ignorant
of what the real circumcision meant and the real Sabaoth,
and understood no better the true meaning of the distinction
between pure and impure animals as laid down in Leviticus.

Taken literally, as the Jews did, this distinction would
mean nothing less than to favour the Gnostic heresy according
to which part of the Divine creation would not be good.   If
God had divided animals into categories, which in the beginning had all been blessed by him equally, it was for our mental
and moral instruction.   In itself, every animal was " pure."
But God wished to make the Jews, carnal beings, understand
the obligation of fleeing those vices which the forbidden
animals symbolised :   " In animalibus mores depinguntur
humani et actus et volontates ex quibus ipsi homines fiunt
vel mundi vel immundi " (§ iii) :   for example, the life of the

---

[1] Cf. xvi (Fausset, p. 56) ; xxx (id., p. 112).
[2] V.g. § ii (Fausset, p.9, I. 5–14).

pig passed in the muck, the thefts of the marten, the haughti-
ness of the swan, the hatred of the owl for the light, etc. . . .
On the contrary, the pure animals represented the virtues
loved by God : are not the ruminants representative of man
who chews without ceasing the Divine precepts ? Do not
the fishes with their rough scales bring to our minds the harsh,
bristling, untutored, solid and grave manner of thought of
virtuous men ?   The forbidding of certain foods was a punishment to the Jews for having preferred the flesh-pots of Egypt
to manna, and taught them temperance. But all that had
passed away. The religion of Christ consisted of something
very different to restrictions of this sort. " Deus ventre
non colitur." Truly pure and holy nourishment was an
unspotted conscience, an innocent life. Does it follow
from this that all excess shall be henceforth lawful (§ vi) ?
By no means. The religion of Christ was also a severe
religion. And those who took pleasure in good cheer, and
filled themselves with undiluted wine even on awaking from
sleep,[1] or gave themselves up to debauchery should be mindful
of this.

The interpretation given by Novatian to the regulations
in Leviticus was not at all new. We already find it in the
letter in which under the name of Aristeus, a hellenised Jew
had endeavoured to explain to the Greeks who despised
Judaism, not only the origin of the translation of the *Septuagint*, but also the motive of those precepts which scandalised
them.[2] It likewise appears in the *Epistle of Barnabas*,[3]
the work of a converted Jew who wrote without doubt in the
first half of the IInd century of our era. Tertullian himself
outlines it in his *Adversus Marcionem*.[4] But in the *De Cibis
Judaicis*, it is developed with a clearness, a choice of examples
and also an ease of style revealing a methodic mind familiar
with the best profane writers. It has been remarked to what
a high degree Novatian carries the spiritual meaning in regard
to enactments about food. He is behind the Christianity of
his time from this point of view. Another interest attaching
to this work is the first opening out, as it were, of the symbolic

[1] This last feature is a reminiscence of Seneca, *Ep.* cxxi, 6.
[2] § 143 ; 144 ; 164 ; 306 (Wendland's ed.).
[3] x, 1-9.
[4] II, xviii.

ideas of the Middle Ages, which was to develop a liking for personifying some human vice or virtue in each animal.[1]

IV

CHRISTIAN antiquity is almost mute as regards Commodian. Gennadius of Marseilles, who seems to have written the first 82 notices in his *De Viris Illustribus* between the years 467 and 469, devotes to him the following paragraph (§ xv) :

" It was through reading our Christian writings, together with profane writings, that he was touched by the faith. He therefore became a Christian, and desirous of offering as a gift to Christ, the author of his salvation, the fruit of his studies, he wrote against the pagans in a mediocre and *quasi* metrical style (*mediocri sermone quasi versu*). With the little familiarity that he possessed with our holy books he showed himself better able to destroy pagan errors than to fortify our own beliefs. This is why in treating of the Divine promises against them he conducted his discussion in a sufficiently gross and, as it were, heavy spirit (*vili satis et crasso ut ita dixerim sensu*) which threw them into astonishment and us into despair. Having studied in the school of Tertullian, Lactantius, and Papias, he inculcated upon his readers a doctrine which is perfectly moral, and above all, the love of voluntary poverty, which he had himself embraced."

One other mention of Commodian appears in the Decretal attributed to Pope Gelasius (P.L., lix, 163) : " The writings of Commodian are apocryphal (that is to say, non-canonical)."

No other ancient writer speaks of him. His works were only printed at a late date. Jacques Sirmond, the Jesuit, drew attention to the *Instructiones* and quoted two pieces from it in his edition of Ennodius (1611). Nicolas Rigault published them for the first time at Toul, in 1649. As regards the *Carmen Apologeticum*, it was only discovered in the middle of the XIXth century by J. B. Pitra in a manuscript of the VIIIth century belonging to the library of Thomas Philipps at Middlehill. Pitra inserted it in his

[1] See H. O. Taylor, *The Mediaeval Mind*, 1914, 11, p. 67–130.

Spicilegium Solesmense, vol. I (Paris, 1852), p. 21 et s.   The poem is without a title and without the name of the author, but the identity of certain verses (for example, *Instr*. I, xxviii, 1, *Carm. Apol.* 229), the similarity of ideas, style and metre, enabled Pitra to attribute it with certainty to Commodian.

Of very moderate interest in themselves, Commodian's works have regained a present-day prominence whereof the personality of the author and the date of his works have been the subject of discussion in recent years.   Before entering upon these discussions, we must give an indication of the contents and the spirit of the *Instructiones* and the *Carmen Apologeticum*.

V

THE *Instructiones per litteras versuum primas* comprises 80 pieces of 6 to 48 verses.   These pieces are " acrostics," that is to say, that the first letters read vertically form one or several words.   Two of them (I, xxxv ; II, xix) are alphabetical, the first letters corresponding to the series of the letters of the alphabet.   The division running into two books (41 pieces + 39) is not very satisfactory.   The division would be better if it were placed after II, iv in accordance with the nature of the subjects.   The title of the collection is explained by verse I, i, 9 : " *Ob ea perdoctus ignaros instruo verum :* " " I who know, instruct in the truth those who are ignorant of it."   The first book is addressed specially to outside unbelievers.   The second book is more esoteric.   In it Commodian sets forth his " eschatological " ideas, then distributes moral and disciplinary counsels to the various classes of Christians—catechumens, matrons, confessors, ecclesiastics, etc.

The *Carmen Apologeticum* comprises 1060 verses grouped two by two.   It opens with a warning by the author to the pagans (1–88) ;   then follows an exposition of a rather vague theology (principally from the point of view of the Trinity) on God, Christ and Revelation (89–578) ;   a demonstration of the necessity of faith for salvation (579–790) ;   lastly, a picture of the end of the world (791–1060).   Speaking generally, the *Carmen Apologeticum* seems superior to the

Instructiones, doubtless because the author has not subjected himself to the limitations of the acrostic. But the spirit animating the two works is the same.

Commodian has none of the speculative spirit which sets forth ideas for the pleasure of seeing them grouped into a system and appealing to each other by natural affinities. In his eyes, as with Tertullian and Cyprian, Christianity was the great, the only matter. He concerns himself with discouraging his enemies and in confirming in their faith those who, although Christians, were tending to forget the duties to which their profession bound them.

He first takes to task the pagans among the unbelievers, and does not spare them his sarcasms. The word *stultus* is his favourite epithet. He directs against them many gibes of this sort : " Poor fool, dost thou think then that Jupiter thunders, he who was born upon the earth and was nourished on the milk of a goat ? And supposing Saturn had devoured him at that time, what wouldst thou have done now that he is dead ? " [1] " Do you dare to call gods statues made of brass ? Make of them therefore rather pots for your use." [2] He inveighs against the " ignorant brutes " whose sluggish hearts are indifferent to the truth, and who, like fatted swine, take pleasure in their bestial delights.[3] How are you to live, however, if life is not ruled by one law ? [4] As for the Jews, " ever froward, and stiff-necked without suppleness,"[5] he reproaches the obstinacy with which they shun the evidences of history. " You will not allow yourselves to be convinced, and therefore shall you be disinherited." [6] In the *Carmen Apologeticum*, he devotes a special piece to them (V. 617–744) in which he stigmatises their pride and their pretence of filling by rites the place of purity of heart which they lack : " Nos sumus electi ! dicentes." [7] Neither does Commodian forget the pagans of Judaistic tendencies who pass their lives " hesitating between two parties " [8] and run to the synagogue and then come back from there to their temples. This equivocal attitude will be their ruin : it will give them over to tortures beyond the grave.

With regard to the believers themselves, he displays little

---

[1] *Instr.*, I, vi, 7–10.
[2] *Ibid.*, I, xx, 6–7.
[3] *Carmen Apol.*, 16 et s.
[4] *Instr.*, I, xxiii, 4.
[5] *Ibid.*, I, xxxviii, 1.
[6] v, 2.
[7] *Carmen Apol*, 676.
[8] *Instr.*, I, xxiv, 1.

M

gentleness, to whatever rank they belong. He reproaches the Christian women with their finery, their curls, their painted eyelids and dyed hair, and all that vain show which they should leave to courtesans.[1] " Triumph over the evil one, ye modest women of Christ, and only display your wealth by bestowing it." He stigmatises too the sumptuous funerals,[2] the brutishness of drunkenness,[3] and frivolous gossiping in Church.[4] Neither do his criticisms spare people connected with the Church, the " Doctors," who in their hopes for the present, accept the persons of men and authorise certain relaxations,[5] and clerics who do not observe the Law which they presume to teach.[6] Quite other is the Christian's ideal. He should fulfil like a man a joyless task[7] in this life which is but a long chain of woes and tribulations :

> " Esto ergo talis qualem vult esse te Christus :
> Mitis et in illo hilaris, nam saeculo tristis.
> Excurre, labora, suda, cum tristitia pugna."[8]

To accomplish this, he must avoid the public shows ;[9] he must consider how little worth are profane studies at the price of rectitude of the will ;[10] he must give alms largely and accept with entire resignation the trials which God sends him. . . .[11]

These chiding exhortations, addressed to the *rudes* (the word signifies not the " ignorant " as G. Boissier believed, but those who were not acquainted with Christianity or who were not inspired with its real spirit), assume a still more urgent intensity in the light of the eschatological views which the poet discloses in certain pieces of the *Instructiones*,[12] and especially in the *Carmen Apologeticum*. G. Monceaux[13] remarked that the picture traced by Commodian of the end of time is the most complete which has been bequeathed to us by the fantasy of the Christian " millenarists." " Guided by his faith and the Bible, Commodian vividly calls up before his eyes these grandiose spectacles which he paints with the enthusiasm of a devotee sure of going to paradise, and with the precision of an ocular witness."

[1] *Instr.*, II, xviii ; xix. [2] II, xxxiii.
[3] II, xxxvi. [4] II, xxxv.
[5] II, xvi, 1–2. [6] II, xxxiv.
[7] I, xxvi, 10 et s. [8] II, xvii, 15–17.
[9] II, xvi, 4–6 ; 21–23 ; *Carmen Apol.*, 207 et s. [10] *Carmen Apol.*, 583–4.
[11] *Inst.*, II, xxxii. [12] I, xli ; II, 1–4 ; xxxix.
[12] III, 479.

The following are the special features of the *Carmen Apologeticum* :

At the end of six thousand years the immortality promised to man will come. Man will rise from the dead, will recognise the truth of the promises which have been made to him, and will feel to the fullest extent his moral and physical happiness (v. 791–805).[1] There will be signs foretelling this resurrection. King Apollyon[2] invades Rome with the Goths ; he treats the pagans harshly, makes the Senate pass under the yoke and contrariwise manifests his entire benevolence towards the Christians. This episode lasts for five months (v. 805–823).[3] Meanwhile, Cyrus arrives, whom Commodian identifies with Nero, who has been held in reserve in a mysterious place for the work he had to accomplish.[4] His coming had been prophesied by Elias during three and a half days.[5] The Jews and Romans fall to adoring Nero and under his leadership take steps to massacre the Christians. Elias makes reprisals with formidable scourges.[6] Notwithstanding, at the instigation of the Jews, Nero causes seven thousand Christians to perish,[7] whose bodies God takes up into heaven (v. 823–865).[8] The persecution redoubles. The Christian people are exiled from Rome.[9] Nero joins two Cæsars[10] to himself, and issues general edicts and orders all to do sacrifice.[11] For three and a half years blood is poured forth. But Nero is to be despoiled of the power which he has abused (v. 865–890). A king rises up in the East and advances towards Rome at the head of four nations (Persians, Medes, Chaldeans and Baby-

---

[1] For a picture of this happiness, cf. *Apocal.*, xxi, 4.
[2] Cf. *Apocal.*, ix, 11.
[3] *Ibid.*, ix, 10.
[4] Some people thought that Nero would come back under another name, in order that the Jews might accept him as a Christ (cf. Victorinus of Pettau, *in Apoc.*, xiii, 16 ; Lactantius, *Inst. Div.*, VII, xvi, 4). The choice of the name of Cyrus here given by Commodian is perhaps explained by Isaias, xliv, 28, and xlv, 1. On the legend concerning Nero, cf. Geffcken, *Nachrichten* of Gottingen, *Phil.-Hist. Kl.*, 1899, pp. 441–462. The incidents relating to Nero are scattered in the following passages in Commodian : *Carm Apol.*, 813–838 ; 851–858 ; 869–874 ; 885–897 ; 909–918 ; 927–935 ; *Instr.*, I, xli, 7–11.
[5] A combination probably of Malachias, iv, 5, with *Apocal.*, xi, 11.
[6] Cf. *Apocal.*, xi, 6.
[7] For the figures, cf. *Apocal.*, xi, 13 (it is there applied however to the enemies of God).
[8] Cf. *Apocal.*, xi, 9 and 12.
[9] *Orac. Sibyll.*, iv, 135.
[10] Cf. *Daniel*, vii, 24.
[11] For the cessation of the *oblatio* to Christ (v. 879), cf. *Daniel*, ix, 27.

lonians).[1] Nero marches against them with the two Cæsars.
They are all three massacred and their bodies become food
for the birds.[2] Their armies pillage Rome, and the proud
city, which deemed itself to be eternal, is burnt and wiped out
(v. 891–926).[3] The victorious king directs his steps to Judea
and endeavours to seduce the Jews by prodigies.[4] " He is
anti-Christ for the Jews, as Nero was for us." [5] Soon the
disappointed Jews are reduced to implore the succour of the
true God (v. 927–940). God then causes the advance of a
people whom he had been keeping in the regions beyond
Persia. This people consisted of nine and a half of the
tribes of the Jews out of the twelve traditional number.[6]
The innocence and happiness of this people are described.
They march towards Judea in the midst of universal rejoicings.
The tyrant flees to the North and raises an army. But he is
taken prisoner and also the devil, and they are both plunged
into flames.[7] The saints enter into the Holy City and
beseech God to raise up the dead as He had promised (v. 941–
992). God begins by making a fire rain down upon the
impious. Very few escape from it. Then is let loose the
final catastrophe heralded by the strident sounds of the
trumpet. During the night, there is a terrifying falling to
pieces of the universe accompanied by the hurling of thunderbolts, the falling of the stars, earthquakes, and the roaring
of the hurricane. A fall of dew protects a few privileged
ones who have been marked out beforehand by Christ. For
the space of seven months, the fire purifies the earth. The

---

[1] These four nations recall perhaps the four angels of the *Apocalypse*. This
was to be the interpretation of St Epiphanius, *Panarion*, LI, xxxiii.

[2] Cf. *Apocal.*, xix, 17 ; 21.

[3] Cf. *Apoc.*, xviii, 7. The idea of a punishment hanging over Rome quoted
as the sinner and the persecutor, is frequent in the *Sibylline Oracles* (III, 356–364 ;
V, 162–178 ; 386–397 ; VIII, 37–49 ; 80–106 ; 165). The Latin apologists only
allude to them with the greatest discretion ; Tertullian, *Apol.*, xxxii, 1 ; St Cyprian,
ad Demetr., xxi (Hartel, p. 336, 8) ; Lactantius, VII, xv, 18.

[4] Cf. *Apocal.*, xiii, 13.

[5] Commodian thus distinguishes *two* Anti-Christs. This duplication is also
met with in Victorinus of Pettau, *in Apoc.*, xiii, 16 (P.L., v, 338 C) ; in Lactantius,
de Mort. Pers. II, who alludes to the popular belief founded on the declarations of
the Sibyl (*quidam deliri credunt . . . Sibylla dicente*) according to which Nero
would appear at the end of time as the precursor of Anti-Christ. See also Sulpicius Severus, *Dial.* II, xiv ; *Chron.* II, xxix, 5 ; St Jerome, *in Dan.*, ix, 29 (P.L.
xxv, 568). Neither the *Apocalypse* nor Hippolytus of Rome mention two Anti-
Christs.

[6] Cf. Esdras, IV, xiii, 40 et s. ; *Apoc.* of Baruch, lxxviii–lxxxvi (Schurer,
esch. d. Jud. Volkes, III, 305).

[7] Cf. *Apocal.*, xix, 20.

humble come down from heaven surrounded by angels. The bodies of the Just rise from the tomb and are borne on the clouds to Christ. The executioners of Jesus rise also from the tomb in order to gaze at this spectacle ; then they are plunged back again into the abyss (v. 993–1060).

The *Instructiones* furnish in a supplement some curious notions which Commodian indicated in the *Carmen Apologeticum*. Thus, according to the succession of events given in the *Instructiones* (II, i ; iii ; iv), the descent of the Heavenly Jerusalem is placed, between the first conflagration of the world (*Carmen*, v. 993–998) and the second (v. 999–1041), when the just receive the recompense which they have merited by their heroic resistance to anti-Christ. " They reproduce in wedlock for a thousand years. There, all the attributes which life on earth distributes in abundance by a perpetual renewing are brought together. No more rain, no more cold, in this golden city . . . ; the light given by lamps is no longer necessary there ; it gleams with the brightness of Him who created it, and night never reigns there " (II, iii, 9 et s.).

VI

APOCALYPTIC reveries inspired from Jewish and Judaeo-Christian sources ; injunctions of unaccommodating severity aimed at Christians who were too much inclined to escape from the rigour of the law of Christ, as much as at outside unbelievers—of such is made up the work of Commodian.

When compared with the rules of classic literature, his language swarms with inaccuracies. He jumbles up declensions and conjugations ; he confuses the query *ubi* and the query *quo ;* he is indifferent to the syntax of agreement and to the rule governing the right relation of tenses. His verses " contain the finest collection of barbarisms which the worst Latinist could have dreamt of." [1] Nevertheless, his style is not that of an *indoctus*. Apart from Holy Scripture, the principal food of his mind, and Christian authors (Tertullian and St Cyprian), Commodian had at least some slight acquaintance with certain profane writers, such as Terence, Lucretius, Virgil, Horace, perhaps also Sallust, Cicero, Tibullus and

[1] Monceaux, III, 483.

Ovid.[1] He makes awkward attempts at different methods—
alliterations, parallelisms between his verses, antitheses, and
piling up of synonyms. He sometimes attains to very forcible
compendious phrases in his turn of expression. But any
appreciation of art was wanting to him ; with the exception
of a few happy points, the whole is prosaic, heavy and maladroit.

As regards his hexameters, they have been compared to
those of a modern schoolboy who knows fairly well the general
rules pertaining to Latin verse in connection with the *caesura*
and the form of the last two feet, but is very ignorant of
quantity. Commodian did manage to write some good
hexameters (there are 37 in the *Instructiones*, and 26 in the
Carmen Apologeticum) ; but for the most part, his versification is wrong because the poet had not an idea of prosody.
Of the usual classical pauses he has hardly retained any but
the *penthémimère* which he almost always uses.[2] He reproduces in the two last feet the classical distribution of words
and accents, but here, as elsewhere, he pours into the traditional mould elements which do not at all belong to it.

Should this clumsy imitation of the classic hexameter
be considered as a fact by itself marking " the beginning of
a new art " ?[3] I think not. M. Monceaux has shown [4]
how in two-thirds of the metrical inscriptions, whether Christian or pagan, which have been discovered in the Roman
provinces, especially in Africa, quantity is confused. On
the other hand, the pause is given to the fifth foot ; a habitual
rhythm in the last two feet is observed ; and, as is the case
with Commodian, the acrostic, assonance, and sometimes
even the rhyme, are preserved. Commodian therefore made
no new innovations. Neither did he prepare the way for
any future innovation, for his verses present nothing in
common with the " rhyming " verses of the centuries that
succeeded.[5]

We may remark, moreover, that the perplexities experi-

[1] Notice is given of these resemblances in Dombart's edition, and in Manitius
(R.L.M., xlv [1890], p. 317, and xlvi [1891], p. 151), Ciceri (*Didascaleion*, II [1913],
363) ; J. Martin (S.B.W., vol. 181, 6, p. 108).

[2] There are also some examples of the *hepthémimère*, and four cases at least of
the *caesura* κατὰ τρίτον τροχαῖον (*Instr.*, I, 10, 8 ; II, 7, 15 ; 11, 10 ; 31, 6).

[3] G. Boissier, *Fin du Paganisme*, II, 37.

[4] III, 430 et s.

[5] On his metre cf. Vernier, in the *Rev. de Philol.*, v. XV (1891) ; Havet, *Métrique*,
§ 496 ; Vrow, *op. cit.* ; and especially Monceaux, III, 481 et s.

enced by specialists relating to the system of versification followed by Commodian [1] will not be removed until we have an edition more faithful to the manuscripts than that of the *Corpus* of Vienna. In more than one place, Dombart has retouched the text in order to accommodate it to the metre which he attributes to his author.

It has been sometimes supposed that Commodian deliberately wished to adapt his methods of expression to an unlettered public which he had specially in view. [2] In itself, this hypothesis does not seem to be unlikely. St Augustine followed the same practice when he wrote his *Alphabetical Psalm* against the Donatists, [3] as he explains in his *Retractiones*. But the case of Commodian appears to be very different. Nowhere does he limit the circle of his readers to the illiterate : In this connection I have pointed out the mistake which people commit about the word *rudes*. If he wrote badly, as did many of his contemporaries, it was in spite of himself and not of set purpose. Passionately convinced in his views and his faith as he was, he would surely have defended them with other weapons if he had not been at bottom rather ignorant notwithstanding certain passing breaths of classic literature.

VII

THE personality of Commodian is still an enigma, and all efforts of the critics have not succeeded in unravelling it or in determining with certitude the period at which he lived. Difference of opinion is considerable in relation to the date of the *Inscriptiones* and of the *Carmen Apologeticum*, since it bears on a period of time extending over more than two hundred years. For long this question had been in dispute

---

[1] These difficulties are extremely perplexing and not a little disconcerting. Boissier and Scheifer declare that Commodian does not take quantity into account at all.   Haussen affirms that the system of the grammatical accent has been in no way substituted by the poet for the system of quantity both before the *caesura* and at the end of the line, and that the quantity is observed to a certain extent. Vernier maintains that Commodian never replaced a short syllable by a long accented one : this critic admits moreover that there are words where the accent is wrongly placed.   Meyer seeks an explanation in Semitic poetry which only takes into account the number of the syllables, and whose principles Commodian blended with those of the *cursus* of prose writers, etc. . . .

[2] Boissier, II, 40 ; and before him Gaston Paris, *Lettre à Léon Gautier sur la versification latine rythmique*, Paris, 1866 (Extract from the *Bibl. de l'Ec. des Chartes*, sixth series, v. II), p. 28.

[3] P.L., xliii, 23–32. Cf. *Retr.*, I, xix.

when in 1906 Brewer was believed by some to have settled it in an important study on Commodian. According to Brewer,[1] Commodian must have been writing neither in the middle of the IIIrd century (Ebert, Boissier), nor at the beginning of the IVth (F. X. Kraus), nor between the years 260 and 350 (Harnack), nor in the second half of the IVth century (Maas), but between the years 458 and 466, in the south of Gaul. This is the conclusion to which Brewer came from considerations of a linguistic order and from an examination of historical allusions which he thought he saw in the *Instructiones* and especially in the *Carmen Apologeticum*. Shortly after the appearance of this learned work, J. Draseke wrote : " There is no longer any question concerning Commodian ; Brewer has offered a definite solution." [2] This was going rather too fast. Draseke's conviction did not impose itself on all minds with the same clearness. A very lively attack was brought to bear upon Brewer's comparisons by M. Paul Lejay,[3] which was soon followed up by Carl Weyman,[4] F. Zeller,[5] d'Alès,[6] Revay [7] and J. Martin.[8] We may say that to-day Brewer's thesis is held to be more than doubtful. This thesis relied in the first place on a passage in the *Carmen Apologeticum* (v. 805–822) in which Brewer thought he recognised more than one incident taken from the capture of Rome by Alaric in the year 410. The following is a literal translation of this passage : Commodian is here indicating some of the signs announcing the end of the world :

" ' But,' some may say, ' when are we to believe that all this is going to take place ? ' Here, in a few words, are the events following which those I am announcing will be realised. There will be many signs which will mark the end of this mighty disaster. But the beginning will be the seventh persecution directed against us. Already he is knocking at our gates and is girding himself with his sword who shall soon cross over the river while

[1] *Forschungen*, A. Ehrhard and J. P. Kirsch, VI, 1–2, Paderborn, 1906 ; *ibid.*, X, 5 (1910).
[2] T.L.Z., 1907, p. 80 ; *ibid.*, 1911, p. 364.
[3] R.C., v. LXIV (1907), pp. 199–209 ; LXVIII (1909), p. 125.
[4] *Theolog. Revue*, v. VII (1908), p. 523 et s. ; vol. VIII (1909), p. 485 et s.
[5] T.Q., vol. XCI (1909), p. 161–211 ; 252–406.
[6] *Rech. de Sc. rel.*, vol. II (1911), p. 479 et s. ; 599 et s.
[7] *Didaskaleion*, vol. I (1912), pp. 455–480.
[8] T.U., xxxix, 4 (1913).

the Goths are making their on-rush. King Apollyon, the name to be feared, will be with them. He will put an end, with sword in hand, to the persecution of the saints. He will march upon Rome with many thousands (of warriors) of his own race, and, by God's decree, he will make some of the vanquished his captives. At that time many senators, made captive, will lament ; and, conquered by a barbarian, they will blaspheme the God of heaven. Nevertheless, these pagans everywhere keep alive the Christians. Filled with joy, they seek for them more as if they were their brothers. As for those living in luxury and worshippers of vain idols, they hunt them down and make the senate pass under their yoke. These are the evils which those who have persecuted the loved ones (of God) will undergo : for the space of five months they will be slaughtered by this enemy."

An analysis of the details of this description is sufficient for us to see that in no particular do they fit in with the information bequeathed to us by historians contemporary with the taking of Rome in the year 410. The invaders are represented as pagans : now the Goths had become Arians from the time of Valens (364–378). Commodian insists on the benevolence with which they favour the Christians exclusively : now, according to Orosius [1] and St Augustine,[2] Alaric displayed equal clemency to the pagans themselves. Lastly, the senate is shown as a pagan *collegium*, and as the stronghold of paganism, and on this account suffers humiliating treatment. How can we apply to the Vth century such a picture of the senate when, by the testimony of St Ambrose, the Christian senators formed the large majority from the end of the IVth century ? [3] In reality, Commodian imagines much more than he can remember ; and, mingling historical touches with recollections of the Apocalypse, he gives an eschatological rôle to the Goths in the middle of the IIIrd century, whose menace the empire had already felt so heavily.

[1] VII, xxxix, 10 (Zangemeister, p. 546, 14).
[2] *De Civit. Dei*, I, 1 (Hoffmann, p. 4, 1, 21) ; III, xxix (H., p. 156, 26 ; 157, 3).
[3] *Ep.* xvii, 9 : " Cum majore jam curia christianorum numero sit referta " ; xvii, 10 : " pauci gentiles," " innumeri christiani senatores." Commodian lays stress in more than one place on the " paganism " of the Senate (*Carmen Ap.*, v. 815–820 ; 824 ; 831–849 ; 851 ; 855 ; 910).

Brewer likewise endeavoured to establish a connection between a passage in the *Instructiones*, II, x (the poet was exhorting certain children who had been carried away by the enemy and reduced to some form of slavery, to re-enter the bosom of the Church when grown up), and a decision of Pope Leo I in the year 458, relating to the question whether it was necessary to re-baptise children who had been carried away by the Vandals, when they returned to the Catholic faith. But certain characteristics are little favourable to the comparison : if these children were captives, how could the poet counsel them to flee " a terrible and ever bloodstained, impious and rebellious race, living the life of brute beasts " (v. 8–9), if that depended upon them ? We are under the impression that this " enemy " is rather the persecuting State which had usurped possession of their young consciences.

The fact is that nothing in the *Instructiones*, any more than in the *Carmen Apologeticum*, reveals that Commodian wrote after the reconciliation of the Church with the Roman authorities. The life of a Christian, as he depicts it, was a life under constant menace,[1] a life of struggle, in which peace itself when it should arrive, would be a " traitor's " peace.[2] One or two passages even offer some curious analogies with certain episodes at the time of St Cyprian, such as the schism of Felicissimus.[3] Nevertheless, it would not be unlikely if Commodian, insufficiently equipped with information on his own account, had applied even expressions of Cyprian to a case different from that which the saint had in view. Taking all in all, I think that we can with some certainty place the works of Commodian between the year 250 and the Edict of Milan (313). St Jerome does not speak of him in his *De Viris Illustribus* published in the year 392 : this was because the illiterate character of Commodian's work would not have contributed to the aims which he professes in his preface. As regards Gennadius, the place given by him to Commodian (between Prudentius and Audentius on the one hand, and between Faustinus and Rufinus on the other) is of little value, for it looks very much as if he knew nothing of him except what he had learnt from the *Instructiones*.

[1] Cf. *Instr.*, II, ix, xiii, xxi, xxv, xxix.
[2] *De Pace subdola* (xxv)
[3] xxv and xxix. Cf. Zeller, in T.Q., 1909, p. 359 et s., for these verbal analogies which are striking.

Commodian was born a pagan.[1] He often deplores his past errors and confesses that he had been given up to every kind of superstition.[2] The *explicit* of the *Carmen Apologeticum* gives him the rank of Bishop : there is nothing in his writings to confirm this information, which perhaps is due to the imagination of a scribe. He calls himself *mendicus Christi*,[3] which may perhaps mean an " ascetic," [4] or " one who solicits alms for Christ." [5] At the head of the last portion of the *Instructiones*, in the place where he gives his own name in an acrostic, these two words *Nomen Gasaei* figure, which so far have had little explanation although hypotheses are not wanting. Do they mean " the man of Gaza " ? [6] Or the name of the " treasurer " ? [7] We cannot tell exactly. If Commodian is believed to have been a native of Africa, or an African by adoption, this is due to his name, his language, his numerous references to St Cyprian, and the use which he makes of the *Testimonia ad Quirinum*. It is possible that a more profound knowledge of " Christian " Latin, and of the history of Christian ideas, will one day permit of absolute conclusions which would be premature at the present time.

[1] The words *parentibus insciis ipsis* (*Instr.*, I, l. 5) have been wrongly interpreted by G. Boissier (*Fin du Paganisme*, II, 39) : they mean " (I used to frequent the temples), my parents being themselves ignorant people " and not ". . . without the knowledge of my parents ".

[2] *Instr.*, I, 1, 4 ; I, vii, 21 ; I, xxvi, 25 ; I, xxxiii, 2 ; *Carm. Apol.*, 3 ; 11 ; 83.

[3] *Instr.*, II, xxxix : *Commodianus mendicus Christi*, is the group of words obtained by reading the first letter of each verse of this piece from the bottom to the top.

[4] Cf. C. Weyman, *Miscell. zu lat. Dichtern*, printed by the IVth International Congress of Catholics at Freibourg (1898), p. 9 et s. Weyman appeals to Cassiodorus, 10th Collatio, in which the expression is used of one " qui de aliena largitate cotidianum poscit auxilium." For the ascetic spirit of Commodian, cf. *Instr.*, I, xxvi–xxviii, and *Carmen Apol.*, v, 579–616.

[5] Monceaux (III, 463 ; cf. 83) remarks upon the insistence with which Commodian solicits the alms of the faithful and scolds them for not giving enough. He regards Commodian as one of those *seniores laici* who (this practice is given as at the beginning of the IVth century, but it goes back to an earlier date without doubt) helped the Bishop in his work of administration.

[6] Gaza, in Syria : the ordinary ethnological term is *Gazensis ;* we find however *Gazeus*, at a rather later date.

[7] *Gazaeus*, derived from *gaza* or *gazum*, treasure, is not established elsewhere.

CHAPTER IV

THE EVE OF THE PEACE OF THE CHURCH

ARNOBIUS AND LACTANTIUS

BIBLIOGRAPHY

I. ARNOBIUS.—P.L., V, 718-1288 ; Reifferscheid, in C.V., vol. IV (1875). For the sole manuscript of Arnobius see Minucius Felix on a former page. The text of Arnobius has drawn the special attention of philologists : Meiser, in S.B.M., 1908 ; Lofstedt, *Arnobiana*, Lund, 1917 (cf. B. ph. W., 1917, 1291) ; Brakman, *Arnobiana*, Leyden, 1917 ; K. Kistner, *Arnobiana*, Progymn. St-Ingbert, Pfatz, etc. . . . A fresh edition of the *Adv. Nationes* is much to be desired.—Consult : Monceaux, III, 241-286.

II. LACTANTIUS.—P.L., VI and VII ; Brandt, in C.V., xix (1890) and xxvii (fasc. 1, 1893 ; fasc. ii, 1897). — Consult : René Pichon, *Lactance*, Paris, 1901 ; Monceaux, III, 287-359 ; Th. Stangl, *Lactantiana*, in Rh.M., LXX, 224-252. Brandt (*Wochensch. f. kl. Phil.*, 29 [1912], 1383) declares that a revision of his own edition is indispensable.—The question as to the authenticity of the *De Mortibus Persecutorum* has lost much of its importance since an almost unanimous agreement has been reached on this long-debated problem between the most authoritative critics. The work was one out of a collection of manuscripts bought by Colbert at the Convent of Moissac (Tarn-et-Garonne), on the advice of Baluze. The latter, when he published the work for the first time (1679), following a much spoilt manuscript of the IXth century (Bibl. Nat. 2627, *Colbert*, 1297), had no hesitation in identifying it with the *De Persecutione* attributed to Lactantius by St Jerome (*de Vir. Ill.*, lxxx). This assignment was almost at once contested by Columbus, in 1684, then by Dom le Nourry in 1710. Brandt, the editor of Lactantius in the *Corpus Script. Eccl. Lat.* has appraised the *rationes dubitandi* (S.B.W., vol. 120 [1890] and 125 [1891]). His reasons were very skilfully refuted by René Pichon (*Lactance*, p. 338 et s.), who won over the assent of Brandt himself (B. ph. W., 1903, 1257). With the exception of a few dissentients (v.g., Silomon, in *Hermes*, 1912, pp. 250-257), the authenticity is commonly accepted to-day. The same does not quite hold good for the two dedications to Constantine included in book I, 1, 13-16, and in book VII, xxvii, 2, of the *Instit. Div.* Brandt and Monceaux consider them to have been interpolated, for the triumphant tone of the author does not at all agree with the work as a whole, in which the suffering anger of an oppressed man is plainly visible. Pichon thinks that the opposition between these pieces and the rest of the *Institutiones* is exaggerated. It is possible, too, that Lactantius himself re-edited his *Inst. Div.* (see Batiffol, *La Paix constant. et le Cathol.*, Paris, 1914, p. 224 et s.). In fact, these dedications are wanting from certain excellent manuscripts. These same manuscripts likewise do not include three theological dissertations in which opinions of a very pronounced dualism are expressed. Monceaux (III, 302) regards them as subsequent additions. According to Pichon, these pieces are conformable to the train of ideas habitual with Lactantius who was rather uncertain as a theologian. Brandt ended by accepting Pichon's point of view (B. ph. W.).

III. Victorinus of Pettau.—P.L., V, 281-344 (reproducing Routh, R.S., III, 451-453, in the *De Fabrica Mundi*); Haussleiter, in C.V., vol. XLIX (1916). See later observations on the manuscripts.

SUMMARY

I. The question of Arnobius.—II. The *Adversus Nationes*. Arnobius and the Bible. His Metaphysical Conceptions.—III. The Christianity of Arnobius.—IV. His Polemics against Paganism.—V. The Rhetoric of Arnobius.—VI. The Opinion of Christians regarding him.—VII. Lactantius. His Life.—VIII. The *De Opificio Dei*.—IX. The *Institutiones Divinae*. Lactantius's Method of Apologetics. Plan of his Works.—X. The Blunders of Lactantius. The Salient Portions of his Work. Stratification of the Views of Lactantius.—XI. The *De Ira Dei*.—XII. The *De Mortibus Persecutorum*. Christian History.—XIII. Conclusions on Lactantius.—XIV. Victorinus of Pettau, first Latin Exegetist.—XV. The *Adversus Omnes Haereses*.

I

THE position which Arnobius occupies in Christian antiquity is exceptional and very curious. After having taught rhetoric all his life at Sicca-Veneria, in proconsular Africa, Arnobius was converted late in about his sixtieth year. His Bishop, a little distrustful of this labourer who had engaged at the eleventh hour, whom he had always known as being very violent against the Christians, demanded from him a pledge of his sincerity.[1] Arnobius thought he could do no better than to transfer to the service of the cause which he had just embraced his sustained eloquence, his concise erudition and his heavy irony. He wrote a work, the *Adversus Nationes*, which appeared about the year 300.[2] It is amusing to observe what this old man and improvised apologist understood of Christianity, and how he mingled adventitious ideas without troubling himself over their incongruities and without considering that his Christian readers might be offended.

II

THE *Adversus Nationes* comprises seven books. Arnobius begins by a refutation of a grievance the import of which Tertullian and St Cyprian have already made us understand.

[1] This story is related to us by St Jerome in *Ep.* LXX, 5.
[2] Probably between the years 304 and 310.

On all sides people were saying that since the Christians had appeared the human race had been afflicted with a thousand ills proving that the offended gods had abandoned the earth. Arnobius draws attention to the puerility of any argument fixing a date for the beginning of these scourges, whose very name goes back to most remote antiquity, so as to make them coincide with the coming of Christianity. How could any-one doubt that these ills proceeded from the general laws of the universe which are in no way subject to our convenience? In any case, there was nothing in the Christian doctrine to justify the wrath of heaven. From this doctrine Arnobius sketches the leading points, after his own fashion, in books I and II. Then he turns round on the pagans: you say that it is because of us the gods load humanity with misfortune. Not at all! If they exist, it is with you that they are angry on account of the gross conception which you have of them, and the incoherent rites by which you pretend to honour them. Books III to VII form the polemic of an ironical and vehement despiser of the Greco-Roman religion. And continually the same sarcastic question crops up: " Is it then on account of such mad conceptions that you persecute us? . . ."

What first of all strikes us in the *Adversus Nationes* is the almost total absence of quotations from Scripture. Arnobius unfolds his line of argument in the abstract; nowhere does he place his support upon the Sacred Books. We barely find three or four passages giving a more or less clear echo of them.[1] Is this discretion, so rarely found in Christian writings of the first centuries, the considered policy of Arnobius? In addressing himself to the pagans, did he avoid on principle laying weight on documents which the pagans could have challenged? This would be to give him a too subtile intention. In several places Arnobius confuses points, or labours them excessively, thereby purely and simply betraying his lack of knowledge. Thus he affirms that Christ was heard by the different nations whom He addressed as though He had spoken in the proper language of each one of them [2]—a manifest transposition of the facts reported on the Day of Pentecost in the Acts of the Apostles. A

[1] Compare Arnobius, C.V., vol. IV (1875), 1, 6 (p. 6, line 7), with *Matthew*, v, 49; ii, 6 (p. 108, l. 26), and *Romans*, xii, 7; ii, 65 (p. 101, l. 11), with *John*, x 7–9; xiv, 6, etc.
[2] 1, 46.

little further on, he greatly exaggerates the prodigies that followed the death of Christ : " Novitate rerum exterrita universa mundi sunt elementa turbata, tellus mota contremuit, *mare funditus refusum est,* aer globis involitus est tenebrarum *igneus orbis solis tepefacto ardore deriguit.*" [1] He had read the gospels very carelessly ! More singular still is his total lack of curiosity as regards the Old Testament. We might say that he had no idea of the filiation between Judaism and Christianity, nor of the link which united the New with the Old Testament. To the pagans who returned against him his accusation of anthropomorphism by bringing forward the anthropomorphisms of the Old Testament, he retorts in these words : " And let them not bring against us the fables of the Jews as if we also attributed different forms to God. . . . In reality, these fables do not concern us and have absolutely nothing in common with us ; or if, as people think, they have a community with us, you must look for more learned doctors who will teach you how to clear up the obscurity and the mysterious words of these writings." [2] Here we have a very rash repudiation and one which does not seem to have caused him any embarrassment. Again, if he had ever opened the New Testament, would he have insisted so much on declaring as incompatible the idea of anger and the idea of Divinity itself ? [3] The God of Arnobius is a God who is indifferent and peaceable, who is neither moved, nor given to vengeance. The Divine impassibility as he imagines it, has an altogether pagan and Epicurean quality. Remarkable minds like Tertullian and Clement of Alexandria had energetically combated this view, and, even at the time when Arnobius was writing, Lactantius devoted a whole work, the *De Ira Dei,* to refuting it. Arnobius has the appearance of considering as null and void all this long labour of Christian thought.

We find the same singularity in his metaphysical conceptions, for example, in what concerns the soul, its origin, its nature and its destinies. [4] In the eyes of Arnobius, it was veritable blasphemy to attribute to God the fatherhood of the soul—a presumptuous filiation invented by human pride. If the soul proceeded directly from God, would God

---

[1] 1, 59.   [2] iii, 12.
[3] i, 17 ; vi, 2 ; vii, 5 ; 36, etc.   [4] See book II.

have permitted that it should fall into so many moral and religious errors ? Would He not have foreseen the consequences of His act as Creator ? From the perfect, only the perfect could come forth : Plato saw this well, and Arnobius does not hesitate to place himself under his patronage. That the soul has for its author some demiurge, " inferior to God, although belonging to His court," [1] appears to him to be the most likely hypothesis. Fashioned in this manner, the soul was certainly corporeal. There was such a close solidarity between the life of the body and the life of the soul that these reciprocal influences implied an identity of material. Was it at least immortal ? in itself, it was not : it may become so when the case arises by virtue of its merits, and thanks to a special favour of God. If it has sinned, it will be plunged into the flames, and these flames will have the effect of rarefying it, and of destroying it little by little in cruel tortures. The immortality of the soul was quite conditional and subordinated to the efforts made in this life to know God and to follow His law. [2]

The principal points of this doctrine come from Plato for whom Arnobius does not spare flattering epithets and whose authority he willingly invokes. If he takes away from God the responsibility of having created souls, if he imagines them as being materially linked with the body up to the last *dijugatio*, it is because he is making use of the conceptions of Plato. He only formally separates himself from the philosopher to deny the pre-existence of souls. But it is not Plato only upon whom he draws. In Arnobius there is a whole series of intellectual influences which intersect each other and do battle in his thoughts. What he says of the demiurge, the artificer of the soul, singularly resembles certain Gnostic dreamings. His views on the corporeal nature of the soul are reminiscent of those of Tertullian in his *De Anima*. If we examine his theory of knowledge, we see that it is related to the empiric point of view of the Stoic school : for him, the soul is a *tabula rasa* on which impressions from without come to be inscribed, and only experimental knowledge can bring certitude. In flagrant contradiction, Arnobius only makes an exception of the idea

---

[1] ii, 36 (C.V., p. 77, 15).
[2] II, 32 and 61 (C.V., p. 74, 13 and 97, 16).

of God, which he declares to be innate. Certain vestiges of Neo-Platonism have been noticed in him. In fact, he is an example of the most surprising eclecticism, and he borrows his explanations in turn from the different systems of lay philosophy.

III

BUT what place then does Christianity occupy in such a complex whole ? Does it form only a secondary part of the edifice ? Does it play only a subordinate and purely accessory *rôle* ? To state this would be to come to a too rapid conclusion.

To begin with, Arnobius was veritably changed and converted by grace : " What blindness ! " he cries. " Up to now I still worshipped images that had come forth from the foundry, gods fashioned by blows of the hammer on the anvil, from the bones of elephants, from pictures, and garlands suspended from ancient trees ; when I saw a polished stone all glistening with oil, I adored it as though some power were present in it ; I paid my addresses to it, I asked favours from a senseless stone. . . . But now, led by so great a master (Christ) into the paths of truth, I know the value of all that, I pay my respect to Him who is worthy of respect, I no longer insult the name of God, and I render unto each one his due." [1] He thus whole-heartedly renounces his former self. I will add that there are certain truths in Christianity which Arnobius appears to have felt with force and sincerity : for example, the majesty of God, whose existence and all-power man recognises as it were spontaneously ; the goodness of Christ, and His divinity. Even here doubtless a scrupulous theologian might find much to reprehend. Arnobius had so much fear of lowering the notion of Divinity by making it have any points of contact with Humanity, that he establishes only a very feeble link between the Divinity and the Humanity of Christ.[2] And, from the purely literary point of view, how much want of taste ! Does he not go so far as to laud Christ in several passages with the same turn of words which had already served Lucretius in his praise of Epicurus ? [3] But if we except these relatively theological and unfortunate

[1] i, 39.   [2] Cf. Tixeront, *Hist. des Dogmes,* Paris, 1908, I, 443.
[3] Compare i, 32, and Lucretius, *de Nat. Rerum,* v, 1 et s. ; v, 471 et s. ; 281 et s.; 592 et s., etc. . . .

N

resemblances Arnobius speaks in a worthy manner of the Saviour and of the immense benefit brought by Him to humanity.

He likewise makes observations on the conditions regulating the acceptance of the Christian belief. Thus he sketches in book II some sort of theory of the necessity of " faith " for life. Every enterprise, he observes, postulates some preliminary faith; such is the absolute law of all our initiatives. Who makes a journey or a voyage, or enters into business transactions without firmly counting upon coming back to his home with his affairs brought to a satisfactory conclusion, etc. ? In the same way, every philosophic doctrine to which we adhere implies that we refer it in a more or less degree to the authority of a master. Therefore, why jeer at the Christians for attaching themselves to Christ ? They were doing nothing more than conforming to the normal methods of human action.

This theory of faith, in itself a legitimate concession to the intelligence, had already been put forward by Origen in his great work against Celsus,[1] and we can find other traces of it in Christian writers of an anterior date.[2] More than a century after Arnobius St Augustine was to give it a far higher meaning and to make of it a real " principle of reason." With Arnobius, it is only an occasional consideration from which he does not dream of deducing all the consequences. Also we must not expect to see him establishing his defence of Christianity on any very profound psychology.

He insists more on the powerlessness of human reason to discover the truth by its natural forces. Arnobius was the first in date of these hardy, and very probably rash apologists who based religious doctrine on philosophic Pyrrhonism. Confessions of incertitude from the great philosophers ; specious arguments on which the most contradictory metaphysical reasonings base their authority ; man's ignorance of the true explanation of the phenomena surrounding him ; the uselessness of his presence in the universe ; the basic equality of man and the animal in spite of the superiority which, in his pride, the former attributes to himself, and in a certain sense even the greater innocence of the animal,

---

[1] I, ii (Koetschau, in C.B., vol. I, pp. 63–64).
[2] V.g. Theophilus, ad Autol., 1, 8.

as an ox, in whose mouth Arnobius places a veritable speech for the prosecution against his master,[1] eloquently affirms,— such are the reasons upon which our author prides himself in order to counsel man to despise himself entirely. He is also as far removed as possible from the optimism of his pupil Lactantius who was so ready to marvel at the beauty and admirable arrangement of the human being. To Arnobius man was a creature without grace and without distinction, miserable and vile.[2] And his conclusion is that we must abandon vain speculations which exhaust our frail reason, in order to give ourselves entirely to God, *ad Dominum rerum tota mente atque anima proficisci*.[3]

IV

IN order to understand the real character of the work, we must remember that it is a speech for the prosecution which Arnobius develops far more than a piece of special pleading ; or rather, it is a furious assault with a prodigality of wounding phrases.[4] He takes no trouble to win over rebellious minds. His aim is only to confound and humiliate. Mythology is his butt ; it bears all the burden of his demonstration.

We must not suppose that the Christians were the first to be shocked at the " scandal " of mythology. The truth is that, if we put aside the *Iliad* and the *Odyssey*, wherein faith in the reality of the events belonging to mythology appears to be entire, lengthy protest had not ceased to make itself heard from the first awakening of critical reflection. There were very few thoughtful minds in Greece who refrained, from motives of respect, from giving expression to their reservations and from offering some more acceptable interpretation. The legends of the past shocked at once their moral and religious

---

[1] vii, 9 (C.V., p. 243, 13).
[2] " Nam quid in homine pulchrum est ? " (iii, 16).   " In humanis vero corporibus quidnam, quaeso, inerat pulchritudinis ? " (iv, 23).   Man was an "animal himself well saw the moral danger of this systematic lowering of man's dignity : *Inst. div.*, II, 1, 2 et s.
[3] ii, 60 (C.V., p. 96, 24).
[4] " O parvuli (Reiff., 28, 24) ; O mentes incredulae, difficiles, durae (34, 27) ; miserum et supervacuum " (ii, 38) ; " animal vile " (vii, 4), etc., etc. Lactantius O nescii (36, 7 ; 50, 13) ; O impii (159, 13) ; O sancti atque impolluti antistites religionum (118, 2) ; O theologi (181, 1) ", etc.

sense of what was fitting, and their reason. And it was on the score sometimes of morality and religion, and sometimes of reason, that they took up their attitude against it.[1]

Did the advocates of Christianity bring to bear any very new methods of exegesis? B. Aubé, whose learned works on the first centuries of our era are well known, wrote in one of his books that Christian polemics had made no fundamental additions to pagan criticism of mythology.[2] Speaking frankly, we cannot contradict him over that. The object the Christian writers had in view was not to interpret mythology, but to demonstrate it as infamous and ridiculous. Among the hypotheses bequeathed to them by Greek philosophy they were content to choose those which best suited their particular purpose. For the most part they confined themselves to seizing upon the evhemerist hypothesis[3] which had in their eyes the advantage of controverting all the pseudo-divine element in paganism on the most ordinary historical grounds. But on the other hand, not daring altogether to deny the prodigies proceeding from the oracles and magic of the pagans, they attributed them to demons. Other methods of explanation which had been tried before did not offer them any attraction. Or rather, they saw the danger of people drawing from them reasons for saving polytheism by lending a more or less philosophic appearance to the most impossible legends. This is why they refused all credence and even violently denounced them,—especially the Stoic method of exegesis, that last refuge of the defenders of Hellenism.

Their wellnigh constant method was irony. To obtain a correct idea of this we must read Arnobius especially. The *Adversus Nationes* is the most complete repertory of Christian criticism of mythology. Archæologists will there find a mass of information on pagan legends, and on the details of their rites and sacred ceremonies. We can clearly see that his erudition is not first-hand. Arnobius draws upon Clement

[1] See Paul Decharme's fine work, *la Critique des traditions religieuses chez les Grecs*, Paris, 1904.—Bodo von Borries, *Quid veteres philosophi de idololatria senserint*, Gottingen, 1918.

[2] *St Justin, Philosophe et Martyr*, 1875, p. 326.

[3] The fundamental conception which Evhemerus had put forth in his famous romance *The Ἱερὰ Ἀναγράφη* may be summed up as follows : " The gods were originally powerful kings whom their subjects, from gratitude or from flattery, deified after their death."

of Alexandria, Tertullian, and other more obscure authors,[1] without counting Cicero, whose *De Natura Deorum* furnished Christian writers with so many valuable resources.   But he developed the traditional themes with such ample fecundity that it is interesting to examine them in his book.   Arnobius was possessed of a realistic imagination of exceptional vigour. His triumph is to seize upon some metaphysical hypothesis, or popular belief, and deduce from it accurately and with the most precise details all the ridiculous consequences which he perceives in it.   The way in which he relates the adventures of Jupiter should be read.   Without any compunction at the most licentious pictures, this pitiless satirist describes the ridiculous positions to which the libidinous god had to stoop ; he imagines all the circumstances of his seductions with a copious *verve* with which the reader ends by being amused in spite of the puerile tinsel of his phraseology.

V

On the whole, Arnobius may be considered as a kind of Voltaire, far less polished, but possessed of an irony almost as impetuous as that of Voltaire himself.   He derives the legends of mythology by a procedure very like that which the Voltaire of the *Taureau Blanc* or of the *Lettres d'Amabed* was to employ against the Bible.   I will add that he was in addition what Voltaire never became in the slightest degree—the most verbose of rhetoricians.   In reading him we seem to be hearing his sonorous and indefatigable voice ; we feel him delighting himself with the amplitude of his periods and the fecundity of his vocabulary.   No theme comes his way without its supplying him with all that it is capable of producing, and even more.[2]   The art of amplification, understood in the most superficial sense, could not be illustrated by

[1] For example, a certain Cornelius Labeo, whom he does not mention by name. He was a philosopher, probably a Neo-Platonist of the Ist or IInd century A.D., who was much interested in the national religion of Rome.   In comparing the *Adv. Nationes* with texts of St Augustine and Macrobius, wherein Labeo is explicitly mentioned, we can see that Arnobius often took him as his point of departure, in order to refute him.   Cf. Kroll, Rh. M., 1916, 309–357 ; Boehm, *De Corn. Labeonis aetate*, Konisberg, 1913 ; Bousset, in *Archiv. f. Religions wiss.*, XVIII, 137.

[2] Thus I, xxxviii (Reiff., p. 24, l. 29 et s.), when enumerating the benefits conferred by Christ, he allows himself to be drawn on to attribute to Him some which do no less than make Jesus to be an initiator into the secrets of universal matter.

better examples than those which may be drawn from the
Adversus Nationes. Interrogations repeated up to the fif-
teenth and twentieth time, apostrophes, exclamations,
antitheses, alliterations, anaphora—the whole arsenal of the
schools can be found. The verbal dexterity of Arnobius is
extraordinary. We suspect that he must have been a great
consulter of glossaries.[1] He delivers his words with the
prodigality of a man sure of not drying up his sources. He
has always two, three, four, or five words for the same idea,
and instead of choosing one of them he piles them all up.[2]
In addition, his tenacious memory furnishes him with a large
quantity of recollections borrowed from classic writers,
and even from the most ancient Latin authors.[3] In his
rounded periods he observes the metrical rules of the *clausula*.[4]
All this goes to make up a style of singular *verve* in which,
as I have said, we end by finding a species of entertainment
which is not of a very high order.

VI

WE shall not be surprised after all this that Arnobius enjoyed
in Christian antiquity only a very mediocre *prestige*. When
St Jerome speaks freely of him, that is to say in his letters
(not in his *De Viris Illustribus*, in which the exigencies of
apologetics are the ruling note), he shows what he makes of
him (*Ep.* lviii, 10). He is moreover almost the sole writer
to make any mention of him. The famous decretal attributed to Pope Gelasius quotes the writings of Arnobius as
" apocryphal," that is to say, not as being unauthentic,
but as being very suspect from the doctrinal point of view.
The same suspicions are to be found in modern times. The
Mémoires of Trévoux, the organ of the Jesuits, only consents
to exonerate Arnobius from Bayle's insidious criticisms after
observing " that he does not hold a sufficiently distinguished

---

[1] Cf. Tschiersch, *De Arnobii Studiis Latinis*, Jena, 1905, p. 39 et s.

[2] Ex.: Reifferscheid, p. 16, 30 ; 164, 16 ; 24, 22 (. . . quid fecerint, egerint,
pertulerint, actitarint) ; p. 58, 1 : " qui estis unius mentis et per easdem vias
placitorum inceditis unitate " ; p. 175, 3 : " victos somnos atque altissimi soporis
oblivione demersos, etc. . . ."

[3] Tschiersch, *op. cit.* (Lucretius, p. 8 et s. ; Plautus, p. 11 et s. ; Cato, p. 16
et s. ; Varro, p. 18 et s.).

[4] Spindler, *de Arnobii genere dicendi*, Strasbourg, 1901, p. 30–32 ; Th. Lorenz,
de clausulis Arnobianis, Breslau, 1910.

rank among the Fathers to urge us keenly to take up his defence." Further, just as with Lactantius, the *Mémorial* refuses him the title of Father. "We should not call them Fathers of the Church while attributing error to them, but rather only give this title to those to whom the common and recognised belief of the faithful accords it."

A Christian who knew nothing of Scripture, or made very little use of it; who misunderstood some of the leading ideas of Christianity and, I will add, formally proscribed all exterior forms of worship,[1] was in fact a very strange Christian! It is matter for astonishment that Arnobius was never invited by his Bishop to revise his work. How are we to believe that the latter could have declared himself satisfied with this token furnished by his white-haired catechumen? However this may be, the interest attaching to the case of Arnobius lies in the contradictions offered by a line of thought which had for long been fashioned on the reading of profane works, and had then been remodelled by a late *crise religieuse* which, powerless to bring into unity these contradictory influences, serenely placed the most anomalous assertions side by side in the same work.

VII

LACTANTIUS too is not an intelligence of the first order. Gaston Boissier often quotes him in his *Fin du Paganisme*, but he did not judge him to be sufficiently "representative" to devote to him a special study. M. René Pichon who wrote a lengthy volume on him instinct with very scrupulous literary sentiment, acknowledges with a good grace that his author is mediocre, "in the Latin sense of the word,—and a little also in the French sense."[2] The very fact that he has been called the Cicero of the Christians,[3] and that he was wellnigh the equal of the classic masters whom he admired in the purity of his style, is proof to us that he kept himself to well-worn grooves: a more vigorous and fresher mode of

---

[1] vi, 2 ; vii, 1 et s.

[2] *Op. cit.*, p. viii.

[3] It was Pic de la Mirandole who gave him that title (*Opera Omnia*, 1573, p. 21). But quite early his name had been associated with that of his model of predilection : cf. St Jerome. *Ep.* lviii, 10 : "quos (libros) si legere volueris, dialogorum Ciceronis ἐπιτομήν (abridgment) reperies."

thought would have upset this fine classic harmony. Even when we exert ourselves to say something good of him it would be puerile to endeavour to cover up the weaknesses in the train of thought of this conscientious professor, whose traditionalism was more pronounced than his critical sense was acute. Nevertheless we carry away with us after reading his works the impression that, notwithstanding his too exclusively literary culture, Lactantius counts in the long series of the first apologists; that the attempt which he made possesses its own originality, and reveals certain interesting modifications in the state of mind of the lettered Christians.

He styled himself L. Caecilius Firmianus qui et Lactantius.[1] People have sometimes tried to make him out an Italian, from Firmum in Picenum. But the ethnological derivative from Firmum would be Firmanus, not Firmianus. From St Jerome's notice of him (*De Vir. Ill.*, lxxx), we may conclude that he was an African. The chronology of his life is little known. However, we possess certain distinguishing marks. He was born a pagan in about the year 250. He studied under Arnobius at Sicca. Nowhere does he mention him by name as his instructor, even in the passage of the *Institutiones Divinae* in which he gives the names of his predecessors. We know that Arnobius wrote his apology very late in life. He appears, besides, to have exercised no influence on the mind of Lactantius. The latter in his turn took up the teaching of rhetoric.[2] He acknowledges that his ability in the art of eloquence was of limited extent, and that he never appeared in the Forum.[3] All the same, he must have acquired a certain reputation for he was nominated for the post of professor in that subject at Nicomedia in Bithynia. Since the winter of the year 285 the town had become the place of residence of Diocletian and had acquired all the importance of an imperial city. In this entirely Greek town he had only a few pupils and was obliged to take to writing : " *Penuria discipulorum* ob graecam videlicet civitatem ad scribendum se contulit," said St Jerome.[4] Possibly this " *penuria* " was not felt until the active measures taken against the Christians deprived

---

[1] The MSS. vary between Caecilius and Caelius. An inscription found at Cirta (C.I.L., viii, 7241) mentions an L. Caecilius Firmianus who must have belonged to the same family. The " qui et Lactantius " is the *signum* or familiar name.
[2] *Inst. div.*, I, 1, 8.
[3] *Ibid.*, 10.
[4] *De Vir. Ill.*, lxxx.

him of his official title of rhetorician. Meanwhile, he had been converted.[1] The terrible persecution of 303 came. Lactantius did not suffer personally any punishment, and remained in Bithynia until 305 or even 306.[2] But when, after the abdication of Diocletian (May 305), Galerius made war upon the schools, Lactantius decided to leave Nicomedia.[3] We do not know where he took refuge during this time of trouble. Possibly he came back to Nicomedia between 311 and 313, when Galerius issued his Edict of toleration (10th April, 311).[4] He had experienced some very hard times, lacking even the necessaries of life, if we are to believe St Jerome's account.[5] His last years were more peaceful than he could have hoped. Constantine appointed him to teach Latin literature to his son Crispus born in 307. Lactantius was then " in extrema senectute." [6] He died doubtless at Trèves but we do not know at what exact date.

VIII

THE first work of Lactantius preserved to us is entitled *De Opificio Dei*.[7] Up till then, he had confined himself to poetry and to the somewhat dry walks of the old learning.[8] Now that he had become a Christian he set himself to do some good work for the use of those whom he called " the philosophers of our sect." The work is not based on the circum-

[1] *Inst. Div.*, I, 1, 8 ; *Epit.*, xliii, 3 ; *de Ira Dei*, 11, 2 ; cf. St Augustine, *de Doctr. Christ.*, II, lxi.

[2] *Inst. Div.*, V, xi, 15.

[3] *Ibid.*, V, ii, 2.

[4] We conclude this from certain indications in the *de Mort. Persec.*, xxxv, 1 and 4 ; xlviii, 1. See, however, Pichon, *op. cit.*, p. 360.

[5] *Chronical* (II, p. 191 Schoene).

[6] *Ibid.*

[7] Composed in 303–4 (Harnack) or at the end of 305 (Monceaux).

[8] St Jerome (*De Vir. Ill.*, lxxx) attributes to him : 1. A *Symposium*. The " tabulated form " arose in Greece and had enjoyed much favour in the philosophic schools (Plato, Xenophon, Aristotle, Aristoxenes of Tarentum, Hieronymus of Rhodes, Prytanis, Epicurus, Persaeus, Lucian of Samosata, Plutarch, etc.). Cf. *Cena Trimalchionis*, in the *Satiricon* of Petronius ; 2. A Ὁδοιπορικόν, an itinerary from Africa to Nicomedia in hexameters ; 3. A work entitled *Grammaticus*, doubtless dealing with questions of grammar ; 4. Four books of letters to Probus, two books addressed to Severus and two books to Demetrianus (these are quoted by St Jerome, *Ep.* lxxxiv, 7, and *Com. in Gal.* II, 4 (P.L., xxvi, 373)). Pope Damasus pronounced these letters very wearisome on account of their length and for the scant interest of the subjects treated therein (the rules of versification, geography, philosophy) : cf. St Jerome, *Ep.* xxxv, 2. The date of these different collections is uncertain ; 5. Two books to Asclepiades, who had himself dedicated a book on Providence to Lactantius (cf. *Inst. Div.*, VII, iv, 17).

stances of current events although the author makes allusion
in it to the clouds held in the sky over the Christians.[1] He
addresses himself to one Demetrianus, a former pupil of his
own, a Christian, and, without giving to his explanations
any supporting aid from Scripture, endeavours to vindicate
Providence from the attacks of certain philosophic schools,
who denounced any Divine work in connection with man,
his soul and his body. Cicero had already undertaken this
task;[2] but, according to Lactantius, he had not understood
how to draw all that might have been possible from such rich
material. To counter the pessimism affected by the Epi-
cureans in order to discredit the very notion of Providence,
Lactantius demonstrates that man is not at all degraded to
the point to which those paradoxical minds had debased him,
since he had to his credit language and reason, which made up
for what he lacked,[3] and that even those very people who
placed the animal superior to him would not go to the
extreme limit of exchanging their alleged meanness as men
against the stupidity of the brutes.[4] Then analysing in
detail the physical constitution of man, he shows the perfect
adaptation of his organs to their end. Next he passes on to
the nature of the soul, whose creation he deliberately attributes
to God, in contradistinction to his former tutor Arnobius.
Here and there some rather *naïve* remarks make us laugh [5]
(similar works by Fénelon and Bernardin of Saint-Pierre
have some difficulty in guarding against these trifling ironies) :
taking him as a whole, this spiritual apology, thoroughly
imbued with Aristotle, Cicero, and Varro, is of value from its
clearness and the æsthetic feeling which dominates it, as
well as its eye to usefulness which is thoroughly in accordance
with Roman tradition.

IX

As soon as he had written the *De Opificio Dei*, Lactantius
occupied his mind with a work of quite another bearing,

---

[1] I, 1 ; I, 7 ; xx, 1.
[2] *De Rep.*, IV, l. 1 ; *de Nat. Deorum*, II, xlvii ; *de Finibus*, III, xviii.
[3] " Quae desunt ratio rependit " (iii, 5).
[4] iii, 12.
[5] V.g. xiii · " Conglobata in nates caro quam sedendi officio apta ! "

and began preparing the materials.[1] In writing his *Institutiones Divinae*, Lactantius had a very clear view of the object which he wished to attain, and of the proper method of approaching it. Formed by his education and also by his profession to hold in esteem things intellectual, he had often suffered from the cultured contempt lavished by educated pagans on Christianity. He himself quite appreciated the fact that those amongst the Christians who constituted themselves the interpreters of divine truths were not always up to the level of their task.

This feeling of inferiority, so painful for his *amour propre* as a proselyte, appears to have been emphasised in Lactantius by the writings of two opponents of Christianity whom he had known when he was teaching rhetoric in Bithynia.[2] The scholarly art and the cruelly skilful arguments made use of by one of them had inflamed him with an ardent desire to refute them, and with them, all those who either in Greek or Latin had accomplished the same detestable task.

It was thus to educated minds that he wished to address himself by preference. Not by any means in any spirit of lofty superiority as was the case with the Gnostic. In nowise did he despise the humble. He knew better than anyone that religion found access more easily to simple and pure hearts because they had fewer secret antipathies to it.[3] But he marks out in his mind the audience which he wished more particularly to convince.

This end dictates the principal features of his methods. Lactantius claims to be making a literary apology adorned with every attraction of style, and capable of charming the most disdainfully punctilious minds. He is not ashamed to confess it; and the desire to write well is co-ordinated in him with a more lofty design, which is to obtain access to minds still obstinate whom he must convince at all costs.

---

[1] *De Opif. Dei*, xv, 6; xx, 2. The *Institutiones* appeared between 304 and 313.

[2] *Inst. Div.*, V, ii. He mentions neither of them by name. One of them was a philosopher by profession: Porphyry has been suggested, but Porphyry had written a work in fifteen books against the Christians. Now Lactantius speaks of a work in three volumes. It is, besides, doubtful if Porphyry was living at the time of Lactantius. The second was a judge. He was referring probably to Hierocles, the Neo-Platonist, the author of a Λόγος φιλαλήθης προς τοὺς χριστιανούς. For the intellectual condition of pagan society at the beginning of the IVth century read some penetrating pages in Father Batiffol's *La Paix Constantinienne et le Catholicisme*, 1914, p. 142 et s.

[3] *Inst. Div.*, VII, 1, 12.

In addition, he understood that the days of pure and simple refutation had passed, and that in face of the imposing systems of pagan philosophy, he must erect an edifice more firmly held together and of a cohesion which should be of a far superior kind. As was to be the case with Bossuet at a later date, he thought that for the defence of Christian doctrine the better part was to " la proposer simplement." The title, *Institutiones*, borrowed from the language of the law, is also significant. Lactantius is the first Latin apologist to offer to the men and women of his time a complete doctrine, elementary without doubt, but connected throughout by the singleness of his inner principle and capable of giving satisfaction to minds keenly appreciative of logic and harmony. Here we have no vague spiritual metaphysics : a whole history of religion is unfolded, a complete moral system is stated, and an entire philosophy is offered for acceptance, dominated by the doctrine of a Providence, the Christian doctrine *par excellence*. We are dealing with a thorough and fully conscious Christian who in his desire to communicate his belief to others does not disguise any portion of it nor extenuate any requirement of faith. As M. Thamin has happily expressed it, the *Institutiones* are " la véritable *Somme* des premières années du IV. siècle."

Newer still is the method of discussion which Lactantius imposed upon himself and which he faithfully followed. Addressing unbelievers, he did not wish to propose arguments which predicated faith in order that their validity might be appreciated. Thus he deliberately puts on one side the testimony of Scripture. It was useless to make use of Scripture to convince minds who judged it to be *vanam, fictam, commentitiam*. In his treatise *Ad Demetrianum* he blames St Cyprian for having so constantly had recourse to it. Proofs taken from the Holy Books were assuredly excellent in themselves, but only for Christians. Others must be convinced by arguments from comparison, " *argumentis et ratione*." When he decided to bring forward some sacred text, he always took care to corroborate it by extracts from other sources in the same sense, which the pagans could not reject. Thus he makes appeal to the authority of philosophers, historians and poets, and to the *carmina sacra*, and oracles, for those whom profane writers would otherwise have left cold. His literary tastes made this excellent method easy and agreeable to him. Sometimes we even see literary recollections intruding into his views at moments when we might have hoped for a less literary fervour : a reminiscence of the *In Verrem* comes rather coldly in connection with the crucifixion of Jesus Christ (IV, xviii). As a rule, however, he restrains them and adroitly makes them serve his purpose.

The two first books (*De Falsa Religione* and *De Origine Erroris*) are given up to a criticism of polytheism : no other point of view of the author is developed in it.

Book III, *De Falsa Sapientia*, has for its object to prove the falsity of pagan philosophy, its contradictions, and its uselessness in practice. Lactantius has little love for the philosophers although his strictures are unequally distributed between the different schools. He treats them very harshly : the arbitrary nature of their constructions, sometimes too the lie direct which their bad morals give to principles which they proclaim so loudly, irritate him and he delivers against them a strong attack. He goes so far as to say that their virtues, if by any chance they *are* virtuous, are as if they did not exist. This is because the echoes of the persecution still rumble in the *Institutiones*, and because certain philosophers had not shown themselves to be the least implacable enemies of the Christian. Moreover the tactics imposed by Lactantius upon himself, as well as his own loyalty, restrained him as a rule on the brink of the abusive exaggeration into which Tertullian had fallen. To defame without measure the leaders of pagan thought would have been to discredit points of agreement which he selected between *their* ideas and Christianity. He savoured too much of a Cicero or a Seneca to believe that even though lacking the faith human reason could not catch any gleam of light ; and it was upon points common to both, and undisputed, found in almost all moral writings (VI, ii, 16–18), that he claims to base the sound foundations of his own in order to make them as broad as possible.

From Book IV (*De Vera Sapientia et Religione*) onwards, Lactantius, without entirely renouncing polemics, sets himself to build up rather than to criticise. He demonstrates the indissoluble union between " wisdom " and religion. He develops the cardinal articles of his faith : God, Christ, miracles, the Incarnation, the Church and heresies. In Book V (*De Justitia*), he makes a study of the idea of " justice," which had been notoriously confused in pagan philosophy. Book VI (*De Vero Cultu*), establishes the fundamental principles of Christian morality, so far as it proceeded from God, its true origin. Lastly in Book VII (*De Vita Beata*), he approaches the highest problems : the wherefore of creation, of the immortality of the soul, and the problem of our latter end ; and he closes his work with an exhortation to fight the good fight for God.

The *Epitome*, by the testimony of Lactantius himself written some time after the *Institutiones* at the request of one Pentadius, reproduces its essential points in a much briefer form, with corrections of details which prove that Lactantius had reconsidered his plan in order the better to adapt it to the daily life of the Christians. It is like an amended second edition of the *Institutiones* after the elimination of useless developments, repetitions and quotations from profane authors.

X

VOLTAIRE showed himself greatly amused over the errors of " that man Lactantius whom the students at the Alexandrian school of his time would have derided if they had deigned to cast their eyes over his rhapsodies." [1] As a matter of fact, it would be easy to draw attention to his insufficiencies from the critical point of view.

With the same credulity as his predecessors (with the exception of St Irenæus and Origen), he makes use of the Sibylline oracles, and of the compilations which had come wholesale from Jewish or Christian hands in which he thought he found so many clinching confessions wrenched from the pagan Sibyls by the force of truth. He had an excellent opportunity of proving any analogies existing between these predictions and his own ideas. He does not suspect either that the books attributed to Hermes Trismegistus might have been written after the advent of Christianity by pagans desirous of making them compete with Christianity itself and of defending the national religion. Impressed by the wonderful knowledge of Trismegistus, and with his marvellous

[1] *Dict. philos.*, article *Ciel matériel.*

similarity to Christian thought, he is happy to bring his example before the pagans in order to prove to them that they were wrong in rejecting his teaching which was so very well adapted to the highest views of their religious philosophy.

Thus a portion of his argument rests simply on wrong interpretations. As a theologian, he does not count. He is a far from trustworthy exponent, and some of his interpretations are wholly lacking in taste.[1] He recklessly plunges into dreams of the Millennium at a moment when, at least in the East, they were tending to disappear under the influence of wiser explanations ; and he is even pleased to give lengthy descriptions of the phases of the strange apocalypse which he announces.[2] His fantastic eschatology is all the more surprising in that the entire work of Lactantius is decidedly that of a man offering a doctrine applicable to a long continuity of mankind. Now he declares that these appalling prodigies would happen before two hundred years.[3] He passively accepts a tradition which should have been repugnant to him, and classes himself among those disciples of the letter, *solius litterae discipuli*, whose superficial exegesis the great Origen when treating of this question of the Millennium, had already denounced more than fifty years before.[4]

We must understand then that Lactantius was possessed of an intelligence of no very great compass. " Utinam tam nostra adfirmare potuisset quam facile aliena destruxit ! "[5] St Jerome mournfully said. Whence is it that each time that he touches upon moral questions, he interests and almost moves us ? It is no longer the aggressive and rough dialectic of Tertullian, or the rather despondent language of St Cyprian : we meet with fine intuitions, and all the *clairvoyances* of a delicate soul which really feels the truth of Christianity and which knows how to make it appeal to the heart. In truth, what is perhaps the most novel trait in Lactantius is the really profound sense which he possesses

---

[1] E.g., *Inst. Div.*, IV, viii, 7.
[2] *Inst. Div.*, VII, xiv–xxvi.
[3] *Ibid.*, VII, xxv, 5.—We may note the following expressions : " The cause of this desolation and of this carnage will be that the name of Rome, which now rules the universe (it costs me much to say this, but I say it because it must happen), the Roman name will be effaced from the earth. The Empire will go back to the East ; once more the East will reign, and the West will be under its heel."
[4] *Periarch.*, II, ii, 2 (P.G., xi, 241–2).
[5] *Ep.* lviii, 10.

of the moral efficaciousness and of the renovation which it has brought to the soul of mankind.

No one before Lactantius had better grasped the difference between the two religions, Christian and pagan, the one consisting principally in the reform of the will by adhesion to certain doctrines bound together and entirely dependent on a God conceived as Father and as Master ; [1] the other resting wellnigh solely on rites in which the " fingers " alone had a part,[2] and which exacted neither purity of heart, assent of the intelligence, nor a right intention. In the love of God lay the norm of every true Christian. Therefore, in order to bring unity to his interior life, the Christian must not suffer the wholly pagan divorce of religion from intelligence. He must not form his philosophy in one way, and his religious life in another, but must identify his religion with his philosophy, the one interpenetrating the other, the one being the other in its foundation. *In sapientia religio et in religione sapientia est.*[3]

In another place, on meeting with a definition of virtue included in some verses of the satirical poet Lucilius, he shows how virtue in the mind of the pagans consisted in *knowing* where good and evil are to be found. This definition is far too intellectual to his taste. What use is there in knowing where good and evil are to be found, if the will is not sufficiently strong to turn us towards the one and away from the other ? Knowledge is a thing extrinsic to the soul, our will lies in our inmost heart and must be the moving spirit. Moreover, to do good implied that we know already what it is, in such a way that the principle advanced by Lucilius, which was false because incomplete, entered into a juster and more comprehensive principle (VI, v).

Again elsewhere he discusses with penetration a statement of the philosopher Carneades. Carneades maintained that the man who would be wholly just cannot escape from falling sometimes into evident follies, since he will speak or act against his most certain interests. An honest man who owns an insanitary house, and who at the moment of selling it feels himself bound in conscience to make known to the purchaser

---

[1] *Inst.,* IV, iii.
[2] Ritus ejus in manu et digitis est (IV, iii, 9), ritum ad solos digitos pertinentem (V, xix, 29).
[3] IV, iii.

its state ; or a man who, in a shipwreck, seeing one weaker than he supporting himself on a plank, shrinks from seizing upon it, and prefers to die rather than to commit an injustice— such a man cannot fail to be taken for a fool. From the purely human point of view, replies Lactantius, this argument cannot be gainsaid. It had caused much embarrassment to Cicero. It was clear that if we limited everything to things of earth, even egoism became right reason, and sacrifice was folly or pure illusion. But if, on the other hand, we hold the doing of our duty by obeying God to be our foremost concern, the sense of the words was changed as it were. Wisdom, as conceived by Carneades, was but a snare and delusion ; folly, on the contrary, was what he exalted under the name of wisdom, in responding to one's immediate interest even though it be to the hurt of another. To the man holding the true principle, everything was clear ; to the man who was ignorant of it, everything remained obscure and disconcerting.

Many other passages could likewise prove to us that in places Lactantius reached the real foundation of the Christian spirit. And what gives a real interest to the study of the *Institutiones* is that we find very different tendencies inter- mingled and confused in them, some the legacy of the past, and others indications of a new spirit. His writings contain more traces than we might think of the *intransigeant* attitude hostile to every concession which had animated certain writers of the first centuries. Lactantius had some liking for logic carried to extreme lengths, the weapon dear to Ter- tullian which, if carried out to the letter, would have extin- guished the possibility of any social life for the Christian and would have cut him off from the civil. Neither trade nor war concerned the Christian : [1] it is true that Lactantius immediately admits that necessity may constrain him, but, only for a moment, and he adhered to the old mistrust which had so long dwelt in the minds of Christians of strict observance against *cupiditas acquirendi* and against the shedding of blood. Lactantius is so unbending over the *Non occides* that in his view a Christian has not even the right to require the penalty of death against an accused man, for " it was equally criminal to kill people by word as by the sword." [2] More severe than Tertullian,[3] who only condemned

---

[1] V, xvi, 2, and I, xviii.　　[2] VI, xx.　　[3] See the *De Idolol.*, xiv.

O

art in so far as it ministered to pagan worship, Lactantius discountenances it without any extenuation. More ruthless than Clement of Alexandria, he denounced perfumes and flowers : if God created them, it was in order that man might exercise his virtue by not making use of them. As regards music, he only authorised it on condition that it be consecrated to the praise of God.[1]

These traits of absolutism are so much the more surprising because, taken as a whole, his work is of a moderate and tranquil tone. Did so much rigorousness enter into the heart of this " University Christian " ? Was he then an implacable adversary of the world in which he lived ? Not at all. He was possessed of a very lively sentiment of the majesty of Rome : he did not believe in the eternity of Rome since he was convinced that the world was shortly coming to an end, but in predicting her fall, he could not help himself from trembling at an announcement which was almost a blasphemy : *Horret animus dicere*.[2] Let me further add that Lactantius had nothing about him as a rule of the intemperate ascetic who derives a sour pleasure from hurling defiance at all the instincts of human nature. He experienced no misgivings on the lawfulness of marriage, on flight in times of persecution, or on a liberal amnesty in matters of penance.

How can we reconcile such irreproachable uprightness and so just a sense of what may be demanded from human frailty, with the violent extremes of thought to which we have just drawn attention ? These incongruities must be explained by the diverging influences which weighed upon his mind. Lactantius was at once a man of tradition and a man of his own time. On one side of him he was very respectful of all that he inherited from past generations of Christians. He even accepted, as we have seen, beliefs already almost superannuated, such as the Millennium, and introduced them somewhat artificially into the material of his work. A horror of war, disdain for commerce, a distrust of all that renders life on earth smoother and more attractive were forms of sentiment which were survivals of a former state of mind, that of the first Christian communities, or at least of certain elements contained in those communities.

On another side, however, Lactantius did not isolate himself from the surroundings in which he was living. We

---

[1] VI, xx, 16.   [2] VII, xvi, 2 ; cf. xxv, 7.

know with what decision he inaugurated a novel method in apologetics, more scientific and more accessible to those whom he wished to win. He must have understood the moral problems which changing times presented. He belonged to a period when the masses were streaming into the Church, when the Church herself was shortly to seal a pact of alliance with the Empire, thanks to which all material obstacles paralysing her free scope were to be removed. Would it be possible henceforth to uphold the Kingdom of God at so high a level above so many hesitating and lukewarm souls ? Must not a system of morality which was strained and seeking after extremes be made more supple, and while preserving virtue and doctrine, give the preference to more moderate solutions ? His good sense said " yes," but the numbing influence of the old rigorism suggested " no " ; and something of these contradictory tendencies which disputed a place in his thoughts and gained the upper hand each in turn, remained in his theological reasonings.

XI

The *De Ira Dei* is plainly announced in the *Institutiones Divinae :* " Some people think that anger is absolutely foreign to God, in as much as God is not subject to passions, which are violent upheavals of the soul, and that every living thing is doomed to perish which experiences the action of their shock.   This thesis shatters the very foundation of true religion.   But let us leave for the moment this question of the anger of God : the material is too abundant and I will defer it for more ample development in a special work." [1]

The following are the terms of reference presented by this problem from the philosophic point of view.

The God of the Old Testament was a severe God, sometimes even cruel ; who loves, hates, is irritated, and takes vengeance : " And I will execute great vengeance upon them, rebuking them in fury : and they shall know that I am the Lord, when I shall lay my vengeance upon them " (Exek. xxv, 17).   Now the idea of God which had been developed in the Greek philosophic schools implied on the contrary ἀπάθεια impassibility, amongst the Divine attributes. On this point,

[1] *Inst. Div.*, II, xvii, 4.

they were almost all in agreement. " Num iratum timemus Jovem ? " Cicero asks in his *De Officiis*, III, 102, where he gives an explanation, as we know, of Greek thought. And he replies : " At hoc quidem commune est omnium philosophorum . . . nunquam nec irasci Deum nec nocere."

The Jewish and Hellenic conceptions were therefore in absolute opposition to each other. Hence arose a great difficulty for minds formed in the Greek school, whose faith forbade them to sacrifice any portion of the Old Testament.

It is curious to see how this conflict of views for some possessed extreme importance, while for others it remained null and void, or of little account. Thus the apologists of the IInd century, Justin, Aristides, etc., in their restrained commerce with profane philosophy accepted the notion of ἀπάθεια—a complaisance which in no wise hindered them from making allusions to the ὀργή Θεοῦ. How these matters could be reconciled they have not troubled to tell us. Similarly, among the Latins at the beginning of the IVth century, Arnobius, as we have seen, insisted with such warmth upon the absolute necessity of the Divine impassibility, that we are justified in asking ourselves how he accommodated his views with the Bible, or even if he had ever read it. There were also others (such as Cyprian and Commodian) who, entirely leaning to the practical, and desirous only for the interests of discipline, brandished over the sinner the threat of the Divine anger without thinking of regarding it from the philosophic point of view.

But for a goodly number of ecclesiastical writers this was a real problem which they felt bound to discuss and to solve. The influence exercised by Greek philosophy on the thought of those whom we might imagine to be most unbending, is striking. Thus Tertullian, in his polemics against Marcion who had taken upon himself to point out the " anthropopathisms " of the Old Testament in order to draw from them a conclusion as to the inferior quality of the God of the Jews. The features to which Marcion took offence —the picture of a God provoked to anger and prompt to vengeance—were just those of which Tertullian was most enamoured. Nevertheless, the objections of the heresiarch moved him more than he cared to acknowledge. This was because he felt that they were inspired by Greek thought,

which alarmed him, whatever he might have said about it.
Also, after having brought divers arguments against it,—
texts from Scripture proving that Jesus Himself had been
a " jealous God " ; [1] teachings of St Paul on God the avenger
and lover of justice ; [2] the folly of taking literally that illusion
of language by which we imagine the Divine nature to be
entirely similar to human nature and susceptible of the same
shortcomings,[3]—we see him making the most unexpected
concession : he admits that it is the Son, the Son alone, who,
destined from all eternity to assume contact with humanity,
invested Himself in some manner from the beginning with the
sentiments and passions of mankind ; that it is He who rages,
repents, pardons, and shows Himself to the Patriarchs in the
Old Testament : and during that time, the Father remained
invisible in His transcendent majesty.[4]

Origen traced out the solution which the Greek Church
should favour. Taking inspiration from Philo, he admitted
that God has acted in regard to man as man himself acts in
regard to the child : God feigns to make experiment of human
affection (anger, repentance, etc. . . .) in order the better
to lead him into the paths of salvation ; but it would be
puerile to take literally the expressions used in the Old Testament, which are adapted to the feeble mentality of the generality of mortals,—for the Divine Essence is excluded from all
" passion."

Lactantius leaves these discussions outside his programme.
They appear to have only a very small interest for him.
More of a jurist than a philosopher, he takes up a very
different point of view. " Sine ira Deum esse credentes
dissolvunt omnem religionem " : [5] " Omne imperium metu
constat, metus autem per iram. . . . Deus autem habet
imperium, ergo et iram, qua constat imperium, habeat
necesse est." [6] To dispute this Divine aptitude was to do
no less than to destroy the doctrine of a Providence. If
God is not angered against the impious, neither does He
cherish the just. The very idea of Providence comprehends
that of a God who knows how to punish just as He knows also

---

[1] *Adv. Marc.*, IV, xxvii.   [2] *Ibid.*, V, xiii.   [3] *Ibid.*, II, xvi.
[4] Cf. *Adv. Prax.*, xvi ; *Adv. Marc.*, II, xxvii : " Igitur quaecunque exigitis
Deo digna, habebuntur in Patre invisibili incongressibilique *et placido*, et, ut ita
dixerim, *philosophorum deo*, quaecunque autem ut indigna reprehenditis, deputa-
buntur in Filio. . . ."
[5] *De Ira Dei*, xxii, 2.   [6] *Ibid.*, xxiii, 4.

how to reward. Moreover—and this was the error made by Epicurean and Stoic philosophies—this Divine anger was pure at its source, possessing no other attribute than holy indignation against evil. It had nothing of the sudden and irrepressible violence which characterised our own. It was patient and long-suffering and it allowed sinners time for repentance. And, faithful to his customary method, Lactantius does not omit to quote certain passages from the Sibylline books where the threat of Divine anger breaks forth, in order to show that the pagan religion itself had a belief in this primordial truth, that God cannot be impassible. In fact, putting aside speculations for which he cares nothing, he draws a picture of a God at once just and good, quite like the father of a family or the head of a State, upon whom their responsibilities imposed the duty of exacting the necessary punishment. And the interpretation which he puts forth is not very different from that which St Augustine was to lay down : " Ira Dei, non perturbatio animi, sed judicium quo irrogatur poena peccato." [1]

XII

The *De Mortibus Persecutorum* is no longer, as was the case with the *De Ira Dei*, a quiet dissertation on the lawfulness of the Divine anger. It is the setting forth of the formidable effects of this anger, partly based on the most recent events.

When the author wrote it,[2] peace had at last been given to the Church. Addressing himself to a certain Donatus, he intones a Hosanna in honour of Providence who had at last brought moral and material repose to the Christians, and who had laid low their enemies at the same time. He sets himself to relate their successive downfalls. He first passes in review in a very summary manner the first persecutors of Christianity, Nero, Domitian, Decius, Valerian, and Aurelian, upon whom a cruel or premature death had avenged their attacks (§ i–vi). Beginning with Diocletian, he comes to contemporary events, and to these he devotes no less than forty-five chapters (§ vii–lii). He starts with the Government

---

[1] *De Civit Dei*, XV, xxv.
[2] 313–4 (Harnack) ; 318–320 (Monceaux).

of the Tetrarchy, Diocletian and Maximian, "Augusti"; Galerius and Constantius Chlorus, "Cæsars"; the hateful exactions of the first three; the cruelties exercised against the Christians by Diocletian, whose hatred, inflamed by Galerius, commanded the general persecution of 303. Then follow the illness of Diocletian, and the intrigues whereby Galerius succeeded in compelling his abdication, and in causing Maximin Daïa and Severus to be associated in the Imperial rule; the abominable cruelties of Galerius when he became supreme; and Constantine, after his escape from his murderous designs, elected Emperor by the soldiers on the death of Constantius Chlorus. The very confusion of these succeeding events (there were no less than six "Augusti" in 307), renders difficult a succinct analysis of the last part of the work. While following closely the tangled web of these circumstances, the author does not forget the particular preoccupation which caused him to undertake the work. What he seeks to demonstrate is the manner in which the hand of God had lain heavy on those Princes who had done evil to the Christians, while it spared and favoured those who had seen fit to recognise the goodness of their cause.[1] One of these persecutors, Severus, was compelled to open his veins (§ xxvi); another, Maximian, had hanged himself (§ xxx); Galerius, a truly ferocious wild beast who deserved the most exquisite form of punishment, died corrupted and devoured by worms (§ xxxv); Diocletian had expired in sorry and destitute circumstances (§ xliii); Maximin Daïa had poisoned himself and his agony had been terrible (§ lxix). Even the families of these cruel men had not been spared (§ l). And the *De Mortibus Persecutorum* finishes, as it had begun, with a hymn of gratitude to the Lord : " The Lord who hath purged the earth of those proud names. Let us then celebrate the triumph of God with joy; day and night let us offer Him our prayer and praise, that He may establish for all time this peace which has been given to us after ten years of war." The leading characteristics of this treatise emerge from this brief glance : the terrible end suffered by the greater part of these wicked rulers had been meted out by the Divine dispositions, not with reference to any particular crime, but especially to the persecuting measures taken against the faithful. " In spite

---

[1] ix, ii.

of the punishment which his crimes had deserved, Diocletian had reigned perfectly happily so long as he did not soil his hands in the blood of the just." Only those had escaped the rigour of heaven who had proved themselves friendly to the Christians, Constantine for example, whose death had been calm and peaceful; "In lecto suo requiem vitae, sicut optabat, accepit." [1] Lactantius had been for a long while penetrated with the conception of Divine vengeance exercising itself upon those who had braved it when the hour came. This he had clearly indicated in the *Institutiones*, and also in the *Epitome*. [2] Is there any need to say that this was by no means a new idea, and that in it Lactantius revealed himself, as Bossuet would have said, as " un homme de l'ancienne marque " ? There is no doubt that the Christian idea of Providence admitted these " special exercises " (of the Divine will) on which, according to some, Lactantius too much insisted. Let us bear in mind, however, something of this complaint. Lactantius is indiscreet in the zeal which he displays in endeavouring to unravel God's designs with the intrepid certitude which he reveals in all their details, as if these had been confided to him from above. All the more that, following the example of Tertullian, he avoids any useful explanation of the fact that " good " emperors had treated the Christians without any clemency. The intoxicating and unlooked-for victory, coming after such severe experiences, had so far confirmed him in his views on the avenging initiatives of Providence, that the least suspension of judgment would have seemed to him culpable and almost sacrilegious scepticism.

What gives a particular value to this work is that Lactantius was compelled by his thesis to give an historic substructure to the demonstration which he was proving. From the point of view of an historical document, what value should be placed on the *De Mortibus Persecutorum?* For some years, critics have appreciably reconsidered the contemptuous views of Lactantius as an historian held by Duruy, Burckhardt and Schiller. M. Maurice has demonstrated his trustworthiness by irrefutable numismatic and

---

[1] xxiv, 5.
[2] *Inst. Div.*, V, xxiii, 1–5. Cf. IV, xxvii, 5 ; V, xxii, 23 ; *Epit.*, xlviii, 4–5. The most important texts are translated in Monceaux, III, 343.

iconographic testimony.[1] M. Pichon, after a minute comparison of the information furnished by Lactantius with what we can gather from contemporary and subsequent historians, comes to this conclusion regarding the *De Mortibus :* " This is not a unique treasure-house of perfect truth ; neither is it a tissue of errors and misstatements : it is a historical source useful to consult and necessary to correct, a source mingled with the truth, with what is likely and with what may be romance, a historical source just like the others, no more and no less." [2] " The more one studies his account," M. Monceaux concludes,[3] " the more one is brought to recognise its rigorous and detailed exactitude. It cannot be denied that Lactantius was wonderfully well informed on the history of official events as also on the *chronique scandaleuse ou anecdotique* of his times." Where Lactantius lays himself open to more real criticism is the way in which he interprets the facts which he had truthfully set down. He is partial ; he hates with such a vigorous hatred the persecuting rulers that he can hardly bring himself to admit that any good could possibly proceed from souls so fundamentally corrupt. Thus, he censures measures which from the political point of view were quite defensible, such as the Tetrarchy, or the financial enactments of Galerius. He is profuse in unfriendly interpretations however fair he wished to be, although the latter trait comes out through much passionate invective.

At the very time when Lactantius was composing his *De Mortibus Persecutorum*, Eusebius, Bishop of Cæsarea in Palestine, himself also one of Constantine's great administrators, was endeavouring to give an account of Christianity from its beginnings in Greek, or more accurately, to make a careful choice and a suitable classification of the documents handed down by tradition. The attitude of mind in which he pursued his task was not essentially different from that of Lactantius. In the mind of Eusebius, ecclesiastical history was evangelical proof of a particular kind. It was an account

---

[1] See numerous mentions of Maurice in Monceaux, III, 347. Add *Comptes rendus de l'Acad. des Inscr. et B.-Lettres,* 1908, p. 146 et s. ; *Numismatique Constantinienne,* vol. I (1908) ; vol. II (1910) ; *Bull. de la Soc. des Antiq. de France,* 1913 (*Nouvelles observations à propos du Labarum,* and various articles) ; B.A.L.A.C. 1914, p. 37 et s.

[2] *Op. cit.,* p. 383.

[3] III, 347.

of the stages by which the Church, firmly established upon the tradition embodied in the Bishops, and illuminated by the Holy Spirit which spoke through her foremost men, had successively passed, before her Providential reconciliation with the Roman power. And in the attempts of dissident sects, Eusebius always perceived the hand of the devil greedy for the ruin of souls, who used every endeavour to arrive at his hateful end. Such had been the innermost tendency of Christian history when, emerging from purely chronological investigations to which it had hitherto confined itself, it conceived higher ambitions ; such it was to remain during the passage of time, setting forth the Divine will by recording the facts by which this will had been manifested. Lactantius had his share in impressing this character upon it. The *De Mortibus Persecutorum* marks a date.

At the present day this work still deserves to be read. Spurred on by passion, the former professor of rhetoric laid bare therein his somewhat tasteless conceits. By a rapid narration of a succession of events, by the dramatic unfolding of certain scenes, and the piquant character of certain features, he stimulates interest from one end to the other and renews it again and again.

XIII

THAT Lactantius was not a great mind is a conclusion emerging clearly enough from the review which we have just made, and there is no need to insist on this again. His train of thought has so little of what was new about it that it felt no need of expression in any other than the old mould of Ciceronian prose. It found itself at home there and did not seek to create from it any other form. The excellent pages of M. René Pichon [1] should be read in which, defining " classic " style, he shows with what happy scrupulousness Lactantius strove to observe its rules and to imitate its elegances ; and his assiduity in " formulating the most novel and special ideas in the traditional language, and in clothing in terms of irreproachable classic purity matters which belonged exclusively to Christianity." A stranger to the attractive originalities of a Tertullian or an Apuleius, he does not deviate

---

[1] *Op. cit.*, p. 307 et s.

from classic syntax except in a small number of points.[1]   He invents no new metaphors and does not resuscitate current expressions.   In revenge, what he possesses in a remarkable degree is the instinct and taste for oratorical style, with its copiousness, its symmetry, and its large, harmoniously-balanced developments.   Everything about him, in form and foundation, gives an impression of disciplined and seasoned balance, and only the revengeful ardour of the *De Mortibus Persecutorum* had a momentary effect of disturbing this balance.

Moreover, the writers who had any traffic with new channels were few.   It was something in those times of changing literary methods, to have preserved a language that was correct, clear and abundant.   Also, more intellectual resources than we might at first suppose that a quiet professor of rhetoric could possess must have been required to form such a personal idea of the needs of contemporary apologetics ; to give so much sequence and careful application in the realisation of the design thus conceived ; to cling with such tenacity to the Christian doctrine of Providence, and to follow up its demonstration with ever-increasing aptitude through a series of works from the altogether tranquil and philosophic deism of the *De Opificio Dei*, to the burning accents of the *De Mortibus Persecutorum.*

What influence had his effort on those cultivated pagans whom he had in view throughout ?   We have no indication which might enable us to gauge it.   He found far more admirers at the beginning of the Renaissance than in Christian antiquity.   Hardly any ecclesiastical writer has been so often published.   Since then, sympathy in his regard has grown colder, and I think, this disfavour is somewhat excessive.   However this may be, his name remains " inseparable from one of the most important facts in history, not only in that of Rome, but of all humanity, namely, the reconciliation of the Church with the Empire and the appearance of the first Christian Government." [2]

---

[1] For example, as regards the agreement of the tenses, and the use of *quod* and even (rarely) of *quia* after verbs of explanation.

[2] Pichon, p. 454.

XIV

It is principally from St Jerome that we derive our knowledge of Victorinus of Pettau. Jerome was interested in Victorinus as the earliest specialist in exegesis among the Latins, and also from his being a compatriot from Illyria. Otherwise he held him in little esteem. While recognising in him a certain amount of learning,[1] or at least some desire of erudition,[2] he allows it to be understood that this attempt was paralysed by his literary unskilfulness[3] and by his incompetence in the Latin language.[4] In addition he reproaches him for having been addicted to the wild dreams of the millennium,[5] after Papias, Irenæus, Apollinaris, Tertullian and Lactantius. According to Jerome, Victorinus had been Bishop of Poetovio[6] (in Upper Pannonia, on the Drave on the borders of Noricum). He certainly died a martyr under Diocletian,[7] but we do not know in what year. His life therefore may be placed in the second half of the IIIrd century. Of the works attributed to him by St Jerome in the *De Viris Illustribus* one only remains, the Commentary on the Apocalypse.[8] There is quite a history attaching to the text of this Commentary. We have it (thanks to the labours of Haussleiter) in four different forms. A manuscript in the Vatican Library[9] mentioned by Angelo Mai gives the first version of Victorinus, which is very strongly imbued with millenarism.[10] A second

---

[1] *Prol. in Is.* (P.L., XXIV, 20): "etsi imperitus sermone, non tamen scientia."

[2] *Ep.* lxx, 5 (Hilberg, in C.V., liv, 707): "licet desit eruditio, tamen non deest eruditionis voluntas."

[3] *Ep.* lviii, 10 (*ibid.*, p. 539): "quod intellegit, eloqui non potest."

[4] *De Vir. Ill.*, lxxiv: "Non seque latine ut graece noverat."

[5] *De Vir. Ill.*, xviii; in *Ez.* XI, xxxvi, 1 (P.L., XXV, 339).

[6] Petavionensis episcopus, *de Vir. Ill.*, lxxiv. It was often read as *Pictaviensis* before Launoy in a dissertation of the year 1653 (2 ed., 1664) restored the true reading and showed that Victorinus had been the Bishop of Pettau and not of Poitiers.

[7] We may conclude this from the manner in which Jerome signalises his name in the *De Vir. Ill.* and elsewhere (v.g. *Adv. Rufinum*, III, xiv). Adon. was the first to state this explicitly in his martyrology (P.L., CXXIII, 389).

[8] For traces of other writings mentioned by Jerome, see Haussleiter, in C.V., vol. XXXXIX, p. xiv et s.—The enumeration of St Jerome is not final: he adds *et multa alia*, a very vague expression of which he makes excessive use in the *De Vir. Ill.* Cassiodorus, *Inst. Div.*, vii (P.L., LXX, 1119) alludes to a comm. by Victorinus on St Matthew; likewise Jerome (P.L., XXVI, 20 and 223).

[9] *Codex Ottobonianus latinus* 3288 A., XVth Century. This manuscript is very difficult to read. There is a photographic reproduction of some leaves in C.V., vol. XXXXIX. There are two copies of this, of the XVth and XVIth Century.

[10] Especially beginning from chap. xix et s.

version is due to St Jerome. At the request of a certain Anatolius Jerome consented to revise the Commentary of Victorinus. He gives an explanation in a prologue wherein, in order to escape the criticisms of his detractors, he is careful not to exaggerate the importance of this revision, which he confined to certain additions, suppressions and corrections.[1] As a matter of fact, a comparison of his rendering with that of Victorinus brings out emendations of a certain importance. Jerome has improved the style of Victorinus; in many passages he has substituted a new Latin rendering of Scripture to that used by Victorinus; his emendations also bear upon the root of things, especially upon his " millenary " passages, nearly all of which he has cut out;[2] to make up for this, he has improved and amplified the rendering of Victorinus by different supplementary paraphrases, some of which are borrowed from Tyconius.[3]

In a later recension, the authorship of which is unknown, the text of the *Apocalypse* carries a more liberal admixture of the editing of Jerome, undergoing some further rather incompetent revision.[4] Lastly, a final recension has united the three preceding ones, with the introduction of some additions and many transpositions[5] under pretext of better methodical arrangement.

Another very short work, the *De Fabrica Mundi*, of which there is no mention in antiquity, was claimed for Victorinus by G. Cave, in the XVIIth century, on account of the super-scription on a manuscript in Lambeth Palace Library,[6] containing a series of fragments and extracts. This assignment is commonly admitted: the mediocre and obscure style, and the ideas coloured by millenarism,[7] clearly favour it. In it Victorinus draws moral and religious lessons from the Creation in Genesis; he insists especially on the virtue of

---

[1] C.V., XXXXIX, p. 14.
[2] The arrangement of Haussleiter's edition enables us easily to take these into account: see C.V., XXXXIX, p. 138, 1 to 154, 18.
[3] Jerome's recension figures in four manuscripts. The two principal ones are the *Cod. Taurinensis lat.*, G.V. 3, XIth century, and *Cod.* 1079 in the Municipal Library of Arras, Xth century.
[4] Six manuscripts. The principal one is the *Codex Harleianus*, saec. ix–x, now in the British Museum.
[5] One manuscript only, *Cod. biblioth. Casinensis* CCXLVII, saec. xi–xii. This is the only text which figures in Migne's *Patrology*, in which Galland's edition is reproduced.
[6] *Cod. bibliothecae Lambethanae Londinensis* 414, saec. x–xi.
[7] See especially § vi (Haussleiter, p. 6, l. 10 et s.).

the number seven, and makes it fit in with his own conceptions of the economy of the universe.[1] The arrangement of this little treatise hardly enables us to think with G. Cave that it originally belonged to a commentary on Genesis or on the Apocalypse.

In a great number of manuscripts of Tertullian there figures an *Adversus Omnes Haereses*, resembling the *De Praescriptione*.[2] This catalogue gives a characteristic summary of thirty-two heresies : the first is that of Dositheus, the last that of Praxeas. There is general agreement in recognising that Tertullian could not have been the author. Taking up a hypothesis already suggested by Œhler (*Tertull. Opera*, II, 752), Harnack proposed to attribute it to Victorinus of Pettau.[3] The arguments adduced by him cannot but have their value. (1) In his *De Viris Illustribus*, § lxxiv, St Jerome quotes an *Adversus Omnes Haereses* among the works of Victorinus. (2) Now Jerome must surely have known the work we are speaking of. In his treatise against the Luciferians, § xxiii there is a passage which, with the exception of a few emendations of form, is a close imitation of the beginning of the *Adversus Omnes Haereses*. Then Jerome only mentions by name one work bearing this title and makes use of just this one which we possess. We have here a presumption favourable to its identification. (3) On the other hand, in a letter addressed to Damasus (*Ep.* xxxvi, 16), Jerome connects the name of Victorinus with that of Hippolytus in relation to the interpretation of the history of Esau and Jacob : " . . . *Hippolyti* martyrii verba ponamus, a quo et *Victorinus* noster non plurimum discrepat, non quod omnia executus sit, sed quo possit occasionem praebere lectori ad intelligentiam latiorem. . . ." Victorinus had thus borrowed certain things in his exegetic treatises from Hippolytus where he followed him very closely. This proceeding of borrowing material conforms with the idea of the relation-

---

[1] *Ibid.*

[2] We do not find it in the *Agobardinus*. It is joined without any special reason to the *De Praescriptione* in the *Paterniacensis* 439, saec. xi. In more recent manuscripts, especially those of the Italian tradition (*Florentinus Magliabechianus*, Conu. sopp. VI, 9, s. xv ; *Florentinus Magliabechianus*, Conu. sopp. VI, 10, s. xv, etc. . . .), the *Adversus Omnes Haereses* immediately precedes the *De Praescriptione*. The first editors of Tertullian printed it after the *De Praescriptione*. Since Rigault it has been separated from it : see Œhler, II, 751 ; Kroymann, 213.

[3] *Zeitsch. f. wiss. Theol.*, xix (1876), 116 et s. ; cf. *Chron.*, II, 430.

ship between the *Adversus Omnes Haereses* and the *Syntagma* of Hippolytus.[1]

The combination is ingenious, nevertheless Harnack himself in the course of time became far less favourable to it ; and, from reasons of matter and form, he confesses that the drawing up of this list is far more intelligible if we place it at Rome about the year 220 rather than at Poetovio at the end of the IIIrd century.[2]

Various other works [3] have been attributed to Victorinus of Pettau, without any of these conjectures appearing to be required. Taking him as a whole, his was a mind of mediocre originality, his temperament that of a follower formed on the school of writers of Greek culture, such as Papias, Irenæus, Hippolytus, and, above all, Origen,[4] and one who appeared, although writing in Latin, to have been ignorant of the Latin literary tradition.

[1] On this relationship, cf. P. de Labriolle, *Les Sources de l'Histoire du Montanisme*, pp. xxxvi–xlviii.

[2] For further details, *ibid.*, p. lxxxiv.

[3] The *Tractatus Origenis de libris ss. Scripturarum*, and a Homily *de Decem Virginibus*, etc.

[4] Jerome insists on different occasions on the subordination of Victorinus to the views of Origen ; cf. Haussleiter, in C.V., vol. XXXXIX, p. viii et s.

BOOK III

THE GOLDEN AGE

OF

LATIN CHRISTIAN LITERATURE

P

CHAPTER I

THE MORROW OF THE VICTORY

BIBLIOGRAPHY

I. FIRMICUS MATERNUS.—P.L., XII, 981-1050 ; Halm, in C.V., vol. II (1867) ; Ziegler, in B.T. (1907).—Consult : Cl. H. Moore, *Julius Firmicus Maternus, der Heide u. der Christ*, Munich, 1897 ; Boll, in P.W., VI, 2365-2379 ; Spiegelberg, *das Isis-Mysterium bei F.M.*, in *Archiv. f. Religionswiss*, XIX (1918), p. 194 ; F. Groehl, *de Syntaxi Firmiciana*, Breslau, 1918 (cf. B. ph. W., 1918, pp. 1231-1235). French Translation in Buchon's *Choix de Monuments primitifs de l'Egl. Chrét.*, 1840, pp. 747-771.

II. RETICIUS of AUTUN.—Consult : *Hist. litt. de la France*, I, 2 (1733), pp. 59-63 ; D.C.B., IV, 544 ; *Chron.*, p. 433.

III. SAINT HILARY DE POITIERS. See TABLE, No. IV.—Consult : Largent, *Saint Hilaire*, 1902 (Coll, *les Saints*, Gabalda) ; Feder, in *Stimmen aus Maria-Laach*, 1911, pp. 30-45 ; C. Weyman, in B. ph. W., 1917, p. 1165 ; Beck, in Z.K.T., 1906, pp. 108 and 305 ; Rauschen, *ibid.*, p. 295 ; H. Jeannotte, *Le Psautier de saint Hilaire de Poitiers*, 1917.

IV. LUCIFER of CALARIS.—P.L., XII, 765-1038 ; Hartel, in C.V., vol. XIV (1886).—Consult : Hartel, A.L.L., 1886, 1-58 ; Kruger, in R.E., XI, 666.

V. *Collectio Avellana*.—Gunther, in C.V., vol. XXXV (1895-8).

VI. *Libellus Precum*.—P.L., XIII, 82-107 ; C.V., vol. XXXV, pp. 5-40.

VII. FAUSTINUS.—*Contra Arianos*, P.L., XIII, 37-80 ; *Fides Theodosio Oblata, ibid.*, 79-80.

VIII. Arian and anti - Arian Literature.—POTAMIUS OLISOPO : *Ep. ad Athanasium* (written about 350, according to Dom Wilmart, *R. Bén.*, XXX [1913], 284) ; P.L., VIII, 1416-1418 : cf. *R. Bén., ibid.* The other works are in P.L., VIII. According to Dom Wilmart, *op. cit.*, the *Epist.* called *Beati Hieronymi de Substantia Patris et Filii et Spiritus Sancti*, published by Guillermo Antolin, in the *Revista de Archivos, Bibl. y Museos*, XII (1908), p. 207, is by Potamius.

IX. FRAGMENTS from BOBBIO.—P.L., XIII, 593-672.

X. *Sermo Arianorum sine nomine auctoris*.—P.L., XLII, 677-684.

XI. *Opus imperfectum in Matthaeum*.—P.G., LVI, 611-946.

XII. *Dissertatio Maximi contra Ambrosium*, in Fr. Kauffmann, *Aus der Schule des Wulfila*, Strasb., 1899, pp. 65-90.

XIII. FOEBADIUS of AGEN.—*Liber c. Arianos* (c. 357-8). P.L., XX, 13-20.

XIV. HOSIUS of CORDOVA.—*Ep. ad Constantium*, P.L., VIII, 1327-1331, and P.G., XXV, 744-748 (translated in Tillemont, VII, 313) ; *Hosii Sententiae* : P.L., VIII, 1317-1328 ; *Ep. ad Papam Julium*, Mansi, *Conc.*, VI, 1909-1910.

XV. EUSEBIUS of VERCELLI.—*Ep. ad Constantium* (355), P.L., XII, 947 ; *Ep. ad Presbyt. et Plebem Italiae*, XII, 947-954 ; *Ep. ad Gregorium*, X, 713-714 (cf. Feder, S.B.W., 162 [1909], p. 64) ; *Symbolum Quicumque* : P.G., XXVIII, 1581-1596 (cf. Turner, in J.T.S., XI [1910], 401-411).

XVI. *Altercatio Heracliana Laici cum Germinio Episc.* (January 366) ; Caspari, K. A., pp. 131-147.

XVII. *Tractatus contra Arianos.*—Sedlmayer, in S.B.W., 146 (1903), p. 11.

On Arian literature in general, cf. L. Duchesne, *Hist. Anc. de l'Eglise*, vol. II (1907); Jacques Zeiller, *Les Orig. Chrét. dans les Provinces Danubiennes de l'Empire Romain*, 1918 (a very full bibliography is given therein).

XVIII. Gregory of Elvira.—The five sermons on the *Cant. of Cant.* have been published by Gotth. Heine, *Biblioth. Anecdotorum*, part I, L., 1848, p. 134.—See further on in detail the works which have been attributed to him.—Consult: P. Lejay, in *R. Bén.*, 1908, 435-457 ; Butler, in J.T.S., 1909, 450-459.

XIX. Marius Victorinus. — Non-Christian works : *Ars Grammatica*, G.L., VI, p. 3 ; *Explanatio* on the *de Invent.* of Cicero, R.L.M., pp. 155-304, and Stangl, *Tulliana et Mario-Victoriniana*, Progr. Munich, 1888, p. 49 ; *De Definitionibus*, P.L., LXIV, 891-910, and Stangl, *ibid.*, p. 17.—Christian works in P.L., VIII, 1019-1236.—Consult : Monceaux, III, 373 et s.

SUMMARY

I. General view of the period opening with the Edict of Milan.—II. The first transports over the victory : Firmicus Maternus.—III. Reticius of Autun, an exegetist. — IV. Struggles over doctrine. Arianism. St Hilary of Poitiers. His life of warfare. His works. The *Fragmenta Historica.*—V. Lucifer of Calaris. The *Libellus Precum.*— VI. Arian and anti-Arian literature. — VII. Gregory of Elvira. — VIII. Marius Victorinus.

I

We now enter upon a new period, that of the first pact between Christianity and the Roman Empire. Promulgated in March 313 by Constantine and Licinius, the Edict of Milan inaugurated a system of liberty, but a liberty already privileged, and one which granted to the Christians something rather more than the just reparation to which they had a right. Constantine was not content with showing his favour to Christianity by the building and endowment of sumptuous basilicas at Constantinople, Nicomedia, Antioch, Jerusalem, Bethlehem (the only one still remaining), Naples, Capua, Ostia and Albano ; by immunities granted to the Catholic clergy ; and by the juridical powers assigned to the Bishops. These favours he intended to be reserved to the orthodox Church—the Church he only entered effectually on his death-bed—to the exclusion of heretics and schismatics. As regards the traditional religion of Rome, he did not hesitate to designate it in an official document by the word *superstitio :* [1] " Too circumspect to suppress the old forms of worship, he contented himself with leaving to them their own life which

[1] The Law of May 25, 323 (*Code Theod.*, XVI, ii, 5 : Mommsen, p. 836) ; inscription at Spello (between 333 and 337). Dessau, p. 705.

was almost at an end, while taking care that no one should be unaware that he was no longer faithful to them." [1]

His policy towards paganism was accentuated in the most rigorous sense by his sons Constans and Constantius. But strange contradictions retarded its effects. Though he forbade sacrifices and pagan worship, Constantius gave proof, on more than one occasion, of a want of logic of which the pagan Symmachus, in the face of arbitrary measures of quite another kind, was later on to take advantage. In his famous *Relatio* addressed in 384 to Valentinian II,[2] he recalled that " Constantius had taken away none of the privileges of the consecrated virgins ; he had filled the priestly offices with nobles ; he had not refused financial support to the Roman ceremonies ; he had followed the Senate with much complacency along the streets of the Eternal City ; he had viewed the temples without emotion ; he had read the names of the gods inscribed on their frontals ; he had enquired as to the origin of those sanctuaries, he had expressed admiration for the architects. . . ."

In these strong measures which were only partially efficacious, there was, however, matter to exasperate minds still faithful to the old religion on account of the fascination which its classic literary souvenirs exercised,—those glorious souvenirs in which it seemed bound up,—or who found in the " mysteries " sufficient outlet for their religious sense. Such minds were still numerous, especially among the upper classes. St Augustine has noted in his *Confessions* (VIII, ii, 3), possibly with some exaggeration, the pagan sympathies of " nearly all the Roman nobility " (*tota fere Romana nobilitas*) in the second half of the IVth century. To Prudentius the word *nobilitas*, taken by itself, meant the pagan aristocracy. Highly placed personages submitted to the unclean and bloody rites of the " taurobola." Amongst those whom we know practised this rite, Claudius Hermogenianus Cæsarius was Pro-Consul of Africa from 368 to 370, and Prefect of the City in 374 ; another, Sextilius Agesilaus Aldesius was director of the principal services of the Chancellery, and member of the Consistory of Public Worship ; yet another, Vettius Agorius

[1] P. Batiffol, *la Paix Constantinienne et le Catholicisme*, 1914, p. 399.
[2] § vi (ed. Seeck, M.G.H., VI, 1, p. 280 et s.). This is translated in my *Saint Ambroise*, Paris, 1908, pp. 37–44. On the visit of Constantius to Rome in 356, see also Ammianus Marcellinus, XVI, x.

Praetextatus, " sacrorum omnium praesul," " princeps religiosorum," as Macrobius [1] calls him, was Prefect of the City in 367, and Praetorian Prefect in 384.[2] The momentary success of the short reaction inaugurated by Julian can be understood. However, twenty years later, St Ambrose could speak of his times as Christian, *christiana tempora*.[3] Ambrose was too clear-sighted to exaggerate the full meaning of this expression. He knew on what compromises so many minds lacking any real devotion depended for their adhesion to Christianity. But from the political point of view the victory of the Christian faith, so long harassed and hunted down, was now no longer in doubt.

" See," cried the poet Prudentius in his *Contra Symmachum* (I, 544 et s.), when speaking of the Senate, " see the Assembly of old Catos donning the white robe of catechumens and laying aside the insignia of High Priest ! Barely a handful of them still remains on the Tarpeian rock ; the rest hasten to the pure sanctuaries of Christianity ; all the Curia of Evander is running to Apostolic sources. At their head are marching the Annii and the Probi. Rome, the illustrious, takes pride in having seen the noble Anicius the first to give lustre to the Assembly of the Chiefs of the City by his conversion. The heir of the Olybrii, after having inscribed his name on the Fasti and having donned the palm-bordered mantle, seeks to lower the fasces of Brutus before the gates of the martyrs, and to bow the axe of the Latins before Christ. The prompt faith of the Paulinii and the Bassi has not hesitated to give itself up to Christ, and to offer to the world to come the proud scions of their patrician race. Need I mention too the Gracchi, those friends of the people, those men invested with power and place at the head of the Senate, who have given orders to destroy the images of the gods, and with their Lictors have consecrated themselves to Christ, the All Compelling."

The pagan historian Ammianus Marcellinus notes on his

---

[1] *Saturn.*, I, xvii, 1 ; I, xi, 1.
[2] Other facts are quoted by Wissowa, *Rel. u. Kultus der Romer*, pp. 98–102. Cf. Geffcken, in *Neue Jahrb. f. d. Kl.*, 1918, p. 109.
[3] *Ep.* xvii, 10 (P.L., XVI, 964) ; cf. St Augustine, *Sermo* xliv, 2 ; Enarr. LIV, 12 ; cf. ii, 5.

side that if the candidates for the Roman Episcopate show so much ardour to compete for this office, it is because practical advantages are not wanting : gifts from Roman ladies, comfortable carriages, magnificent robes, and repasts whose luxury is not surpassed by kings.[1] However ill-natured, this remark reveals the prestige and state with which the Bishop of Rome was surrounded.

The reconciliation of the Christian Church with the Roman State held consequences of the first order for the future of Christianity : "In our days," observes M. Paul Lejay,[2] "people are too much inclined to limit its importance. Until the peace of the Church, the hostility of the public powers had weighed heavily on the life of the Christian communities. On the day when it had been definitely removed we see the Church coming forth, as it were, from a long winter, consolidating and developing her ranks, discussing her hierarchical powers, defining the lines of her doctrines, drawing up the formulæ of her faith, regulating her worship, surrounding the holy places with public marks of veneration, providing holy retreats for souls desirous of perfection, and giving to the Latin half of the Church a more faithful version of the Bible. All these fruits are the harvest of the IVth century." This expansion of the spiritual power of the Church and of her material prosperity made itself felt too in the domain of literature. Still we must exclude from our survey the rich output of Athanasius, Basil, Gregory of Nazianzen, Gregory of Nyssa, John Chrysostom, Synesius, or Ephrem, in order to confine ourselves to works written in Latin. In Biblical exegesis, speculative and moral theology, the hymns of the Church, didactic, epic, and lyric poetry, Christian effort was manifesting itself in every direction. Even art, from this time onward, became a "complete system of instruction, a theology in images, an *apologia* in sculptured design."[3] We can measure the importance of this revival if we consider that profane literature had no other representatives at that time than men like Libanios, Symmachus, Macrobius, or Claudian.

[1] *Res Gestae*, XXVII, iii.
[2] R.H.L.R., 1900, 187.
[3] L, Bréhier, L'Art Chrétien, 1918, p. 107,

II

UNDER the name of J. Firmicus Maternus we possess two
works of quite dissimilar character : a manual of astrology,
Matheseos Libri VIII, the most ample legacy from antiquity
we have on this subject, and the *De Errore Profanarum
Religionum*.[1]

Did the same Firmicus write both these works ?   Cl. H.
Moore's study scarcely allows us any doubt.   The two works
were written at a distance of some years apart, one between
335 and 337, the other (the *De Errore*) between 346 and 350.
The author of the *Mathesis* informs us that he was born in
Sicily ;[2] now the author of the *De Errore* was personally
acquainted with that country.[3]   Lastly, the resemblance
in details of language and analogy of expression are striking :[4]
taken together, identity of authorship seems to be imperative.

The *Mathesis* is dedicated to Lollianus Mavortius, Governor
of Campania.   Firmicus himself belonged to the order of
Senators.   He tells us that he had at first devoted himself to
the Bar, and that disgusted, by the annoyances and enmities
which the exercise of his profession had brought him, he had
finally given it up.   His eight books on Astrology according
to his intention were to contain " omnem disciplinam divinae
matheseos."   There are, however, *lacunae* and mistakes :[5]
the author agrees that he was not very cognisant of the
matter of which he treats.   He works upon Greek and Latin
sources, the origin of which he rarely defines, being anxious
above all things (as he confesses) to annex a new province for
Roman literature.[6]   We need not lay too much stress upon
this technical treatise here.   It will suffice to note the curious
tendencies which appear in it.   Firmicus counsels certain
prudent restrictions in the use to be made of astrological
conclusions.   Care must be taken to make no deductions on

---

[1] Dom Morin (*Histor. Jahrb.*, 1916, pp. 229–266) attributes to Firmicus the
Consultationes Zacchaei et Apollonii (P.L., XX, 1071–1166) ; likewise, with reservations, A. Reatz, in *der Katholik*, XXI (1919), p. 300 et s.
[2] I *Prooem.*, iv : " Siciliae situm, quam incolo et unde oriendus sum ". Cf.
VI, xxx, 26.
[3] *De Err.*, vii (description of the neighbourhood of Henna).
[4] These resemblances are shown in Ziegler's edition, L., 1907.   One of the most
significant is in *De Err.*, xxvi, 3 ; cf. *Math.*, V, *Praef.* 3 (Skutsch, p. 280, line 17).
[5] See Boll, in P.W., VI, 2374.
[6] V *Prooem.*, iii.

matters of State nor upon the Emperor. Lord of the Universe, the Emperor, by reason of his very divinity, was immune from stellar influences.[1] What is most significant, from our point of view, is that Firmicus seems to be concerned with different moral problems connected with his favourite science. He seeks to reconcile, in an otherwise very superficial manner, regard for the moral order and respect for Astrology.[2] He wishes people to approach this science with a pure and sober heart, for he is compelled to have daily intercourse with the gods.[3] The prayers with which he opens books V and VII are written in accents that are almost Christian.

We could not reasonably venture to maintain that he had already embraced the faith when he wrote his *Mathesis* and was projecting other works of the same kind.[4] Astrology had been for long held suspect by Christianity [5] as being contrary to the very idea of a Providence whose free decisions could not be bound by anything. By pretending that destiny is immutably written in the stars, the astrologers seemed to render superfluous all recourse to the true God. What we can say is, that Firmicus betrays certain inner dispositions which render less surprising the fact of his conversion, which happened during the ten years separating the *Mathesis* from the *De Errore Profanarum Religionum*.

The beginning of the *De Errore* is wanting : the two first leaves have been torn from the only very much spoilt manuscript, a Vaticanus Palatinus (n°. 165, Xth century) from which Mathias Placius Illyricus made the first edition at Strasbourg in 1562, and which Bursian discovered at the Vatican in 1856. Firmicus arraigns firstly divination by the elements : water (the cult of Osiris and Isis), earth (cult of Cybele and Atys), air (cult of *Juno Caelestis*), and fire (Persian, the Magi, the cult of Mithra) ; and he points his more or less scandalous anecdotes with pathetic exhortations addressed to those who favoured those ridiculous figments. He then applies (§ vi,

---

[1] *Math.*, II, xxx, 4 et s.
[2] I, vi, 3.
[3] II, xxx, 1.
[4] V, i, 38 ; VIII, i, 10 ; VIII, iv, 14.
[5] See *Dict. of Christian Antiquities*, Lon., 1893, art. *Magic* and *Astrology ;* R.H.L.R., 1903, p. 431 et s., and 1906, p. 40 ; *Rev. Histor.*, vol. LXV (1897), p. 262 et s. The Christian attacks upon these practices have not yet been studied in any deep manner.

et s.) the critical method of Evhemerist exegesis to a series of other beliefs, especially to those coming from the East which were particularly dear to pagan religious sentiment (the *Liber* of Crete and that of Thebes ; the Ceres of Henna ; Adonis ; Jupiter Sabazios ; the Corybantes ; and the Cabires of Macedonia) : parricide, adultery, pederasty, theft, incest,—there was no crime which these gods did not authorize by their example, or by the legends relating to them.[1] Firmicus even gives an eloquent discourse on the sun, dealing with the identification which some people sometimes wish to establish between Bacchus and the heavenly body of light, and protests against such extravagance and invites them to listen rather to the Divine Word (§ viii, 1–3). A few chapters are devoted to explaining the etymology of the names of certain gods : Serapis (Σάρρας παῖς, the child of Sarah), was the Joseph of Scripture, worshipped by the Egyptians in a manner he would certainly never have wished ; the Penates (from *penus*, provisions) were originally only the daily meats by which man sustained his life, etc. These fancies are followed by (xviii, et s.) very precious information from an historical point of view on the signs, and symbols or passwords, used in the mysteries.[2] " I have eaten from the dulcimer, I have drunk from the cymbal and have learnt in their true meaning the religious mysteries " (cult of Atys and the Eleusinian Mysteries) ; " Hail, new spouse, hail, new spouse, hail, new light ! " (Mysteries of Iacchus) ; " Alas ! O thou who hast two horns and two shapes ! " (Mysteries of Bacchus) ; " Be of good courage, ye initiates of the god set free ; for ye shall be freed from your woes " (Mysteries of Isis, Atys or Adonis) ; " The bull is father to the serpent, and the serpent is father to the bull " (Mysteries of Dionysus).

The refutations of Firmicus and the resemblances indicated by him between these formulæ and passages from the Bible have not much interest. But what are significant in quite another way are the energetic appeals to the secular

---

[1] xii, 5.

[2] M. Paul Foucart writes in this connection (*Les Mystères d'Eleusis*, Paris, 1914, p. 377) : " Firmicus Maternus made a mistake, I think, about the value of these formulæ and their use. It was not a password used by the initiates to recognise each other, but a reply to the question put by the ministers of the temple ; each of the recipients declared that he had accomplished the acts enjoined by the ritual." Cf. *ibid.*, p. 383 ; and Graillot, *Le Culte de Cybèle* (Bibl. des Ec. franç. d'Ath. et de Rome, fasc. 107 [1912], pp. 132 and 543).

arm with which he points his demonstrations. He turns to
the Emperors Constantine and Constans (*sacratissimi imperatores, sacrosancti imperatores, sacrosancti principes, domini
imperatores*) and implores them to destroy, once for all, these
demoralizing and impious forms of worship :

" Needs must, most holy Emperors, that you extirpate
these abominations, destroy them, and apply to them
the most severe enactments in your Edicts. Suffer
not this fatal and senseless delusion longer to soil the
Roman Universe. . . . There are some who refuse,
hide away, and passionately crave after their own ruin.
Nevertheless, assist these unhappy men, deliver them,
they perish ! If God from on high has entrusted the
Empire to you, it is that you may heal these wounds. We
know what peril their crime makes them run, what punishment is reserved to their error : better to free them
from it in spite of themselves than to abandon them in
their full contentment to their ruin." (They are like
sick men who ask for food likely to do them harm, and
it is necessary to make them take the most active
remedies and to suffer the cautery of fire and sword.
Once healed, they will realize the benefit of this constraint). . . . " As for you, most holy Emperors,
necessity commands you to overcome and to punish this
evil. God orders you in His Law to pursue with your
severity in every place the crime of idolatry. Hearken
and merit in your sacred minds what God ordains for
this crime " (then follows the text of Deuteronomy, xiii,
6–10, 12–18).

And again :

" It wants but little, thanks to your laws, for the devil
to be completely overthrown, for idolatry to be extin-
guished, and for this fatal contagion to be stamped out.
Already the poison has lost its virulence ; each day, the
food for profane passion grows less. Rear the standard
of faith : this is the rôle which Divinity has reserved
to you. Thanks to His favour, you have overthrown
in a wonderful manner all your enemies by whom the
Roman Empire was becoming enfeebled. Give to it the

revered mark of law. Draw up sanctions, promulgate
the necessary edicts. . . . In His benevolence, Christ
has reserved to His people through the work of your
hands the destruction of idolatry and the overthrowing
of profane temples." . . . "Strip without misgiving
from the temples the ornaments which these gods,
out of your revenues, fashion in the fire of your foundries,
and in the furnaces of your mines. Confiscate for your
benefit all their offerings ; make them your own. From
the time of the overthrowing of the temples, the Divine
Power has not ceased to add increase to your own
might. . . ."

There is something a little painful in the spectacle of this
intolerance on the part of those who had formerly been
persecuted, and, scarcely delivered from their own nightmare,
were hastening to become persecutors in their turn. These
vengeful exhortations did not remain a dead letter. If the
work of Firmicus is of the year 346, it may have contributed
to the promulgation of the rigorous edict of that same year
which (these are the very words used in the edict), ordered
sacrifice to be discontinued and the closing of the temples
in order "to take away from those who had strayed the
occasion of sin." Some years later (353–356), the provisions of a similar law passed in 341 were renewed. As
regards the Christians, extenuating circumstances were
certainly not wanting, and Gaston Boissier has skilfully
pleaded them : [1] "Their feelings of anger and hate can be
understood," he observes ; "Paganism was the enemy, the
implacable enemy who, for three centuries, had prevented
them from living in peace, whom they had all been brought
up to fear and to abhor. . . . After all, paganism had given
the example of these rigours ; the first to strike with the
sword, it seemed just that they should perish by the sword."
Then too, they were in the first enthusiasm of a victory which
seemed like a miracle. The reaction traced by the Emperor
Julian was to counsel more prudence and discretion, while
at the same time it was to revive the hopes of the pagans
which had for some time disappeared. It remains to say that
such a sudden evolution cannot fail to be disheartening

[1] *Fin du Pag.*, I, 67, 69.

to those who remember the fine words which Lactantius at the beginning of the IVth century had written about the duty of exercising persuasiveness and of discountenancing all violence in religious controversies.[1]

The *De Errore Profanarum Religionum* deserves a careful commentary, the material of which would be easy to find in the learned works published during these last few years on the pagan mysteries. The work is not tedious : an ardent rhetorical style gives life to it. Moreover, when we appraise what Firmicus owed to his Christian predecessors [2] (Cyprian especially, for his quotations from the Bible, Minucius Felix and Arnobius), and the turns and expressions which he gathered from his profane models (Terence, Sallust, Ovid, Titus Livius, Virgil, Plotinus, Porphyry, etc.), his own original contribution appears modest. But he has the merit of putting together a very precise documentation of the contemporary forms of the cults which he wished to denounce as absurd and abominable.

In addition, his work shows us the extravagant transports caused to certain Christians of passionate temperament by the astonishing turn of fortune which seemed to place the forces of the Empire at the service of their faith. It appeared to them that so unlooked for a triumph, such a stroke of Providence, should at once display all its effects, and that it was necessary that the truth, henceforth sure of its future, should exercise its indefeasible right by doing away with obstacles capable of retarding its march.

III

RETICIUS, Bishop of Autun, was one of the great influences of the Church in Gaul in the first years of the IVth century.[3] He played an important part in the Synod of Rome held in 313, when Donatus was condemned,[4] and at the Synod of Arles in 314.[5] St Jerome attributes to him a voluminous work against Novatian, and a *Commentary on the Canticle of Canticles*. In the *De Viris Illustribus*, where his purpose is to

[1] *Div. Inst.*, V, xx, 9 (C.V., XIX, p. 468). Cf. *Epitome*, liii.
[2] Cf. Ziegler's edition, p. xlv.
[3] St Jerome, *De Vir. Ill.*, lxxxii ; St Augustine, *Contra Jul. Pelag.*, I, iii, 7.
[4] Augustine, *ibid.*
[5] St Optat, I, xxiii.

enhance the prestige of Christian literature, Jerome refrains from letting us know what little merit he conceived for this *Commentary*. More liberal in his letters,[1] he notices its insufficiencies, not so much from the point of view of its form as of its interpretation : Reticius must have forgotten the first duty of the exegetist, which is to facilitate for the reader the understanding of the text which he has undertaken to paraphrase. The *Commentary* of Reticius was still existing in the XIIth century : Béranger quotes a fragment of it in his *Apologie d'Abélard*.[2] Since that date all traces of it have been lost.[3]

IV

THAT the advantage of friendship with those in high places has not always been an unmixed benefit for the Church, is shown unmistakably by the life of St Hilary of Poitiers.

The IVth century was the period of the great controversies in doctrine,—Arians, Priscillianists, Origenists, Donatists, Manichæans, and Pelagians. Of these intestine dissensions none was graver or more disintegrating for the Christian faith than the controversy raised by Arius. The fundamental economy of Revelation was threatened. In addition, the Emperors when constituting themselves the protectors of Christianity were fully determined to place her in a state of tutelage and to take sides, in the name of their omnipotence, in the factions which had been let loose. The favour manifested by Constantius towards the partisans of Arianism as against the holders of the faith of Nicaea might have been a deciding factor in the development of events if the admirable tenacity of a St Athanasius in the East, and of a St Hilary in the West, had not offered a counterpoise. The first " Doctor "[4] of the Latin Church, St Hilary appeared in the light of history for the space of only ten years, but during this short period lasting from 355 to 367 his action was of sovereign efficacy.

[1] *Ep.*, xxxvii, 3.
[2] P.L., CLXXVIII, 1864.
[3] According to St Jerome, *De Vir. Ill.*, 97, Fortunatianus of Aquileia, another exegetist, wrote in the time of Constantine.
[4] This title was officially conferred upon him in the XIXth century by the Decree *Quod potissimum* of the Congregation of Rites (29 March 1851) and the Apostolic Brief *Si ab ipsis* (13 May 1851).

Hilary was born at Poitiers in the first years of the IVth century. His family which occupied a high position was pagan.[1] In the Gaul of the IVth century, which was " an Italy much more than a Province," [2] Hilary received a very careful education. In the introduction to his work on the Trinity he gives the motives which determined his conversion. He had felt keenly that he would never be contented with material and bestial (*beluinae*) enjoyments, with idleness and riches. An upright life securely swathed in the prudent maxims of Epicureanism no longer satisfied him. He had a hunger after the Divine which the contradictions of philosophy ill satisfied. Contact with the Sacred Books brought light into his soul which up till then had been in darkness and uncertainty. We know nothing of the period between his baptism and his becoming a Bishop. He had been married, if we may believe the poet Venantius Fortunatus, who wrote his life in verse at the end of the VIth century. We have even a letter from Hilary " to his daughter Abra " ; but it is so affected that it is hard to believe it authentic.

Once Bishop of Poitiers, Hilary shortly after 350 made no delay in entering upon the struggles which were to fill his life. Up till then he had remained quite outside the Eastern disputes on the ὁμοούσιος and the ὁμοιούσιος,[3] and had rested in the quiet possession and preaching of the truths he had acquired.[4] His first work, the *Commentaries* on St Matthew, in which he treats of different questions connected with the text of the Gospel, although he does not give any continuous paraphrase of it, shows him to be faithful to the tradition of the Trinity held by Tertullian and Novatian : the formulæ of Nicaea had not yet exercised any influence on him. The Synods of Arles (353) and of Milan (355), the exile of Paulinus of Trèves, Eusebius of Vercelli, Lucifer of Calaris, and Denys of Milan, opened his eyes to the Arian menace : " *Horum furori respondere* animus exarsit," he remarks.[5] He resolutely opposed Saturninus, the Primate of

---

[1] In Ps. 146, 13 (C.V., vol. XXII, p. 853, 1, 9).
[2] The expression is from Pliny the Elder, *Hist. Nat.*, III, iv. It was still truer in the IVth century than in the Ist. For his education at Poitiers, cf. Ausonius, *Prof.*, xi, 46–48 ; *Epigr.* xlvii, 2, 208.
[3] He confesses this himself : *De Syn.*, xci : ". . . fidem Nicaenam nunquam nisi exsulaturus audivi."
[4] Cf. *De Trin.*, I, xiv.
[5] *Ibid.*, I, xvii.

Arles, who had gone over to the Arian idea. The ardour of his proceedings marked him out to the Arian Bishops as a dangerous adversary. At the Synod of Béziers (356) they prevented him from offering a defence of Athanasius and the faith of Nicea, denounced him to the Emperor as a factious person, and obtained a sentence of exile against him.

Hilary was banished to Phrygia.[1] He profited largely during this unhappy time to add to his intellectual perfectioning. He initiated himself into Greek Christian literature (it would be interesting to know on what theologians he nourished his thought). It was a form of culture which was already somewhat rare at this time, and conferred upon him a superiority among the dialecticians of the West, of which his *De Trinitate*, composed during his exile,[2] bears the stamp. In these twelve books he was principally stirred against the Arians, although his polemics were sometimes aimed at the Sabellians, the Jews and the Gnostics. He was well aware of the extent of the evil against which he desired to forearm men's minds.[3] Here and there he traces with *clairvoyance* the Arian psychology—that *haeretica subtilitas* which played upon words in order to deceive the simple, and adapted itself so complacently to *prudentia saeculi*. The discussions of Hilary disclose on more than one page the penetration of his mind, and enable us to understand the details of the Arian contention. Evidence of this has been preserved to us, thanks to him.[4] On such a question, the difficulty of which dismays him,[5] St Hilary makes his readers understand that the words which he is obliged to employ, and the images and comparisons he uses, are hopelessly inadequate to the ineffable truths which he has to render intelligible, and that they should only see in them distant approximations destined to lead them from the known to the unknown.[6] The *De Trinitate* is one of the monuments of lofty Christian speculation of the first centuries : never up till then had the problems of Christology been examined in the West in such minute detail. The *De Synodis*, which

---

[1] Cf. St Jerome, *De Vir. Ill.*, c ; Hilary, *De Syn.*, lxiii.

[2] Cf. *De Trin.*, X, iv (P.L., X, 346) : " Loquemur exsules per hos libros, et sermo Dei, qui vinciri non potest, liber excurret."

[3] Cf. XI, 1 : " . . . multis jam per omnes ferme Romani imperii prouincias ecclesiis morbo pestiferae hujus praedicationis infectis."

[4] Cf. the letter of Arius to Alexander, VI, v.

[5] II, v.   [6] I, xix.

is joined to the *De Trinitate* in nearly all the manuscripts, presents a speculative character in only certain portions (§ lxvi–xcii). The principal object of the work, which is addressed to the Bishops of Gaul, the two Germanies, and Britain, is to put the people of the West in touch with the struggles in the East against Arianism. Thus Hilary is led to quote and to appraise several formulæ of the faith of the East :—the second formula of Sirmium (357), clearly Arian in colour, the twelve anathemas of Ancyra (358), the formula of the Synod of Antioch *in encaeniis* (341), the " confession " of Philippopolis (343–344), and the first formula of Sirmium (351). It is a precious work from the historical point of view ; it prepared the way to appeasing men's minds by giving them a clearer view of the questions in dispute, and the position of the opposing parties.

The authority of Hilary made itself felt even in the East. Although a Latin Bishop, he was invited to take his place at the Synod of Seleucia in 359, and there he upheld the conclusions of Nicea against the semi-Arian majority and against the Anomoeans. He likewise took part in the deputation sent to Constantinople to inform the Emperor of what had taken place at Seleucia. Saturninus of Arles was at that moment at Constantinople. Hilary solicited an audience of Constantius. We possess his petition, the *Ad Constantium Augustum*. In it he went over in twelve chapters the circumstances of his unjust exile, and begged the Emperor, in the interest of peace between the East and the West, to hearken to the language of the authentic faith, which had been altogether confused by intrigues, subtilties, and vain disputes. Constantius did not heed the prayer of Hilary. Thereat the latter allowed his indignation to burst forth in a pamphlet which perhaps was not published until after the death of the Emperor (3rd Nov. 361). After enumerating the attempts made by the Arians and protected by Constantius, Hilary did not hesitate to compare him with the worst persecutors :

" I will therefore cry aloud to thee, Constantius, what I would have said to Nero, what Decius and Maximin would have heard from my lips. Thou art fighting against God, thou art laying waste the Church, thou persecutest the Saints, thou dost hold in detestation the proclaimers of Christ, thou dost overthrow religion, a tyrant not of human things, but of things Divine. Up to now I have said what crimes are common to thee and to those persecutors : learn now those which proceed from thyself alone. Thou dost falsely pretend to be a Christian, and art a fresh enemy to Christ ; precursor of anti-Christ, thou art accomplishing his works of darkness. . . . Thou dost distribute the Episcopal Sees among thy partisans and thou dost replace good Bishops by evil ones. Thou dost imprison priests, thou dost put thine armies in the field to terrorise the Church, thou dost assemble Councils, and thou dost constrain to impiety the Bishops of the West who are shut up at Rimini after having frightened them with thy menaces, and weakened them with hunger enfeebled as they are by winter, and led astray by thy falsehoods. . . ." [1]

Such intrepid activity was matter to be feared by the Arians of the East. They had Hilary sent back to Gaul under the pretext that he was " *discordiae seminarium et perturbator Orientis.*" [2] Received with great demonstrations of joy in his Episcopal city, Hilary had no mind to give himself the least rest. To drive out Arianism from Gaul was the task he pursued without intermission. After various Provincial Synods, the Council of Paris, held in 361, anathematised Auxentius, Ursacius, Valens and Saturninus, the leaders of the Arian movement. The Nicene doctrine triumphed in Gaul ; Hilary carried the war into Italy. A conference at Milan brought him into opposition with Auxentius, the Bishop. The latter extricated himself by making use of equivocal methods, and St Hilary, who protested, received orders to leave Milan. [3] He obeyed, but in his *Contra Auxentium* he denounced the underhand proceedings of his adversary, " that angel of Satan, that enemy of Christ, that cursed despoiler, that renegade from the faith which he confessed by a lie and which he outrages by blasphemy." [4]

His last years passed in his diocese were fruitful in exegetic and historical works. A disciple of Origen, [5] he applied the

---

[1] § vi–vii.
[2] Sulp. Severus, *Chron.*, II, xlv, 4.
[3] *Contra Aux.*, § viii.
[4] § xii.
[5] Cf. St Jerome, *Ep.* xxxiv, 3.

methods of allegorical interpretation to the study of the Psalms in his *Tractatus super Psalmos*, which has only come down to us in an incomplete form :[1] in it the Psalms are explained in their function of *evangelica praedicatio*. The *Tractatus Mysteriorum*, discovered in 1887 by Gamurrini in the famous manuscript of Arezzo, is conceived in the same spirit and, although much spoilt, clearly presents the purpose of Hilary :

"Every work contained in the sacred volume," declares Hilary, " announces by word, explains by facts, and corroborates by examples the coming of our Lord Jesus Christ, sent by His Father, and born a man of a Virgin, through the operation of the Holy Spirit. From the beginning of the world, Christ, by authentic and absolute prefigurations (fulfilled) in the person of the Patriarchs, gives birth to the Church, washes it clean, sanctifies it, chooses it, places it apart and redeems it : by the sleep of Adam, by the deluge in the days of Noe, by the blessing of Melchisedech, by Abraham's justification, by the birth of Isaac, by the captivity of Jacob. . . . The purpose of this work is to show that in each personage, in every age, and in every act, the image of His coming, of His teaching, of His resurrection, and of our Church, is reflected as in a mirror."[2]

And further on :

"These acts, signified by the different personages (in the Old Testament), but understood and fulfilled in Christ alone, it is fitting should be preserved to posterity in works written and drawn up. Thus future generations, instructed in the actions of former times, may con-

---

[1] There are remaining the paraphrases of *Ps.* 1, 2, 9, 13, 14, 51–69, 91, 118–150. Certain references mentioned by Hilary reveal evident lacunæ. The MSS. thus give us only a *selection.*—The commentaries on *Ps.* 15, 31, and 41 are not authentic. There are some additional fragments in R.B., vol. XXVII (1910), p. 19. The word *tractatus* carries two principal acceptations in ecclesiastical language. It means (1) a treatise, a commentary, explanations principally on the Bible (v.g. the African Confessors, in St Cyprian, *Ep.* lxxvii, 1 ; the " *Tractatus super Psalmos* " of St Hilary of Poitiers ; St Jerome, *de Vir. Ill.*, xxxvii, xlviii, xlix, etc.) ; (2) a discourse (cf. Ps. Cyprian, *de Op. et Eleem.*, xii [Hartel, III, 1, p. 383] ; St Augustine, *Ep.* ccxxiv, 2 [C.V., vol. LVII, p. 453, l. 5]) : " . . . tractatus populares, quos Graeci homilias vocant " ; Optat, *Contra Parmen,* vii, 6 : " . . . Omnis tractatus in ecclesia a nomine Dei incipitur et ejusdem Dei nomine terminatur ".

[2] § 1 (C.V., LXV, p. 3, l. 10 et s.).

template the present even in the past, and may venerate the past still more in the present. . . ." [1]

Such is his method : St Jerome, who under the influence of Origen, was in his turn to practise it, recognised its difficulties which Hilary hardly seemed to have foreseen.

Of his Commentaries on Job there only remain two fragments. Doubtless therein Hilary made no great effort as he did elsewhere to expound the mystical relationships of the *typica significantia*.

But he was not unmindful of the Arian question, or rather, his mind remained obsessed with it. The *Fragmenta Historica* do great honour to his zeal as an historian. They deserve special attention by reason of their importance as a fountain-head for ecclesiastical history and also on account of the problems in modern criticism which they arouse.

The dogmatic conflicts of the IVth century provoked, as we know, the formation of several very valuable documentary collections both in the East and in the West. It was necessary to find suitable material for their polemics and to provide the means of enlightening public opinions. We should bear in mind the pieces included by St Athanasius in his *Apologia* against the Arians, in his *History of the Arians* addressed to the Monks, and in his treatise on the *Decrees of the Council of Nicea ;* the letters collected by Arius and Alexander ; the Συναγωγή of Sabinus of Heraclea ; the *Gesta Purgationis Caecilii et Felicis,* etc. . . . More complete than any other, the collection known under the title *Fragmenta Historica* is drawn up on a very similar plan : there are letters from Popes, Bishops, and Emperors, Acts and Decrees of different Councils, and professions of faith, each contribution as a rule being connected to the preceding one by a more or less lengthy explanatory text.

These *Fragmenta Historica* were first published in Paris in 1598 by Nicholas le Fèvre according to the edition which Pierre Pithou, who died two years before, had already compiled and nearly finished. Pithou had worked on a manuscript of the XVIth century in which the fragments had been classed under two series, one anonymous and the

[1] *Ibid.,* ii, 14 (C.V., p. 37, l. 5).

other attributed to St Hilary by name. Le Fèvre took into account this division and attribution of authorship ; nevertheless, for chronological reasons he inverted the order of the series, placing the anonymous series second. A century later, Pierre Coustant, the Benedictine, admitted that *all* the documents included in Pithou's manuscript were fragments of a great historical work on the Councils of Rimini and Seleucia [1] written by St Hilary : this is why in his edition of the works of St Hilary which he published in 1693, and which has long been held as an authority, he called the whole collection *Fragmenta ex libro sancti Hilarii Pictaviensis Provinciae Aquitaniae*, etc., after arranging them under a more exact chronology, the name which, variously abbreviated, has since passed into ordinary usage.

Charged by the commission of the *Corpus Script. Eccles. Latinorum* to bring out a certain number of the works of Hilary—the *Fragmenta Historica* among others—Father Feder, a Jesuit, took in hand the study of the tradition of the manuscript and the historical contents and origin of this collection as a preliminary,[2] which he designated under the title *Collectanea Antiariana Parisina*, without prejudice.

Feder established in the first place that the Cod. Parisin. Armamentarii lat. 483, of the IXth century (A) preserved in the Arsenal Library, of which Fèvre and Coustant were ignorant, is the archetype of the two manuscripts utilised by them, namely the Cod. Pithoeanus (T) now lost, and the Cod. Paris. lat. 1700, of the XVIIth century (C), which latter moreover is only a copy of T. He also drew up a list of other manuscripts wherein appear many isolated pieces from the *Coll. Antiar. Par.*, and furnished complete references to the printed collections (especially those dealing with Councils) in which these several documents had been inserted.

He then took in hand to settle the origin of these *Fragmenta Historica*. The name of Hilary of Poitiers figures at the head of the second series of the Manuscripts—which the first resembles very closely as a matter of fact. Now this notion is confirmed by the intrinsic study of the fragments composing the above series. Thus the opening piece is by

---

[1] This work is attested by St Jerome in his notice on Hilary (*De Vir. Ill.*, § C) : " Est ejus . . . liber adversum Valentem et Ursacium, historiam Ariminensis et Seleuciensis synodi continens."

[2] S.B.W., CLXII, 4 (1910) ; CLXVI, 5 (1911) ; CLXIX, 5 (1912).

all evidence an introduction to a historico-polemic work
by a Bishop who played an important part at the Council of
Béziers, who made vain attempts to obtain an audience
of the Emperor, and was determined to fight to the end for
Athanasius and the Nicene confession of faith. How is it
possible not to recognise Hilary under this description ?

Moreover this attributing of the authorship to him is
hardly contested. But there is this fine point about it : are
these extracts material for a work which Hilary had not been
able to finish, or are they extracts from a finished work
which we no longer possess ?   It is to the second solution that
Father Feder rallies. By a series of considerations in which
the historical analysis of the texts in dispute and the evidence
of contemporary events mutually help each other, he advances
the following hypothesis. In 356, immediately after the
Council of Béziers (and not during his exile at Constantinople
from 359–360 as had been believed since the time of Coustant),
Hilary wrote an historical and polemical work which was
none other than the *Liber adversus Valentem et Ursacium*
mentioned by St Jerome. Many fragments of this work are
still in existence, namely two and probably three from the
Fragmenta Historica,[1] to which must be added two other
documents which have come down to us under the misleading
and now obsolete title *Ad Constantium Liber Primus*—the
letter from the Council of Sardica to the Emperor Constantius
and the narrative text accompanying it.

Father Feder borrowed the essential portion of these
views from a remarkable article by Dom A. Wilmart which
appeared in the *Revue Bénédictine* in 1907,[2] but while he
appropriated Dom Wilmart's ideas, Father Feder systematised them and carried them further than Dom Wilmart
wished to do. He thinks that St Hilary wrote a sequel to
his work against Valens and Ursacius about December 359,
after the Councils of Seleucia and Rimini. What he was
wishing to do on this occasion was to influence the Bishops
who had " fallen " at Rimini to retract. The *Epistola
legatorum Synodi Seleuciensis ad legatos Synodi Arimensis,*

---

[1] The *Praefatio ad opus historicum,* the *Varia ex actis synodi Sardicensis,* also
doubtless the *Epistola synodi Sardicensis Orientalium.*

[2] " *L'Ad Constantium liber primus* de Saint Hilaire de Poitiers et Les Fragments
historiques."

and probably also seven other of the *Fragmenta Historica* would belong to this second portion.

As regards those *Fragmenta* not susceptible of being classed in the two first portions of St Hilary's work against Valens and Ursacius, Feder supposes that they were incorporated in a third portion which appeared in 367, shortly before or after the death of Hilary.

The formation of the collection such as we now have it could be explained as follows. An anonymous writer, with the view of giving a fresh account of the Arian struggles, must have extracted for his own purposes from Hilary's work the numerous documents which the latter had included in it, and added thereto ample marginal notes. These useful *excerpta* were transcribed and circulated at an early date; certain indications enable us to state that the collection was made up in Italy at the beginning of the IVth century.

Clearly, conjecture occupies a large space in these combinations; it could not be otherwise on such a matter. At any rate, the leading ideas on the literary enigma offered to the curiosity of critics by the *Fragmenta Historica* are henceforth defined in a useful manner. And it is interesting to discover in the great Bishop the Roman taste for administrative conciseness and methodical order which furnished these oratorical contests with documents and facts.

St Hilary also made use of poetry in giving expression to his views. He was the first to write hymns for the Church in Latin. Isidore of Spain affirms this,[1] and before him St Jerome had noted the *Liber Hymnorum*.[2] His sojourn in the East had given him the opportunity of appreciating the effective propaganda of which the use of sung words is capable. Had not Arius composed songs for the use of sailors, millers, and travellers, set to profane airs?[3] This method of the Gnostics[4] had been revived and Hilary thought good to appropriate it. We know that he experienced difficulty in imposing the use of the chant of the Church upon his compatriots.[5] In 1887 a few hymns were known under his name,

---

[1] *De Eccl. Off.*, I, vi (P.L., LXXXIII, 743).
[2] *De Vir. Ill.*, c.
[3] Cf. Philostorgius, H.E., II, xxvii (P.G., LXVI, 464).
[4] Texts in P. de Labriolle's *La Crise Montaniste*, p. 62 et s.
[5] Jerome, *ad Gal.*, I. II: " Hilarius . . . Gallos in hymnorum carmine indociles vocat."

without sufficient guarantee of authenticity. The Arezzo manuscript has given three which might reasonably be attributed to him. The first piece, *Ante saecula qui manes* is written in the rhythm known as second asclepiad (one glyconic line followed by a minor asclepiad). The four last strophes are missing. There follows next—after a gap of six leaves in the manuscript—the piece *Fefellit saevam* in iambics of six feet; the first five strophes are missing. These two fragments are alphabetical. The third hymn, *Adae carnis gloriosa*, is in catalectic trochaic tetrameters; the end has been lost. These three pieces (to which some critics add a few others of a more or less resemblance) are dogmatic in character, which is specially pronounced in the *Ante saecula* treating of the relationship of the Son to the Father. In the second hymn the soul regenerated by baptism explains how Christ has triumphed over death and made the resurrection possible. The third celebrates Christ, the heavenly Adam, and His first victory over Satan. The versification shows many licences, especially a rather frequent hiatus.[1] These are clearly the kind of hymns, at once liturgical and popular, which it was necessary to oppose to the Arians in order to imprint on the memory the essential truths which the former were threatening.

St Hilary was thus a man of action and a fighter even in his verses. One thought only filled his life and made it one whole—the fight against Arianism. He was persuaded that the entire faith was at stake, that this rationalistic theology, this formalistic and literal exegesis, would kill the Catholicism that had been handed down. He had no hesitation in calling the Arian Bishops " anti-Christ " : *nominis antichristi proprietas est, Christo esse contrarium.*[2] Giving the appearance of preaching Jesus Christ, but in reality denying Him since they would only give Him attributes by means of which He could in nothing be distinguished from the creature, the angel or man ; carrying out this detestable work under the mask of a false piety ; seeking their support in the " world," and basing it on *ambitio saecularis,* and on *suffragia terrena,* whereas the Apostles themselves had known how to struggle

[1] For example, in the *Ante saecula*, lines 26, 32, 53, 72.
[2] *Contra Auxentium,* § ii.

against every power leagued against them—is how he up-braids them, and with these familiar grievances he mingles pity for the Christian people thus deceived by bad shepherds : " *Sanctiores aures plebis quam corda sunt sacerdotum.*" [1]

Hilary possessed the qualities of a leader of men, and this he showed wherever he went, in the East as well as in the West. His reputation was immense.[2] He enjoyed the *prestige* of having suffered for his ideas. How can we deny him the title of " disciple of truth,"[3] which was his ambition ? Then too the eloquent vigour of his language completed the effect of a very noble example.

In contradistinction to many other ecclesiastical writers Hilary never concealed his desire to write well. At the beginning of his great work on the Trinity he asks God to grant him " verborum significationem, intellegentiae lumen, *dictorum honorem.* . . ." [4] In another place, in his Commentary on the Psalms,[5] he declares that " he who treats of the word of God should do honour to the Author of that word, even in the beauty of his phrasing, just as those who compose the wording of a king's rescript must proceed with diligence and care in order to be worthy of the dignity due to a prince." He always drew up the plan of his works with an eye to wise composition,[6] and here and there excused himself for having allowed himself in the ardour of discussion to be drawn further than the limits he had set.[7]

In addition he had received a good formation as a scholar. He did not know Hebrew,[8] but he had learnt Greek in the East.[9] He had some knowledge of philosophy[10] and natural sciences.[11] In a word, he had at his disposition all the resources giving a wide range of culture to a man who has not been endowed with an original style and a form of expression

---

[1] *Ibid.*, iii–iv.
[2] We have the witness of St Jerome on this point, *Ep.* xxxiv, 3 : ". . . ubicumque romanum nomen est, praedicatur."
[3] *Contra Const.*, xii.
[4] I, xxxviii (P.L., X, 49).
[5] xiii, 1 (P.L., IX, 295).
[6] Cf. *De Trin.*, I, xx et s. : " Nihil enim incompositum indigestumque placuit afferre."
[7] *Ibid.*, V, xii (X, 136).
[8] Cf. *In Psalm*, cxxxviii, 43 (P.L., IX, 775) ; cxlii, 1 (IX, 805) ; and St Jerome, *Ep.* xxxiv, 3.
[9] St Jerome (*ibid.*) is too exact when he wrote : " Graecarum quoque litterarum *quandam aurulam* ceperat."
[10] Cf. the introduction to the *De Trinitate*.
[11] *De Trin.*, XII, liii ; *In Ps.* cxxxiv, 11 ; lxviii, 29 ; cxx, 12, etc.

of his own. It is classic, and formed in the school of Quintilian, whom he imitates occasionally, but with more discretion than a phrase of St Jerome [1] would allow us to suppose. His periods are of an oratorical amplitude, with an abundance of similes which are too rigorously developed and driven home,[2] and endings adroitly balanced off.[3]

The strong vigour of eloquence does not permeate Hilary's writings. With Villemain we might say that it is on a lower level than the genius of the author, and that all this contentious and arid theology only half expresses him. But a burning sincerity breathes throughout which does not exclude charity. A fanatic like Lucifer of Calaris, himself passionately anti-Arian, was to attack Hilary for the concessions he made by his practical liberalism. He is a worthy figure in the list of those skilful and powerful organisers of Christianity, the Fathers of the Church, victorious, but harassed by intestine discords almost as grievously as it had been persecuted till lately from without.

Hilary died in 367, on the 1st of November, without doubt.[4]

V

PUTTING on one side all question of literary talent, Lucifer of Calaris (Cagliari, in Sardinia) makes one think of Tertullian whose *intransigeance* and restrictions he copied. Exiled with three other Bishops shortly after the Council of Milan (355)[5] for having refused to subscribe to the condemnation of St Athanasius, when the greater part of those who took part in it were weak enough to adhere to it, Lucifer lived in different countries from 356 to 361. We find him successively at Germanicia in Syria Commagene, Eleutheropolis in Palestine, then in the Thebaid. It was here he was found by the edict of the Emperor Julian who recalled to their Sees

---

[1] *Ep.* lxx, 5 : "Hilarius . . . duodecim Quintiliani libros et stilo imitatus est et numero." Cf. Kling, *De Hilario Pict. artis rhetoricae* . . . *studioso.* Fr.-i.-B., 1910, p. 31.

[2] There is a characteristic example in the *De Trin.*, XII, 1.   "Longis interdum periodis involvitur," Jerome caustically remarks, *Ep.* LVIII, 10. Hilary uses fifteen times running *cum* in a complementary sense : *In Ps.* li, 6.

[3] Kling, *op. cit.*, p. 33 et s.

[4] See the discussion on the date in Feder, S.B.W., vol. CLXII, fasc. 4, p. 126.

[5] Athanasius, *Hist. Arian.*, xxxiii et s. (P.G., XXV, 732 ; XLI, 741) ; Sulp.-Severus, *Chron.*, II, xxxix.

the Bishops who had been exiled or interned by the decision of the Council, with the secret design of rekindling hostile feelings within the bosom of Christianity.

Lucifer's writings were all written during his exile, and were aimed uniformly at Constantius who is treated therein without any attempt at conciliation. Their titles are significant beforehand in their brevity : No truck with heretics (*De non conveniendo cum haereticis*) ; Saint Athanasius (*De Sancto Athanasio*) ; No pity for the enemies of God (*De non parcendo in Deum delinquentibus*) ; Let us die for the Son of God (*Moriendum esse pro Dei Filio*). These pamphlets, largely reinforced by texts specially taken from the Old Testament, which have come to us in one only manuscript (*Vatic.*, 133, ix–x cent.), have as their object to stigmatise the policy of Constantius, his complaisance towards the Arians, those sons of darkness,[1] and his claim to justify them by alleging his then prosperity to be a kind of dispensation from God, while there were so many examples which showed the long delay of the inevitable vengeance of heaven.[2] Lucifer also protests against the procedure observed at the Council of Milan when St Athanasius was condemned without having been heard (*De Sancto Athanasio*). As against the Emperor who had taxed him with arrogance he alleges his duty as a Bishop to proclaim the truth without respect of persons (*De non parcendo*). The *Moriendum Esse*, a mosaic made up from Tertullian, Lactantius, the letters of St Cyprian,[3] and the *De Laude Martyrii*, shows the energetic temper with which Lucifer declares himself ready to leave everything in order to defend the orthodox belief proclaimed at Nicea.

The imperial prerogative was not wanting in a certain longanimity since it put up with such intemperate language without wrath. " He allowed himself to be called the Ahab of the Christians by the new Elias." [4] Possibly he thought these anathemas too uninteresting to trouble about. Lucifer had no claim as a man of letters ; he boasted of it and affected to have been brought up on the Bible alone.[5] For skill in

[1] C.V., XIV, p. 20, l. 4.
[2] *Ibid.*, p. 35, l. 7.
[3] Especially letters vi, x, xxxvii, lv (perhaps also lviii). See Merk, in T.Q., 1912, p. 1 et s.
[4] Duchesne, II, 340.
[5] C.V., XIV, p. 256, l. 6 ; p. 294, l. 23 ; p. 306, l. 19 and 23.

developing arguments he substituted a wealth of quotations from Scripture. Anchored upon certain unshakable principles, he deemed it to be superfluous to strengthen them by any demonstration from reason. Philologists (rather than men of letters or even theologians) find something to glean from his combative writing, whether in the text of the version of the Bible or in his language packed with anacoluthons, ellipses, and smacking of the popular orator.[1]

Towards the end of his life this passionate defender of orthodoxy outlined a movement very similar, as I have said, to what had already been effected by Tertullian. When Pope Liberius and Bishop Athanasius were inclined to exercise indulgence in regard to those Bishops who had allowed themselves to sign a formula favourable to the Arians at the Council of Rimini (359), Lucifer opposed their pacificatory desires with all his force. He rallied to his uncompromising views Hilary the Deacon, and Gregory the Bishop of Eliberis, about whom we shall have to speak on a future occasion. Hilary went so far as to maintain that the defaulters at Rimini, and those who followed them,[2] must be rebaptised. Such rigour was no longer in season and condemned Lucifer to remain by himself or nearly so. He spent the last years of his life in his diocese in Sardinia, and died there about the year 370–371.

Some of his partisans caused talk up to about the year 384. The *Collectio Avellana*[3] contains a *Libellus precum*,[4] a kind of petition addressed in 383–4 to the Emperors Valentinian II, Theodosius, and Arcadius, by the priests Faustinus and Marcellinus, as a form of protest against the annoyances to which they were exposed on the part of the Catholics, and against the odious name of " Luciferians " by which they were caricatured. An imperial rescript recog-

---

[1] Hartel's study in A.L.L., III (1886), p. 1, of Lucifer's Latin is well summed up in the *Rev. de Philol.* (*Revue des Revues*), 1888, p. 197–199.

[2] St Jerome, *Dial. adv. Lucifer*, xxi (P.L., XXIII, 175) and xxvii.

[3] A collection of more than two hundred pieces put together by an unknown scholar who lived in Rome in the time of Pope Vigilius (537–555). This collection comprises letters, edicts, etc., of emperors, magistrates, Popes, and Bishops and spreads over the years 367–553.   The Ballerini brothers gave it this name in the XVIIIth century, because they thought (wrongly) that a manuscript in the Umbrian Convent of Santa Cruce in Fonte Avellana (now *Vaticanus* 4961) was the principal source from which the collection was drawn.

[4] This title is not attested by the written manuscript. It was invented by J. Sirmond, who published the work for the first time in 1650.

nised the reasonableness of their request.[1] We possess also two other *opuscula* of Faustinus, composed as a guarantee of the purity of their orthodoxy. In one, the *Fides Theodosio Imp. Oblata*, he defends himself against any leaning to Sabellianism; in the other, the *De Trinitate sire de Fide contra Arianos*, he enlightens Flaccilla the Empress on the fundamental points of the Arian controversy.

The literary activity of the Luciferians may also have assumed a more subtle and underhand form. They were suspected, for sufficiently striking reasons, of having fashioned weapons to be used for the glory of their cause which was dear to them and too little understood—in particular, two pretended letters of St Athanasius to Lucifer,[2] and the first eight books of the *De Trinitate* by the pseudo-Athanasius.[3]

VI

WE must also glance at the Arian and anti-Arian literature which reflects the burning polemics of the time, but offers little real attraction except for theologians and students of the history of doctrine. The confusion surrounding these thorny controversies reveals but few agreeable surprises.

The writings on the Arian side are by no means numerous. We know the fate of heterodox literature, and what dangers it must have run in avoiding so many occasions for its destruction.[4]

We may make passing mention of Potamius, Bishop of Olisopo (Lisbon), a supporter of Arianism in the Episcopacy of Spain. We have a letter from him to St Athanasius, also two sermons, one on Lazarus, and the other on the martyrdom of Isaias, which are characterised by a deliberate seeking after the horrible. The writer complacently describes in detail the different phases of the decomposition of the body of Lazarus in the tomb, and notes its deliquescence and putrid odour; he lets us hear the *stridor* of the saw through the body of Isaias and follows its hideous progress.

---

[1] P.L., XIII, 107–108.

[2] We have only the Latin text : P.G., XXVI, 1181 et s. ; C.V., XIII, 322 et s.

[3] P.L., LXII, 307–334. Books IX–XII form another work, and they have been wrongly incorporated with the first eight in the *Patrol. lat.* See L. Saltet, B.L.E., 1906, 300.

[4] Cf. P. de Labriolle, *Les Sources de l'Hist. du Montanism*, 1913, p. ix–xiii.

The Vatican Library and the Ambrosian Library at Milan share a palimpsest containing curious fragments of Arian origin. This palimpsest came from the Monastery of Bobbio. " The monks of the Abbey of Bobbio, founded by St Colomban in 613, to whom had been given the task of combating the influence of Arianism which had been perpetuated in Italy by the Gothic, and afterwards by the Lombard, domination, were obliged to collect ample Arian material in their library." [1] These twenty-one fragments all refer to Arianism, with the exception of the last two which are made up from extracts from an apocryphal work, the *Ascension of Isaias*. Angelo Mai first edited them in 1828. They belong to different works, of a homiletic, dogmatic, or polemical character. There is no positive difficulty in attributing them to the same author, whom certain indications invite us to look for among the Bishops of the region of the Danube. Maximin, Auxentius of Durostorum, and Palladius of Ratiara, have been suggested, but no deciding reason enables us to place any likelihood on its authorship. Another palimpsest from Bobbio, also deciphered and published by Mai, has given us fragments of a commentary on St Luke. In it there are mingled very characteristic statements of " homoian " Arianism with its edifying phraseology. [2]

The treatise by St Augustine, *Contra Sermonem Arianorum*, has preserved for us an anonymous Arian sermon (*Quidam sermo Arianorum sine nomine auctoris sui*) used as a preface to it. In the same way an Arian commentary on Job has slipped in among the works of Origen. These little treatises are of a tiresome mediocrity. This is not the case with the *Opus imperfectum in Matthaeum*, an " incomplete " collection of homilies on the Gospel of St Matthew, of which St John Chrysostom has long been regarded as the author, although Arian doctrine is there betrayed in statements lacking no ambiguity. [3] St Thomas Aquinas (who probably read the work in an amended edition) declared that if he had to choose between owning Paris or this book, he would choose the *Opus imperfectum*, if the choice were given him. In it the author speaks in the tone of a Bishop, with much force and

---

[1] J. Zeiller, *Les Orig. chrét. dans les Prov. Danubiennes*, etc., 1918, p. 491.
[2] *Ibid.*, p. 499, where the principal texts are quoted.
[3] *Ibid.*, p. 474.

authority, and extreme bitterness at having seen the erroneous doctrine of Nicea triumph over that of Arius. He also wrote— he alluded to it himself—Commentaries on St Mark and St Luke. Can he be identified with Maximin ? This hypothesis does not pass the bounds of mere probability. The same may be said of a learned attempt to show that the work had been written originally in Greek, which does not seem to have resulted in any sound conclusions.[1]

The *Dissertatio Maximini contra Ambrosium* (such is the title coined by Kauffmann, its first editor) is without literary value. But it is of real importance from the point of view of the Arian attitude towards St Ambrose and of the fortunes of Arianism in Illyria. This compilation is compressed in the margin of a manuscript at Paris (Bibl. Nat. lat. 8907) containing the two first books of St Ambrose's *De Fide* and the Acts of the Council of Aquileia. It comprises three distinct parts. First it is a commentary on a part of the Proceedings at Aquileia ; we know that the Council of Aquileia, which opened on the 3rd September 381, and of which Ambrose was the moving spirit, deposed summarily Palladius of Ratiara (Arcer), and another Illyrian Bishop, without doubt Secundianus of Singidunum (Belgrade), both convicted of Arianism. The Commentary, which is by the Goth Bishop, Maximin, follows the debates in the Council step by step. In a second portion, Maximin quotes various evidence in favour of the Arian doctrine, among others a letter in which Auxentius, the Bishop of Durostorum and a disciple of Ulfila, relates the life of his master. A profession of faith by Ulfila himself is inserted in this letter, which is a source of information of the first order on the life of the Arian apostle of the Goths.[2] After a space, which was no doubt left by the copyist in order to transcribe other texts which were finally neglected, comes the testimony of Palladius —a vehement diatribe against the *De Fide* of St Ambrose, and against his diplomatic methods. The collection closes with a brief appendix which relates the failure of the steps taken by Ulfila, Palladius, and Secundianus, and their partisans, before Theodosius. This last paragraph must

[1] Cf. Stiglmayr, Z.K.T., XXXIII (1909), p. 594–597, and XXXIV (1910), p. 1–38 ; p. 473–499. See also Dom Capelle in R. Bén., 1922, pp. 224-233.

[2] Cf. Jacques Zeiller, *op. cit.*, p. 440 et s. This profession of faith is quoted on p. 461.

have been added afterwards in the Vth century, and is not by Maximin.[1]

On the orthodox side we may mention the *Liber contra Arianos* by Foebadius of Agen, who, during St Hilary's exile, held a position of some prominence in Gaul. His mind was without originality, for whom Tertullian's *Adversus Praxean* seems to have been his favourite work, to judge from the clippings and abridgments which he took from it for his treatise addressed to the Bishops of Gaul. In it he aims especially at the second formula of Sirmium (357) which was strongly tinged with Arianism, and at Bishop Hosius of Cordova who had weakly subscribed to it.

Hosius was a hundred years old at the time ; this fact explains his error, which his sturdy and long-held sympathy with Nicea made so unexpected, and which he was soon to disavow on his death-bed. When already a very old man he had taken an important position at the Council of Nicea, and had presided at the Council of Sardica, at which apparently the canons were drawn up under his immediate influence. Isidore attributes to him in his *De Vir. Ill.*, § v, two small works which have not come down to us. All that remains by him is a letter to St Athanasius, and another to Pope Julius.

Eusebius, born in Sardinia, and Bishop of Vercelli in 345, after having been for some time a Lector of the Church in Rome, became a courageous co-operator in the work of St Hilary, and suffered exile in 355–6, at the same time as Lucifer of Calaris. He lived at Skythopolis in Palestine, then in Cappadocia, and afterwards in Upper Egypt. Julian's edict set him at liberty ; he died on the 1st August 370 or 371. The Church venerates him as a martyr. Among the treasures of the Cathedral of Vercelli is preserved a manuscript of the Gospels, written very probably in the IVth century, perhaps even by the hand of Eusebius, representing one of the most famous pre-Hieronymean texts.[2] According to the testimony of St Jerome,[3] Eusebius of Vercelli had translated the *Commentaries on the Psalms* by Eusebius of Cæsarea, leaving out passages of doubtful orthodoxy. We

[1] *Ibid.*, p. 484–488.
[2] Cf. P.L., XII, 9–948. The text has been re-edited by Cardinal Gasquet in the *Collectanea Biblica*, fasc. 111, Rome, 1914.
[3] *De Vir. Ill.*, xcvi. Cf. *Ep.*, lxi, 2.

have only a few letters of his. Some have wished to attribute to him the *Symbolum Athanasianum*, called the *Quicumque*.[1]

The most original of this group of anti-Arian writings is the *Altercatio Heracliani Laici cum Germinio Episcopo Sirmiensi de fide Synodi Nicaenae et Arimensis Arianorum*. It is dated the 6th of the Ides of January, 366. In it we must see, not an imaginary dialogue but an authentic tilt between Heraclianus, a layman, representing the orthodoxy of Nicea, and Germinius the Bishop of Sirmium[2] professing Arianism. Heraclianus who was thrown into prison with two other confessors, vigorously kept up the dispute, which bore upon the divinity of the Holy Spirit as much as on that of the Son. The arguments used are not those of dialectics : at a given moment at the Bishop's orders Heraclianus is boxed on the ears by a reader and a deacon. Nevertheless Germinius refused to hand him over to the imperial justice as urged by the shouts of the crowd. The whole setting of this colloquy has movement and life. It will be noticed that the profession of faith pronounced in the course of the debate by Heraclianus is taken word for word from a passage of Tertullian's *Apologeticum* (§ xxi).

Let me mention further among extant traces of anti-Arian literature a *Tractatus contra Arianos*, the fragments of which, included in a papyrus of the VIth century at Vienna (Cod. 2160, Theol. C 50a) following after St Hilary's *De Trinitate*, are not unworthy of our attention. This work seems to go back to the second half of the IVth century.

VII

To Gregory of Eliberis (Elvira, in Betica) St Jerome attributes quite justly some *tractatus* written "*mediocri sermone*," and an "elegant book" *de Fide*.[3] Modern commentators have been far more generous, and his "heritage" has been swollen with a quantity of additions of which I should not dare to say all formed part of the original stock.

A great enemy of Arianism,[4] pitiless towards all com-

---

[1] Cf. C. H. Turner, in J.T.S., I (1900), p. 126.
[2] Cf. Feder in S.B.W., vol. CLXII, fasc. 4, pp. 100–104, on Germinius.
[3] *De Vir. Ill.*, cv.
[4] St Jerome, *Chron.*, *ad ann.* 2386, i.e. 370 A.D.

R

plaisance where the Arians were concerned, the fine rigidity
of his orthodoxy deserved the praise meted out to it by the
Luciferian compilers of the *Libellus Precum.*

A manuscript (XIth century) in the Church of St Vincent
de Roda, in Aragon, imputes five sermons to him on the Canticle of Canticles, which were published by Gotthold Heine in
1848. Owing to the disturbance produced by the Revolution
of 1848, Heine's publication had passed unnoticed. Dom
Wilmart brought it back to the light in 1906,[1] and used it
as a criterion to restore other works to Gregory,—in the first
place the famous *Tractatus Origenis*, which were published in
1900 by Mgr. Batiffol and Dom Wilmart himself. These
consist of twenty homilies, nineteen of which are on the Old
Testament, and one on the mission of the Holy Spirit, written
by a clever allegorist of moderate literary talent and saturated
throughout with Minucius Felix, Tertullian, Novatian, Origen,
Hippolytus and St Hilary. The first editors, accepting the
tradition of the manuscript,[2] attributed them to Origen
whose Greek rendering must have been translated, as they
thought, by Victorinus of Pettau. Certain indications[3]
compel us to recognise that this is no case of a translation
but that we are confronted with a Latin original. It was
necessary to go in search of some author who wrote in the
Latin tongue, a difficult and often deceptive endeavour.
Novatian appeared to be the one, but a deeper examination
rendered the combination difficult to adhere to, and disclosed
the likelihood of a post Nicene origin for the *Tractatus.*
Dom Wilmart found a " close parallelism " between these
Tractatus and Gregory's sermons on the Canticle of Canticles :
" The same methods of style, the same system of quotations,
the same turn of exegesis, the same theological trend ; or,
if you prefer, the same characteristic traits reappear throughout, clearly and well defined—a ready suppleness of expression, original views on the Bible, freshness of allegory, and
doctrinal *naïveté*, not excluding firmness." [4] What is very
singular is that the *Tractatus* (sic) *Origenis*, which combat
errors such as anthropomorphism or *patripassianism*, do not

[1] B.L.E., 1906, pp. 233–299.
[2] An Orleans manuscript, no. 22, Xth century ; one at St Omer, no. 150, XIIth
century.
[3] V.g. p. 6, 1 ; " ex *humo homo* dicitur."
[4] B.L.E., 1906, p. 249.

breathe a word about the Arian question which outweighed all others in the life of Gregory. This objection has an answer to it ; we have said that St Hilary himself only interested himself very late in Arianism. The West showed some strange ignorances, but it did not fail to make its impression notwithstanding.

A sermon on Noah's Ark, a " type " of the cross, has since been " restored " to Gregory,[1] and the *Liber de Fide* which St Augustine erroneously imputed to St Gregory of Nazianzen,[2] and has come down to us in two editions, the second of which bears traces of retouching by the author.[3] The question of the ὁμοούσιος is frankly approached this time.[4]

VIII

ST AUGUSTINE has related the attractive history of C. Marius Victorinus in his *Confessions* (VIII, ii). He obtained it from a priest, Simplicianus by name, who had been the intimate friend of Victorinus. Born in the African Pro-Consulate about the year 300, Victorinus followed the calling of rhetor in Rome. He was accounted one of the wisest and most eloquent men of his time. He had even allowed a statue to be erected in his honour in the Roman Forum (or perhaps in the Forum of Trajan). In spite of a certain urbanity natural to him which he preserved throughout his life, he does not spare the Christians some hard knocks of this kind : " In the opinion of the Christians the following argument is not conclusive :—' If she brought forth a child it was because she had connection with a man ' ; nor this either :—' If he was born, he will die.' For the Christians admit the existence of a Being who was born without the intervention of man, and who did not die." Augustine tells us that his heart was " the impregnable retreat of the devil " (*pectus, quod tam inexpugnabile receptaculum diabolus obtinuerat*, VIII iv, 9), and that his tongue, like a sharp arrow, had slain many souls.

In order the better to combat Christianity, he set himself to read assiduously " Holy Scripture and all the Christian

[1] *R. Bén.*, XXVI (1909), p. 1.
[2] *Ep.* cxlviii, 10. It occurs in various places in Migne (XX, 31 ; XVII, 549 ; LXII, 449, and P.G., XXXVI, 669).
[3] Dom Wilmart, in S.B.W., vol. CLIX (1908), fasc. I.
[4] V.g. P.L., XX, 35 ; 37–38 ; 39 ; 40 ; 41 ; 44 ; etc.

literature." Undertaken with a frankly hostile intention this inquiry was to start him on the way to unexpected conclusions. He felt a growing sympathy springing up within him for the doctrine against which he was seeking weapons. He went so far one day as to say privately to Simplicianus, " Don't you know well that I am already a Christian." To which Simplicianus replied, " I shall not believe you, and I shall not count you as a Christian so long as I do not see you in the Church of Christ." " Do walls then make men Christians ? " Victorinus laughingly exclaimed. The fear of causing sorrow to his friends and arousing lively hatred for some time made his steps slow along the road he was taking. One day, however, blushing over his delays, he said suddenly to Simplicianus, " Come to the Church ! I mean to be a Christian." Without restraining his joy (*non se capiens laetitia*), Simplicianus at once conducted him to it. Victorinus passed through the various stages of a catechumen, " *mirante Roma, gaudente ecclesia*," St Augustine says. When the day came on which, as was customary, he was to make his public profession of faith, the Roman clergy offered to read it to him behind closed doors so as to spare his *amour propre*. Victorinus refused. He mounted on the platform. His name passed from mouth to mouth, then a great silence fell and " he pronounced the formula of truth with such a fine confidence that all would have liked to seize him and give him a place in the deepest recesses of their hearts " (. . . *volebant eum omnes rapere intro in cor suum*).

Up till then he had given himself up to learned works and metaphysics. It is not easy to discern in the *Ars Grammatica* what portion properly belonged to him and what should be attributed to a grammarian, by name Aphtonius, whose work seems to have been compiled with his own. His commentary on Cicero's *Inventione* is not important otherwise than in informing us of the method of instruction followed by the rhetoricians in the IVth century. A *De Definitionibus* which had strayed in among the writings of Boethius should be restored to him. But it was in philosophy that Victorinus interested himself far more than in philology or grammar (" qui philosophorum tam multa legerat et dijudicaverat," St Augustine remarks). As a confirmed neo-Platonist he had translated Porphyry's *Isagogé* [1] and apparently various works of Plotinus.[2] It was he who initiated St Augustine into neo-Platonism at a critical period in his views, and it was from his example that he received a decisive impulse. *Exarsi ad imitandum,* he confesses. Victorinus also translated Aristotle's *Categories* and the Περὶ ἑρμηνείας, thereby exercising a leading influence on the logicians of the Middle Ages through the intermediary of Boethius.

A dialectician before everything else, he applied his aptitude and taste to the defence of the Christian faith once he had embraced it. The Arian dispute attracted him especially on account of its metaphysical rather than its historical character. He brought to it his customary charm [3] sounding a different note amid those hard-hitting polemics, and his firm belief in the sovereign competence of the reason even where it bases its support on Scripture.[4] St Jerome appraised the works of Victorinus somewhat harshly. He finds them very obscure and accessible only to the learned (". . . valde obscuros, qui nisi ab eruditis non intelliguntur ").[5] In another place [6] he reproaches him with his ignorance of Holy Scripture (certain portions of which he had commented upon). " It is no use being eloquent," Jerome remarks ; " it is not possible to discuss competently a subject one knows nothing of." As a matter of fact, there is no doubt that Victorinus had read the Bible closely ; but as he had become a Christian very late, and was wholly penetrated with neo-Platonism, he did not see his way, like so many others, to renounce the philosophy which had been dear to him ; he endeavoured rather to draw attention to the help which even orthodoxy might derive from it in the arduous comprehension of the relationship of the Son to the Father (which he

---

[1] A restored version by P. Monceaux of this Latin *Isagogé* by Porphyry appears in *Mélanges Havet*, Paris, 1909, pp. 296–310 (following one of the commentaries of Boethius).

[2] On this point see Alfaric, *L'Evol. intell. de St Augustin*, 1918, p. 375.

[3] In his discussion with Candidus, the Arian, of which a little work entitled *Liber de generatione divina* (P.L., VIII, 1013–1020) has been preserved, and which is connected with the refutation of the Arians, he calls his adversary *O generose Candide, O mi dulcissime Candide*, etc. . . . There is also a letter from Candidus to Marius Victorinus (P.L., *ibid.*, 1035).

[4] He felt the danger of this prepossession and says : ". . . Ne quis blasphemiter intellegens meum dogma dixerit, omnia enim a sancta Scriptura et dicuntur et sunt " (*Adv. Arium*, I, xlvi ; P.L., VIII, 1076-C.).

[5] *De Vir. Ill.*, ci.

[6] *Comm. in Gal.*, Praef.

represents as analogous to that of the One and the νοῦς of the metaphysics of Plotinus),[1] of the theory of creation,[2] and the explanation of original sin.[3]   Deep down in the mind of Victorinus, the system of Plotinus holds a place of first importance.   From this proceeded certain statements and certain rather disquieting reserves,[4] sincerely Christian as he had become.   He would never have accepted the Christian doctrine if he had not had the happy astonishment of finding so many occasions of " utilising " his favourite concepts, to which he strains in more than one place to refer it.

His style has force, movement and even a kind of pious melody (as for example in his three hymns to the Trinity). Victorinus formed for the Latin of the West a new language of philosophy which was to be of great help to the logicians and metaphysicians of the Middle Ages.   He tried, as far as he could, to transpose Greek expressions into Latin and apologises when he cannot find the equivalents.[5]   To sum him up, Victorinus, without having a great mind himself, has influenced great minds.   In the history of ideas he has his place, more by what he has transmitted than by what he created himself.

---

[1] See details and references in Tixeront, *Hist. des Dogmes*, II, 266 ; 268.
[2] *Ibid.*, p. 273.
[3] p. 278.
[4] He admits that man is under the influence of the stars so long as he is not a Christian and has not acquired *in suis actibus libertatem* (*ad Gal.*, II, 3 ; P.L., VIII, 1175–6).   The same idea comes out also in Hippolytus of Rome and Clement of Alexandria.   The manner in which he expresses himself on the resurrection of the body has an idealism which might lend itself to equivocal interpretation (*ad Eph.*, ii, 9 ; P.L., VIII, 1274 A).   He seems to attribute to matter a maleficent power by which original sin might be explained (*Adv. Arium*, I, xxvi ; P.L., VIII, 1060 A), etc.
[5] V.g. *Adv. Arium*, II, ix (P.L., VIII, 1095 A) ; *ibid.*, II, xi (1097 A).

CHAPTER II

ST AMBROSE, BISHOP AND DIPLOMAT

BIBLIOGRAPHY

THE first edition of the works of Ambrose appeared in Venice in 1485. No decided progress in establishing the text was realised before the edition brought out by the Benedictines Du Frische and Le Nourry, published in two sets in Paris between 1686 and 1690. The Benedictine edition was reproduced by Migne, P.L., vol. XIV-XVII. A very faulty re-impression of Migne, with fresh pagination, was brought out in 1879. It also served as the basis of P. A. Ballerini's edition, published in Milan between the years 1875 and 1883. Ballerini was satisfied with collating certain Milanese manuscripts. His work, handsomely produced, has been severely criticised. A large portion of Ambrose's exegetic treatises have found a place in the *Corpus Script. Eccl. lat.*, through the labours of Schenkl. See Table V.

Consult: Tillemont, vol. X (1705), p. 78, a conscientious and indispensable guide; A. Baunard, *Histoire de St Ambroise*, 2nd ed., Paris, 1872, very ably combined, but more literary than scientific; Th. Foerster, *Ambrosius, Bischof von Mailand, eine Darstellung seines Lebens und Wirkenes*, Halle, 1884, an excellent monograph; Duc de Broglie, *Saint Ambroise*, Paris, 1899, important for the political activity of Ambrose.—A large number of pieces have been translated by P. de Labriolle, and combined with analyses, in his *St Ambroise*, Paris, 1908 (P.C.).—Ihm has set out the chronology of Ambrose's works in the *Jahrbucher fur Klassische Philologie, Supplementband*, XVII (1890), p. 1 et s., following the results already obtained by the Benedictines Du Frische and Le Nourry. Many fertile discussions are included also in Rauschen's work, *Jahrbucher der christlichen Kirche unter dem Theodosius dem Grossen*, Freiburg-im-Breisgau, 1897.

The language of Ambrose has not yet been thoroughly studied. Useful indications will be found in Steier's *Jahrbucher fur Klassische Philologie, Supplementband*, XXVIII (1903), pp. 553-562; Francesco Lora, *Saggio sintatico comparativo su Girolamo, Agostino, Ambrogio*, Padova, 1900; Engelbrecht, *Philologisches aus Augustinus und Ambrosius (Zeitsch f. die oesterr. Gymnasien*, LVII, 7), C.W. (Carl Weyman), Rh.M., 1909, p. 328; P. Canata, *De Synt. Ambrosiana in libris qui inscrib. de Officiis*, Catanna, 1911.—We may mention also in connection with the iconography of Ambrose an article by Wieland in the *Römische Quartalschrift*, 1909, p. 132 et s.

SUMMARY

I. A Bishop in the IVth century. The rôle of St Ambrose.—II. His life until becoming a Bishop.—III. His intellectual formation.—IV. His political action. The Altar to Victory. The affair of Callinicum. The Penance of Theodosius.—V. His literary work. The *De Officiis*.—VI. Treatises on the ascetic life.—VII. Exegetic Treatises.—VIII. Dogmatic Treatises and the Ambrosian Hymns.—IX. The Prestige of St Ambrose.

I

On a page of his *Études Historiques*,[1] Chateaubriand has given in forcible language the *rôle* of a Bishop in the IVth century : "There is nothing more complete or well filled than the life of the prelates of the IVth and Vth centuries. A Bishop baptised, acted as confessor, preached, prescribed private and public penances, issued anathemas and lifted excommunications, visited the sick, ministered to the dying, buried the dead, ransomed captives, gave relief to the poor, the widows and orphans, founded hospitals and lazar-houses, administered the goods of his clergy, adjudicated as a Justice of the Peace in private suits and arbitrated on the quarrels between different cities. At the same time he published treatises on moral, discipline, and theology, wrote against heresiarchs and philosophers, interested himself in science and history, dictated letters to people who consulted him on one or other religion, corresponded with Churches and Bishops, monks and hermits, sat in Councils and Synods, was called in by Emperors to advise them, was charged with the arrangement of affairs, and despatched to usurpers and barbarian princes to disarm or restrain them : three powers—religious, political, and philosophical—were concentrated in the Bishop."

The features of this picture drawn by Chateaubriand were provided for the most part by the life of St Ambrose ; and we are not surprised a few lines further on to encounter the name of the Bishop of Milan.

In St Cyprian and St Hilary we have already admired finished examples of those magnificent churchmen who were the light and support of so many souls. But how different was their lot to that of Ambrose ! Proscribed and hunted down by the Roman authority, Cyprian could only develop his initiatives in a setting that was relatively narrow. For reasons of another kind, Hilary felt in an equal degree the weight of the animosities engendered by power. Ambrose, during nearly twenty years, from 378–397, was the adviser of Gratian, Valentinian II and Theodosius, and the dispenser of imperial favours, and on more than one occasion gave them

---

[1] *Etude, Œuvres complètes*, ed. Pourrat, Paris, 1836, vol. V, p. 268.

the assistance of his diplomacy [1] when their authority was in need of it. This favour, however justified it was, suffered its eclipses, we need hardly say; it could not fail to exasperate those at the imperial court who wished to monopolise it to the exclusion of Ambrose. The Bishop rode victoriously over the most dangerous crises. He had made himself too formidable owing to the close solidarity uniting him with his people, and too necessary on account of the wisdom of his counsels, that he could easily be put down and dispensed with. Responsible for the future prosperity of the Empire, how could Gratian, Valentinian II, and Theodosius have misunderstood the absolute devotion with which the fervour of his Roman patriotism inspired the Bishop? The interests which he defended were as dear to him as to themselves; with them he suffered the first assaults upon the majesty of Rome inflicted by the barbarians; his reverence for the *res publica* was part and parcel of his faith itself.

Little by little there formed in this lofty mind the magnificent idea of a Christian Empire whereof the Catholic faith should be the cement: " O sacred nail," he cried in his funeral oration on Theodosius (alluding to the Nail of the Cross which Helena had sent to Constantine to set in his diadem), nail which holds the whole world together, and which serves as ornament to the brow of sovereigns in order that those who have long persecuted the faith may become its heralds: *ut sint praedicatores, qui persecutores esse consueverunt!* " [2] Dying before the taking of Rome by Alaric, Ambrose did not live to see the overthrow of this grandiose dream under the shock of invasions. That he should have been able to conceive it is a sign of the times, and marks the fresh stages that Christianity had passed through on its painful and then triumphal road.

II

WE do not know the exact date of the birth of Ambrose. [3]

---

[1] See P. de Labriolle, *op. cit.*, p. 95 et s., on his painful missions to Maximus.
[2] P.L., XVI, 1465.
[3] We have three principal sources for learning the character and life of Ambrose :
(1) Ambrose in his works, especially his correspondence (91 letters) ; and a passage in *Ep.* xlviii, 7, enables us to conjecture that he took pains himself to form a kind of collection of his letters. (2) The biography of Ambrose, written by the deacon Paulinus about twenty-five years after the death of the Bishop. This *Vita*

It should be placed between the years 330 and 340.[1] His
family had been Christian for a fairly long time; among
its members it counted a martyr, Sotheris a virgin, who had
been put to death during the persecution of Diocletian.
Ambrose's father exercised the high function of Pretorian
Prefect among the Gauls, at Trèves. When he died, his
widow brought her three children, Ambrose, Satyrus and
Marcellina, to Rome. We have hardly any details of the
early life of Ambrose; but he undoubtedly received the
education of the young of his class. He passed through the
school of grammar and rhetoric, and received the imprint
of this intellectual discipline like so many others.

The example of his father could not but incite him to
enter upon the same *cursus honorum*. He attached himself
to the person of Sextus Petronius Probus, Pretorian Prefect
of Italy from 368-376, and his powerful protector conceived
so much esteem for him that it was not long before he entrusted him, after a short period under his own immediate
direction, with the government of the Provinces of Liguria
and Aemilia, with the title of Consul.

Ambrose thus settled at Milan, the Episcopal See of which
was then filled by Auxentius who belonged to the Arian party.
When Auxentius died a year after the arrival of Ambrose,
the choice of his successor occasioned lively debate among
the Christians of Milan, of whom some were partisans of
Arius, while others held firmly to the orthodox faith. The
opposing factions met in the basilica to discuss the matter.
Ambrose, fearing trouble, felt he ought to be there in person.
Paulinus, his biographer, tells us (§ vi), " He was haranguing
the crowd when the voice of a child suddenly cried, ' Ambrose
Bishop ! ' All the people repeated this cry, and thereupon
the disputing between Arians and Catholics gave place to
a marvellous and incredible unanimity." Ambrose was
little expecting such an honour. His first motion was to

Anbrosii was translated into Greek. Papadopoulos-Kerameus published in 1891
at St Petersburg a Greek text which should go back to the VIIIth or IXth century.
Paulinus throughout aims at edification. (3) Indications and testimony of ecclesiastical contemporaries; these *testimonia* are to be found in Ballerini's edition, I,
p. xvi et s. There is in existence a *Commentary* on the blessing of Jacob (cf.
Genesis, xlix) which is ascribed to Paulinus of Milan. It is printed in P.L., XX,
715-732. Dom A. Wilmart has recently drawn attention to a manuscript of
Troyes, no. 804, IXth century which gives the real author as Adrevald, doubtless
the monk of Fleury-sur-Loire who died in 878 or 879. See *R. Bén.*, 1920, pp. 57-63.
[1] Cf. *Ep.* lix, 4.

fly from it. But unexpected though it was, the choice
appeared so excellent to all that he had to resign himself to
submit. The Italian Bishops and then the Emperor Valentinian gave it their approval. Ambrose received baptism
(it had been deferred until then according to the custom of
those times), and eight days after, the priesthood, on the
7th December, 374.

III

AMBROSE, suddenly made a Bishop under the impulse of
popular enthusiasm, found himself in a very paradoxical
position. Without any preliminary theological training or
any special education for it, he had, right from the outset,
to exercise Episcopal authority, " to instruct before having
even learnt," [1] as he confesses with his customary simplicity.
If we may attribute to him with certainty a rather free
translation of the *Wars of the Jews* by the historian Josephus,
which several manuscripts ascribe to him (while others give
a certain Hegesippus as the author),[2] we must conclude
that even before his episcopate he had interested himself
in religious history. But taking everything into account,
the attribution of the authorship to him rests extremely
doubtful.

The very high conception which he formed of his duties
made him feel keenly what was wanting in him on the speculative side proper. His first care then was to read assiduously
Holy Scripture in order to make of it his life's blood and his
food. There are few ecclesiastical writers as fruitful as he
in quotations from the Bible. I would not dare to say that
the modern reader would always find them perfectly oppor-
tune or could bear them without some impatience. But
Ambrose would not have understood that anyone could

---

[1] *De Off.*, I, l. 4 : " . . . Factum est ut prius docere inciperem quam discere."
Cf. *de Paenit.*, II, viii, 72.

[2] Text in P.L., XV, 1961–2224 ; special edition by C. Fr. Weber and J. Caesar,
Marburg, 1864. Bibliog. in O. Scholz, *die Heges. Ambrosius Frage*, Breslau,
1913.—The translator alludes in his preamble to a Latin transposition in the form
of a historical account of the four books of Kings which he had already made. This
indication led Dom Morin (*R. Bén.*, 1914, pp. 83–91) to suppose that the true author
was Dexter, the son of Pacian of Barcelona, to whom St Jerome dedicated his
De Vir. Illustr. The work on the Kings was preserved in a Latin account of the
death of the Machabees which may be read in twenty manuscripts.

wish to divert him from exploring as widely as possible the source of all truth and all philosophy.

Again, he had to make himself familiar with the workings of Christian thought, whether to fit himself to be able to interpret the Scriptures, or for theological controversy. The curious thing is, that in spite of his practical and realistic mind which should have brought him in touch with the West, he almost entirely neglected their writings. He was unacquainted apparently with Tertullian and St Cyprian. There is hardly anyone except Hippolytus of Rome who drew his attention. It was to Eastern writers that his sympathies and curiosity went out. He felt their superiority from the speculative point of view, and that in them he would find ready to his hand the weapons he needed in his struggle against the heterodoxy of the times. It was a short step for him to find himself at once on their side. Philo and Origen became his masters in exegesis. For moral and dog-matic instruction he had recourse to the most well-known Greek ecclesiastics of his day, Athanasius, Basil, Cyril of Jerusalem, Didymus, Epiphanius and Gregory of Nazianzen, making himself master of their writings with avidity, even of those which had only just appeared. We see him making use of the theological discourses given by Gregory of Nazianzen at Constantinople in 380, for his own *De Spiritu Sancto* which was written during the first half of 381.

In this way, by constant study of the sacred Books and the best Greek and Hellenistic exegetists and theologians, he was successful in acquiring the foundations of ecclesiastical learning in which he was wanting; these were rather jumbled and lacking in order, but failing any striking originality it revealed in him a remarkable power of assimilation.

The constant practice of public speaking obliged him to filter and clarify this adventitious theology for the benefit of those he was instructing, and he made it his own, thanks to his labour in adaptation. His catechetical instructions at the same time provided him with the matter for nearly all his works. After he had spoken he wrote it down either from his own notes or memory, or from a report taken down in shorthand; it sufficed him to arrange the subject matter and any connecting links, and the book was ready at the cost of a slight revision. This was clearly a risky method as far as artistic presentment was concerned. How could Ambrose prevent a few of the gaps permissible in a spoken discourse, and even some of the ready witticisms in which a public audience delight, from creeping into his explanatory renderings ? He remained faithful to this method, however, to the end of his career ; it economised valuable time, and once he saw that it did not compromise edification which was his sole thought, it mattered little to him that a few fastidious minds were so narrow as to find fault with it.

IV

MOREOVER, the domain of literature properly speaking was not that in which Ambrose showed his full capacity, and in which his labour was most fruitful. Direction of souls, and the utilisation of different characters and circumstances for the benefit of the Church formed the real field in which he triumphed. We must therefore first study his practical activity—not in all its consequences, but selecting a few significant features.

One of the most famous episodes of his public life, the matter of the Altar to Victory, brought him up against the followers of the pagan religion. From the year 380 his ascendancy over Gratian was firmly established. Gratian was pleased to regard him as a father and guide, and possibly it was at his (Ambrose's) instigation that in 382 he decided to renew the struggle against paganism which had been suspended for the past eighteen years by the policy of toleration pursued by Valentinian I. By an edict he deprived the colleges of their priests and the vestals of their revenues. The allocations allotted to the exercise of their religion were suppressed for the benefit of the public treasury, and the same thing happened to the foundations bequeathed to these colleges by legacy. Finally, as the crowning point of these vexations, Gratian ordered the removal from the Chamber of the Curia of the famous statue to Victory which from the time of Augustus had stood upon an altar, as the symbol to the Senators in their Assembly of the glorious Roman past.

The Senators who were pagan resolved to send a deputa-

tion to Gratian praying him to annul so wounding a measure.
But their Christian colleagues, who already formed a majority
in the Curia, formally refused to associate themselves with
them and, through the intermediary of Ambrose and Pope
Damasus, made known to the Emperor their decision.
Gratian did not receive the deputation.

In the following year, on the 25th August 383, Gratian
fell at Lyons beneath the blows of the usurper Maximus.
Valentinian II, still very young—he was about twelve years
old—assumed the responsibilities of power. The pagan party
thought this a good opportunity to return to the charge.
At that time, in 384, Symmachus, one of the most distinguished representatives of that party, occupied the position
of Prefect of Rome. The Pretorian Prefect of Italy, Vettius
Agorius Praetextatus, was also a confirmed follower of the
ancient religion. The occasion seemed to be propitious.
Towards the middle or the end of the summer, Symmachus
drew up his famous Report which a delegation of Senators
placed in the hands of the young Emperor.[1]

Modern critics have found this petition cold and half-
hearted. It is deserving of a more favourable appreciation.
Written in a style of sober elegance, its mission was to defend
" ancestral institutions, and the rights and destinies of the
fatherland " :

> " What ! Is the Roman religion outside the rights of
> Romans ? " exclaims Symmachus. " Freedmen share
> the legacies which have been bequeathed to them :
> we do not refuse to slaves the legal advantages which
> testamentary dispositions concede to them : and shall
> noble virgins, ministers of a sacred cult, be excluded
> from the possessions which come to them by succession ?
> What profit to them to devote their chastity to the public
> safety, to assure protection from on high for the Empire
> so long as it shall last, to bring to your arms, to your
> eagles, the agency of friendly powers, to offer up for
> you their efficacious vows, if they have not the enjoy-
> ment of common law ? " (§ 13).

And, calling up the mighty image of Rome in a kind of
prosopopoeia, he puts into its mouth words instinct with

[1] Ed. Seeck, M.G.H., VI, 1, p. 280.

majestic sorrow in order to deplore the assaults of which such venerable traditions had just been the victim.

When read at the Emperor's Council this document produced a powerful effect. Christians and pagans seemed for one moment to be agreed to give it a favourable reply. Ambrose understood that he would have to act at once. In a letter to Valentinian (*Ep.* xvii) he took steps to show him how groundless were the grievances of which Symmachus had made himself the interpreter :

> " They come and make complaint of their losses—those who were so little sparing of our blood and who have laid our Churches in ruins ! . . . They claim their privileges from you when, but yesterday, the laws of Julian refused to us the right devolving upon all to speak and instruct. . . ." (§ iv).

By what right did the pagans claim to impose on their Christian colleagues, in the same Curia even, the statue of a religion condemned by them ? Ambrose implored Valentinian in the name of his dead brother and on the conscience of a Christian Emperor, to reject the petition :

> " The present question is one concerning religion, and I intervene therefore in my capacity as a Bishop. . . . If a decision contrary to us be taken, we Bishops cannot accommodate ourselves to it with a light heart, nor dissimulate our opinion. You may lawfully come to Church, but you will not find there any priest, or he will only be there for the purpose of protesting " (§ xiii).

This warning had its full effect. Valentinian decided, against the advice of his council, to make no change in the measure proposed two years before by Gratian. The rebuff to the pagan party was complete. To make it still more damaging, Ambrose drew up a detailed reply to the petition of Symmachus in the form of a letter to Valentinian (*Ep.* xviii). Taking the arguments of Symmachus one by one, he set himself to destroy any close connection between the glory of Rome and the sacred rites of the official religion. He let fall the heavy weight of his irony on the desolation of the vestals and the priests deprived of their revenues, and to these well-paid offices of devotion opposed the magnificent disinterestedness of the Church :

> " The Church possesses nothing, except it be the faith : therein are her revenues, therein her benefits. The maintenance of the poor is her patrimony. Let our adversaries tell us how many captives their temples have ransomed, how many poor they have supported, and to how many exiles they have provided the means to live ! "

Then sharply rebuking the reactionary complaints of Symmachus and his superstitious cult of the past, he does not hesitate to affirm the inevitable character of the evolution through which humanity, freeing itself from religious forms henceforth passed away, was advancing towards a truth becoming more and more luminous and complete.

His cause was heard. In spite of many attempts ventured upon before Theodosius, Valentinian II and Eugenius, the pagan element never succeeded in regaining entirely what it had lost. And it is an undoubted fact that the Bishop of Milan was the principal instrument in this humiliating defeat.

The affair of Callinicum, quite a local incident, only deserves to be mentioned here because we see in it very fully the inflexible and high-handed firmness of the Bishop once the *prestige* of the Church appeared to him to be threatened.

During the year 388, Theodosius was informed by a report from the *Comes Orientis*, the commander of the Roman troops in the East, that very serious disorders had broken out in the town of Callinicum, one of the chief cities of the province of Osroene (Mesopotamia). Some monks who had been roughly handled by the partisans of a Gnostic sect had set fire in reprisal to one of their sanctuaries. A still more vexatious proceeding, and one to which the Emperor gave special attention, was the burning of a Jewish synagogue at the instigation of the Bishop of the town.

Anxious for the preservation of public order, Theodosius judged that strong measures should be taken. He ordered the synagogue to be rebuilt at the cost of the Bishop, whom he considered to have been responsible.

On receiving news of this, Ambrose, who was at Aquileia,

returned in all haste to Milan, with the intention of formally opposing the step taken by the Emperor. Seeing that he was by no means inclined to grant him an audience, he addressed a letter to him (*Ep.* xl), in an attempt to induce him to withdraw his decision. He reproached him for not having even called for a report from the Bishop, and for having condemned him unheard. He recalled to his recollection similar proceedings on the part of the Jews, when they had often taken the gravest responsibilities upon themselves without much notice having been taken of them. He protested, above all, against the injury done to the Catholics, who had been humiliated before the Jews and obliged to rebuild with Christian money a synagogue, a den of impiousness. " If my personal credit is too weak," he concluded, " deign to call together any Bishops you please. Let them examine what can be done without bringing harm to the faith. In questions pertaining to money, you consult your Comites : is it not still more just to consult, in matters of religion, the ministers of the Lord ? " (§ 27).

This urgent presentation of the case did not produce at first the effect which Ambrose had hoped. The Emperor made no reply to it. Ambrose then resolved on a bold stroke. He has himself related in a letter to his sister (*Ep.* xli) the setting of the scene he made use of. In a full Church he reminded the Emperor in a series of allusions from his Bishop's throne of the responsibility of his duties, and of the debt of gratitude to heaven he had incurred, and invited him to " protect the body of Christ " in order that Christ Himself might protect his Empire. At the conclusion of his sermon he stepped down :

" ' Is it of me that you have been speaking ? ' the Emperor asked : ' I said what I thought to be my duty in order to help you.' ' Yes,' he replied ; ' the order I gave to have the synagogue restored by the Bishop was too harsh, but I have softened it down. The monks are much too forward ! ' I remained standing some little time, and then said to the Emperor, ' Act so that I can offer the Holy Sacrifice for you in full assurance. Lift the weight off my soul.' The Emperor, who was seated, made a gesture of agreement but without any

s

formal promise. I stayed planted in front of him. He told me he would amend his rescript. I asked him to issue at once his commands on the matter. . . . He promised me that this should be done. ' I have your word ? ' ' I give it.' Then only did I go up to the altar which I should not have approached if he had not made me a positive promise " (§ 27–28).

Such was the firmness with which Ambrose dared to speak to so powerful a man as Theodosius once it seemed to him that the Emperor was trespassing beyond his right.

Still more famous is the penance which he imposed upon him after the massacre of Thessalonica. The seat of the Governor of Macedonia, Thessalonica in 390 was the theatre of a rising springing from trivial causes in which a certain number of functionaries perished. Theodosius was profoundly annoyed at this. Ill advised by his counsellors, he sent a savage order which he did his best to revoke soon afterwards, but when too late. A large part of the people of Thessalonica, who were assembled in the circus under the pretext of a display, were massacred by soldiers let loose upon them.

When the news of this dire event became known in Milan, many Bishops happened to be assembled at a Synod there. The general view was that a public expiation should be demanded from the Emperor. Ambrose, whose close relations with Theodosius were well known, felt that it was incumbent upon him to obtain his submission and to make him understand that he was excluded from the Church on account of his crime and that he could only obtain re-admission at the price of sincere repentance. He did not wait for Theodosius, then absent from Milan, to return; though in great ill-health himself, he left the city and addressed confidentially letter li to the Emperor from a distance. After some discreet remonstrances that Theodosius had purposely kept himself away while he was devising these abominable reprisals, he made known to the Emperor categorically the duty incumbent upon him—the duty to repent and do penance, the example of which had been given to him by David and other personages in the Bible. Together with phrases testifying to his affection he introduced a note of menace: it would be impossible for him as a Bishop to offer the Holy Sacrifice before a sinner who had done nothing to restore the communion of the Church. What was the attitude of Theodosius in face of this respectful summons ? That he brought himself to repent is certain ; but over the details of this historic penance modern criticism raises serious difficulties.[1] According to the Greek historian Theodoret,[2] when the Emperor wished to enter the Church Ambrose stepped in front of him and forbade him to set foot within the sacred precincts. Even to this day, in Milan, an ancient column marks the spot where tradition states the Bishop and Emperor met. Unfortunately Theodoret has mingled many blunders with his account, which renders it suspect. Neither Rufinus, St Augustine, nor Ambrose himself, speak of any such impressive exclusion. There is here then a very obscure historic problem.[3] Moreover, the renown of Ambrose does not rest in any degree on one or other of the solutions presented to us ; if the episode related by Theodoret were nothing but pure fiction, we still have the fact that the confidential letter of Ambrose to Theodosius was sufficient to decide the Emperor to undergo the humiliation of a public penance, which is attested unanimously by contemporary evidence.

Taken as a whole, we can say that the religious policy of Ambrose had a triple object in view : first, the protection of the Church against all violence or indiscretion on the part of the State : " In questions affecting the faith, it is the Bishops who are the judges of Christian Emperors, and not the Emperors who are the judges of the Bishops." [4] Next, to make the civil power respect the moral law, even in acts deprived of any religious character, under pain of the censure of the Church. And lastly, to seal a close union between Church and State of such a kind that, far from placing the different religions on the same level, the State should unfailingly show its special and single favour to the Catholic religion, and discourage all others.

We are not called upon to approve *en bloc* all the steps taken by Ambrose in the politico-religious affairs in which he was mixed up. Was his success over the incident of

---

[1] Cf. my *Saint Ambroise*, p. 136–147.
[2] *Hist. eccl.*, V, xvii (P.G., LXXXII, 1232).
[3] It deserves fresh examination.
[4] *Ep.* xxi, 4.

Callinicum of such a kind that we can give whole-hearted praise to it ? Certainly Theodosius might have proceeded with less heat and more caution than he first showed, by waiting for an explanation from the Bishop, and making the town pay the expense, and not the Bishop in his own person. But in all justice, total immunity would have been to show excessive leniency likely to encourage the promoters of disorder.

With this reservation once made it is impossible not to see in Ambrose a habitual and very noble regard for equity. Thus he did not hesitate to brand in most vigorous terms the inhumanity of the Bishops who wrung from the imperial power the punishment of death for Priscillian and his partisans under the pretext of magic and immorality, but in reality for heresy.[1] He was far from thinking that the State should be indifferent in matters of doctrine, and freely suffer them to dispute for the possession of souls ; but he did nothing to counteract that genuine liberalism towards persons which the State observed. Never were high pagan officials discharged from their posts once they were serving well,[2] and St Ambrose was the first to render service to them when he could.[3]

It was a benefit that, outside any desire for political domination, there should rise in face of the all-powerful Emperor another power strong enough, although unarmed, to impose a moral check upon him, and oblige him to confess his faults when the occasion arose. It was through Ambrose that the people learnt what clement mediation, what sheltering guardianship the Church was henceforth to offer to the caprice and violence of their princes—a lesson it was not likely to forget through succeeding ages.

V

IT is time we came to the literary work of St Ambrose. I have already hinted that it provides some disappointments. Ambrose had neither the depth and gift of verbal creation of

---

[1] *Ep.* xxvi.
[2] The poet Prudentius noted this : *Contra Symmachum*, I, 616 et s.
[3] See the letters of Symmachus to Ambrose, M.G.H., VI, 1, 80 and 82, with introduction, p. cxxviii.

a St Augustine, nor the ardent imagination, the impassioned fire, and scientific aptitude of a St Jerome. The most interesting portion is his Correspondence. In it the man of action is depicted, with his energy, practical wisdom, and real goodness, the attractiveness of which was felt so keenly by those who knew him. In some places, occasionally, we are a little disappointed to see him wasting time over the little elegances of style, and the imitations and mannerisms of a past age which the taste of the period represented as literary excellence. Ambrose's composition is seldom irreproachable, and his form of expression itself lacks originality. Burdened with more urgent tasks, he never had the time to improve on the form or to aim at perfection.

Nevertheless his books, into which he was far from putting his principal energy and the best of himself, do not fail to offer considerable interest from the point of view of a record of his ideas. They are of value as documents on the moral doctrines of Christianity in the second half of the IVth century.

We know with what subtle and penetrating considerations St Ambrose's *De Officiis Ministrorum* has inspired a critic like R. Thamin.[1] The work is one of those which enable us to *mark the point* forming a landmark on the road followed by succeeding generations. Certainly Christianity has been incessantly concerned with moral problems, both theoretical and practical, but with the exception of the *Institutiones* of Lactantius, a very miscellaneous work by an honest, conscientious mind of limited scope, there was not yet in the IVth century any synthesis comparable to those which the Greeks, and after them, the Romans, had sometimes attempted.

In his *De Officiis* Ambrose nowhere assumes the tone of a thinker who is proposing to give a *Summa* of the moral principles with which he had identified his faith and life. Far from proclaiming any such ambition he seeks the most modest *formulæ ;* it is a simple conversation on moral questions which he wished to have with his clergy, by means of which he took occasion to rectify many philosophic ideas current among the pagans. He even declares that he is little concerned to present any methodical explanation and that it is

---

[1] *Saint Ambroise et la morale chrétienne au IVᵉ siècle. Etude comparée des traités De Officiis de Cicéron et de Saint Ambroise,* 1895.

sufficient for him to paraphrase the beautiful examples of which the Scriptures offer such a rich harvest.[1]

In fact, there is much freedom of choice and disconnectedness in the work. There, as elsewhere, Ambrose observes a very free style, to which his habit of preaching had accustomed him. Again, whom was he addressing? Were they the clergy only, or the Christian body? Was it a strictly clerical system of moral doctrine that he outlined, or one that was simply Christian? His hesitation is sometimes excusable; hence a certain lack of clearness and unity.

It remains to say that Ambrose followed Cicero very closely both in his general scheme (in spite of certain digressions which were necessary to his particular point of view) and in the setting forth of his ideas, and sometimes even in his expressions. I have already indicated in what spirit he made this kind of transposition,[2] and the fresh support he supplied to many precepts of tradition. In each one of his exhortations we find, on analysis, an amalgam of Stoicism and Christianity, but it is the latter which forms the preponderating and decisive element. Nowhere do we obtain a clearer idea at what particular point the basic doctrines of Christianity—the belief in a Providence, the firm trust in the immortality of the soul and of a reward beyond the grave, and especially faith in Jesus Christ—have ousted numerous moral problems.[3]

VI

THE treatises on the ascetic life present a special side of the moral teaching of Ambrose, and make us understand one of the favourite forms of his propaganda among the faithful.

From all parts of Italy, and even from Africa, young girls were coming to Milan to take the veil. These *opuscula* are derived, at least partly, from the sermons delivered by Ambrose in honour of virginity. The *De Virginibus*, the first in point of date, goes back probably to 377. In it Ambrose states that when he wrote it he was *nondum triennalis sacerdos*. It was addressed to Marcellina, his sister, who

[1] Cf. I, xviii, 72.
[2] Introd., p. 31.
[3] In this connection see Brochard's reflections, *Etudes de Philos. anc. et de Philos. moderne*, p. 493.

had herself made her profession of virginity, and who, associating herself in all the works of her brother, had become the spiritual directress of some young girls who had resolved to live in the same state. Shortly afterwards, the *De Virginitate* appeared (in which Ambrose refutes objections raised by the *De Virginibus*), and the *De Viduis* in which the Bishop addressed himself exclusively to widows. In 391, thirteen or fourteen years afterwards, he wrote the *De Institutione Virginis*, on the occasion of the taking of the veil by Ambrosia, a young girl who had been intrusted to his ministrations. Lastly, the *Exhortatio Virginitatis*, published in 393, is nothing else than a sermon preached by Ambrose at Florence on the occasion of the commemoration of the martyrs Vitalis and Agricola.

Ambrose did not nourish any systematic hostility against marriage. With his customary good sense and his care for strict fairness, he also abstains from certain brutal misogynisms of which ecclesiastical writers have not always been sufficiently sparing. He guards himself against wishing to discountenance or discredit marriage. He regarded it as a permanent union which divine law forbids to be broken, and one in which the husband should predominate and be the *gubernator*. On the question of re-marriage, he is much more severe. From an early date Christian tradition had looked suspiciously at a second marriage. Ambrose too saw in it a mark of weakness, a want of self-control. Notwithstanding this, he refuses to consider it in the light of a sin : *Neque enim prohibemus secundas nuptias, sed non suademus.*[1] And if he discountenances it, this is entirely from ascetic reasons and considerations of a practical order which he does not omit to develop in full detail. As regards the state of virginity, it is in his eyes that virtue which is pre-eminently Christian. It existed of course among the pagans, but in their case it was inspired by purely temporal motives. In the Christian religion alone was virginity practised from supernatural motives and it enhanced itself by an incomparable moral purity. He had no hesitation, therefore, in order the more cogently to urge souls to renunciation, in marking the worries which usually accompany the state of marriage, and in praising in the most enthusiastic terms the incom-

[1] *De Viduis*, xi, 68.

parable sacrifice consummated by the virgin. He endeavoured also to unravel the difficulties in the moral and even economic order which were raised in Milanese society against the maxims he was advocating. Furthermore, all these criticisms, although he refuted them one by one, must break in pieces against an argument which, in the opinion of Ambrose, would dispense with the necessity of giving any others. And this was that virginity, as a vocation freely chosen, is of divine institution which the Virgin Mary protects with her example and patronage.

Such in broad lines is the doctrine of Ambrose on marriage, re-marriage, and virginity. He has certainly contributed in large part to attach to the ideal he thus traced the high value it has retained in the bosom of Catholicism.

VII

As I have already said, nearly all the works of Ambrose were spoken before being written out ; and if they were put into writing it was because he wished that what he preached should be heard beyond the circle of his Milanese audience which was too narrow for his taste. It was to his pastoral eloquence that he owed his most efficacious influence over souls. On this point, we have the direct testimony of St Augustine, a constant hearer of Ambrose even before his own conversion : " I was very zealous," he relates in his *Confessions* (V, xiii), " in hearing him deliver his dissertations in the midst of the people, and his words held my irresolute attention. In truth, I was not curious, I was even disdainful, over the deeper matters, *but the sweetness of his discourse enthralled me.*"

We know that one of the favourite themes on which Ambrose loved to expatiate was the immorality of the contrast existing between the extreme poverty of some and the unbridled luxury of others. Particularly significant from this point of view is his sermon on Naboth which most likely dates from one of his last years. With a vigour which recalls the invective of the Roman satirists and moralists, he brands the greed of the rich and the oppression they make weigh heavily on the poor. He even does not shrink from reminding

them of the altogether conventional and arbitrary character
of human property. The " political economy " of Ambrose,
if it is not too ambitious a term, is penetrated through and
through with charity and love.

To gain an idea of his catechizing, we must read his *De
Mysteriis*. In it St Ambrose addresses the catechumens who
had already received Baptism and the Eucharist, and explains
to them the profound signification of the ritual which had been
carried out before them or upon them. In order to anticipate
objections or doubts which might arise in their minds, he
takes pains to demonstrate to them that nothing is indifferent
in what they had seen, that everything carried a mysterious
meaning and a moral efficacy, and was the instrument of
regeneration prefigured in so many writings of Scripture.

Constant recourse to Scripture was the usual method of
St Ambrose in his sermons. " Holy Scripture," he wrote to
Bishop Constantius,[1] " is a sea which has in itself deep
meanings and all the mystery of prophetic riddles." To the
deciphering of these riddles he devoted his exegetic treatises
which form the bulk of his work.

At the outset we are astonished that St Ambrose found
leisure to draw out such copious paraphrases from the Scriptures in the midst of a life taken up by so many diverse cares.
But when we come to analyse them the matter is fairly
intelligible. It was out of his daily task of preaching that he
produced the greater part of these lesser works.[2] Thus the
Exameron (to take this as an example) is made up of nine
sermons which were preached on six days running during
Lent. Six homilies are included in the first, third, and fifth
books—two in each book. The other books, the second,
fourth and sixth, are composed of only one homily each.
And here and there we are able to mark traces of their origin,
which Ambrose had not troubled to remove : the finishing
words or resumption of a sermon ;[3] an allusion to the day
which is declining ;[4] and to the fatigue of his listeners.[5]

It is beyond dispute that in his time Ambrose had real
renown as an exegetist. From all parts people consulted

---

[1] *Ep.* ii, 3.
[2] Sauvage and Tougard re-edited (Paris, 1895) a sermon by Victricius of
Rotomagus (Rouen), *De Laude Sanctorum* : cf. P.L., XX, 443. See E. Vacandard's
Saint Victrice, Evêque de Rouen (iv–v cent.), 1903 (Coll. *Les Saints*).
[3] *Exam.*, I, vi, 24 ; V, xxiv, 92.   [4] V, xxiv, 84.   [5] VI, 1, 1.

him on difficulties presented by the Old and New Testament. Nevertheless, from the historical point of view, his method of interpretation offers nothing really fresh.   In no way aiming at writing scientific treatises on sacred hermeneutics, but solely desirous of offering his sheep the truths pertaining to salvation in a form most fitted to move them, Ambrose from preference employed what is called the allegorical method of exegesis.   From the first days of Christianity St Paul had employed it ; it had, besides, for long been held in honour among the Jews, who themselves owed the idea to Greek philosophy.   Thus quite a tradition authorised its use ; but it was especially in the East, in the hands of Clement of Alexandria and Origen, that the use of allegory had been raised to a system with deliberate intention.   According to Origen, allegory should serve to exclude from Scripture any contradictions, improbabilities, and those " stumbling blocks," " pitfalls," and " mysteries " which it had pleased the Spirit of God to sow " in the faith and the records," and conse- quently it should distinguish the real intentions of the inspired authors from appearances, and render clear the sub- stance of their teaching.

It would not be accurate to say (as sometimes has been wrongly said), that St Ambrose was the first to introduce allegorical exegesis in the West.   In order to render this assertion null and void, it is sufficient to mention the names of Tertullian, the author of the *De Cibis Judaicis,* and St Hilary of Poitiers.   But Ambrose gave to it special import- ance because it enabled him to multiply *ad infinitum* edifying considerations in connection with texts, and to combat effectively the heretics with whom he happened to be dealing. Was it not by this means that he made a conquest of the intelligence of Augustine who was still imbued with very many Manichaean prejudices ? [1]   His special authorities were Philo the Alexandrine Jew, and Origen.   He mentioned them but rarely by name ; he even came to combat their views.   But in point of fact he used them as his favourite guides to get beyond the literal meaning to what he calls the *sensus altior* or the *subtilior interpretatio.*[2]

Allegorical exegesis is no longer to modern taste.   We know the Bible far less well than the Christians of the first

---

[1] *Confessions,* vi, 4.
[2] A very accurate analysis of his different methods will be found in Kellner's *Ambrosius als Erklarer des alten Testaments,* Regensburg, 1891.

centuries who made it their favourite and almost sole sustenance.

Let us learn however to recognise in it the principle of an art which, at least in the order of architecture, was to produce marvels, and of a profoundly idealistic conception of the universe. It is the allegorical interpretation of the Bible which has habituated Christian thought to seek symbols for everything, to go in search of pure spirit behind outward appearances, and to see in each form the mark or covering of an idea. This mystical conviction, so different from the proceeding usual in science, was to impose upon generations of writers, liturgists, and artists, the search to decipher the handiwork of God, wherein everything consisted of prefiguration, instruction, and mystic concordance suitable to engendering piety. The genius of the Middle Ages already was breathing in the exegetic work of St Ambrose.[1]

It is in this class of writing too, especially in the *Exameron,* that Ambrose most developed literary quality properly so called, rhetorical effect and distinction. The *Exameron* became the model and the principal source of those *Mirrors* from nature in which the theologians of the Middle Ages represented the picture of the universe even in the order of the creation. At Chartres, Laon, Auxerre, Lyons, Bourges, and many other towns, the six days' work has been sculptured in synthetic representations on the sides of our Cathedrals.[2]

VIII

WE do not possess all the dogmatic treatises of St Ambrose. Three works at least have been lost, the *De Sacramento Regenerationis sive de Philosophia,* to which St Augustine often alludes; the *Ad Pansophium Puerum,* attested by Paulinus, his biographer (§ 28); and the *Expositio Fidei,* from which Theodoret, Bishop of Cyr, quotes a fragment.[3] Among those which have come down to us we must mention first the *De Fide.* The two first books, written in 378 at the express desire of Gratian, bear the impress of the haste in

[1] See H. Hauvette, *Dante,* 1911, p. 281 et s.
[2] The Greek and Latin *Examerons* have been studied by F. Egleston, in *The Hexaemeral Literature,* Chicago, 1912; cf. K. Gronau's *Posidonios und die judisch-christliche Genesisexegese,* L. and B., 1914. A special study of St Ambrose's *Exameron,* its sources and its philosophy, would be a useful contribution to the history of Christian thought.
[3] *Eranistes,* ii.

which Ambrose had composed them. The general outlines of the subject are sketched out rather than deeply fathomed, as even the author acknowledges.[1] In 380, two years later, Ambrose revised his treatment of it and gave it all the fulness which he thought it deserved. At this period of controversies and heresies it was important to fortify the young Emperor with precise ideas upon the *depositum fidei*. Ambrose wrote this treatise at the very time when Gratian, informed of the disasters which the imprudence of Valens was preparing for the Empire, was making ready to start for the East. This is how at the end of the second book (II, xvi, 136), Ambrose breaks off for a moment in his exposition of doctrine to express to the Emperor in a " chant de guerre à la fois pieux et patriotique," [2] his good wishes for his victory, and to affirm the solidarity henceforth established between the religion of Christ and the destinies of Rome. The three books of the *De Spiritu Sancto*, likewise dedicated to Gratian, were put together in 381. In order to deal with this difficult question Ambrose availed himself of the principal resources of contemporary Greek theology. We recognise in the *De Spiritu Sancto* ideas from Athanasius, Cyril of Jerusalem, Basil, Didymus of Alexandria, Gregory of Nazianzen, and Epiphanius of Salamis. St Jerome, who always was very sparing in his praise of Ambrose, could not refrain from discharging an epigram at his indiscretion shown in these borrowings.[3] Even before Ambrose had completed the work, the challenge of two Arian chamberlains at the court of Gratian [4] led him to deliver a public statement on the mystery of the Incarnation; from this instruction issued the *De Incarnationis Dominicae Sacramento* which appears to have been published between the *De Fide* and the *De Spiritu Sancto*. The *De Paenitentia* was written between the years 380 and 390, and was directed against the partisans of Novatian who had remained faithful to that heresiarch's ideas after the lapse of a hundred and thirty years. In the first book Ambrose claims the absolute right of the Church to bind and loose sins, and refutes the arguments which

---

[1] III, l, 1.
[2] De Broglie, *Saint Ambroise*, p. 28.
[3] P.L., XXIII, 103 (Preface to the translation of the *De Spir. Sancto* by Didymus of Alex.).
[4] Cf. the *Life* of Ambrose, by Paulinus, § 18.

those rigorists deduced from certain texts from Scripture. The object of the second book is to inculcate the necessity of penance for expiation and pardon. In fact, it does not enter into the mind of Ambrose to mitigate in the slightest degree those just satisfactions which are required for the wiping out of sins ; but his natural moderation made him feel acutely the imprudence of the attitude of the Novatians, and the danger arising from the apparently heroic demands which that sect did not shrink from proclaiming.

Doctrinal considerations are not absent from the *De Excessu Satyri* either. The first book is nothing more than the setting down in writing of the touching funeral oration which Ambrose delivered in the Cathedral at Milan on the day of his brother Satyrus' funeral. In the second book is incorporated the sermon given seven days later before the tomb. It contains further outpourings of memories and regrets, but also quite philosophic developments on the universal and beneficent law of death, the rigour of which was wonderfully softened by the promise of the resurrection. The same concern is evident in the hymns which Ambrose wrote in iambic dimeters to serve as a useful vehicle for the propagation of orthodox ideas against the Arians, as St Hilary had done before him. Of the hymns, which are called Ambrosian, four are certainly authentic,[1] the *Æterne Rerum Conditor*, the *Deus Creator Omnium*, the *Jam surgit Hora Tertia*, and the *Veni, Redemptor Gentium*. Eight others are doubtful, and critics differ in their opinion as to the correctness of attributing them to Ambrose. In 386 Ambrose had preferred to undergo a regular siege, shutting himself up in the Porcian basilica with a multitude of the faithful, rather than hand it over to the Arians as the Court had ordered him to do at the instigation of the Empress Justina. In order to keep up the spirits of this crowd of people who had nothing to do, it occurred to him to introduce into the office the alternating chant of psalms and hymns. This custom seems to have had its rise at Antioch, and from there it had passed into use among the Christian communities of the East. Thanks to Ambrose, it soon spread throughout the West.[2]

[1] See Ermoni's "Ambroise (saint) Hymnographe", in the *Dict. d'Arch. chr. et de Lit.*, I, 1347 et s. ; Walpole, Notes on the text of the Hymns of S. Ambrose, in J.T.S., 1908, p. 428–436.

[2] Paulinus, *Vita S. Ambrosii*, § 13, Saint Augustine, *Conf.*, ix, 7.

IX

IT is sufficient to run through the list of *testimonia* collected
in modern editions to realise that Ambrose was soon considered by his contemporaries, in the East as well, as a
" pillar of the Church," " the pearl glistening on the finger
of God," and " the flower of Latin writers." From his see
at Milan he exercised a kind of moral primacy over the
Churches in Illyria. This was well seen at the Council of
Aquileia (3rd September, 381); it was manifestly he who
laid down the summary procedure through which, in spite
of their subterfuges, the Arian Bishops Palladius of Ratiara
and Secundianus of Singidunum found themselves punished
by being deposed.[1] He laboured from a distance at the
conversion of a German tribe, the Marcomanni. His
biographer relates (§ 36) that in the last years of the IVth
century, Frigitil, their queen, asked him to instruct her
in the Christian religion by correspondence. Ambrose
acceded to her wishes and, animated always with his desire to
serve Rome, begged her to work upon the mind of her husband
to remain at peace with the Empire. A few years later,
Ambrose, together with Jerome, Gregory and Augustine,
was to be numbered among the Doctors of the Church,
who at first were four in number, as we know—" like the four
rivers of Paradise," remarks a monk of the Middle Ages.[2]

[1] J. Zeiller, *Le Christianisme dans les Provinces Danubiennes*, p. 328 et s.
[2] *Ioannis monachi liber de miraculis* (viii–ix cent.), ed. Hoferer, Wurzburg,
1884, p. 47.

CHAPTER III

THEOLOGIANS OF THE SECOND ORDER

BIBLIOGRAPHY

I. AMBROSIASTER (c. 366-384), P.L., XVII, 45-508.—Consult: Cumont, R.H.L.R., 1903, p. 417 ; Wittig, *der Amb. Hilarius (Sdraleks Kirchengesch. Abh.* 4, Breslau, 1906) ; Souter, in *Expositor*, 1914, pp. 224-232.

II. DONATISM.—Consult: Monceaux, vols. IV and V.

III. ST OPTATUS.—P.L., XI, 883-1082 ; Ziwsa, in C.V., vol. XXVI (1893). One of the *tractatus* published by Dom Morin in 1917 " *Sermo in Natale infantium qui pro Domino occisi sunt*" (p. 170) is attributed to Optatus in the *Cod. Aureliensis*, 154, s. vii/viii.—French Translation by Pierre Viel, 1664.—Consult: L. Duchesne, *Le dossier du Donatisme*, in the *Mél. d'Arch. et d'Hist. publiés par l'Ecole franc. de Rome*, X (1890), p. 589-650 ; Monceaux, V, 241-306.

IV. TYCONIUS.—P.L., XVIII, 15-66 ; F. C. Burkitt in T.S., 3, 1 (1894). The *Commentary on the Apocalypse* was still in existence at St Gall in the IXth century. Some fragments of it have been published in the *Spicilegium Casinense*, III, 1 (1897), p. 261 et s. An attempt at its reconstruction by J. Haussleiter in *Zeitsch. f. Kirchl. Wiss. u. Kirchl. Leben*, VII (1886), pp. 239-257. Cf. H. L. Ramsay in R.H.L.R., 1902, pp. 433-444.—Consult: Hahn, *Tyconius-Studien*, L., 1900 (*St. zur Gesch. der Theol. u. der Kirche*, 6, 2); Monceaux, V, 165-219.

V. PACIAN.—P.L., XIII, 1051-1090 ; Peyrot, Zwolle, 1896 (mediocre). Dom Morin, from reasons of similarity of style which are hardly conclusive, attributes to Pacian the *Liber ad Justinum* often imputed to Victorinus (*R. Bén.*, 30 [1913], p. 286-293).

VI. FILASTER OF BRESCIA.—P.L., XII, 1111-1302 ; Marx, in C.V., vol. XXXVIII (1898).

VII. GAUDENTIUS.—P.L., XX, 827-1006.

VIII. ZENO OF VERONA. — P.L., XI, 253-528. A critical edition by Giuliari, Verona, 1883 ; 2nd ed., 1900, unchanged.—Consult: Monceaux, III, p. 365-371.

IX. HILARIANUS.—P.L., XIII, 1097-1114. These works are dated the 24th and 25th March 397. Re-edited by C. Frick, in the *Chronica Minora*, I, Leipzig, 1892 (B.T.), p. 153-174. See also Mommsen, M.G.H., XIII, 415.

X. NICETA OF REMESIANA.—P.L., LII ; A. E. Burn, *N. of R.*, Cambridge, 1905 : The *Sermones de Vigiliis* (Burn, pp. 55-67) are in P.L., LXVIII, 365-376 ; the *Sermones de Psalmodiae Bono* (Burn, pp. 67-82), in P.L., XXX, 232 ; the *De Ratione Paschae* (Burn, pp. 93-111), in P.L., LXXII, 49-52 and P.G., XXVIII, 1605-1610 ; the *Ad Lapsam Virginem Libellus* (Burn, pp. 112-131), in P.L., XVI, 367-384. Burn's edition has all the importance of a leading basic work. Consult: W. A. Patin, N., *Bischof von R.*, Munchen, 1909.—Numerous observations on the language of Niceta in A.L.L., 1906, p. 481 et s. See also Patin, chap. v.

XI. PRISCILLIAN.—Schepss, in C.V., vol. XVIII (1889).—Consult: E. Ch. Babut, *Pr. et le Priscillianisme* (*Bibl. de l'Ecole des Hautes-Et.*, sc. histor. and philol.), fasc. 169. A. Puech, in the *Journal des Savants*, 1911, and B.A.L.A.C., 1912, p. 81 ; 161.

SUMMARY

I. Ambrosiaster. — II. Donatism. Optatus of Milevis. Tyconius. — III. Pacian of Barcelona.—IV. Filaster of Brescia. Gaudentius. V. Zeno of Verona.—VI. Hilarianus.—VII. Niceta of Remesiana.—VIII. The Affair of Priscillian.

I

SINCE the XVIth century, under the name of Ambrosiaster (pseudo-Ambrose), people have designated the anonymous author of a commentary on the Epistles of St Paul (excluding the Epistle to the Hebrews), which was incorrectly ascribed to St Ambrose in the Middle Ages and possibly even in the time of Cassiodorus.[1] This paraphrase is really remarkable and is one of the most interesting bequeathed to us by Christian antiquity. Of an original mind, well versed in the methods of the Law, and possessing very positive views combined with pointed satirical humour in regard to prominent men in the Church, the author carefully avoids losing himself in the mists of allegory. This disregard of the allegorical method is almost a unique case at that period. Before everything else he aims at a clear comprehension of his text, and sets himself to draw practical lessons therefrom for the use of Catholics. Let me add, he had his eyes open as to the times in which he was living. His commentary is a precious source for understanding the pagan mysteries—those of Anubis, Mithra and especially Cybele— whose vitality remained still so powerful in the second half of the IVth century, and we can gather from it the persistence of the belief in astrology by the Christians themselves.[2]

The problem of the identity of Ambrosiaster is particularly irritating. We even know that he wrote in Rome soon after Julian the Apostate,[3] in the time of Pope Damasus [4] (366– 384). Now this period is fairly well known to us, and it is strange that so vigorous a personality as this " Ambrosiaster," should not be able to be clearly established. All the more

---

[1] *Instit. Div.*, viii (P.L., LXX, 1120). Ambrose had promised some homilies on St Paul in one of his letters (*Ep.* xxxvii, 1-2).
[2] Cf. Cumont, R.H.L.R., VIII (1903), p. 417 et s.
[3] *In II Thess.*, ii, 7 (P.L., XVII, 457).
[4] *In I Tim.*, iii, 14 (XVII, 471).

so because another work, the *Quaestiones Veteris et Novi Testamenti*,[1] (wrongly printed among the writings of St Augustine), presenting a series of discussions on doctrine, Scripture, and polemics which are nearly always interesting, must be restored to him.[2]

Conjectures are not wanting. Dom Morin has shown a special fecundity in this respect. He first thought of the Jew Isaac,[3] and the combination offered sufficient attraction for certain critics still to adhere to it, even after he had relinquished it. This Jew Isaac, after having been converted to Catholicism, took an active part in the competition of Ursinus with Damasus for the Episcopal See of Rome; he even brought a serious accusation in law against Damasus, the matter of which we are ignorant; his suit went against him and caused him to be exiled to Spain by Gratian. Isaac ended by returning to the synagogue.[4] A Paris manuscript (VIIIth–IXth centuries) has preserved a *Liber Fidei de Sancta Trinitate et de Incarnatione Domini* by him.[5] Dom Morin thought he noted certain analogies of language between it and the *Quaestiones* and *Commentary* on St Paul. Also the caustic turn of mind of Ambrosiaster, and the special importance he appears to attach to a host of particulars more or less connected with Judaism were features which seemed to him remarkably applicable to the accuser of Damasus. The identification, however, entails

---

[1] *Quaestio* in ecclesiastical language means an examination of passages of Scripture which are hard to understand. Several of St Augustine's works contain this word in their title: *De diversis quaestionibus ad Simplicianum*, etc. Cf. Souter, in T.S., VII, 4, p. 8. Ed. in P.L., XXXV, 2213–2416, and C.V., vol. L (1908), by Souter. There have been three renderings of the *Quaestiones*: one contains 151 questions, the second, amended and abridged, 127 questions, and the third (which was made between the VIIIth and IXth centuries) 115 questions.

[2] The demonstration given by Al. Souter, *A Study of Ambrosiaster*, in T.S., VII, 4 (1905), p. 23–160, is quite conclusive.

[3] R.H.L.R., IV (1899), p. 97.

[4] Cf. Mansi, *Conc.*, III, 626, and *Coll. Avellana*, no. 13. Isaac is probably alluded to by St Jerome, *in Tit.*, iii, 9 (P.L., XXVI, 595).

[5] P.G., XXXIII, 1541–1546 (published shortly after 374).—Certain recent critics (Wittig, Scholz, etc.) have ascribed to Isaac various works of unknown origin; for example, the *Gesta inter Liberium et Felicem episcopum* (C.V., XXXV, 1), the *Fragmenta contra Arianos* (S.B.W., 146 [1903], p. 11), the *de Bello Judaico* of Hegesippus (P.L., XV, 1962), the *de Concordia Matthaei* (P.L., XVII, 1011), a tract on St Matthew (Mai, *Nova Patr. Bibl.* I, 1, 477), the famous *Mosaicarum et Romanarum legum Collatio* (Hyamson, Oxford, 1913; Mommsen, *Coll. libr. juris ante-justiniani*, B. 1890) wherein several provisions in Roman Law are represented as being already in existence in the Bible, the fragment of a Comm. on St Matthew (Mercati, *Studi e Testi*, Rome, 1903; Turner, J.T.S., 1904, 218), and an *Expositio Fidei Catholicae* (K.A., p. 304).

T

serious difficulties.[1]   Four years later,[2] Dom Morin brought forward another person, Decimus Hilarianus Hilarius,[3] a man connected with the State, concerning whom, moreover, there is no evidence enabling us to say that he made any practice of writing, even occasionally. Finally, in 1914, after comparing the biography written by Evagrius with the personal information escaping from the writings of Ambrosiaster, and the Latin of the translation of the *Life of St Antony*, by Evagrius, with the Latin of Ambrosiaster, he decided to identify the latter with Evagrius of Antioch.[4] It may be that this fresh conjecture in spite of its being presented as " undeniable and certain," may not enjoy a longer fortune than its predecessors.[5] The worst thing that minds curious about Christian literature will have to fear is to read the works of Ambrosiaster, resigning themselves to remaining ignorant of the real name of this penetrating and caustic exegetist.

II

WE need not relate in detail here the history of Donatism which absorbed almost all the vitality of the Church in Africa in the IVth century. Taking birth shortly after the persecution under Diocletian, under the pretext that certain Bishops who had handed over the Sacred Books (*traditores*) were unworthy any longer to remain as directors of their flock, this movement quickly developed, and neither the

---

[1] (1) The author says himself (*Quaestio* cxiii ; Souter, p. 310, 22) : " Cum in errore degeremus in quo nunc manent Pagani . . .", which seems to imply that he had been previously a pagan, not a Jew.   Other texts to the same effect, but not so pronounced, are quoted by Brewer, Z.K.T., 1913, p. 214–216.—(2) The beginning of *Quaestio* cxx resembles completely the opening of a homily by a priest ; now it does not appear that Isaac belonged to the clergy.

[2] R.B., XX (1903), p. 113.

[3] Pro-Consul of Africa in 377 ; Prefect of the City in 383 and 408 ; Pretorian Prefect of Italy in 396.   Cf. C.I.L., VIII, 1219 (an inscription at Vaga, in Africa). Ambrosiaster is quoted by St Augustine under the name of " Sanctus Hilarius " (*Contra duas Epist. Pelag.* IV, iv, 7 ; cf. *Ambros.* v, 12 [P.L., XVII, 92]).

[4] R.B., XXXI (1914), p. 1–34.

[5] The expressions *ac per hoc*, and *hinc est unde*, real peculiarities of style with the author of the *Commentary* on the Epistles of St Paul, and of the *Quaestiones*, are not found in the *Life* of St Antony.   Ambrosiaster shows a certain antagonism to the Greek ecclesiastical writers.   Now Evagrius was from the East and did not come to Italy before 363–4, when he was already married.   Lastly the silence of St Jerome in his *De Vir. Illustr.* on such important works is difficult to understand.   His notice of Evagrius (§ cxxv) only makes very vague allusion to *diversarum ὑποθεσέων tractatus* not yet published.   Dom Morin points out these objections himself, but does not succeed in lessening their importance.

intervention of the imperial power nor the conferences arranged between Catholics and Dissidents succeeded in checking it. Very many elements foreign to the initial causes of this crisis violently stirred up the passions of both sides :—old disputes in connection with the necessity of re-baptising, on the duty of keeping the Church immaculate, and on the obligation to seek martyrdom. Local patriotism and personal matters ended by embittering the conflict in which " circumcelliones," [1] robbers and incendiaries, mingled their lawless violence.

Like all great movements based on ideas, Donatism brought forth a fairly considerable amount of literature, of which we are in a position to form an approximate estimate thanks to the detailed refutations of orthodox polemists,[2] which remained for long without any serious reply from the Catholic side. It will be noticed that Donatism, unlike Arianism, had its seat in the West. There do not appear to have been any Greek Donatists, and there was no Greek Donatist literature.

Ought we to make a distinction between Donatus the Great, Bishop of Carthage, and Donatus, Bishop of *Casae Nigrae*? [3] It is at least doubtful, and it is possible that this duplication of names may have been invented afterwards by the Donatists. However this may be, the head of the sect composed a large number of writings, also a *liber de Spiritu Sancto*, which bordered on Arianism according to St Jerome.[4] All of this is lost.

Parmenianus is known to us through St Augustine's *Contra Epistulam Parmeniani* and the treatise of Optatus of Milevis. Although a Spaniard or a Gaul, he became the head of the schismatic church in Africa, and Bishop of Carthage after the death of Donatus. He only took posses-

---

[1] The original form of the word seems to have been *circelliones* (from *circellus* meaning *fibula* : cf. schol. *ad* Juvenal., vi, 379), that is, the " continent ". The sobriquet *circumcelliones*, grafted in derision on to the first, has another signification, that of *circum cellas vagantes*. Donatus restored the original sense by the term *agonistici* (Optat. III, iv) : *agonisticus* meaning *miles Christi :* cf. St Augustine, *Enarr. in Ps.* 132. See Reitzenstein, in the *Nachrichten Gott.*, 1914, 1, p. 90.

[2] Monceaux (V, 35 et s.) has devoted a special study to the *passiones* of the Donatist martyrs.

[3] Cf. Dom Chapman, in *R.B.*, 1909, p. 13 et s. ; Monceaux, IV, p. 20, note 1 ; V, 99 et s.

[4] *De Vir. Ill.*, xciii.

sion of his Episcopal See just after the abrogation by Julian the Apostate of the Edict of Constantius, which from the year 347 had kept the Donatist leaders in exile.   He had the heavy task of reorganising the sect in the midst of the trouble which Julian (perhaps purposely) had let loose, and he was remarkably successful.   He was a man of high intellect and a certain moderation ;   his Catholic opponents spoke of him with deference.   In a long treatise of five books written possibly about the year 362–3 immediately after his return to Africa, he attempted an apology of the Donatist Church [1] to the detriment of Catholicism.   In his *Letter to Tyconius* he hit back vigorously against his criticisms in regard to his co-religionists.   His collection of *Psalms* was intended as an incentive to the piety of the Donatists.[2]

In 411, Gaudentius of Thamugadi (Timgad) was one of the seven advocates of Donatism at the Conference of Carthage presided over by Marcellinus, who helped to win the cause for the Catholics, and was a delegate from the Emperor Honorius.   In 420, when the Tribune Dulcitius promulgated his edicts against the Donatists, Gaudentius declared that rather than hand over his basilica he would prefer to be burnt in it together with his following.   It was then that at the request of the embarrassed Tribune St Augustine wrote his *contra Gaudentium* which brought him a pamphlet in the form of a letter from his opponent which he answered in a second book.   We do not know the issue of this affair,[3] which should be placed about the year 420–1.

We must further mention Vitellius to whom Gennadius [4] ascribes a *De eo quod sint mundo Dei servi*, and *Adversus Gentes*, and divers works relating to the *regula ecclesiastica ;* Cresconius the grammarian, also refuted by Augustine in 406 ;   the priest Macrobius [5] who later on was to become the secret head of the Donatist community at Rome and had written, when still a Catholic, a *Liber moralis ad Confessores et Virgines*.   The *dossier* of Petilianus, the Donatist Bishop of

---

[1] There is a reconstruction of the plan of this treatise by Monceaux in the *Journal des Savants*, 1909, p. 158 et s., i.e. the *Hist. litt. de l'Afr. chr.*, v, 227 et s.

[2] Cf. St Augustine, *Ep.* LV, xviii, 34.

[3] Monceaux has described it in detail in the *Rev. de Philol.*, XXXI (1907), p. 111–133.

[4] *De Vir. Ill.*, iv.   Gennadius places him in the time of Constantius (337–350).

[5] *Ibid.*, v.   The *de Singularitate clericorum* has been attributed to Macrobius : see above, and Monceaux, V, 151 et s.

Cirta, has become far more important,[1] thanks to the research of M. Monceaux; it comprises an *Epistola ad presbyteros et diaconos Donatistas adversus Catholicam*, two letters to St Augustine, a *Liber de Schismate Maximianistarum*, an *Epistula de ordine partis Donati*, a *de Unico Baptismo*, and different discourses given at the Conference of Carthage in 411. These titles and a few meagre fragments can be established by the writings of St Augustine.

The most interesting personality among the Donatists is this same Tyconius over whom Augustine was so much exercised. "He was a Donatist, but of a very special kind, a layman who mixed himself up in theology and was able to enlighten the Bishops thereon, a man of study who observed with interest the disputes between the Churches, and who in the independence of his views claimed to preserve his freedom of speech, a philosopher who knew the Bible better than anyone else but interpreted it in his own way without fearing to clash with opinions already established . . . , lastly, a polemist solicitous for the truth, ready to allow that his opponents were not always in the wrong and to tell his friends that they were not always in the right."[2] There is nothing so detestable to parties as those censorious minds who refuse to submit their judgment to sectarian catchwords. In two works which have been lost, the *de Bello Intestino*, written about the year 370, and the *Expositiones Diversarum Causarum*, in 375,[3] but of whose contents we have some approximate knowledge thanks to allusions thereto by St Augustine, Tyconius did not hesitate to controvert the Donatists on a certain number of points without making any breach with the Donatist Church. Parmenianus, the head of this schismatic Church, refuted him in that *Letter to Tyconius* which, some years later, St Augustine in his turn was to turn against him.[4] Tyconius was finally condemned in 380 by a Donatist Council.

He also wrote a *Commentary on the Apocalypse* of which

[1] *Rev. de Philol.*, XXX (1906), p. 218 et s.; XXXI (1907), 28 et s. *Hist. litt. de l'Afr. chr.*, V, 309–328.

[2] Monceaux, *Journal des Savants*, 1909, p. 162: cf. *Hist. litt. de l'Afr. chr.*, V, 165 et s.

[3] Titles mentioned by Gennadius, *de Vir. Ill.*, xviii.

[4] The *Letter to Tyconius* is analysed by Monceaux, *ibid.*, p. 164 et s. *Hist. litt.*, V, 231 et s.

various later commentaries on the same book enable us to form some idea. But the work which is most admired was his *Liber Regularum*, written about 382, which may be considered as the first manual of Biblical hermeneutics to appear in the West. The object of Tyconius was to establish rules of interpretation enabling edification to be drawn from the Bible from every portion as it were, even from passages the most unpromising in appearance. From the first beginnings of Christianity texts from the Bible had largely been used by exegetists, polemists, compilers of *tractatus*, etc. ; repertories had even been formed in which every one might seek according to his requirements. But there remained a considerable residue, a *prophetiae immensa silva*, in the words of Tyconius, the moral and religious significance of which did not appear at first. Tyconius flattered himself that he had discovered a method by means of which these sterile and neglected texts might be assimilated with the efficacious ones : " Si ratio regularum sine invidia, ut communicamus, accepta fuerit, *clausa quaeque patefient et obscura dilucidabuntur. . . .*" These *regulae* seem to us to be passably ingenious ; what is certain is that his contemporaries were enraptured with them. While recommending that Tyconius should only be read with due care,[1] St Augustine embodied his seven rules of exegesis in his *De Doctrina Christiana*,[2] thus perpetuating the influence of this vigorous, original, and in more than one case, disconcerting mind.

III

THE first Catholic champion against Donatism, and the most remarkable before St Augustine to do full justice to it, was Optatus, Bishop of Milevis, in Numidia. In 366 or 367 he undertook to reply to Parmenianus, whose subtile dialectics troubled many of the faithful. The Donatists avoided debates in public ;[3] it was in order to reach them in spite of their evasiveness that he wrote his *Libri contra Parmenianum Donatistam*.

The work originally comprised six books. In the 1st

---

[1] *De Doctr. Chr.*, III, xxx.
[2] *Ibid.*, xxx–xxxvii. These rules are explained in Monceaux, V, 182 et s.
[3] *Contra Parm.*, I, iv.

Book Optatus traces the history of Donatism. To do this, he collected ten salient points which he placed in an appendix, and refers his reader to them on different occasions. The authenticity of these documents thus inserted has been contested. Optatus has even been suspected of having been only a forger. Mgr. Duchesne has conclusively proved, as against Seeck, the hollowness of these accusations. The following are the conclusions at which he arrives: "There is no possible reason to doubt the sincerity of St Optatus of Milevis, but we must recognise that he did not handle his documents with the same skill as St Augustine. Neither the accounts given by St Optatus, nor the arguments brought forward by him, should be struck out from the list of historic sources as regards the origins of Donatism. We only need the assistance of other information at our disposal for purposes of classifying and interpreting them." On the other hand, his most recent historian, M. Monceaux, notes in him "two fundamental qualities—loyalty and a taste for precision." The polemics of Optatus present valuable information to theologians; for instance, when he opposes the great Catholic Church, whose centre and connecting point[1] is Rome, to the little Donatist Church; when he defines the "marks" of the Church; when he lays down the rôle of the minister in the administration of the Sacraments (V, iv: *sacramenta per se esse sancta, non per homines*). Let us note too that in Book III, vi–vii, he outlines some kind of justification for the action of the secular power against heresy. His style slightly errs in over-emphasis, but it is clear, accurate, and not without humour.

Twenty years after the publication of his treatise, Optatus took it up again, as it seems, and retouched it in places; then he added a seventh book of a gentler tone addressed to the Donatists in general (Parmenianus died in 391), in order to answer the contradictions which his criticisms had provoked. This seventh book was not finished, and it is possible that other hands may have inserted certain rather maladroit interpolations. St Jerome was not yet aware of it in 392 when he wrote his notice of Optatus in § cx of his *De Viris Illustribus*.[2]

[1] II, ii.
[2] Cf. Dom Wilmart, in R.S.R., 1922, p. 271-302, on a sermon by St Optat. for the Feast of Christmas.

Pacian need not detain us long. Before everything else he was a somewhat reactionary theologian who thrived on the legacy of ideas bequeathed by Tertullian and St Cyprian, but he knew how to combat with tact and humanity certain rigorist prejudices which went so far as to exclude in perpetuity the sinner from the Church under the pretext of preserving her entire " virginity."

When Bishop of Barcelona, a recrudescence of Novatianism brought him up against a certain Sympronianus, who approved of the severity affected by that sect. Three letters of Pacian remain to us out of the correspondence exchanged between them. In the first, the Bishop claims for the orthodox Christian the right to call himself Catholic in view of the multiplicity of sects. In it this oft-quoted phrase appears : " Christianus mihi nomen est, Catholicus vero cognomen " (1, 4). Sympronianus having again written to him sending at the same time a tract on Novatianism, Pacian gives expression to his views on Novatian himself in a second letter. Then, after having read over again at his leisure the objections of his adversary, he refutes them radically in a third letter in which he quotes numerous extracts. The main idea of Sympronianus is summed up at the beginning of the letter in these words : " . . . quod post baptisum paenitere non liceat ; quod mortale peccatum Ecclesia donare non possit, immo quod ipsa pereat recipiendo peccantes." It is the same spirit as Tertullian's in his *de Pudicitia* when he had become a Montanist, and, whose side the Novatianists of the IVth century still took.

Pacian wrote with taste ; his irony is not lacking in point. He was a lettered man who had read and retained his Cicero, Virgil, and Horace. We have further a *Sermo de Baptismo* in which he points out the renovating effects of baptism on the soul (" . . . aperiam quid fuerit ante gentilitas, quid fides praestet, quid baptismus indulgeat ") ; a *Paraenesis, sive Exhortatorius Libellus ad Poenitentiam*, in which he defines the different kinds of sins, and upbraids those of the faithful who from false pride conceal their faults or who after confessing them evade the necessary expiation, and ends by setting forth the rewards promised to those who loyally carry it out.

He also wrote a *Cervulus* directed against the amusements

of an altogether pagan license which marked the new year. There are numerous allusions in Christian literature to this kind of Carnival which was accompanied by many disorders.[1] Pacian gives such a *piquant* description of them that he was accused (he himself mentions ironically this insinuation at the beginning of the *Paraenesis*) of encouraging the very people he was endeavouring to dissuade from them. Unfortunately the work has not been preserved.[2]

According to St Jerome he died in the reign of Theodosius in extreme old age, before the year 392, the date on which Jerome wrote a short notice of him in his *De Viris Illustribus* (§ cvi).

IV

THE immense heterodox literature of the first Christian centuries has almost entirely perished, such of it, at least, as remains in its original tenor. We are able to form some idea of it from Catholic refutations and the works of heresiographers. The list which in a certain number of manuscripts is joined to Tertullian's *De Praescriptione*,[3] is one of the first specimens of this kind of investigation, a fresh attempt at which we find in the mediocre compilation of Filaster.

" You express a keen desire that I should write something short on all the heresies contrary to the doctrine of our Lord which have swarmed since His coming. . . . Filaster, the Bishop of Brixia (Brescia), whom I have seen with St Ambrose of Milan, wrote a book on the above ; he even made mention of the heresies which showed themselves among the Jewish people before the coming of the Lord, and he counted twenty-eight ; as regards the heresies which have arisen since the establishment of Christianity he counted one hundred and twenty-eight. Epiphanius, Bishop of Cyprus . . . collecting the heresies during the time preceding and following our Lord, only found eighty. Both were endeavouring to

---

[1] Cf. *The Mediaeval Stage*, Oxford, 1903, vol. II. App. N. ; see also the thesis of Boethius mentioned further on, on St Caesarius of Arles.

[2] Dom Morin, basing his view on similarities in language, further ascribes to Pacian : 1. the *De Similitudine carnis peccati*, included in the Paris MS. 13344, IXth cent. (R. Bén., 1912, p. 1 et s.) ; 2. the *Liber ad Justinum Manichaeum* (P.L., viii, 999–1010), usually imputed to C. Marius Victorinus (R. Bén., 1913, 286 et s.).

[3] See above, p. 222.

do what you are asking of me, and you see how the number of sects differs ; this would not have happened if what had seemed a heresy to the one had also seemed a heresy to the other. We must not believe that Epiphanius was unaware of the heresies which Filaster knew of, for I find Epiphanius far more learned than Filaster. . . . But it cannot be doubted that over such a matter the two authors were not in agreement as to what was and what was not heretical ; and as a matter of fact, it is difficult to decide this fully. . . . Consider then whether perhaps I had not better send you St Epiphanius' book ; I think he has spoken on this matter with more light than Filaster. . . ."

This appreciation of St Augustine in a letter to Quod-vultdeus [1] should be borne in mind, but we cannot avoid still further accentuating our unfavourable opinion of Filaster from it.

We know very little of even the personality of Filaster. A sermon by Gaudentius, his successor, suggests the idea of a restless and travelled controversialist [2] who throughout the Roman world disputed with pagans, Jews, heretics (especially with Auxentius, the Arian Bishop of Milan), and entered into private and public oratorical contests, even in Rome itself. Whatever Marx, the last editor of the *Liber de Haeresibus* may say, Filaster was most likely of Latin origin ; the characteristics of his language are in favour of this hypothesis. [3]

As to his low intellectual level, it is as low as you like to place it. He had a clumsy mind and though professing to be a heresiologist was incapable of defining with any precision the very concept of heresy, [4] and sought in a puerile manner to

[1] *Ep.* ccxxii.
[2] See the *Sermo de vita et obitu Filastri* (P.L., XX, 998) : " . . . Circumiens universum paene ambitum Romani orbis, dominicum praedicavit verbum. . . ."
[3] A good demonstration of this is to be found in P. C. Juret's *Etude gramm. sur le Latin de Saint Filastrius*, a thesis at Fribourg-en-S, 1904 (Roman. Forsch., xix [1906], p. 130 et s.), p. 4–5.
[4] We should say in exculpation that this concept was only made clear fairly late. *Heresy* and *schism* were for long rather confused : see Buonaiuti in *Athenaeum*, IV (1916), p. 168–180 ; Monceaux, IV, 161–2 ; Bayard, *Le Latin de Saint Cyprien*, 1902, p. 183. But how can we admit statements like this (§ cii) : " Alia est haeresis quae terrae motum non Dei jussione et indignatione fieri, sed de natura ipsa elementorum opinatur " ?

establish an artificial symmetry in his notices.[1] There is a paragraph in the *Liber de Haeresibus* which defies the most careful endeavours to interpretate. With all the assurance of mediocrity, Filaster rejects *en bloc* human science, the *inanes sententiae philosophorum*, and the *deliramenta poetarum*, the *mendacia historiographorum ;* every quotation he makes from profane works seem to have been drawn, not from the original texts, but from the ecclesiastical sources he utilises. It is difficult to verify these sources for he mixes up his own extracts with others and with his own personal discoveries.[2] It hardly seems open to doubt, although this has been contested, that he had before him the *Panarion* of St Epiphanius. The *Panarion* must have been finished towards the end of 376, or in the course of the year 377. A thorough examination of the ideas given in the *Liber de Haeresibus* leads us to place its compilation between 385 and 391. Now at this time important works passed very quickly from the East to the West.

We know from Gaudentius, the panegyrist of Filaster, that he was in the East when news came to him of his election as Bishop of Brixia. He hesitated to assume the responsibility of this charge, but St Ambrose and other Bishops wrote to him such pressing letters that he decided to accept it. A highly considered personage, he took part in the embassy sent to the imperial court at Constantinople by Honorius and Pope Innocent I, when St John Chrysostom was condemned to exile. His sermons were held in high esteem. A chance circumstance decided him to put in writing a few of them. A certain Benevolus, *magister memoriae* to Valentinian II, and a pious official who was so attached to the faith of Nicea that he gave up his position rather than collaborate in the law of the 23rd January 386 drawn in favour of the Arians, had been unable through illness to hear the ten sermons delivered by Gaudentius during Easter week. At his request, the Bishop consented to write them out.[3] He added five *tractatus*, four of which were on the Gospel and one on Machabees. Six other writings may be

---

[1] Augustine gives the division selected by Filaster (28 + 128). Filaster divides these 128 heresies which arose during the Christian era into two series of 64 + 64, the first of which is classed κατὰ διαδοχήν, and the second κατὰ δόξαν.

[2] For a full discussion see my *Sources de l'Hist. du Montanisme*, 1913, p. xxxvi et s.

[3] Gaudentius gives these reasons himself (P.L., XX, 827 ; 830).

ascribed to him for serious reasons, namely, the *De Ordinatione sui*, the *De Dedicatione Basilicae*, the *Ad Paulum Diaconum*, the *De Petro et Paulo*, and the *De Vita et obitu b. Filastrii* (groundlessly suspected by Marx). His style is simple and correct and shows a classic formation.

V

IT is not open to doubt that there was a Zeno, Bishop of Verona, during the second half of the IVth century. In a letter addressed to Syagrius, Bishop of that city, about 386, St Ambrose expresses himself as follows regarding a nun unjustly suspected : " Before giving the matter any consideration you have formed a preconceived opinion against a girl *to whom Zeno, of holy memory, had given his esteem and whom he had sanctified with his blessing.*" [1] We also possess a sermon of Petronius of Bologna delivered at Verona for the anniversary of Zeno, who was the patron of that city.[2] It is singular that neither St Jerome nor Gennadius mention him in their lists of *illustres*. St Jerome seems to have been unaware that his contemporary Zeno possessed any qualifications as a writer. Nevertheless a dozen manuscripts have preserved to us sixteen well-developed sermons and seventy-seven much shorter under his name.[3] Certain indications make us think that Zeno must have been of African origin. One of these *tractatus* is devoted to Arcadius of Cæsarea, an obscure martyr of Mauretania. The author closely imitates Tertullian, St Cyprian, Lactantius, and even Apuleius ; he has gone so far as to find some of his similies in the most *risqué* scenes from the voluptuous sophist of Madaurus.[4] Several of these writings are directed against the Arians,

---

[1] *Ep.* v, 1.

[2] The most recent edition is that given by Dom Morin in the *R. Bén.*, XIV (1897), p. 3 et s. Dom Morin has published *ibid.* for the first time following the *Monac.* 14386, Xth cent., another sermon of Petronius " *in die ordinationis vel natale episcopi.*" The contents of these sermons prove that Petronius was not the Bishop of Verona, contrary to the superscription on the manuscript. The notice by Gennadius (*De Vir. Ill.*, xlii) styles him as Bishop of Bologna.

[3] The manuscripts in reality give 104 sermons, but 11 of them are not by Zeno. A difference in the writing of the oldest manuscript, the codem *Remensis*, has enabled this discrimination to be made.

[4] Compare Zeno, iv, 3 (p. 38, Giuliari) : " Venerem . . . connexis manibus se tegere conantem, immo animi sui vitium et corporis demonstrantem " ; and Apuleius, *Metam.*, II, xvii : " In speciem Veneris . . . reformata . . . feminal rosea palmula potius obumbrans de industria quam tegens verecundia."

pagans and Jews. Others are dissertations on doctrine or moral exhortations. In connection with the history of dogma in the IVth century, as also with that of the Christian religion, the liturgy, and Christian archæology, much may be gleaned from his pages, with their studied and even flowery arguments.

VI

JULIUS QUINTUS HILARIANUS was a Bishop in the Pro-Consulate of Africa. In his *De Mundi Duratione,* he endeavoured to define the duration of the universe by the light of the *Lex Dei,* disregarding the "verbiage" of profane science.[1] As reckoned by Hilarianus, there still remained to humanity 101 years of life at the end of the IVth century.[2] Towards the end, Antichrist would prevail; then after the revolution of the 6000 years allotted to the world, there would come the resurrection of the dead, the reign of 1000 years (the millennium), the universal judgment, the total destruction of the heavens and earth, and finally, the descent of the City described in the Apocalypse, wherein the just would be happy for ever. In order to understand the importance attached during the first centuries to this kind of calculation, we must remember the long continued anxiety of the Christians regarding the date of Christ's second coming. Practically the Christians were resigned to dispose themselves and arrange their daily life as though the *parousia* were only an uncertain quantity. Nevertheless belief in an end of the world that was fairly imminent remained alert and active : it was one of the mainsprings of their individual morality. The benefits to be anticipated from a Christian chronology were to enlighten them as to whether this gloomy disquietude as to the future might be laid to rest in each one's mind, or whether, on the contrary, it should make them more anxious on account of the proximity of the final catastrophe. At that time they would have deemed rather strange the discouragement felt by modern exegetists when confronted with the difficult task of reconciling the chronological ideas of the Old Testament either with each other, or with those of profane history. Hence the zeal of the old interpreters. However irksome to us their calculations may be, we should under-

---

[1] Cf. the opening.　　　　　　　　　　[2] § xvii.

stand the value they had for their contemporaries. Where we see only a skeleton framework of somewhat fantastic additions, they read the secret of their own personal destiny and that of the universe, and believed that they had pierced the riddle of the mysterious and dreadful to-morrow.

In the *De Die Paschae et Mensis*, Hilarianus develops and claims to unravel three problems relating to the fixing of the festival of Easter from the course of the moon. He sums up his conclusions in § xiv, and establishes the difference between the Jewish and Christian calculation. " Aliud est pascha nostrum, aliud Judaeorum." In all this chronology, there is more numerical fantasy than solid and real science. According to the *De Duratione*, § 1, the two *opuscula* form a division into two of a previous work in which they were at first united.

VII

Niceta of Remesiana was the apostle of Catholicism among the Danubian races. His Episcopal city of Remesiana (Palanka), not far from Nisch, was in Lower Dacia on the road from Naissus to Sardica. But the evangelising activity of Niceta certainly extended beyond the limits of his ecclesiastical boundary.

Christian antiquity has not overlooked his name. Paulinus of Nola, who received two visits from him, expresses in his poem XXVII his joy at the thought of seeing him soon,[1] on the occasion of the approaching anniversary of St Felix. Poem XVII is a " Proempticon "[2] in 85 strophes addressed to Niceta on his return to his own country. In it Paulinus alludes to the happy propaganda carried out by Niceta amidst the barbarian tribes as far as the Riphaean mountains (in the north of Scythia) :[3]

> " Quaque Riphaeis Boreas in oris
> Adligat densis fluvios pruinis,
> Hic gelu mentes rigidas superno
> Igne resolvis."

Again in another place he speaks of the " venerabili

[1] Verses 148 et s.
[2] Cf. F. Iager, *das antike Propemptikon u. das* 17 *Gedicht des Paulinus v. N.*, Munich, 1913.
[3] Lines 201 et s. Cf. v. 249.

episcopo atque doctissimo Nicetae, qui ex Dacia Romanis merito admirandus advenerat. . . ." [1] The second visit of Niceta to Paulinus of Nola should be placed in 400. He also figures as one of those to whom the letter of Germanius to his colleagues in Illyria was addressed in 366 or 367.[2] Letters XXI and XXII of Pope Innocent I imply that he was still living in 409–414.[3] The above are the only data left to us concerning his life.

We should do wrong to regard as certainties the hypotheses tending to ascribe to Niceta various anonymous writings. Paulinus of Nola informs us that Niceta encouraged around him a taste for Church hymns.[4] Two treatises, the *de Vigiliis Servorum Dei*, and the *de Psalmodiae Bono*, are attributed to him in several manuscripts : the first enumerates the advantages of *meditatio nocturna* during which the soul retreats better into itself than in the midst of the bustle of the day ; [5] the second combats the view of those who did not see the use of Church music,[6] and explains to them their error both from the point of view of tradition as also of the evident benefit their piety draws from it.[7] People have been led on this account to think that Niceta might very well have been the author of the *Te Deum* which was already known everywhere by the IVth century.[8] Various manuscripts of this rhythmic prose give the name of Niceta or Nicetius : "Thus," Mgr. Duchesne remarks, "this celebrated hymn, which all Christendom sings in its moments of deep emotion, may have first resounded from a hidden corner of ancient Moesia." [9] It would be an interesting fact. Nevertheless, specialists in Latin euchology are far from considering this as definitely established. Similarly the reasons given for placing to the account of Niceta the *de*

[1] *Ep.* xxix, 14.
[2] Quoted in Burn, p. 138.
[3] Cf. Burn, p. liv.
[4] *Carmen* xvii, 90 ; 109 ; 262 ; xxvii, 315 ; 500.
[5] Cf. § viii (Burn, p. 65).
[6] § ii : "Scio nonnullos, non solum in nostris, sed etiam in orientalibus esse partibus, qui superfluam nec minus congruentem divinae religioni aestiment psalmorum et hymnorum decantationem."
[7] It will be noted that Niceta ascribes the *Magnificat* to St Elizabeth (§ ix ; Burn, p. 76, l. 21 ; § xi, Burn, p. 79, l. 4). Origen had already been aware of this attribution (*Hom.* vii *in Luc* ; P.G., XIII, 1897 c.). Cf. Burn, p. clv in the edition mentioned.
[8] From the testimony of Cyprian of Toulon in the year 530 (M.G.H., *Epist.* III, 436). Cf. Dom Morin, R. Bén., XI (1894), p. 48–77, who favoured the conjecture.
[9] *Hist. anc. de l'Egl.*, III, 181.

Ratione Paschae and the *Epistula ad Virginem Lapsam* present nothing to carry our assent.

The notice by Gennadius (*de Vir. Ill.*, xxii) has enabled the *Libelli Instructionis*, written for candidates for baptism, to be reconstructed through the accident of a series of learned discoveries. Niceta is here seen, in his polemics against Arianism or Macedonianism, in the light, not of a theologian of complicated speculations, but as a catechist skilful in simplifying difficult questions. He shows the gift of lucid explanation for which Cassiodorus later on was to praise him : [1] " Si quis vero de Patre et Filio et Spiritu Sancto aliquid *summatim* praeoptat attingere, *nec se mavult longa lectione fatigari*, legat Niceti (sic) episcopi librum quem de fide conscripsit. . . ." Gennadius had said of him, *Simplici et nitido sermone.* It is in a style suited to pastoral instructions in which only the essential points of doctrine require to be touched on and defined. Elsewhere Niceta could be vehement and almost pathetic when he wished to appeal to the deeper sensibilities of his hearers.

On the whole, it is fortunate that the efforts of philologists have been successful in restoring some kind of vitality to this apostolic figure who from the time of Baronius had been confused with Nicetas of Aquileia or with Nicetius of Treves. " In studying the sum total of his work we are led to conceive that at various periods in Illyricum, first in connection with Victorinus of Pettau and afterwards with Niceta at the end of the IVth century, a centre of theological activity hitherto little known, to which the situation of this country lying between the two worlds which met there, give it a place apart." [2] In any case, a history of Christian evangelisation should keep a place for the name of the Bishop of Remesiana, the civiliser of the barbarians, whom he made Roman in making Catholic.

> " Orbis in muta regione per te
> Barbari discunt resonare Christum
> Corde Romano placidamque casti
> Vivere pacem." [3]

---

[1] *Inst. Div litt.*, § xvi.
[2] J. Zeiller, *Les orig. chrét. dans les Provinces Danubiennes*, p. 556.
[3] Paulinus of Nola, *Carmen* xvii, 257 et s.

VIII

THE question of Priscillian has always aroused particular interest among Church historians, whether orthodox or not. Has not Priscillian been considered as the first victim of the " secular arm," of the power of the State put at the disposal of the Church ? The facts are well known, and it will be enough to recall them very briefly.

Born in Spain in the middle of the IVth century, of noble birth, wealthy, and a man of high culture, Priscillian began to spread abroad his theories of doctrine about 370–375, especially, as it appears, in the district of Merida Cordova. He found numerous adherents among educated people and women. Two Bishops, Instantius and Salvianus, joined him. But his propaganda was violently opposed by two other Bishops, Hydatius of Merida and Itacius of Ossonaba, who displayed extraordinary zeal to compass his ruin and were capable of every sort of violence and deceit. In October 380, a Council at Saragossa had to pronounce on the Priscillianist " heresy," and condemned, if not Priscillian by name, at least the ideas which were attributed to him.[1] Hydacius and Itacius thereupon turned to the imperial power and obtained from Gratian a decree of banishment against the " Manichaeans," a term sufficiently vague which comprehended in the current usage the Priscillianists themselves. Priscillian, who had just been consecrated Bishop of Avila, was obliged to go to Aquitania. There too he made proselytes ; Euchrotia, the wife of Delphidius the rhetorician, and her daughter Procula, attached themselves to him and followed him to Italy, where his personal pleading before Pope Damasus and St Ambrose did not obtain for him any advantage. However, thanks to the good offices of Macedonius, *magister officiorum*, and of Volventius, Pro-Consul of Africa, he secured the annulment of the edict issued by Gratian and was able to return to his own country. Meanwhile Maximus had been proclaimed Emperor by the legions in Britain, and, desirous of securing the support of the Catholic clergy, he relegated the matter to a synod assembled

---

[1] On this vexed question, cf. Cirot, in *Bull. Critique*, 1897, no. 18 ; Babut, *Priscillien et le Priscillianisme*, p. 40 ; Puech, in the *Journal des Savants*, 1891, p. 343, and in B.A.L.A.C., 1912, p. 173.

U

at Bordeaux (384).   Instantius was deprived of his Episcopal
See.   Priscillian refused to recognise the competence of
the Council of Bordeaux, and committed the imprudence
of appealing to Maximus himself.   After being taken to Trèves
he was condemned to death on the report of the prefect
Evodius, together with four of his partisans, including
Euchrotia, and was executed.   Sulpicius Severus[1] has
acquainted us with the motives of this condemnation :
" . . . convictumque *maleficii* nec diffitentem obscenis se
studuisse doctrinis, nocturnos etiam turpium feminarum
egisse conventus nudumque orare solitum . . ." : immorality
and magic were the charges brought, to the exclusion of the
crime of heresy.[2]

Hydatius and Itacius had worked underground in order to
obtain this bloody outcome.   Violent protests were raised
among the Catholics themselves against their abominable
proceedings.   The former was obliged to resign from his see ;
the latter was deposed.   St Martin of Tours and St Ambrose
gave expression to their reprobation in forcible terms.   The
scandal also was great on the part of the pagans.   In his
panegyric on Theodosius, written in 389, the Gallic rhetorician,
Latinus Pacatus Drepanius, a friend of Ausonius, speaks with
horror of these Bishops turned executioners " who assisted
in person at their torture and went to feast their eyes and ears
on the sufferings and groans of the accused." [3]

The curiosity of learned people was therefore keenly excited
when eleven treatises ascribed to Priscillian appeared in
1889 in the *Corpus Script. eccles. latinorum*, vol. XVIII,
thanks to the labours of Schepss.   These treatises, with no
name of the author, figure in a manuscript of the Vth or VIth
century belonging to the library of the University of Wurzburg.   They had drawn the attention of Ruland, the librarian,
who made a copy of them.   This copy passed into the hands
of Dollinger, the historian, who did not edit it himself but
suggested that Priscillian must be the author.   Dollinger's
conclusion was accepted by Schepss.

[1] *Chron.*, II, L, 8.
[2] As regards the *nudum orare solitum*, we must remember that nudity, partial or
complete, was one of the conditions exacted in magic practices.   See references in
Lejay, R.H.L.R., 1903, p. 317.
[3] *Paneg. lat.* (Baehrens, p. 217).

The hopes aroused by this discovery have been sadly deceived. In the first place, the style of the collection is very different from what one had a right to expect from an author whom Sulpicius Severus represents as *facundus . . . , disserendi ac disputandi promptissimus*, etc. Clumsy, obscure, and involved lucubrations, scarcely relieved here and there by specimens of a rather fervid form of dialectics, constitute the sole profit gained by the disappointed scholars. Secondly, the enigma of Priscillian's doctrine was made little clearer by the publication from which so much had been expected. The most qualified historians of dogma had sadly to acknowledge this on the morrow of the appearance of Schepss' work. From his languid and dreary sentences one can certainly pick out statements that might be held suspect on the right of freely interpreting the Scriptures in the name of the gift of prophecy whose prerogatives God had not limited,[1] and on the use of apocryphal writings which the author would have liked to incorporate in an enlarged canon of Scripture.[2] But these indications do not go far.

The results of this disappointment have been twofold. If it is so difficult to discern " heresy " in any definite form in the writings of Priscillian, might this not be because his orthodoxy was not deserving of the disqualifications to which it was subjected ? M. Babut undertook with vigour and skill the paradoxical task of the rehabilitation of Priscillian in history. After examining the *dossier* of Priscillianism, he distinguishes two groups of documents. First, what he calls the " dossier primitif," wherein he includes among other writings the treatises of Schepss. If we are reduced to this series, " the condemnation of Priscillian would appear to have been not only unjustifiable, but also inexplicable." [3] Secondly, the accusing documents which appeared, especially after the year 400, imputing to Priscillianism an extraordinary multiplicity of errors. According to Babut's conception of him, Priscillian was above all things " a man of opposition and an innovator " [4] who " sincerely attempted a compromise between the free tendencies of his own personal religion and the demands of orthodoxy " [5] and finally became the

---

[1] Schepss, p. 32.   [2] *Ibid.*, p. 44, 10 ; 52, 11 ; 53.
[3] Babut, p. 15.   [4] P. 167.   [5] P. 128.

victim of the " machinations of worldly Bishops who feared the rigour of his precepts and the purity of his ideal."

An ingenious thesis, which raises more difficulties than it solves. If Priscillian's ideal was irreproachable, why did the Council of Saragossa condemn him ? Why did Ambrose and Damasus show the door to the Bishop of Avila ? Why did Bishop Delphinus, who was present at the Council of Saragossa, forbid him to enter Bordeaux ? Why has Sulpicius Severus, who esteemed the condemnation of Priscillian iniquitous, such harsh words for his errors ? How likewise explain the severity of St Jerome ? [1] Lastly, if Priscillian had not been a heretic, through what misunderstanding did his immediate followers undoubtedly so become ?

In spite of the generous efforts of Babut, a revision of the question of Priscillian is not incumbent upon history.

An examination of the Wurzburg treatises led Dom Morin [2] to a conclusion of another kind from which it is far more difficult to escape. Out of these eleven treatises, there are eight which are hardly more than homilies devoid of historic value. The three first, namely the *Liber apologeticus*, the *Liber ad Damasum episcopum*, and the *De Fide et Apocryphis* have an entirely different bearing. Critics are agreed in considering the *Liber Apologeticus* as a plea delivered before the Council of Bordeaux in 384. On this count, remarks Dom Morin, it is impossible to admit that Priscillian can have been the author. As a matter of fact, Priscillian denied the competence of his ecclesiastical judges ; he refused to be heard by them and preferred to appeal to the Emperor. [3] Under these circumstances it was another who pleaded the cause of the Priscillianists, and Sulpicius Severus mentions him by name : *Instantius prior jussus causam dicere. . . .* [4]

The Wurzburg treatises therefore cannot have been written by Priscillian ; they should be restored to Instantius. Another indication strengthens this conjecture. We read in the *Liber ad Damasum* (p. 46, l. ii) the following passage : *nos tamen non omittentes in causa fidei sanctorum judicium malle quam saeculi.* These words are suitable in the mouth

---

[1] *Ep.* lxxv, 3 ; *Comm. in Is.* xvii, 64 (P.L., XXIV, 622) ; *Ep.* cxxxiii, 3.
[2] R. Bén., 1913, p. 158 et s.
[3] Cf. Sulpicius Severus, *Chron.*, II, xlix.
[4] " Jussus causam dicere " was what Sulpicius Severus wrote. " Quod jubetis " he said at the beginning of the work (Schepss, p. 4, I. 2).

of Instantius who undertook to defend his ideas before the
Bishops assembled at Bordeaux.   How can we attribute
them to Priscillian since he rejected the authority of the
ecclesiastical tribunal in order to entrust his case to a
secular court ?

Dom Morin's hypothesis seems to be very judicious.   It
explains the literary mediocrity of the Wurzburg treatises,
and the mild note of heretical " pravity " which we are
astonished to notice therein.   If it definitely stands the proof
of time and the acuteness of the critics, there will hardly
remain anything else to the credit of Priscillian except the
Canones in Pauli Apostoli epistulas.[1]   These are a kind of
theological digest of St Paul composed of quotations and
references which for a long time were held to have been
written by St Jerome, and after the mistake had been discovered, were retouched by a Bishop of the name of Peregrinus
to insure their perfect orthodoxy.   Attempts have been made
(on no serious grounds) to identify Peregrinus with the
Spanish monk Bachiarius, to whom we are also indebted
for a *Liber de Fide* and a *Liber ad Januarium de Reparatione
Lapsi*.[2]

Priscillianism kept up a disquieting vitality up to the Vth
century.   The sect approached nearer and nearer to Manichaean ideas.   A fairly abundant literature was born from
these polemics ;   on the Priscillianist side we may mention
the names of Tiberianus,[3] Asarbus,[4] Latronianus (a very
distinguished poet, if we may credit St Jerome),[5] and
Dictinius,[6] and on the Catholic side those of Itacius,[7] Olym-

---

[1] This compilation, likewise published by Schepss, p. 107 et s., was fairly well
known in Spain and France during several centuries.   Schepss was aware of 17
manuscripts dating from the IXth to the XVth centuries.   It is possible that in the
mind of Priscillian it was originally meant for a controversial work for the purpose
of showing the conformity of his theology with that of St Paul.

[2] P.L., XX, 1019–1062.   Th. Stangl (B. ph. W. 1917, p. 868–888) considers
this identification doubtful.   Dom de Bruyne (R.B., XXXI [1914–19], p. 384)
rejects it expressly.   I have analysed Stangl's interesting notice of Bachiarius in
the *Revue de Philologie* (*Revue des Revues*, 1918).   Dom Morin has published in
B.A.L.A.C., 1914, p. 117 et s., divers hitherto unpublished fragments of which
Bachiarius might be the author.   The whole work of this personality seems to
merit a study ;   his writings are not at all insignificant.

[3] St Jerome, *De Vir. Ill.*, cxxiii.

[4] Priscillian, *Liber Apol.*, I (Schepss, p. 3).

[5] *De Vir. Ill.*, cxxii.

[6] Cf. *Ep.* xv, 16, of Pope Leo Ist.   We can reconstruct the main gist of his
work entitled *Libra*, from St Augustine's *Contra Mendacium*.

[7] Isidore of Seville, *De Vir. Ill.*, xv.

pius,[1] Pastor,[2] Syagrius,[3] and Turibius of Astorga.[4] St Augustine himself attacks the Priscillianists more than once in his letters, in his *Contra Mendacium,* and his *Ad Orosium contra Priscillianistas et Origenistas.*

[1] Gennadius, *De Vir. Ill.,* xxiii.
[2] *Ibid.,* lxxvii.
[3] *Ibid.,* lxvi.
[4] Cf. Migne, LIV, 693. On these different personages, see Kunstle, *Anti-priscilliana,* Fr. i. B., 1905, and Dufourcq, *Etude sur les Gesta Martyrum romains,* vol. IV (*Le Néo-Manichéisme et la légende chrétienne*).

CHAPTER IV

CHRISTIAN POETRY IN THE IVth CENTURY

BIBLIOGRAPHY

I. The Small Poems. See Table VI.—There is a general *resumé* in Manitius, *Gesch. d. christlich-lat. Poesie*, Stuttgart, 1891 (mediocre, but useful analyses); G. Boissier, *La Fin du Paganisme*, vol. II, book IV.

II. Juvencus.—P.L., XIX, 53-346; Marold, in B.T. (1886); C.V., XXIV (1891, Huemer); some translations in F. Clément's *Les Poètes chrétiens*, 1857, p. 1-11.

III. Paulinus of Nola.—His works are in Migne, vol. LXI, and in C.V. (Hartel, 1894), vols. XXIX and XXX. Hartel has included in an appendix four poems whose authenticity is contested, the *Carmen ad conjugem*, the *C. de nomine Jesu*, the *C. ad Deum post conversionem et bapt. suum*, and the *C. de domesticis suis calamitatibus.*—A French anonymous translation of his letters in prose, Paris, 1703; 1724. Some pieces in verse and prose are translated in Anot. de Maizières' *Nouveaux choix de Pères latins*, 1853, vol. IV and V; the notice of Pacatus written by his pupil Uranius (Migne, LIII, 866), is included in the above, vol. II, p. 144. See also the *Chefs-d'oeuvre des Pères de l'Eglise*, vol. XIV; Félix Clément, *op. cit.*, pp. 88-161. P. de Labriolle's *la Corresp. d'Ausone et de Paulin de Nole*, 1910.—The chronology of Paulinus' works is often a difficult matter; cf. E. Ch. Babut, in the *Annales du Midi*, XX (1908), pp. 18-44, and Rauschen's *Jahrbucher der christl. Kirche*, 1897.—On his works as a whole, consult: Lagrange, *Hist. de saint Paulin de Nole*, 2 vols., 1882; A. Baudrillart, *Saint Paulin, évêque de Nole* (coll. *les Saints*), 1905.—There are many useful observations in P. Reinelt's *Studien uber die Briefe des hl. P. v. N.*, Breslau, 1904, and Philipp's *Zum Sprachgebrauch des P. v. N.*, Erlangen, 1904 and L. Kraus' *die poetische Sprache des Paulinus Nolanus*, Augsburg, 1918.

SUMMARY

I. General view of Latin Christian Poetry.—II. Paraphrases of the Bible. Juvencus. Cyprian's *Heptateuchos*.—III. Didactic Poems.—IV. The *Centos*.—V. Paulinus of Nola. The Conversion of Paulinus. Paulinus and Ausonius.—VI. The Letters of Paulinus.—VII. His Poems.

I

In his History of the Church (III, xvi), the Greek historian Socrates relates that following the edict of the Emperor Julian which forbade the Christians to explain the pagan classics, the two Apollinares, father and son, the former a professor of grammar at Laodicea in Syria, and the latter Bishop of Laodicea, made an attempt to reconstitute *en bloc* for the benefit of educated Christians the profane works on which they were forbidden to comment in public. The father drew up a grammar " consonant with the Christian faith," which doubtless means that his examples were taken from Christian authors or counterfeited in conformity with the faith ; he translated the books of Moses into heroic verse, paraphrased the historical books of the Old Testament, and drew from them epopees and tragedies. He purposely made use of the greatest possible number of the traditional metrical forms of Hellenic literature in order to popularise them among the Christians. His son transposed " the Gospels and the doctrine of the Apostles " in the form of Platonic dialogues.

Julian died soon after ; the law he had introduced became inoperative, and all this counterfeiting of profane literature, in the words of Socrates, " retained no more importance than if it had never existed." [1]

It is well to know something of the attempt by the Apollinares in order to understand the spirit inspiring the majority of the Christian poets in the Latin tongue whom we are going to review. What slightly diminishes the interest of their works is that we are too much aware of a desire to assimilate them to profane literature ; we can discern a concerted purpose, an artificial effort, rather than the freedom of spontaneous inspiration which relieves itself in its utterance. Their intention is to oppose the *certa fides* to the *mendacia* of the classics (these are the terms used by Juvencus), and by the same forms as those employed in the classics. In order to reach a public very different from the cultivated circles at which they usually aim, they only very exceptionally shake themselves free from these forms consecrated by long usage.[2] Christian poetry in Latin was only able to rise to real and true originality in the Church hymn. Nevertheless the IVth century offers us one name at least which

---

[1] Sozomenes, who also gives details of this improvisation (H.E., V, xviii), judges it differently : " If mortals did not attach value solely to what is old, if they could shake themselves free from inveterate routine, the writings of the Apollinares would have been read with no less pleasure than the works which they were intended to supersede."

[2] This was the case with St Augustine in his *Alphabetical Psalm*.

should be remembered—that of Paulinus of Nola,—and a talent exceeding the mediocrity of the common level.

II

THERE is a whole group of poems which are nothing else than paraphrases of episodes, more or less developed, taken from the Old Testament, and, less often, from the New.   The magnificent poetry of the Bible, the Mosaic cosmogony in particular, offered rich material which was largely exploited.   In order to realise the secret of the Christian versifiers, we must understand the ideas which they obeyed.   It was a question with them, in the first place, of being helpful to young minds by instilling into them sacred teaching transposed in an attractive form, expurgated of those difficult details with which certain episodes in the Bible might oppress their youthful imaginations.[1]   Then, imbued with another thought which as we know obsessed the cultivated Christians, they hoped to conquer the intellectual and learned *élite* by the charm of their poetry, and bring them back to God by those flowery paths which were not forbidden by Him.   "It matters little," Sedulius was to say in the dedicatory Epistle of his *Carmen Paschale*, " it matters little by what path each one arrives at the Faith, provided that once he has entered upon the road to liberty he does not fall again into the pitfalls of servitude which lately held him captive."   Lastly, a commentary of the Bible in verse enabled them to develop certain dogmatic and moral interpretations, to refute adverse doctrines on the origin and formation of the earth, and to unveil the mystic signification hidden beneath the dry covering of the texts.   Apologetics also thus found their place in it.   One would not like to say that poetry always comes into its own.   In any case this series of poems, without being absolutely barren of happy features, does not reveal any original talent,—no Milton, Tasso, not even a du Bartas or a Maurice Scève.   Description abounds formidably, the kind of description defined by Guizot,[2] " which is less anxious

---

[1] We shall notice that with the exception of Dracontius, who allows himself some rather profane details, the creation of woman in Eden does not provoke any perilous descriptions.   The *Metrum in Genesin* (v. 123) drily gives in a hemistich :   *Mulier de costa viri fit :*   that is all.

[2] *Hist. de la Civilis. en France*, vol. II, ch. xviii, p. 60.

to make people see objects than to make them understand them, which observes and goes through them, taking pains to enumerate and display every part ; in such a way that such and such a person, such and such a fact, if it had been simply mentioned or indicated by one sole characteristic, would have been real and visible to the imagination, but now only appears discomposed, cut in pieces, dissected, and destroyed." Again, these professorial amplifications are supported entirely on quotations. The author of the *Metrum in Genesin* [1] becomes moved over Adam and his posterity in terms recalling the melancholy of Virgil when deploring the sad destiny of the young Marcellus : " O happy man, formed by the same hand of God which hurleth the thunderbolt (*summi cui dextra tonantis est pater*) ; O too happy, thou who takest from heaven (*Olympo*) both thy origin and thy shape ! If thou dost not become the prey of the deadly vices of the earth, if thou dost not allow thyself to be seduced by error, thou shalt be a god (*numen eris*) and, mounting to heaven, shalt marvel at the kingdom which by His own mouth the Father hath promised to virtuous men ! " I have underlined certain expressions of " classicism " rather foreign in a Christian subject. Tartarus, the vale of Tempe, the Styx, Avernus, the Elysian Fields, and material from mythology of every kind find a place in these verses aiming at being epic, amid a quantity of shreds torn from Ovid and Virgil. It is something like Claudian with less colour, brilliancy, and richness of imagination. At any rate, this rather servile respect for past masters, shared alike by Christians and pagans, preserved the art of poetry from a ruin still more complete by substituting imitations which are not always without skill, in place of their feeble inspiration.

If Commodian must be put on one side as certain critics (wrongly without doubt) wish to do as far as the IVth or even the Vth centuries are concerned, the Spanish priest Gaius Vettius Aquilinus Juvencus should be reckoned the first Christian poet in the Latin tongue.

We must, however, mention a little poem anterior by a few years, the *Laudes Domini*, in which the anonymous author who knew his Virgil very well, in connection with a miracle which had taken place " in the country of the Eduens "

---

[1] Lines 125–30 (P.L., L, 1287 ; C.V. III, 283, and XXVII, 231).

(a Gallic tribe whose capital was Bibracte, Autun) sings the praises of Christ Who, together with the Father, created the world and came to ransom it. In any case, Juvencus was the first to try and utilise Christian ideas in any large measure by methods borrowed from traditional classic technique.

> " Versibus ut nostris divinæ gloria legis.[1]
> Ornamenta libens caperet terrestria linguæ . . ."

St Jerome informs us that he wrote his *Evangeliorum Libri* in the reign of Constantine, about the year 329.[2] The idea of drawing from the sacred Books matter for a Christian epopee must have come naturally to lettered Christian writers. The literary Roman criterion (the most perfect expression of which we find in Horace) was firmly bound up in a hierarchy of subject matter, and gave the palm to the epic poem.[3] What honour to the Faith to prove that it could become the principle or leaven in a revival of this kind of literature which was so highly esteemed !

" I would sing," Juvencus declares, " the noble deeds of Christ on earth." In his conception, therefore, it was highly appropriate to reproduce the Gospel in a kind of epopee, and his invocation to the Holy Spirit takes the place of the Prologue, the traditional invocation to the Muses. As his basis he takes St Matthew's text which he read from one, or several, pre-Hieronymic Latin versions, and availed himself on occasion of St Luke, St John, and, more rarely, of St Mark. The 3190 lines of the poem are divided into four books which otherwise do not coincide with the contents of each of the four Gospels.

The great difficulty encountered by Juvencus—many other Christian poets after him were to bruise themselves against this stumbling-block—was his very respect for the Word of God, and his fear of offending God by misrepresenting the fabric of the sacred Books. By applying in all its rigour such a principle or scruple all poetic endeavour would have become impossible. Juvencus was obliged here and there to prune, transpose, and even elaborate—especially in his descriptions of nature, where his ready and *facile* talent found

---

[1] iv, 805.
[2] *De Vir. Ill.*, lxxxiv ; *Chron. ad annum* 2345 ; cf. Juvencus, iv, 806 et s.
[3] Cf. Horace, *Sat.*, I, iv, 43.

itself more justified in breaking ground. But he is not at his ease, and this is somewhat too apparent. Equally timorous both as a classic and as a Christian, he has no other concern than to plant his footsteps as closely as possible in the tracks of Virgil—his favourite model—or in those of Lucretius, Statius, and a few others.[1] Evangelical simplicity does not emerge without damage from these laborious adaptations. The *Transeat a me Calix Iste* is watered down as follows :

> " Si fas est, genitor, calicis me transeat hujus
> Incumbens valido nobis violentia tractu,
> Sed tua jam veniat potius quam nostra voluntas
> Quæ tibi decreta est tantis sententia rebus."

The *Jam foetet* becomes :

> " Crediderim corpus motu fugiente caloris
> Fetorem miserum liquefactis reddere membris."

Modern critics are very sensitive to these errors of taste. A certain phrase of St Jerome seems to imply that he had already felt their maladroitness (*Ep.* lxx, 5). Nevertheless, Juvencus founded a tradition, and his initiative sufficed to assure him the respect of his Christian successors who often essayed to imitate this imitator.[2] His renown was widespread throughout the Middle Ages,[3] but it hardly lasted beyond it.

The *Heptateuchos* of the poet Cyprian has only been known to us in its present form for a few years. In 1560, G. Morel, following a manuscript in the library of the Abbey of St Victor, Paris—to-day this manuscript is in the Bibliothèque Nationale, and is numbered 14758—published a short poem of 165 lines entitled *Genesis*. In 1735, the Benedictines Dom Martène and Dom Durand added to this fragment 1276 lines after a MS. in the Abbey of Saint Germain-des-Prés (Bibl. Nat. no. 13047). In 1852, Cardinal Pitra completed this *Genesis* by the addition of 57 lines (*Spicil. Solesm.*, vol. I). The three manuscripts which he had examined, namely two at Laon (IXth century), and one at Trinity College, Cambridge (Xth century), enabled him in 1888 to include

---

[1] The peculiarities of his versification are mentioned in edition C.V., p. 163. He frequently makes use of rhyme. He ventured on some verbal creations: *auricolor* (1, 356) ; *flammivomus* (*Prol.*, 23) ; *flammicomans* (iv, 201) ; *flammipes* (ii, 546) ; *altithronus* (*Prol.*, 24 et *passim*) ; etc.

[2] Cf. Huemer's edition (C.V.), p. viii.

[3] *Ibid.*, p. xiv.

in his *Analecta novissima Tusculana*, six other poems on the
books following *Genesis*, viz. Exodus, Leviticus, Numbers,
Deuteronomy, Josue and Judges. The "Heptateuch" was
complete. The name of Cyprian was found in an old catalogue
of the Xth century of the manuscripts of St Nazaire de Lorsch,
and in one of the manuscripts at Laon. Who was this
Cyprian? Was he the author of the *Caena Cypriani* which
had been inserted among the apocryphal writings of St Cyprian,
or the priest Cyprian to whom Letter CXL of St Jerome is
addressed? This we cannot venture to decide. In any case,
he was a lettered man, familiar with Virgil, Ovid, Persius,
Juvenal, and Lucan, and also with several Christian poets,
and one who was not without a certain technical skill : thus,
for different portions of a more lyrical turn, he substitutes the
phalecian hendecasyllable in place of the hexameter (v.g.
Exodus, 507–542 ; *Numbers*, 557–567 ; *Deuteronomy*, 152–
278). His prosody is otherwise somewhat fanciful, and he
makes an unpleasing abuse of the old Roman practice of
alliteration.

It is probable that the poetic efforts accomplished by
Cyprian were more numerous than we can judge at the present
time, for isolated verses have been discovered relating to
the four books of Kings, the two Paralipomena and Job.
We find also in old catalogues traces of a translation in verse
of Judith and Esther. Perhaps Cyprian had attempted to
put into verse the whole of the Old Testament, leaving himself
free to omit from his scheme (as we see he had done in different
places) those portions which did not lend themselves to
transposition.

III

ANOTHER series of writings is connected with the didactic
order which enjoyed a long popularity in Rome. "We may
say . . . that by recalling Lucretius, Virgil, and even
Manilius, it aimed at the highest elements in the Roman soul,
and that it responded to its most noble and most treasured
aspirations."[1] Since the IIIrd century this vigorous tradition had lost its flavour in mediocre works such as the
Cynegetica of Nemesianus, the *de Re Rustica* of Palladius

[1] A. Puech, *Prudentius*, p. 161.

and several others. The Christian writers had the merit of understanding the advantages of a method of exposition or of polemics, offered by a class of literature which had such deep roots in the Roman past.

The de Cruce [1] (called also the de Pascha, and the de Ligno Vitae) deserves special mention. The " tree of life " was the cross raised on Golgotha, wood " cut from a barren tree " which notwithstanding " extended its branches on both sides," and " covered the whole world in order that the nations of the earth might ever find in it their nourishment and their life, and might learn that death also could die." And its fruits savouring of salvation produce a marvellous renewing in those who before having recourse to it " have obliterated the shameful defilements of their past life, and have washed their bodies in the sacred stream." All this symbolism is presented with simplicity and feeling. The de Ternarii Numeri Excellentia,[2] attributed to St Ambrose, celebrates in 14 hexameters the surpassing virtue of the number three. Subtilty delighting in refinements, and making play in allegory and symbol, had for long been exercised on the mystery attaching to numbers and to their secret correspondence with certain beliefs. Did not St Augustine himself take pleasure in it ? [3] The de Naturis Rerum, which an Oxford manuscript likewise attributes to St Ambrose (it is not known whether rightly or wrongly), celebrates the almightiness of God in nature under a title very similar to that chosen by Lucretius the Epicurean.[4] The Ad quemdam Senatorem [5] is an urgent, but courteous warning to a Senator and former Consul (v. 27), who, after having embraced Christianity for several years (v. 43–44), had abandoned it for the religion of the Magna Mater. The author (he is given as St Cyprian in the manuscripts !) is astounded that a man of his distinction should return to those absurd and bloody rites, and expresses the hope that when he grows old the backslider will abjure them. " As I am not unmindful that you are a lover of poetry," he remarks, " I have tried to turn poet

[1] TABLE VI, no. 3. See Brandt in B. ph. W., 1920, 424–432 (a study of the text : Hartel cannot have followed the best MSS.).
[2] Ibid., no. 22.
[3] Cf. Knappitsch, Augustins Zahlensymbolik, Progr. Graz, 1905.
[4] TABLE VI, no. 16.
[5] No. 21.

in order to make answer to you, and I hasten to write these verses to make you ashamed." The piece is very clear in language and of a very lively turn. The *Invectiva contra Nicomachum* was written during or immediately after the pagan reaction attempted by the Emperor Eugenius, in 392–394. Virius Nicomachus Flavianus, several times Praetorian Prefect, Consul in 394, and an historian of a certain talent, had shown himself one of those most attached to the ancient religion [1] among the members of the Roman aristocracy ; he died before the Emperor Eugenius. The *Invectiva* celebrates the fall of this influential adversary of Christianity and draws therefrom a pretext to turn into somewhat heavy ridicule the superstitions of the pagans, and the cult of Isis and of the *Magna Mater*. This poem, whose style is clumsy and versification rather incorrect, has been preserved to us in one single manuscript, the *Cod. Paris.* 8084, of the VIth century, which also includes the poems of Prudentius. The *Carmen adversus Marcionem*,[2] in five books and 1302 lines, was published in 1564 by George Fabricius from a manuscript now lost, but which doubtless came from the monastery of Lorsch where the poem was ascribed to Tertullian. Comparison with the authentic treatise of Tertullian against Marcion proves that the poem was incorrectly attributed to him. The names of Marius Victorinus, Victorinus of Pettau, and Commodian, have been suggested. The date of the writing of the *Carmen*, as also the place where it was written, cannot be defined with certainty.[3] In addition to Tertullian, the author exploits a few other Christian writers, Theophilus, St Cyprian, etc. His narrative is dull and confused in spite of a certain correctness of diction, and is strangely flat after Tertullian's ardent, caustic, and passionate prose. Fabricius made the mistake of retouching the text arbitrarily with the view of giving it a more classic colour. Certain restorations of the original text are possible, thanks to a poem

---

[1] He translated into Latin, with hostile intent, the *Life of Apollonius of Tyana*, by Philostratus.

[2] No. 14.

[3] A recent study by Karl Holl, S.B.B., 1918, p. 514–559, comes to the conclusion that this poem must have been written in the south of Gaul during the last quarter of the Vth century. His argument relies on two passages, the list of the Popes (iii, 275 et s.), and the legend that Adam was buried at Golgotha (ii, 160 et s.). See my analysis in the *Revue de Philologie, Rev. des Rev.*, 1919, p. 53 ; also T.U., XLII, 4 (1919), p. 161–2

entitled *Versus Victorini de Lege Domini*,[1] made up of lines taken from the *Carmen adversus Marcionem*.

Two manuscripts, the *Codex Veronensis* 163 (IXth century) and the *Vossianus* Q 33 (Xth century), St Gregory of Tours,[2] and an anonymous grammarian of the early Middle Ages,[3] attribute the *Carmen de Ave Phoenice* [4] to Lactantius. This poem relates in 85 distiches the legend of the Phœnix, its life in a sacred wood in the remote East (v. 1–58) as the bird-priest of the Sun, its voluntary death every thousand years on a palm-tree in Phœnicia in which it builds a nest for this purpose (v. 59–98), and finally its resurrection and the transfer of its remains to the Temple of the Sun in Egypt (99–170). The legend of the Phœnix was popular in antiquity. Herodotus [5] had learnt it from Egyptian priests without attaching too much credence to it. More than one Roman writer had re-echoed it, among whom was the sober-minded Tacitus, in his *Annales*.[6] Tacitus relates it in full detail in connection with the alleged reappearance of the Phœnix in Egypt during the Consulate of Fabius and Vitellius (34 A.D.). Always distrustful and divided as regards the " marvellous," he adds, " all this is uncertain and exaggerated by fables. Moreover, it is incontestable that this bird sometimes appears in Egypt." Pliny the Elder [7] too had his doubts : *haud scio an fabulose*. The legend, developed and added to in a greater or less degree, was to preserve its vitality down to the last days of Latin literature, and Claudian was to sing it in one of his idylls. Quite early the Jews had appropriated it as a symbol of the resurrection. The Christians followed their example. Towards the end of the Ist century, Clement of Rome considered the story of the Phœnix in his letter to the Corinthians,[8] and concluded in these words, " Can we then find it strange and astonishing that the Creator of the Universe should make those creatures live again who served Him in a holy manner and with the confidence of a perfect faith, since He makes us behold in a bird the magnificence of His promise ? " A large number of Christian authors treated

---

[1] Cf. Brandes, in *Wiener Studien*, XII (1890), p. 310. This poem is included in the *Vaticanus Regin.* 582, of the IXth or Xth century.
[2] *De Cursu Stell.*, § 12 (M.G.H., *Scr. rer. Merov.*, 1, 2, p. 861).
[3] G.L., v.g. 477, 14 et s.   [4] TABLE VI, no. 1.
[5] II, lxxiii.   [6] VI, xxviii.
[7] *H. Nat.*, X, ii.   [8] xxv–xxvi.

it in the same spirit. At the beginning of the VIth century, the poet Dracontius again brings it forward among examples of resurrection offered by nature.[1] This form of zoology applied to Christian doctrine was altogether to the taste of the first centuries.

The author of the *Carmen de Ave Phoenice* only makes extremely discreet use of the fable in the service of Christianity, so much so that we might feel some doubt whether he had any other object in view than to develop incidents which provided him with a sufficiently brilliant poetic theme. Nevertheless, certain features, without being very clearly marked, reveal the Christian, and under the rather ordinary guise of description there is hidden a mysticism which knew how to extract from traditional common-places congruities suited to the faith.[2] It can neither be proved, nor is it unlikely, that it was Lactantius who adapted the story in this manner.

The idyll *de Mortibus Boum*,[3] in 33 asclepiad strophes, is a work by a friend of Paulinus of Nola,[4] the rhetorician Severus Sanctus Endelechius, a man of Gallic origin, who taught in Rome at the end of the IVth century. Aegon is struck by the sadness of Buculus. The latter informs him that in two days the terrible epidemic which, starting in Pannonia had spread through Illyria and Belgium, had carried off his whole flock. Tityrus, another drover, had preserved his own intact. Tityrus explains how a cross laid on the foreheads of his cattle had protected them efficaciously. Buculus and Aegon at once decide to have themselves initiated in the safe-guarding faith. Without equalling the great descriptions of the classics, that given by Buculus of this scourge is rather expressive and strong.

IV

THE universal admiration in which Virgil was held had early provoked certain minds gifted with ingenuity to compose whole poems out of verses taken from the *Bucolics*, *Georgics* and the *Æneid*, and twisted more or less skilfully into meanings

---

[1] *Carmen de Deo*, I, 650–660.
[2] For example, v. 93 : "Animam commendat " (cf. St Luke, xxiii, 46) ; v. 64 : "hunc orbem, mors ubi regna tenet " ; v. 25 : "fons in medio est, quem vivum nomine dicunt " ; v. 163–170 : in praise of chastity.
[3] TABLE VI, no. 15.
[4] Paulinus, *Ep.* xxviii, 6.

X

quite unforeseen by the bard of Mantua : "We see to-day," Tertullian had already noted,[1] "issuing from Virgil some entirely different fable in which the subject is adapted to verse and the verse to the subject. Hosidius Geta 'pumped up' entire (*plenissime exsuxit*) his tragedy *Medea* from Virgil. One of my relations, among other literary pastimes has explained the *Pinax Cebetis* by means of the same poet." This "labour of the rag-picker" (*more centonario*), as Tertullian calls it, had become the fashion : we possess fairly numerous specimens of "centos."[2] The poetess Proba, a Christian lady of the highest aristocracy, the granddaughter, daughter and mother of Consuls, conceived the idea of relating by the same method the principal episodes of the Old Testament as far as the Deluge,[3] and of the New Testament, to the Ascension.[4] She wished in this way to assist her children more easily to engrave the sacred history on their memory. It was a chimerical undertaking, the difficulties of which no device could surmount. Proba was compelled to substitute for the names of the personages in the Gospel vague designations such as *Deus*, *Dominus*, *Magister*, *Heros*, *mater*, *vates*, etc. Only the name of Moses, *Moseus*, due to its consonance with that of Virgil's *Musaeus*, succeeded in finding a place in her verses. And then how could she express in profane hemistiches the Conception of the Virgin, the flight into Egypt, the Crucifixion, etc., even by changing the circumstances of the events and persons as she sometimes permitted herself to do, or by allowing herself liberties in prosody which Virgil would not have tolerated ? We can understand the annoyance which these well-intentioned imitations (of which we have a few other specimens),[5] caused to St Jerome's good sense.[6] The decree ascribed to Gelasius places Proba's work among the "apocrypha" reserved for private reading.[7]

1 *De Praescr. Haer.*, xxxix, 3.
2 They are to be found collected in P.L.M., IV, p. 191–240.
3 V. 29–332.
4 V. 333–688.
5 TABLE VI, nos. 2, 5, 23, 24.
6 *Ep.* liii, 7 (C.V., LIV, 454, 1, i).
7 P.L., LIX, 162. Cf. Isidore, *de Vir. Ill.*, xxii.

V

A PROFOUND sensation was created in high Gallo-Roman society when, in 393, it learnt that Meropius Pontius Paulinus, one of the foremost personages in the Empire, the owner of vast domains in Gaul and Italy, a Senator, and Procurator of Campania since his twenty-first year, was definitely renouncing the life of the world, and was thinking of becoming a monk.   And this too, not in the decline of life when a man's powers become unsteady and disillusionment increases, but at the age of forty, in his full intellectual and physical maturity.[1]

For some years his friends had already seen that his soul was undergoing a change, and that he was gradually detaching himself from everything, and suspected that the influence of his wife, Therasia, a pious Spanish woman, strongly supported the secret working of his mind.[2]   But could any-one have expected such a complete rupture, the alienation of his magnificent landed properties—the *regna Paulini*,[3]— which he was selling in order to distribute his wealth among the poor ?   What was to become of the empire, menaced as it was by the barbarians, if its most valiant defenders thus made default ?   Also was it right that at a time when the public offices of the State constituted so heavy a burden, the richest should dispense themselves from them, and leave all the weight on other men's shoulders ?   The restless state of patriotism, the important interests affected, and lastly, the spirit of enjoyment humiliated by the spirit of sacrifice—all these sentiments of different value united to render the scandal more impressive.   Paulinus was aware of the unpopularity of which he was the object.   He suffered on account of it without doubt, but he was determined to effect the necessary cutting adrift.   Besides, his wife, in complete harmony of soul, shared with him all his renunciations.

He had not reached this point all at once.   Born of a Christian family, religious considerations were aroused in him fairly early.   When quite a young man, he had been keenly struck by the miracles which he had seen taking place

---

[1] He was born at Bordeaux in 353 or 354.
[2] Cf. Ausonius, *Ep.* xxviii, 31 (Peiper, p. 284).
[3] *Id., Ep.* xxvii, 116.

at the basilica of St Felix, at Nola, which belonged to his family.[1] He had then entered upon his career of high position, and for some years lived happily the life of the world at Bordeaux. In a prayer to the Creator in 19 hexameters which he wrote at that time, he expressed no other desire than to take advantage of the lawful pleasures of life [2] in full security.

A somewhat mysterious occurrence, a grave peril from which he thought his escape had been wholly due to the protection of St Felix, seems to have contributed greatly to detach him from the life of the world : " Thy goodness, O my Father and guardian (he is addressing the Saint) hath never belied itself. Following after the death of my brother, I found myself in danger ; out of the trial of my brother there arose against me a like accusation ; the public assessor had already come to view my possessions in order to auction them. It was thou who wast able to remove my neck from under the sword, my patrimony from the state treasury, and thus save for the Lord Christ my goods and my person." [3] He had doubtless nearly fallen a victim to some juridical murder set on foot by the usurper Maximus with the sole object of confiscating his riches. What is certain is that from 390, his desire for " conversion " (we can see in what sense to understand this word) was more and more felt. He was baptised, which had been put off until then ; he settled in Spain with Therasia, and remained there four years at least. There, about the year 393–4, husband and wife decided to live a life of continence and poverty.

We may truly say that no one was more painfully astonished at so disconcerting a report than Ausonius, the aged rhetorician. He had had Paulinus as his pupil at the University of Bordeaux. He had taken the greatest satisfaction in him, had placed his highest hopes on his future, and had continued his connection with him by the affectionate intercourse of letters, verses, and presents. He highly appreciated the poetic talent of Paulinus. An abridgment in verse, which he undertook, of three books of Suetonius on the Kings had delighted him especially.[4] He recognised therein the

---

[1] *Carm.* xxi, 367 et s. (Hartel, II, p. 170).
[2] *Carm.* iv.
[3] *Carm.* xxi, 414 et s. (Hartel, II, p. 171).
[4] Ausonius, *Ep.* xxiii (Peiper, p. 267).

happy fruits of the discipline he had inculcated; he saw himself reflected in his disciple. And here was Paulinus, so dear to him, renouncing the life of the world, leaving Aquitaine to bury himself in Spain, and selling his worldly possessions. . . . But what then? And his abstract of Suetonius, his poetry, his Latin culture? Was he going to deny himself all these things? Ausonius could not endure such a perplexing condition of things, which was aggravated by the long silence of Paulinus. He wrote to him four letters in verse, one after the other, begging him to speak, to give some explanation, and to come back; and in these hexameters, full of the most cordial and sincere sentiments, he multiplied choice legends of mythology, and the wide common ground existing between themselves, as though the better to recall to his old pupil the beautiful things he seemed to be forgetting.

Paulinus at last replied, also in verse. A certain literary coquetry was always to remain with him—the only vanity in which he did not deny himself some pleasure. While lavishing on his old master the most affectionate terms, he gave him categorically to understand that the pastimes in which he begged him to continue his interest seemed to him from now onward to be too frivolous, and that another kind of discipline, which monopolised his thought, his heart, and his whole being, had taken the savour from that wherein he had occupied his youth.[1]

In spite of all his protestations of respect and tenderness, nothing could be more mortifying to Ausonius, nor make him see better at a glance the chasm which had been opened between their two spirits, formerly so like-minded.

Looking around him, Ausonius began to perceive more and more that to some minds elegant phrases were not a sufficient incentive to life, and this discovery plunged him into a kind of stupor. He saw Patrician men and women undertaking long pilgrimages to the Holy Land. He saw an illustrious advocate like Sulpicius Severus imitating the renunciation of Paulinus, and at the same time marvellous fishers of souls like St Martin and Romanus of Blaye, bringing about the most astounding conversions among the masses. At the end of the IVth century a gust of asceticism was

---

[1] I have translated and commented on this *Correspondence*, Paris, (Bloud), 1910.

blowing over the whole of the West. Piety, confidence, and faith were stirring up Christian believers to the work of conquest and struggle. Even in the immediate surroundings of Ausonius, his grandson Paulinus (of Pella), although still quite a child, was giving indications of a desire to consecrate himself to the service of Christ, and just at first his parents were not opposed to this. The old man was able from his daily experience to observe the prodigious difference which separated his own quite external and formal Christianity from a Christianity that was truly felt and was deep.[1]

By contrast, the *prestige* of the sacrifices freely consummated by Paulinus and Therasia was extraordinary among the people. On Christmas Day 394, or 395, the population of Barcelona, in a tumultuous access of enthusiasm, practically compelled Paulinus to receive the priesthood at the hands of Bishop Lampius, although he was not at all in the prescribed canonical conditions.[2] Soon afterwards Paulinus decided to retire to Nola by the tomb of St Felix. He embarked with Therasia for Narbonne, and was welcomed most warmly by St Ambrose who wished to enrol him among his clergy,[3] at least nominally, and far more coldly by Pope Siricius, the reasons for which Paulinus does not define.[4] He passed the last thirty-five years of his life at Nola in the exercise of mortification and prayer. What remained to him of his patrimony he devoted to building a new basilica to St Felix, which was inaugurated in 403. In 409, on the death of Bishop Paulus, he received Episcopal dignity. If he had had a mind so commonplace as to wish to be revenged on those who had detracted from his life, he could have found a striking opportunity when in the year 410 he witnessed the arrival at Nola, miserable and frozen with terror, of the fugitives fleeing before the hordes of Alaric. The flood of the barbarians had passed over those rich domains, those white villas, and those good things which had rendered Gallo-Roman life so pleasant and so agreeable that to renounce them had seemed folly.

---

[1] On the Christianity of Ausonius, see *ibid.*, p. 53–63. Ausonius' works have been edited by Peiper (B.T., 1886) and Schenkl, M.G.H., 5, 2 (1883). French translation by Corpet in Panckoucke's and in Nisard's collection.

[2] Paulinus, *Ep.* l, 10 ; iii, 4.

[3] *Ep.* iii, 4.

[4] *Ep.* iv, 13–14. That he should have been suspected of Priscillianism (see Babut, R.H.L.R., 1910, p. 109 et s.), is a paradox which the most refined subtilty has not succeeded in rendering likely.

Latin civilisation, whose seductiveness and requirements they had lately opposed to his vow of asceticism had resolved itself into dust.

He died on the 22nd June 431, at the age of 76 or 77. His body was buried in the basilica of St Felix ; later on, it was to be transferred to the Church of St Barthélemy in Rome.

VI

HIS work is divided in the *Corpus Scriptorum Ecclesiasticorum Latinorum* into one volume of prose and one of verse.

The prose writings are all in letters. A panegyric on Theodosius, composed by Paulinus in 394–5 on the occasion of the victory of the Emperor over Maximus and Eugenius, has not come down to us. Hartel gives 51 letters in his edition.[1] *Ep.* xxxiv, which is a sermon on well-doing, must be set apart. We possess only a fragment of *Ep.* xlviii. The authenticity of *Ep.* xlvi and xlvii, addressed to Rufinus, without being improbable, is uncertain.[2] These letters are scattered between the years 394 and 413 ; one only, the 51st, must be placed between 423 and 426. Their chronology is rather difficult, for they are not disposed in the manuscripts according to their order in point of time.

It is not open to doubt that Paulinus was esteemed by his contemporaries as one of the most remarkable of letter writers. St Augustine,[3] and St Jerome [4] speak of his letters with an enthusiasm which appears to be sincere ; St Jerome goes so far as to compare him to Cicero : " *In epistolari studio prope Tullium representas*," he wrote to him. We find less pleasure in them than these eminent correspondents, and for these reasons.

In the first place, there is an excessive abundance of quotations from the Bible which is rather overwhelming. " More than any other Catholic writer of the time," Babut very well remarks,[5] " he multiplies extracts from the Bible. Sometimes there are passages or entire verses, more often

---

[1] There are at least 14 or 15 which have been lost, according to the allusions given in them : cf. Reinelt, p. 54 et s.
[2] There are arguments in a contrary sense in Reinelt, p. 45, Philipp, p. 67.
[3] *Ep.* xxvii, 2 ; clxxxvi, 40.
[4] *Ep.* lviii, 11, and lxxxv, 1.
[5] R.H.L.R., 1910, p. 129. Cf. Philipp, p. 77.

scraps of two or three words or simple allusions. . . . The quotations, or quasi-quotations, are only on rare occasions distinguished from the text by a word which qualifies them, such as *scriptum est* or *dicente apostolo*. As a rule, they are incorporated in the sentences. Paulinus tangles up his own words and what he quotes. He incessantly expresses his own thoughts by means of expressions taken from Scripture, or rather his own thoughts seem made up of a continuous flow of Biblical *souvenirs*. We have here a special kind of literature written for a scholarly few, the full savour of which escapes us. . . ." Let me add that Paulinus, beneath his camel's hair shirt, which was a present from his friend Sulpicius Severus, was a man of letters according to the taste of his age and of his old professor Ausonius. He takes care to excuse himself here and there when any reminiscences of profane literature come into his mind,[1] but these repentances are fugitive. As a matter of fact, his prose is adorned with all the flowers of rhetoric, and nowhere exhibits any repugnance to diffuse developments carefully and even meticulously prepared.[2] He is regardless only of the fact that there should be some limit even to what is pleasing, and that discretion is a virtue in a writer. Lastly, his letters in prose all refer to the time when the form of his thought and life was definitely settled. He gives us no confidences in connection with the stages through which he passed as an opulent patrician before arriving at this point of humility and detachment. Hence our curiosity is somewhat disappointed.

Notwithstanding, this part of his work offers some interest. Many illustrious names of the period are mentioned. His correspondence with Sulpicius Severus is particularly attractive. Linked with Sulpicius in close friendship, Paulinus had preceded him in the path of asceticism, and Sulpicius wished to regard him as his spiritual guide, although the modesty of Paulinus refused to allow this. They had been victims of the same adverse comments, and the same outcry, on account of their breach with the world. They felt themselves so fully united in heart that Paulinus liked to consider that their affection had been predestined.[3] It is in their

---

[1] See Philipp, p. 58 et s.
[2] E.g. : *Ep.* xxiii, 10 et s. (Hartel, I, p. 167).
[3] *Ep.* xxiii, 15.

letters especially that the quality of the religious sentiment residing in the choice souls of those times can be seen. The letter to Jovius [1] fairly well indicates the position taken by Paulinus in the debated question of the lawfulness of utilising the old learning, which was always arising again. A cultured Christian, Jovius took pleasure in Plato, Xenophon, Demosthenes, Cato, Varro and Cicero, and allowed himself to be imbued with certain ideas on chance and fortune somewhat incompatible with Catholic sentiment. While giving large praise to his intellectual qualities, his *facundia* and his *doctrina*, Paulinus begs him not to allow himself to be captivated by the " pernicious charm " of pagan literature. Let him take from it the qualities it is able to impart, *linguae copiam et oris ornatum*, but as a man who arms himself with hostile weapons in order to make a better use of them, and let him turn them to the service of true wisdom. It is practically the theory of Jerome ; from this time onward there was agreement on this question among minds of any scope of vision. Disputes on matters of doctrine are not absent even from these letters. But Paulinus was not of a bellicose temperament ; he was a gentle and modest man of profound humility and charity who did not at all think that he need espouse the heated quarrels of the great champions of orthodoxy, although on fundamental points he sided with them.

VII

THERE is general agreement in according a marked preference to his work in verse. Paulinus was thoroughly acquainted with the *technique* of poetry ; he had been educated in a good school. Like Ausonius he uses great diversity of metres. In the same piece he passes on from the hexameter to the iambic trimeter, then to the elegiac, to go back finally to the form used at the commencement.[2] Like Ausonius again, he had at his service the whole lexicon of the revered poets Virgil, Horace, Ovid and Statius ; from Ausonius himself he made flattering extracts.[3] His memory was so loaded with reminiscences that he, so scrupulous about everything bearing on the

---

[1] *Ep.* xvi (Hartel, I, 120).
[2] *Carm.* xxi : cf. x, xi, xxxiii.
[3] See Philipp, p. 19–57.

faith, came to apply to his own beliefs turns of expression coming in a straight line of descent from the poets of paganism. He calls St John the Baptist " *semideumque* virum " ; [1] he depicts Christ enthroned on high in heaven in these words : " *Inridebat eos caelesti Christus ab arce.*" [2] He said of the child Celsus, who died at the age of eight and whose intelligence appeared to be full of promise, that his parents feared the revenge of some kind of jealous Nemesis : " *Gaudebant trepido praesagi corde parentes dum metuunt tanti* muneris invidiam.*" [3] This method, moreover, was customary with nearly all the Christian poets of the first centuries and only appears to have provoked very rare protests.

The classification of his poems does not present any difficulty. I have already drawn attention to his correspondence with Ausonius. [4] In it Paulinus does not seem to be so very different from Ausonius intellectually, but his Christianity awakened in him new refinements. When he describes the moral transformation which had taken place in him, his self-abandonment to the Divine will, his concern as to his state in the future life, it is *his* soul speaking to ours in spite of the trivial niceties of style over which he still lingers. [5] The group of poems in honour of St Felix include no fewer than 14 pieces of varying length. [6] Every year Paulinus wrote one for January 14th, the anniversary of the death of the saint and of his " birth " into life eternal. [7] The subject ran the risk of seeming monotonous. Without completely avoiding this difficulty Paulinus very skilfully diversified his matter, relating either the chief episodes in the life of the Saint, or the miracles that had been accomplished through his intercession. These poems provide a host of original features in connection with the history of popular devotions. [8] His description of the new Basilica of St Felix is deserving of the attention of those interested in Christian art. [9] We can also

---

[1] *Carm.* vi, 252.   [2] *Carm.* xvi, 122.   [3] *Carm.* xxxi, 29.

[4] *Carm.* x ; xi.   On the course taken by this correspondence, see P. de Labriolle, *op. cit.*, p. 51.

[5] Cf. x, 19 et s.

[6] *Carm.* xii–xvi ; xviii–xxi ; xxiii ; xxvi–xxix. *Carmen* xii has 29 lines, *Carmen* xxi, 858. These poems were written between the years 395 and 407.

[7] *Carm.* xiv, 2 : " Qua corpore terris occidit et Christo superis est natus in astris ".   Hence its title *Natalicia* (cf. *Ep.* xxviii, 6).

[8] G. Boissier has skilfully brought some of these out (*Fin du Pagan.*, II, 94 et s.).

[9] *Carm.* xxvii–xxviii.

gather precious sidelights on the interior evolution of Paulinus [1] who is less discreet here than in his prose, and on the religious struggles of the period which he visualises more than once without however falling into the tone of the polemist.[2]

He found another source of inspiration in the Bible whose inexhaustible fruitfulness for a poet in search of a style worthy of the pen of a Christian he pointed out to Jovius.[3] Paulinus was the first of the numerous line of poets to imitate the Psalms.[4] Renewing the attempt of Juvencus, he also paraphrased the Gospel in 330 hexameters in order to celebrate St John the Baptist.[5] He has been reproached with emasculating the Hebrew poetry to excess; desirous of edification before everything else, his tender and restrained soul chose instinctively the points likely to touch, while doing his best to tone down what might give offence to unbelievers.

He did not go so far as certain kinds of literature much favoured among the pagans, which he only appropriated in order to infuse a new spirit into them. Of this kind is the *Epithalamium* which he composed for the marriage of Julian (the future Julian of Eclana, the opponent of St Augustine) and Titia;[6] his Christian spirituality eliminates from it all appeal to voluptuousness to the taste of writers like Catullus and Claudian; the *Propemticon* addressed to Niceta, the apostle of the Dacians, and Bishop of Remesiana;[7] the *Consolatio* in which, in connection with the mourning of Pneumatius and Fidelis who had lost their son Celsus, he tenderly recalls the memory of his only son who had died not long since in Spain shortly after his birth.[8] Other pieces resemble the familiar swing of one of Horace's epistles,[9] or assume the gravity of inscriptions intended to explain to the people the mural paintings in their Churches.[10]

[1] *Carm.* xxi.
[2] *Carm.* xxvii. R. Pichon has shown that Paulinus, without naming him, refutes some of the arguments of Vigilantius, the heresiarch (R.E.A., XI [1909], p. 237–242).
[3] *Carm.* xxii, 149 et s.
[4] *Carm.* vii, viii-ix (Ps. 1, 2, 136).
[5] *Carm.* vi.
[6] *Carm.* xxv.
[7] *Carm.* xvii. Lucilius, Corn. Gallus, Propertius, Tibullus, Horace, and Statius had largely exploited the same class of writing. See above, p. 302.
[8] *Carm.* xxxi.
[9] *Carm.* xxii; xxxii.
[10] Compare the *Dittochaeon* by Prudentius. If the *de Obitu Baebiani* (*Carm.* xxxiii) is by Paulinus that would prove that he composed *epigrammata* of the same order for private and domestic use.

We see how varied was his *facile*, smooth and limpid talent, and how much his efforts must have contributed to the Christianising of Latin poetry. Paulinus had no genius, but he possessed the gift of restraint, a delicacy that is sometimes charming, and a happy turn of mind for intimate and personal poetry. " We see springing forth in him some drops from that stream which overflowed so abundant and clear from St Gregory of Nazianzen, and so tumultuous from St Augustine." [1] It was largely due to him that Nola became " one of the holy cities of the West." [2] Paulinus himself was admired less for the quality of his poetry than for that of his soul, and for the magnificent example which he had given of the renunciation of his worldly possessions. *Praestantissimum praesentium temporum exemplum* Sulpicius Severus called him. [3]

---

[1] A. Puech, *Le poète Prudence*, p. 157.
[2] H. Delehaye, *Les Orig. du Culte des Martyrs*, Brus., 1912, p. 347.
[3] *Vita Martini*, xxv.

CHAPTER V

ST JEROME AND HIS TIMES

BIBLIOGRAPHY

I. St Jerome.—See Table No. VII. The fundamental work on St Jerome is no longer Grutzmacher's *Hieronymus*, 3 vols. L. and B. 1901-1908, but Cavallera's still unfinished *St Jérôme, Sa Vie et ses Oeuvres*, 2 vols. (Paris and Louvain, 1922). On St Jerome's language, cf. H. Goelzer's *Etude lexic. et gramm. de la latinité de S. Jérôme*, 1884 ; A. Ottolini's *La rettorica nelle Epist. de Girolamo da Stridone*, Cremona, 1905 ; C. Kunst's *de S. Hier. studiis Ciceronianis* (Diss. *philol. Vindob.*, vol. XII, p. 2 [1918]) ; Reiter in *B.* ph. W., 1919, pp. 642, 666, 690 ; L. Laurand, in R.S.R. 1919, pp. 371-2.

II. Rufinus.—The work of Rufinus is very scattered and has not yet been collected into a *Corpus.*—A. Translations. St Basil's *Instituta monachorum* were published by Holstenius, *Codex regularum monasticarum et canonicarum*, Augsburg (1759), I, 67-108 ; the nine discourses of St Gregory of Nazianzen appear in C.V., XLVI (1910): Migne, P.G., XXXVI, 735, only gives the prologue. Origen's *de Principiis* is to be found in P.G., XI, 111-414, and in C.B. (1913, by Koetschau) ; *the History of the Church* by Eusebius of Cæsarea, in P.G., XX, 45-906, and C.B. (1903-1909, by Schwartz and Mommsen): the two last books, which deal with the years 324-395, are by Rufinus himself, and are also to be found in P.L., XXI, 461-540 ; O. F. Fritzsche issued at Zurich in 1873 the *Epistula Clementis ad Jacobum*; the *Sententiae* of Sextus are in Gildemeister, Bonn 1873, and A. Elter's *Gnomica*, L. 1892 ; the *de recta in Deum fide*, in C.B. (1901, by Van de Sande Bakhuyzen). The other translations are included in vols. I, XII, XIII, XIV, XVII, XXXI, XXXII, of *Patr. Grecque*; the *Historia Monachorum* is in P.L., XXI, 623-688.—B. Personal works. P.L., XXI, 295-688.—C. Works unauthenticated. *Ibid.* The *Commentarius in prophetas minores tres Osee, Joel et Amos* should be by Julian of Eclana, according to Dom Morin, *R. Bén.*, XXX (1913), 1-24. Dom Wilmart, *R. Bén.*, XXXI (1914), 258-276, restores to Lithbert, Abbot of St Rufinus Abbey (XIIth century) the *Commentarius in LXXV Davidis psalmos.*

III. The Pilgrimages to the Holy Land.—*Itiner. Burdigalense* (in the year 333), P.L., VIII, 783-796 ; Geyer, in C.V., XXXIX, 1-33 ; *Peregrinatio Aetheriae* (about 395), C.V., *ibid.*, 35-101 ; W. Heraeus, Heidelburg 1908 (*Samml. vulgarlat. Texte*, I) ; *Eucherii quae fertur de situ Hieros. urbis* (Vth century), C.V., pp. 123-134 ; *Breviarius de Hieros.* (Vth to VIth century), C.V., pp. 151-155. See Geyer for accounts of a later date.—Consult: F. Cabrol, *Etude sur la Peregrinatio Silviae, les Eglises de Jérusalem, la discipline et la liturgie au IVᵉ Siècle*, Paris and Poitiers 1895 ; J. Anglade, *de latinitate libelli qui inscriptus est Peregrinatio ad loca sancta*, 1905 ; E. Lofstedt, *Philol. Kommentar zur Per Aetheriae*, Upsala 1911. English translation of the *Peregr. Aetheriae*, by J. H. Bernard, London 1891.

IV. Sulpicius Severus.—P.L., XX, 95-248 ; Halm, in C.V., vol. I (1866) ; text and French translation of the *Chronica* by Lavertujon, 2 vols. 1896-1899 ;

the edition of the *Vita Martini*, by Dubner-Lejay, 1890.—Consult: H.
Goelzer, *Gramm. in Sulpitium Severum observationes*, 1883.—French transla-
tion of the works of Sulpicius Severus by Herbert and Riton in the *Biblioth.
Panckoucke*, 1848-9, 2 vols.

SUMMARY

I. St Jerome's Destiny.—II. His early years.—III. The Biographies of the
  Monks.—IV. The *Chronica*.—V. The translations of Origen.—VI. St
  Jerome in Rome. The Council of Patrician Women. The Satirist.
  —VII. The *Discussion between a Luciferian and an Orthodox*. The *Adv
  Helvidium*.—VIII. St Jerome the Translator of the Sacred Books.
  The First Phase.—IX. His Departure for the East. The Second
  Phase.—X. St Jerome and the *Hebraica Veritas*. St Augustine's Reser-
  vations.—XI. The Commentaries on the Bible—XII. The *de Viris
  Illustribus*. The *Adv. Jovinianum*. The *Contra Vigilantium*. The
  Dialogues against the Pelagians. — XIII. The Origenist Dispute.
  Rufinus of Aquileia.—XIV. The Personality of St Jerome.—XV. The
  Pilgrimages to the Holy Land. The *Peregrinatio Aetheriae*.—XVI.
  Sulpicius Severus.

I

AMONG the leading representatives of Christian thought in
the IVth century St Jerome had a special career.

At a time when high ecclesiastical positions already
possessed influence and *prestige*, he was neither a Bishop as
were St Hilary, St Augustine, or St Ambrose, nor an Arch-
bishop, as was St Basil, nor a Patriarch, as was St John
Chrysostom. It is true he might have been Pope but for the
animosities he aroused. He himself tells us that from the date
of his sojourn in Rome, from 382 to 385, the close intimacy
which united him with Pope Damasus had marked him
out in the eyes of almost every one as his eventual successor.
"... *Totius in me Urbis studia consonabant. Omnium
paene judicio dignus summo sacerdotio decernebar.*" [1] A cabal
drove him from the Pontificate, and we can believe that he
consoled himself for this without difficulty since he was able
to retain his precious liberty. He accepted the priesthood
on one express condition namely that of remaining a monk
and free from any link with the life of the world.[2] We can
see in him a very clear purpose to eliminate from his life anything that could intrude upon his complete independence
and impair its fruitfulness.

Neither had he, like the great pastors whose names I have
recalled, vast congregations to feel the power of his words.

---

[1] *Ep.* xlv, 3.   [2] *Contra Ioh. Ierosolym.*, c. xli.

We have some homilies of St Jerome ; nearly a hundred
have been discovered during the last few years.[1] But these
are altogether familiar allocutions, " whispered in a corner
of the monastery," [2] as he himself says, and delivered to his
monks at Bethlehem. Properly speaking, they did not reach
the Christian public.

And so this man who for nearly forty years was one of the
lights of Christianity and fashioned so many souls after his
own ideal, owed all his influence to his qualities as a scholar
and still more to his initiatives as a man of action. Cut off
from external aids his own personality accomplished everything. Let me endeavour to describe him in his process of
formation and in the work of his maturity.

II

THE exact date of the birth of Jerome (*Eusebius Hieronymus*)
is unknown. Plausible calculations place it between the
years 340 and 350.[3] In his *de Viris Illustribus* [4] he informs
us that he was born at Stridon, and that this town before its
destruction by the Goths was situated on the confines of
Dalmatia and Pannonia. An inscription, published in 1882,[5]
enables us to localise Stridon in the neighbourhood of the
modern town of Grahovo. Stridon belonged to the Roman
province of Dalmatia.

His parents were Christian. " From the cradle I was
brought up on the milk of the Catholic faith," [6] he wrote.
He was, however, not to receive baptism until much later,
in accordance with the custom at that time very general,
which theologians such as Gregory of Nazianzen, Gregory of

[1] Dom Morin in 1897 brought to light 59 homilies by Jerome on the Psalms,
10 on the Gospel of St Mark, and 10 more on different texts from the Bible (A.M.,
III, 2, p. 373). For an account of his discovery see R.H.L.R., I (1896), p. 393–434,
Revue d'Hist. eccl., I (1900), p. 75 and 78, and R.B., XIX (1902), p. 113–144. In
1903 Dom Morin further published 14 homilies on the Psalms, and 2 homilies on
Isaias, known already, but whose authenticity was disputed (A.M., III, 3).

[2] *Ep.* cxii, 22 : " Mihi sufficit cum auditore vel lectore pauperculo in angulo
monasterii susurrare."

[3] Cf. Grutzmacher, vol. I, p. 45 et s.

[4] § 135.

[5] *Corpus Insc. lat.*, III, 4, 9860. This inscription was found graven on a stone
marking the boundaries of Stridon and Salviae. Mgr. Bulic has shown that the
doubts cast on its authenticity have no serious foundations (*Festschrift fur Otto
Benndorf*, Vienna, 1898, p. 276–280).

[6] *Ep.* lxxxii, 2.

Nyssa, and St John Chrysostom were already combating. His family was in easy circumstances; they held landed property, and there still remained a few more or less dilapidated *villulae*[1] even after the passage of the barbarians. As a young man Jerome went to Rome to finish his education which had begun in his native town. He there had for his professor in grammar, the famous Donatus, the commentator on Terence and Virgil, and the author of the manuals *Ars Major* and *Ars Minor*, on which from the end of the IVth century to beyond the IXth the interpretation of grammarians was to base itself. With the exception of St Augustine perhaps no other Christian author was more strongly nurtured on the pith of the classics than Jerome.

His life as a student was not irreproachable. As often happens in the case of those who resolve to live a stricter life after a period of dissipation, Jerome was to retain in his heart both the sting and the remorse for his past as a young man. He carried away from it the conviction that the dangers offered by life are such that inevitably frail souls (that is to say almost all) must succumb to them unless they place between themselves and temptation a barrier that is almost impassable. This was the leading motive for his asceticism and the reason why, without making of the religious life an absolute obligation, he constantly praised it as the best, and as the one offering the greatest moral security.

It was in Rome, however, that he was ultimately baptised. At the conclusion of his studies he travelled in Gaul with his friend Bonosus. He touched at Trèves, and there seems to have resolved to embrace a life of mortification.[2] We find him shortly afterwards at Aquileia in Illyria. He formed one of an association given up to the practice of asceticism, of which Chromatius, the future Bishop of Aquileia, was the leading spirit.[3] Then, coming to an abrupt decision, he left for the East after bidding farewell to his relatives at Stridon.

A group of pilgrims set forth with him on the road to Jerusalem. But he saw his companions dropping off on the

---

[1] *Ep.* lxvi, 14. Jerome was obliged to sell these in 397 in order to maintain his institution at Bethlehem.

[2] *Ep.* iii, 5; *Comm. in Gal.*, Preface of I, II.

[3] Some Commentaries (P.L., XX) by Chromatius, Bishop of Aquileia, still exist (P.L., XX). Cf. P. de Puniet in the *Rev. d'Hist. Eccl.*, VI, 1905, p. 15–32; and Paschini in *R. Bén.*, 1909, 469–475.

journey; Innocent and Hylas the slave died, and Niceas, a sub-deacon, returned to his own country. Jerome himself fell ill at Antioch. After recovering, he delayed some time in that city to attend the lessons of Apollinaris of Laodicea. His vocation as a great "intellectual" had already been indicated. He would not separate from his books which he had bought not so long back in Rome, and which he was shortly to carry with him into solitude. He had also just applied himself to the study of the Greek language which was an indispensable instrument for his future task.

Nevertheless, he felt his desire for the monastic life to be swerving. The news that his friends Bonosus and Rufinus had already made the sacrifice, and had settled, one on the coast of Dalmatia, and the other in Nitria, made him blush at such vacillations. He buried himself in the desert of Chalcis on the frontier of Syria, fifty miles from Antioch. He was to remain there three years, from 375 to 377.

He courageously accepted the hard life practised by the monks of the desert. He gives a picture of himself, his body covered with a hideous sack, black with sweat and dust, lying on the bare ground, drinking water and sustaining life on uncooked food. This physical wretchedness did not guarantee him from the worst temptations :

> " I, even I, who from fear of Gehenna had condemned myself to such a prison tenanted only by scorpions and wild beasts, often felt myself transported into the midst of girls dancing. I was pale from fasting, and my imagination was boiling over with desire in a frozen body wherein the fire of my passions wrought frenzy." [1]

After days and entire nights passed in groanings and anguish, fearing his cell as though the accomplice of his thoughts,[2] he would take flight anywhere to still more rugged spots, and sometimes a kind of ecstasy came to flood him with sweetness in the midst of his prayers and tears.

Happily intellectual work brought him its aid which was sometimes painful, but always efficacious. It was in the desert of Chalcis that he learned the Hebrew tongue under the

[1] *Ep.* xxii, 7.
[2] " Ipsam quoque cellulam meam, quasi cogitationum mearum consciam, pertimescebam." (*Ibid.*)

Y

direction of a lettered Jew who rendered him the most scholarly service.[1] His initiation was a severe penance :

" Relinquishing there," he relates,[2] " the skilled turns of Quintilian, the flood of eloquence overflowing from Cicero, the gravity of Frontonius, and the charm of Pliny, I set myself to learn the Hebrew alphabet and to study a language of guttural and heavy-breathing words.[3] Much effort as I had expended and many the difficulties I had suffered, how many times in desperation did I not break off from a study which the stubborn desire for knowledge made me resume again afterwards, I alone can testify, I who have toiled so hardly, and with me those who then shared my life. And I render thanks to God for any delicious fruit I now gather from so bitter a sowing."

Moreover, except during those periods when his vexed soul sought isolation, he was not too far from the civilised world so as not to be able to keep up a connection with his friends through the interchange of letters. He had books [4] sent to him through them, and he offered them in exchange Bibles copied under his own supervision by *alumni* trained for the purpose. He even had the happiness of receiving a visit from his friend Evagrius.[5] An essay (lost) commenting on the prophet Abdias dates from this period, also the *Life of Paul of Thebes* of which I shall speak further on.

The desert would have held a real attraction for him if he had been allowed to live there in peace. But the interests and concerns which Jerome had thought to flee soon came to start him off again. Antioch, the metropolis of Syria, had for many years been a prey to disputes on matters of doctrine which kept on increasing in intensity, and its echoes reached the desert of Chalcis. Three parties, those of Miletius, Paulinus, and Vitalis, were affirming with equal asperity their orthodoxy as regards the Trinity ; all three could boast of sympathies that were worthy of respect and alleged themselves to be in full agreement with the *cathedra Petri*.[6] The *formulæ* on which they were disputing were not very familiar

---

[1] *Ep.* xviii, A, 10.   [2] *Ep.* cxxv, 12.   [3] *Stridentia anhelantiaque verba.*
[4] See *Ep.* v, 2.   [5] *Ep.* vii, 1.
[6] *Ep.* xvi, 2, *ad Domasum :* " Meletius, Vitalis atque Paulinus tibi haerere se dicunt."

to the western mind of Jerome, who suspected some snare.[1]
Moreover, almost every day fanatics from the different parties
came to extort from him his profession of faith, and treated
him as a heretic when it did not square with their own.[2] In
his uncertainty Jerome thought to solicit the advice of Pope
Damasus. He wrote to Damasus a first letter in which he
celebrated the unique *prestige* of the See of Rome and declared
himself ready to side with the opinion of Damasus whatever
it might be.[3] This letter received no reply. He wrote
a second,[4] to which Damasus does not appear to have replied
either. Jerome was feeling weary of these continuous
summonses to which he was being subjected by the monks,
his brethren in the desert.[5] Their pretensions to regulate
consciences became unbearable to him. " I am ashamed to
say this ; " he wrote, " we condemn the universe from the
depth of our cells ; huddled under sackcloth and ashes we
pass judgment on our Bishops. What is this pride, more
suited to kings, doing under the habit of the penitent ?
Chains, squalor, and long hair are outward signs of a remorse
which groans, and not emblems of domination ! " [6] Many
solitaries, vexed by this indiscreetness, abandoned the desert
where they had previously shut themselves off, " preferring,"
as they said, " to live in the midst of wild beasts rather
than with Christians of that kind." [7] As soon as the season
permitted Jerome bent his footsteps towards Antioch.

Rome had just recognised Paulinus as an orthodox
Bishop.[8] He conferred, or rather imposed, the priesthood
on Jerome.[9] It was understood that he was to remain
free from any pastoral or liturgical obligation. Notwithstanding his troublesome experiences in the desert of Chalcis,
he remained profoundly attached to his monastic ideal, and
to his twofold profession of scholarship and asceticism, upon
which he had already begun to regulate his life.

He knew Gregory of Nazianzen at Constantinople whither
he went shortly, and learned to profit by his instructions in
exegesis[10] while at the same time he conceived from his studies
an admiration for Origen, for which he was later on to repent

---

[1] *Ep.* xv, 3–4.   [2] *Ep.* xvii, 2–3.   [3] *Ep.* xv.
[4] *Ep.* xvi.   [5] *Ep.* xvi, 2.   [6] *Ep.* xvii, 3.
[7] *Ibid.*   [8] St Ambrose, *Ep.* xii.
[9] *Contra Joh. Hierosolym.*, xli.
[10] *Comm. in Is.*, vi, 1 (Migne, xxiv, 93) ; *Ep.* i, I ; lii, 8, etc. He willingly
called Gregory *praeceptor meus.*

for having given too strong expression. He was still living there when the second Oecumenical Council began in May 381. But another Council was about to open in Rome. He decided to accompany thither Paulinus of Antioch and Epiphanius of Salamis.[1] Possibly Pope Damasus, to whom his talents were known, had given him a personal invitation to come and meet him there.

III

HE settled there in the year 382.

His reputation as a writer had preceded him. Let us cast an eye over his labours prior to his sojourn in Rome (382–385).

He had already inaugurated with his *Life of Paul* that series of biographies of monks which he was to continue a little later with his *Life of Malchus* and his *Life of Hilarion* (published between the years 386–391).[2] Already stories about these holy people were popular, at least in the countries where they had lived. Jerome was content to gather them together, giving to them of set purpose the charm of a very simple style, and to reconstitute the atmosphere of the marvellous with which the imagination of the crowd surrounded the anchorites. In this way he made up real little historical romances which were amusing as fairy tales, but which were profitable to the conscience in quite another way on account of the moral lessons emerging from them. Just like one of Perrault's Fairy Tales he began " Once upon a time there was an old man called Malchus. . . ." And then were seen the extraordinary adventures of young men who, disgusted with the world, or driven away by persecution, had taken refuge in the desert. Jerome outlined certain features of the usual scene with a few touches which were always the same— a grotto serving as the cell of the hermit, a spring at which he quenched his thirst, and a palm-tree whose leaves woven together supplied a ready-made garment. He depicts the solitaries giving themselves up to the most rigid fasting in

---

[1] *Ep.* cviii, 6 ; cxxvii, 7.

[2] He had formed the project of writing a kind of history of the Church in a series of monographs of the same kind (cf. *Vita Malchi*, I). He did not follow up this idea, neither that of a history of the reigns of Gratian and Theodosius which he was considering in 381 (*Chronicle*, ed. Helm, p. 7).

order to mortify their flesh and to free their souls from evil suggestions. Thus Hilarion, the founder of monachism, from the age of 21 to 27 years, during the first three years consumed only 17 gallons of lentils soaked in cold water, and for the three following years dry bread and water and salt ; from the age of 27 to 30, he supported himself on wild herbs without oil. But illness compelled him nevertheless to add a little oil to his frugal *régime*, which he kept up to his 63rd year. Then, feeling his strength growing weaker, he thought that an old man had fewer needs than a young one. He therefore cut down his bread from the age of 64 to 80. His daily food and drink then weighed barely five ounces. He passed the rest of his life in this manner. This practice of abstinence won for him great renown and also a special power over created beings. By killing in himself all material desires he made himself master over matter and made it subject to his law. Not only did he exorcise those possessed, and heal the sick, but even the animals and the elements became subject to him. At his bidding the devil came forth from the body of a camel which had been all foaming and maddened by it. He compelled a boa to climb upon a heap of logs and allow itself to be burnt. And with three signs of the Cross he caused the sea, which a cataclysm had projected beyond its limits, to retire to its bed.

The History of Paul and Antony contains the same mixture of facts which are probably accurate (they are rather difficult to disentangle) and of more or less fantastic poetic rendering. There is no reason to add that in Jerome's mind these stories were solely meant to amuse. They are consistent with his apostolate, although possessing somewhat more liberty of fancy. Jerome was not unaware that in all great matters some element of imagination and fantasy finds entrance. Why should not the very strangeness of these far-off stories be the prelude to some generous vocation by stirring up the imagination ? In any case, the edifying intention in them is strongly marked here and there. Thus the Life of Paul introduces a parallel between the deceits of the joys of the world and the happiness, fruitful in quite another way, of the eremitic or monastic life. The monks themselves gathered useful lessons from the life of Malchus who had retired from the world, and then experienced a nostalgia, and had tried to get back to it, and thereby exposed himself to tragic misadventures the vicissitudes of which Jerome gives in detail.

We may say that through these lives of solitaries, the success of which was considerable, Jerome gave a fresh character to hagiographic literature. For long the acts of the martyrs, and the heroism of " witnesses " to the faith, had constituted its basis. But the era of bloodshed was finished. The struggle now, no less bitter, was that of man against himself, the example of which must be set forth for the piety of the faithful. Henceforward, the lives of saints, their works, and their *traits* were to become the food of religious souls—the genuine romance of which they would be justified in reading with pleasure because at the same time they would purify themselves.

IV

IN the year 379–380, doubtless during his sojourn at Constantinople, Jerome wrote the *Chronicle* dedicated to a certain Gallianus, and to Vincentius, to whom was also to be dedicated another of his works, namely his translation of Origen's *Homilies*.

The χρονιχόι κανόνες of Eusebius of Cæsarea served as his model. We no longer possess the original work of Eusebius, but we are able partly to reconstruct it, thanks to an Armenian version published for the first time in 1818,[1] and to a large number of *excerpta* transcribed by other chronographers. In a first part (χρονογραφία), Eusebius set forth the chronological systems of the Chaldeans (according to Alexander Polyhistor, Abydenos,[2] and Josephus) ; of the Assyrians (according to Abydenos, Castor, Diodorus and Cephalion) ; of the Hebrews (according to the Old Testament, Josephus, and Clement of Alexandria) ; of the Egyptians (according to Diodorus, Manetho, and Porphyry) ; of the Greeks (according to Castor, Porphyry, and Diodorus) ; and of the Romans (according to Dionysius of Halicarnassus,

---

[1] In Armenian, by J. B. Aucher, at Venice ; in Latin, by J. Zohrab and A. Mai, at Milan. A German translation of the Armenian *Chronicle* has been given by J. Karst, 1911, in C.B., *Eusebius*, vol. V.

[2] The author of a history of Chaldea, written in the time of Antoninus (*Fragm. hist. gr.*, iv, 279–285).

Diodorus and Castor). The second part, by far the most important, was made up of a series of synchronous tables (χρονικόι κανόνες), in which figured the principal facts of universal history, especially those of sacred history, together with references to different computations (the years of Abraham, the Olympiads, the years of Rome, and the dates of Dynasties). The object set himself by Eusebius was to show the great antiquity of Moses ;[1] in addition, he desired to provide for the period posterior to the coming of Christ a chronological equipment for the *History of the Church* he was meditating. For his point of departure he took the year of Abraham's birth (2016–5 B.C.) and defined five divisions : (*a*) from Abraham to the taking of Troy ; (*b*) from the taking of Troy to the first Olympiad ; (*c*) from the first Olympiad to the second year of the reign of Darius ; (*d*) from the second year of the reign of Darius to the death of Christ ; (*e*) from the death of Christ to the twentieth year of the reign of Constantine.

Such is the work which Jerome undertook to introduce into the West in a Latin translation. He contented himself with making a translation pure and simple of the first part. In the sections following, inasmuch as his work was destined for the West, he felt he ought to insert a large number of facts dealing with general history, and especially with Roman history and even Roman literature. Lastly, this time without any guide, he continued the *Chronicle* of Eusebius from the twentieth year of Constantine down to the year 378, the date of the death of Valens.

This *opus tumultuarium*, as Jerome himself calls it, who confesses to have dictated it *velocissime*,[2] thus offers to us a threefold aspect in the form of a translation, a revision, and an original work. He had, however, felt its technical difficulties ; he indicates them in his preface[3] while apologising beforehand for any negligences of his scribes.[4] He conscientiously prepared his ground. His own personal sources have been carefully marked down ;[5] they are numerous

---

[1] Schoene, II, p. 5 (cf. Helm, p. 9, I, 5 et s.) : " Nam Moyses . . . omnibus . . . quos Graeci antiquissimos putant senior deprehenditur, Homero scilicet et Hesiodo Trojanoque bello ", etc. . . .

[2] Helm, p. 2, I, 12.   [3] *Ibid.*, p. 4–5.   [4] *Ibid.*, p. 6, l. 4.

[5] Mommsen, *Gesamm. Schriften*, VII, p. 606 ; Bauer, S.B.W., vol. CLXII (1909), 3 Abt., p. 42, 1.

—Eutropius, Suetonius, Rufius Festus, Ammianus Marcellinus, Aurelius Victor, etc. But we suspect that the *taedium operis* dulled his brain in more than one place. There are mistakes in translation and an often arbitrary and strange choice of events in what he writes down as memorable. Thus in the year 356 A.D., the murder of a monk by the Saracens ; referring to the year 374, the following note occurs : "*Aquileienses clerici quasi chorus beatorum habentur* " ; he does not seem able to get away from himself nor from anything that interested him personally. The same thing applies to his likes and dislikes : for this same year he had noted down the departure of Melania, the elder for Jerusalem, and in this connection recalls that she had deserved the name of Thecla [1] on account of her virtues, especially her humility; he crossed out this flattering mention when he fell out with her over Origenism.[2]

Notwithstanding, the work has rendered great service. To judge of this it is only necessary to examine a modern history of the Church, or even a history of Roman literature. The history of empires was represented to the Middle Ages, " just as the history of the Popes was contained in the notices in the *Liber Pontificalis*." [3] The *Chronicle* has been one of the fundamental books upon which all researches on the past of mankind have been based.[4]

V

WE know Origen's singular fate. This eminent mind, this powerful intellect, and the glory of Christianity in the IIIrd century, was to become a hot-bed of disputes and a firebrand of discord for a long series of generations. Familiar with all the systems of Greek philosophy and the speculations of the Gnostics, but at the same time deeply attached to the

[1] Helm, p. 247.

[2] Rufinus, *Contra Hier.*, II, xxv. But it is incorrect to accuse him of having substituted the name of Florentius for that of Rufinus : cf. Cavallera, in B.L.E., 1918, p. 318.

[3] Duchesne, *Liber Pontif.*, Preface to vol. I.

[4] To understand the different lists in the *Chronicle* requires a certain preliminary initiation. One will do well to consult the *Paléographie Latine* by Steffens-Coulon, Paris, 1910, p. 17. Useful concordance tables of the different reckonings are given by Schürer, *Gesch. der judischen Volkes*, 3rd ed., I, p. 773, and by Ginzel, *Handbuch der mathem. Chronologie*, at the end of vol. II.

rule of faith, Origen had conceived the idea of a vast synthesis in which to incorporate the fundamental principles of the Christian doctrine about God, Man, the Universe, and Scripture which was the source of all truth. This " summa " of theology, the book of *the Principles* (Περὶ Ἀρχῶν), Origen wrote at Alexandria shortly after the year 220, no doubt making use of the conferences which for twenty years he had been giving at the Catechetical School, to which educated Christians and half-converted pagans, or at least people curious about matters pertaining to Christianity, came in crowds. In spite of the respect which Origen's admirable clearness and genius had won for him, his methods did not escape arousing uneasiness. These misgivings only grew more pronounced in certain circles later on. Origen's orthodoxy was furiously attacked and passionately defended. These quarrels lasted for centuries, always being rekindled after long periods of quiet. The " errors " of Origen were to be explicitly condemned at Constantinople by the Councils of 543 and 553.

That Jerome was at first an admirer of Origen, and his faithful disciple, was evidence which one day his adversaries were to exploit against him, and which he himself was not able to cover up. The immense erudition of the Alexandrine Doctor had literally subjugated him and he found no words too strong to express his enthusiasm for such a model. We shall speak of the disagreeable consequences he was thus preparing for himself.

During the years 379 to 381, St Jerome rendered in Latin fourteen homilies of Origen on Jeremias, a like number on Ezechiel, and nine on Isaias.[1] He was to continue these translations during subsequent years. He had a clear conception of the character of his task as translator and explains himself in more than one passage.[2] His view was that the interpreter should translate *latine* (that is, *in good Latin*) and not merely *in latinam linguam*. A word-for-word servility seemed to him an absurd subjection; he claimed for himself the examples of Terence, Plautus, Caecilius, and Cicero himself the translator of Plato, Xenophon, Æschines and Demosthenes. But he also indicated that a translation of the Scriptures demanded a much more scrupulous literalness

---

[1] For the manuscript translation, see B.A.L.A.C., 1914, 309.
[2] See his Preface to Origen's *Homilies* on Jeremias and Ezechiel; *Ep.* lvii to Pammachius; *Ep.* cvi, 3.

than that required for a non-canonical text, even the order of the words having a symbolic value in the Bible. Here, where we are able to compare his Latin with the Greek of Origen, we see how alert in him was that taste for humanism and fitting language which is one of the surest marks of his talent.[1]

VI

JEROME'S memory is indissolubly bound up with that of the Roman Patrician ladies whose counsellor and friend he was. In Albina, Marcella, Asella, Fabiola, Principia, and still more, perhaps, Paula, her daughters and her grand-daughter (for Jerome knew the two generations of which Paula was the grandmother),[2] we hear the echo of the names which Jerome's correspondence brings down to us, in whose souls he could contemplate the most faithful reflection of the ideal he carried in his own heart.

Before Jerome came to Rome a certain number of Roman ladies belonging to the highest nobility had been accustomed to meet at the house of one of them, Marcella, who had established a kind of conventicle in her palace on Mount Aventine. She wished to create in the midst of the town which was still half pagan, and in which the Christians themselves did not always set an example, a little Thebaid where they could freely discourse upon holy things, read the Scriptures, and sing Psalms. This *coterie* of women was persuaded of the super-eminent virtues of the religious life, whose austerities they endeavoured to imitate in the midst of the bustle of the world.

When Jerome arrived in Rome in 382, his activity as a letter-writer had already made him known as a Hebrew scholar of the first order.[3] It was soon learnt that he was much appreciated by Pope Damasus, and that on questions of

---

[1] Cf. Klostermann, in T.U., N.F. I (1897), p. 2 and 33.

[2]

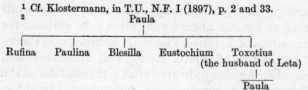

Paula

Rufina — Paulina — Blesilla — Eustochium — Toxotius (the husband of Leta)

Paula
(for whom a plan of education was outlined by Jerome in letter 107).

[3] Eighteen letters in our collection are anterior to 382. Cf. the list drawn up by Grutzmacher, *op. cit.*, I, p. 99.

philology he readily consulted him. Lastly his letters revealed his proselytising interest in the eremitic life which he had himself lived in the desert of Chalcis, and which he was in a position to advocate from his own knowledge. One of his letters in particular, addressed to his friend Heliodorus,[1] who had at first thought of following Jerome into the desert and had then reconsidered it, had vividly struck the minds of people on account of its eloquence (very artificial in our opinion), but altogether to the taste of the time.[2]

Jerome was greeted with enthusiasm by the circle whose aspirations I have described. During the three years which he passed in Rome he became the centre and oracle of the gatherings on the Aventine. There existed a kind of harmony, already established between the souls which he was called upon to direct, and his own tastes. These women of quite superior education were passionately interested in Biblical studies. Many of them, Marcella, Paula, Blesilla and Eustochium, already knew Hebrew, or learnt it in order to study the Scriptures and sing the Psalms in the same language in which they had been written. To Jerome they were not only his pupils, but his fellow-workers. Marcella especially, according to the testimony of Jerome, put such intelligent questions as to be instructive in themselves,[3] and Jerome published a volume of letters written in reply to the difficulties which she submitted to him. We can see from them that scholarship retained all its severity in this intellectual intercourse. Jerome had no need to vulgarise nor render it insipid. We may say that the influence of this feminine curiosity, which here took so noble a form, reappears in all the works of Jerome. How many times did he not decide to put himself to the task of translating some commentary of Origen, or to clear up some portion of Scripture, only because Marcella, Paula, or Eustochium had asked him to do so![4] In dedicating to them a certain number of his driest works,[5]

---

[1] Ep. xiv.

[2] Jerome himself recognised later on that this declamatory letter, at least in its form, was a jeu d'esprit of his earliest youth. Cf. Ep. lxx, 2.

[3] Ep. lix, 11 : Magis nos provocas quaestionibus, et torpens otio ingenium, dum interrogas, doces. Cf. Ep. cxxvii, 7.

[4] For the Homilies of Origen, cf. P.L., XXIV, 219 ; for the commentary on Ezechiel and Isaias, P.L., XXV, 76 ; XXIV, 17 ; for the commentary on Ecclesiastes, P.L., XXIII, 1061 ; for the Epistles of St Paul, P.L., XXVI, 440.

[5] The commentaries on Sophonia (P.L., XXV, 1337), on Isaias (XXIV, 17), and on Ezechiel (XXV, 15) are addressed to Paula and Eustochium.

Jerome might draw upon himself the ridicule of foolish men : [1] in reality he was only acquitting himself of a debt of gratitude towards those women who had inspired them.

But St Jerome's intercourse with these remarkable women was not limited to questions of scholarship and exegesis. He was really their director ; that is to say, by tracing out for them a certain type of life accounted the most perfect, he assisted them to get nearer to it in the midst of the miseries and weaknesses of everyday life. In this capacity he was the first of the line of such men as St Francis of Sales, Bossuet, and Fénelon. " Like them, he had the privilege of being the confidant of the most aristocratic souls of his time and of working upon moral material of a high quality." [2] But he counselled them to make sacrifices and renunciations far sterner than Fénelon ever required of the Comtesse de Montberon, or Bossuet of Madame de Luynes. Real religious life as conceived by Jerome consisted in the giving up of all joys, in fastings, mortifications, and tears ; above all, in celibacy, to the preservation of which all the other ascetic exercises co-operated. There are moments when we might say that Tertullian's spirit, violently hostile to nature and rejoicing in the deprivations which he imposed upon it, lived again in Jerome, so much vigorous conciseness, such plain-spoken directness does he use in inculcating the virtues which he loved.

Moreover, those to whom he addressed these rigorous counsels were not likely to find them too inexorable. They had already given up all those vanities whose nothingness he was seeking to show them. He confirmed them in a disposition they had already acquired, rather than imposed any change of life. But on numerous occasions, when going outside this circle thus won in advance, his efforts to expand the ascetic life encountered, even in Rome, the most violent opposition, and not only among laymen.

He was not spared either equivocal insinuations or direct attacks. " Why does he occupy himself always with women, and never with men ? " " If the men would question me about the Scriptures, I should not talk to the women," he

---

[1] Cf. *Praef. in Sophon.* ; Rufinus, *Apol.*, ii, 7 (P.L., XXI, 589) : *Puellis quoque et mulierculis scribens.* . . .

[2] Thamin, *Saint Ambroise et la morale chrétienne au IVe siècle*, Paris, 1895, p. 386.

replied. What provoked the greatest exasperation were the *piquant* phrases he discharged at society in Rome. In Jerome there was the stuff of a Juvenal ; he readily compared himself to Lucilius. His letters are full of satirical portraits of extraordinary *verve*. One day he was denouncing worldly women, " the women who daub with vermilion and I don't know what other paints, their cheeks and eyelids ; whose plastered faces, disfigured with too much whitening, make one think of idols ; who cannot drop an involuntary tear without it hollowing out a streak ; . . . who make-up their heads with the hair of others, and furbish up for themselves a tardy youth over their senile wrinkles." [1] Another time it was false devotees who suffered : " A robe of dirty brown, a coarse belt, unclean hands and feet . . . but the belly which is not seen gorged with meats." [2] Even the clergy were not spared. For certain smart ecclesiastics, with curled hair, perfumed, skittish, and of the butterfly kind, prototypes of the gallant abbés of the XVIIIth century, Jerome reserved his most biting ridicule. A frame of mind whose sharpness his friends endeavoured to temper with a half-laugh,[3] was bound in the nature of things to create a coalition against him of all those whom he had belaboured. When Blesilla, the daughter of Paula, died, they accused Jerome of having killed her with fasts. The people tried to knock him down and all the monks with him, on one occasion.[4] We can guess too whether their tongues did not shoot forth their most viperish gibes against the school of asceticism (*castitatis chorus*) of which Jerome was the spiritual master. Not one of those noble women on the Aventine was spared.[5] As long as Pope Damasus lived, Jerome held up against the storm. But after the death of his protector all support was withdrawn from him and he had no other resource but to leave that " Babylon " [6] where it was not permitted to be a saint with impunity.

VII

During these three years of Roman life, during which he contracted strong friendships and tenacious enmities which

---

[1] *Ep.* xxxviii, 3. [2] *Ep.* xxii, 27. [3] *Ep.* xxvii, 2.
[4] *Ep.* xxxix, 5. [5] *Ep.* xlv, 4. [6] *Ibid.*, 6.

were to accompany him right to the end, Jerome did not write any very important work. Twenty-six letters (*Ep.* xix to xliv) belong to this period. It is not certain that the *Discussion between a Luciferian and an Orthodox* was not written a little earlier, in the year 379 or 380 : in a tone of moderation which he was not to practise very much longer, Jerome sets forth the reasonable requirements of the Church as regards the Arians who desired to re-enter her bosom, and he makes a fictitious adversary, the disciple of Lucifer of Calaris, recognise the enormity of the punishments which the latter demanded against these repentant men. The debate centred in a very lively engagement between the two disputants, while stenographers took down their arguments.

The *Adversus Helvidium* strikes a *piquant* note in another way. Jerome's ascetic propaganda in Rome, in addition to so many other forms of opposition, had brought forth a polemical pamphlet wherein a layman named Helvidius thought there was no better way to ruin Jerome's contention as to the superiority of celibacy than to attack the doctrine of the perpetual virginity of Mary. We do not know exactly who Helvidius was. Gennadius puts him down as a pupil of Auxentius, the Arian Bishop of Milan.[1] According to Jerome, he was a man of mediocre talent.[2] However, he thought it advisable to reply in a short work of twenty-two chapters.

Helvidius directed his principal attack upon the belief in the immaculate virginity of Mary *post partum*. He made much of certain texts in the Gospel, such as Matth. i, 18–20 ; i, 25 ; Luke ii, 7, and viii, 20. He also invoked the authority of Tertullian (*de Mon.*, viii ; *de Virg. Vel.*, vi ; *de Carne Christi*, vii) and that of Victorinus of Pettau. Jerome rejected the authority of Tertullian : " De Tertulliano quidem nihil amplius dico, *quam Ecclesiae hominem non fuisse.*" He affirms that Helvidius interpreted badly the views of Victorinus.[3] But he takes particular exception to the passages from the Gospel on which Helvidius had set store. He discusses them with power and precision, and most of the solutions which he favours, for instance the question of the

---

[1] *De Vir. Ill.*, xxxii (P.L., LVIII, 1077).

[2] 1: ". . . Hominem rusticum et vix primis quoque imbutum litteris ; . . . ut discat aliquando reticere, qui numquam didicit loqui." § xvi : " Praetermitto vitia sermonis, quibus omnis liber tuus scatet. Taceo ridiculum exordium : O tempora ! O mores ! etc. . . ."

[3] § xvii (P.L., XXIII, 201).

" brethren " of Jesus, have become traditional in the bosom of the Catholic Church. The *Adversus Helvidium* is the first treatise by a Latin specially devoted to Mariology, and this realm of ecclesiastical knowledge is largely due to Jerome.[1]

The two last chapters oppose the moral and religious advantages of celibacy to the worries entailed by marriage. After discussing many trivial details Jerome gladly gives rein to his rhetorical eloquence. He confesses that *rhetoricati sumus, et in morem declamatorum paululum lusimus.* Helvidius emerges from this bout riddled with shafts : [2]

> " O thou most ignorant of men," Jerome exclaims, " without taking the trouble of consulting the Scriptures thou hast soiled with thy slime the Virgin. Legend speaketh of a fool who, in order to be talked about, found nothing better to do than to set fire to the temple of Diana. . . . Following the example of this monstrosity, thou also hast fouled the sanctuary of the Holy Spirit by presuming to make issue therefrom a whole cartload of brothers and sisters. . . . Behold thee arrived at thy goal ; thy crime hath rendered thee famous ! "

VIII

IT was when in Rome that St Jerome entered upon the task which was to fill twenty years of his life, namely the revision and translation of the Sacred Books.

At the end of the IVth century many far-seeing minds felt the need of a general recasting of the Latin translations of the Bible. Pope Damasus had the good sense to see that he had ready to his hand the kind of man required to carry out successfully such a task. He knew Jerome for a technician familiar with the Greek language and one who was capable of clearing up delicate questions of *textual* criticism. He therefore begged him to take in hand, not a fresh translation of the New Testament,—an initiative which at the outset would have seemed too daring,—but a simple revision of the Latin translations.

---

[1] Cf. J. Niessen, *die Mariologie des hl. Hieronymus*, Munster i W., 1913 (and B.A.L.A.C., 1914, p. 304).

[2] § xvi (Turmel's translation, p. 174).

" You wish me to draw forth from an old work a new one," Jerome wrote to him. " I shall have to become the judge of copies of Scripture scattered over the whole world, and after having seen their discrepancies to decide on the text which is conformable with the Greek original. A pious labour without doubt, but what peril in this presumption to judge others, to be judged by opinion in my turn, to change the language of old men, and to bring the world already growing grey to the first beginnings of infancy ! " [1]

In spite of his misgivings which were not fantastic Jerome set himself to the work. His method was the following : He took a certain number of Latin versions and the oldest Greek manuscripts which he could procure ; [2] where the Greek disclosed evident misinterpretations in the Latin he corrected them ; when the versions offered meanings which were sufficiently divergent, he chose the one which seemed to him to approach most nearly to the Greek.

His retouches were not equally thorough in the different portions of the Gospels. He was deeply concerned to upset as little as possible anything that western Christianity was accustomed to, and proceeded with greater or less discretion according to his mood.[3] Did he likewise revise the remainder of the New Testament ? The matter is not certain, and since the time of Erasmus and Lefèvre of Etaples it has often been disputed ; it seems at least to be very likely.[4]

In any case, the revision of the *Psalter* from which came

---

[1] *Praef. in quattuor Evang.* (P.L., XXIX, 525).

[2] He seems to have examined the versions of the Italo-Roman type to the exclusion of those of the African type. One of these manuscripts in our possession, the *Codex Brixianus*, provides a text fairly close to that used by Jerome. Cf. Harnack, *Beitr. zur Einl. in das Neue Test.* VII (1916), p. 6. His Greek manuscripts resembled those represented to us by the *Sinaiticus* and the *Vaticanus*. Taking all in all, Harnack is of opinion that the critics have not up till now attached sufficient value to Jerome's revision, and that not one of our Greek manuscripts is as near to the original text as Jerome's Latin translation (S.B.B., 1915, no xxxvi–xxxvii, p. 569).

[3] His adjustment to the *graeca veritas* is seen especially in the beginning of Matth. and in the second portion of John ; it appears less in Mark, and very little in Luke.

[4] See Durand in R.S.R., 1916, p. 531 et s. ; Harnack, *Beitr. zur Einleitung in das Neue Test.*, VII (1916), p. 11. The texts which make one lean towards the affirmative are *Ep.* lxxi, 5 (Hilberg, in C.V., LV, p. 6, I. 10) ; *Ep.* cxii, 20 (*ibid.*, p. 391, I. 3) and *de Vir. Ill.*, cxxxv. Cf. however Lagrange, in R.B., 1917, pp. 445–447, and 1918, pp. 254–257 : Fr. Lagrange does not think that Jerome revised the Epistles of St Paul.

the *Psalterium* called *Romanum*, dates from this same period.[1] Jerome amended the text according to the Greek of the *Septuagint*.

On the whole, the labours of Jerome marked a progress of which competent people were sensible. St Augustine, whose express reservations on certain of Jerome's later undertakings we shall mention, gave his approval to this one. Nevertheless, criticism was not wanting already. In his Letter XXVII to Marcella, Jerome takes exception to certain *homunculi* whom he calls two-legged asses, who, in the name of tradition and of the inspired nature of the Gospels, were protesting against his corrections. This was only the prelude of storms to come. The first phase was to a great extent accomplished without too many obstacles. Besides, the protection of Damasus was extended over Jerome.

IX

FROM the day when he no longer possessed it, he understood that he must leave. He departed for the East. His special friends Paula, and Eustochium, her daughter, soon decided to follow him. Jerome has recounted their journey (*Ep.* cviii). In spite of the entreaties of their family they embarked, taking with them a few young girls destined, as they hoped, to form the nucleus of a convent. They made a prolonged stay in Palestine and Egypt, and contemplated the spots with which Scripture had familiarised them beforehand. In 386, they finally settled in Bethlehem. Paula employed what she had kept of her fortune to build several convents— one for men over which Jerome took the direction, and three others for women which she administered herself.[2] Hostels for the use of pilgrims were also built. Then began the happiest period in the life of Jerome and of his companions. Shortly after their arrival the latter wrote to Marcella a letter full of mysticism and tenderness in which they depicted their joy.[3] While watching over strict economy in the convent

---

[1] Jerome states this formally (P.L., XXIX, 117).
[2] Up to the time of her death in 404. Eustochium succeeded her.
[3] *Ep.* xlvi. They begged Marcella to come and join them. She did not come. There was much more independence and self-possession in her than in her friends. The latter only lived upon feeling: Marcella was an "intellectual" before everything else.

they delighted in humbling themselves to the most lowly duties, attending to the lamps, sweeping the rooms, and lighting the fires.[1] Jerome often saw his friends; he commented on the Scriptures for them, and charged them with many duties which helped him in his work. It was at Bethlehem, in his cell which he called his paradise, that he wrote the greater part of his works. In addition, he opened a school for young boys whom he instructed in grammar, and commented upon the classic authors.[2] But the best part of his time was absorbed by the monastery; he showed his monks how to copy manuscripts, thus giving the model to those laborious communities who in the Middle Ages saved so much of the *débris* of the old civilisation.

He had already learnt Hebrew in the desert of Chalcis. He took it up again with renewed ardour under the direction of a Jew named Bar Anina who gave him lessons for money— by night in order to avoid the animosity of his co-religionists.[3] Gaston Paris has remarked, not without astonishment, that " not one of the Fathers of the Latin Church up to the time of St Jerome appears to have known Hebrew nor to have been concerned to learn it." [4] The Septuagint had sufficed to establish the authority of the Old Testament in a world in which the Greek language predominated. But Jerome possessed the critical capability which drove him to go back to the sources, for he knew how many deformations a text must inevitably undergo when it is transposed into another language.

Origen's *Hexaples* which he went through in the library at Cæsarea,[5] strengthened this conviction in him. The object of Origen in this vast work had been not so much to give a correct edition of the Greek Bible as to establish, with the view of composing so many disputes between Jews and Christians who were each reciprocally dealing with forgeries, the status of the Jewish and Christian Bible respectively. Arranged in six columns, the *Hexaples* (the original manuscript of which was in fifty large rolls) presented

1 *Ep.* lxvi, 13.
2 Cf. Rufinus, *Apol.*, ii, 8 (P.L., XXI, 592).
3 *Ep.* lxxxiv, 3 (Hilberg, in C.V., LV, p. 123, l. 8).
4 *Journal des Savants*, 1883, p. 387. Cf. the article *Hebrew Learning among the Fathers*, by the Rev. C. J. Elliot, in D.C.B., II, 851–872.
5 " Ἑξαπλοῦς Origenis in Cæsariensi bibliotheca relegens semel tantum scriptum repperi." (*Commentarioli in Ps.*, ed. Morin, p. 5.) See Cavallera, II, p. 88.

synoptically the Hebrew text of the Old Testament in Hebrew characters, the Hebrew text in Greek characters, the Greek translation of Aquila, the Jew, contemporary with Hadrian, the Greek translation of Symmachus, the Jew, in the time of Septimus Severus, the Greek translation of the Septuagint, and lastly that of the Jew Theodotion (about 180 A.D.). For certain books there were three more supplementary columns in which anonymous Greek versions were inserted.[1] In addition, the text of the *Septuagint* was marked with certain signs (which had become traditional since the time of Alexandrine criticism)[2] intended to show the bearing of this text upon the Hebrew text. The *obelus*[3] signified words or passages added in the Greek ; the asterisk disclosed the *lacunae* appearing in the Greek ; the termination of the additions or omissions was shown by two dots.

This methodical arrangement decided Jerome in the autumn of 386 to enter upon new undertakings. He revised the *Psalter* for the second time, following the system of the *Hexaples* by using the critical signs employed by Origen.[4] From this revision emerged the *Psalterium* called *Gallicanum* from its having been the first to be in general use in Gaul. He also translated the book of Job [5] from the Greek of the *Hexaples*, using the same system of signs, the *Proverbs*,[6] *Ecclesiastes*,[7] the *Canticle of Canticles*,[8] and the *Paralipomena*.[9] It is possible that he may have proceeded further in this work, of which a theft almost completely defrauded him.[10] We only have in their entirety the Psalter, and the book of Job.[11]

---

[1] There is a description of the *Hexaples* by Jerome in the *Comm. in Titum*, iii, 9 (P.L., XXVI, 595).

[2] The origin of these goes back to Aristophanes of Byzantium about 257-180 B.C. or even to Zenodotus (IIIrd century). See J. E. Sandys, *A History of classical Scholarship*, Cambridge, 1906, p. 127.

[3] From the Greek ὀβελός, a brooch. The form was this ÷ or -. On these critical signs, cf. St Epiphanius, *de Mens. et Ponder.*, viii and xvii (P.G., XLIII, 243-244 and 265) : Isidore of Seville, *Orig.*, I, xx. Serruys has shown that Anastasius the Sinaite has given a clearer and more satisfactory interpretation of them than that by Epiphanius, which is derived from his, but has mistakes in it (*Mél. de l'Ecole de Rome*, XXII [1902], p. 189 et s.).

[4] Cf. P.L., XXIX, 117.

[5] St Augustine, *Ep.* civ, 3, in Hilberg, C.V., LV, p. 239, l. 21.

[6] *Praef. in libr. Salomonis*, P.L., XXIX, 403.

[7] *Ibid.*

[8] *Ibid.*

[9] XXIX, 401.

[10] *Ep.* cxxxiv, 2 (P.L., XXII, 1162).

[11] We must add to these extracts from the three books of Solomon in the St Gall manuscript no. 11 (cf. C. P. Caspari, *das Buch Job*, 1893, pp. 5-7) ; S. Berger, *Quelques textes latins inédits de l'Ancien Testament* (notices and extracts from the

X

BUT more and more one thing became obvious to his mind. Any critical investigation of the Old Testament should be based neither on the Latin texts which were often faulty, nor on the Greek of the Septuagint, which was not sufficiently close, but on the original text wherein God Himself had spoken, the *Hebraica veritas*. The only rational solution therefore was to neglect the intermediaries and translate direct from the Hebrew. This was a considerable undertaking but one from which St Jerome did not recoil once his conscience as a scholar had decided, sustained as he was by the thought that he was at last to dispossess the Jews of the privilege upon which they plumed themselves, of being the only people to read the Divine Word in its authentic tenor. This he accomplished between the years 390 and 404. As he finished a book or group of books he dedicated it to one of his followers, together with a foreword which provides us with more than one valuable piece of information. He only left on one side the books which he considered as non-canonical or doubtful, *Wisdom*, *Ecclesiasticus*, *Baruch* with the *Letter of Jeremias*, the first and second Book of *Machabees*, the third and fourth Book of *Esdras*, and the additions to the Book of *Esther*. Considerations foreign to canonicity, properly so called, decided him to translate also the additions to the Book of *Daniel* (but marking them with the *obelus*), and the Books of *Tobias* and *Judith*. For the portions written in Chaldaic he obtained the assistance (at least at the commencement) of a Jewish interpreter who translated to him aloud the Chaldaic into Hebrew, and Jerome transposed it accordingly into Latin.[1]

How was this enterprise, so honourable to Catholic scholarship, received by St Jerome's contemporaries ? With great distrust and even hostility outside the group of his faithful

MSS., vol. XXXIV, 2) ; quotations from the *Proverbs* in a Pelagian writing of the year 430, and in Cassian (cf. P. Vaccari, *Un testo dommatico e una versione biblica,* in *Civilta Cattolica,* vol. IV [1913], p. 196). Dom de Bruyne drew attention in the R. Bén., July 1914, pp. 229–236, to fragments of the preface to the book of *Esther,* which, contrary to the opinion of Martianay, he wished to connect with Jerome's version from the *Hexaples.* The result of this would be, therefore, that Jerome must have also revised the book of *Esther.*

[1] *Prol. in Tob.* (P.L., XXIX, 23 et s.).

friends. He was doing nothing less than relegating to a second place the translation of the Septuagint : this was the delicate point. " People must consider the attachment of the first Christians to the letter of the Scriptures, and to the authority of the Septuagint which had been universally used by the Fathers in their commentaries, was accepted and read in the churches, and held as inspired by the unanimous opinion of the Doctors. It was not a question of completing them in Hebrew, but of a total recasting. Thousands of phrases were to disappear, others were to be added, the order of several books was to be changed, and at every step a different sense was to be encountered. It was a matter of reducing to silence the Messianic prophecies, of abandoning the text used by the Apostles which they had consecrated by their infallible authority ;—in other words, as the conservatives said, Jerome intended to lower the Catholic Church before the pretended scholarship of the Jews." [1] There was a wild outcry against this *falsarius et sacrilegus* [2] who dared to lay hands upon the venerated text of the Septuagint which was authenticated by every tradition. Despite his natural moderation, St Augustine himself was moved. The first revision from the Greek accomplished by Jerome had met with his full approval. But the idea of a new translation from the Hebrew was invincibly repugnant to him. He could not restrain himself from letting Jerome hear his views. " And in the first place," he asked him, " can you seriously hope to do better than the former translators of the Hebrew text ? "

" It is a matter of astonishment to me that there is still in the Hebrew something which has escaped so many interpreters, past-masters in their knowledge of this language. I am not speaking now of the Septuagint ; I do not wish to formulate any precise opinion on their conformity in design or inspiration which is more noticeable in them than if they had been by one and the same author, still more, because such a privilege should, in my opinion, indisputably extend to them a

[1] Lagrange, in B.L.E., 1899, p. 41.
[2] *Prol. in Evang.*, P.L., XXIX, 558 ; *Apol.*, II, xxiv (P.L., XXIII, 468) ; *in Ezech.* (P.L., XXV, 327). And again P.L., XXVIII, 179, 505, 1137, 1141, 1308, etc. . . .

pre-eminent authority. But what strikes me especially is that those who after them laboured to translate the Scriptures and who are accounted to have been most careful to render accurately the genius of the Hebrew expressions and turns, not only are not agreed among themselves, but further have passed over so many difficulties which must now be exhumed and placed in their proper light. For, to come to the point, those passages are clear or obscure. If they are obscure, we may permit ourselves to believe that it is possible for you to be mistaken about them just as much as they were. If they are clear, how can we suppose that they were mistaken ? " [1]

St Jerome's retort to this dilemma is an argument *ad hominem* and betrays a little nervousness :

" I will borrow from you," he wrote to Augustine, " your own argument. What the former writers who have preceded us in the Lord have explained in their commentaries on Holy Scripture is either obscure or clear. If it is obscure, how have you dared to discuss after them matters which they did not know how to elucidate ? If it is clear, it were a vain undertaking to search out explanations which could not have escaped them." [2]

But Augustine had further objections, and other scruples, and after having read the translation from the Hebrew of Job he laid them before Jerome with his customary gentle firmness, as a Bishop desirous for the good of souls before all else. If the West were to adopt the new version and read it in public, would there not then be disagreement between the Latin Churches and the Greek, who were firmly attached to the Septuagint ? [3] If a controversy arise on any passage in Scripture, recourse to the Greek is easy, but could they imagine having recourse to the Hebrew with which no one was acquainted ? [4] And then, too, was Jerome's translation so reliable as he believed it to be ?

[1] *Ep.* lvi, 2, *Ap.* St Jerome (Hilberg, C.V., LIV, p. 497, l. 1).
[2] *Ep.* cxii, 20 (Hilberg, C.V., vol. LV, p. 389, l. 25).
[3] *Ep.* civ, 4 (in Jerome ; Hilberg, C.V., LV, p. 240, l. 15).
[4] *Ibid.*, p. 240, l. 19.

" We have come to this that a brother Bishop, having ordered your translation to be read in the church to which he was accredited, people were disturbed because you had rendered a passage from the prophet Jonas in a very different manner from that which had grown old in all their memories and which so many generations had repeated. All the people were in an uproar; the Greeks, especially, passionately accused you of having falsified the text; so much so that the Bishop (the scene took place at Oea) was obliged to consult the Jews. Whether from ignorance or malice the latter affirmed that the tenor of the Hebrew was conformable to that given in the Greek and Latin copies. Our Bishop found himself obliged to rectify the passage as being erroneous in order to retain his people who were on the point of abandoning him. It seems to me therefore that you, even you, may have misunderstood certain passages, and you can guess to what consequences that might lead in the case of a text which it is impossible to correct from the point of view of the original, the language of which is not in use." [1]

The fact was that Augustine saw no serious reason to upset so many interests and venerable traditions, and energetically counselled Jerome to confine himself to giving a good translation of the Septuagint which was known everywhere and which the Apostles themselves had used.[2]

We can guess how much Jerome suffered at seeing the advantages of his initiative thus misunderstood. " If my work gives offence," he observed sadly, " no one is bound to read it. I leave people to find delight in drinking the old and in despising my new wine." [3] To reasons in the practical order he opposed reasons in the scientific, namely, the value of a translation made from the original, *ut scirent nostri quid Hebraea veritas contineret;* [4] his own care for accuracy despite stories like that of the Bishop of Oea, the foundation for which he formally disputed; [5] the mistake of thinking

[1] *Ibid.*, 5 (p. 241).
[2] *Ibid.*, 4 and 6.
[3] *Ep.* cxii, 20 (Hilberg, in C.V., LV, p. 390, l. 24).
[4] *Ibid.*, 20.
[5] *Ibid.*, 21. See also P.L., XXVIII, 604, 1185, 1394; 1473; XXIX, 426.

that the Greek Bible presented any unity, or had undergone no alterations,[1] and the occasional independence of Christ and the Apostles as regards the Septuagint in their quotations from the Old Testament.[2]

He felt himself sustained by his profound conviction that the future would decide the dispute in his favour. In this he did not deceive himself. Jerome's version was gradually introduced into the practical use of the Churches. St Augustine himself had recourse to it in certain cases.[3] It is not our task to describe here the history of the Vulgate in the Middle Ages,[4] nor the vicissitudes which resulted in the declaration of the Council of Trent ordering "*ut haec ipsa vetus et vulgata editio, quae longo tot saeculorum usu in ipsa ecclesia probata est . . . pro authentica habeatur.*"[5]

XI

ST JEROME did not rest satisfied with translating Holy Scripture; he endeavoured also to facilitate its understanding by following it up with commentaries. He completed these exegetic works at Bethlehem. I have already described with what ardour the admirable women who lived under his eyes demanded fresh lights without ceasing.

In these, as elsewhere, Jerome's method in working was not irreproachable. His natural impulsiveness made the meticulous slowness required in critical work painful to him; he yielded to a haste which he acknowledged with humility

[1] *Ep.* cxii, 19 ; and P.L., XXVIII, 1389 et s.
[2] *Apol.* II, xxxiv (P.L., XXIII, 477), etc.
[3] Cf. *de Doct. Christ.*, IV, vii.
[4] See Samuel Berger's fundamental work, *Hist. de la Vulgate pendant les premiers siècles du moyen-âge*. It will be noticed that St Jerome employs the word *vulgata* to describe the translation of the *Septuagint* (*In Is.*, lxv, 20 ; *in Oseam*, vii, 13) : it is a translation of the Greek word κοινη. In the Middle Ages the term *vulgata editio* was still sometimes used to designate the *Septuagint*. It was only after the Council of Trent that it was ordinarily applied to St Jerome's translation. In its present condition, the *Vulgate* comprises (1) the old Latin translation not revised by Jerome (as regards certain non-canonical books of the Old Testament) ; (2) the old Latin translation revised from the Greek (in the case of the Gospels ; possibly for the rest of the New Testament ; and for the Psalter [Gallican]) ; (3) the translation made by Jerome from the Hebrew (for the Old Testament, with the exception of certain apocrypha). For present-day schemes for the revision of the *Vulgate*, cf. Jaquier, *Le N.T. dans l'Eglise Chrétienne*, Paris, 1913, II, 195 ; J. Denk, *der neue Sabatier*, L. 1914.
[5] Denzinger-Bannwart, *Enchir. Symbol. et Definitionum*, 1908, no. 785. The principal modern edition of the *Vulgate* is that of Wordsworth & White, Oxford, 1889 et s.

in order to be excused, but without always succeeding in being pardoned. The *Commentary* on Abdias was dictated in two nights ; that on St Matthew in two weeks ; he cleared off the Epistle of St Paul to the Ephesians at the rate of a thousand lines a day.[1] From this arose a prolixity which nearly approaches to chatter, also an annoying tendency to pile up opinions which had been given at an earlier date on any particular Scriptural difficulty, instead of making his own selection and putting it forward. His lexicographical and topographical writings on the Bible come from Origen especially, and also from Philo (through the intermediary of Origen), but Jerome has also included in them the results of his original researches. Richard Simon irreverently declared as regards the *Liber de nominibus Hebraicis* that " if any one were to think of presenting to the public a work like that he would be hissed by everybody." [2] Far better equipped with implements, modern minds have been quick to look down upon the toil of the first clearing of the ground. Let us at least recognise St Jerome's great merit and his truly scholarly concern to make comprehensible the texts he was endeavouring to explain, by surrounding them with all positive information capable of elucidating them. With rare exceptions this was not at all the form of exegesis in favour in his time. They much preferred allegorical exegesis, which, starting from the principle that the sacred text hid a mysterious meaning which the letter veiled far more than it explained, endeavoured to extract it even by means of the most fantastic interpretations. The fashion was so strong that Jerome himself could not get away from it. His ideal would also have been, so far as we can see, to mingle the two forms of interpretation, historical and allegorical,[3] or to overlay one with the other.[4] In any case, he strove to associate with this somewhat puerile bent, wherein vanity found play,[5] investigations less flattering to the imagination, but fruitful in other ways for a full understanding of the past.[6]

---

[1] I have mentioned other facts in B.A.L.A.C., 1914, p. 238.
[2] *Lettres choisies*, I, 310.
[3] *Comm. in Nahum*, § 2 (P.L., XXV, 1243).
[4] *In Isaiam, Pref.* (P.L., XXIV, 20).
[5] *Ibid., Pref.* 1. V (P.L., XXIV, 158).
[6] He remarks in the *Prologue* to Isaias how little prepared was Roman taste, permeated with rhetoric as it was, to understand the importance of these researches.

XII

WE must cast an eye over those works of his mature age which do not enter into the ample framework of his Scriptural writings, especially the *De Viris Illustribus* and the *Adversus Jovinianum*.

The *De Viris Illustribus* was written at Bethlehem in the year 392 at the request of Dexter, the son of Pacian (Bishop of Barcelona then dead) and a Pretorian Prefect. This work was dedicated to Dexter.

The idea of Jerome was to draw up a list of Christian writers, but in a much briefer form, on the lines of the *De Viris Illustribus* of Suetonius, which was a series of notices written in the year 113 in which the most distinguished representatives in Roman literature found a place. " Suetonius enumerated the poets from the time of Livius Andronicus, the orators from Cicero, the historians from Sallust, the philosophers, and lastly, the grammarians who formed only one book. In each of these books he doubtless gave the names in chronological order, as in the last." [1] It was a common practice among the pagans to jeer at the intellectual mediocrity of the Catholics. What better means could be found to show them their error or bad faith than to enumerate the writers by whom Christian literature was honoured ?

> " Let them learn then—men like Celsus, Porphyry and Julian, those mad dogs raving against Christ—let their partisans learn, men who imagine that the Church has neither philosophers, orators or doctors, the breadth and the talent of the men who founded, developed and embellished her ; let them cease accusing our faith of having nothing else to show than rustic simplicity, and let them rather recognise their own ignorance."

Jerome therefore took in hand to supply a few brief notices of all those who " from the time of the Passion of Christ up to the fourteenth year of Theodosius *de scripturis sanctis memoriae aliquid tradiderunt*."

The list comprised 135 sections, the first of which is

---

[1] Macé, *Essai sur Suétone*, Paris, 1900, p. 244.

devoted to Simon Peter, and the last to St Jerome himself, who kept back to the end his own notice among this succession of "illustrious men." The first 78 are closely dependent upon the *Ecclesiastical History* and the *Chronical* by Eusebius of Cæsarea. Jerome is content to include the particulars found therein save in a few rare cases (*e.g.* 12 ; 53 ; 58 ; 66 ; 67 ; 68 ; 72 ; 74 ; 75). It thus happens that he reproduces the mistakes of Eusebius, and even makes others himself, which we can rectify by reading his model.[1] In reality, he was rather poorly acquainted with the early Christian literature of the IInd century, or rather, being contented to transcribe Eusebius, he did not take the trouble to revive what he knew. From § 79, Jerome continues by himself. As regards a certain number of writers, such as Tertullian, Minucius Felix, Cyprian, Novatian, Victorinus of Pettau, etc., he is our one and precious source.

We must bear in mind the particular object he proposed to himself if we would understand certain of his methods. Thus, in his desire to enhance the importance of the writers he speaks about, he is prodigal to excess of laudatory epithets —*elegans, utilis, pulcherrimus, valde utilis,* which he adds to the information copied from Eusebius. Further, desirous of swelling his list at all costs, he does not hesitate to enter the names of heretics, such as Tatian (§ 29), Bardesanus (§ 33), Asterius (§ 94), Photinus (§ 107), and even under various pretexts, profane writers such as Philo the Jew (§ 11), Flavius Josephus (§ 13), and Justus Tiberiensis (§ 14). St Augustine expressed his regret to him that he had not taken the trouble to insist more strongly on the errors of the heresiarchs whom he thus incorporated in the ranks of the Christian phalanxes.[2] The fact is that they played somewhat the *rôle* of " substitutes " destined to make up the number, and Jerome had not been at pains to blacken them too much.

Even in these simple notices the personality of the author betrays itself in a curious manner. More than once Jerome makes the length of his chapters accord with his sympathies or antipathies. When dealing with a Didymus (§ 109),

---

[1] E.g. § xxxix, he includes under one person Quadratus the author of an apology presented to Hadrian in 124, and Quadratus Bishop of Athens who lived in the time of Marcus Aurelius (161–180). See also P. de Labriolle, *Les sources de l'Histoire du Montanisme*, Paris, 1913, p. xx et s.

[2] *Ep.* xl, 6 (P.L., XXXIII, 157).

or a Gregory of Nazianzen (§ 117), he makes generous allowance. To make up for this, St John Chrysostom (§ 129), then but a simple priest at Antioch it is true, only has three lines. As for St Ambrose (§ 124), Jerome metes out to him the following statement :

> " Ambrose, the Bishop of Milan, is still writing to-day ;
> as he is living, I shall avoid giving my judgment in order
> not to expose myself to the contradictory reproach of
> too much flattery or too much frankness (*ne in alterutram
> partem aut adulatio in me reprehendatur aut veritas*)."

The serenity proper to the historian and critic was not his strong point. But after all the work has left landmarks for posterity whose loss would be irreparable. He kindled the zeal of various writers to continue his work, such as Gennadius in the Vth century ; Isidore of Seville in the VIIth, and Honorius of Autun in the XIIth. An unknown hand translated it into Greek between the VIIth and IXth centuries. This translation has been preserved in MS. C. 11, XIVth century, in the Library at Zurich.

The *Adversus Jovinianum* was written in 392–3 at the request of Pammachius, the son-in-law of Paula. According to St Jerome Jovinian had at first led a very severe life, then little by little he was seen to be giving up this first rigour, and to be taking to a much freer manner of living. Perhaps he had made an endeavour to react against the excesses of the asceticism of the East such as were becoming naturalised more and more among a portion of Roman society, and which Jerome did not cease to recommend. Was he influenced by personal motives which were more or less unmentionable ? We can only suppose so if we listen to Jerome alone. Nevertheless, neither St Ambrose, nor Pope Siricius, nor St Augustine insinuate anything of the kind against him, and our sense of justice demands a due reserve. Already in 390 a Council held in Rome had condemned him, together with eight of his partisans. He took refuge in Milan, but St Ambrose was swift to renew this condemnation by a Synod held in 391. Meanwhile, Jerome received in Rome the *Commentarioli* composed by the heresiarch, and notwithstanding the poor style of Jovinian (I, i), he determined to write a refutation.

Jerome reviews Jovinian's doctrine in four theses.

In the first place, Jovinian had proclaimed the equal merit after baptism of virgins, widows, and married women, provided that their " good works " were of equal merit. He was concerned to vindicate the state of marriage against its detractors, including among them those who, without formally discrediting it, showed a greater esteem for celibacy. He based his contention upon Genesis ii, 24 ; and Matthew xix, 5 ; he appealed to the example of persons in the Old and New Testaments who were married ; he also invoked the authority of the Apostle Paul in his Ist Epistle to Timothy. And from all these examples he made the deduction that marriage, even when repeated, was not in itself inferior to any other manner of life. St Jerome's reply is a discussion of the texts before everything else. He exerted himself to prove that those relied upon by his opponent were misleading or were annulled, or at any rate were limited, by other texts in an opposite sense. In addition, he did not deny himself any extravagance in his views or any violence in his expressions. It is a kind of semi-paradoxical contest from which the *prestige* attaching to marriage emerges somewhat impaired.

We must realise that this question of marriage, its advantages and its disadvantages, had much concerned the moralists of old. The theme " εἰ γαμητέον " (ought one to marry ?) was dear to popular philosophy. We see it treated of by Hierocles, the Stoic, in the Ist or IInd century of our era, and in the *excerpta* which Stobaeus, the compiler, has preserved of him. Hierocles recommended marriage from the political and civic point of view. For him it represented, as Cicero has said in his *De Officiis* (I, xvii, 54), *principium urbis et quasi seminarium reipublicae.* He also extols it as the entire union of two beings, a union of the body, and a union of the soul, ". . . μεχρὶ τῶν σωμάτων, μᾶλλον δὲ καὶ αὐτῶν τῶν ψυχῶν." He mentions the benefit of the presence of an industrious woman in the house, the useful help which the children, when they have grown up, give to their parents, and the care which the latter receive from them in their old age. In his eyes, marriage from its nature was a light burden. What weighed it down to the point of rendering it unbearable to many was the lack of reason, the ἀφροσύνη of so many men, who allow themselves to be drawn into it by the sole consideration of beauty or fortune.

These discussions περὶ γάμου, in which Chrysippus had already perhaps had a hand, recur in the writings of many other Stoic moralists, or of those with Stoic tendencies, such as Dion Chrysostom, Seneca (*Ep.* 94), Eudorus, etc., and even the rhetoricians had taken it up. We also hear therein the arguments of the detractors of marriage. He who marries, they contended, exposes himself to the humiliation of being deceived by his wife, to the grief of losing his children, to the prolonged weariness of living side by side with a woman who is a *coquette*, extravagant, cross-grained, etc. . . . Tertullian certainly had made use of this satirical tradition in his work (now lost) *de Nuptiarum Angustiis*. Jerome in turn appropriated it in his *Adversus Jovinianum*, happy in the thought that the worldly women of Rome would rear up under the pricks of the expressions which he was letting loose against their sex.[1]

His refutation of the second proposition of the heresiarch was appreciably shorter.[2] In addition, it was far more abstract in character, and more specifically theological, and in this domain of speculation Jerome is rather less at his ease. Jovinian claimed that whosoever received baptism in full faith could not, after this rebirth, be led into sin by the devil. Perhaps there was in his mind a secret co-relation between this second thesis and the first. From the moment that it was enough to receive baptism in the requisite conditions in order to become the permanent habitation of God, it mattered little what was the particular state adopted by anyone after baptism. It became then only a secondary element, the importance of which there was no need to accentuate. To this line of argument Jerome replied with facts not with reasoned statements ; it was a fact that the best may fall, as had Moses, Aaron, David, Solomon, and Peter the Apostle. How then could they believe in the indefectibility of those who had been baptised ?[3]

The third thesis of Jovinian[4] went to maintain that there

---

[1] I, x : "Licet enim in me saevituras sciam plurimas matronarum . . . tamen dicam quod sentio." On all these matters, see Bickel's *In Senecae philosophiae fragmenta*, vol. I. *Fragm. de Matrimonio*, L. 1915, p. 191 et s., 356; Fr. Buggenhagen, Περὶ γάμου . . . Bale, Zurich, 1919.

[2] II, i–iv.

[3] II, iv : "(Baptisma) sicut priora peccata dimittit, sic in futurum servare non potest, nisi baptizati omni custodia servaverint cor suum."

[4] II, v et s.

was no difference between abstaining from food and partaking of it with thanksgiving. He thus aimed at diminishing the merit of fasting. Here Tertullian's *de Jejunio* provided Jerome with the greater part of his arguments (he also borrows some from the philosopher Porphyry), and prompts him as to the tactics to pursue. It consisted in treating his opponent as a glutton who erects an array of imposing principles in order to mask the hankerings of his voracity. Nevertheless in this apology of the practice of fasting he is careful at times not to go too far, and shows that he does not share in any degree the error of certain heretics who condemned the work of the Creator.[1]

In his fourth and last proposition, Jovinian asserted the identity of the rewards which all who had preserved their baptismal faith and purity would obtain in heaven. Therefore we were to conclude from this that the hierarchy which people wished to establish between the different *states* was chimerical. One just man was worth as much as another just man, by whatever means he had preserved himself in his state of justice. Jerome met him with reasons from Scripture (e.g. I *Cor.* xv, 22 ; 39 et s. ; II *Cor.* v, 10) and also from good sense ; how could God be so unjust as to reward with identical remuneration merits which were so obviously of unequal value ? There were shades and degrees of good as well as of evil.

In his peroration,[2] he resumes his abusive and truculent tone :

"And now for a last word to our Epicurus sweating out passion (*subantem*) in the midst of his gardens among young men and young women. Thou hast for thy followers the plump, the well-fed, the well-washed. All the pretty boys, all the youth with curled hair that I see, and their well kept locks and cheeks painted with vermilion, form thy flock, or rather all that trash grunts among thy pigs. . . ."

The work finishes with an enthusiastically-worded reproach against the city of Rome where the doctrine of Peter is seated unshakable upon the rock of Christ.

This work, full of vigour, if not of good taste, did not

---

[1] II, xiv. [2] II, xxxvi.

meet with the success which Jerome had promised himself. His friend Pammachius had bought a good number of copies of it in Rome : he made speed to withdraw from circulation those upon which he could lay hands, in face of the impression that was produced.[1] From another quarter Domnio communicated to Jerome quite a long list of passages begging him to correct or to explain them.[2] Jerome had to defend himself in an apologetic letter addressed to Pammachius.[3] In it he repeated that he had not at all intended to condemn marriage, nor to glide into a kind of Manichaeism on account of his misgivings about flesh-meat and wine ; he also invoked the liberty permitted to a polemical work.[4] These were grumbling excuses, in which were mingled sharp attacks against certain people who, he affirmed, only gave themselves airs of indignation in order to defame him.

Thirteen or fourteen years after, in 406, he had again to break a lance against Vigilantius, a priest from Gaul, who was reviving certain theses which had already been combated by Jerome, and in addition attacked the veneration with which the tombs of the martyrs were surrounded, the vigils which it was customary to pass in their Churches, and various liturgical practices. Jerome had personal reasons for little liking Vigilantius whom he had welcomed with goodwill at Bethlehem on the recommendation of Paulinus of Nola,[5] and who had repaid him by retailing unfriendly stories about him.[6] As soon as his works came into his hands he retorted with a short and furious diatribe in which reasoning holds only a feeble place, as though such a sorry adversary was not worth the trouble of refuting in detail, and in which he hustles, abuses, cleaves him in two, and even reproaches him with his name, on which he does not disdain to make puns.[7]

This wordy vigour seems to have already been somewhat appeased by the year 415, in which Jerome wrote his *Dialogues* against the Pelagians. It was St Augustine who, through the

---

[1] *Ep.* xlviii, 2 (Hilberg, in C.V., LIV, 347).

[2] *Ep.* L. 3 (*ibid.*, p. 391, l. 16).

[3] *Ep.* xlix (xlviii, in Vallarsi).

[4] For a curious theory as to the duplicity that was permissible in works of this kind, see *ibid.*, 13 (Hilberg, p. 368).

[5] *Ep.* lviii, 11.

[6] *Ep.* lxi.

[7] He calls Vigilantius *Dormitantius* (as an enemy to pious vigils). I note that Cicero expressly approved of this play of words on proper names : *de Orat.*, II, lxiii, 257.

intermediary of his disciple Orosius, had engaged him in a struggle which he held so much at heart. St Augustine praised the accurate expression of Catholic doctrine [1] contained in his *Dialogues*. Of the two disputants, the one, Atticus, represents the orthodox point of view, the other, Critobulus, the opposite opinion; the theses are presented in the presence of each other, turn by turn, and this alternation obliged Jerome to observe the form of a certain amount of impartiality.

XIII

THE evening of his life was saddened by quarrels over Origenism in the course of which he had to struggle against the most mortifying personal attacks. There is no reason to relate here all the phases of this unhappy strife ; [2] we must at least give an outline of the character of some of the protagonists who were mixed up in it, and point out where they parted company.

In the last years of the IVth century the renown of Origen was still shining with a bright light in spite of the efforts of certain men to cloud it over. The entry of a redoubtable adversary into the lists was to change all that. At the beginning of the year 374, Epiphanius, the Bishop of Salamis, assigned to himself the task of ruining Origen and Origenism in Catholic opinion. To anyone who may still doubt that the most extensive erudition can be joined in the same mind to a real mediocrity of intelligence and the most obstinate prejudices, Epiphanius may be presented as a fairly successful specimen of this displeasing amalgam. Personally he was a man of edifying piety and of a life worthy of respect ; but burning over with a somewhat mischievous zeal he had constituted himself a hunter of heresies, and scented in Origenism a magnificent prey.

We have mentioned all that Origen represented to the laborious youth of Jerome, the respect and admiration which he had devoted to that illustrious exegetist, and his promptness in taxing with ignorance anyone who refused to

---

[1] *Ep.* clxxx, 5.
[2] It is traced in a very vivid manner in J. Brochet's work, *Saint Jérôme et ses ennemis*, 1905. But Brochet is not always correct in the chronology of his facts : see the important studies of Holl and Julicher in S.B.B., 1916, p. 226 et s. (and my analysis in the *Rev. de Philol., Rev. des Revues,* 1917).

2 A

recognise in him the Instructor of the Churches from the time of the Apostles (*post apostolos Ecclesiarum magistrum nemo nisi imperitus negabit*).[1] What then were the influences under which this unexpected revival took shape in his mind about the year 400 ?

We must here introduce upon the scene a new personage who was to play an important *rôle* in this crisis, the enigmatic Tyrannius Rufinus.

Rufinus was born at Concordia, near Aquileia. He had made the acquaintance of Jerome in Rome where they were both studying, and their friendship was strengthened into affection in the ascetic little circle at Aquileia. When this group was scattered, Rufinus, who had become a monk, attached himself to the person of Melania, a rich patrician lady ;[2] he became in some degree her director of conscience and her indispensable counsellor. In November 372, they both left for the East. They first stopped in Egypt ; Rufinus prolonged his stay there while Melania went on to Jerusalem and there founded a monastery where Rufinus rejoined her in 378. The influence of Origen was at that time altogether predominant in the East, especially in Egypt with the monks. Rufinus submitted to it all the more readily because he had not any very vigorous originality of mind. If we cast an eye over his works (almost all of them written after the year 397), we see that, apart from his polemical writings and one or two exegetic treatises, they are made up of translations. Rufinus had observed that in the West people knew Greek less and less, while thinkers of the breadth of mind of Origen were entirely ignorant of it, even in high ecclesiastical spheres. He told himself that it would be a useful task to translate the leading works of Greek theology, even at the cost of a few free renderings and amendments, into as correct and elegant Latin as possible.[3]

When Jerome and Paula arrived in Palestine (386),

---

[1] *De Nomin. Hebr. Praef.*

[2] She was Melania, the elder, the daughter of Marcellinus who was Consul in 341. Her grand-daughter, Melania, the younger, the wife of Pinianus, settled at Bethlehem in 414 with her mother Albina, and Pinianus, her husband.

[3] Let me mention here the anonymous Latin translation of the *Acta Archelai* (C.B., Beeson), which must have been made at the end of the IVth century. These two dialogues between Bishop Archelaus and Manes constitute one of the most important sources of the History of Manichaeism. The "palatine" translation of the *Pastor of Hermas* (ed. Gebhardt and Harnack, in *Patrum apost. op.*, fasc. 3, L. 1877) is of the same date.

Melania and Rufinus held a leading position in Jerusalem. Inasmuch as pious pilgrims were settling in Jerusalem, little jealousies and occasions of variance were successfully avoided for several years. But in 392, a certain Aterbius (possibly sent by Epiphanius) came to ask Jerome and Rufinus to condemn Origenism, the progress of which was then evident in Palestine. Jerome could not fail to experience some perplexity. Up till then he had before everything else regarded Origen as the interpreter of the Scriptures rather than as a bold constructor of ideas ; the sanctity of Epiphanius, his wide erudition, and zeal for orthodoxy, must have intimidated his judgment and have awakened in him a fear of deviating from the right path if he obstinately clung to defending an entire theological system which he had hardly investigated up till that moment. Briefly, he associated himself in the reprobation of the errors of the great Alexandrine which Aterbius pointed out to him. Rufinus entirely refused to receive Aterbius. This different attitude created at the outset a certain constraint between the two friends.

Meanwhile Epiphanius, who was almost an octogenarian, thought good to come in person to Jerusalem (doubtless about Easter of the year 392) in order to combat directly the epidemic of Origenism with which John, the Bishop, was infected. An oratorical duel, wherein, under an external aspect of palpitating courtesy, opposing passions were boiling, set them one against the other in the chapel of the Holy Sepulchre. John refused all disavowal of Origenism. Epiphanius then left the city in the dead of night and took refuge in the monastery at Bethlehem. He formally invited the monks to break off from Jerusalem, and in order that they might not advance the necessity of their liturgical requirements he ordained almost by force Paulinianus, Jerome's own brother. Some months later he launched against John of Jerusalem a decisive ultimatum wherein he summoned him to pronounce his views as regards Origenism. Jerome translated this letter in order to place *au courant* his friend Eusebius of Cremona who did not know Greek. His translation fell into the hands of Rufinus. John and Rufinus might well believe that Jerome associated himself personally with the campaign opened by Epiphanius.

Then began a war of subterranean manœuvres, intrigues

and traps, with intervals of rest, and verbal reconciliations, to begin again with still more intensity and treachery. In 397, Rufinus, who had returned to Italy, made the Origenist quarrels fashionable there, and enlisted in his rancour Jerome's old enemies. With a cleverness which was very like perfidy he affected to place under the patronage of Jerome his own efforts in favour of Origen, and recalled the numerous evidences he had given in former days of his admiration for the author of the treatise *de Principiis*. Jerome protested : " I praised," he stated, " the exegesis of Origen and not his doctrine, his genius, not his faith, the scholar and not the propagandist." [1] Driven by these polemics far beyond his first hesitations, he opposed to the toned-down translation of the *de Principiis* which Rufinus had just given, another translation in which the systematic omissions of Rufinus were repaired, in order that the perilous temerities of Origen might appear in their full light.[2] But shortly after, Rufinus by a singular *volte-face* disavowed Origen in order to concentrate all the ardour and all the spleen of his polemics upon Jerome. To the *Apologies* of Rufinus Jerome felt bound to reply with his three books *Contra Rufinum*, in which he laid bare the crookedness of his old friend, his quibbles, and his " traps for foxes," and congratulated himself that he was at last able to tear off the mask from him : *levius est inimicum cavere quam hostem latentem sub amici nomine sustinere* (ii, 35).

This time his vigorousness got the better of the elusive suppleness of his adversary. Rufinus took the course of silence. He shut himself away at Aquileia and buried himself in his labours as a skilful translator up to the day when fleeing from the barbarians he was obliged to take flight to the East with Melania, accompanied by her daughter Albina, Melania the younger and Pinianus the husband of the latter. But death overtook him in Sicily (410).

Jerome himself died on the 30th September, 420, in his cell at Bethlehem. He had experienced the sorrow of seeing the passing away before him of his pious and learned friends who had remained tenderly faithful to him through all his troubles.

[1] *Ep.* lxxxiv.
[2] Of these translations see the large edition of the *de Principiis* by Koetschau (C.B., 1913) and my review of them in B.A.L.A.C., 1914, pp. 287–290.

XIV

I HAVE endeavoured to give a succinct idea of the *rôle* and personality of St Jerome. I have thinned down as little as possible the magnificent *relief*, while quite realising that certain features of it may have seemed singular to minds who conceive of sanctity under the somewhat conventional aspect of benevolent gentleness. At this valuation Jerome would be a saint out of his frame. His ardent imagination, his fiery though disciplined passions, and his violent and eruptive nature, connect him with all sides of humanity as it is. He is profoundly human. But what is most remarkable about him is it not just this, that with his altogether impulsive temperament he consistently subordinated the multifarious activities of his life to a sharply defined end ? The goal to which his every effort converged was the good of the Church. He rendered immense services to her. By his revision of the Bible he unified and fixed the text in which Christians read the Word of God. By his fervour for the ascetic ideal he indirectly raised the moral level of the faithful and the clergy, for the sight of renunciations is assuredly the best propaganda, even for those who are not willing or who dare not raise themselves to such a height. And at the same time, he spread appreciation of a celibacy devoted to good works, a fruitful celibacy, thereby preparing the way for the marvellous monastic expansion of the Middle Ages. Lastly, as a writer, he has enriched the entire domain of classic literature—exegesis, literary history, biography, polemics, and even the funeral oration, for certain letters of his on his friends who had died are nothing else. He was thus assured of the greatest influence upon the literature of the Middle Ages in the West. And by an exceptional fate his gifts as a man of letters and as a scholar, and the brilliancy of his style closely resembling the classics which he imitated even in their methods, preserved for him a like admiration among the men of the Renaissance. There were perhaps among the Fathers of the Church characters more delicate, more nicely shaded, more subtile—that of an Ambrose or an Augustine, for instance. But there was not one more vigorous, nor one whose life, expression, and fire, we can better grasp through the dead letter after the lapse of so many centuries.

XV

IN a letter addressed to Marcella, Jerome's friends, Paula and Eustochium described with pious and *naïve* ardour their happiness in the privileged East : [1]

"We are able to see here the foremost personages in the world. . . . All the most brilliant people in Gaul hasten to come here. From the recesses of his land, which the ocean separates from our own world, the Briton, as soon as he has made any progress in religion, leaves behind his Western sun and seeks a city he only knows by reputation, and because he has read of it in Holy Scripture. How describe the Armenians, Persians, the people from India, Ethiopia, and Egypt neighbour to Palestine and so fruitful in solitaries, from Pontus, Cappadocia, Coele-Syria, Mesopotamia, and the entire East ?

"Here the only rivalry is in humility. The least of all takes rank with the first. We have no difference in our garb, nothing which seeks to be admired. We dispose ourselves as we will without risk of censure or praise. We do not rend each other here with gnashing teeth as people do elsewhere. No luxury, no voluptuousness : but so many spots for prayer that one day would not suffice to visit them. . . . Oh ! when will come that day when a breathless courser will bring us the news that our Marcella hath set foot in Palestine, when the choirs of monks and the multitude of virgins will everywhere spread abroad the news ; . . . that day when it will be vouchsafed to us to enter with thee the grotto of the Saviour, to weep with His sister at the sepulchre of Christ, to mourn there with His Mother, to kiss the wood of the Cross, and to ascend in mind and soul with the Lord the Mount of Olives ; to see Lazarus rise again swathed in bands, and to contemplate the waters of the Jordan purified by the baptism of Jesus. . . . We will go to Nazareth, and will see the 'flower' of Galilee, for Nazareth meaneth 'flower.' Not

[1] *Ep.* xlvi, 10 et s.

far from there we will visit Cana, where the water was changed into wine. We will climb up to Itabyrium, etc. . . ."

One of the notable facts of the IVth century was just this ardent piety which from this period carried so many Christian men and women to the Holy Land there " to adore" as St Jerome says (*Ep.* xlvii, 2), " the track of the footsteps of the Saviour, and to see there in all their freshness the traces of the Nativity, the Cross and Passion."

The influx of pilgrims into Jerusalem was not however without its disadvantages. Less optimistic at certain times than these patrician mystics, St Jerome does not hesitate to dissuade Paulinus of Nola from going there : [1]

> " Do not imagine that your faith will suffer some loss from not coming to Jerusalem, and do not think that we are better because we live here. . . . If the spots which have witnessed the accomplishment of the mystery of the Cross and of the Resurrection were not in a city which is over populated, wherein we find a Curia, a garrison, prostitutes, actors, and buffoons, just like in other cities ; if they (the Holy Places) were only frequented by solitaries, all the solitaries assuredly should wish to fix their habitation here. But what folly to give up the world, to leave one's country, to leave the cities behind and to follow the calling of monk in order to live far from one's own house amid a population far denser than in one's own fatherland ! People flock to Jerusalem from all the corners of the universe. This city is full of all sorts of people, and we see here such a throng of men and women that one is obliged to put up with many a sight here which one may succeed in some measure in avoiding elsewhere."

He had however not so long back said that pilgrimages to the Holy Places were " a part of the Faith " (pars fidei),[2] and a passing fit of ill-humour did not alter this conviction in him. We see this well from the way in which he relates in his *Epitaphium Paulae* the journey of Paula to Galilee.

[1] *Ep.* lviii, 4 et s. (C.V., LIV, 532). Compare St Gregory of Nyssa, *Ep.* ii.
[2] *Ep.* xlii, 2.

This letter of consolation (*Ep.* cviii), addressed to Eustochium —one of the most moving which came from his pen—is further interesting from its detailing the whole series of stages by which the descendant of the Gracchi and the Scipios travelled, up to the point of her settling in her cell at Bethlehem : the island of Pontia, Methone (south of Messenia), Cyprus, Seleucia, Antioch, Coele-Syria and Phœnicia, various spots in the Holy Land, Jerusalem, and lastly, Bethlehem, which was to be the point of departure for another tour which she made through Palestine and Egypt.

We possess other accounts of travels in the Holy Land, written by the pilgrims themselves. There are two which belong to the IVth century, the *Itinerary from Bordeaux to Jerusalem* which refers to the year 333, and the *Peregrinatio* called *Aetheriae*, which the opinion of the most competent critics assigns to the last quarter of the IVth century.

The *Itinerarium a Burdigala Hierusalem usque et ab Heraclea per Aulonam* (Aulona in Illyria, on the coast of the Ionian Sea) *et per urbem Romam Mediolanum usque*, with no name of the author, is hardly more than a list of names of places written by a pilgrim who leaving Bordeaux for Jerusalem returned to his native town by way of Constantinople, Rome, and Milan, after a sojourn of some months in the Holy Land. His wellnigh only concern is to take note of the distances between the stages of the posting houses (*mutatio*) at which he stopped, the cities which he passed through, and the rest-houses (*mansio*) where he stayed the night. The portion devoted to the Holy Land assumes a slightly less arid turn, but still closely resembles a simple catalogue, with the addition of references to the Bible. The whole work is of the most forbidding dryness.

The *Peregrinatio Aetheriae* has a different character. It was discovered by Gamurrini in the same manuscript at Arezzo which also provided him with the *De Mysteriis* and fragments of hymns attributed to St Hilary. This manuscript of the XIth century had previously belonged to Monte Cassino. Dom de Bruyne [1] has discovered since then some

---

[1] R. Bén., XXVI (1909), p. 481 et s. The work by Petrus Diaconus, *de locis Sanctis* (XIth century), in which the *Peregrinatio* is utilised, also enables us to fill in certain *lacunae* (cf. Geyer, in C.V., vol. XXXIX, p. xiv).—History of the manuscript of Arezzo in the Revue du Monde catholique, 1888, I, p. 21 et s.

fragments of the *Peregrinatio* in a manuscript at Madrid (IXth century).

It is the account of a pilgrimage to the Holy places made by a woman. She addresses her " sisters " (*dominae venerabiles sorores, dominae animae meae, dominae sorores, dominae, lumen meum*) in an affectionate and sprightly tone, and it is on their account that she puts down in writing her impressions and recollections. The account is incomplete. The portion which has been preserved shows us the traveller at the foot of Mount Sinai. From there she goes to Jerusalem which is her connecting point. Some time after she proceeds to Mount Nebo in Arabia (x, i), comes back to Jerusalem, starts again for the *Ausitis regio* on the confines of Idumaea and Arabia in order to see the tomb (*memoria*) of Job there (xiii, i), and, after another stay in the Holy City, considers returning to her own country. But before doing so she is anxious to go further, into Mesopotamia, in order to visit the solitaries living there, whose wonderful lives she had heard people speak of, and also the tomb of St Thomas, at Edessa (xvii, i). She sets out therefore from Antioch to Mesopotamia and, after her curiosity has been satisfied (*ut sum satis curiosa*, she confesses, xvi, 3), she makes her way to Constantinople by way of Antioch, Cilicia, Cappadocia, Galatia, Bithynia, and the sea (xxii–xxiii). It is at Constantinople too that she writes the account of her travels (xxiii, 10). Thinking that her " sisters " will be interested in it she adds a kind of appendix on the liturgy followed by the Church in Jerusalem (xxiv, i). This supplement by itself is almost as long as the portion of the narrative proper still remaining ; further, the end is missing.

The tone of the work is perfectly simple and relieved from all rhetorical phraseology. The interest proceeding from it is real, but we must describe its nature. Amateurs of the picturesque would be disappointed. The pilgrim is not insensible to the beauties of nature ; the powerful and " terrible " volume of the Euphrates reminds her of the course of the Rhône,[1] but on a larger scale ; she finds pleasure in describing the wide views she obtained from the top of Mount Nebo.[2] But she does not drive to death the epithet " rare " ; *vallem infinitam, valde pulchram, vallem pulchram satis et*

---

[1] xviii, 2 (Geyer, p. 61). [2] xii, 3, p. 53.

amoenam, vallem amoenissimam, hortos pulcherrimos, hortus gratissimus, are the sober adjectives which suffice for her.[1] What she is eager for (and it is almost the only thing), is to contemplate the spots whose names she knows from the Scriptures or from pious legends, and to realise at first-hand the moving stories with which her nun's imagination is full. Guided by the monks whom she collects around her with a *naïve* confidence very sure of itself, she makes them show her, as she says, " singula loca, quae semper ego juxta scripturas requirebam." [2]   A prayer, and a repetition from the Psalms carry to God on each occasion the testimony of her gratitude for the happiness she has just tasted.

If we exclude the specifically literary point of view, the *Peregrinatio* is a precious document. We find in it a host of topographical information, sufficiently succinct for scholarship to draw material from it. Philology can gather therein specimens of late Latin in general use. But it is especially in the history of the liturgy that we are appreciably enriched : " The woman who wrote these pages gives us in their most minute detail a description of the liturgical ceremonies and the offices of each day. She tells us of the principal Feasts in the ecclesiastical year at a time when other writers remained mute upon this subject, or only furnished a few vague and incomplete particulars." [3]

Who was the author of the *Peregrinatio?*   It is a much-discussed question which seems to have received a solution, not indeed certain, but one that is reasonable and plausible. The pilgrim must have occupied a certain rank, if one may judge from the regard with which she was received both by the clergy and the official authorities who placed at her disposition soldiers for her protection. Gamurrini proposes that she should be recognised as the sister-in-law (he was wrong : the sister) of the Consul Rufinus who, on the testimony of Palladius (*Hist. Lausiaca*, LV, i), made the journey from Jerusalem to Egypt at the end of the IVth century. She was called Σιλβανία, and Gamurrini renders this name in Latin by Silvia. A work by Dom Férotin, which appeared in the *Revue des Questions Historiques* [4] in 1903, reopened the debate. Dom Férotin draws attention to a letter included in a manu-

---

[1] I, i ; xiii, 2 ; xvi, 2 ; ix, 4 ; iv, 7.   [2] vii, 2, p. 47.
[3] Dom Cabrol, *op. cit.*, p. 5.   [4] Vol. LXXIV, p. 367 et s.

script in the Escurial, wherein Valerius, a Spanish monk, who lived in Galicia in the second half of the VIIth century, writing to the monks of Vierzo (*fratres Bergidenses*) in order to kindle their zeal puts before them the admirable example of the journey to the East accomplished by the virgin Aetheria through every kind of difficulty.[1] From the way in which he describes the meritorious trials of Aetheria we can see to all appearances that he has in his mind the alleged Silvia.[2]

Was Aetheria a native of Galicia, or did she come from one of the convents of Marseilles or Arles ? The researches of philologists have not cleared up this debated point. It is still very difficult in the present state of our knowledge, and it may always remain so, to distinguish precisely the specific characteristics of different forms of national Latinity, and to be able to state for certain what is a " Gallicism," a " Hispanism," or an " Africanism." Neither does the comparison between the Rhône and the Euphrates, which I mentioned above, authorise a very solid conclusion : the traveller may have seen the Rhône and noticed its impetuous course without having lived on its banks.

There is no decisive reason to bring down the date of the *Peregrinatio*[3] to the middle of the VIth century. Attention has been drawn to the relatively few sanctuaries of the martyrs which attracted her notice : in the VIth century these would have been looked for in more places. The *terminus post quem* is provided in § xx, 12 : to a request by the pilgrim who was desirous of visiting the country where Thare lived (cf. *Genesis* xi, 28), the Bishop to whom she wrote informed her that the cities of Nisibis and Hur were not accessible to the Romans, this region being under Persian domination. Now the Persian rule was extended over the country from the

---

[1] This letter had been printed already in Migne's *Patr. Lat.* (LXXXVII, 421). There is a critical edition by Z. Garcia, in A.B., XXIX (1910), p. 393 et s. The manuscripts of the letter of Valerius (several have been discovered) give the following forms : Etheria, Echeria, Eiheria, Aeiheria, Egeria. The form Aetheria is to be preferred on account of a passage in which the author appears to suggest a play upon the words : ". . . ut . . . *aetherea* hereditaret regna " (Garcia, p. 398).

[2] M. Paul Lejay is rather sceptical (R.C., 1909, i, 165) : " The combination which has provided the name Etheria is ingenious ; but a fresh discovery would suffice to overturn this house of cards. An agreement in literals between two texts of this kind proves nothing : there were already Baedekers or Vasari, copied without shame by the Stendhals of the period."

[3] This is Meister's theory (Rh.M., LXIV [1909], 327–392), refuted by Deconinck (R.B., 1910, pp. 432–445), Baumstark (*Oriens Christ.*, I [1911], pp. 32–86), Weigand Byz. Zeitsch., 1911, pp. 1–26), Delehaye (A.B., XXXI [1912], p. 346).

year 363 : after the death of the Emperor Julian (26th June, 363) Jovian was forced to cede to Sapor the five provinces on the other side of the Tigris in return for a thirty years' peace.[1] The *terminus ante quem* is doubtful : Aetheria wrote (xix, 2) : " Pervenimus Edessam. Ubi cum pervenissemus, statim perreximus ad ecclesiam *et* ad martyrium sancti Thomae." At first sight we should be tempted to say that she made a distinction between the Church and the tomb of the Apostle. Now we know that the relics of St Thomas were transferred in 394 to the Church itself. But it is not certain that the " et " is disjunctive.[2] However this may be, a certain number of indications, especially in the liturgical order, strongly urge us to place the *Peregrinatio* at the end of the IVth century.

It would be a departure from our plan to examine in this place the other accounts of pilgrimages which succeeding centuries from the Vth to the VIIIth have bequeathed to us. But we may at least draw attention to the importance of these narratives of travel, and, speaking generally, of the journeys to the Holy Land, from the point of view of the history of civilisation. They had the effect of widening in the West the knowledge of geography and history which was tending to become restricted on account of the breaking up of the great Roman unity. They prepared the way from a distance for the great crusading movement. The veneration of relics and the liturgy received the impression of Oriental usages, especially of those of the Church in Jerusalem. Many a legend (like that of the Grail) had the same origin, and there is nothing in the monumental, iconographic, and decorative art of the Middle Ages which does not reveal the influence of Syria and Palestine.

XVI

SULPICIUS SEVERUS also powerfully collaborated in developing in the West the taste for asceticism. He was a native of Aquitaine.[3] Born in the year 360 of Christian parents, a student at Bordeaux, and an advocate of renown, a rich marriage

---

[1] Ammianus Marcellinus, XXV, ix.
[2] See p. 65 and p. 70, two passages which provide significant parallels.
[3] Gennadius, *de Vir. Ill.*, xix ; *Dial.*, I, xxvii, 2.

which had united him with a family of consular rank seemed
to bring him every chance of happiness, when his young wife
died. From that moment Sulpicius Severus resolved to
turn to a life of piety and renunciation. The example of his
special friend Paulinus—the future Paulinus of Nola—offered
him encouragement during this turning-point in his conscience,
and his wish was likewise favoured by Bassula, his mother-in-
law, by whom he was loved affectionately. For some years
he lived in the neighbourhood of Elusa (Eauze) in Aquitaine,
and also at Toulouse and Elusio (Font d'Alzonne) in Narbonne.
The reputation of St Martin gave him a keen desire to know
the illustrious Bishop. He went to Tours in 396, having
in his mind, as he later confessed, to write his biography one
day.[1] From that time, as he states, he did not fail to visit
him at regular intervals, as often as twice in the same year.
Martin's influence put an end to the trouble that was working
in his soul. From another quarter the letters of Paulinus
exhorted him from a distance to complete his sacrifice.
Sulpicius had sold already a portion of his goods, but poverty
made him afraid.[2] It was only in 399 that he realised his
project of breaking with the world, thereby stirring up a
scandal almost as lively as that recently aroused by Paulinus.
Paulinus dissuaded him from replying to the abuse of his
detractors.[3]

Sulpicius settled at Primuliacum [4] with his mother-in-law
and a group of pious friends, giving himself up entirely to his
literary labours from which he hoped for some glory for the
Church and for himself. According to the notice of him
given by Gennadius, he received the priesthood : what is
certain is that the " lay " note is appreciable in his writings.
Gennadius states that after having had some leanings towards
Pelagianism he soon recognised his error, and punished
himself by inflicting on himself an absolute silence up to
the day of his death. We have no means of checking this
information.[5]

---

[1] *Vita M.*, xxv.
[2] Paulinus of Nola, *Ep.* xi, 12–13.
[3] *Ep.* 1, 2.
[4] There is some controversy in localising *Primuliacum*. See Abbé L. Ricaud,
Sulpice-Sévère et sa Villa de Primuliac à Saint-Sever-de-Rustan, Tarbes, 1914,
who reviews these discussions, p. 179 et s.
[5] It should be taken with caution. See T. R. Glover, *Classical Review*, 1899,
p. 211.

The *Chronica* is only a " popular " work. Sulpicius wished to present a short history of Christianity written in an attractive manner, and capable, in spite of its pre-determined brevity, of interesting the educated public.[1] This sort of abridgment was then much in favour ; we may call to mind the *Breviarium* of Eutropius, and that of Festus, etc. Sulpicius begins his narrative with events at the Creation, and takes it down as far as the Consulate of Stilicho (400). Giving special attention to the chronology, he analyses the books of the Old Testament which he read from the Greek of the Septuagint ; as regards the New Testament, he abstains out of respect from mentioning the historical events related therein.[2] He found a useful guide in Eusebius of Cæsarea whose *Chronicle* he makes use of without mentioning the name of the author, nor those of any of his profane authorities, contenting himself with informing his reader [3] once for all that he was going to avail himself of *historicis mundialibus*.[4] As regards certain episodes about which he was especially informed his account is more fully developed, as for example the Priscillianist affair at the end of the second book. M. Babut thought he had detected certain affinities in Sulpicius with that sect. Certainly Sulpicius felt keen animosity against some of those who had most warmly combated the doctrines of that heresiarch ; he did not forgive the partisans of Itacius the accusations which they had dared to bring against St Martin himself, and the indignation which he felt on this account may have had its counterpart in diminishing his personal objections to the theories of Priscillian. But if each of the expressions which he employed in his *Chronicle* to qualify Priscillianism be weighed, it will be seen whether gentleness is their leading characteristic.[5] This little work is written in a quick, nervous style, showing much distinction. Sulpicius, from the moment of his conversion, had made an undertaking with himself not to read profane [6] authors any more, but he continued to profit by the solid grounding he

---

[1] See the beginning, I, i.
[2] *Chron.*, II, xxvii, 3 (Halm, p. 82).
[3] I. i.
[4] Bernays (*Ueber die Chronik des S.S.*, in *Ges. Abhandl.*, II, 167 et s.) remarks that he ransacked the works of Greek historians unknown to us for the account of the Diadochi.
[5] II, xlvi, 1 ; 4 ; 5 ; 6 ; 7 ; xlvii, 3, 4 ; xlviii, 2, 3 ; xlix, 9 ; li, 5.
[6] Cf. Paulinus of Nola, *Ep.* xxii, 3 ; cf. v, 6 and xxx, i.

owed to them. Very little read in the Middle Ages—we only have one single manuscript of it, a *Palatinus*, now *Vaticanus* 824, of the XIth century—the *Chronicle* regained the high favour of scholars after the Renaissance.

His immense literary popularity Sulpicius Severus owes to his works on St Martin : his *Life*, written during the last months of 396 and appearing in 397, after the death of Martin ; the three complementary letters recording his last moments ; and the two *Dialogues* [1] only published in 403–4. These last are made up of a conversation lasting two days between Sulpicius Severus, Gallus, a former monk from Marmoutier and a pupil of St Martin, and one Postumianus returned from the East, during which they compare some of the wonders wrought by St Martin with those of the Eastern Christian ascetics.

If there is one saint with whom the most " independent " of historians have dealt sympathetically, or even with some sort of piety, it is assuredly St Martin. Gaston Boissier hails him as " the ideal French saint." [2] " Excluding Christ," Camille Jullian [3] wrote, " no character in Christianity has exercised, whether living or above all dead, such a lasting influence. . . . In all the history of Christianity he is the phenomenon most like the initial phenomenon, the name, the life and the memory of Christ." E. Ch. Babut [4] reproaches these learned men for continuing a hagiographic tradition the authority for which he thinks is more than suspect, without taking this into account. He is concerned to diminish the value of the testimony of Sulpicius Severus concerning St Martin. Babut states that in order to put together the portrait of his hero, Sulpicius Severus borrowed more than one *trait* from the *Life of Antony* by St Athanasius, and from St Jerome, and St Hilary, and utilised a quantity of material taken from books which he boldly incorporated in his biography, presenting them as authentic facts concerning St Martin. " The Life of St Martin," Babut wrote, " is a veritable anthology of marvellous events taken from different sources which Sulpicius arbitrarily placed to the credit of his

---

[1] Editions anterior to those of Halm give three ; but the best manuscripts show no division in the middle of the first dialogue (cf. Halm, p. vii).
[2] *Fin du Pagan.*, II, 59.
[3] R.E.A., vol. XII (1910), p. 260.
[4] *Saint Martin de Tours*, Paris, p. 146.

hero." The literary habits of the time authorised, it is true, a large amount of fiction in narratives of this kind, but Sulpicius would have somewhat abused the right of *mendacium* which was then allowed to " aretologists " or recorders of miracles. Babut's conclusion is that we know almost nothing of the real character or of the authentic *rôle* of St Martin ; that he must have been a poor man whose reputation was much contested during the second part of his life ; and that the historians, too partial to the writings of Sulpicius Severus, have *naïvely* indulged in the " sophisme du document " which " consists in presuming, when dealing with times about which few texts have been preserved, that men and facts have had in real history the same importance as written history had assigned to them."

In order to appraise with justice Babut's contention the work of Sulpicius Severus should be read through again. A somewhat puzzling impression is left. The literary ability of Sulpicius is outside the question. Possibly too Babut was wrong in disputing, as he has done, the facts narrated, since he allows that Sulpicius may have stayed " some months " at least in close contact with Martin (p. 60). What is more disturbing are his asseverations as to his veracity which, amid so many strange and sometimes burlesque and even " scatological " [1] episodes, he awards to himself. If his conscience had been easy, would he have felt the need of making oath at every incident that he was speaking the truth ? In fact Babut has shown in an excellent chapter (p. 73 et s.) how Sulpicius more than once enriched his narrative by covertly copying from antecedent *Lives*, or by exploiting traditional themes. This does not denote the scrupulous accuracy which he would have us believe was so alert in him. Since the famous *Life of Antony* by Athanasius, it was an understood thing that all Christian biography had to be a kind of " epopee of miracles." [2] Hence the necessity for the biographer to make search on all sides for the means to swell the number of these *virtutes*. More than once we ask ourselves which of these two dispositions we must suspect in Sulpicius— a boundless credulity, or the secret wish to amuse himself at the expense of his readers. Babut is not the first critic to

[1] For instance, *Vita M.*, xvii, 7.
[2] The expression of Cam. Jullian in R.E.A., 1911, p. 328.

raise doubts as to his perfect ingenuousness, but he adduced new reasons to mistrust him, and we must agree after reading it that to write a historically true life of St Martin is a difficult matter in the present state of our sources of information.

We must not conclude from this, as Babut has done, that St Martin was only a personage of limited consequence in real history. If he had left behind in Gaul no profound memory, no luminous track, would the work of Sulpicius Severus, however enthusiastic and skilful, have been sufficient to elevate him to such a destiny ? Such a consideration is not without its difficulties.

Babut attaches great importance to the fact that, apart from Sulpicius Severus and Paulinus of Nola, and excepting also the epitaph by Foedula in Vienne (which must have been engraved between the years 410 and 440), Martin's name was not mentioned in the literature of Gaul of the first half of the Vth century. From this he concludes that the Bishop did not occupy in the counsels of his time the place assigned to him by Sulpicius, and that the effects of the apotheosis stage-managed by him were only realised after the generation which had known the real Martin had disappeared. These deductions are rather hazardous. In the history of the literature of the first centuries of Christianity there are many of these disconcerting silences. Could it be believed that Tertullian nowhere makes mention of Hippolytus of Rome nor of Clement of Alexandria, or that neither Hippolytus nor Clement of Alexandria quote Tertullian ? St Ambrose does not speak of St Jerome, nor does Athanasius mention the name of St Hilary. We could find other puzzling instances of the same kind. To be in a position to impute them to ill-will, or a voluntary indifference, we should have to possess in its integrity the literature of the period. And again, pure chance sometimes plays singular tricks.

Such as it is, the portrait of St Martin, more hagiographic in the *Life*, and more familiar in the *Dialogues*, gave keen delight to the first readers to whom it became known. In Rome people disputed for copies of it.[1] It became the model for lives of the Saints. Paulinus of Nola, Hilary of Arles

---

[1] See especially *Dial.*, I, xxiii (Halm, p. 176): "Deinde cum tota certatim urbe raperetur, exultantes librarios vidi, quod nihil ab his quaestuosius haberetur, siquidem nihil illo promptius, nihil carius venderetur."

2 B

in his *Life of St Honoratus*,[1] Uranius in his *Death of Paulinus of Nola*,[2] Possidius in his *Life of Augustine*, Paulinus of Petricordia (Périgueux) in the six books of his *Vita Martini*,[3] Gregory of Rome in his *Dialogues*, Gregory of Tours, and Fortunatus, all took their inspiration from it. Hundreds of manuscripts of the work of Sulpicius exist,[4] the fame of which has come down to modern times.

The character of the author himself is one of the most complex of the end of the IVth century. There is some enigma about Sulpicius Severus : how far did this finished man of letters, *ecclesiasticorum purissimus scriptor*, as Scaliger called him, personally credit the stories he related so well ? We can suspect a good deal of malice in him if we are to judge from the caustic terms in which he censures certain monks, and the Bishops of his time, above all.[5] He remains an interesting and original figure, even if we refuse to attribute to him all the *arrière-pensées* with which people have been pleased to complicate his personality.

[1] Migne, L, 1249–1272.

[2] *Ibid.*, LIII, 859–866.

[3] *Ibid.*, LXI, 1009–1076. C.V., XVI (1888, Petschenig). It is a panegyric in verse, written about the year 470, the three first books of which are based on the *Vita S. Martini* of Sulpicius, the two following on the *Dialogues*, and the sixth on information furnished by Perpetuus, Bishop of Tours. French translation by Corpet, 1852 (Coll. Panckoucke). Some pieces are translated in F. Clément's, *Les Poètes chrétiens*, 1857, pp. 267–281.

[4] Halm distinguishes two groups, the *Italica* (a basic manuscript, a *Veronensis* of the VIIth century) ; the *Gallica* and the *Germanica* (a basic manuscript, a Quedlinburgensis [Quedlinburg in Saxony] of the IXth century).

[5] *Vita M.*, II, xx, i ; xi ; xxvii ; *Dial.*, I, ii, 3–4 ; I, xxiv, 3 ; I, xxvi, 3, etc. ; *Chron.*, II, li, 19. Halm has not sufficiently studied the written tradition concerning Sulp. Sev. See Delehaye, art. quoted, p. 8 et s.

BOOK IV

THE BREAK UP OF THE EMPIRE

CHAPTER I

SAINT AUGUSTINE AND AUGUSTINIANISM

BIBLIOGRAPHY

THE Benedictine edition of St Augustine has quite a history (cf. Kukula, in S.B.W., 1890, 1893, 1898 ; and Ingold, *Hist. de l'éd. Bénéd. de S. Augustin*, Paris, 1903). Begun, at the suggestion of the great Arnauld, by the labours of Dom Delfau and Dom Robert Guérard, the work appeared to be imperilled on a first occasion in 1670, these two religious having been relegated to a distant abbey possibly on account of certain outspoken views on the abuses to which the *commendam* of the abbey had been put. Dom Blampin took their place and prosecuted their task with zeal. The printing was put in hand on the 5th October 1677, and the first volume appeared in the beginning of 1679. A staff of diligent workers, among whom were Dom Pierre Coustant, Dom Claude Guénié, Dom Nicolas Goyzot, and Dom Martène, pushed the work on with their best endeavours. A few slight skirmishes had already revealed that unfriendly eyes were watching the undertaking from afar. The real battle opened in 1678 with an anonymous pamphlet which purported to have been written by "one of the most important ecclesiastics in Germany," in which the Congregation of St Maur were accused of favouring the errors of Jansenius. Suspicion naturally fell upon the Jesuits, and, as a matter of fact, the letter seems to have been written by one of them, Père Langlois.

Certain members of the Episcopate already were showing some feeling in the matter. But Bossuet energetically took up the defence of the Benedictines before the king. Other anonymous libels were published. The Benedictines had decided at first to make no reply. They were soon obliged to abandon these tactics which might have turned to their prejudice. Replies and counter-replies were abundant. The most skilful plea put forth in favour of the Congregation of St Maur was that by Bernard de Montfaucon (under the signature of D. B. de Rivière). This strife, the many episodes of which it is impossible to relate here, was terminated on the 7th June 1700 in the complete victory of the Benedictines : a decree of the Holy Office condemned three of the pamphlets which had been directed against them, in particular the famous letter of the "German" ecclesiastic which had kindled the fire. Some weeks later, the General of the Congregation presented to the king the last volume of "this edition of St Augustine which had caused them so much trouble." On different occasions, 1707, 1712 and 1730, their adversaries endeavoured to revive the quarrel, but without success.

For the different editions, see TABLE VIII.

A good French biography of St Augustine is still wanting. Very attractive from its charm of style as is Louis Bertrand's *Saint Augustin* (Paris, undated), with its sequel *Les plus belles pages de Saint Augustin*, published in 1912, it is far from reproducing the complex character of the original.

The Bibliography of St Augustine is given in the *Dictionnaire de Théol.*

Cathol., vol. I (1909), 2284-2286, 2457, art. *Augustin*, by E. Portalié. The recent study by Père Batiffol, *Le Catholicisme de Saint Augustin*, 1920, is of first importance for understanding the mind of Augustine. There are many interesting views in Père Alfaric's *L'Evolution intellectuelle de Saint Augustin*, published in 1918.

Detailed studies will be mentioned in the foot-notes.

SUMMARY

I. The taking of Rome by Alaric.—II. The Soul of Augustine.—III. His Life. The Stages of his Conversion.—IV. Augustine after his Conversion.—V. Polemics: Manichaeans; Donatists; Pelagians; Arians. Exegetic Treatises.—VI. *The City of God.*—VII. The *de Catechizandis Rudibus.*—VIII. The *de Doctrina Christiana.*—IX. Correspondence.— X. Sermons.—XI. Conclusions on St Augustine.—XII. The Disputes for and against Augustinianism. Cassian. St Vincent of Lerins. Faustus of Riez. Arnobius the Younger. Marius Mercator. St Prosper of Aquitaine.—XIII. Evagrius.

I

ON the 24th August 410, Rome was taken by Alaric, defaced, and profaned,—Rome, the Mother of all civilisation, the creator of Law, the mistress of the races of the earth. It was an appalling event and produced a feeling of stupefaction. " My voice left me," wrote St Jerome, " and sobs choked my speech. The city which had conquered the whole world is herself captive. What can I say ? She perished from hunger ere perishing by the sword.[1] That famous city, head of the Roman Empire, is laid waste by fire. There is no spot which is not receiving fugitives from Rome.[2] I was desirous of setting to work to-day studying Ezechiel, but at the very moment when I began to dictate, I felt such anguish in thinking of the catastrophe in the West, that the words ceased to come to me. For long I remained silent, bethinking me well that this was a time for weeping. . . ." [3] The idea of the eternity of Rome was deeply rooted in all minds. Without denying themselves occasional mention of the blemishes which had soiled the history of the city, the Christian apologists themselves willingly accepted this idea since the close union between Church and State had been realised.

All these illusions found themselves weakened, and, while the faith of some was shaken, paganism, harassed by the laws in force against it, but always alive and sullen in many hearts, reiterated the old grievances which attributed

[1] *Ep.*, cxxvii, 12.   [2] *Ibid.*, cxxviii, 4.   [3] *Ep.*, cxxvi, 2.

all the misfortunes of the empire to the anger of the gods who had been outraged and disowned.[1] " Ah ! if sacrifices were still offered ! If they immolated on the altars of the gods as in former times, the ills under which we now suffer would not have come, or they would have been over by now ! " [2] " The body of St Peter is in Rome," people murmured, " the body of St Paul is in Rome, the body of St Laurence rests in Rome, the bodies of so many other holy martyrs find their resting-place in Rome, and Rome is destitute. . . . Where then are the *memoriae apostolorum ?* " [3] Such were the comments heard in Africa.

Under these mournful aspects the Vth century opened. And they knew not the succession of misfortunes to which Western civilisation had been handed over. Never had mankind greater need of a consoler and guide capable of raising their souls above their material and moral misery, and of bringing the virile encouragement of *Sursum corda.*

II

" From his distant Africa," wrote Mgr. Duchesne, " Augustine shed his light over the whole of Christendom. To the men of his own time he uttered profitable words. He knew how to explain their own souls to them, to console them for the cala- mities of the world, and to guide their understanding through mysteries. He was amiable to all. Fanatics were calmed down by him, the ignorant were enlightened, and thoughtful minds were sustained in the traditions. He was the instructor of the entire Middle Ages. Even now, after the inevitable attrition of so many centuries, he is still the great authority in theology. It is through him in a special manner that we have

---

[1] See the *Carmen de Providentia* (P.L., LI, 617–638), written about the year 415 in South Gaul. Translation in Poizat's *Les poètes chrétiens*, Lyons, p. 291 (reproduced in Dom Leclercq's *les Martyrs*, III [1904], p. 313).

[2] " Non enim desunt quorundam voces titillantes aures ecclesiae dicentium : O si sacrificaretur ! O si diis immolarentur solita ! Quoniam aut non venissent, aut iam finirentur ista quae patimur mala." These lines are taken from a sermon *de Tempore barbarico*, which Dom Morin, the editor of St Augustine's *Tractatus* (1917), attributes to Quodvultdeus.

[3] St Augustine, *Serm.*, ccxcvi, 6 ; cf. cxi ; cxxxvi, i ; cv, 12.

intercourse with Christian antiquity. In certain aspects he is for every age. His soul—and what a soul! passed into his writings ; in them he still lives ; on some pages he will always cause tears to fall. . . ." [1]

Theologian, philosopher, moralist, and tireless champion, it is really through his exquisite sensibility that St Augustine has remained the contemporary of successive generations. Who does not call to mind the meditations of the mother and son in the discreet household at Ostia, and the intimate tenderness of these loving hearts who for long had been separated by the " tumults of the flesh " and were reunited on the eve of the day on which Monica was to die, in order that they might dream together rapturously of eternal things without forming any other wish than to taste in heaven a joy similar to what they were then feeling (*ut talis sit sempiterna vita quale fuit hoc momentum intellegentiae cui suspiravimus*) ? [2] No convert knew how to pray like Augustine, with such humility, compunction, remorse for his *prisca flagitia*, and such astonishment that God had not damned him for his long ingratitude. He would love God alone, but he reminds himself that he had loved " the perishable beauty of the body, the brightness of the light, the soft melody of *cantilenae*, the delicious scent of the flowers, and limbs made for embracing by the flesh," [3] and out of all these sweet things purified, transfigured, and idealised, he made the mystic perfume of his love for the " Father of mercies."

Let no one be deceived however ! In that soul of burning charity, expert in discovering words of flame wherewith to address his love to God,[4] there dwelt also the formidable rigour of the dialectician. Into how many anxious hearts has not his doctrine on grace struck dismay, and the terrifying fate reserved for the greater part of the mass of lost ones (*massa perditionis*) of which humanity consisted in his eyes ! Did he not go so far as to consign to hell little children who had died before being baptised, depriving them even of that

---

[1] *Hist. anc. de l'Eglise*, III, p. viii.
[2] *Conf.*, IX, x, 25.
[3] *Ibid.*, X, vi, 8.
[4] " Unum et multa, pulchritudo, dulcedo, Deus pulcherrimus, Deus dulcissimus, odor suavitatis, interior melodia, motus cordis, affectus, passio, suspirare, accendi, flagrare, ascendere, rapi, intrare, deseri, sponsus, sponsa, amplexus, frui Deo mihi adhaerere Deo bonum est," etc. It was Augustine who created a large number of the expressions of Catholic piety.

medietas, that intermediate state which the Pelagians claimed for them ? [1]

Let me add that his interest in scholarship was moderate. From this point of view he differed profoundly from St Jerome, whom he little understood, and whose efforts in the domain of Scripture he appeared to discourage. Exegetists who wish for a broader interpretation of the Bible are disappointed not to find any support in Augustine. The perfect accuracy of the Biblical chronology,[2] the reality—historic and not symbolical—of all the events recorded, the greater weight of the account in the Bible over profane history, and a refusal of any checking by means of the latter—such were the principles of Augustine, and time was only to further strengthen them in him.

How came these inflexible theories to be firmly set in a mind formerly accustomed to so many metamorphoses ? And how could this theological rigorism be united with a foundation most richly endowed with humanity, moderation, and kindness ? It would require a very delicate psychology to unravel this. Nevertheless the history of his previous life is significant : it is in his personal experiences that we shall find the starting-point of several of the conceptions with which his name is connected.

III

WE possess three sources for the history of the life and works of St Augustine. First his biography by Possidius,[3] Bishop of Calama in Numidia, who had been his pupil and remained his friend. Written shortly after 430, this panegyric contains interesting details on the inner life of Augustine and on his last moments. Then we have the *Retractations*.[4] The Latin word *retractationes* does not convey quite the same sense as the corresponding word in French (or English). It was like a synonym for *curae secundae*, and indicated the

[1] *De peccat. meritis et remiss.*, I, xxviii, 55. He makes however one concession to pity : the *damnatio* to which these little ones are vowed will be *omnium mitissima* (*ibid.*, I, xvi, 21). Public sentiment around him protested against the rigorousness of his interpretations : *Sermo*, ccxiv, 1 et s.

[2] See, on the other hand, St Jerome's perplexities, *Ep.*, lxxii, 5, *ad Vitalem*.

[3] P.L., XXXII, 33–66. French translation in the *Œuvres de Saint Augustin* by Péronne, Ecale, Vincent, etc., Paris, 1870, vol. I, p. 1 et s.

[4] There is an important study by Harnack, S.B.B., 1905, II, 1096–1131.

work of the author in going over his writings at a distance of
time in order to bring them into line. Possidius calls this
work *de Recensione librorum;* the title is significant. He
could not otherwise make headway against the traditional
title attested by St Augustine himself. From the year 412,
Augustine was thinking of looking over his writings and
calling attention in a special work to passages which seemed
to him to be capable of improvement.[1] He did not find the
leisure to do this until much later, in 427, when he was
72 years old; he was still only able to revise his treatises,
to the exclusion of letters and sermons. The *Retractations*
are divided into two books. The first is devoted to the
treatises which Augustine had written as layman and as
priest: in it he examines 167 passages. The second deals
with his treatises written when he was a Bishop; the progress
of his thought rendered it necessary for him to retouch
52 passages. It will be noted that in his last thirty works he
raises only 13 sentences for discussion. The reason is that
his orthodoxy had become more and more scrupulous and
circumspect. This tendency shows itself on almost every
page of the *Retractations*. With absolute frankness Augustine
blames and disavows his former complaisance in regard to
profane philosophy, that of Plato especially, and of other
Christian authors of insufficient orthodoxy, such as Origen.
He corrects some of his Scriptural interpretations, and
softens down some of his statements on doctrine, for example
on the question of the soul's origin, in regard to which he
hesitates in choosing between " traducianism " and " creation-
ism." Henceforth he was determined to seek his rule of
thought in the Bible only, and not elsewhere. The *Retractations,* taken as a whole, amount to a theological *erratum,*
and form a very valuable descriptive list. Lastly, there
are the *Confessions,* so highly valued since their first appearance,[2] and which stand out as the most moving book of antiquity on the interior history of a soul.[3] St Augustine did
not utter these confidences to justify himself in the eyes of
posterity, as did Jean Jacques Rousseau, nor to compel it to
agree that no one was a better man than he. Penetrated

---

[1] *Ep.,* cxliii, 2.
[2] *De dono persever.,* xx; *Retract.,* II, vi.
[3] On the " form " *Confessions,* cf. Misch, *Gesch. der Autobiographie,* I, Berlin,
1907, and the study of this work by Paul Lejay, R.C., 1908, II, p. 313.

through and through with remorse for his sins, if he made up his mind to recall them it was because he wished the marvellous effects of divine grace to be seen in his own case. In considering from what an abyss Augustine had been rescued every sinner was to feel heartened to deserve his own redemption through his own efforts. Augustine " confesses " therefore his own falls at the same time as the glory of God. The absolute veracity of this document has been often suspected. In comparing with it his writings very nearly contemporary with the final crisis related in it, we have to ask if Augustine did not unconsciously project over his past certain dispositions of his soul which in point of time came after the phase to which they relate. Such self-deception would only be very natural. We shall see, however, if the difference in *tone* between the *Confessions* and the writings of Augustine as a catechumen are not explicable by very simple reasons, and if there is any just cause to substitute far less authorised conjectures for the testimony he brings himself concerning his moral and religious evolution.

Aurelius Augustinus was born on the 13th November 354, at Thagaste, a small town in Numidia.

In his *Confessions* he begins the history of his life at the cradle, anxious to note down the awakening of evil inclinations, even in his heart as an *infans*.[1] He attended the school at Thagaste to learn the first rudiments. His mother, Monica, a very fervent Christian—his father, Patricius, was a pagan— did her best to develop the sentiment of religion in him. Later on he was to say, " *Religionis verissima semina mihi a pueritia salubriter insita.*"[2] Nevertheless, in accordance with the custom prevailing in the IVth century, she did not have him baptised, foreseeing the temptations he would one day have to encounter and the wisdom of an amnesty thus deferred.[3] Having been sent to Madaurus, the next village, to follow his studies, he there learnt Greek ; it is not correct to allege that he forgot[4] it afterwards, but he was only in

[1] See I, vii, 11.
[2] *De duabus anim.*, i.
[3] I, xi, 18.
[4] He acknowledges in two places that he was not much of a scholar as regards Greek (*Contra litt. Petil.*, II, xxxviii, 91 ; *de Trin.*, III, i, i). Nevertheless the texts collected by H. Becker, *Augustin, Studien zu seiner geistigen Ertwicklung*, L. 1908, pp. 122–131, prove that he had picked up more than a superficial acquaintance with it.

moderate sympathy with that language from that time, as a brutal master had disgusted him with it. Mathematics likewise interested him very little. To make up for this he read with delight the *Æneid*, and his compositions in style won him many little successes.

Notwithstanding his limited means Patricius had conceived high ambitions for his son. He had in mind to send him to Carthage to finish his education. While he was getting together the necessary money, Augustine came back to Thagaste, in the summer of 369. He was then sixteen years old. These months of idleness did his morals no good. He turned into an open *mauvais sujet.* He tells us that among other exploits he and some comrades one day robbed the pears from a pear-tree—not a very serious peccadillo—for which, however, he preserved a keen remorse because he had felt for the first time his inclination to do evil for evil's sake, and to taste what was forbidden simply because it *was* forbidden.[1] Thanks to the munificence of Romanianus, a rich inhabitant of Thagaste, he was able at last to set out for Carthage, a seat of learning, but also a city of pleasure.[2] There he threw himself into pleasure with all the ardour of a passionate soul eager for a risky life, dreading nothing more than a " pathway without snares." [3] " *Nondum amabam et amare amabam. . . .*" From the day when he was loved and loved in return, there were jealous suspicions, quarrels, and all the ardour and all the misery pertaining to sensual *liaisons.* As with the emotions of the heart and the flesh, those aroused by the theatre also awoke in him a profound echo, especially when they caused him to shed tears, stirring him to the bottom.[4] Nevertheless he attended assiduously the school of rhetoric, and took no part in the turbulent proceedings of some of his comrades who had formed themselves into bands of *eversores* (smashers) who were much dreaded by quiet folk. He preserved a substratum of seriousness even in his life of dissipation, the irregularity of which moreover we must not exaggerate, since he informs us himself that he was faithful to his concubine as *to a wife.*

When he was 19 (373) he read Cicero's *Hortensius.* In this dialogue, of which we only possess fragments, Cicero

---

[1] II, iv, 9.

[3] " *Viam sine muscipulis* " (*Conf.*, III, i. i).

[2] Cf. *Contra Acad.*, II, ii, 3.

[4] III, ii.

replied to the criticisms of Hortensius against philosophy
with a magnificent eulogy of this form of intellectual activity,
more capable than any other of setting a man in the way of
real happiness, which consisted, not in deceptive material
enjoyments, but in the life of the mind. From reading this
Augustine himself dates the awakening of his desire for
" wisdom," and a kind of renewal of his sensibility : " *Ille
vero liber mutavit affectum meum. . . .*" [1] " *Surgere coeperam,
ut ad te redirem. . . .*" The call of the infinite sounded
low in his predestined heart. Here we see him started on
the road ; and through many a stage, often painful, he was
not to pause right to the end.

He set himself to study the Scriptures, for owing to the
evident influence of his early education he could not rest
satisfied with any wisdom which was absolutely stranger
to the name of Christ. But the unskilful form of the Latin
translations of the Bible soon repelled him.[2] Disappointed,
he threw them aside as incomprehensible and barbarous.

He turned to the Manichaeans, who were very numerous
in Africa.[3] The sect promised him " truth," and that promise
alone was sufficient to draw him in his then eager state of
mind.[4] It kept its hold over him for some time afterwards
by many ties which he well defined. (*a*) The Manichaeans
claimed to impose no truth on any one before that truth had
become evident to the one who was to accept it. Now,
just then, his own understanding, sharpened by his school
exercises, was very strong in Augustine, and rendered the
method of authority used among the Catholics painful to
him.[5] (*b*) The criticisms directed by the Manichaeans
against the Old Testament, and the ironical questions they
put regarding certain licences granted by God to the Patriarchs, disconcerted Augustine. Having as yet only a very
imperfect idea of the working of Revelation, he was not far
from considering their objections unanswerable.[6] (*c*) He also
acknowledges that he had some difficulty in conceiving
God as a purely spiritual Being. It seemed to him that all
that is must be corporal, in whatever rarefied and quintessen-
tial manner the word be understood. Now the Manichaeans

---

[1] III, iv, 7.   Cf. *de Vita beata*, I, iv.   [2] III, v.
[3] III, iv, 8 ; cf. III, vi, 10.   [4] *De Util. Credendi*, i.
[5] *Conf.*, III, vii.   [6] VII, vii, i.

precisely admitted nothing but matter more or less subtilised.[1]
(d) The doctrine of the Manichaeans of two co-eternal Principles—the one the principle of good, and the other of evil—
having both placed their imprint on every creature, made
clear in his eyes the problem of the origin of evil, and exonerated him from his sins before his own conscience.[2] (e)
Lastly the name of Jesus Christ, which the sect mingled with
their metaphysical conceptions, effectually reassured him
and made him in sympathy.

During nine years, from the age of 19 to 28, he was to
continue this sympathy, in spite of the grief of the pious
Monica, whom these aberrations greatly distressed.

About his twentieth year (c. 374), he had become a professor in his native town, Thagaste.[3] He continued his
liaison with the same woman who had presented him with
a son, Adeodatus. In spite of his adhesion to Manichaeism
his soul was unsatisfied, and he sought his path in books.
Curious to understand everything, astrology attracted him
for a time, but a certain Vindicianus, a man of Pro-Consular
rank, and better instructed than he in the nothingness of
that pseudo-science, half succeeded in undeceiving him.[4] Then
the death of a dear friend reduced him to such an extremity
of sorrow [5] that he determined to leave Thagaste for Carthage
where a post as rhetorician had been offered him.[6]

He remained there about eight years. It is here that he
wrote his first work, which we no longer possess, the *de
Pulchro et Apto*. He was not long in casting away his illusions
regarding Manichaeism. The fantastic conceptions of Manes
on certain questions of accurate knowledge where it was
possible to verify them personally, had always seemed strange
to him, and it astonished him that Manes represented them
as being inspired. The Manichaeans whom he continually
interrogated evaded his questions. Now there arrived at
Carthage a Manichaean Bishop named Faustus, who was
reputed by all to be eloquent and learned. Augustine
hastened to place before him his doubts. But he only could
reply with elegant phrases and ended with the simple con-

---

[1] V, x, 18.
[2] III, xi, 20 ; IV, i, i.
[3] *Conf.*, IV, iv, 7. Cf. Possidius, *Vita*, i–ii.
[4] IV, iii, 5.
[5] See his fine pages on friendship : *Conf.* IV, v, 10, to IV, viii, 13.
[6] IV, vii, 12 ; cf. *C. Acad.*, II, ii, 3.

fession that he did not understand much about those kind of things. Thereupon Augustine felt his keen ardour of hitherto sensibly cooled down.[1]

In the autumn of 383 (it seems) he left Carthage for Rome,[2] where higher appointments and more disciplined classes of students were held out to him. Although, disabused of the sect, he had kept up some acquaintance with the Manichaeans; he first lodged with an " auditor " and fell seriously ill. What proves that the idea of becoming a Christian still held only a very moderate influence over him, is that he had no wish to be baptised at this critical moment.[3] He had reached a certain scepticism which caused him to find some semblance of good sense in the doubts of the academician philosophers, in whose view man could not attain to the full understanding of any truth.[4]

He had already opened his classes in Rome and collected a certain number of students. These proved themselves to be less boisterous than those at Carthage. But Augustine discovered that it was no unusual thing for these young people, notwithstanding the engagement they had entered upon, to leave one school *en masse* and betake themselves to another. Such want of good faith displeased him, and he gladly seized the opportunity given to him, thanks to the recommendation of Symmachus, Prefect of Rome, to go to Milan in the capacity of master of rhetoric (384).

He was going to meet there the chief instrument in his definite conversion. St Ambrose was such an important personage at Milan that Augustine could not refuse to go and present himself to him. He was touched with the fatherly kindness with which the Bishop received him : " *Eum amare coepi,*" he said.[5] He was drawn to attending the sermons of the Bishop. The outer form of these allocutions attracted him from the beginning. He flattered himself that he was attentive only to the quality of his language. But the teaching of St Ambrose little by little penetrated into his mind, and forced him to reflect. Up till then he had considered certain Catholic doctrines to be untenable, and to his surprise he was beginning to find out that they were nothing of the kind. Explanations of the Sacred Books such as St Ambrose

---

[1] V, iii, 6 ; V, v, 8 ; V, iii, 2.   [2] V, viii.   [5] V, xiii, 23.
[3] V, ix, 16.   [4] V, x, 19.

was giving appeared to him to be fully satisfactory. His intellectual appreciation, freshly conceived, decided him to break definitely with Manichaeism. Monica, who had rejoined him, learnt of this breach with joy, and could not refrain from telling him that she was convinced that she would see him a faithful Catholic before she died.[1] She began to follow assiduously with her son Ambrose's pastoral instructions. Augustine would have liked well to confide himself more completely to Ambrose, but the Bishop's life was so wholly taken up that he found neither opportunity nor courage to have a thorough explanation with him.[2]

He thus remained in a state of suspense and perplexity, half won over, but fearing to deceive himself once more, and dreaming somewhat *naïvely* of obtaining " in the order of things not seen " the same certainty which made him affirm that seven and three make ten.[3] He felt however that it was a greater test of loyalty to require a belief in what was not susceptible of demonstration, as did Catholicism, than to undertake to prove everything, and then to extricate themselves by means of ridiculous fables according to the tactics of the Manichaeans. He had lost his prejudices against the Bible. In considering the problem of liberty the riddle of which pursued him, a profound instinct warned him that responsibility was not a vain word : " *Cum aliquid vellem aut nollem, non aliud quam me velle ac nolle certissimus eram et ibi esse causam peccati mei jam jamque animadvertebam.*" [4] But with these accurate intuitions there were still mingled many divagations. Also he felt himself unable to shake off the bonds to which his senses had accustomed him. Without pleasure, life did not seem to him to deserve the name, and became a kind of punishment, *non vita, sed poena.*[5] His mother thought of arranging a marriage for him. The woman with whom he was living was removed : he lost no time in taking another. He was then nearly thirty years old. Eleven years had already passed since he had felt himself inflamed with a fine ardour for wisdom. He experienced profound bitterness at finding himself still so far from the ideal which in his youthful enthusiasm he had formerly set before himself.

[1] VI, i. [2] VI, iii, 3.
[3] VI, iv, 6.   [4] VII, iii, 5.   [5] VI, xii, 22.

Meanwhile, certain Platonist books which had been translated into Latin by Victorinus the rhetorician came into his hands.[1] Augustine does not mention the titles. It is commonly thought that they referred to works by Plotinus and Porphyry.[2] He was keenly struck by the points of resemblance between the teaching he found therein and certain articles of Catholic doctrine, on the Word for instance ; he was also struck by what was wanting in them : "*Non habent illae paginae vultum pietatis hujus, lacrymas confessionis, sacrificium tuum, spiritum contribulatum, cor contritum et humiliatum. . . .*"[3] His reading of these books was the point of departure of new reflections on God, on himself, and on the true nature of the evil which is in the world, and correspondingly many metaphysical difficulties with which he had hitherto been confronted, vanished. He felt in himself a great impulse towards God, but this uplifting was still hampered by many a fall back, in which his will to become better gave way.[4] For beneath the intellectual drama whose vicissitudes were being enacted within he perceived the insidious murmur of his passions, his " old friends " which " drawing him by their garb of the flesh," [5] cunningly counted over the sacrifices to which he would have to consent if he wished to be logical with himself. Certain examples of recent conversions, that of Victorinus in particular,[6] made him ashamed of his weakness and indefinite temporising : "*Ita rodebar intus et confundebar pudore horribili vehementer. . . .*"

The decisive moment in the crisis came in July 386.[7] The scene is well known : a day of poignant struggles between the " two wills," *illa carnalis, illa spiritalis ;* an immense desire to weep ; Alypius, his special friend, present and awaiting the issue of a battle which was nearing its end before his eyes ; the solitude he had sought at the foot of a tree in a garden ; the cry of a child coming from a neighbouring

---

[1] VII, ix.

[2] Cf. *Contra Acad.*, III, xviii ; *Ep.* cxviii ; *de Vita Beata*, iv (the text from *Plotinus* is the only one to remember) ; *Cité de Dieu*, VIII, vii and xii ; Grandgeorge, *S. Augustin et le Neoplatonisme*, published 1896, p. 36 et s. ; Ch. Elsee, *Neo-platonism in relation to Christianity*, Cambridge Univ. Pres. ; P. Alfaric, *L'Evol. intell. de Saint Augustin*, 375 et s. ; 400 et s. See also Boyer, *op. cit.*

[3] VII, xxi, 27.

[4] VII, xvii, 23 : *pondus hoc, consuetudo carnalis.* . . .

[5] VIII, xi, 26.

[6] See above p. 259.

[7] VIII, xii.

2 c

house : [1] " *Tolle, lege ; tolle, lege :* take it and read " ; the Bible opened at hazard, and Augustine's eyes falling on the verse from the Epistle to the Romans wherein St Paul calls upon the faithful to renounce voluptuous pleasures and to " put on Jesus Christ " ; all the shadows dissipated and the sense of security coming to inundate his soul with sweetness. . . .

Augustine did not receive baptism until eight months later, on the 24th April 387. In the interval he retired to a property situated at Cassiciacum, not far from Milan, which his friend Verecundus the grammarian had placed at his disposal, and he stayed there till the beginning of Lent 387. He had need of mental quiet ; in addition, he was suffering from his chest. He shared this studious retreat with Monica, his mother, his brother Navigius, his son Adeodatus, and some friends among whom were Alypius and Romanianus. The *contra Academicos,* the *de Vita Beata,* and the *De Ordine* resulted from the philosophic discussions which constituted the favourite recreation of the learned and pious company with which Augustine had surrounded himself. A stenographer took them down, and the transcriptions, revised and retouched by Augustine who adapted them to a Ciceronian style, formed the matter of these " dialogues," which cannot be said to be fictitious since they more or less reproduce faithfully authentic conversations.

Critics have been astonished to find in them no traces of the moral torment which is unburdened in the last chapters of the *Confessions.* The peaceful calm of these metaphysical discourses scandalises them. Just as if on the morrow of this dearly-bought victory some kind of relaxation must not have made itself felt in the soul of Augustine, and as if in these same works whose tranquil tone amazes them one is not able here and there to mark the track left by his inner life, his devotion, and tears in secret to which his companions were in no way privy ! [2]

---

[1] *De vicina domo.* Knoll has had the maladroitness to accept the text *de divina domo,* on the authority of only one manuscript, the *Sessorianus,* of the VIIth–VIIIth century.

[2] See especially *De Ordine,* I, iii, 6 ; I, viii, 22 ; I, x, 29. He was hoping that philosophy would assist him to *understand* what he already *believed* (*C. Acad.,* III, xx, 43). In a letter to Nebridius (*Ep.* iv, 2), which should belong to this period, he expresses his surprise at his craving to reason things out at those very moments when he *felt* his faith most vividly.

A few months after his baptism, his thoughts turned to going back to Africa with his relatives. But his mother died at Ostia on the journey, in the autumn of 387. In the immense sorrow which he felt Augustine could tell himself that she had at least enjoyed in her last days the full realisation of the dream of her whole life.

IV

AT this point the narrative portion, properly speaking, of his *Confessions* comes to a halt. Augustine could have continued further the history of his life from 388 to 398, the approximate date of his writing the work. But he only wished to relate the thirteen years of vagueness and uncertainty during which he was seeking for the *truth* which he had found and cherished ever after. Certainly the development of his views was not at an end; it was to remain ceaselessly active and vibrating, with a strong tendency to eliminate all those elements not specifically Christian which he had at first fostered : from the year 386 their standpoint was fixed, and only that mattered in the eyes of Augustine. Moreover, the three last books of the *Confessions* consist of little more than mysticism and philosophy.

After a short stay in Carthage, he retired to Thagaste and remained there three years (388–391) in laborious meditation in which he associated his friends. He was considering a kind of encyclopædia of the " liberal arts "—grammar, logic, rhetoric, music, geometry, arithmetic, and philosophy (to take the place of astronomy) ; he only realised a small portion of this. He also began his polemics against the Manichaeans ; still quite close in point of time to the errors in which he had remained so long, it was from them that he wished especially to preserve men's minds. In order the better to mark his renunciation of his previous ambitions he sold his little inheritance and distributed the proceeds among the poor. In his own words, he had bid good-bye to all the hopes of the world.[1] He would have liked to establish a monastery and live there in piety, work, and friendship. His elevation to the priesthood in 391 was quite unexpected. He had gone to *Hippo Regius* in the hope of winning a soul there which seemed

[1] *Sermo,* ccclv, 2 (P.L., XXXIX, 969).

ready to offer itself to God ; he discovered that Valerius, the old Bishop, who felt a keen desire to be supported in his public preaching by an assistant priest, was opening his mind to his people at that very moment. The acclamation of all at once designated Augustine. He received the priesthood with anxious humility, requested of Valerius a leave of some months in order to make a profound study of the Scriptures which he would be obliged to teach, and then came back to set himself to his task. The Bishop made over to him a garden near the church, and half realising his own personal design, Augustine founded there a kind of community where his friends formed a group from which, on the testimony of Possidius,[1] ten Bishops were later to come. Towards the end of 395, Valerius made known his intention of conferring Episcopal ordination himself upon Augustine. The practical unanimity of the African Bishops approved his initiative, in spite of the canonical difficulty created by the 8th Canon of Nicea, which forbade duality of Bishops in the same city. Valerius died shortly afterwards. Augustine remained Bishop of Hippo until his death. He died at the age of 76 on the 28th August, 430, at the beginning of the siege of the city by Genseric, king of the Vandals.

V

DURING nearly thirty-five years he guided with pre-eminent authority the religious thought of his age, and even drew fresh ardour from the opposition he encountered. He was a polemist of prodigious resources who in the height of his debates had always present the law of charity in his heart, and was the great sower of ideas over which theology was to dispute indefinitely.

It would be a disproportionate task to examine here every one of the treatises composing his immense output of work. We must content ourselves with a rapid classification which will be followed by a more detailed examination of some of his writings of preponderating historical importance.

---

[1] Possidius does not give their names. We know at any rate Alypius who became Bishop of Thagaste in 394 ; Evodius, Bishop of Uzalum (the *de Fide contra Manichaeos* [P.L., XLII, 1139–1154] is very probably by Evodius) : see also Dom Morin, *R. Bén.*, XIII [1896], pp. 481–486, and XVIII [1901], pp. 241–256) ; Severus, Bishop of Milevis ; Profuturus, Bishop of Cirta ; Possidius himself, Bishop of Calama.

Manichaeans, Donatists, Pelagians, and Arians were the principal adversaries with whom Augustine had to measure himself.[1]

Manichaeism had spread through every part of the Roman [2] world in the IVth century. Its partisans were recruited both from the old Gnostic sects (the Marcionists in particular), and from among those who were seeking to reconcile as far as they could some sort of link between Christianity and their taste for rationalism and freedom of criticism. Of the fantastic theories of Manichaean mythology the West scarcely knew any but that of dualism : the others were carefully wrapped in mist so as not to startle people. It was this reasonable attitude which had formerly attracted Augustine's youth. The principal promoter of Manichaeism in Africa since 383 was Faustus of Milevis, a Bishop of the sect, one of the most skilful sophists but a man of very superficial learning, whom Augustine had consulted. Various Manichaean works were current in the country—the " Letter on the Foundations of Mani," a work by Adimantus, and another by Faustus himself.[3] At Hippo, Fortunatus a Manichaean priest had made many partisans. Augustine entered on the contest, as I have said, in 388 directly after his baptism. He only had to follow it up actively until about 405. His method consisted not only in written refutations, but in public addresses. A disputation begun on the 28th August 392 ended in the overthrow of Fortunatus. Another conference held on the 7th December 404, against the Manichaean priest Felix, turned out likewise a complete success for Augustine ; Felix agreed to anathematise Mani and his doctrine. Naturally anxious to probe the matter to its depths Augustine was not content to refute the theories of the sect. From these debates he drew positive conclusions in the philosophic and theological order on the relationship between knowledge and faith, on the origin and nature of evil, on free will, and on the economy of Revelation whether shown in the Old or the New Testament.[4]

[1] For the history of heresies in general, see TABLE VIII, no. 114.

[2] Cf. Em. de Stoop, *Essai sur la diffusion du Manichéisme dans l'Empire romain* (derived from the labours of the Univ. of Ghent, Fac. de Phil. et Lettres, 38 fasc. (1909)) ; Dufourcq, *Et. sur les Gesta Martyrum romains*, vol. IV, published 1910 (and my account in the *Rev. Crit.* of the 16th June, 1910, pp. 463–470) ; Prosper Alfaric, *Les Ecritures manichéennes, leur constitution, leur histoire*, 1918 ; *id.*, *L'Evolution intell. de S. Augustin*, p. 65 et s. ; 279 et s. (important).

[3] *Conf.*, V, iii ; cf. A. Bruckner, *Faustus v. Mileve*, Bâle, 1901.

[4] TABLE VIII, nos. 14, 15, 16, 18, 20, 21, 22, 30, 35, 42, 54, 55, 56, 81, 103.

In the same way, his polemics against the Donatists drew him on to define with wonderful penetration the essence of the Church, without ever losing sight of the sentiment of her vitality in this subtle investigation. The Donatists, puritanical and mischief-makers, kept up an epidemic state of discord in Africa which was tormented by this perpetual anarchy. Much more, they awakened terrible scruples in the hearts of numerous Catholics by continuing to repeat that the efficaciousness of the Sacrament depended upon the state of holiness of the minister, and that their Catholic ministers were under the grave suspicion of administering only invalid sacraments. Augustine had a formidable combination to deal with : men like Petilianus, Gaudentius, and Parmenianus were by no means opponents of a negligible quantity. Apart from his numerous polemical treatises,[1] in order to discomfit them by reaching the masses he wrote an *Alphabetical Psalm* in 287 lines, each strophe of 12 lines being followed by this refrain : "*Omnes qui gaudetis de pace, modo verum judicate.*" M. Monceaux [2] has remarked how wrong the learned writers who make a study of the origins of our versification have been to neglect this piece. A fixed number of syllables, the *caesura* always in the same place, rhythm or assonance, balanced hemistiches with two fixed accentuations — these " fundamental elements of Roman verse " discover themselves in the *Alphabetical Psalm*, from which Augustine of set purpose had excluded entirely all the prosody of tradition.[3] It was in the course of these struggles with Donatism that Augustine, who had at first favoured as wide a toleration as was possible,[4] was led to express a wish for the direct coercion of the State in certain cases, and to acknowledge that some " wholesome fear " [5] might be of advantage since in actual fact it brought back to the fold the hesitating and timorous, or prevented them from leaving it—a principle which he himself would never have applied except with his customary moderation,[6] but one in the course of centuries that was to produce formid-

---

[1] TABLE VIII, nos. 25, 47, 48, 51, 57, 64, 65, 66, 90, 91, 102. Cf. Batiffol, *op. cit.*, I, 125 et s.
[2] III, 495 et s. See also Monceaux, VII, 81 et s.
[3] *Retract.*, I, xx.
[4] *Ep.* xxiii, 7.
[5] *Ep.* xciii, 10 (P.L., XXXIII, 326) ; *Contra litt. Petil.*, II, lxxxiii.
[6] Cf. *Ep.* c and cxxxiv. See Batiffol, *op. cit.*, II, 228 and 335. See also Monceaux, VII, 215 et s.

able results which Augustine for certain would not have
advocated.

In his works written against Pelagianism,[1]—the first in
date, the *De Peccatorum Meritis*, is of the year 412,—St
Augustine has perhaps given the best expression of his inner
nature as fashioned by the experiences of his life. In the
course of those long years of uncertainty and painful interior
struggles he had tasted in very truth all the joys of a passionate
existence. Rhetoric, philosophy, dialectics, music, mathematics, poetry—none of the walks of knowledge known in
his time were strangers to him. He had felt the keen delights
of friendships and of love. The satisfaction springing from
a career in life had likewise not been denied to him. But
these pleasant things had been more than half spoiled by the
weaknesses of a will which had been too easily overcome by the
" bird-lime " of pleasure. He retained from those years a fear
of his senses, of the *inquietus ardor libidinis*, and a sure knowledge of the infirmity of the human will. He conceived
life as a long succession of temptations (*ista vita, quae tota
temptatio nominatur*),[2] and as " a forest full of ambushes and
perils." [3] To cut off the various forms of concupiscence,
both of the flesh and of the mind,[4] was the task to which he
had consecrated his efforts. We can guess what he must
have thought of the ideas of Pelagius, the British monk,[5]
and of his disciple Caelestius, on the radical soundness of
nature and the absolute power of free will.[6] They repre-

---

[1] TABLE VIII, nos. 70, 71, 77, 78, 85, 89, 98, 99, 100, 104, 108, 109, 116, 117,
118. The doctrine of Augustine on grace did not take clear shape until the year
397 (*de div. quaest. ad Simplic.*). In his *de libero Arbitrio*, he had not given to
grace its full share, and from this fact the Pelagians later on were careful to make
objections to it.

[2] *Conf.*, X, xxxii, 48.

[3] X, xxxv, 56 ; cf. 60.

[4] Cf. X, xxx et s.

[5] Pelagius was more probably a Briton than an Irishman (cf. Roger, *L'enseign
des Lettres class. d'Ausone à Alcuin*, 1905, p. 214). Gennadius devotes a short
notice to him, *de Vir. Ill.*, § xliii. Of his numerous writings we have an *Epistola
ad Demetriadem* (412 or 413) : (P.L., XXX, 15–45 and XXXIII, 1099–1120),
a *Libellus fidei* addressed to Pope Innocent 417 (P.L., XLV, 1716–1718 and XLVIII,
488–491). A. Souter has restored the original text of his *Commentarii in epistulas
S. Pauli*, London, 1907. Dom Morin attributes to him a work, *De Induratione
Cordis Pharaonis* (*R. Bén.*, XXVI, 163). On Pelagius consult Batiffol, *op. cit.*,
vol. II, p. 349 et s. ; Bruckner, *Quellen zur Gesch. d. Pelag. Streites*, S.Q. ii, 7
(1900). All we know of Caelestius are the names of certain of his works. There
is a notice of him in Gennadius, § xlv.

[6] In 1890 Caspari published at Christiania some writings of Pelagian origin
which Dom Morin attributes to the British Bishop Fastidius (*R. Bén.*, XV, 1898,
491–493). Gennadius (*De Vir. Ill.*, LVI) mentions a *De Vita Christiana* by this

sented to him a formidable psychological misinterpretation. His opposition to these enormities was so keen that it disconcerted a large number of theologians and of the faithful. We shall follow the current of ideas arising from his opposition to these theories.

His anti-Arian writings are far fewer than the preceding.[1]

It was not until 418 that Augustine was led to concern himself with Arianism in connection with an anonymous Arian sermon which had been submitted for his examination. Two years before his death he again provoked a debate in public with Maximinus, an Arian Bishop, who took up a very disloyal attitude in it.

We will only say a word here on his exegetic treatises which are, in contradistinction, very numerous.[2] It was from the Bible, the *veracissima Scriptura*, wearied as he was with the speculations over which he had delayed too long, that he asked for the solution of the riddle of man and the universe. Time caused his evolution to take the form of a fidelity becoming increasingly more strict to the letter of the sacred Books, and to a certainty of their indefectibility becoming more and more strengthened. We shall find again in his *de Doctrina Christiana* an indication of some of the principles from which he formed the substructure of his commentaries on the Old and New Testament.

Let us now fix our attention at rather greater length on some of his leading works.

VI

It would be difficult to meet with one more ample, more rich in ideas, than the *City of God*. This book which originally had only been begun to meet a " particular case," or for a polemical purpose between the years 412 and 426, was developed into a masterly synthesis of doctrine, wherein place was found for an entire history of mankind, the whole system of Christian beliefs, and all the imposing drama exhibiting

Fastidius, which is perhaps the same as that appearing in P.L., XL, 1031, and L. 383. We have a *De Damnatione Pelagii atque Caelestii Hereticorum*, by Aurelius of Carthage, written in the year 419 (P.L., XX, 1009).

[1] TABLE VIII, nos. 92, 112, 113.

[2] TABLE VIII, nos. 15, 24, 26, 28, 29, 37, 38, 39, 43, 53, 82, 83, 84, 95, 96.

before our eyes the old struggle between the " Divine City " and the " Terrestrial City," right up to the final apotheosis of the one and the swallowing up in the abyss of Gehenna of the other.

After the fall of Rome, as we know, many went about repeating the old accusation against Christianity that it had been a leaven of decadence for the City. Uneasiness was general in all classes of society. Augustine understood that this could only be dispelled by a real renewing of public mentality.[1] This was the reason of his writing the *City of God*. He worked at it for thirteen or fourteen years ; but from the beginning he had conceived its vast proportions,[2] and it was owing to his responsibilities which were too heavy [3] for him that he delayed its completion for so long.

Whoever has read the *City of God* from beginning to end will recall having felt here and there some misgivings the causes of which, on analysing them, have been fairly apparent to him. In the first place, the composition of the book is much too lax for modern tastes. Augustine had a plan : he summarised it in his *Retractations*, II, xliii, and we see him taking trouble to mark the different divisions in the *City of God* (cf. II, i ; III, i ; IV, i and ii ; VI, i ; IX, i ; XI, i ; XVIII, i ; XIX, i). But he is nowhere in a hurry to come to a head and, anxious before anything else to bring peace to men's minds, he approaches as he goes along all the questions with which he knows they were preoccupied at the time. These digressions have their interest : in the long run they become somewhat fatiguing.

What is much more disconcerting still is the apparent lack of preciseness in his notion of the " city " which is floating between heaven and earth without our being able to understand in places if we are to attribute to it a value which is purely metaphysical, or if we ought to understand it in a realistic sense.

Augustine uses the words " City of God," and " terrestrial city " right from the beginning of the work. He does not think it necessary to excuse the novelty of the expression which he would not have failed to do if he had run any risk

---

[1] His first attempt to combat this spirit is in *Ep.* cxxxviii.
[2] See the first pages of the *De Civit.*, and I, xxxv.
[3] *Retract.*, II, xliii.

of mystifying his public. We must therefore look for ante-cedents for this conception of the word " city." We find very striking ones in Plato (in *Leg.*, p. 713 A), and among the Stoics (according to Clement of Alex., *Strom.*, IV, xxvi), less pronounced in Philo, Seneca, and Plotinus. In reality it was the Bible which had familiarised Christian readers with the notion of the divine " city." At the beginning of Book XI Augustine refers expressly to Scripture ; he quotes *Psalm* LXXXVI, 3 : " Gloriosa dicta sunt de te, civitas Dei," and also *Psalms* XLVII, 2, 3, 9 ; XLV, 5 et s. The writer of the *Epistle* to the *Hebrews* alludes to the πίλις promised by God to men who believe (xi, 10, 16 ; xii, 22 ; xiii, 14). Likewise the *Apocalypse*, iii, 12 ; xxi, 2. The concept was therefore traditional. Moreover, Tyconius the Donatist, whose exegetic skill was held in high appreciation by Augus-tine, had appropriated it and had brought it out in strong relief in his *Commentary* on the Apocalypse written shortly before 380. He marks the opposition between the *civitas Dei* and the *civitas diaboli* in the following terms : " Hae duae civitates, una mundo et una desiderat servire Christo : una in hoc mundo regnum cupit tenere, et una ab hoc mundo fugere. . . . Hae utraeque ita laborant in unum, una ut habeat unde damnetur, altera ut habeat unde salvetur." Augustine was struck by this parallel and registered it in his memory. He makes use of it in his *De Catech. Rudibus*, §§ 31 and 37, in the *De Vera Religione*, § 50, in the *Enarr. in Ps.* LXI and LXIV, and in the *in Ps.* CXXXVI ; he also amply developed it in the *De Civitate Dei*, as we know.

What then was this " city " as conceived by Augustine ? Primarily the grouping, which is ever being renewed, of men who regulate their lives in accordance with the Divine Will, or upon purely worldly and almost always corrupt principles. " Quod (genus hominum) in duo genera distribuimus, unum eorum, qui secundum hominem, alterum eorum, qui secundum Deum vivunt ; *quas etiam* MYSTICE *appellamus civitates duas.* . . ." (XV, i). These two cities, considered thus in their mystical and symbolic aspect, are intermingled and con-fused together down here, " perplexae in hoc saeculo invicem-que permixtae " (I, xxxv), until their sorting out at the Last Judgment. Further, in composing his picture of each of these cities Augustine borrows numerous traits from the historical realities of the past and present. His terrestrial city was really the *societas improborum*, but it was also the State, pagan in so far as it was wanting in justice, which should be its principal mainspring, owing to the failures of its rulers. In the same way the divine city was the collectivity into which enter the souls liberated from sin by grace, the *communio electorum*, but it was also the Church Militant struggling against her enemies while awaiting the triumph reserved for her. Augustine invariably places in juxtaposition the realistic and the symbolic point of view : hence arises some confusion to anyone not alive to this.

" What an occasion and what a theme ! Rome taken, paganism imputing to the new faith this last downfall, this irreparable overthrow of all the grandeur of the past ; in its turn, Christianity throwing back these misfortunes upon the entire ancient civilisation, and to that frail city which had been vaunted as eternal opposing another city which was really eternal and could only accomplish her destiny in the bosom of God, but which was beginning already in the souls of those who believe and pray." [1] Augustine has been accused of ungraciousness in regard to Rome in the hour when this noble victim succumbed. However, he was not insensible to the magnificence of her past *rôle*. He praises her worship of honour and her love of glory—very mixed virtues doubtless, but yet worthy of drawing a divine blessing—which had made her historical greatness.[2] But all the same one feels a sense of solidarity unfolding itself in the *De Civitate Dei*. Christianity had realised, in the light of facts, that it bore within itself the principle of its own development and the guarantee of its destinies, and that— whatever useful support the power of Rome had been able to bring to it—it was henceforth strong enough to prosper without that support, or to create others. Though the City of man might topple in ruins there would still remain the fervent and luminous City of God, to which all upright wills and all pure hearts had access.

Generations of men were to nourish their thoughts and their hopes on all these similitudes.[3] I would not dare to

---

[1] Paul Janet in the *Rev. des Deux Mondes*, March 15th, 1856, p. 388.
[2] V, xv and xxi.
[3] See B. Gaffrey, *die augustinische Geschichtsanschauung im liber ad amicum des Bischofs Bonitho v. Sutri*, Langelsalza, 1918 ; E. Bernheim, *Mittelalterliche Zeitanschauungen . . .* , Tubingen, 1918.

affirm that a study of this grandiose work to-day would
make it appear equally convincing in all its parts.[1] But
the idea of co-ordinating the evolution of humanity with the
great battle between believers and unbelievers is a general
view which has as much value and more, without doubt,
than many other generalisations of the same kind. It requires a certain amount of prejudice to declare that one must
not speak of the philosophy of history in connection with the
City because divine foreknowledge " renders nugatory the
evolution of history," and that the conception of " progress "
would have been lost upon Augustine.[2]

We must also emphasise (since this is sometimes misunderstood) the features which Augustine gave to his definitions
of the pagan State, at first sight so severe and crushing. Its
formidable antagonism to the *civitas caelestis*, as represented
by him, would make one think that he wished it to come to a
miserable end. He does manage however to allow it a certain
justitia civilis ; he praises the State in its capacity of guardian
of public order, the safeguard against anarchy, and the power
that produces the incontestable benefit of peace. In addition,
faithful to the precepts of St Paul, he commends to Christians
a patient submission to established authority, whatever it
be : " pessimam etiam, si ita necesse est, flagitiosissimamque
rempublicam . . . tolerare . . . jubentur." [3] His personal
ideal is a Christian State in which true faith reigns, a pledge
for the welfare of all, wherein the Church is recognised as
the dispenser of all higher moral life, and can count upon
the secular arm in its struggles against heresy, and where the
king has no other care but to use his authority in the service
of God : " suam potestatem ad Dei cultum maxime dilatandum
majestati ejus famulam facit." [4] From this point of view the
policy of the Christian emperors already gave him wide
satisfaction, and he does not hesitate to characterise

---

[1] It would be an interesting thing to draw up a table on this matter. The
question of the sources used by Augustine have hardly been studied, except for
the first ten books, by S. Angus, in " The Sources of the first ten Books of A. *De
Civit.* D.," Princeton, 1906. The *City of God* provides considerable material in
the matter of history, political science, and theology. Cf. Schilling, *die Staatsund
Soziallehre* des hl. Augustinus, Freib. i. B., 1910, a systematised repertory of the
writings of Augustine on politics and sociology.

[2] H. Scholz, *Glaube u. Unglaube in der Weltgeschichte,* L. 1911, p. 150 et s.

[3] II, xix.

[4] V, xxiv.

his age as truly Christian.[1] But it was in the Middle Ages especially that the principles of Augustine were to exercise their most efficacious influence. Gregory VII was often to avail himself of them in his struggles with the civil powers. St Thomas of Aquinas incorporated a large number in his theory of the State. And was Charlemagne, a great reader of the *City of God*, dreaming of anything else than a Christian conqueror such as Augustine had already defined as one who " places his authority at the service of Divine Majesty in order to spread the worship of Him as widely as possible " ?

VII

THE *De Catechizandis Rudibus*, written in 400, is addressed to Deogratias, a deacon of Carthage. " On the Art of Catechising, for the use of those who are ignorant of Christian Doctrine," is the sense of this title. Deogratias had admitted to Augustine the embarrassment and discouragement he had more than once experienced in his duties as catechist, and had asked him for his advice and a system. Augustine begins with kind consolation, showing him that there is nothing exceptional in his case. That thought is always in advance of its expression was a fact well known to all who speak or write, and it required to be somewhat simple to be disturbed over translating badly into speech what one felt strongly :

> " I myself am almost always dissatisfied with what I have said. I would like to say something better ; I play with this something in my mind before trying to express it in speech. And when I perceive the inferiority of this expression I suffer because my tongue renders so imperfectly the sentiments of my heart." [2]

The essential thing was to love what one was doing ; and very usually the pleasure which one derived from the task of teacher passed on to the listeners and became the measure of the attention they would give. There was nothing that communicated itself so easily as tediousness if there be no alacrity proceeding from a cheerful teacher.

[1] *De Vera Rel.*, III, iii ; *De Cons. Evang.*, I, xxvi, 40 ; *Sermo*, cv, 6, 8 ; *Ep.* cxi, 2 ; *De Gratia Christi et de pecc. or.*, ii, 17–18, etc.
[2] § ii.

For the teaching of Holy Scripture, of the Old Testament especially, experience suggested certain principles with which it was good to inspire oneself. In the first place, not to put oneself to the pains of either relating or even summarising all the facts included therein, but to choose a few of the most wonderful and most moving, and then extract all the juice, and be satisfied with brief allusions for the rest. To inculcate in their minds the essential idea that everything in Scripture up to the coming of Christ was a figure of what had been realised in Christ and His Church. Once this truth was grasped it mattered little if the details were omitted. Also, to make the catechumens understand that the Redemption was essentially a work of love, and that human love ought to respond to divine love by passionate obedience to the divine law. To question each one as to the personal motives which were urging him to the faith in order to make him feel God better in the changes through which his own experiences were passing. Lastly not to be afraid of insisting on the promises of the Resurrection which were so much laughed at by pagans and sceptics, and upon the punishments beyond the grave, not forgetting to forewarn the simple of the scandal which the feebleness of some of those already in the Church might offer to them.

Such is the general system recommended by Augustine. But he takes pains also to foresee and study certain special cases.

First, the case of the merely educated man (*liberalibus doctrinis* excultus)[1] who reaches Christianity. It was probable that a postulant of this quality had already occupied himself for some time with matters concerning the faith. There was no need therefore to weary him with making him go over the rudiments. But it would be a good thing to enquire what books he had read and how and when his aspiration towards the faith took shape. If by chance these have been heretical works, he should enlighten him upon them by basing himself on the authority of the universal Church. Certain authors, Catholics who were dead, favoured heresy, however, in some pages of their writings : he must equally know in what points their views were incompatible with true orthodoxy.

[1] § viii.

More delicate was the case of a catechumen who was an " intellectual," a former pupil of grammarians and rhetoricians, and already initiated into all the curiosities of the mind.[1] The first step to attempt was to give him a taste for Christian humility, and to show him that it was a more serious thing to sin against good morals than against grammar. If he was successful in piercing the envelope containing his classical prejudices, in making him understand the seriousness of human life, and the greater importance of what one does than of the refinements of the intellect, a considerable step would have been made. As regards Holy Scripture, the taste for this could not be given to people of this kind except by representing it to them as a book of mystery, fruitful in deep meanings upon which the intellect must exercise itself in a broad manner. This is a significant passage which helps one to penetrate the state of mind of the lettered pagans, and explains the fondness of the Christian interpreters for allegorical exegesis.

> " One must make them see how great is the profit from these matters which are hidden beneath a veil, and for that very reason are called mysteries, and how much these obscure riddles sharpen a love for truth and dissipate the weariness and distaste inspired by any notion too easy to discover."

Lastly Augustine enlarges upon the disposition of mind in which the catechist should endeavour to place himself in order to react against moments of dryness and carelessness. He shows him how to arouse the attention of a class which has become a little sleepy and how to keep up their spirits. As a conclusion to the treatise, he gives a specimen " instruction " for the use of uneducated postulants, which is simple, direct, practical, and wonderfully adapted to the minds of common people.

VIII

WE have already marked the importance of the *De Doctrina Christiana* from the point of view of the destinies of the old learning during the preceding centuries of Christianity.[2]

---

[1] § x.   [2] Cf. p. 27.

There are certain notions developed in this work which are worth while drawing attention to again, all the more that Augustine, having completed his work three years before his death, must have given them in their final form.[1]

Augustine's object was to provide a method of interpreting the Scriptures both for the understanding of the text itself and also for giving an account of the results attained (*modus inveniendi quae intellegenda sunt et modus proferendi quae intellecta sunt*).

Of the first three books, which are of an altogether technical character, only a few features need be specified here. In chapter x of book II, Augustine recommends the Christian exegetist to learn Greek and Hebrew for cases where the Latin translations appeared obscure or doubtful. He was ignorant of Hebrew himself ; [2] we remember that he had not supported St Jerome when the latter made his vigorous attempt at *Hebraica veritas*.[3] Some change had thus come over his sincere mind ; he no longer limited the investigations of the exegetist to the Latin translations, nor even to the *Septuagint* —which, nevertheless, still remained in his eyes the privileged version.[4]

In chapter xv of book II we find the famous passage on the *Itala*, which has been the cause of so much vexatious confusion. St Augustine mentions the multiplicity of Latin versions of the Bible, some very servile, others rather more free, which latter he prefers. There was one to which he assigns the palm, the *Itala*, in which clearness was united to a scrupulous fidelity : " Among the translations we must place the *Itala* above all others for it comes closest to the words, and the idea stands out clear in it : *In ipsis autem interpretationibus Itala ceteris praeferatur ; nam est verborum tenacior cum perspicuitate sententiae.*"

[1] The original text, which was abandoned by Augustine in 397, went as far as chapter iii, xxxvii, of the complete work finished in 427. "Cum imperfectos (libros) comperissem," Augustine explains (*Retr.*, II, iv, i), " perficere malui quam eis relictis ad alia retractanda transire. Complevi ergo tertium. . . . Addidi etiam novissimum librum et quatuor libris opus illud implevi." To attempt to restore the first edition, as Dom de Bruyne has done, who supposes that Augustine remodelled the work from cover to cover in 427 (*R. Bén.*, 1913, p. 301 et s.), is an undertaking which seems to be rather chimerical (cf. Cavallera, B.L.E., 1915–6, p. 420 et s.).

[2] *De doct. chr.*, II, xvi, 23 ; cf. *Conf.*, XI, iii, 5.

[3] See above, p. 357.

[4] *Ep.* lxxi ; lxxxii ; *Enarr. in ps.* 87, 10 ; *de Civit. Dei*, XVIII, xlii–xliv.

What exactly was this Itala ? Many different answers
have been given. To Ronsch, the *Itala* was . . . the *Afra*,
a version of African origin ! Other modern critics, F. C.
Burkitt, for instance (*The Old Latin and the Itala*, in *Texts
and Studies*, IV, 3), and, more recently still, Dom de Bruyne
(*Rev. Bénéd.*, XXX [1913], pp. 294–314), have wished to
identify the *Itala* with St Jerome's version. In the VIIth
century this was already the interpretation of Isidore of
Seville (*Etym.*, VI, iv). This gives rise to such great difficulties that it must be rejected deliberately.[1]

The *Itala*, as its name indicates, could be no other than
a version accustomed to be used in the " diocese " of Italy,
which at the time of Augustine included Verona, Aquileia,
Brescia, Ravenna and Milan.[2] From the moment that
Augustine put it forward against the other translations
which were current in large numbers (" *Latinorum interpretum
infinita varietas*," he wrote in the *De Doctr. Chr.*, II, xvi),
it is altogether unreasonable to attribute this name to the
Latin translations anterior to St Jerome taken in bulk, and
it is an erroneous assignment which must at last be given up.[3]

In interpreting the Scriptures, all the resources of profane
knowledge, with the exception of those confined to superstition, would not be superfluous. Nevertheless Augustine
is careful to mark that the Bible to a certain degree surpassed
all other books : " Nam quidquid homo extra didicerit,
si noxium est, ibi damnatur ; si utile est, ibi invenitur." [4]

In book III he indicates with much minuteness the different
ways of solving the difficulties which result from the letter
of the Scriptures, or from the apparent sense of certain
passages which are disconcerting as regards morality. Allegorical exegesis should render good service [5] in the last case.

---

[1] See Cavallera, in B.L.E., 1915–6, p. 416 et s., and W. Ruting, *Unters. uber
Augustins Quaestiones u. Locutiones in Heptateuchum*, Paderborn, 1916, pp. 360–366.

[2] The adjective *Italus* is a poetic use. But the prose writers of the imperial
age employed it fairly frequently instead of *Italicus* (e.g. Pliny, *Hist. Nat.*, III,
liv ; Arnob. *Adv. Nat.*, II, lxxiii ; St Augustine, *City of God*, III, xxvi, etc.).
Cf. Sittl, in A.L.L., XI (1900), p. 124 ; Wölfflin, in S.B.M., 1893, I, p. 256.

[3] The Commission of the *Thesaurus Linguae Latinae* of Berlin has incorporated
it in its system of reference. Wölfflin nevertheless in 1893 drew attention to the
inconveniences it presented (S.B.M., 1893, I, p. 273). The two books *De Vocatione
Omnium Gentium* (P.L., XVII, 1073, and LI, 647) have likewise wrongly been
attributed to Prosper. The author is unknown.

[4] II, xlii.

[5] III, xxii.

2 D

No interpretation which set forth the *caritas Dei et proximi* could be altogether erroneous.[1] He counsels the use of the seven rules of Tyconius the Donatist which were excellent notwithstanding the partial heterodoxy of their author.[2]

Book IV is very important from the point of view of the literary ideas of St Augustine.[3] He recommends the Christian professor to study rhetoric. When any technique of eloquent phraseology was encountered it should be assimilated, lest a bad service be done to the interests of truth by excluding it with less skill than that shown in the passage it was intended to combat. To instruct, to please, to touch, were, in the opinion of Augustine as of Cicero, the ends of eloquence. But it was only in St Paul and the prophets that he sought for his examples. According to him, Scripture offers specimens of every variety of style. It was lawful to follow the models presented in it, or those put forward by the best Christian writers, such as St Cyprian or St Ambrose. But the rule governing all presentation of the truths of faith was clearness; the susceptibilities of good language must not prevail against that fundamental law. If one spoke, it was in order to be understood.[4]

IX

Of the 276 letters of St Augustine[5] which we possess 53 have reference to his correspondents. This series is spread over forty years (from 386–7 to 429) : it therefore only reflects in a very incomplete manner Augustine's immense activity as a letter writer.

His letters do not possess the literary and brilliant turn of those of St Jerome. There are no animated scenes, and no

---

[1] I, xl.

[2] III, xxx et s.

[3] There are some views in Zurek, *Diss. philol. Vindobonenses*, VIII (1905), pp. 69–109. Hendrickson's article in the *Amer. Journ. of philol.*, 1905, p. 276 et s., treats of little more than the differences of style in Augustine.

[4] *De Doctr. Chr.*, IV, x, 24.

[5] 270 were collected and classified by the Benedictines; 2 letters and a fragment have been discovered since the Benedictine edition, and figure in Migne (XXXIII, 751 ; 789–792 ; 929–938) ; 2 letters published by Goldbacher (C.V., XXXIV, 2, p. 444 and XLIII, p. 648), following manuscript 3479 in Cambridge University ; 1 letter published by Dom Morin in R. Bén., XVIII (1901), pp. 241–256, from the *Monacensis* Clm 8107, IXth century. Goldbacher also gives in vol. LVII of the C.V., p. 44, an unpublished fragment of four lines of a letter to Bonifatius, from the *Codex Augiensis* XCV, Xth century. The letters of Augustine are in P.L., XXXIII, and in C.V., vol. XXIV, XXXIV and LVII.

biting satires. He only very rarely betrays himself or becomes expansive.[1] Sometimes we meet with a slight trace of malice, but he very soon recovers himself, being entirely taken up with his purpose and bent solely on the demonstration he wishes to give.

They are of varying length. Some are compressed into short notes. Others take the form of veritable treatises which can only be classed as letters from the fact of the names which appear at the beginning and end : for instance *Ep.* clxxxv to Count Boniface, which St Augustine in his *Retractations* himself entitles " *liber de correctione Donatistarum.*" [2] Letter ccxiii is still further removed ; it is a stenographic report of a meeting held in the Church of Peace at Hippo on the 26th September 426, at which Augustine obtained the assent of his flock to the priest Heraclius being his successor in the Episcopal chair of that city.

From the point of view of the history of religion, and even that of civilisation, this collection is of first importance. Year by year we feel the *prestige* of Augustine growing. He is the revered *Pope* to whom the eyes of Western Christendom were turned, and to whom the Emperors themselves judged it indispensable to address a copy of the official letters which they sent to the Primate of Carthage. He was consulted on every side, and these enquiries, even on the most delicate [3] and sometimes preposterous matters,[4] brought forth replies full of forbearance. He gives comfort and advice with eagerness and inexhaustible kindness, and is as ready to provide a community of religious women with a detailed rule of life,[5] as to treat of the great questions of grace, free will, or the lawfulness of a career as a soldier.

X

St Augustine was not accustomed to write out beforehand the sermons he was to deliver, except on rare occasions.[6]

---

[1] *e.g.* at the beginning of *Ep.* cclxi.
[2] Likewise the letters mentioned in Table VIII.
[3] Cf. *Ep.* cclxii : the wisdom of his directions in the case of a private quarrel between husband and wife will be noted.
[4] Cf. *Ep.* ccv, in which we see Consentius enquiring of him " utrum nunc corpus Domini ossa et sanguinem habeat, aut reliqua carnis lineamenta."
[5] *Ep.* ccxi.
[6] Cf. *de Trin.*, XV, xxvii, 48 ; *Retract.*, II, xxxii, 2.

He would not have had the time to do that. He contented himself with a preliminary meditation bearing principally on the texts from Scripture which he intended were to form their structure. If we are to believe his biographer Possidius he sometimes even abruptly changed his subject under the pressure of some unexpected circumstance. Stenographers,[1] sometimes the faithful themselves, took down his words.[2] This is how a certain number of them have survived. Victor of Vita informs us that this ran away with much of his time.[3] Among the sermons to which Possidius, Cassiodorus and others, allude, there are some which do not figure in our very incomplete collection. To make up for this, many were fraudulently written under Augustine's name. The task of modern editors has been to separate the genuine from the false. Unfortunately the valuable revision represented by the *Retractations* is wanting in his sermons and letters.[4]

The interest offered by these sermons is very unequal. Many are made up merely of paraphrases of verses from the Bible over which the attention of the most zealous reader wavers a little. The interest revives upon seeing Augustine unfolding not only the strength of his deep faith, but also the candour of his humility, in order to reach the inner feelings of his hearers which was the source of his invigorating power. Far from placing himself above the heads of those he was instructing in doctrine, he acknowledges himself to be as weak as they, and includes himself in the rebukes he delivers to them. The language in which he speaks to them is curiously composite. The methods of rhetoric betray themselves on more than one page; there are alliterations, metaphors, plays upon

---

[1] *In Ps.* li, 1 (P.L., XXXVI, 600).
[2] Possidius, § vii.
[3] *Hist. Persec.*, I, iii, ii.
[4] The Benedictines have distinguished 363 authentic sermons, 31 doubtful, and 317 apocryphal. They divide the sermons into four classes—*sermones de Scripturis* (1–183); *s. de tempore* (*i.e.* Feasts of the Liturgical year, 184–272); *s. de sanctis* (273–340); *s. de diversis* (341–363). The oldest sermon we possess is no. 214, of the year 391; the latest, sermon 345, after the year 428 (cf. P.L., vol. XXXVIII–XXXIX). Since the Benedictine edition, other sermons have been published by Michel Denis (P.L., XLVI, 813–940); Fontani (XLVII, 1113–1140); Frangipane (XLVI, 939–10004). Dom Morin has discovered in a manuscript of the IXth century, now at Wolfenbüttel (no. 4096), a collection of homilies, forty-one of which are not yet published. He attributes thirty-three of these to St Augustine (*S. Aurelii Augustini tractatus sive sermones . . . edidit G. Morin*, Campoduni and Monaci, 1917). This collection must have been made in the time of Cæsarius of Arles. Dom Morin had published previously two other authentic sermons (R. Bén., VII, 260; 592; VIII, 417; cf. IX, 173).

words,[1] etc.; but he approaches closely turns of phrase which are in distinctly popular language wherein we see certain marks similar to those in use in languages of Latin origin : *Nunquam fecit tale frigus* (never before was it so cold) ; *metuo ne ibi vos habeam fatigatos ; multa habemus dicere vobis*,[2] etc. He wrote in his *de Doctrina Christiana* (IV, x) : " More often than not, to speak in popular language (*loquendi consuetudo vulgaris*) is more useful for expressing things than the correctness of language of lettered men." There should be much material in the sermons for reconstructing life in Africa at the beginning of the Vth century, the survivals of paganism, the relations between the pagans and Christians, as well as the frenzy for public shows and the sensual ardour of those races upon whom Augustine essayed unweariedly to impose the law of Christianity, with its refinements and austerities.

XI

Noverim me, noverim te (*Solil.*, II, i) : to know God, and to know the human soul formed the twofold object towards which the mind of Augustine was drawn with an ever fresh impetus. He was the most philosophic of the Fathers of the Primitive Church. We will say more : among the Latin Fathers he is the only one who really possessed speculative genius and the gifts of a close thinker. He embodied some of the purest sources of the old philosophy, especially those of Platonism ; but he searched into them with a gaze that was too *clairvoyant* not to enrich with his own personal contribution their lofty lessons which he made his own.

Moreover, his philosophy did not pride itself on any independence. He made his submission resolutely to the faith and to the Church. Augustine accepted whole-heartedly the authority of Catholicism, and all his dialectic efforts were used only to justify it in a rational manner, and to make it understood by those who had not yet felt its benefits. The Bible and the Church were for him the very foundations of truth, and every construction not based upon them seemed in his eyes destined to ruin. Notwithstanding, he appreciated

---

[1] " Distulit *securim*, dedit *securitatem* (72, 2). *Perpetua et Felicitas*, coronis martyrii decoratae, *perpetua felicitate* floruerunt," etc.

[2] S. 25, 3 ; 37, 17 ; 215, 9.

learning, and was less distrustful of it than a St Hilary or a St Ambrose ; he would not subject his faith to it, but his mentality in deciphering its riddles, and his life.

Minds inclined to be critical find more satisfaction in the works of St Jerome than in his. His very humility sometimes rendered him credulous, and Manichaeism had made the minutiæ of exegesis excessively distasteful to him. The vigorous mind of Jerome had more defensive power than Augustine's and greater resistance to what was unacceptable. But what detachment from self was in Augustine, what true modesty in face of the admiration which his contemporaries were not sparing in showing him, what passionate flights, what ardent meditations ! He was all charity and all love.

In a letter to St Bernard, Peter the Venerable calls him *maximus post apostolos ecclesiarum instructor*. Not that certain of his teachings did not provoke, as we shall see, bitter opposition. But his thoughts have become as it were the substance of Christian literature ; they have been present in the thick of all the battles of the spirit during the centuries past.

XII

THE thesis of Augustine on human free will and predestination—that harsh doctrine which consigned to Hell the greater part of the human race, the real " leaven of iniquity," with the exception of a privileged few to whom God had vouchsafed the wholly gratuitous gift of His grace—aroused keen opposition in several quarters of the Christian world. Eighteen Bishops in Italy and Sicily preferred to resign their Episcopal sees rather than subscribe to the condemnation of Pelagius and Caelestius formulated in the *Tractoria* of Pope Zosimus. The most irreconcilable of them was Julian of Eclana, a polemist formidable from the force of his logic and the clearness of his language.[1] Deposed and in exile, Julian waged strife with Augustine who during twelve years found himself obliged

---

[1] Cf. A. Bruckner, *Julian von Eclanum*, in T.U., XV, 3 (1897) *id., die vier Bucher Julians von Ecl. an Turbantius*, B. 1910 ; Batiffol, *op. cit.*, II, 490 ; Dom Morin, R. Bén., 1913, pp. 1–24, wished to restore to Julian the commentary by the Pseudo-Rufinus on the Prophets Osee, Joel, and Amos (P.L., XXI, 959–1104), and that this commentary be re-edited from the *Parisinus* 12148. Alb. Vaccari attributes to him a commentary on Job, published in 1897 in the *Spic. Casinense* under the name of the priest Philippus (*Un commento a Giobbe di Giuliano di Eclana*, Rome, 1915). There is a notice of Julian in Gennadius, *de Vir. Ill.*, xlvi.

to sustain his attacks and reply to them. It is only from numerous and long quotations copied out by Augustine that we are able to form any idea of the *Four Books to Turbantius* and the *Eight Books to Florus*, in which Julian combated his views. The ideas of Pelagius had also found some favour in Britain. Many Bishops were advocating them there, and their moral integrity brought much support to the doctrine they defended. In order to refute them Pope Celestine was obliged to send Bishop Germanus of Auxerre, who crossed over the English Channel accompanied by St Lupus, Bishop of Troyes.[1] In spite of the thoroughness of the efforts of Germanus, who soon became a legendary figure among the Britons, the concepts of Pelagius lasted on for a long time still in the land of his birth.

But it was especially in southern Gaul that opposition to him was organised and vigorous.[2] At Marseilles, John Cassian (c. 360–435) openly took part against Augustine. His influence was great. Born in Scythia,[3] if we may give credence to Gennadius, and brought up in a monastery at Bethlehem, he had lived for ten years with the monks of the Egyptian Delta and Desert of Nitria. Ordained deacon at Constantinople in 404 by St John Chrysostom, next a priest in Rome, Cassian founded about the year 415 two monasteries at Marseilles, one for men and the other for women. His twelve books *de Institutis coenobiorum et de octo principalium vitiorum remedio*,[4] finished in the year 426, give in detail, with numerous examples, the stern rules of the monasteries in Palestine and Egypt, and the moral tribulations to which the monks were specially subjected (among these eight *vitia*,

---

[1] A letter from Lupus to Talasius of Angers appears in P.L., LVIII, 66.

[2] In addition to the names we are about to mention, we must bear in mind those of various Gaulish ecclesiastical writers, such as Petrus Chrysologus, Bishop of Ravenna, 433–450 (his sermons, many of which are not authentic, are in P.L., LII, 183 and 665); Valerianus, Abbot of Lérins, and Bishop of Cemele (homilies and a letter are in P.L., LII, 691–758); Bishop Maximus (a letter to Theophilus of Alexandria; cf. Dom Morin, R. Bén., XI [1894], p. 274); Leontius of Arles (a letter to Pope Hilary, written in 462, in P.L., LVIII, 22–23); Ruricius of Limoges (82 letters in two books: P.L., LVIII, 67–124, C.V., XXI, p. 348 et s. [1891, Engelbrecht], and M.G.H., VIII [1887, Krusch]).

[3] *De Vir. Ill.*, lxii. According to Merkle, this should refer to the Dobroudja, cf. T.Q., 1900, pp. 419–441. See the discussion by Petschenig in C.V., vol. XVII, p. iiii, who thinks that he was a native of Provence. There is no doubt that Gennadius intended a Latin town in Scythia, which presents nothing extraordinary.

[4] Migne (who reproduces the edition of Gazet, Douai, 1616), XLIX, 53–476; C.V., vol. XVII (1888, Petschenig). French translation by Saligny, published 1663, Lyons, 1685. Study by Paucker on the Latinity of Cassian in the *Romanische Forschungen*, II (1886), pp. 391–448.

he mentions " sadness ") together with the means of healing them. His twenty-four *Collationes* (c. 429),[1] in three parts (i–x ; xi–xvii ; xviii–xxiv) and each preceded by a preface,[2] initiate the Christian public into the spiritual life of the monks. These two works formed a kind of code of monachism.[3] They were translated into Greek,[4] a privilege the exceptional character of which I have already mentioned. Lastly the *de Incarnatione Domini contra Nestorium* in seven books written in 430 by request of the future Pope Leo, give evidence of the zeal of Cassian for orthodoxy.[5] Now this stern writer, holding profane [6] learning in little favour, steeped in asceticism and austere studies, and a man whose influence was great with the most pious minds in Gaul, distinctly attributed the initiative to good to the human will in his thirteenth *Collatio* (§ viii, ix, xi), divine grace coming afterwards to add an *incrementum.*

The solitaries of the Isle of Lérins (to-day St Honorat) on the south-east coast of France were hardly more favourable to Augustine's views. Founded by St Honoratus, afterwards Metropolitan of Arles (426), in the first years of the Vth century, the Monastery of Lérins had become one of the centres of Catholic theology in Gaul, and a nursery of Bishops for that country.[7] In his *de Laude Eremi* [8] St Eucherius, the

---

[1] The *collatio* was an exercise much in vogue amongst the monks. They made known their personal difficulties, and those in the intellectual and moral order, to their Abbot, who suggested a solution for them. This custom was already enjoined in the rule of St Pachomius for the East, and in the XIIth century it was still in existence in the West.

[2] P.L., XLIX, 477–1328 ; C.V., vol. XIII (1886, Petschenig). French translation by Saligny, P. 1667, Lyons, 1687 (excluding the thirteenth *Collatio*).

[3] Herwegen, *Beitr. zur Gesch. d. alten Mönchtums*, Munster i. W. 1912 (an analysis of Cassian's rules).

[4] On the testimony of Photius, *Bibl.* 197. A *résumé* in Greek of the *de Instit. Coen.* may be found in the *Patr. grecque*, XXVIII, 849 et s. under the wrong title of *Epist. ad Castorem.* K. J. Dyovouniotis published in 1913 from *Cod.* 593 in a Meteorite monastery, *Collationes*, i, ii, vii, viii, in Greek. Cf. *R. Bén.*, 1913, 477, on the Greek translations of certain of Cassian's works.

[5] P.L., L, 9–272 ; C.V., vol. XVII.

[6] Cf. *Coll.*, XIV, xii et s.

[7] Cf. Cooper-Marsdin, *The History of the Islands of the Lérins*, Cambridge Univ. Press, 1914.

[8] § xlii. St Eucherius wrote various works destined to spread the taste for monastic life and to facilitate the understanding of the Bible : cf. P.L., L. vol. XXXI of the *Corpus* of Vienna (1894, Wotke) includes the *Formulae spiritalis intellegentiae*, the *Instructionum libri duo*, the *Passio Agaunensium martyrum*, the *Epistula de Laude heremi ;* also different letters addressed to Eucherius by Salvianus, Hilary and Rusticus. French translation by Gregory and Collombet (together with Vincent of Lérins), published 1834. Salonius and Veranius, the two sons of Eucherius, were Bishops like their father ; we owe to the former a few writings of mystical exegesis (P.L., LIII, 967–1012).

future Bishop of Lyons, who had joined the community in 410, extolled the charm of the setting chosen by Honoratus : " Watered by health-giving springs, rich in verdure, spangled with flowers, full of the charm of fragrance and sweet sights, my dear Lérins presents to those who enjoy her an image of that paradise which they should possess."

From Lérins came the famous *Commonitorium*,[1] written in 434 [2] by that enigma " Vincent of Lérins." [3] Few works of Christian antiquity have had such striking attention as the *Commonitorium*, I mean in modern times.[4] Not that Vincent gives evidence of much individual originality as regards the fundamentals of his doctrine.[5] We can discern in the *Commonitorium* many echoes of Tertullian's *de Praescriptione*, and it is equally certain that Vincent derived much profit from his reading of St Augustine's writings, in spite of certain hostile *arrière-pensées*. But he has the merit of having meditated on the ideas of his predecessors and of having enclosed them in clear, striking, and decisive formulæ, which seem to have imposed themselves in some cases upon posterity. We know his famous criterion, so often invoked, so seldom applicable, and which the Church has never made her own except under reserve : [6]

> " In the Catholic Church we must carefully adhere to what has been believed everywhere, always, and by all (*quod ubique, quod semper, quod ab omnibus creditum est*). For that is what is truly and properly ' Catholic,' as is shown by the meaning and etymology of the word itself, which comprehends the universality of things." [7]

To make up for this, his theory of progressive doctrine [8]— operating through organic growth and not by the addition of elements which were originally foreign to it, and consisting

---

[1] *Commonitorium* properly means "notes consigned to writing to aid the memory" (Baluze). Cf. F. Brunetière and P. de Labriolle, *St Vincent of Lérins*, Paris, 1906 (French translation with detailed introduction), and Koch, in T.U., XXXI, 2 (1907). P.L., L, 637–686 (which reproduces Baluze). Special editions by Jülicher, in S.Q., 1895, and Rauschen, in F.P., 1906.

[2] We gather the date from § xxix, 7.

[3] We owe the little we know of him to Gennadius, *de Vir. Ill.*, § lxv.

[4] More than 150 editions and translations can be counted since the XVIth century.

[5] Cf. Brunetière and P. de Labriolle, p. lxiv et s.

[6] *Ibid.*, p. lxxxv et s.

[7] *Common.*, ii, 6.

[8] xxiii.

in disengaging and placing in their own proper light the truths
implicit in the *depositum fidei* and not yet perceived—has
become the *quasi*-official doctrine of the Church.[1] Vossius [2]
was the first to suspect that this work of St Vincent of Lérins
might well have formed a portion of the semi-Pelagian
dossier. What Vincent says in chapter xxvi, 8, of this
sect which held out to its adherents " a special and strictly
personal grace " which people received " without labour,
without effort, without giving oneself any trouble, and without
even asking, or seeking, or knocking at the door for it," [3]
is very congruous, according to Tillemont himself,[4] " to
the unfavourable meaning which the semi-Pelagians gave
to the doctrine of grace, in order to discredit it in the minds of
people." Other indications suggest the same conclusion.
Without doubt it would be an altogether exaggerated view
to uphold (as some have done) that the *Commonitorium* as
a whole is fundamentally only a polemical treatise against St
Augustine. Vincent of Lérins had an intention which was
much more general : he wished to place in the hands of the
Church a weapon which might serve for all time against
heretics. But it is also strongly probable that he had in his
mind the illustrious Doctor of Hippo on more than one
page, and that Augustine's personal point of view remained,
in short, *privata opiniuncula* (xxviii, 8), and was not capable
of prevailing against the old unanimous view of the Church.

In the year 433, Faustus, the future Bishop of Reji (Riez,
in Provence), was appointed Abbot of the Monastery of Lérins.
In his *de Gratia libri duo*, written against the priest Lucidus,
a partisan of predestination, Faustus adhered to the views of
Cassian in his essentials. Moreover the decree of the pseudo-
Gelasius included this work, together with all the writings
of Cassian himself, among the *apocrypha*. A prolific writer,
Faustus in the words of Gennadius had the reputation of
" an eminent Doctor," [5] and we possess a fairly large number

---

[1] Whatever may have been said, Newman did not have a very different conception of the development of doctrine : cf. *Critical and Historical Essays*, London,
1871, vol. I, p. 287.
[2] *Hist. de controversiis quas Pelagius ejusque reliquiae moverunt*, Leyden, 1618,
l. I, § 9.
[3] " Etiamsi nec petant, nec quaerant, nec pulsent." Cf. St Augustine, *de
Dono Persev.*, xxiii, 64 : " Adtentant ergo quomodo falluntur, qui putant esse
a nobis, non dari nobis, ut petamus, quaeramus, pulsemus."
[4] *Mém.* . . . , XV, 860–1.
[5] " Viva voce egregius doctor et creditur et probatur." (*De Vir. Ill.*, lxxxvi.)

of his writings. The assignment of certain of them to him is open to discussion.[1]

Arnobius the Younger, who was thus named in order to distinguish him from Arnobius the rhetorician, the master of Lactantius, has attracted the attention of critics during recent years. It is impossible to gather any explicit account of him from the writings of antiquity. He appears to have given himself out as a monk.[2] There is no decisive reason to suppose he was a Gaul.[3] In any case, he lived in Rome, or was in very close relations with people in Rome about the year 450. We have some *Commentarii in Psalmos* [4] of his, in which he too combats the views of St Augustine upon grace. Possibly he is the author of the *Expositiunculae in Evangelium*,[5] short notes of no great significance, and of the *Conflictus Arnobii Catholici cum Serapione Aegyptio*,[6] directed against Monophysitism. Dom Morin attributes to him in addition a curious *Libellus ad Gregoriam* which Isidore of Seville ascribed to St John Chrysostom : [7] the work is addressed to Gregoria, a Roman lady, who lived in the imperial palace on the Palatine, and found herself in disagreement with her husband ; the author points out to her the virtuous diplomacy which will again insure happiness in her household.[8]

Dom Morin likewise restores to Arnobius the Younger the treatise in three books known by the name of *Praedestinatus*,[9] which was discovered by J. Sirmond the Jesuit in a manuscript of Rheims Cathedral, and published by him in 1643.

---

[1] Texts in P.L., LVIII. The *Corpus scrip. eccl. lat.*, vol. XXI (1891, Engelbrecht) includes the *de Gratia*, the *de Sp. Sancto*, twelve *Epistulae*, of which two are addressed to Faustus, and thirty-one *sermones*. Others yet to appear are the sermons edited by Gagny, 1547 ; the *Tractatus* edited by Pierre Pithou, 1586 ; the *Tractatus de Symbolo*, edited by Caspari (*Alte u. neue Quellen zur Gesch. d. Taufsymbols*, Christiania, 1879, p. 250). The authenticity of certain sermons has been discussed (cf. Dom Morin, R. Bén., IX, 49 ; X, 62), and of a letter (*ibid.*, VIII, 97), and the identification of the *Adversus Arianos et Macedonianos* mentioned by Gennadius (cf. Dom Cabrol, R.Q.H., XLVII, 232). The letters of Faustus appear also in M.G.H., VIII. French translation of the letter to Lucidus, in *l'Histoire de Boèce*, by Gervaise, 1715.

[2] Comm. in Ps., P.L., LIII, 486 and 552.

[3] Cf. Dom Morin, *Etudes, Textes, Découvertes*, I, p. 341.

[4] Migne, LIII, 327–570.

[5] LIII, 569–580, published completely for the first time by Dom Morin, *Anecd. Mareds.*, III, 129–151 (cf. R. Bén., XX [1903], pp. 64–76).

[6] LIII, 239–322.

[7] De Vir. Ill., xix.

[8] Critical text published for the first time by Dom Morin, *Etudes, Textes, Découv.*, I, pp. 383–439.

[9] P.L., LIII, 587–672.

The purpose of the *Praedestinatus* was to attack the doctrine of predestination in a roundabout and circumspect form and with every kind of effusive respect for St Augustine.   In the first book the author, careful to vouch for his own personal orthodoxy, ushers in his exposure of the " heresy " of predestination by drawing up a list of heresies teeming with involuntary carelessness, wilful misrepresentation, facts very like the latter, and falsehoods.[1] The second book offers a defence of the said heresy, which is refuted in the third. Dom Morin, basing himself on parallelisms of expression and thought, supposes[2] that the preface, the first, and the third book, are the work of one and the same author, and that this author is no other than Arnobius the Younger.

Whatever value we should attach to the resemblances indicated by Dom Morin, a grave difficulty makes us hesitate to ascribe to Arnobius the responsibility for the whole of these writings, which Dom Morin is disposed to swell still further. How could the convinced semi-Pelagian who betrays himself in the *Commentarii* and in the *Praedestinatus*, finally subscribe in the *Conflictus* to the Augustinian thesis ? Dom Morin supposes that Arnobius had thrown off the ideas of Pelagius " as the increasingly clear action of the authority of Rome, which did not take a light view of questions such as these, made him see his opportunity."   If such an evolution was really produced in the mind of Arnobius, the case of this monk toning down from motives of prudence and discipline the *odium theologicum* which he had at first shed forth so bitterly, would be an interesting one.[3]

Some of the most convinced admirers of St Augustine hesitated to follow him on the question of grace. Such, on the testimony of St Prosper, was the state of mind of Hilary,[4] the Bishop of Arles, " a man of great authority and much addicted to spiritual studies," who expressly

---

[1] See my *Sources de l'Hist. du Montanisme*, pp. cxiv–cxxvii.

[2] *Etudes*, etc., p. 315 et s.

[3] The most complete work upon Arnobius is Dom Morin's, *Etudes, Textes*, etc., pp. 309–382. See also H. Kayser's, *die Schriften des Arnobius Junior*, *dogmengesch. u. litt. unters.*, Gutersloh, 1912 ; J. Scharnagl, *Zur Textesgestaltung des Arnobianischen Conflictus*, in *Wiener* Studien, 1916, 2, pp. 382–384.

[4] *Ep.* ccxxv, 9, ad Augustinum. Cf. the notice of Gennadius on Hilary of Arles, § lxix.   He wrote the *Life of Honoratus*, his predecessor (P.L., L, 1249–1272). A few other pieces are doubtfully assigned to him, e.g. the *Metrum in Genesin*, and the *Versus in natali Machabaeorum*.

reserved himself upon this point. But none the less Augustine did not lack warm partisans quite ready to enter the lists on his side, such as the Gaulish monk Leporius,[1] whom he had succeeded in turning from Pelagianism in 418, and who wrote a book in order to give an account of his error and of his recovery therefrom, and Aurelius, Bishop of Carthage.[2] Among his most active supporters, two laymen, Marius Mercator and Prosper of Aquitaine, take the first place.

Marius Mercator was probably a native of Africa. In the year 418 he sent to Augustine from Rome two works (apparently now lost) against the partisans of Pelagius and Caelestius.[3] A few years later, in 429, he is to be found at Constantinople, ever active against Pelagianism, and also against Nestorianism. His knowledge of Greek enabled him to make known in the West various works by heresiarchs such as Theodore of Mopsuesta, Nestorius, and Proclus, which would not have come down to us without him. He also translated into Latin the polemical writings of Nestorius against Pelagianism, and of St Cyril against Nestorianism. He thus undertook a task very similar to that which Rufinus had so usefully fulfilled.[4] Mercator died probably after the year 451.

The personality of Prosper, although not commanding, and of a too abject docility, deserves a more careful study.

Born in the South of Gaul in the year 390, Prosper of Aquitaine (*Tiro Prosper* was his name, according to the manuscripts of his *Chronicle*) learned to understand Pelagianism about the year 428 from St Augustine's *de Correctione et Gratia*. The purpose of his life and the field for his activity were revealed to him by reading this work ; although only a layman, he determined to follow up Pelagianism under all its forms and to defend the illustrious Bishop of Hippo

[1] *Libellus emendationis sive satisfactionis ad episcopos Galliae :* P.L., XXXI, 1221–1230.

[2] *De damnatione Pelagii atque Caelestii haereticorum* (419) ; P.L., XX, 1009–1014.—Capreolus (430–437), the successor of Aurelius, reserved his efforts to combat Nestorianism : P.L., LIII, 843–858.

[3] Cf. letter cxciii of Augustine to Marius Mercator. It has sometimes been wished to identify one of the two works to which St Augustine alludes with the *Hypomnesticon contra Pelagianos et Caelestianos* (P.L., XLV, 1611–1664).

[4] The fragments of his translations are in P.L., vol. XLVIII. Likewise his own works : the *Commonitorium super nomine Caelestii* (published first in Greek [429], then in Latin [431]) ; the *Commonitorium adv. haer. Pelagii et Caelestii vel etiam scripta Juliani* (431–2) ; the *Comparatio dogmatum Pauli Samosateni et Nestorii* (431), and the *Nestorii blasphemiarum capitula* (431).

against his detractors. He did hardly anything else, both in prose and verse, during the space of thirty years.

In 428 or 429 he warned St Augustine [1] of the opposition aroused by his writings on grace among certain circles in Marseilles, who judged his theory of gratuitous predestination to be contrary to the traditional feeling of the Church, and even dangerous from the point of view of edification. He begged him to throw light on these difficult questions by further explanations. We know that St Augustine, urged on likewise by Hilary,[2] another layman, wrote for both of them the *de Praedestinatione Sanctorum* and the *de Dono Perseverantiae*.

Prosper then undertook to explain to Rufinus, one of his friends, the nature of the problem of grace (*Ep. ad Rufinum de gratia et libero arbitrio*),[3] next he fell upon St Augustine's opponents (he died in 430) with ever fresh ardour, without allowing himself to be intimidated either by the talent of men like Vincent of Lérins (*Pro Augustino responsiones ad capitula objectionum Vincentianarum*), or the prestige of Cassian the model of the ascetics (*De gratia Dei et libero arbitrio liber contra Collatorem*).[4] His most curious work is the Περὶ ἀχαρίστων, *hoc est, de ingratis*, in 1002 hexameters. He plays upon the double meaning of the word *ingratus*, "unprofitable" and "despiser of grace." This poem, which Guizot hails as "one of the happiest essays in philosophical poetry which have been attempted within the bosom of Christianity,"[5] is entirely made up of theological disquisitions against semi-Pelagianism, the heir to Pelagianism. In the first part are found the well-known verses (quoted in honour by Bossuet in his *Sermon sur l'Unité de l'Eglise*) upon Rome who "held captive by the authority of religion what she no longer held by the force of arms,"[6] as well as a fine eulogium of St Augustine.[7]

Although Prosper in his prose recognises the virtues of his opponents (in his letter to St Augustine), he treats them with no benevolence in his verse. The disquisition in the *de*

[1] *Ep.* ccxxv (among the letters of Augustine).
[2] *Ep.* ccxxvi.
[3] Translated into French in the *Œuvres de Saint Augustin*, by Péronne, Ecalle, Vincent, vol. XXXII.
[4] Translated *ibid.*
[5] *Hist. de la civil. en France*, IVth.
[6] Line 39 et s.
[7] Line 99 et s.

Ingratis is at least clear and bright, however difficult the subject may be; sometimes even it warms into elegance born of the ardour of his belief in St Augustine, which accepts with enthusiasm the rigorousness and even the obscurity of his master's doctrine.

> " If you ask why from among the innumerable multitude of men upon earth, God chooses some to be reborn in Jesus Christ and leaves others to perish, although the same condemnation surrounds all men, and nothing but grace distinguishes creatures who are equal in merit, *we are not so rash as to seek further* in order to penetrate into channels hidden from us or to plant our footsteps in inaccessible paths."

To the *de Ingratis* we may add a series of short poems, for example, two epigrams in verse against an *obtrectator Augustini*, the sarcastic epitaph on the Nestorian and Pelagian heresies, and 106 epigrams in which are transposed into verse various views from the *Liber Sententiarum* which Prosper had himself compiled from the writings of Augustine.

The only work in which Prosper partially gets away from the sole idea which absorbed his intellect and devotion, is his *Chronicle*. In it he develops St Jerome's *Chronicle* by calling to his aid the annals of the Consuls (*consularia Italica*), and brings it down at first to the year 445,[1] and then in a second revision, to the year 455.[2] The work has no real historical importance until after the year 425, on which date the information given by Prosper becomes independent.

He died in 463. It is not correct to make him Bishop of Riez. He remained a layman to the last, but owing to the favour in which he was held by Pope Celestine, and Pope Leo I, whose secretary he became in 440, and to his solid theological foundation and the consistent character of his ardent con-

[1] This is the *Chronicon* called *vulgatum*.
[2] This is the *Chronicon* called *intergrum*. Among the Chronicles more or less directly related to the Chronicle of St Jerome, we might also mention that of Hydatius († in 468) which goes from 370 to 468 (Migne, LXXIV); that of Count Marcellinus († after 534), from 379 to 534, interesting on account of the Empire of the East (Migne, LI); that of Marius of Avenches († 593), from 455 to 581 (Migne, LXXII); that of Victor of Tunnuna († 569), from 444 to 567, in the portion which has been preserved (Migne, LXVIII); and that of Jean de Biclaro who continued after Victor the years 567 to 590 (Migne, LXXII). All these Chronicles were collected by Mommsen in the *Chron. Minora*, vol. II (M.G.H., XI [1894]).

victions, he exercised considerable influence on ecclesiastical thought in the middle of the Vth century.[1]

Without entering into the views of semi-Pelagianism the Roman Church displayed much reserve on the theories of Augustine. The ardent controversies of that period were to revive many centuries later with a virulence which is well known.

XIII

In the year 440 Evagrius the Gaulish priest endeavoured in his *Altercatio legis inter Simonem Judaeum et Theophilum Christianum*,[2] to go back to the tradition of the literary dialogue in use in Christian apologetics in the middle of the second century. His rendering is of an almost *naïve* simplicity. " Fuit igitur altercatio legis inter quemdam Simonem Judaeum et Theophilum Christianum. Judaeus igitur sic ait. . . ." This forms all the prelude. Once the discussion is entered upon Theophilus takes a larger and larger share in it and lavishes on his opponent significant texts from the Old Testament. Soon the Jew begins to waver ; for conscience' sake he still brings forward a few objections, which are quickly refuted ; finally he acknowledges himself beaten, asks to be baptised and utters a prayer to God to give him grace, which closes the colloquy : The forfeit had been fixed from the beginning : " Quod si tu me hodie viceris, facito Christianum : aut ego cum te superavero, faciam Nazaraeum ludaeum." We are far from the zest and *finesse* of the *Octavius*, or even from the supple dialectics of one of St Augustine's similar dialogues.

[1] The history of the editions of St Prosper is summarised by L. Couture, in B.L.E., 1900, pp. 270–282, which shows the use of his works made by Jansenism in the XVIIth century. There are interesting modern quotations in J. J. Ampère's *Hist. litt. de la France avant le XIIth century*, II, p. 50 et s. Migne (vol. LI) reproduced the edition of Luc Urbain Mangeant (Paris, 1711). The *Chronicle* is also printed in M.G.H., IX, 1, p. 341 (1892, Mommsen). We cannot assign to Prosper with any certainty the *De promissionibus et praedictionibus Dei* (P.L., LI, 733) ; the *Poema conjugis ad uxorem* (P.L., LI, 611 ; C.V., XXX, 344) ; the *De Providentia Divina* (P.L., LI, 617) ; the *Confessio Prosperi* (P.L., LI, 607) ; the *Praeteritorum sedis apostolicae episcoporum auctoritates de gratia Dei* (P.L., LI, 205 ; L, 531). The matter is discussed in Valentin's *S. Prosper d'Aquitaine*, Paris, 1900, who likewise makes a study of the language and style of Prosper.. French translation of the *de Ingratis*, by Lemaistre de Sacy, 1646 and 1650 ; of the complete works of Prosper, by Lequeux, 1762 ; various of his writings have been inserted in the translation of St Augustine, vol. XXXII.

[2] P.L., XX, 1165–1182 ; Harnack, T.U., I, 3 (1883) ; Bratke, in C.V., vol. XLV (1904). Critical notes by Stangl, in B. ph. W., 1915, nos. 23 to 26. Harnack's thesis, according to which the *Altercatio* was a translation or a resetting of the *Debate between Jason and Papiscus*, by Ariston of Pella (about the year 140) has not been favourably received.

CHAPTER II

THE CHURCH AND THE BARBARIANS—OROSIUS—
SALVIANUS—LEO THE GREAT—VICTOR OF VITA

BIBLIOGRAPHY

I. Orosius. The *Commonitorium de errore Priscillianistarum* appears in P.L., XXXI, 1211-1216 (and XLII, 665-670), also in C.V., vol. XVIII, pp. 149-157 (Schepss): the *Liber Apologeticus* is printed in P.L., XXXI, 1173-1212, and C.V., vol. V, 600-664 (C. Zangemeister); the seven books *Historiarum adv. Paganos*, are in P.L., XXXI, 663-1172; C.V., vol. V, 1-564; B.T. (Zangemeister, 1889). A letter to St Augustine *de Haeresibus* is mentioned in S.B.W., vol. LXXXIV (1877), p. 533; it is in the British Museum, Add. MSS. 24902, fol. 37 v.—Consult; G. Boissier, *Fin du Pagan*, vol. II, p. 398 et s.

II. Salvianus.—Text in P.L., LIII; M.G.H., I, 1 (Halm, 1877); C.V., VIII (Pauly, 1883). French translation by Grégoire and Collombet, 2 vols., Paris, 1833. A reliable study of the language of Salvianus, which is very interesting, is needed. J. H. Schmalz has drawn attention to certain grammatical peculiarities in B. ph. W., 1915, No. 32/33, cols. 1041-1046. —Consult: Boissier's *Fin du Pagan*, vol. II, p. 410 et s.; Waltzing's *Tertullien et Salvien*, *Mélanges de Borman*, 1919, pp. 13-17.

III. Leo the Great.—P.L., LIV-LVI (116 Sermons, of which 96 are authentic; 173 letters, of which 143 are by Leo himself). Amelli published in 1882 two letters written to Leo, one from Flavianus of Constantinople, and the other from Eusebius of Dorylaeum: these documents were re-edited by Mommsen in 1886, in the *Archiv. d. Ges. f. aelt. Geschichteskunde*, XI, 361-8.—Consult: Turner in the *Miscellanea Ceriani*, Milan, 1910; Ad. Régnier, *S. Léon le Grand*, 1910 (coll. *les Saints*). French translation of ten sermons and nine letters in the *Chefs-d'oeuvre des Pères de l'Eglise*, vol. XIV (1838), pp. 129-310; translation of all the sermons by the Abbot of Bellegarde, 1701.—The *Sacramentarium Leonianum* has been edited by Feltoe (c. 1897); cf. Migne, LV, 21-156.

IV. Victor of Vita.—P.L., LVIII, 180-216; Halm, in M.G.H. (1879), III, 1; Petschenig, in C.V., VII (1881). French translation in Dom Leclercq's *Les Martyrs*, III (1904), pp. 348-407.

SUMMARY

I. Orosius and Augustine. — II. The Seven Books *against the Pagans*.— III. The *de Gubernatione Dei*, by Salvianus. — IV. Pope Leo the Great.—V. *The History of the Persecution by the Vandals*, by Victor of Vita.—VI. Vigilius of Thapsus.

433

2 E

I

THE name of Orosius is naturally connected with that of St Augustine. Like Alypius, Quodvultdeus,[1] and many others, Orosius was his disciple and friend, and had scarcely any other ambition than to live upon his doctrines, and to develop them subject to his master's corrections.

Paulus Orosius was a native of Spain, perhaps of Tarragona.[2] Born about the year 390, he entered orders and was attached apparently to the clergy at Bracara, in Gallecia. His admiration for Augustine brought him in 414 to Hippo. Augustine welcomed him kindly, and quickly recognised his real moral and intellectual[3] qualities, and after keeping him a short time with him sent him to St Jerome in Palestine in order both to help him to finish his education in doctrine, and to transmit to Jerome by a trusty messenger certain questions on the origin of the soul,[4] over which he was preoccupied at that time.

In the meantime, Orosius, who had been able to observe at close quarters in his own country the Priscillianist doctrine, inscribed to Augustine a *Commonitorium de Priscillianistis et de Origenis errore.* Augustine replied to it without delay with a treatise *contra Priscillianistas et Origenistas ad Orosium.*

Having arrived at Bethlehem, Orosius soon became St Jerome's auxiliary in his polemics which at that time were being directed against the Pelagians. In this way he felt sure of giving pleasure to St Augustine and no thought could have acted as a keener spur to him. In the last months of 415 he wrote a *Liber Apologeticus*, a veritable indictment of Pelagian-

[1] Various works have been recently restored to Quodvultdeus with more or less probability : sermons (*S. Aur. Augustini tractatus sive sermones inediti*, published by Dom Morin in 1917, pp. 181, 191, 196, 200) ; a *Liber de promissionibus et praedictionibus Dei*, reproduced by Migne in the appendix to the works of St Prosper of Aquitaine, P.L., LI, 734–838 (see Schepens, R.S.R., 1919, pp. 230–243).

[2] He wrote *Tarraconem nostrum* (*Adv. Pag.*, VII, xxii, 8).

[3] *Ep.* clxvi, 2.

[4] *Ep.* clxvi. It appears probable that Orosius also took with him *Ep.* clxvii and certain other writings for the purpose of placing Jerome *au courant* with Augustine's ideas on grace. Cf. Brochet, *Saint Jér. et ses ennemis*, 1906, p. 451 et s. In December 415, during his stay in Jerusalem, the relics of St Stephen were discovered by the priest Lucianus of Kaphar Gamala, who wrote out in Greek an account of this *inventio*, which was soon translated into Latin by Avitus of Bracara, a Spanish priest, who happened to be there (P.L., XLI, 805–818). Orosius later on brought some of these relics to Minorca, where many Jews were converted on this account : related by Severus, Bishop of Minorca, in P.L., XLI, 821–832, and XX, 731–746.

ism, for the use of the Fathers assembled at the Council of
Diospolis (on the coast of Palestine) in December of that
same year.[1] But this "lamentable" Council, as Jerome
called it, in no way resulted in the confounding of Pelagius,
and Orosius returned disappointed to Augustine at the beginning of 416.

Acting on his advice he set himself to his great work,
the *Adversum Paganos Libri VII*, and laboured at it with so
much ardour that by 417 he had almost finished it.[2]

II

THIS history is directly connected with the *City of God*,
particularly with Book III wherein Augustine set down the
reckoning of the evils suffered in former days by Rome which
the gods had been powerless to avert. Augustine considered
that his outline might be gone over and amplified with
advantage in order to do away with the grievance of the pagans
over what they supposed were exceptional misfortunes at
the beginning of the Vth century. Orosius clearly explains
this design in his preface. What he wished to do was to collect
from the record of different nations the most significant
examples of the ills of humanity—wars, pestilences, famines,
earthquakes, floods, the ravages caused by thunderbolts and
hail, cases of parricide and turpitude—and to classify these
calamities in the form of a kind of history of the world.[3]

In the nature of things Orosius could not examine a very
large number of documents in only two years. He would
very much like us to believe that he made use of very many
sources of information. As a matter of fact, he extracted
what he knew from a small number of Latin authors (not
counting the Old and New Testament). The *Chronicle*
of Eusebius, remodelled and continued by St Jerome, provided him with the outlines of his plan. He supplied himself
with his facts from an *Epitome* of Titus Livius, from Cæsar's
Commentaries (which he attributed to Suetonius),[4] from
Tacitus, Justin, Florus, Eutropius, Rufinus, and St Augustine

---

[1] Cf. Frankfurth, *Augustinus u. die Synode zu Diospolis*, B. 1904.
[2] He gives the number of years since the creation of the world to the time
at which he was writing as 5618 (VII, xliii, 19 ; Zangemeister, p. 564).
[3] See the Prologue ix–x ; cf. I, xxi, 21.
[4] VI, vii, 2.

himself.[1] His account has special interest after the year 378, for his written sources of information for that period have not been preserved.

This abundant subject matter, with which he confesses he is somewhat overwhelmed,[2] is divided into seven books : I. A short description of the terrestrial globe. A history of the world down to the founding of Rome, which he places in the year 752 (B.C.). II. A history of Rome down to the conquest of the city by the Gauls, together with a synchronous account of the history of the Persians from the time of Cyrus, and of the Greeks down to the battle of Cunaxa. III. Events in Roman, Greco-Macedonian, and Hellenistic history down to the year 290 before the Christian era. IV. The Pyrrhic wars down to the destruction of Carthage. V. Rome, from the destruction of Corinth to the first civil war. VI. The wars against Mithridates down to Augustus and the birth of Christ. VII. The period of the Emperors down to 417 A.D.

In order to understand the methods employed in the *Adversum Paganos*, we must remember that considerations of a mystical order, rather than technical requirements, suggested them to Orosius in more than one place. If he divided his work into seven books, it was because St Augustine had given prominence in his *City of God* (XI, xxxi) to the special virtues of the number 7—the total made by the first uneven number (3) and the total of the first two even numbers (4)[3]—the number of the day on which God rested after the Creation, etc. . . . In the same manner, if he admitted four great Empires—the Macedonian in the North, the Assyrio-Babylonian in the East, the Carthaginian in the South, and the Roman in the West—it was because the Prophet Daniel's interpretation (VII, 3–27) of his dream favoured that classification. He thought he saw mysterious chronological coincidences between the refounding of Babylon by Semiramis and the conquest of that city by the Medes, and he notices that the same lapse of time separated the founding of Rome and her conquest by Alaric. These enigmatic coincidences appearing among the multiplicity of events in history disclosed in his eyes the constant

---

[1] The verification is easy thanks to the notes in Zangemeister's edition, and to the index, pp. 684–700.

[2] *Pref.* to Book III.

[3] Augustine makes 4 the first even number (*totus par*).

action of Providence which had ordained them and which regulates the onward march of humanity down to its minutest detail.

But the considerations which had determined him to undertake his work inclined him also to emphasise especially events of the past of a particular kind. What mattered to him was to demonstrate that in spite of their childish bewailings, his contemporaries were not appreciably to be more pitied than those of any other period in the world's history. He remarks on that illusion of the imagination or of the sensibility which readily makes us believe that no misfortune can be worse than what we are suffering at the present moment, like some man who, after having been devoured by fleas all night, is of opinion that his loss of sleep was more trying than when a raging fever had recently held him in its grip.[1] It is therefore upon the sufferings of generations of men, on the harsh dealings of nature, and on the ferociousness of mankind, that Orosius dwells more readily in order to arrange an instructive picture, a kind of chamber of horrors of history, looking at which his contemporaries shall blush for their grumblings. Besides, was the present as appalling as they pretended ? For his part, Orosius doubted it, and resolutely held out an optimistic view. Thus, after tracing the war between Sparta and Athens, he makes this observation :[2]

" We esteem lightly those afflictions which weighed down Greece during so many long years. What we cannot put up with now is that the course of our pleasures should be interfered with, and that our passions experience some weariness. There is, however, this difference between those times and our own, that they put up with those intolerable ills with a steadfast heart because they were born to them, because they lived among them and knew no other better state, while our people, accustomed from long date to the serenity of their undisturbed condition and of their pleasures, are moved by the slightest shadow of worry and anxiety. Please God they may pray to Him who can dissipate this alarm however

---

[1] Preface to Book IV (Z., p. 204).
[2] I, xxi, 18 (Z., p. 78).

trifling it be, and to Whom they owe a continuity of peace unknown to other periods ! ''

In another place,[1] in connection with a terrible invasion of locusts which had alighted upon Africa during the Consulship of M. Plautius Hypsaeus and M. Fulvius Flaccus (in the year 125 B.C.), he remarks that no such formidable scourge had ever been reproduced since the era of Christianity. There were still many incursions of these insects, *sed tolerabiliter laedunt.*

Even towards the barbarians only recently so hateful in the eyes of an Ambrose, or a Prudentius, Orosius feels within himself much indulgence. Of course he loves *Romania,*[2] and appreciates the benefits springing from Roman civilisation, and appears to believe still in the solidity of its foundations. But he considers the barbarians to be capable of improving. They perpetrated horrors, it was true : at least they were not incapable of repenting[3] of them. In short, without his views on the future of Latin Hegemony being very clearly pronounced, Orosius was half resigned already to vicissitudes which the preceding generation could not accept without revolt.

Written with a certain warmth of eloquence in language wherein an imitation of the classics, particularly of Virgil, has left many traces, the Histories of Orosius enjoyed a wide influence in the Middle Ages. We possess more than two hundred manuscripts, one of which is a *Laurentianus* of the VIth century. Their compiler became in his turn a source of information for Count Marcellinus, Jordanis, Bede, Isidore and Gregory of Tours. At periods of an inferior state of learning this kind of work was preferred to all others. Moreover, its leading idea was interesting : Orosius contributed in a remarkable degree to make the history of Christianity a field for apologetics by using it to describe the action of Providence in the vicissitudes of mankind.

---

[1] V, xi, 6 (p. 302). We may also compare III, ii, 14 (p. 145).
[2] He is one of the first to employ this term as a literary expression (III, xx, ii ; VII, xliii). We also meet with it in the *Vita Augustini,* by Possidius, VI. It is of older use in Greek. See Gaston Paris, *Mél. linguist.,* I, p. 18.
[3] VIII, xl, 10.

III

MORE than twenty years passed between the appearance of the work of Orosius, written in 417–418, and that of the *de Gubernatione Dei* by Salvianus, composed between the years 439 and 451. The advance of the barbarians had become too evident, their strength had been too brutally asserted for any observer capable of perspicacity to retain the least doubt as to the final overthrow of the Roman power. Already they held the greater part of Gaul, Spain and Africa ; every year the independent territories were becoming more shrunk. In the face of all these calamities the Christians themselves were murmuring vehemently against Providence which was allowing the arms of the orthodox to be defeated by Arian or pagan invaders, and seemed to be heedless of the fate of the Christian Empire.

It was Salvianus who set himself to reassure the despondency of public opinion on this point.

Gennadius informs us in his *de Viris Illustribus*, § lxvii, that Salvianus was a priest of the Church at Marseilles. We have a few letters of his, nine, to be exact ; we see from the fourth that he had married, when quite a young man, Palladia the daughter of a pagan, and that he had a daughter, Auspiciola ; that he and his wife a few years later both resolved to embrace the ascetic life, and that the parents of the young woman were so vexed over it that they quarrelled with them. From certain indications in his writings, Salvianus must have been a native of Trèves.[1] Part of his life was passed at Lérins, and then at Marseilles ; he also made a sojourn in Africa.[2] He died at a fairly advanced age.[3] This is about all we know of him.

Gennadius mentions different works by Salvianus which have been lost. Besides the above-mentioned letters, and the *de Gubernatione Dei*, we have nothing else but a work in 4 books called by Gennadius *Adversus Avaritiam*, but *Ad Ecclesiam* in the manuscripts, and by Salvianus himself,[4] and anterior to the *de Gubernatione*, because it is mentioned in it.[5] Under

---

[1] *De Gub.*, VI, xiii, 72 (text doubtful) ; VI, xv, 84 ; VII, vi, 25 ; *Ep.* i, 5.
[2] V, xvi, 70.
[3] " Vivit usque hodie in senectute bona," Gennadius wrote, about the year 470.
[4] *Ep.* ix.
[5] IV, i.

the pseudonym of Timothy, Salvianus addresses those who on their death-bed neglect to leave of their possessions to the Church, and who end by placing the seal on their lifelong cupidity by this last exercise of avarice. According to him, this oblation of their earthly riches for the benefit of the Church, provided that it was accompanied by tears and compunction, was the best way to blot out the sins of the past.[1] He imposed this obligation upon all states of life, lay as well as religious, and claimed to justify it by a series of texts from Scripture with which he confronted good common-sense motives, especially the perplexity of parents who may be disturbed at the thought of leaving their children deprived of all resources.

Such an uncompromising injunction leads us to distrust somewhat his good judgment and critical sense. Possibly the *de Gubernatione Dei* may go some little way to remove this ambiguous impression.

This work comprises eight books, the last of which was uncompleted.[2] Salvianus begins by reproving those whom the despondency caused by those melancholy times had induced to have doubts of Providence. Afterwards in book III he enters upon the essence of his thesis.

If Christians complained, it was doubtless because in worshipping the true God they thought they were entitled to have the benefit of a protecting guardian. But in what does this faith consist from which they claim exceptional treatment as their proper due ? Does it not consist essentially in observing the commandments of God ? Salvianus had now reached his point. He then goes on to endeavour to demonstrate that not only did the ills under which Christians were suffering in no way reflect upon Providence, but that if Providence did not chastise so many outrages daily committed against His law, only in that case might they doubt the reality of His action. The crimes, shameful actions and wickedness of the *plebs Romana* were the direct cause of so many calamities. " (Deus) ideo nos perferre haec mala patitur, quia meremur ut ista patismur." [3]

He then contrasts in a long catalogue abounding in

---

[1] *Ad Eccl.*, I, x.
[2] An argument begun in VII, i, 2, does not appear in it either.
[3] IV, liv.

picturesque features, the vices of the Roman civilisation with the qualities of the victorious races, which were mingled with faults, without doubt, but were unquestionable. This arresting comparison is continued right to the end of the work.

To the Romans he attributes every kind of moral enormity —drunkenness, lying, pride and perjury. *Proprium est Romanorum paene omnium malum.*[1] He considers the Africans still worse : they might be called the sink into which the turpitude of the whole world had come to empty itself.

" From the point of view of our lives and our acts, we are worse than the barbarians, heretics, and pagans. No exception can be made to this, except for the religious (*omnes religiosos*), and a few lay people who are like religious (*deinde nonnullos etiam saeculares religiosis pares, aut, si id nimis grande est, aliqua tamen religiosis honestorum actuum probitate consimiles*). As for the rest, all, or nearly all, are more culpable than the barbarians."[2]

To possess the Catholic law was, without doubt, an immense advantage, but all the more must they render themselves worthy of it. " Quod lex bona est, nostrum non est ; quod autem male vivimus, nostrum est."[3] Equal in vice, their knowledge of this divine law only aggravated the responsibility of the Romans as compared with the responsibility of the barbarians.

Salvianus admired many virtues in the invaders. They loved one another : " *Mutuo amant*, omnes paene Romani se mutuo persequuntur."[4] They also saw poor people, widows and orphans preferring to go and live among the Goths and Bagaudi, and that they were not at all disappointed with their choice. They were chaste, especially the Goths and the Saxons.[5] They were unacquainted with the impure exhibitions of the circus and theatre.[6] With them, fornication was a crime, while the Romans gloried in it.[7] By certain energetic measures they had put an end, especially in Africa, to horrors at which the Romans did not blush.[8] " An incredible and unheard of thing, they had succeeded in obliging them to observe modesty."[9] It must not be denied

---

[1] VII, lxii.   [2] IV, lxi.   [3] *Ibid.*
[4] V, xv.   [5] VII, lxiv.   [6] VI, xxxv.
[7] VII, xxiv.   [8] VII, xciv.   [9] VII, cvii.

that they were heretics ; but that again was the fault of the Romans. " Etiam ipsae quondam haereses barbarorum de Romano magisterio fluxerunt, ac perinde etiam hoc nostrum crimen est, quod populi barbarorum haeretici esse coeperunt." [1]

How could they be surprised that God had given them Aquitaine and almost the whole of the Empire, inasmuch as they were accomplishing therein a wholesome work ? [2] In short, theirs was a purifying *rôle :* " Barbari ad emendandam nostrarum turpidinum labem extiterunt." [3]

This comparison between *Romania* and Barbary all to the honour of the latter marks a new development in the evolution sketched by Orosius. Salvianus already was half resigned to the fall of Rome. Certain historians, like Hauréau,[4] have angrily reproached him for this kind of treason. Even among the Gallo-Roman aristocracy such instances of turning round were by no means rare in the Vth century.[5] Moreover, we must guard ourselves against unreserved agreement with the fervid paradoxes of Salvianus. One or two generations after him St Cæsarius gives us a lively picture of the bestiality of these barbarians who were so dear to the heart of Salvianus, and of their propensity to drunkenness, homicide and sensuality. But it would not be surprising if, with his fiery eloquence, his highly-coloured fervour and thundering rhetoric formed in the school of the Fathers more than in that of the classics, Salvianus contributed to incline men's minds to accept the new state of things which was in process of formation amid so many tribulations and trials.

IV

HOWEVER, the cult of Rome the eternal had not been crushed out of all hearts. Pope Leo the Great celebrated in magnificent terms in the middle of the Vth century the wonderful fortunes of that City which had placed under her hegemony so many different races in order to diffuse the Gospel more efficaciously and had now become still more majestic in her spiritual power than ever she had been in former days in

[1] V, xiv.
[2] VII, xxiv.
[3] VII, xciv.
[4] *Mém. de l'Acad. des Inscr. et belles-lettres,* vol. XXVI (1867), p. 142.
[5] Cf. Roger, *L'Enseign. des lettres class. d'Ausone à Alcuin,* p. 62.

all her grandeur of the flesh.[1] The short sermons of Leo
are full of doctrinal vigour which was not impaired by any
excessive seeking after verbal effects. His language is strong
and simple, altogether worthy of that admirable Pontiff,
who knew how to protect Rome from the threat of Attila,[2]
who ransomed her from the cruelty of Genseric[3] and more than
any other of his predecessors strengthened the sovereign power
of the Papacy.[4] But it was not only by his practical skill
and firm suppleness that St Leo acquired œcumenical
authority ; it was also by his wide knowledge as a Doctor[5]
of the Church. In the course of the disputes relating to
Eutychianism, in his famous letter to Flavianus[6] he provided
the Council of Chalcedon with the elements essential to the
dogmatic decisions which were there arrived at. At the same
time in the West he followed up the active remnant of Manichaeism and Priscillianism, exacted a formal retractation
from those Pelagians who were anxious to re-enter the Church,
and imposed on all the feeling that in the universal anarchy
of the time there was no other form of method and unity
than in the Catholic Church.

V

THE *Historia persecutionis Africanae provinciae temporibus
Geiserici et Hunirici regum Vandalorum* which we owe to

---

[1] *Sermo 82, In natali apost. Petri et Pauli,* § 1 (P.L., LIV, 422).
[2] Cf. St Prosper's *Chron. ad a.* 452.
[3] *Ibid., ad a.* 451.
[4] Cf. *Ep.* xvi ; xlvi, 2. It was he who, in face of the encroachments of Bishop
Hilary of Arles, obtained from the Emperor Valentinian II in 445 an edict " ne
quid praeter auctoritatem sedis istius inlicitum praesumptio attentare nitatur "
(v. *Ep.* x–xi). We must mention here a few of the Popes who had preceded him.
The letters and decretals of Pope Siricius (384–399) are in Migne, XIII, 1115–1196 ;
those of Anastasius I (399–402), *ibid.,* XX, 51–80 (a letter to Venerius, discovered
in 1871 in a manuscript in Brussels, has been re-edited by J. Van den Gheyn in
R.H.L.R., IV [1899], pp. 1–12) ; those of Innocent I, XX, 463 et s. ; those of
Zosimus (417–418), XX, 639 et s. ; those of Boniface I (418–422), XX, 749 et s. ;
those of Celestine (422–432), L, 417 et s. ; those of Sixtus III (432–440), L, 581 et s.
Cf. K. Silva-Taronca, *Ueberlieferungsgesch. der Papstbriefe des 4, 5 u. 6 Jahrhund.,*
in Z.K.T., 1919. The famous decretal *de recipiendis et non recipiendis libris,*
attributed, without doubt inaccurately, to Pope Gelasius, and which might pass
as the prototype of the *Index librorum prohibitorum,* has been much studied in
recent times : Dobschutz, in T.U., 38, 4 (1912), de Bruyne, R. Bén., 1913, 187–207
and 315–333. The authentic writings of Gelasius are in P.L., LIX : there is a
study of his language in A.L.L., XII, 1 et s.
[5] The title of Doctor of the Church was decreed to him by Benedict XIV
in 1754.
[6] *Ep.* xxviii (of the 13th June, 449).

Bishop Victor, of Vita in Byzacene (south of Tunisia), comprises three books—and not five according to the incorrect division of the old editions.[1] The work relates the persecutions which the Vandals made the Christians undergo from the time of their invasion of Northern Africa (429) down to the death of Huneric (484). Victor wrote it in the year 486 when in exile on the confines of Tripoly. He made a special point of describing the abominations committed by the Arian barbarians, and the appalling sufferings inflicted on Bishops, priests, consecrated virgins, and simple believers. The history of Victor of Vita gives the impression of a long and painful *Passio martyrum*. In more than one case the author is at pains to note that he was a witness of the facts he is reporting, or that he saw the victims. He is careful to insert official documents in his narrative, for instance, Huneric's edict authorising all liberty of preaching to be given to the Arian Bishops ; the mandate preparing the conference of Carthage in 484 ; the *libellus fidei* of Eugenius, Bishop of Carthage (1. II) ; and a second edict of Huneric against the Catholics, the prelude to fresh atrocities (1. III). The accounts given by Victor have the attraction of the horrible : he lingers over descriptions of the worst tortures, counting up the blows and making you see the palpitating flesh. He seeks after oratorical effects and willingly borrows turns and words from the language of poetry ; but this striving after effect is joined to a remarkable lack of concern for, or ignorance of, the traditional morphology and syntax.

VI

VIGILIUS of Thapsus (Thapsus in Byzacene) was present at the Conference held in Carthage (1st February 484) between Catholic and Arian Bishops,[2] described by Victor of Vita in his *History of the Vandal Persecution*. Of the treatises claimed for him by Chifflet, a Jesuit, in his edition of 1664 (reproduced by Migne),[3] there are only two which are certainly authentic—

---

[1] Cf. F. Ferrère, in the *Rev. de Philol.*, 1901, pp. 110–123, 320–336.

[2] Among the works which kept alive the persecution of Arianism, and polemical writings, we should mention a letter by Eugenius of Carthage (P.L., LVIII, 769), an *opusculum* by Cerealis of Castellum in Mauretamia (*ibid.*, 757), and a letter of condolence by Autoninus Honoratus of Cirta (L. 567).

[3] T. LXII.

the dialogue *contra Arianos, Sabellianos et Photinianos,* and the five books *contra Eutychetem.*[1] In the first of these two works Vigilius mentions a book written against the Arian Bishop Marivadus (II, xlv), and another work against the Arian Bishop Palladius (II, L). These appear to have been lost ; the works printed by Chifflet under the same headings are not by Vigilius.[2] There are no serious reasons for claiming for him the other treatises collected by Chifflet.

[1] For the different literary and theological problems connected with the works of Vigilius, cf. Ficker's *Studien zu Vigilius von Thapsus,* Leipzig, 1897.

[2] The first probably belongs to Itacius of Ossonuba ; the second to Phebadius of Agen, as regards book II at least (*de Fide orthodoxa contra Arianos*), for book I simply reproduces the acts of the Synod of Aquitaine (381).

CHAPTER III

CHRISTIAN LATIN POETRY IN THE Vth CENTURY

BIBLIOGRAPHY

I. PRUDENTIUS.—Bergman, a learned Swede (S.B.W., CLVII [1908], Abh. V), has enumerated 320 manuscripts of the poetry of Prudentius. Of these manuscripts 27 only contain all the works of the poet; the greater number belong to the Xth century; they are divided into two classifications which enable us to distinguish the order of succession of the poems, and in the second, the relationship of the last two hymns of the *Cathemerinon* to the *Peristephanon*. The most important manuscript is the Puteanus *sive* Parisiensis 8084, of the VIth century (*Bibl. Nat.*). Bergman has promised a critical edition of Prudentius. The last in date is that of Dressel, Leipsic, 1860. Migne (vols. LIX and LX) reproduced the edition of Arevalo, Rome, 1788. Special edition of the *Psychomachia* by Bergman, Upsala, 1897 (with commentary). A good selection by Lietzmann, K.T., No. 47/49 (1910).

The most important work on Prudentius is undoubtedly A. Puech's thesis, *Prudence, Etude sur la Poésie latine chrétienne au IVᵉ siècle*, Paris, 1888. To this must be added the series of articles by Paul Allard in R.Q.H., vol. XXXV to XXXVII, and P. Chavanne's work on the *Patriotisme de Prudence* in R.H.L.R., IV (1899), p. 385. A study on the language of Prudentius will be indispensable after Bergman's edition has appeared.

The *Apotheosis* has been partially translated in Felix Clément's *Les Poètes chrétiens* . . . , 1857, pp. 139-161. The *Cathemerinon* is also translated in Bayle, 1868, and in Anot de Maizières, *Nouveau Choix de Pères latins*, 1853, vol. V, pp. 126-199; specimens of the *Contra Symmachum*, in Clément, *op. cit.*, pp. 88-138. Poizat has translated a few of the hymns of Prudentius into French in *Les Poètes chrétiens*, Lyons-Paris, 1902, p. 243.

II. ORIENTIUS.—Text in P.L., vol. LXI, 977-1000 (reproducing Martène), and in C.V., XVI, 171 (1888, R. Ellis). French translation of the *Commonitorium* and of the prayers in Louis Bellanger's *Etude sur le poème d'Orientius*, Paris, 1902, pp. 293-339.

III. ALETHIA.—P.L., LXI, 937-970 (Migne was so mistaken as to reproduce the fantastic edition of Gagny (Lyons, 1536) instead of that of G. Morel (1560)); C.V., vol. XVI, p. 335 (1888, Schenkl).

IV. PAULINUS of PELLA.—The *Eucharisticos* is not included in Migne; the best edition is that of Brandes, in C.V., XVI, pp. 263-334. French translation by Corpet, in *Les Oeuvres d'Ausone* (Panckoucke's collection), I, 348 et s.—For the language of Paulinus, cf. Devogel's *Etude sur la Latinité et le style de Paulin de Pella*, Brussels, 1898.

V. CLAUDIANUS MAMERTUS.—Text in P.L., LIII, 697-790 (reproducing Gallandi); and in C.V., vol. XI (1885, Engelbrecht), which only gives the *de Statu animae* and the *Letters*.

VI. DRACONTIUS.—Text in P.L., LX (the *Hexaemeron* [i.e., *Laudes Dei*, I. 118-754] also figures as a separate piece in vol. LXXXVII); in M.G.H., XIV (1905, Vollmer); and in P.L.M., vol. V (1914, Vollmer, amended).—

The *Orestis Tragoedia* and the *Carmina minora* (an anthology of Verona gives to them the title of *Romulea*, probably a synonym for *Latina* [*carmina*]) is in M.G.H., pp. 197 and 132, and in P.L.M., V.—For their language, see M.G.H., p. 431 et s.

VII. Sedulius.—There are numerous manuscripts of the poems of Sedulius, of which two are *Bobienses* of the VIIth century giving the *Carmen Paschale*, whose *prestige* was considerable in the Middle Ages (see Manitius, *Gesch. d. lat. Litt. d. Mittelalt.*, under *s. u. Sedulius* in the Index).—Text in P.L., XIX, 533-754 (reproducing Arevalo, Rome, 1794); C.V., vol. X (1885, Huemer).

VIII. Sidonius Apollinaris.—Text in P.L., LVIII (reproducing Sirmond, Paris, 1614); and in M.G.H., VIII (1887, Lutjohann). A small edition by P. Mohr, 1895 (B.T.).—French translation by Grégoire and Collombet, 1836, 3 vols., and by Eug. Baret, 1887 (Nisard's collection).—Consult: Paul Allard's *Saint Sidoine Apollinaire* (*les Saints* collection), 1910. There are some valuable remarks on the grammar in Eug. Baret's *Oeuvres de Sidoine Apollinaire*, 1879, pp. 106-123. Cf. especially Lutjohann's *Index*, p. 449 et s.

SUMMARY

I. Prudentius. His Life.—II. The *Cathemerinon.*—III. The *Peristephanon.* —IV. Didactic Poems. The Patriotism of Prudentius. The *Psychomachia.* The *Dittochaeon.*—V. The Poetry of Prudentius.—VI. The Poem of Orientius. The *Alethia.*—VII. Paulinus of Pella.—VIII. Claudianus Mamertus.—IX. Dracontius.—X. Sedulius.—XI. Sidonius Apollinaris.

I.

" I have lived, if I mistake not, for fifty years, to which seven more must be added. . . . Their limit is not far off, and I see coming the days which are near to old age. What have I done of any use in so long a time? My childhood shed tears beneath the resounding strokes of the ferule. Then, already disabused, I put on the toga, and learned to utter culpable lies. Then came vice unabashed, and outbursts of sensuality, and every foul and perverse naughtiness soiled my youth—what remorse and what disgust! Wordy battles next armed my restless spirit; an unreasonable obstinacy to come off best threw me into painful predicaments. Twice I have governed noble cities under the authority of the laws, rendering justice to the good, and bringing fear to the guilty. At last the good pleasure of the Prince honoured me with a high post in the army and placed me near his person in the highest rank. And all this time life was in flight, my hair was growing white, and I forgot that I was born when old Salia was Consul (348). . . . Well, well! May my sinful soul cast off its follies, and if it cannot render homage to God through its merits, may it do so at least by its voice ! ''

These biographical details and the secret of his call to poetry are given to us by Prudentius in the Preface to his Poems, published by himself in the year 405. An advocate, a high official, perhaps even a *comes primi ordinis*, he felt the need of making amends for the sins of his life, and for his tardy poetical efforts he predicated the merit of repentance and expiation.

In this same preface (v. 37 et s.) he enumerates the series of poems which he is presenting to his readers :

> '' May these hymns string together day to day, and may no night pass without singing praises to the Lord (the *Cathemerinon*), may my voice combat heresies (the *Apotheosis*), defend the Catholic faith (the *Hamartigenia*), tread the pagans under foot (the *Psychomachia*), prepare, O Rome, the way for the fall of thine idols (the *Contra Symmachum*), and dedicate its verses to the martyrs, and laud the Apostles (the *Peristephanon*).''

Apart from the poems thus designated by Prudentius in paraphrases (the vagueness of the term *Psychomachia* will be noted), Gennadius ascribes to him a *Tropaeum*—doubtless it should read *Dittochaeon*—and a *Hexaemeron* of which we have no other source of information.

The traditional division of the works of Prudentius is into lyrical and didactic poems, and it is best to keep to it.

II

THE *Cathemerinon* is a collection of twelve hymns, the first six of which are intended to celebrate the different '' mystical moments '' of the Christian's day. A hymn for cock-crow (i) ; the morning hymn (ii) ; a hymn for before and after meals (iii–iv) ; a hymn for the hour when the lamps are lighted (v) ; a hymn before going to sleep (vi). The round of daily acts is now closed. Hymns vii and viii praise the virtues of fasting, the latter being specially written for the ninth hour which marks the end of the day. Hymn ix (*Hymnus omni horae*) is a canticle of thanksgiving to Christ, whose chief miracles are recalled. Hymn x is addressed to the dead, and holds out to them the resurrection. Hymns xi and xii celebrate the Feasts of Christmas and Epiphany.

Only a small portion of this lyrical work has passed into use in the liturgy of the Church.[1] The reason for this is because Prudentius of set purpose departed from that extreme simplicity which St Ambrose and St Hilary had made the rule by their Church hymns. Side by side with the popular acatalectic (i, ii, xi, xii) iambic dimeter, and catalectic (vi), he made use of metres and strophes of a far more ambitious character—the iambic in six feet (vii); the catalectic trochaic tetrameter (ix); the hypercatalectic dactylic trimeter (iii); the catalectic anapæstic dimeter (x); the phalecian hendecasyllable (iv); the short asclepiad (v); and the sapphic strophe (viii). He wished to write a literary work, that of a *scholarly* poet as they would have called it in the days of Catullus and Horace. The same claim is betrayed in the composition of his pieces. Prudentius endeavoured to amplify and illustrate his subject by inserting extracts and descriptions from the Bible. He cultivated a literary development with the conscious and avowed desire of embodying some little of the distinction still shed by the classic poets. " A sentiment which was not Christian, that of human renown, a love which was not Christian, that of art esteemed and aimed at for its own sake, are seen to be at the bottom of this new form of inspiration, and the genius of other days on its way to disappear, but immortal in spite of all, creeps in and mingles with that of the age which was springing to birth." [2] This great attempt was not without its fruit. Prudentius hits upon some happy developments, and verses of bright and delicate colouring, such as the following on the Holy Innocents, in the hymn of the Epiphany (v. 125 et s.) :

" Hail, ye blossoms of martyrdom, whom, on the very threshold of life, Christ's persecutor hath mown down, like budding roses in a sudden gust of wind—First victims of Christ, tender flock of sacrifice, innocently ye sport with palm and crown at the very foot of the altar. . . ."

---

[1] For example, some of the strophes in hymns i, ii and xii.
[2] A. Puech, *Prudence*, p. 97.

We have to recognise that such touching and original accents are very seldom repeated in these hymns. For so grandiose an attempt Prudentius had need of greater inspiration; he required also a more accurate appreciation of proportion which would have warned him against writing at such length,[1] and would have obliged him to subordinate the different parts of the same piece to the general purport, instead of making each development bring out everything he thought possible to extract from it.

III

THE same failings of taste sometimes obtrude themselves in a still more glaring manner in the *Peristephanon* (i.e. a poem " on the crowns " [of the martyrs]), the leading idea of which is nevertheless so interesting.

The eminent dignity of the martyr in the eyes of the primitive Church is well known. The sentence of Pascal: " Je crois volontiers les histoires dont les témoins se font égorger," [2] sums up the impression of every age. In the eyes of the first Christian generations the martyr represented the perfect Christian in faith and love; on the part of his brethren he was esteemed worthy of eternal veneration as the highly-privileged depositary of the power of the Holy Spirit. In order to do honour to the dead martyrs Christianity appropriated the traditional funeral customs of the pagans, leaving itself free to modify them in accordance with its own ideals. The bodies of the martyrs were laid in the midst of the tombs of simple believers, outside the town; and it was there that the people gathered for the usual commemorations. When once security had been definitely achieved in the IVth century, these ceremonies were surrounded with more imposing circumstance, and assumed the character of real popular festivals. In every spot of Roman territory basilicas were rising up from the ground. The celebration of the feasts of a great number of martyrs tended by degrees to break through the restricted limits in which they were at first confined. An anniversary, which originally had been a kind of family affair, and special to a particular community, became almost general.

---

[1] The shortest piece, the viiith, is in 80 verses; the xiith has 208.
[2] Brunschvigg's edition, § ix, pensée 593, p. 595.

The custom was established of invoking the martyrs and of begging their intercession. From their relics power was held to emanate which appeared to be capable of being communicated, and the efficaciousness of which made itself felt both in healing and exorcism. Many of the faithful sought the privilege of being buried in the vicinity of their tombs, and the names of martyrs were readily given to children in order to assure them protection and safeguard.[1]

Prudentius who shared in these sentiments of veneration for the *witnesses* to the faith with a full union of heart and enthusiasm, conceived the bold project of making their martyrdom the subject of a series of lyrical poems.

We can mention hardly any former attempt other than that made by Damasus, Bishop of Rome (366–384), the first Pope (as appears likely) to have endeavoured to accomplish any literary work in Latin.[2] But the attempt by Damasus had a very different character. A great builder and restorer of edifices intended for worship, his design, in the words of Rossi, was "to include not only certain chosen monuments of the Roman Church, but indeed all, and especially those connected with the martyrs, in the ample circumference of the suburban cemeteries, and to adorn them with historic *tituli*, for present and future instruction." Majestically engraved by Furius Dionysius Filocalus, an engraver of much taste, the inscriptions of Damasus were eagerly read and copied out by pilgrims visiting the *mirabilia* of Rome. Many of these marbles were broken by the Goths in the VIth century; fortunately collections of them in manuscript had been early made. The interpretation made by Rossi has largely contributed to determine the tests of authenticity of these inscriptions composed by Damasus.[3] From the literary

---

[1] See the excellent book dealing with all these matters by Delehaye, *Les Origines du Culte des Martyrs*, Brussels, 1912.

[2] See above, p. 52, for Victor I; for Sixtus II, and the treatise by the pseudo-Cyprian *ad Novatianum*, p. 163, note 1. Two letters in Latin of Pope Cornelius (251–253) figure in the series of letters of St Cyprian (*Ep.* xlix, L); five others have been lost, which we can take note of, thanks to allusions by St Cyprian (*Ep.* xlv, i; xlviii, i; L; lix, 1–2). There is a special edition of the two letters which have been preserved, by G. Mergati, *D'Alcuni nuovi sussidi per la critica del testo di S Cipriano*, Rome, 1899, pp. 72–86. A decision of Pope Stephen relative to the baptism of heretics is quoted by St Cyprian (*Ep.* lxxiv, 1). The letters of Pope Liberius (352–366) are in P.L., vol. VIII: of these there are four (*Studens paci, Pro Deifico, Quia scio*, and *Non doceo: ibid.*, 1365–1372) which have occasioned much discussion as to the orthodoxy of Liberius: See Zeiller, in B.A.L.A.C., 1913, pp. 20–51.

[3] These tests are three in number: the testimony of Damasus himself, the style, and the form of the characters. Cf. Ihm, in Rh. M., vol. L (1895), p. 491 et s.

point of view it must be confessed that they hold little but disappointment : " No worse verses," Mgr. Duchesne somewhat irreverently declares, " have ever been transcribed in such profusion. If only they had been merely bad ! But they are void of all history, obscure, and contain scarcely anything but banalities." [1]

There does not seem to be any doubt that Prudentius knew these vague and colourless Virgilian inscriptions, with their metrical inaccuracies. *Peristephanon XI* is, in one portion at least, only an amplification of one of the inscriptions of Damasus. Notwithstanding, Prudentius has nowhere made mention of Damasus by name. Such attempts must have appeared paltry to him by the side of the series of poems he had in view.

It was especially Spanish and Roman legends which he undertook to adorn with his art and poetry in the fourteen hymns of the *Peristephanon.*

" Hispanos Deus adspicit benignus ! " [2]

His local patriotism reserved to the Spanish martyrs poems i, iii, iv, v, vi, and viii, in which he celebrates in succession two Spanish soldiers, the brothers Hemeterius and Celedonius, who had been put to death for having refused to sacrifice to pagan altars ; Saint Eulalia of Merida ; eighteen martyrs of Cæsaraugusta (Saragossa) ; the deacon Vincentius, also of Saragossa ; Bishop Fructuosus of Tarraco (Tarragona), and his two deacons ; and the martyrs of Calagurris (Calahorra). To this series we may add poems vii and x, the former relating to the Pannonian martyr Quirinus, Bishop of Siscia (Sissek in Croatia), and the latter to St Romanus, a deacon of Cæsarea, veneration for whom had been spread in Spain, also poem xiii consecrated to the life and death of St Cyprian, a martyr reverenced by the whole Church. The other poems were inspired in Prudentius by a journey he made to Rome in the year 402 or 403. A moved and fervent pilgrim, he went through the Holy City, its sanctuaries, and

---

[1] *Hist. anc. de l'Egl.*, II, 482. Cf. *Anal. Bolland.*, XVI, 239. Migne reproduced in P.L., vol. XIII Merenda's edition (Rome, 1754). The best edition is Ihm's *Damasi epigrammata* (*Anthol. lat. supplementa.* I, Leipzic, 1895), French translation by Dom Leclercq in the *Dict. d'Arch. chr. et de Lit.*, art. *Damase.*

[2] Hymn vi, 4. Paul Allard has given in R.Q.H., 1885, p. 353 et s., a very successful specimen of criticism on the sources of Prudentius. The enquiry might be further developed.

its catacombs, studied the tablets in the churches and deciphered the inscriptions, and in this way he was able to mingle many descriptions with the accounts of the martyrdom of such Roman martyrs as St Laurence (II), St Cassian (IX), St Hippolytus (XI), St Peter and St Paul (XII) and St Agnes (XIV), wherein modern archæologists find valuable aid for their own personal investigations. The words in which he gives his impression of the catacomb in the Tiburtine Way, though less " romantic " than the famous account of St Jerome in his *Commentary on Ezechiel* (XL, 5), is not lacking either in accuracy or picturesqueness :

" Not far from the walls of Rome and the cultivated zone which surrounds them a concealed crypt opens its deep entrenchments. The steep slope of a path returning on itself leads through the windings of this retreat, from which light is absent. For daylight hardly reaches the first opening of the entrance and only then lights up the threshold of the vestibule. In proportion as one advances into the labyrinths of the cavern darkness becomes denser, although from time to time openings made in the vault of the roof permit a brilliant ray of sunlight to penetrate. In the midst of the obscure turnings formed by narrow chambers and dark galleries crossing each other, a little daylight thus falls from above into the entrails of the hill. In the bottom of the subterranean crypt it is still possible to see the gleam and to follow the light of the absent sun." [1]

Rome the beautiful, *pulcherrima Roma* [2] from the magnificence of her buildings, if not from the purity of her morals, had inspired in Prudentius an admiration of which the *Peristephanon* [3]—as also other works of this poet—bears the mark. He commiserates his compatriots living so far from her. But it was Christian Rome, with her basilicas, baptisteries, marbles, paintings and mosaics, which had especially attracted the gaze of the wonderstruck provincial ; and Prudentius was capable of being a close observer and a trusty

---

[1] *Perist.*, xi, 155–168. I am using Paul Allard's translation, R.Q.H., XXXVI (1884), 48.

[2] *Perist.*, xi, 231. Cf. Virgil, *Georg.*, ii, 534.

[3] *Perist.*, ii, 529.

witness of the manifold outward signs by which victorious
Christianity then gave evidence of its vitality.

As regards the real character of these poems and their
artistic construction, more than one reservation must be made.
Prudentius nourished his inspiration from various sources—
fama, that is popular traditions, the liturgy of the Church,
figured representations, inscriptions, especially the literature
of the later *Acta*, so different from the admirable and touching
accounts written in the first centuries (such as the *Martyrdom*
of St Polycarp, the *Letter* relating to the martyrs of Lyons,
the *Passio* of Perpetua and Felicitas, etc. . . .). He accepts
and reproduces the current stories, conventions, and declamatory rhetoric of their vexatious form of hagiography.
Let us not condemn the scenes of torture which he is pleased
to describe : " the rare cruelty " (as d'Aubigny was to say
in his *Tragiques*) [1] of these " exquisite deaths " have their
place in the oratorical jousts between judge and accused.
What is most painful is the grandiloquent verbosity which he
puts into the mouths of his martyrs : by turns ironical and
losing all self-control (did not the gentle Eulalia, brought up
under her mother's wing, spit in the face of the Praetor ?),
his heroes and heroines weary the patience of the magistrates
and that of the reader by interminable harangues in which
the commonplaces of traditional apologetics are mingled
with still more tiresome notions. St Romanus develops
at great length the strange idea that torture is not so exceptionally dreadful inasmuch as ordinary illnesses, such as
pleurisy, fever, gout, rheumatism and surgical operations,
inflict almost parallel sufferings on the patients. [2] St Laurence
draws an almost ludicrous parallel between physical ills
and the ills of the soul, and ends his list with a pun at the
expense of the judge to whom he declares that he (the judge)
is suffering from *morbus regius* (i.e. jaundice). [3] One, " under
examination," utters no fewer than six tirades—the two
last of 32 and 93 lines—after his tongue had been cut out ! [4]
Prudentius does not know how to keep himself within limits ;
he has a tendency to prolixity and declamation owing to the
natural bent of his Spanish temperament nourished on Roman

---

[1] Lalanne's, ed. 1857. *Les Feux*, p. 178.
[2] *Perist.*, iii, 127.
[3] *Ibid.*, ii, 264.
[4] *Perist.*, x, 133 et s. ; 426 et s. ; 587 et s. ; 801 et s. ; 928 et s. ; 1007 et s.

rhetoric but little understanding the models of lofty reason offered by the classics which he was endeavouring to out-rival.

This lack of literary tact is all the more regrettable because brilliant pieces, well-finished developments, and skil-fully arranged strophes are not rare in the *Peristephanon*. The attempt realised by Prudentius is worthy of respect. And what variety of metre, what technical virtuosity ![1] But all the archæological and historic interest of this work, and certain happy successes, cannot hide its weakness of con-struction and the mistakes of a somewhat uncertain good taste.

IV

ANOTHER series of poems is of the didactic kind, so well suited to the Roman temperament, and to the best and most glorious Latin tradition, and it was natural that Christianity, eager to instruct souls in order to conquer them, should appropriate it in its turn. These are the *Apotheosis*, the *Hamartigenia*, the two books *Contra Symmachum*, the *Psy-chomachia* and the *Dittochaeon*.

Preceded by a double prelude, one in 12 hexameters, the other in 56 iambic lines grouped together in twos and threes, the *Apotheosis* refutes in 1084 hexameters a certain number of errors concerning the Trinity, and the Divinity of Christ. Prudentius first takes to task the " Patripassionist " heresy of Praxeas (1–177), and then Sabellianism (178–320). His polemics are then turned against the Jews (321–551), a " blind and deaf " nation who obstinately shut their ears to the Divine voice whereas almost the whole world had learned to listen to its accents :

" It hath known the coming of the Lord, this people
     whom the sun of Iberia sees when it sets, and whom
     the East lightens with its first rays. The penetrating

---

[1] Here is a table of the metres he employs : i (120 lines) ; in catalectic trochaic tetrameters ; ii (584 lines) : acatalectic iambic dimeters ; iii (215 lines) : hyper-catalectic dactylic trimeters ; iv (200 lines) : sapphic strophes ; v (575 lines) : acatalectic iambic dimeters ; vi (162 lines) : phalecian hendecasyllables ; vii (90 lines) : glyconics ; viii (18 lines) : elegiacs ; ix (106 lines) : dactylic hexa-meters and iambic trimeters grouped together in verses ; x (1130 lines) : iambic trimeters ; xi (246 lines) : elegiacs ; xii (66 lines) : archilochian ; xiii (106 lines) : archilochian ; xiv (133 lines) : hendecasyllable Alcaics.

force of the word of the Gospel hath pierced the frosts of Scythia, and its warmth hath dissipated the misty cold of Hyrcania; delivered from its icy bonds, the Hebrus, coming to birth in the Caucasus, rolls to the foot of Rhodope its cool waters. The Getae are made gentle; the Gelonian, ferocious barbarian, fills with pure milk his cup emptied of blood; the blood of Christ will furnish him with a holy potion. Already the countries of Atlas inhabited by the perfidious Moor have learned to consecrate on the altars of God their bearded kings. . . . And among the sons of Aeneas, the purple prostrates itself suppliant before the altars of Christ, and the lord of the world adores the standard of the Cross!" [1]

Like the Jews, the Ebionites denied the divinity of Jesus. Prudentius opposes to them the prodigies which surrounded His birth, and especially the succession of His miracles (552–781). He declares that those who deny Christ will be the prey of everlasting night, and this gives him occasion to study the nature of the soul, its origin, and the punishments beyond the grave (782–951). Christ alone escaped death. Prudentius launches a final assault against the Manichaean docetism, and concludes his poem with a vigorous affirmation of his belief in the Resurrection.

The *Hamartigenia*, in 966 hexameters preceded by a preface of 63 iambic trimeters, treats of only one question, the origin of evil as connected with Marcion's Gnostic dualism, which is interpellated right from the beginning. Prudentius arraigns dualism: he who admits two gods can just as well admit thousands. The father of evil was Satan, the corrupter of mankind and of nature. In this connection the poet gives some specimens of the vices of his times, and with special vigorousness takes exception to the artifices of the *toilette* in blameworthy use among women—Why has God permitted evil? (637 et s.):

"Si non vult Deus esse malum, cur non vetat? inquis."

Because that was the sole means of leaving to human action man's free choice between the lord of life and the lord of death. This choice will be confirmed by posthumous rewards.

[1] *Apoth.*, 424 et s.

The description given by Prudentius of the torments of Hell (824 et s.) and the joys of Paradise is one of the most circumstantial left to us by Christian literature of the first centuries :

" Carpunt tormenta foventque
Materiem sine fine datam : mors deserit ipsa
Aeternos gemitus, et flentes vivere cogit."

In conclusion, he expresses the hope of meriting a not too vigorous punishment, if the " immense light " be denied him.

These two poems are not at all negligible. Certainly the doctrine contained in them is hardly original. Although he was treating of questions in which his age took a lively interest, Prudentius avoided throwing himself into the quarrels of the time. Some people have thought to discover allusions to Priscillianism in them.[1] They must be very vague ; and why should Prudentius have avoided mentioning Priscillian by name ? As a matter of fact, he preferred to inveigh against errors which had been classified and refuted long before. Nearly all the substance of his theology comes from Tertullian, whose *Adversus Marcionem, Adversus Praxean,* the *De Carne Christi,* and perhaps the *De Patientia,* he had read. Where Prudentius is seen to advantage is in explanation and detail. He had an appreciation of ideas, and the gift of explaining clearly and of illustrating them with significant examples. He had that passion which animates and gives colour to everything, and a sincere attachment to the beliefs he was burning to propagate, like some Christian Lucretius. A great number of his developments are interesting in connection with the history of manners, and there is something in his poetical mythology, and in his race of demons, the enemies of mankind whose ambushes he describes, which has made certain possibly too indulgent critics, think of the pictures of a Dante or a Milton which are powerful in another way.

Written between the spring of the year 402 and the summer of 403, the two books *Contra Symmachum* came twenty years after the famous incidents the vicissitudes of which we have related.[2] M. A. Puech[3] is inclined to think that there may

---

[1] Kunstle, *Antipriscilliana,* Freib.-i.-B., 1905, p. 170 et s. Cf. Bergman's ed. of the *Psychomachia,* p. xxviii ; he is much less positive than Kunstle.
[2] P. 270 et s.
[3] *Op. cit.,* p. 195.

have been, shortly before 402, a fresh attempt on the part of Symmachus, or of his party, to extort from the son of Theodosius the favourable decision which had been obstinately refused by his predecessor. At the beginning of book II Prudentius seems to say that the *orator catus* had come back to the charge. The allusion is however very far from being explicit. Doubtless Prudentius simply saw in this episode an interesting historical subject the rich matter of which he tried to exploit.

The work comprises two books. The first opens with a preface in 89 asclepiads in which Prudentius recalls the shipwreck of St Paul on the coast of the island of Malta, and how he rendered the bite of the viper innocuous : in this account in the Acts (xxviii) the poet saw in miniature a symbol of the destiny of Christianity itself. There follow 658 hexameters in which the triumph of the faith is celebrated, notwithstanding the vitality which, thanks to certain influences, paganism still preserved. Theodosius pronounces a long discourse summoning Rome to detach herself from her gods and to adore the Cross. Further, it was to Christianity that all the promises of the future were to come :

"Turn your looks towards the people : how many are there who do not shun with disgust the altar of Jupiter, tainted with impure blood? All those people who dwell in high garrets and run about the muddy streets of the city, and who eat the bread which is served out to them from the high steps, hasten to visit on Mount Aventine the tomb wherein repose the ashes of Peter, our beloved Father ; or else they go in crowds to the palace on the Lateran whence they return with the holy Chrism and the sacred character of the Christian. What then ! Can we still doubt, O Christ, that Rome is consecrated to thee and hath passed under thy laws ? . . . ." [1]

The first book closes with a fine eulogium on Symmachus, *Romani decus eloquii*, in regard to whom the poet observes in this polemical work the most exact rules of courtesy.

In the preface to the second book, in 66 eloquent glyconics

---

[1] I, 545 et s. ; 579 et s.

Prudentius invokes the presence of Christ. Then he unfolds in 1131 hexameters a refutation of the *Relatio* of Symmachus, making use of almost the same answer which St Ambrose had given.

The work is interesting for more than one reason. We find vigorous traits in it worthy of the strong realism of Juvenal; for example, when Prudentius jeers at the tardy marriages of the Vestals (II, 1080 et s.) :

> " Vesta on her return is weary at last of all this virginity; her period of service over, her sacred work accomplished, the aged Vestal is in haste to marry; she leaves the hearth she has guarded all her youth; she carries to the nuptial couch her well-won wrinkles and, newly married in a frozen bed, learns to know transports that are but lukewarm." [1]

But the most curious aspect of this work is the ardent patriotism breathing through it, which the poet associates with his beliefs without any difficulty. Prudentius had a respect and a love for Rome, and accepted the doctrine of her immortality in the same spirit that Horace or Virgil would have felt. He venerates all the outward marks by which the might of Rome was expressed, whenever they were not opposed to the faith. The *prestige* of the Senate remains unimpaired in his eyes; he calls the Senators *pulcherrima mundi lumina*. He uses words of respect and devotion in speaking of the emperors. Even to Julian the Apostate he had previously rendered impartial justice in the *Apotheosis :*

> " He flourished in the days of my childhood, and I remember him. A very courageous general, a wise lawgiver, famed for his eloquence and his valour, he preferred the religion of his fathers to the true religion, and was the zealous upholder of three hundred thousand gods. I have seen that prince, faithless to God, but not to Rome (*Perfidus ille Deo, quamvis non perfidus Urbi*), bowing his august head before the feet of a Minerva made of clay, etc." [2]

The reverence of Prudentius for Rome, and his confidence in her eternal destinies, are closely bound up with his religious

[1] II, 1078 et s. [2] *Apoth.*, 450 et s.

convictions. Looking down the vista of past centuries Rome seemed to him to have fulfilled a kind of mission set by Providence. By grouping together under her hegemony all the peoples of the world she had been a powerful instrument for the propagation of Christianity :

"Would you know, O Romans, the true cause of your accomplishments, the real reason of that glory which hath placed the world under your yoke ? These races speak different languages, their kingdoms have diverse religions : God willed to make of them a society, to submit their customs to the unity of the same empire, and to make all accept the same yoke, in order that religion might draw together the hearts of men ; for there could not be a union worthy of Christ unless one spirit only held all nations joined together. . . . In every part of the world men live this day as fellow-citizens of the same city, and their children by the same hearth. The administration of justice, the forum, commerce, the arts, and marriages, draw together the inhabitants of the most distant shores. These are the fruits of the victories and triumphs of the Roman Empire : in this way was the path prepared for the coming of Christ, and the road constructed by a long peace under Roman government. . . . The world, O Christ, now possesseth Thee, the world brought into unity by the *Pax Romana*." [1]

In the *Peristephanon*, II, 433, he placed this prayer in the mouth of the martyr Laurence :

"O Christ, grant unto thy Romans that their city may be Christian, that city through whom Thou hast given the same faith to all the cities of the world (*per quam dedisti ut ceteris mens una sacrorum foret*). May all their scattered members be united under one sign ! May the universe turn in submission, may their city, mistress of all, turn ! . . . May Romulus become a believer, and Numa himself believe in thee ! "

---

[1] II, 582 et s. Compare Claudian's lines, *de Consul. Stilich.*, III, 138 :
"Haec est in gremium victos quae sola recepit,
Humanumque genus communi nomine fovit."

The Roman patriotism of Prudentius is so sensitive on this point that he surpassed that of Symmachus. The poet does not mean to admit that the gods had nothing to do with the working out of the grandeur of Rome, for their action might be enlarged on by only recalling the exploits of a Corvinus or the Fabii (II, 555 et s.). He protests against the pessimism into which Symmachus was tempted to fall when he gave importance to certain indications of the wrath of heaven against Rome for being heedless of her traditions. No, never had the Empire been so happy, so flourishing ; as for those who were threatening her, as for the Barbarians, there was more difference between them and the Romans than " between the quadruped and the biped, between the dumb and one able to speak, between the Christian and the pagan " (II, 814 et s.).

A curious state of mind which facts, the rulers of the world, were not long in modifying at the centre of Christendom. We have already followed this transformation in the case of St Augustine, Orosius, and Salvianus. During all these first years of the Vth century before the inrush of the barbarians, it became still more general, and the vehemence with which Prudentius knew how to give expression to it should suffice to lend an exceptionally historic bearing to the *Contra Symmachum*.

The battles of the soul, and the struggle between Christianity and paganism, form the subject of the *Psychomachia*, a kind of epopee with an apologetic intention, which takes the shape of a long allegory. The preface, in 68 iambic trimeters, relates an episode in the history of Abraham ; then the poem, in 915 hexameters, opens with a Virgilian ring :

> "Christe, graves hominum semper miserate labores[1] . . ."

First the Faith is advancing :

> ". . . agresti turbida cultu,
> Nuda humeros, intonsa comas, exserta lacertos."

The first enemy who dares to come to the attack is the *veterum Cultura Deorum* (l. 29). But the faith lays it low, and the *legio victrix* composed of a thousand martyrs shouts

[1] Cf. *Æneid*, VI, 56 : " Phoebe, graves Trojae semper miserate labores."

with joy.   Other battles take place between *Pudicitia* and *Sodomita Libido* (l. 40–108), Patience and Anger (109–177), *Superbia* and the army led by Humility and Hope (178–309). *Superbia* falls into a pit digged by *Fraus*, and Humility cuts off her head.   But here a more formidable enemy comes forward, *Luxuria*, with her perfumed hair, wandering eyes, and languid voice. . . .

> "Delibuta comas, oculis vaga, languida voce.
> Perdita deliciis, vitae cui cause voluptas" (l. 310).

She hurls at the army composed of the virtues, not javelins, but violets and rose leaves whose corrupting scent (*male dulcis odor*) insinuates itself languorously among them. Fortunately *Sobrietas* finds the words necessary to reanimate their failing courage, and *Luxuria* falls under their blows. Her army, made up of *Jocus, Petulantia, Amor, Pompa,* and *Voluptas*, scatters, leaving behind an ample booty of which Avarice and her daughters, true Eumenides, wish to take possession.   Pity (i.e. *Operatio*)[1] saves the situation.   The army of the Virtues is then victorious.   Concord (l. 644) gives the signal to go back to the camp to which the triumphant troops take their way singing like the Israelites after the passage of the Red Sea.   But she is wounded by a treacherous blow from Discord (l. 665) who, summoned to give her name, confesses that she is called *Haeresis* (l. 710). Discord develops her views on Christ (Prudentius is hitting at Arianism and Gnosticism—perhaps also at Priscillianism, but that is open to doubt) ; Faith ends by piercing her tongue with a dart, and invites the holy assembly to raise in honour of Christ a temple spangled with gems, sapphires, amethysts, and topazes.   A prayer of thanksgiving to Jesus concludes the poem (888–915).

Thus the method consistently employed in the *Psychomachia* is allegory, in the sense of personifying purely abstract notions.   This method was no stranger to Greek literature,[2] and Roman taste had accepted it from a long date.   We have only to call to mind the abstractions so often deified in the old religion of the Romans[3]—the dialogue between

---

[1] L. 573.

[2] An example in Egger's *Essai sur l'hist. de la Critique chez les Grecs*, Paris, 2nd ed., 1886, p. 41.

[3] Cagnat-Chapot's *Manuel d'archéol. Rom.*, I (1917), pp. 460–466.

Luxury and Poverty in the prologue to the *Trinummus* of
Plautus, the *mala gaudia mentis* of the Hades of Virgil (*Aen.*,
VI, 273 et s.), Claudian's description of the gardens of Venus
in the *de Nuptiis Honorii et Mariae*, peopled by *Pallor*, *Irae*,
Licentia, *Perjuria*, *Voluptas* and *Lacrimae ;* and again in
Christian literature itself, we have the portrait of Patience
as drawn by Tertullian : " If we would like to picture her
countenance and apparel, her face is tranquil and peaceful,
her forehead smooth with no wrinkles from anger or grief . . ."
(*de Pat.*, xv) ; and there is the procession of adultery in the
de Pudicitia, v, led by idolatry which goes before, and by
homicide which follows after, both of whom protest their
complete solidarity with her. " It is very natural," observes
M. Puech, " that a Christian who sees in temptation the work
of the Devil, should be led, more than another, to translate
into exterior images the struggles of within, and to give a
visible reality to the adversaries whom he supposes present
to him." This was very much the view of Prudentius : he
intended, under a poetical form, to translate the " inner
sedition " of the soul, the tumult of which was only appeased
by faith :

> " Et omnes
> Virtutum gemmas componat sede piata " (l. 910).

Taken as a whole the poem leaves an impression of
pedantic heaviness clinging to an almost continuous imitation
of the epic style of Virgil. All these abstractions abuse one
another, embrace, and put each other in the wrong, repeating
the words and gestures of the heroes in the *Æneid*. And
what eloquence is expended in these fictitious encounters
from which flows blood too pale to cause emotion ! Discourses on Chastity, Anger, Patience, Pride, Hope, Sobriety,
Operatio, Discord, Concord, Faith—there is scarcely one of
these vices or virtues which the poet does not dower with his
inexhaustible verboseness, interrupting his narrative, and
again resuming it with a *Dixerat* or a *Haec ubi dicta dedit*
after the manner of Virgil. Furthermore we should be
ignorant of the spirit of the Middle Ages to be astonished that
this was recognised in the *Psychomachia*, and that this poem
became one of their favourite books. Their theologians,
miniaturists, and sculptors (the Roman more than the

Gothic) on many an occasion found in it matter for their dialectics or the motives of their inspiration.[1]

There remains the *Dittochaeon*. The title of this work is rather enigmatic : without doubt we must derive it from the two Greek words διττὸς ὀχή meaning " twofold nourishment," in allusion to the Old and the New Testaments. It is a collection of 49 quatrains in hexameters intended for the explanation of pictures : twenty-four refer to the Old Testament, and twenty-five to the New. Paintings and mosaics were largely employed in the religious edifices from the IVth century,[2] and inscriptions were often placed before them in order to interpret them to the faithful, " ut littera monstret quod manus explicuit," as Paulinus of Nola expressed it.[3] The following are the subjects of some of the works of art briefly commented on in the *Dittochaeon*—in what Church we do not know : *Adam and Eve ; The Oak of Mambre ; Sara's Tomb ; Joseph recognised by his brethren ; Moses receiving the Law ;* the *House of Rahab the Harlot ;* the *Captivity of Israel ; Mary and the Angel Gabriel ;* the *Angels announcing the Glad Tidings to the Shepherds ;* the *Massacre of the Innocents ;* the *Resurrection of Lazarus ;* the *Passion of the Saviour ; St Peter's Vision,* etc. . . . The descriptions of these historic scenes are of great interest in the study of Christian iconography.

V

CONSIDERING the work of Prudentius as a whole we cannot refuse to admire a poetical effort which transformed the liturgical hymn into a Christian ode, which drew from the ample literature of the *Acts of the Martyrs* rich epic and lyrical material, which placed didactic poetry at the service of the new faith, and largely exploited the allegorical method. The poetry of Prudentius is absolutely Christian in its inspiration. Certain private opinions have been noticed in him, for instance,

[1] See Mâle's *L'Art relig. au XIII s. en France,* 3rd ed., 1910, p. 124 et s., 150 ; L. Bréhier's *L'Art Chrétien,* 1918, p. 203 et s.
[2] Cf. St Paulinus of Nola, *Natale,* IX, 515–635 ; X, 15–27 ; 167–179 ; *Ep.* xxxii, 17 ; Biraghi, *Disticha ad picturas sanctas in Basilica Ambrosiana,* in continuation of the *Inni sinceri di sant. Ambrogio,* Milan, 1862.
[3] *Natale,* IX, 584–585.

concerning the rest accorded to the damned on the night of the Resurrection : [1] there are hardly any authentic Fathers of the Church in whom analogous views may not be noted. Prudentius does not pride himself in playing at being an original thinker, and his sole wish is to infuse into the souls of his readers the enthusiasm for the faith held in common by the faithful with which he himself is animated. But this singer of Catholic doctrines is at the same time a Roman of the good old stock, formed in the school of Lucretius, Virgil, Horace and Juvenal, familiar, too, so it appears, with the Greek language. He accepts all the firm Roman traditions on condition that he may purify them. Although impassioned, there is nothing of the fanatic or iconoclast about him. He respects the manifestations of Roman genius both in art and literature, and in their civil and political life :

> " O Senators," he exclaims, " wash ye your marbles stained with the blood of victims : may the statues, works of great artists, rear themselves white and pure. In them we have the fairest ornaments of our fatherland ; but may no unworthy use from henceforth soil these monuments of an art which has for too long been turned aside from its proper end." [2]

Bentley calls him " *Christianorum Maro et Flaccus.*" Virgil and Horace were in truth his favourite models. A rather bold innovator as regards matter and verbal creations, his style is closely imitated from the phraseology of Virgil, and he tried to reproduce in his metres, so varied in form, the technical suppleness and dexterity of Horace. He had no need, in speaking of himself, to exclaim : " *Audi poetam rusticum,*" [3] or to declare that " a love for the precious names of the martyrs interferes little with the rules of versification, for when one speaks of the Saints one never speaks amiss or incorrectly." [4] Such commonplaces are somewhat insincere. In fact he emancipated himself from the popular forms preferred by Christian poets anterior to him, and almost the only one with whom he may be compared as regards diversity of metre, is Ausonius.

---

[1] *Cathem.*, L, 125.
[3] *Perist.*, II, 574.
[2] *Contra Symm.*, I, 501–5.
[4] *Ibid.*, L, 165.

This combination of Christian thought and classic forms often produces curious incongruities in Prudentius. Like the great Venetians of the XVIth century, he intermingles heterogeneous elements in his composition. He describes Sodom as being destroyed with its *tabularia, forum, balneae, templa* and *madidae propinae*.[1] At the marriage of Cana, Christ changes the water into Falernian wine, " *fit falernum nobile*." [2] Biblical and Roman forms are constantly mixed up in his verses, together with anachronisms whose simplicity is not without its savour.

Taken as a whole, he is not far short of deserving to be called a great poet. With a little more moral substance, or originality in psychological observation, and with a finer sense of proportion, he would almost have realised that fusion of the two " learnings " which the most lettered Christians of the first centuries had always dreamed of, without daring to acknowledge it.

VI

" In the towns, estates, country-side, cross-roads, villages, and all along the roads wherever you looked, nothing was seen but death, woe, destruction, disaster, fire, and mourning ; in short, entire Gaul was nothing but a smoking funeral pyre." These lines from the *Commonitorium* [3] of Orientius make us think that this poet must have witnessed the vast desolation of Gaul ravaged by invasions since the first years of the Vth century. At the beginning of his *Life of St Martin*,[4] Fortunatus mentions Orientius after Juvencus and Sedulius, and before Prudentius, Paulinus of Périgueux and Avitus. Scrupulous critics have decided to identify him with St Orens, the Bishop of Auch,[5] who in 439, in the name of Theodoric king of the Visigoths at Toulouse, presented himself before the Roman generals Aetius and Littorius, in order to solicit peace from them.[6]

Orientius, whose birthplace the three *Lives* drawn up by the Bollandists give as in Spain, must have been living in

[1] *Hamart.*, 758 et s.
[2] *Cathem.*, IX, 28.
[3] *Common.*, II, 181 et s.
[4] I, 140.
[5] L. Duchesne, *Fastes Episc. de l'Anc. Gaule*, II, 96.
[6] *Acta Sanctorum*, 1st May, p. 62.

Gaul in the first half of the Vth century. His *Commonitorium* is an exhortation in elegiacs written for the purpose of instructing his readers as to " what are the means which open Heaven to us and put death to flight." Without concealing that he himself had escaped with great difficulty from the " slough of sensuality " he wishes the experiences of his life to be serviceable for their good. In the first book, after having besought Christ in a prayer, which takes the place of the old invocation to the Muses, for " the gift of good speech and thought," he enumerates the blessings of God, recommends the law of charity to one's neighbour, and details the promises of the Resurrection and immortality ; he then goes on to precepts in the practical order—to beware of women, " the first cause of evil on earth," whose deceptive beauty turns into hideousness with advancing years : " When therefore thou dost behold a young girl of fair countenance and charming manner, turn aside thine eyes, or lower thy head " ; to preserve oneself also from envy and cupidity, and to love peace. The second book enjoins mistrust of praise, draws a rather spirited portrait of the drunkard losing his dignity and his equilibrium, and lays bare how vain do honours appear at the approach of inevitable death, the prelude to the tremendous divine judgments.

This poem, or rather sermon in verse (for the tone is consistently oratorical) on the vanities and miseries of the world, reads easily. What is especially wanting is originality of expression. There is some truth in Fauriel's [1] judgment when he is astonished at the " inability of ecclesiastical literature to rise to simple and severe forms—forms in harmony with the basic nature of its subject." If we take away from this poem of Orientius (as we might from many other productions of this period) what the poet owes to Virgil, Ovid, Horace and even Martial, Catullus, and Juvenal, without counting the Christian poets, little else remains but the merit of having pieced together this *marqueterie*, and the honour due to his outspoken convictions.

The *Commonitorium* has come down to us in only two manuscripts, an *Aquicinctensis* (i.e. a MS. of Anchin, near Douai), now lost, which only contains the first book and formed the basis for the edition of Martin Antoine Delrio

[1] *Hist. de la Gaule mérid.*, I, 430.

(Antwerp, 1600), and a *Turonensis* of the Xth century, which contains the two books and was used by Dom Edmond Martène in his edition of 1700. Stolen from Tours by the famous Libri, this manuscript was sold to Lord Ashburnham ; thanks to Leopold Delisle, the French Bibliothèque Nationale regained possession of it in the year 1888. It announces " twenty-four prayers of Orientius " to follow the *Commonitorium*,[1] but only gives two, in iambics of 6 feet ; the strophes are of three lines with a refrain of two lines. It is probable that these pieces were written for liturgical use.

The *Alethia*—the Latin for the Greek word ᾿Αληθέια, Truth—follows the story in Genesis from the creation of the world to the destruction of Sodom. The first book (547 hexam.) corresponds to the three first chapters of Genesis ; the second (558 hexam.) to the four following ; the third (789 hexam.) embraces chapter viii, verse 20, to chapter xix, verse 29. In spite of certain slight difficulties, we can identify this poem with that attributed by Gennadius (*de Vir. Ill.*, lxi) to one Victorinus or Victorius, a rhetorician of Marseilles : the only manuscript of the *Alethia*[2] gives as the author " Claudius Marius Victor, *orator Massiliensis.*" Victor was a lettered man, familiar with Lucretius, Virgil and Ovid. His object, as he shows in the *Precatio* at the beginning, is to instruct the youth, *teneros formare animos :*[3] he also carefully leaves out indecent incidents, such as that relating to the daughters of Lot, and dissembles the wickedness of Sodom. It is with the same intention to instruct that he outlines certain philosophic doctrines, such as atomism and the eternity of matter,[4] and certain practices such as astrology.[5] While paying homage to his " truly Christian and pious sense," Gennadius declares that Victor " only expressed ideas of a very slight value because no one had instructed him how to understand the Scriptures." It is not impossible that Gennadius, with his known tendencies, was rather annoyed

---

[1] We must note that this title is not provided by the manuscripts, which only give *S Orientii versus* and *Versus libri S Orientii*. It goes back to Sigebert de Gembloux, a writer of the XIth century, and was preferred by Delrio and Martène.

[2] *Parisin.* 7558, IXth century (which comes from Tours).

[3] V, 1, 104–5.

[4] I, 22–32.

[5] III, 139–148.

that a layman and a man of letters like Victor should dare to appropriate the Bible and effect a number of transpositions of the facts in the sacred narrative, even though he offered his excuses [1] while doing so.

Following the *Alethia*, a *S. Paulini Epigramma* in 110 hexameters figures in the manuscript : it is a satirical dialogue upon Gallo-Roman morals—masculine and feminine— at the beginning of the Vth century. The unknown author (he has been sometimes identified, at a guess, with Paulinus, Bishop of Béziers [c. 400–419]), gives his opinion that the hardest trials have not reformed the vices of his compatriots.[2]

VII

WE see clearly in the *Eucharisticos* (616 hexameters) which Paulinus of Pella wrote in 459 when he was over 80 years old among what vicissitudes certain lives were passed in those troublous times.

"Conditio instabilis semper generaliter aeví." [3]

He was born at Pella in Macedonia. His father there fulfilled the office of Prefect, and then was given the high position of Pro-Consul of Africa, and the child was taken to Carthage. Eighteen months later he was brought to Rome, and then to Bordeaux, the home of his ancestors : *Tandem majorum in patriam. . . . Burdigala veni.* There he first came to know his grandfather, who was then Consul.

It has been deduced from these indications that Paulinus must have been the grandson of Ausonius, who was Consul in the year 379. Two different theories have been put forward by the critics : some identify the father of Paulinus with Hesperius, the son of Ausonius, who was Pro-Consul of Africa in 376 ; [4] others with Thalassius, the son-in-law of Ausonius, who was Pro-Consul of Africa in 378, whose son

---

[1] *Prec.*, 119.

[2] V. 91 et s. Text in Migne, LXI, 969–972, and in C.V., xvi, 499 ; French translation in Clément, *op. cit.*, pp. 247–252. This passage should be noted : " If St Paul and Solomon be left on one side, if a Dido recite Virgil, a Corinna Ovid, if they (women) applaud the lyre of Flaccus or the Muse of Terence, it is we (men) who are responsible."

[3] *Euchar.*, v. 540.

[4] Tillemont, *Hist. des Empereurs*, V, 710–11 : Kruger in R.E., article *Paulinus v. P. ;* Schenkl, in his edition of Ausonius.

was Paulinus by a first marriage.[1] In any case, we do not know of any other Consul than Ausonius connected with Bordeaux during those years. The relationship of Ausonius to Paulinus is therefore hardly open to doubt, although the former has nowhere made any allusion to his grandson Paulinus.

" The enlightened solicitude of my irreproachable parents fashioned my mind from childhood so as never to expose my reputation to the attacks of scandal. And although this reputation, surely acquired, obtained its measure of esteem, I would nevertheless have preferred the kind of praise which would have been reserved for me if, in agreement as were the wishes of my parents at first with my own, these had persisted in the design of consecrating me from my childhood to Thy service, O Christ. More wisely inspired for my welfare, their pious solicitude would have freed me from the passing pleasures of the flesh in order to enable me to gather the eternal fruits of the future life." [2]

There seems to emerge from this enigmatic passage that the parents of Paulinus, after favouring a precocious religious vocation, afterwards withstood it. They somewhat spoilt the child who was of rather delicate health, and he obtained from their indulgence the gratification of all his whims— horses, dogs, hawks, toys, rich clothes, etc. . . . Paulinus gives us the information that during his adolescence he restrained himself from yielding to the seductions of women of independent position in life, who were much disposed not to show themselves too timid, and that he contented himself meritoriously with availing himself of the charms of the domestics who were in the service of his parents (contentus domus illecebris famulantibus uti) ! At the age of twenty he

[1] Peiper, in his edition of Ausonius, pp. ci and cxv ; Brandes, in his edition of Paulinus of Pella ; Seeck, M.G.H., VI, i, p. lxxvii. Seeck remarks that instructions xv, 7, 3 (10th March, 376), and 1, 32, 2 (8th July, 376) of the *Theodosian Code*, are addressed to Hesperius, Pro-Consul, while instructions 1, 15, 8 (21st January, 377), and viii, 5, 34 (25th February, 377) are addressed to Hesperius, Praetorian Prefect. Hesperius was therefore Prefect of the Gauls from the beginning of the year 377. Now Paulinus informs us that his father was at Pella when he was born and that afterwards he was for eighteen months in Africa as Pro-Consul, that is to say, up to the end of 377. This raises a difficulty.—I remark that this would form a more serious difficulty if we were not aware of the lack of preciseness customary with the ancient poets on questions of chronology.

[2] Cf. Brandes, C.V., vol. XVI, p. 295.

was married off ; he became a man settled in life, active, but fond of a comfortable existence, the security of which was not long in being endangered by subsequent events :

> " I desired a commodious house with large apartments arranged for all kinds of weather according to the different seasons of the year, a table neat and well garnished, slaves young and numerous, furniture in plenty and suited to different uses, silver plate more valuable from its design than from its weight, artists of every kind skilful in promptly carrying out my commissions, stables full of well-fed horses, and strong and elegant carriages for taking drives."

He was thirty when the barbarians penetrated into the " very entrails of the Roman Empire." At first he had only praise for the Goths, who bestowed upon him important positions of dignity. But, by a grievous change of fortune, he soon saw himself despoiled of his possessions, driven from his home which was left in ashes, and besieged in Bazas by the Goths and Alani whom he skilfully found means to set against each other. He would have liked to flee to the East where he still retained a few possessions. He was unable to succeed in doing this, and moreover his wife had no desire to take this step. All these trials ripened his conversion, which he did not complete until fairly late, when he was about 46 years old. In addition, he lost successively his mother-in-law, his mother, his wife, and one of his sons who was already a priest. He lived poverty stricken on the meagre remnant of his patrimony, first at Marseilles and then at Bordeaux. A Goth had the honesty to remit to him the money for a small property which had formerly belonged to him, thus saving him from a too lamentable old age.

The account of this progressive downfall, interspersed with words of thanksgiving after the manner of St Augustine in his *Confessions*, is very attractive, and reflects the uncertainty and misery of that period of dissolution.

VIII

BROTHER of the Bishop of Vienne in Dauphiny, Claudianus Mamertus was a priest in that same town, where he died in

474. " In this master," Sidonius Apollinaris declares in the epitaph which he wrote on him, " a three-fold literature (*triplex bybliotheca*) shone forth—Roman, Attic and Christian. . . . Orator, dialectician, poet, author of sermons, geometrician and musician, he excelled in unravelling the knots of problems and in striking with the sword of his speech the sectaries who harass the Catholic faith. . . ." The generous terms employed by Sidonius in praising his friends are well known. Moreover Claudianus Mamertus is not at all wanting in merit. Gennadius [1] rightly calls him " *Vir ad loquendum artifex et ad disputandum subtilis.*" In his *De Statu Animae* in three books written in 469 and dedicated to Sidonius, he defends the theory of the incorporeity of the soul—substance without doubt, but not quantitative nor subject to the category of space—against the contrary speculations of Faustus of Riez and Gennadius. We have, further, two letters in his name addressed, one to Sidonius Apollinaris, and the other to the rhetorician Sapaudus of Vienne, in which he deplores in significant terms [2] the lack of intellectual curiosity of his contemporaries ; also a few poems which we cannot attribute to him with certainty, or which we should even formally deny having been written by him. A mention added to the notice in Gennadius, missing in most of the manuscripts of the *De Viris Illustribus*, attributes to him the *Pange Lingua Gloriosi.* But it appears certain that Venantius Fortunatus was the author of this famous hymn. Sidonius makes two allusions to hymns written by his friend [3] which may account for this erroneous attribution.

IX

THE principal work written by Dracontius, the *De Laudibus Dei*, was not published in its entirety until 1791 by the Jesuit Arevalo, from two manuscripts in the Vatican which ascribe it inaccurately to St Augustine. Up till then only the portion relating to the history of the Creation, the *Hexaemeron*, was known, which had been detached at an early date from

---

[1] *De Viris Ill.*, lxxxiv.
[2] P.L., LIII, 783 ; C.V., XI, p. 203.
[3] *Ep.* IV, iii, and in the *Epitaph* to Cl. Mamertus.

the poem, and had been touched up in the VIIth century and 59 lines added by Eugenius II, Bishop of Toledo.

The *Laudes Dei* was written by Dracontius under rather tragic circumstances. An advocate of repute at Carthage, *vir clarissimus*, a poet skilled in the art of exploiting the traditional themes of rhetoric and mythology (we possess a certain number of detailed narratives of his, and even a tragedy, the *Orestes*, in 974 hexameters),[1] he had the misfortune to displease Gonthamond (484–496) king of the Vandals, for having lauded in one of his poems an enemy of his. Gonthamond confiscated his goods and cast him into prison.

Under the title of *Satisfactio ad Guthamundum*, Dracontius endeavoured to excite the pity of his persecutor by a humble avowal of his fault, the exposure of his misery in prison, and a promise to celebrate the exploits of the king. This elegy in 153 verses did not succeed in altering the mind of Gonthamond. It was then that Dracontius set himself to his great didactic poem in three books. He still makes a few allusions in it to his sad state : *Quanto cecidi de culmine lapsus* (III, 653), *Me . . . catenarum ferrato pondere pressum* (III, 721). But he rises above these personal considerations to celebrate the action of Divine grace in the world wherein everything hangs upon the *irae* and the *pia vota* of God (I, 10). Descriptions and didactic pieces—for example, in the second Canto on Arianism,[2] and on the origin of evil,[3] and in the third Canto, his criticism of paganism [4]—alternate with passages of a more lyric character, with prayers in the form of hymns,[5] and with regrets for his own past.[6] The part wherein he relates the Six Days' Work is one of his most successful. Striking analogies have been noticed between Canto VIII of Milton's *Paradise Lost* and the happy developments wherein Dracontius describes the wonder of Adam at the spectacle presented by the earthly Paradise, and then the desire he feels for some other created being with whom to share his happiness.[7] There are real beauties of detail in this poem, which was greatly appre-

---

[1] It is really a narrative in epic form.
[2] II, 60 et s.
[3] II, 245 et s.
[4] III, 257 et s.
[5] I, 683 et s. ; II and IV, at the beginning ; II, 154 et s.
[6] III, 566 et s.
[7] I, 348–358.

ciated in the Middle Ages and reveals the familiarity of Dracontius with Christian as well as with classic poets.

X

WE know next to nothing about the life of Sedulius. In a dedication in prose addressed to the priest Macedonius, he informs us that while he was spending his time to no purpose in *saecularia studia,* the Divine pity touched him and decided him to write some work which might strengthen his readers in the right way after he had first attracted them by the " honey " of his poetry for which they were so eager.   According to an indication which appears in trustworthy manuscripts,[1] he learnt " philosophy " in Italy when still a layman, and wrote his works in Greece in the time of Theodosius II and Valentinian III, that is to say, in the middle of the Vth century.[2] A flattering mention of Sedulius in the decree *de libris recipiendis,* issued by the pseudo Gelasius, and the fact that his *Paschale Carmen,* discovered among his papers, was collected and put in order by Turcius Rufus Asterius, who was Consul in 494,[3] are indications which hardly allow of any doubt as to the period in which he lived.

> " While pagan poets delight to celebrate fictitious events in pompous and emphatic terms, under the mask of tragedy, or in the language of the comedy of Geta, or in any other form of poetry ; while they cause to live again the poison of impious events, and laud heinous crimes, and, from no other necessity but custom, trace on papyrus from the Nile thousands of falsehoods, why should I, who am used to chant the Psalms of David to the sound of the ten-stringed instrument, keep silent on the resplendent miracles of Jesus Christ, our Saviour ? "[4]

[1] C.V., X, p. 5.

[2] The anonymous author of this short notice gives it as having been taken from the appendix added to St Jerome's *de Viris Ill.,* by his disciple Paterius (?). If it was Gennadius (the text is evidently mutilated), we shall have to admit that the paragraph relating to Sedulius must have been lost for it does not appear in the *de Vir. Ill.* of that author.

[3] We derive this information from a mention which appears in the oldest manuscripts of Sedulius.   This Asterius is the same man who made a revision of Virgil (cf. the celebrated *subscriptio* to the *Codex Mediceus,* 39, i, Vth century, now at Florence).

[4] *Carmen Pasch.,* I, v. 17–26.

St Paul wrote in his 1st Epistle to the Corinthians (v, 7) : " Etenim Pascha nostrum immolatus est Christus." It was this verse which suggested to Sedulius the title of his poem, *Paschale Carmen*. His object was to celebrate the wondrous facts of the life of Christ, His miracles especially, not simply for the pleasure of describing them in verse, but also to draw from them the doctrinal and moral teaching to which they lent themselves. Of the five books, written in hexameters, the first, a kind of introduction, after an appeal to the pagans who found themselves being impelled to give up their sterile errors,[1] treats of some of the wonderful events in the Old Testament, without regard to abrupt transitions ; the three following give an account of the wonders of Christ from His birth to His triumphant entry into Jerusalem ; the fifth comments on the episodes of the Passion, making use of rhetorical description and allegory. Sedulius bases himself throughout on St Matthew and St Luke ; from the beginning of book V, he *alters* the information given by the four evangelists. He avails himself, on occasion, of authorised commentaries, such as those of St Ambrose and St Augustine. He does not bind himself to a strictly literal rendering of the sacred text, and allows himself free paraphrases whenever he sees it is advantageous for the edification of the reader.

Later on he took the trouble to transpose his poem into prose. He entitled this reconstituted work *Opus Paschale*, to distinguish it from the *Paschale Carmen*. His friend Macedonius got him to undertake this work in order that he might repair (as he explains in the preface), the omissions which the *angustia metricae necessitatis* [2] had imposed upon him.

Gaston Boissier, who some time back had the curiosity to compare the *Opus Paschale* with the *Paschale Carmen*,[3] found the verse of Sedulius much more simple and easy to understand than his prose. This inferiority in the *Opus Paschale* does not proceed simply from the difficulty of finding fresh expressions in which to repeat the same things ; it consists in the abuse (of which Sedulius was also guilty) of the employment of terms of forcible signification to express

---

[1] V, 38 et s.
[2] The most accurate analysis of the poem is that made by Th. Mayr, in his *Studien zu dem Paschale Carmen*, a thesis written at Munich, 1916, pp. 5–33.
[3] *Revue de Philol.*, VI (1882), p. 28 et s.

the simplest things,[1] and especially in his mania for paraphrasing, which was held in check by the rules of versification but which freely found vent in prose, often for the childish pleasure of giving a more suitable termination to a sentence.[2] Briefly, in his poetry, the imitation of the classic poets—of Virgil, who was the model consistently studied—maintained to a certain point the old language, and even the old prosody.[3] Less fettered by tradition, his prose was susceptible in a greater degree of being infused by the bad taste of the period.

Sedulius further wrote two hymns in honour of Christ, one of 55 distiches which affected the form of *versus echoici* or *serpentini*, in which the first words of each hexameter were repeated in the second part of the pentameter;[4] the other, which is alphabetical, is in iambic dimeters grouped in verses of four lines. The Catholic liturgy has taken a few of the verses of the second poem into use—the *A solis ortus cardine* for the Feast of Christmas, and the *Hostis Herodes impie* for the Epiphany.

XI

Sidonius Apollinaris (*C. Sollius Modestus Apollinaris Sidonius*) was born at Lyons on the 5th November 431 or 432 at the time when the city was still entirely Roman, and died in 487, the subject of a Visigoth king. Brought up on the strong traditions of Rome, whose majesty he keenly appreciated, and whom he calls *domicilium legum, gymnasium litterarum, curiam dignitatum, verticem mundi, patriam libertatis, unicam totius mundi civitatem*,[5] he thought it right to

---

[1] *Adorare consulatum,* for " sing the praises of a consulate " ; *sublimare convivium,* for " to honour a festivity with his presence " ; etc.

[2] The man born blind begs his sight of Jesus. Sedulius expressed this in his verse by *lumen petere,* in prose by *oculatae copiam claritatis postulare* (IV, 212). In connection with the massacre of the Innocents, he writes in the *Paschale Carmen,* " *Haec laceros crines nudato vertice rupit, illa genas secuit* " ; and in the *Opus Paschale,* IV, 123 : " Haec effusam vultibus comam miseranda dilacerans crinalis damni foeditate nudum cervicem sauciabat ; illa madidas lacrimosis imbribus genas unguium protervitate sulcabat." The terminations of Sedulius have been studied by J. Candel, Latin thesis, Toulouse, 1904.

[3] We notice besides in Sedulius some irregularities in his prosody—syllables of short accent made long when he wishes to be emphatic, and long syllables shortened when he wishes to express hesitation, etc. . . . See Huemer's edition, p. 394.

[4] Ex : *Primus ad ima ruit* magna de luce superbus : Sic homo, cum tumuit *primus ad ima ruit.*

[5] *Ep.* I, vi.

SIDONIUS APOLLINARIS 477

repay with his verses the forbearance of the invaders " having their heads perfumed with rancid butter." The life of this great personage, somewhat puerile as regards his literary performances, but of great honesty and good intentions, embodies the best elements of Gallo-Roman nobility in the Vth century, faithful to Rome, sacrificed by her, and finally reduced to relying only on themselves.[1]

His grandfather, Pretorian Prefect of Gaul, was converted in 408 in the reign of Theodosius.[2] His father held the *insignia* of the same high post under Valentinian III. In 452, Sidonius, when still very young, married Papianilla, a young girl who belonged to an illustrious family of Auvergne. On the 1st January 456 he was called upon to deliver before the Roman Senate the panegyric upon his father-in-law, Flavius Eparchius Avitus, who had been chosen emperor the previous year by the deputies from the Gaulish nobility assembled at Beaucaire (*Ugernum*). The success of this poetic feat won for him a bronze statue in the Forum of Trajan.[3] Shortly afterwards Avitus, owing to the threats of certain disaffected members of the Roman aristocracy, found no other means of saving his life than to accept the Episcopal see of Plaisance. Another panegyric,[4] this time addressed to the Emperor Majorian, preserved Sidonius from the animosity of the new prince, and even advanced him in his estimation.

From 461 to 465 Sidonius led the comfortable life of a great landed proprietor on his estate at Avitacum, with his wife and three children. A fresh literary exploit—the panegyric on Anthemius, who in his turn had become Emperor of the West[5] —obtained for him in 468 the dignity of Prefect of Rome, and, at the expiration of his term of office, the title of Patrician.

He looked forward to enjoying in peace his remaining years, when, in circumstances of which we are ignorant, he was elected in 471 or 472, to the Episcopal see of Arverna (Clermont-Ferrand). His social *prestige*, his talent as a writer, his administrative experience, and also his great piety (which often finds expression in his *Letters*) marked him out for this high office with the lively approbation of the Gallo-Roman

---

[1] Sources of his biography : a notice in the *de Viris Ill.*, of Gennadius, § xcii; the works of Sidonius and especially the poem included in *Ep.* IX, xvi.
[2] *Carmen* xii, 7.   [3] *Carmen* vii.
[4] *Carmen* iv.   [5] *Carmen* ii.

Episcopate. He had not sought this unexpected promotion, but he did not flinch from any of his new duties which political events rendered heavy and formidable. He organised the resistance against Euric the Arian and his Visigoths who, in 474, had attempted the invasion of Auvergne. But that province was soon after handed over to them by a duly authorised treaty signed by Nepos, the Emperor. *Facta est servitus nostra pretium securitatis alienae*, as Sidonius,[1] who had raised courageous protests, mournfully stated. As a punishment, Euric had him taken to the fortress of Livia not far from Carcassonne,[2] but decided afterwards to give him back his liberty. Sidonius, whose material interests were rendered very precarious, once more made use of his familiar methods with a view to soften the disposition of his new master ; the poem included in *Letter* viii could not but be pleasing to the vanity of Euric. Sidonius was bound to acknowledge that throughout his career, at the price of certain necessary concessions, his writings had served him well.

Twenty-four poems and one hundred and forty-seven letters in nine books make up the works of Sidonius, who was much admired by his contemporaries in the Middle Ages, and whose high favour only paled in the time of the first humanists.[3] In his poems, the show pieces and the *nugae* (detailed descriptions, letters in verse, epithalamia, etc.), should be distinguished ; his favourite metres are the hexameter, elegiacs, and the hendecasyllable. His prosody is correct, and he only allows himself licences on very rare occasions. As regards his letters, they were collected and published by himself at the request of his friends in successive portions, the Ist book in 469, the IInd about 472, books V to VII about 474–475, book VIII a little later, and book IX about 479. When once he had become a Bishop he deemed it suitable to give up the " frivolous exercises " in which he had delighted until then. " I fear," he declares, " that a reputation as a poet may in some degree sully the strictness necessary in a priest." [4] Notwithstanding, on more than one occasion he falls into introducing some passages in verse into his letters.

The fundamental interest of the writings of Sidonius lies

---

[1] *Ep.* VII, vii.
[2] *Ep.* VIII, iii ; IX, iii ; Vaissette, *Hist. du Languedoc*, I, 501.
[3] As evidenced by Baret, *op. cit.*, pp. 102–106.
[4] *Ep.* IX, xii, and IX, xvi, line 45 et s.

in their being historical documents. Even from his most
artificial productions from the point of view of composition,
historians and lovers of the picturesque are able to glean
valuable details : for example, the portrait of the Huns in his
Panegyric on Anthemius, and of the Franks in his *Panegyric*
on Majorian ; and there are many other revealing sketches
which Chateaubriand in the course of his immense reading
as a young man was careful to note. Without the letters
and poems of Sidonius the political and social history of
Gaul at this period would be almost empty of facts for us.
When by chance Sidonius resigns himself to be simple and to
describe without adding any embroidery any incident which
he has witnessed, he is a *piquant* and amusing story-teller.[1]
He also knew how to render himself an eloquent interpreter
of Gallo-Roman patriotism on more than one occasion :
letter VII, vii, written when Auvergne was about to be detached from *Romania*, is a noble page which deserves not to
perish. Devoted to his province and to his flock, faithful
to his friends and profoundly " sociable," the character of
Sidonius commands our sympathy.

He has also made known to us the literary life of Gaul
in the Vth century. Personally, he was a very learned man.[2]
Upon his numerous correspondents [3]—poets, orators, philosophers, lawyers and simple men of letters,—he lavished such
laudatory epithets that if we took them seriously we should
have an impression of an immense intellectual activity
flourishing within the Gallo-Roman society. The following is
a specimen of his amiable hyperbole :

> " When your book," he writes to Claudianus Mamertus
> who had sent him his *De Statu Animae*, " unfolds its
> scholarship against what it is opposing, it proves itself
> equal to authors in both languages in point of
> morals and learned attainments. It thinks like Pytha-
> goras, it distinguishes like Socrates, it explains like
> Plato, it shrouds its meaning like Aristotle, it flatters

---

[1] See *Ep.* V, xvii ; I, xi ; III, xii (with P. Allard's interpretation of certain
details which are often little understood, *Saint Sidoine Apoll.*, p. 75).

[2] The echo of Tibullus and Silius Italicus, almost forgotten for at least two
centuries, comes back with him. The history of Roman literature owes some interesting scraps of information to him, for example, on the wife of Lucan, who married
again ; and on Seneca the tragedian, whom he formally distinguishes from the
philosopher Seneca (*Carm.* ix, 232), etc.

[3] They will be found mentioned in Teuffel, III, no. 466, p. 435.

like Aeschines, it is impassioned like Demosthenes, it is flowery like Hortensius, it inflames like Cethegus, it urges on like Curio, it temporises like Fabius, it feigns like Crassus, it dissimulates like Cæsar, it counsels like Cato, it dissuades like Appius, it persuades like Tullius ; and, to come to a comparison with the holy Fathers, it instructs like Jerome, it is destructive like Lactantius, it establishes like Augustine, etc. . . ." [1]

Then follow in succession : Hilary, John (Chrysostom), Basil, Gregory, Orosius, Rufinus, Eusebius, Eucherius, Paulinus and Ambrose. . . . A quotation like that is sufficient to gauge the watermark of any mind. It warns us also to check the grandiloquent admiration of Sidonius. We can then see that these vaunted correspondents, however slightly acquainted, or however saturated, with literary ability they might be, did not surpass the level of Sidonius himself ; they have the same touching fervour for things of the intellect, the same insufficiency in power of criticism, and in profound learning.[2] In his moments of *clairvoyance* Sidonius has well glimpsed certain aspects of this decadence,[3] but he did not succeed in correcting all its effects on his own account.

Where this is most apparent is when he strives to imitate the methods, the routine, and the pseudo-literary commonplaces of which Juvenal had declared himself to be already weary three and a half centuries before.[4] We see him furbishing up in his verse and prose the forms of address, the enumerations, the amplifications, the scholarly echoes, and the mythological banalities with which his memory, loaded up with so much reading,[5] unremittingly supplied him. And all this is set in tortuous phraseology, painful, and often obscure owing to its far-fetched and affected character, wherein worldly elegance finds itself side by side with obsolete phrases of a Latin which was already breaking up,[6] and

---

[1] *Ep.* IV, iii.

[2] See Roger's *L'Enseign. des lettres class. d'Ausone à Alcuin*, 1905, pp. 67–75.

[3] *Ep.* V, x, 4 ; II, x, i (he was complaining that the rush of barbarism was eating into the Latin tongue) ; IV, xvii, 2.

[4] *Sat.*, i.

[5] An attempt to reconstruct his library appears in Allard, *op. cit.*, p. 133. A notice of the " sources of information " in M.G.H., VIII, p. 384 et s.

[6] The comparative in two words (*Plus celsos . . .*) ; inflections replaced by prepositions (*nebula de pulvere*) ; an infinitive replaced by *quod* or *quia*, with the indicative or subjunctive, etc.

with unexpected verbal creations.[1] It requires an effort to read Sidonius Apollinaris, and one dare not say that it invariably finds its reward.

This was not the opinion of the learned men of his time. Sidonius largely contributed to the formation of the poetic style then in vogue, and this imitator was almost as often copied as some of the authorised classics.

---

[1] Cervicositas, saeculiloquus, familiarescere, phthisiscere, crepusculasceus, etc. . . .

BOOK V

ON THE THRESHOLD OF THE MIDDLE AGES

CHAPTER I

WORKS IN VERSE

BIBLIOGRAPHY

I. AVITUS.—Text in P.L., LIX, reproducing Sirmond (Paris, 1643); in Ul. Chevalier, *Oeuvres complètes de Saint Avite évéque de Vienne*, Lyons, 1890; in M.G.H., VI, part 2 (1883, Peiper [excellent]).—Various pieces translated in F. Clément, *op. cit.*, pp. 323-353.—Consult: H. Goelzer, *Le Latin de Saint Avit* (*Biblioth. de la Faculté des Lettres de Paris*, fasc. XXVI [1909]).

II. ENNODIUS.—The manuscripts give the works of Ennodius in a very confused order. Sirmond (Paris, 1611), reproduced by Migne, LXIII, 13,364, and followed likewise by Hartel, C.V., vol. VI (1882), attempted to introduce a logical classification. Vogel, M.G.H., VII (1885), preferred to keep to the order, or rather disorder, of the manuscripts.—French translation of the *Letters* by the Abbé Léglise, Paris, 1906.—Consult: A. Dubois, *La Latinité d'Ennodius* (Clermont-Ferrand), 1903.

III. VENANTIUS FORTUNATUS. — Text in P.L., vol. LXXXVIII, reproducing the edition of the Benedictine A. Lucchi (Rome, 1786-7). For an account of the history of the editions of Fortunatus, see Ch. Nisard, in the *Rev. de l'Enseign. second.*, 1885, II, p. 276 et s. (cf. id., *le Poète Fortunat*, 1890, chap. i). The *Parisinus*, No. 13,048, VIIIth/IXth century represents a special tradition, and provides 31 pieces not contained in the manuscripts of the other tradition. These poems were published by Guérard in 1835. They do not appear in Migne, except the first three, which had already been published before. The most complete edition is the *Mon. Germaniae histor.*, vol. IV (1881-1885: Leo, for the poetry; Krusch, for the works in prose): the criticism is very conservative, perhaps excessively so (see Rey in the *Rev. de Philol.*, XXXI, 190).—French translation of the poetry of Fortunatus by Ch. Nisard and E. Rittier, Paris, 1887 (Nisard's Collection); translation of the *Life of St Radegonde*, by R. Aigrain, 1910. Study of the grammar of Fortunatus by A. Meneghetti in the *Didaskaleion*, 1916, pp. 195-298; 1917, pp. 1-166 (*La Latinita di Venanzio Fortunato*, Turin, 1917).

N.B.—The writings placed under the name of Amoenus in P.L., LXI, 1075-1082, belong to Prudentius and Fortunatus. This Amoenus was doubtless a mere compiler of extracts.

SUMMARY

I. The Decline of Latin Learning. — II. Avitus. — III. Ennodius.—VI. Venantius Fortunatus.

I

WE know to what degree the mournful presentiments which strained at the hearts of men at the time of the first inrush of the Vandals, Alani, and Suevi at the beginning of the Vth century were justified and even surpassed by events. During all that century torrential invasions broke like surf over Gaul, Italy, Spain and even Africa. The wealth, works of art, and all the refined outer garb of the privileged classes were scattered and broken up by ignorant and brutal hands, and, what was still more disastrous,—for it was not only the upper classes who were to suffer from it—the established institutions were included in the catastrophe, or at least seriously shaken. The public schools in particular found themselves almost wholly disorganised in more than one part of the Empire. They were able to maintain at first in the principal cities a small handful of active and lettered men. Then they became rarer, and the greater number disappeared. Teaching was only given, when it could be provided at all, by private tutors to whom the members of the aristocracy entrusted their children. There were still educated individuals who sometimes associated together in groups when circumstances permitted, but the general level of education— that culture which can only be handed on by uninterrupted effort—declined progressively, and presented a fragile and precarious appearance when once the framework, indispensable to its continuity, had been rent asunder.

Those who endeavoured to become writers in the midst of the prevailing ignorance deserved some merit. The infinite value of the privileged ages during which good taste had acquired all its delicacy and preserved all its balance cannot be better understood than by reading them. There were, however, cultivated intelligences who retained the taste for good style and a genuine respect for that literary tradition which they flattered themselves they were perpetuating. They sought to preserve themselves from the incorrectness of language spoken all around them—two specimens quoted by H. Goelzer in his fine work on St Avitus (p. 2) give a sufficient idea of this increasing corruption. But they seem to have grown unaccustomed to attach importance to the root base of things, to thought itself; they are only careful of their language, and its expression, which they embroider in order to please. They endeavour to overdo each of their phrases. Nothing can be more insipid than their niceties. Also they make few innovations in matter of style. H. Goelzer and Max Bonnet have taught us to recognise in the system they followed the methods used in rhetoric during the first centuries of the Empire; they did nothing more than press them to their utmost limits, sometimes even to absurdity. The already distant influence of an Apuleius developed all its harmful effects in them.

II

BORN at Vienne in Dauphiny about the year 450 of a family from Auvergne who had settled in Burgundy, the son and grandson of Senators, Avitus was raised to the Episcopal chair of his native town in 490 and died in 518. His *rôle* as a Bishop was extremely important. He presided as Metropolitan of the Gauls at the Council of Epaonia in 517.[1] From Arianism he brought back to Catholic orthodoxy, Sigismond, the son and successor of Gondebaud, king of Burgundy. He had the reputation of being a formidable extirpator of heresy.[2] We still possess his *Contra Eutychianam Haeresim Libri Duo*, which dates from 512–513, and his *Dialogi cum Gundobado Rege vel Librorum contra Arianos reliquiae*.[3] His works in prose consist of 98 letters, 2 homilies on the Rogations, and 72 short fragments of sermons. Among his contemporaries he was considered one of the most brilliant writers of his time. It was to his poetry especially that he owed this reputation. The *De Laude Virginitatis* in 666 hexameters, addressed to his sister Fuscina, develops the ecclesiastical theories on the inconveniences of marriage and the advantages of virginity.[4] The work in which Avitus shows his full scope is the *Libelli de Spiritalis Historiae Gestis* (he thus names it in one of his letters),[5] which may be

---

[1] Hefele Leclercq, *Hist. des Conc.*, II, 2, 1031 et s.
[2] Gregory of Tours, *History of the Franks*, II, xxxiv.
[3] The *Collatio Episcoporum contra Arianos coram Gundobaldo Rege* (P.L., LIX, 387) is a mistake of Vignier's. Cf. Julien Havet, *Questions Méroving*, 1885, vol. II.
[4] Note especially this development (line 164 et s.): " . . . Dominum passura cubilis Servit in obsceno tolerans conubia lecto."
[5] *Ep.* xliii.

considered the most remarkable poem inspired by the Book
of Genesis in the Vth century. The first book (325 lines)
treats of the origin of the world ; the second (423 lines),
of original sin ; the third (425 lines), of the Judgment of God.
Guizot remarked that these three cantos form a whole, the
strong texture of which is a forerunner of the *Paradise Lost*.[1]
A fourth book follows on the Deluge (658 lines) and a fifth
on the Passage of the Red Sea (721 lines). Avitus published
the work himself in 507, without having had, as he tells us,
leisure to correct it. He confesses that he had thought of
making up a collection of his poems to form a volume of a fair
size, but the sack of Vienne in 500 caused the loss of nearly
all of them.[2]

Once we admit the principle of his poetry which treats
subjects specifically Christian by means of the methods
inherited from the classics, and in order to build Noah's Ark
takes toll of Pelion, Pindarus, Ossa and Atlas,[3] we must
acknowledge that brilliant and happily-conceived pieces are
not wanting. In the scene of the Temptation, the gradual
rising of evil curiosity in the soul of the woman and the
trembling concessions which lead her on to the full accom-
plishment of her fault—all these *nuances* are described with
a psychological *finesse* which is too rare in these essays of
schoolmen grown old. The preacher of chastity reveals himself in the complaints which he puts into the mouth of Adam :

"Alas ! It was then for my destruction that this
woman was joined to my life ! She whom Thy command
hath given me for companion is the woman who, herself
overcome, hath undone me by her baleful counsels,
and hath driven me to taste the fruit which she knew
already. . . . I have been deceived, but it was Thou
who hadst made me trusting by giving marriage unto
me and by tying these knots full of delight. *Happy man
had I spent my life alone without ever knowing hymeneal
bonds !* "[4]

While freely exploiting the Genesis of old, Avitus does not

---

[1] *Hist. de la Civil. en France,* II (1840), 71.
[2] See the *Prologue* in prose to his brother Apollinaris, Bishop of Valence.
[3] Cf. *de . . . Gestis,* IV, 299 et s.
[4] III, 98–107.

forget the times in which he was living, and compares the
sorrows of Adam and Eve with those endured by their sad
posterity—devastated cities, social upheavals, and the calamities of invasion. " There is no evil which this world, full
of iniquity and woe, doth not commit and endure : its downfall is imminent, the measure of crime is full up. . . ." [1]

Avitus was a lettered man, a *scolasticus*, as they said in
those days. He had received lessons from the rhetorician
Sapaudus whom Sidonius and Mamertus held in high esteem.
He knew grammar very well,[2] and included in an almost equal
admiration Virgil and . . . Sidonius Apollinaris. Consistently concerned with good diction, he only made rare concessions to popular language. His style, refined and artificial,
precious and dainty, also furnishes an excellent choice of
examples whereby to illustrate the history of literary decadence. All the methods dear to Latin writers from an
early date (fulness of expression, paronomasia, antithesis,
alliteration) are used by him without discretion. H. Goelzer [3]
considers, nevertheless, after an " exhaustive " examination,
that, though completely bound to the same school as the other
Gallo-Roman writers, Avitus is less inflated and less obscure
than most of them.

III

ENNODIUS was a native of southern Gaul. He was born
probably at Arles, in the year 473 or 474, of a family of consular rank, but his education and ecclesiastical career were
passed in northern Italy. Like Sidonius Apollinaris he realised
the type of rhetorician-Bishop, but with more sonorous
humanism and unprofitable virtuosity than even the former
possessed.

Becoming Bishop of Ticinum (Pavia) about the year 513,
he was charged with important missions. Pope Hormisdas
sent him on two occasions, in 515 and 517, as Legate to the
court of the Emperor Anastasius at Constantinople, in order to
bring about unity between the churches of the East and the
West. He also mingled in politics. He believed in the
benevolent intentions of Theodoric, accepted his advances,

---

[1] III, 359–361.
[2] See *Ep.* lvii (p. 85, Peiper).
[3] *Op. cit.*, p. 713 et s.

and in 507, a few years before his Episcopate, delivered a grandiloquent panegyric in honour of the king.

He was considered a fine scholar. But his writings consisted of little else than uttering mere trifles in harmonious and well-balanced phrases, or in verse formed on Virgilian *recipes*. His 297 letters are of an elegant turn, and incredibly void of ideas, although some of his correspondents bore the names of Symmachus, Boethius, Hormisdas, etc. Ennodius lingers over academic exercises on the model of the *controversiae* of old : " Against a man who placed a statue of Minerva in a wrong place " ; " Against a father who had been unwilling to ransom his son who had fallen into the power of pirates and who later begs him to come to his assistance." He pushes his admiration for the classics as far as to imitate the licence of a Martial in several of his epigrams. The Christian does however appear in a certain number of pieces, for example, in a *Life of Epiphanius*, Bishop of Pavia (conspicuous for its harangues like those put into the mouths of their characters by the old historians) ; in a *Life of Antony* a monk of Lérins, a *Eucharisticum de Vita sua*, a *Libellus* supporting the Synod of Rome in 502, a *Paraenesis Didascalica*, addressed to two young people, etc. The last-mentioned exhortation mixes up in a strange way the most contradictory points of view : Ennodius recommends to his young friends the Christian virtues, *verecundia*, *fides*, *castitas*, but also the assiduous practice of the liberal arts, especially rhetoric, which at its good pleasure can make an innocent man appear guilty, and a guilty man innocent !

" Qui nostris servit studiis, mox imperat orbi."

Most of his productions which have come down to us seem to have been written before his Episcopate. That is perhaps an excuse. In any case they betray the superficial and entirely academic character of the culture with which he was enamoured, and which in some amusing commonplace he sometimes made a pretence of repudiating : " Cessent anilium commenta poetarum, fabulosa repudietur antiquitas ! "[1] A study of his language reveals a real effort at correctness of grammar. He tried his best to keep to the rules. But he could not succeed in the impossible attempt to perpetuate the

---

[1] *Ep.* I, ix (Léglise's translation, p. 96).

old rules of Latin literary style in an age when Latin
was becoming more and more corrupt; some colloquial
expressions mingle strangely with the traditional rhetorical
language.

What one would like to find among so many faded ele-
gancies, and phrases made up from the *recipes* of the schools,
would be some energetic language based on a vigorous thought,
some idea springing from a fresh sensation. But his exaggerated literary mould comes between himself and reality.[1]

IV

THE life of a troubadour wandering through the countries
of the West, impelled by curiosity and a liking for scenes on
a large scale, and especially by devotion; repaying in com-
plimentary verses the good offices of those who gave him
shelter; and then his vagrant career finding its *métier* once
for all in the most fervent, the most respectful, the most
enthusiastic friendship for a most charming and pious woman
—these traits sum up the career of Venantius Honorius
Clementianus Fortunatus, whom we may regard as the last
representative of Latin poetry on the threshold of the Middle
Ages.

Born about the year 530 at Duplavilis near Treviso,
Fortunatus was educated at Ravenna, and received there
some smattering of grammar, rhetoric, and law. His fortunate recovery from an affection of the eyes led him to set
out for the tomb of St Martin to whom he attributed his
cure.[2] He took by no means the shortest route to reach Tours.
He travelled by way of the Julian Alps, Noricum and Rhetia,
crossed the upper Danube and the Rhine, and stopped for
some time at the court of Sigebert, king of Austrasia, whose
marriage with Brunehaut in 566 he celebrated in an *epithalamium* in which he entrusted to Venus and Cupid their

[1] We may connect the name of Ennodius with that of Rusticus Helpidius,
the author of a *De Christi Jesu Beneficiis*, in 149 hexameters (P.L., LXII, 545–548),
and of certain inscriptions written for the purpose of explaining representations
from the Bible (*ibid.*, 543–546). The *De . . . Beneficiis* was re-edited by W.
Brandes, Brunswick, 1890. A protégé of Ennodius, Arator, subdeacon of the
Church in Rome, published in 544 a paraphrase in verse of the Acts of the Apostles
(P.L., LXVIII, 63–246) dedicated to Pope Vigilius. New edition by Hubner,
Neissen, 1850.

[2] Cf. his *Vita Martini*, IV, 689 et s. ; Gregory of Tours, *De Virt. Mart.*, I, xv.

glory and happiness. On arriving at the end of his journey after two years of adventurous travels, "sometimes asleep, fatigued by my tramping when not made heavy with wine," [1] his pilgrimage accomplished he pushed on again to the Pyrenees, came back to Poitiers and there came to know Radegonde.[2]

The wife of the murderer of her parents and the oppressor of Thuringia her fatherland, Queen Radegonde had finally obtained the permission of her husband Clotaire to consecrate herself to the monastic life. She had founded at Poitiers the monastery of Notre Dame (soon afterwards called the monastery of Sainte-Croix), the direction of which she entrusted to her spiritual daughter Agnes. Both highly cultivated, the two nuns had no difficulty in winning the devotion of the itinerant poet who was doubtless little accustomed to such delicate attentions as theirs, and who received from them mystical intercommunion of soul, and flattering praise, and even a certain amount of innocent spoiling in the way they skilfully humoured a slight greediness which was his favourite shortcoming.[3] Fortunatus did not forget Italy, but yielded to the powerful attraction which kept him at Poitiers (567); besides, his country was at that time invaded by the Lombards. He became Radegonde's secretary, perhaps her responsible agent (*agens in rebus*), at least occasionally. He was ordained priest, and in 597 succeeded Bishop Plato in the Episcopal see of Poitiers. Radegonde had already been dead some ten years (13th August, 587). Fortunatus constituted himself the first biographer of that incomparable woman, *gemma Galliae pretiosissima*, as he described her in his litanies.

His works consist of Lives of saints, hymns and circumstantial poems.[4]

Besides his biography of St Radegonde, he wrote in prose a life of St Albinus, Bishop of Angers († 550 c.), and of St

[1] *Carm., Praef.*, § iv.

[2] See R. Aigrain's *Sainte Radegonde* (coll. les Saints), 1918. An excellent critical account.

[3] The scandal which certain critics, like J. J. Ampère, have experienced over these little mouthfuls which are in fact somewhat frugal, does honour to their own sobriety. See *Carm.* xi, xvi et s.

[4] There is no serious reason to ascribe to St Radegonde the poem on the devastation of Thuringia and the letter to Artachis (M.G.H., IV, 271 and 278) as proposed by Ch. Nisard (*Rev. Histor.*, 1888, *Le Poète Fortunat*, 1890, chap. iii). Cf. E. Rey, *Rev. de Philol.*, XXX (1906), p. 124 et s.

Hilary of Poitiers († 367), as well as a *Liber de Virtutibus S Hilarii;* a life of St Germanus of Paris [1] († 575 c.), of St Paternus of Avranches († 565 c.), of St Marcellus of Paris, and of St Severinus of Bordeaux († 482), which last has not been preserved. Historians can find in them much interesting information about the times in which his heroes lived.

The *Life of St Martin,* dedicated to Gregory of Tours, with whom Fortunatus had been in relations since 573, comprises no less than 2243 hexameters, in four books. The poet does little more than embellish the outline drawn by Sulpicius Severus and Paulinus of Périgueux; [2] moreover he was able to complete his poem in two months.

Partially incorporated in the liturgy of the Catholic Church, his hymns represent the best claim to his moderate reputation, which the mediocrity of his other writings would have only indifferently assured. Fortunatus is the author of the *Agnoscat Omne Caelum* and the *Vexilla Regis Prodeunt,* in acatalectic iambic dimeters and verses of four lines in almost regularly recurring rhyme, and of the *Pange Lingua Gloriosi* in catalectic trochaic tetrameters and verses of three lines. Possibly from among the seven hymns considered as doubtful by modern critics, two or three should also be ascribed to him.[3]

It is in relation to the eleven books of *Carmina,*[4] or *Miscellanea,* together with certain prose writings, that we can best judge his literary ability. Letters, elegies, consolatory addresses, epithalamia, panegyrics of kings, Bishops, important personages, churches, country houses, etc., " toasts," funeral inscriptions (intended to be read rather than engraved), nearly always in elegiacs—the foregoing form

[1] See Batiffol's *Etudes de Liturgie et d'Archéologie Chrétienne,* 1919, p. 245 et s. on an *Expositio Liturgiae Gallicanae* attributed to St Germanus of Paris (P.L., LXXII, 83–98).

[2] Book I is the *Vita Martini* to xviii, 3 ; II, the same, to the end of the work ; III, forms the *Dialogues* ii, 1 to 13 ; IV, the *Dial.* iii, 1 to 17.

[3] Dreves (in V.M., 3, 3 [1908]) attributes to him hymns i, vii, viii in the *Appendix spuriorum* of M.G.H.

[4] Note the preface addressed to Gregory. He expresses a modest astonishment that his friend attaches so much importance to these *nugae,* and mentions that he wrote them haphazard in the course of his wanderings in the West (. . . *paene aut equitando aut dormitando conscripserim*). Books I–VIII comprise the poems written up to the year 576 ; Book IX, those of the years 577–584 ; Book X (note at the beginning his explanation of the *Pater*), those of the year 585 ; Book XI and appendix nos. x–xxxi which opens with an *Expositio Symboli* in prose taken from Rufinus, embody the pieces addressed to Radegonde and Agnes. Possibly these two last books may not have been published by Fortunatus himself.

practically the entire subject matter of the collection which
the poet exerted himself to put together at the request of
Gregory of Tours.[1] His social position—very different from
that of Sidonius, Ennodius, and Avitus—and the long-con-
tinued precariousness of his means of existence, had forced
him to flatter abundantly, and of this he made a speciality.
In cases where we can check what he metes out to his protectors we can see the quality of this court homage. He
lauds Chilperic's taste for letters ; now Gregory of Tours
relates that when the king meddled in versification he mixed
up short syllables with long, and did not conform to any
known system of metre.[2] J. J. Ampère [3] speaks in fairly
appreciative terms, though somewhat ill-naturedly, of the
" literary career of Fortunatus, the last of its kind, humble,
traversed, subservient, ever bowing before the conquerors,
but possessed of a kind of childish vanity and pitiful satisfaction." We see, he adds, " his decrepit and mincing muse,
smirking in superannuated coquetry as the barbarian chiefs
passed before him, and paying them his humble reverence
and little pretentious compliments. . . ."

The talent of Fortunatus lay especially in his facility :
he triumphed in poetic improvisation. But his insufficient
education (although he knew Horace, Virgil and some of the
Christian poets) was a poor safeguard against grammatical
irregularities and faults in quantity.[4] He was well aware of
this, in which connection he has made very humble confessions
whose sincerity might be believed more easily if their form
had been less affected.[5] His own shortcomings in no way
discouraged his output, which brought him honour and profit,
and, however mediocre, caused once more a last reflection of
Latin culture to gleam forth among the barbarians whom he
portrays with " their goblet of maple wood in their hands,
drinking health after health, and uttering a thousand follies
calculated to arouse their God Bacchus " (*Carm.*, *Praef.*, § v).

[1] *Carm.* IX, i, 99 et s.
[2] *Hist. Franc.*, V, xlv, and VI, xlvi.
[3] *Hist. litt. de la France avant le douzième siècle*, vol. II (1839), p. 350.
[4] See the *Indices* in M.G.H., IV, 389 et s.
[5] *De Vita Mart.*, I, xxvi, 30 et s. ; *Carm.* X, iii, i ; II, ix, 5 et s.

CHAPTER II

WORKS IN PROSE

THE HANDING ON OF THE LEGACY OF ANTIQUITY

BIBLIOGRAPHY

I. FULGENTIUS OF RUSPA.—P.L., vol. LXV, reproducing L. Mangeant, Paris, 1684. See notes further on.

II. ST CAESARIUS OF ARLES.—P.L., vol. LXVII. Besides the sermons collected in Migne under the name of Caesarius, several appear in vol. XXXIX of the *Patrologie Latine* in the appendix to St Augustine's sermons (the list is drawn up by Paul Lejay in R.H.L.R., 1905, p. 184), and Dom Morin has published six hitherto unpublished sermons in the *R. Bén.*, XIII (1896), p. 97 ; fifteen others, *ibid.*, XVI (1899), pp. 241, 289 and 337.— A portion of the homilies of Caesarius were translated into French in the XVIIIth century by Dujat de Villeneuve, Paris, 1760, 2 vols. A reliable study on the language of Caesarius is wanted ; see Dom Morin's observations in *Mélanges Cabrières*. Later on the writings attributed to Caesarius will be mentioned.

III. BOETHIUS.—The works of Boethius are in P.L., LXIII-LXIV. The *De Consolatione Philosophiae* (523-4) has been edited by Peiper, Leipsic, 1871.—French translation by Oct. Cottreau, Paris, 1889. The *Commentaria in Porphyrium* (506-7) are in C.V., vol. XLVIII (1906, Schepss and Brandt). Special editions of the *De Arithmetica L. Duo* and the five books *De Musica*, by G. Friedlein, in B.T. (1887) ; of the two books *In Librum Aristotelis de Interpretatione*, by C. Meiser, in B.T. (1897-1900) ; of the *Liber de Diffinitione*, by Th. Stangl (*Tulliana et Mario-Victoriniana*, Munich, 1888) : as a matter of fact, this last work is by Marius Victorinus.

IV. CASSIODORUS.—Texts in P.L., vol. LXIX-LXX, reproducing, with certain additions, the Benedictine Garet (Rouen, 1679). The chapter in *Inst. Div.*, relating to grammar figures in Keil's *Gramm. Latini*, VII, 210-216 ; the chapter on rhetoric is in R.L.M., p. 495 et s. Mommsen has given the *Chronicle* in M.G.H., XI (1894), pp. 109-161 ; the *Variae, ibid.*, xii. (1894), in collaboration with Traube.—A *Compendium* of the *Inst. Div.*, going back to the Middle Ages, has been published by Lehmann in the *Philologus*, 1914/1916, pp. 253-273, following the *Vat. Lat.* no. 4955, XIth century.—Translation of the treatise *On the Soul* by Stephane de Rouville, 1874 ; and of the *Historia Tripartita*, by Loys Pianeus, 1568.

V. ST GREGORY OF TOURS.—Texts in P.L., LXXI, 161-1118, and in M.G.H., *Scriptores Rerum Meroving.*, vol. I (Arndt. Krusch and Bonnet). The *Liber de Miraculis b. Thomae* was published by Max Bonnet, *Supplem. Codicis Apocryphi*, I (L. 1883), pp. 96-132. — French translation of the *Historia Francorum* by H. Bordier, Paris, 1859-1862 ; by the same, the *Book of the Miracles and the other works of Gregory of Tours*, 4 vols., Paris, 1857-1865 (Société de l'Histoire de France).

VI. ISIDORE OF SEVILLE.—The works of Isidore of Seville figure in

495

vols. LXXXI-LXXXIV of Migne, reproducing Arevalo (Rome, 1797-1803). Vol. LXXXI includes interesting data on the life and writings of Isidore.— Special editions of the *De Natura Rerum* by G. Becker, Berlin, 1857 ; of the *Chronica* and the *Historica Gothorum*, by Mommsen, M.G.H., vol. XI (1894) ; of the *Etymologiae* or *Origines*, by W. M. Lindsay, Oxford, 1911 (with useful *Indices*).—Dzialowski, *Isidor u. Ildefons als Literarhistoriker*, Munster i. W., 1898, has amended the text of the *De Vir. Illustribus*, from Arevalo.—The Arevalo-Migne edition is of great value on account of the commentaries which are included.

SUMMARY

I. Fulgentius of Ruspa.—II. St Caesarius of Arles.—III. Boethius, "The First of the Scholastics." — IV. Cassiodorus. — V. St Gregory of Tours. His Hagiographic Works. The *History of the Franks*. Gregory's Learning.—VI. St Isidore of Seville.—VII. Conclusion.

I

THE contention which identifies Claudius Gordianus Fulgentius, Bishop of Ruspa in Byzacene, with the mythologist Fabius Planciades Fulgentius is based on specious reasons, to say the least, drawn either from certain coincidences in their lives, or from certain analogies in their style.[1]

We possess various works by this mythologist,[2] the best known of which is the *Virgiliana Continentia*, wherein the mystical sense attaching to the *Æneid*—taken as a figure representing human life—is elucidated by the methods of allegorical exegesis. The episodes related in the poem are represented as so many veiled lessons suitable to make people love virtue. As regards the Bishop, we know that he was born in 468 at Telepta, in Byzacene, of a Senatorial Carthage family, and that he died in 532. According to his *Life*, written by one of his pupils in 533-534,[3] he knew Greek and also spoke it (§ iv-v). He was exiled to Sardinia by king Thrasamund, together with more than sixty Bishops, and was recalled first in 515, and definitely in 523. A faithful disciple of St Augustine, whose trend of thought he diligently assimilated, he combated Arianism and Semi-Pelagianism in a series of works of which the literary capacity is not always equal to the vigour of his religious views (*Contra*

[1] Cf. O. Friebel, *Fulgentius, der Mytholog und der Bischof* (in the *Studien zur Gesch. u. Kultur des Altertums*, V, 1-2 [1911]), which gives a bibliography of the historical facts connected with the question.

[2] R. Helm's edition, L. 1898. He has made clear the identity of the two Fulgentii with the best arguments (Rh. M., LIV [1899], pp. 111-134).

[3] P.L., LXV, 117-150. Mentioned by Isidore of Seville, *De Vir. Ill.*, xiv.

Arianos ; De Trinitate ad Felicem Notarium ; De Veritate Praedestinationis et Gratiae Dei ad Joannem et Venerium, etc.).   Bossuet calls him " the greatest theologian of his time," which does not mean that Fulgentius was an original thinker, but that he had formed a most lucid and sure conception of doctrine from Augustine's writings.

II

CAESARIUS was born in 470 in the district of Chalon-sur-Saône. He joined the clergy at Chalon in 484, was instructed at Arles by the priest-rhetorician Julianus Pomerius,[1] and succeeded Eonius, Bishop of Arles, in 503.   On two occasions, in 505 and 513, he incurred the disfavour of Alaric II, and Theodoric, for political reasons.   The restoration of the seat of the Primacy of the Gauls to Arles, which he secured from Pope Symmachus (514), still further increased the *prestige* which his personal gifts had won for him.   He died on the 27th August 543.[2]

It is not possible to determine the order in which his works were written nor to assign to them any precise dates.   We possess a *Regula ad Monachos*[3] of his, and a *Regula ad Virgines*[4] (he founded in his diocese a convent of nuns over which he placed his own sister as Superior) ; four *Epistulae*, and a *Testamentum*.[5]   Various other works are attributed to him.[6]   But the best part of his pastoral activity Caesarius

[1] Pomerius wrote various works (cf. Gennadius, § xcviii) : his *De Vita Contemplativa* is in Migne, LIX, 415–520.

[2] Noticed in Gennadius, § xcvii.   *Vita Caesarii* by his pupil Cyprian of Toulon (P.L., LXVII, 1001–1121, and M.G.H., *Script. rer. Meroving.*, III [1896], 433–501). We have a letter of Cyprian's addressed to Maximus of Geneva (M.G.H., Epist. iii [1892], pp. 434–436).

[3] P.L., LXVII, 1099–1104.

[4] *Ibid.*, 1105–1121.   Cf. Dom Leclercq on these *Regulae*, Dict. *d'Archéol. chr. et de Lit.*, art. *Cénobitisme*, col. 3199 et s., and Malnory especially, *Saint Césaire d'Arles*, Paris, 1894.   One will notice that one of the articles of the *Rule* of St Caesarius enjoined on the nuns the transcribing of manuscripts.

[5] P.L., LXVII, 1135–1138.   The *Testamentum* has been re-edited by Dom Morin, *R. Bén.*, XVI, 1899, p. 100 et s.

[6] (1) A Treatise on the Trinity for the fragments of which we must go to Mai's *Nova Patrum Bibliotheca*, I (Rome, 1852), p. 407 ; Reifferscheid's *Bibl. Patrum Italica*, I, 174, note 5 ; Dom Morin's *Mélanges Cabrières*, I (Paris, 1899), p. 109.— (2) A work against the Semi-Pelagians, published by Dom Morin, R. Bén., XIII (1896), p. 433 et s.—(3) *Capitula Sanctorum Patrum, ibid.*, XXI (1904), 225–239.— On the other hand, Dom Morin disputes the authorship by Caesarius of the *Statuta Ecclesiae Antiqua* (cf. R. Bén., XXX [1913], pp. 334–342), which L. Duchesne and P. Lejay attribute to him.

2 I

gave to his sermons.[1] The author of the *Vita Caesarii* informs us that he despatched some copies of them throughout Gaul, Italy and Spain. Critics have succeeded in restoring to him a good number which had been confused under other names, or had remained anonymous, and which certain favourite tricks of style have enabled them to identify.

The form of eloquence shown by Caesarius is familiar and animated, entirely bent upon being practical, even when it touches on what is speculative. He largely utilised his predecessors, the homilists. He copied out sentences or even whole pages from Origen, St Augustine, Fulgentius, and Faustus of Riez, but with adaptations and abridgments, in which he reveals his concern not to disconcert his hearers who for the greater part were uneducated [2] and whose moral sustenance consisted in his sermons, and to only use forms of expression which might be understood by all.

"If I wished to explain the Scriptures in the order and in the language used by the holy Fathers, the food of doctrine could only reach a few learned men, and the rest of the people, the multitude, would remain famished. That is why I humbly beg that the ears of the learned will consent to tolerate unpolished expressions in order that the Lord's flock may receive the celestial food in simple and plain language ; and since the ignorant may not rise to the height of the learned, may the learned deign to descend to the ignorance of their brethren. . . ."

This popular way of speaking revivified the society of that period with all its brutality, vice, and secret and stubborn attachment to pagan practices.[3] The historian would be very wrong to neglect the *Homilies* of Caesarius. As regards

---

[1] Other writers of sermons or letters in his time were Eleutherus, Bishop of Tournai (cf. P.L., LXV, 83–102) ; Remigius, Bishop of Rheims (*ibid.*, LXV, 963–975, and M.G H., *Epist.* iii [1892], pp. 112–116) ; Aurelianus, Bishop of Arles (P.L., LXVIII, 385–408, and M.G.H., *Epist.* iii, 121–126).

[2] Cf. P.L., XXXIX, 2325.

[3] Cf. A. Malnory's *Saint Césaire, Evêque d'Arles*, 1894 ; P. Lejay's *Le Rôle Théologique de Césaire d'Arles*, in R.H.L.R., 1905, pp. 444–487 ; R. Boese's *Superstitiones Aretalenses e Caesario collectae*, Marburg, 1909 (an interesting study which embraces sermons, canons of the Councils, books on penance, etc.). Very significant too, from the point of view of the survival of pagan practices, is the *De Correctione Rusticorum* by Martin of Bracara (Caspari's edition, Christiania, 1883), who was writing in the north of Spain between the years 560 and 580. Martin's writings (P.L., LXXII) are full of reminiscences from Seneca.

his claim to be called a theologian, he will notice the fidelity
with which he followed the views of St Augustine on grace.
He had however visited Lérins, the old stronghold of Semi-
Pelagianism.   But it was to the tradition of Prosper and
Hilary that he adhered and not to that of Cassian and Faustus
of Riez.   Moreover, even in Rome Popes Gelasius I (492–496)
and Anastasius II (496–498) resolutely favoured Augustine's
views and pushed them further on certain points than Augustine himself would have liked to do.   The Semi-Pelagian
reaction had been greatly checked by the end of the Vth
century even in Gaul where not long since it had seemed to
be winning the day.

A man of action, preacher, moralist and instructor of the
barbarians, Caesarius at the beginning of the Merovingian
age was " one of the leaders of the Church in Gaul, one of the
founders of her discipline and of any learning she was to retain
through two centuries of twilight." [1]

III

The " first of the Scholastics," Anicius Manlius Severinus
Boethius belonged to the illustrious *gens* of the *Anicii*, who,
in the course of the IVth and Vth centuries had given to the
Empire a long series of high officials.[2]   They had become
Christians in the middle of the IVth century : [3] we shall see
that we have no reason to doubt that Boethius was one
himself like all his race.   Born in the year 480, Boethius
entered the service of the Arian king Theodoric.   His father
had been Consul in 487 ; he himself became Consul in 510,
and had the pride of seeing his son promoted to the same
dignity in 522.[4]   Theodoric readily entrusted him with the
most delicate missions.   Deep disgrace brutally cut short this
brilliant career.   For having undertaken the defence of the
Senator Albinus who was accused of maintaining secret
correspondence with Justin I, the Emperor of the East,
Boethius found himself thrown into chains (doubtless at

---

[1] Paul Lejay, in R.H.L R., 1905, p. 137.
[2] P.W., I, 2198 et s.   Genealogical table, *ibid.*, p. 2201.
[3] Prudentius, *Contra Symm.*, I, 548 et s. ; Zosimus, VI, vii, 4 ; C.I.L., XIV,
1875.
[4] Cf. the *Variae* of Cassiodorus, II, 40 ; II, 41 ; I, 45.

Pavia). Accused of high treason, and also of magic, he died under torture in 524.

The motives for his condemnation were solely political. Nevertheless he had served the Catholic cause in face of the hostility of his irascible master, and died with admirable resignation. He was included among the martyrs [1] at an early date and honoured as such at Pavia and Brescia.

In spite of the heavy administrative functions whose charge he had assumed, Boethius only lived for things of the mind : " Cum in omnibus philosophiae disciplinis ediscendis atque tractandis summum vitae solamen existimem . . ." : it is with these words that the *De Syllogismo Hypothetico*, one of his treatises, opens, and they sum up wonderfully the rule of his life. After learning Greek at Athens a knowledge of which had become very rare in the West, he assigned himself the task of translating into Latin the whole of Aristotle, and the whole of Plato, of commenting on them, and of showing their fundamental agreement in the majority of the problems of philosophy.[2] In this way he resumed the *rôle* (to the profit of Catholic theology) of interpreter played by Rufinus and St Jerome more than a century before.

He was only able to carry out a small portion of his plan. Those of his works which remain deal with Aristotle as an eminent theorist in logic, and with his commentators and imitators, such as Cicero and Porphyry. Thanks to Boethius the Middle Ages learned how to discourse on the five " universals " and on the " categories," and to construct syllogisms in accordance with the rules laid down by Aristotle ; it was not until much later, at the beginning of the XIIIth century, and through the intermediary of translations from the Arabic, that they came to know the moral and metaphysical works of this philosopher.

Boethius likewise provided the schools with precious manuals in his *Institutio Arithmetica*, wherein he paraphrased the *Introduction to Arithmetic* by Nicomachus of Jerassa, the Pythagorean ; in his *Institutio Musica*, proceeding from the same source, and in his *Geometria*, derived from Euclid.

But his greatest renown rests upon his *Consolations of*

---

[1] Martyrology of Adonius (P.L., CXXIII, 107).
[2] In *Libr. Aristot. de Interpret.*, II, ii, 3 (a leading passage) ; cf. *In Categ.* (P.L., LXIV, 201).

Philosophy, which, as the Abbé Gervaise wrote at the beginning of the XVIIIth century, " has been the delight of all thoughtful minds for twelve centuries, and has been translated into as many different languages as there are races in Europe." With prose and poetry [1] intermingled the work is divided into five books of which the following is the gist.

It opens with a few mournful verses which Boethius wrote in prison " at the dictation of the stricken Muses." Suddenly he seemed to see by his side " a woman of imposing countenance, with eyes full of brilliancy and possessed of wonderful penetration, of bright complexion, and imbued with youthful vigour although she was so full of years that she had all the appearance of belonging to another age." With a few angry words the apparition put to flight the group of the Muses, and then bending over Boethius she dried his eyes dim with tears. Boethius then recognised the companion of his youth and mistress of his life, Philosophy.

She had come to console him. She reminded him of the injustices of which thinkers like Socrates, Anaxagoras, Zeno, Seneca and others, had been the victims, and invited him to lay bare his wounds that she might dress them. Boethius related to her the intrigues under which he had fallen. What they had aimed at was his integrity as an administrator whose uprightness wearied their wicked envy, and as the defender of the Senate which had so ill repaid him its debt of gratitude. In his own personal misfortunes Boethius perceived (and it was this that disconcerted him most) the triumph of injustice, and a serious check inflicted upon the eternal rules of right morality.

To this cry of distress Philosophy replies with calm firmness. She undertakes to reveal to him the fundamental truths wherein his ulcerated soul may find healing.

" It is because thou dost not know what is the last end of things that thou believest in the power and the happiness of wicked men and criminals. It is because thou hast forgotten by what laws the world is governed

---

[1] The same arrangement is found in the Encyclopædia of Martianus Capella, in the Vth century, in Alexander's Greek story revised by Julius Valerius at the beginning of the IVth century, and in the *Satiricon* of Petronius in the Ist century. It has its remote origin in the *Satire* of Menippus.

that thou dost imagine that all these vicissitudes of destiny float about without any direction." [1]

She begins by pouring out for him a first soothing draught (1, II). He grieves over the caprices of Fortune : but was it not the practice of that witch to abandon in an inexplicable manner those on whom she had been lavishing her favours ? Did it count for nothing that he had been loaded with good things by her ? And in his trials did not Boethius still retain a few of them ? [2] Moreover were these benefits, if estimated at their true value, worth the attachment which the generality of men gave to them ? Fortune did better service to mortals when she is contrary to them than when favourable, because she then reveals herself in her true self and frees them from the superstition with which they honour her unduly.

Boethius confesses that he is already somewhat softened and relieved (Book III). But Philosophy holds in reserve a still more efficacious moral therapeutic. She goes back to the quality of the good things pursued after by mankind. Riches, honours, power, glory and pleasure have after all no other value than that which unstable opinion attaches to them. " Not only are they unable of themselves to procure happiness, but they cannot even be considered as the road leading to it." In reality, it is God who is the sole, the sovereign good. It is through Him alone that man can be happy. In him are reconstituted the scattered elements of happiness, on which man lays a greedy hand almost blindly, without knowing that their only value lies in their being brought together in the Divine Unity.

Boethius, although half won over by this persuasive reasoning, still retains a grievous objection (Book IV). How " under the rule of the beneficent Master who governs the world, doth evil pass unpunished or how can it exist ? " Philosophy disposes herself to initiate him into still more lofty problems in order to resolve this difficulty :

---

[1] P.L., LXIII, 654.
[2] " Sed hoc est quod recolentem vehementius coquit. Nam in omni adversitate fortunae infelicissimum genus est infortunii, fuisse felicem," Boethius replies. Dante, who was familiar with the *Consolatio* recollected this passage in the well-known lines, " Nessun maggior dolore, che ricordarsi del tempo felice nella miseria." *Inferno*, V, 119 et s.

" I will fasten wings to thy soul which shall enable it to mount up to higher regions in order that henceforth delivered from all anxiety thou mayst regain safe and sound thine own country under my guidance, by following my paths, and suffering thyself to be borne on by me." [1]

She then enters upon the mysterious question of the nature of good and evil. The good is the opposite of evil : if it be proved that the former possesses power, it is therefore because the latter has none ; and reciprocally, if the powerlessness of evil be demonstrated, the force of good must be recognised. This is the conclusion to which Philosophy leads Boethius by a succession of subtile remarks. Evil is synonymous with *nothing*. In the absolute meaning of the word, wicked men *are not*, since they depart from those very laws which make man what he is by nature destined for.—But, retorts Boethius, they do not persecute the good any less for all that !—Their misfortune is all the greater, and if they rejoice in impunity, it is an added calamity since it perpetuates their iniquity. Philosophy declares that she is not willing to invoke another kind of argument taken from the rewards beyond the grave. She prefers to reply to a fresh question put by Boethius who cannot see how, in the obscure apportionment of good things and misfortunes, God is different from blind chance. She discloses to him the real nature of Providence to whom fate itself is subordinate, being only " the variable and succeeding chain of all those events the working out of which God hath prepared." If happiness and misfortune seem to be distributed without discernment, it is because we are ignorant of the designs by means of which God apportions to each one of us the trials from which we are able to draw our own purification.

What is Chance (Book V) ?   Philosophy hesitates over this secondary question. Finally she decides to give a definition of Chance, but in order to pass at once to the essential problem of free will. Liberty was an undoubted truth. Nevertheless it had its degrees :

" The human soul is necessarily more free so far as it is permitted to remain in the contemplation of the Divine

[1] P.L., LXIII, 788.

Intelligence ; it is already less so when it turns its migration in the direction of the body, and still less when it finds itself imprisoned in its wholly material members. But its slavery is extreme when, given up to vice, it forfeits the possession of Reason which is proper to it." [1]

How was liberty to be reconciled with the Divine foreknowledge ? Philosophy scouts certain current solutions of this difficult problem to bring forward another. The knowledge possessed by the Divine Being in no way resembled our own. It soars above the succession of time, and sees, in the simplicity of its cognition, all things as though they were present.

The *Consolatio* has no conclusion. Evidently Boethius had not time to put the last touches to it.

This work seems beforehand to give the lie to Rochefoucauld's ironical maxim : [2] " Philosophy triumphs easily over past and future ills ; but ills that are present triumph over her." Even in the agony of a harsh captivity Boethius was able to free himself from the dejection caused by his own misery in order to raise his eyes to the great problems of the destiny of man. Who cannot admire the strength shown in such an emancipation ? Even to-day the *Consolatio* is read with interest in spite of its certain lack of balance—more evident in the last three books especially—the forerunner of the quibbles dear to the Middle Ages. A compelling and soothing movement carries the discussion to higher and higher altitudes. Boethius gathers together all the lessons of the noble wisdom of antiquity to create from them the substance of his Προτρεπτικός εἰς Θεόν, of his exhortation to turn towards God which is the end and aim of all creatures. Turn by turn we hear echoes of Aristotle, Plato, Seneca, Cicero, also Tibullus and Virgil. Many other reminiscences mingle in the *Consolatio* with no displeasing incongruity because Boethius blends them with skill into a whole which is his special gift.

This idealistic discussion is nowhere based on the Scriptures, and the name of Christ does not appear in it. It was from considerations of the reason alone that Boethius

---

[1] *Ibid.*, 836.
[2] Gilbert's edition, I, p. 39, and especially p. 22.

drew the material for his argument. People have wondered at this so far as to allege that he was not a Christian.[1] There is one difficulty nevertheless in accepting this interpretation : several treatises on Catholic theology under the name of Boethius have come down to us. Must we then deny his authorship ? Some critics do not recoil from this excision. But this hypothesis is shown to be without foundation since Alfred Holder[2] discovered at the end of a manuscript of the Xth century coming from Reichenau and belonging to the library at Karlsruhe, an extract in which Cassiodorus attributes to his kinsman and friend Boethius by name the *De Sancta Trinitate*, *Capita Dogmatica*, and the *Liber contra Nestorium*. The debate is thus closed : Boethius was a Christian. Let us not compare him, as has Gaston Boissier,[3] with the Tertullian of the *De Anima*, nor with Minucius Felix, nor with Ausonius : analogies could be but superficial. Let us rather compare him, in company with Boissier, this time more happily inspired, with the St Augustine of the treatises written at Cassiciacum. However profoundly convinced of the truths of the faith, Boethius recognised the right which Augustine had claimed not long before, of advancing solutions of the problems dominating life and giving to it its meaning and proper end, which were purely philosophical but fully compatible with the faith. The Middle Ages were nowhere shocked at this method. The *Consolatio Philosophiae* was one of the books on which it was brought up.[4] We possess some 400 manuscripts[5] of it, and we know of more than 20 commentaries. These figures are significant, and from them we are able to estimate the action of this masterpiece on Western thought.[6]

[1] On this question cf. A. Hilderbrand's *B. und seine Stellung zum Christentum*, Regensb. 1885 ; G. Boissier, *Journal des Sav.*, 1889, 449.

[2] Cf. Usener's *Anecdoten Holderi, ein Beitrag zur Gesch. Roms in ostgotischer Zeit*, published in *Festschrift der 32 Philolgenvers, zu Wiesbaden*.

[3] *Journal des Sav.*, 1889, 456.

[4] As regards religious art in particular, see E. Mâle's *l'Art Religieux* au XIIIᵉ siècle, 3rd ed., Paris, 1910, p. 114 et s. ; Bréhier's *l'Art Chrétien*, 1918, p. 284.

[5] There are some views on the manuscripts of Boethius in S.B.W., vol. 144, pp. 1–8 : Engelbrecht claims that a distinctly conservative criticism should be reserved for the *Consolatio*. Observations on his style, *ibid.*, pp. 15–26, his syntax (pp. 16–36), his choice of words (pp. 36–51), his metre (pp. 53–58). F. di Capua has shown in the *Didaskaleion*, III (1914), pp. 269–303, that Boethius observed the rules concerning the ending off of sentences with infinite natural good taste.

[6] The question of the sources used in the *Consolatio* deserve to be studied. According to Usener (Rh. M., XXVIII, 398), Boethius borrowed from Aristotle's *Protrepticos*, either directly, or through a translation, the greater portion of books

IV

THE family to which Flavius Magnus Aurelius Cassiodorus belonged was one of those which deemed it wise and politic to place themselves in the service of the barbarian kings as the Roman power declined. His father was Pretorian Prefect at the court of Theodoric. Born at Scylacium (Squillace),[1] on the south-east coast of Italy, Cassiodorus was himself Quaestor (507–511), Consul (514), Governor of Lucania, *Magister Officiorum* and Pretorian Prefect (from 533–536). His *cursus honorum* thus followed its course uninterruptedly during forty years, and under four successive kings, to whom his administrative aptitude and scholarly gifts rendered him indispensable. In 540, he renounced his worldly honours and retired to the monastery of Vivarium.[2] Beyond his desire to render his salvation more sure another preoccupation had decided him upon this retreat. He was concerned at the lack of serious interpreters of Holy Scripture.[3] Already some years previously, in agreement with Pope Agapetus he had thought of founding in Rome a school of Biblical studies [4] similar to that which had been the glory of Alexandria in the days of Clement and Origen, or to the one which was still flourishing at Nisibis in Mesopotamia. The death of Agapetus after only one year of his Pontificate, and unfavourable political circumstances had brought this project to nothing, and he now resumed it in a more modest form at Vivarium. Here he wrote his theological works and died shortly after the year 575 at the age of nearly one hundred.

Even during his life in the world, Cassiodorus had written

II and III, and the beginning of book IV. The two-thirds of the remainder of the work was made up of reminiscences from Aristotle and neo-Platonism. The observations made by E. Kennard Rand (*Harvard Studies in Classical Philology*, XV [1904], pp. 1–28) tend to recognise much more independence in Boethius than Usener supposes. G. A. Muller, *die Trotschrift des Boethius*, Berlin, 1912, insists on the connection between Boethius, and Plato, Aristotle, and Cicero's *Hortensius* (see pp. 40 and 51 for certain significant resemblances to this last work).

[1] There is a fascinating description of Scylacium in the *Variae*, XII, xv.

[2] The *Monasterium Vivariense* took its name from the fish ponds constructed by Cassiodorus, who was then Pretorian Prefect, near his native town (cf. *Variae*, XII, xv, 14). Another habitation, more secluded, was arranged by the monks who desired solitude, on Mount *Castellum* (*Inst.*, I, xxix).

[3] *Inst.*, I, *Praef.*

[4] *Ibid.*

historical works—a Chronicle of the Universe (*Chronica*) from Adam down to the year 519, drawn up at the request of Eutharic, Consul that same year, from the records of Titus Livius, Aufidius Bassus, the Chronicle of Ravenna and that of St Jerome ; [1] a History of the Goths (*de Origine Actibusque Getorum*) written between the years 526 and 533 at the command of Theodoric (the original has been lost and we only get an idea of it from the *Getica of Jordanis*, who made extensive use of it) ; [2] twelve books of *Variae*, or 468 pieces of an official character, worded in a grandiloquent, florid, and unmeaning style, which became the model of the chancelleries of the Middle Ages ; the last in date is of the year 527 ; and a *De Anima* reflecting the ideas of St Augustine and Claudianus Mamertus.

With the assistance of a collaborator, Epiphanus the *scolasticus*, he wrote in his retreat at Vivarium the *Historia Tripartita*, compiled rather carelessly from Socrates, Sozomenes and Theodoret ; and a translation of the *Antiquities of the Jews* by Josephus whom he qualifies with some exaggeration as *paene secundus Livius*. To these we must add the *Complexiones in Psalmos*, a wordy commentary on the Psalms.

The work on which his best reputation rests is the *Institutiones Divinarum et Saecularium Litterarum* in two books.[3] The first treats of spiritual reading, that is to say, the study of the Bible. The purpose of Cassiodorus, to which he desired to incline his monks, was a full understanding of the sacred Books. He taught them that the mere reading of the canonical texts was not sufficient to grasp all their meaning and that profane sciences—geography, grammar, rhetoric, dialectics, and astronomy—powerfully co-operated to this end.[4] He also exhorted them to copy manuscripts of the Scriptures with a care worthy of such a task, renewing

---

[1] On the subsequent fate of this *Chronicle* in the Middle Ages, cf. Paul Lehmann, *Cassiodorstudien*, in *Philologus*, LXXI (1912), pp. 278–281.

[2] The works of Jordanis are in M.G.H., V, 1 (1882, Mommsen). French translation by A. Savagnier, in the Panckoucke collection, vol. LXXI (1842), and in the Nisard collection.

[3] This is the most authentic title according to V. Mortet, R. ph. XXIV (1900), pp. 103–110. The work must have been written about the middle of the VIth century, in 543–4 according to Franz, Ebert and Mortet ; in the years 543–555, according to Mommsen. Lehmann, *Philologus*, 1912, p. 290, does not think that the *Div. Inst.* could have been finished before 551–562.

[4] I, xxv et s. (P.L., LXX, 1139).

the advice which St Martin had previously given to the cenobites of the monastery at Tours [1] a hundred and fifty years before, and laid down the prudent limits within which their fondness for making corrections in the text should be restrained through respect for the divine Word, even though the grammar or style should suffer from this forbearance. A library of books, purchased at great expense and kept in nine *armaria*, provided them with all the necessary requirements.[2]   To those of them who did not feel an aptitude for literary work he recommended agriculture and gardening, bringing to their notice the help they would find in the works of certain specialists of former days, Gargilius Martialis, Columella, and Aemilianus Macer.   The second book of the *Institutiones* comprises seven chapters concerned with the " liberal " arts, whose method and precepts, as represented by the theorists of antiquity and by certain Christian authors like St Augustine and Boethius, Cassiodorus reviews.

The *De Orthographia*, written at the age of 93, completes the *Institutiones* by giving rules for the art of writing and punctuating correctly.

We have already mentioned, when treating of the preservation of the old learning,[3] how fruitful in initiative Cassiodorus was. He communicated to his monks a taste for intellectual work ; he provided them with books and taught them how to profit by them ; and while co-ordinating in the exegesis of the Bible the methodical researches to which he impelled them—the somewhat narrow view previously held by the Fathers of the IVth century—he guarded against all condemnation of the pagan writers and made many extracts from them.   In this way he founded a tradition of work and criticism which was to be renewed after him, and which assures for him the eternal gratitude of Western civilisation.

In addition, some of his friends under his persuasion devoted themselves to render in Latin a selection of Greek works.   One of them, Mutianus, translated the *Homilies* of St John Chrysostom on the Epistle to the Hebrews.[4]

---

[1] Sulp. Severus, *Vita S. Martini*, vii.

[2] For the probable contents of this library, see Olleris, *Cassiodore Conservateur des livres de l'Antiquité Latine*, 1841, pp. 54–68 ; A. Franz, *M. Aurelius Cassiodorus Senator*, Breslau, 1872, pp. 80–92.

[3] P. 28.

[4] P.G., LXIII, 237.

Denys the Less attacked a series of Greek writings with special reference to the domain of Canon Law ; [1] Bellator translated Origen's *Homilies ;* [2] Epiphanus the Scholastic took as his share Socrates, Sozomenes, Theodoret, and a compilation of what he thought he recognised (but erroneously) as a Commentary by Didymus on the Catholic Epistles.[3] The translation of the *Hypotyposes* of Clement of Alexandria probably came from this same group of writers [4] of whom Cassiodorus was the soul, and whom he inspired with his own love of work. This is the last time that Greek learning, soon to be consigned to oblivion in the West, excited the zeal of an intellectual *élite*.

V

THE " Father of our History," as Claude Fauchet called him in the XVIth century, was born on the 30th November, probably of the year 538, at Arverna (Clermont-Ferrand). He came from a family of Senatorial rank on the side of his father Florentius and of his mother Armentaria, and was " allied both by birth and piety [5] with all that was most illustrious." He was called Georgius Florentius, but took the name of Gregory in memory of his maternal great-grandfather St Gregory, Bishop of Langres from 506–7 to 539–540. After a pious and studious youth under the direction of his mother, his paternal uncle Gallus, Bishop of Clermont, and Avitus who succeeded Gallus in the same Episcopal See, he went to Tours in 563 in the hope of recovering his health at the tomb of St Martin, and he was not disappointed. He had then just been ordained deacon. Ten years later, in 573, at the age of 35, he was chosen to be Bishop of Tours, the religious centre of Gaul. He devoted himself to his charge with complete abnegation amid innumerable difficulties during the twenty years of his episcopate. " In him we possess an admirable type of the Bishop of the VIth century," wrote Gabriel Monod. " The *rôle* that he played

---

[1] P.L., LXVII.
[2] Cf. Cassiod., *Inst.*, I, vi.
[3] P.G., XXXIX, 1749.
[4] Cf. Cassiod., *Inst.*, I, viii.
[5] Cf. genealogical table drawn up by G. Monod in his *Et. crit. sur les sources de l'Hist. mérov.*, in the *Recueil de Travaux Originaux ou Traduits Relatifs aux Sciences Historiques*, fasc. 2 (1872), p. 27.

in the events of his time, together with the respect of all his
contemporaries by which he was surrounded, and his remarkable intellectual activity joined to his ceaseless practical zeal,
disclose in him an intelligence superior to the times in which
he lived however much, in his humility, he pretended the
contrary. But it is his character which commands our respect. . . . A Bishop devoted to the interests of his diocese
and those of the whole Catholic Church, he drew from his
faith an intrepid courage to withstand the acts of violence and
injustice committed by the barbarians, and a moral nobility
and a spirit of charity and disinterestedness which rightly
won for him the title of Saint. He was a perfect representative of the Church which alone in the world at that time
represented intellect and morality." [1]

Gregory died on the 17th November 593 or 594.

His work as a hagiographer [2] is full of curious features.
From nowhere else can lovers of folk-lore draw more abundant
material. The miraculous, of course, has the first place,
because Gregory aimed at edification before all things, and because in the eyes of his somewhat rough public these strong
methods appeared much more compelling than theological
arguments. He himself thought likewise. He built up
rather a strange conception of the power of miracles (*virtus*),
an emanation of the Infinite *Virtus* and liked to describe
their beneficent or terrifying effects. One quotation will
suffice :

"The tomb (of St Peter) placed beneath the altar
(of the church in the Vatican) is a most rare piece of
work. He who would offer prayers at it opens the
grille surrounding it, approaches the sepulchre, and
passing his head through a small window in it, asks
what he has need of ; his prayers are granted immediately provided only that they be lawful. Should
he wish to take back some relic from the tomb, he casts
upon it a piece of cloth which he has first weighed,
then with vigils and fasting he prays fervently that the

[1] *Ibid.*, p. 142.
[2] The *Septem Libri Miraculorum* comprise the *In Gloria Martyrum* (written in
590), the *De Virtutibus S. Juliani* (between 581 and 587), the four books *De Virtutibus Martini* (I and II, written between 574 and 581 ; III in 587 ; IV between
591 and 593). The first six books were touched up afterwards by Gregory.

power of the Apostle will deign to grant his wish. If
the faith of one acting thus be sufficient, the cloth,
when he has taken it from the tomb, is so filled with
divine power that it weighs much heavier than before." [1]

" This page," remarks H. Delehaye, the Bollandist, " has
a very legendary colouring, and it is difficult to persuade oneself that the strange experience of weighing was ever put to
the proof. But what can be said of the state of mind of a man
who does not hesitate to recount anecdotes like these ? " [2]
Gregory was living in the VIth century, and we must not
expect from him a critical mistrust which did not exist in his
times. The flowers of pious expression sometimes found in
his *Lives* of the Saints have at least original freshness and
charm.

Gregory, from his character and inner disposition, was the
most loyal of historians. It is this very candour which
gives so much value to his *History of the Franks*, especially
in regard to events which he personally records. [3] The
first four books which go down to the death of Sigebert
(575), form one complete whole and end in a chronological
summary. In the first book he gives a history of the world
from Adam down to the death of St Martin (397), based
on the Bible, St Jerome, Orosius, the Martyrologies, etc.
Beginning with the second book, he unfolds the history of the
Frankish kings, luxurious, brutal, and good from caprice or
under the influence of Heaven. From the fifth book, his
work assumes the character of personal memoirs, which are
those of a well-informed observer. Gregory nourished a
vigorous hatred against the enemies of the Church, but as he
quotes his facts conscientiously, the impartiality of his
account enables us to rectify the partiality of some of his
judgments. As for the " phlegm " with which he has been
sometimes reproached, [4] is it not preferable that he should

---

[1] *De Gloria M.*, I, xxviii.
[2] *Les Origines du Culte des Martyrs*, Brussels, 1912, p. 142. Other texts are
noticed by Hébert, R.E.A., XVIII (1916), pp. 123–141. See also A. Marignan's
Etudes sur la Civilisation Française, vol. I, *La Société Mérovingienne ;* vol. II,
Le Culte des Saints sous les Mérovingiens, 1899.
[3] Cf. a list of these events in Monod, *op. cit.*, p. 105. For Gregory's sources,
ibid., p. 73 et s. Books I–IV of the *Historia Francorum* were written in 575 ;
V–VI, in 580–585 ; VII–X, § 30 in 585–591, and § 31 of book X, in 594.
[4] Ampère, *Hist. Litt.*, II, 300–301.

have maintained it amid all the horrors which he relates, rather than weary the reader with repeated outbursts of indignation ?

The *De Cursibus Ecclesiasticis*, written between the years 575 and 582, enumerates in succession the seven wonders of the world (the foremost, according to Gregory, was Noah's Ark), and then the seven marvels wrought by God (the tides, the germination of plants and fruits, the phœnix, Mount Etna, the fountain at Grenoble, the sun and the moon). Gregory is thus led to give some indications on the movement of the stars.   He gives his purpose in the following words :

> " I do not instruct in science, and I do not aim at sounding the future, but I will show how the course of the day should be filled logically with the praises of God, *that is to say, at what hours he who desires to pursue with diligence the service of God should rise during the night to pray.*"

Modern opinions differ somewhat on the question of Gregory's " learning."   Let us hear him defining his abilities with his customary ingenuousness : [1]

> " The cities of Gaul allowed the cultivation of literature to decline, or rather to perish. . . . Not one man could be found who, as a grammarian versed in dialectics, was able to depict (the events of the time) either in the language of prose or that of verse. The greater portion often bewailed this and said : ' Woe upon our times, for the study of letters hath perished from among us, and no one in the whole world can be found to tell us by his writings what is happening in our days ! ' Pondering over these laments . . . , I could not keep silent, in my uncouth style, either upon the strife of the wicked or the lives of the good, attracted especially by that saying which hath often struck me among our people when I heard it, that ' very few understand a rhetorician when he offers a dissertation, but many, an ignorant man when he speaks (*philosophantem rhetorem intelligunt pauci, loquentem rusticum multi*).' "

[1] *Hist. Franc., Procemium.*

And again :

" Although these books be written in an unpolished style (*stilo rusticiori*), I conjure nevertheless all the priests of the Lord who shall rule over the Church at Tours after me, who am unworthy, never to cause them to be destroyed. . . ."[1]

" I fear," he confesses elsewhere,[2] " that if I undertake to write, people will say to me ; ' Dost thou think, ignorant man that thou art, who hast not the calling thereof (*O rustice et idiota*), to place thy name among those of the writers ; or dost thou hope to gain acceptance by the competent of this work of thine, void of grace and of art, and lacking all knowledge of style ? Thou, who hast no practice in letters, who knowest not how to distinguish the nouns, who often takest the masculine for feminine, the feminine for neuter, and in place of the neuter dost use the masculine ; who canst not even employ the prepositions [3] as is suitable, the proper use of which hath been regulated by the most illustrious authors, since thou dost place them on occasions which require the accusative before words in the ablative, and inversely ; dost thou think that people will not see that it is a case of a slow heavy ox trying to play in the *palaestrum,* or of a sluggish ass endeavouring to flit across the court of players at ball ? ' Nevertheless, I will make reply, ' It is for you that I labour, and thanks to my rusticity (*per meam rusticitatem*), you will be enabled to exercise your knowledge.' . . ."

Critics like Ozanam,[4] and even Fustel de Coulanges,[5] agree in seeing in these apologies only a half sincere affectation of modesty, or only an echo of that long tradition which liked every ecclesiastical writer to oppose his *rusticitas,* solely desirous of the truth, to the inflated, cadenced and

---

[1] H.F., X, xxxi.   See the whole of the end of the chapter.

[2] *De Gloria Conf., Prooemium.*   See also the *Preface* to the *Vita Martini,* and *passim* (M.G.H., p. 33, 12 ; 668, 27, etc.).

[3] According to a computation by Max Bonnet in his *Le Latin de Grégoire de Tours,* 1890, p. 522, Gregory makes about 20 per cent. of mistakes in his use of his prepositions.

[4] *La Civil. Chrét. chez les Francs,* 1872, p. 479.

[5] *La Monarchie Franque,* 1888, pp. 2–3.

frivolous language of the rhetoricians.   Ozanam found Gregory
" *tout pénétré d'antiquité.*"   This was coming to too quick
a conclusion.   Gregory knew Virgil [1] rather well ; he quotes
two passages from Sallust ; [2] he speaks of Pliny, Aulus Gellius, [3]
Cicero [4] and the Theodosian Code, [5] but there is nothing to
show that he had read them.   This is all that his alleged
impregnation with profane learning comes to.   Besides,
does he not himself say that he had been drawn exclusively
towards sacred literature ? [6]   As regards his language, the
ample work of Max Bonnet provides us with all the elements
of a practical appreciation.   " The extremely rich vocabulary
of Gregory," the eminent philologist writes, [7] " owes its
abundance, after preserving an immense majority of the old
words, not only to his use of expressions borrowed from all
the different varieties of Latin, Greek, and sometimes the
languages of the barbarians, but especially to his adoption of
new preferences which are very diverse and often very
unexpected.   Briefly, the inflections were preserved.   However, some breaches were made in them, both by alterations
in sound which naturally extend to all, and by false analogies
which only show themselves very capriciously.   One word will
follow ten times the old inflection, and at the eleventh he
will confuse it in a new rendering, led away by some kind
of resemblance.   His syntax and vocabulary are furthest
removed from classic Latin.   *There is hardly one line that one
could pass as having been written at the good period.*   His
tendencies and methods of style are those of a self-taught
man anxious to do like the professional writers, but who feels
his powerlessness to imitate them.   Time after time he
strives after this, and then gives it up.   From this results
a strange contrast between worn-out forms of eloquence
and a fresh and rugged originality ! "

Taken as a whole, we have reason to believe that the
declarations of Gregory were sincere.   He had a profound and
sorrowful feeling of his literary insufficiency, and it was well
founded.   It was a scrupulosity which did him honour,

---

[1] Numerous instances are noticed by Karl Sittl, A.L.L., VI, 560.
[2] H.F., IV, xiii ; VII, i.
[3] *Vitae Patr., Proœm.*
[4] *Gloria Conf., Proœm.*
[5] H.F., IV, xlvii.
[6] *Vitae Patr.,* ii.
[7] *Op. cit.,* p. 751.

as it proves that having had a glimpse of some few classics or imitators of the classics, Gregory understood his shortcomings, and regretted that his early bringing up had not enabled him to repair them. It remains to be said that modern readers find a charm in this *naïveté* which did not exclude the language of rhetoric, but was incapable of sustaining the effort for long, and which preserved him throughout from those *finesses* of the *littérateur* in an age when imitation of the old writers was so rapidly degenerating into a perverted taste. What could he not have given us if he had known how to "develop" (*dilatare, extendere*) and "embellish" his writings (*ornare paginam*),[1] instead of having left this perilous task to more skilful hands, as he regretted ?

VI

A WRITER who undertook to-day to treat single-handed of theology, heresiology, polemics, chronology, history, biography, symbolism, law, the liturgy, grammar, etymology, cosmography, natural history, mineralogy, ethnology, agriculture, and the arts of building, clothes and cooking, would have hard work to make himself taken seriously. The Middle Ages, which did not always distinguish very clearly between real knowledge and compilation, nevertheless celebrated Isidore of Seville as the embodiment of the *doctor egregius*. If they mistrusted the quality of Isidore's vast range of knowledge at least they had good reason to feel very grateful to the laborious excerptor who did not spare any pains in collecting and handing on to future generations the positive information he had culled in the course of his immense reading. Far less original than Boethius whom on more than one occasion he has utilised, Isidore fulfilled an analogous *rôle* in a much more varied domain. He provided for later centuries a useful *summa* of the science of antiquity the results of which he condensed in his manuals. Not that he was particularly favourable to Greco-Latin learning. He counselled his monks against the reading of "gentile"[2] books. But, without ignoring the danger of profane literature, he loved it for its own sake, and flattered himself with

---

[1] *Vita M.*, II, Pref.
[2] *Regula Monach.*, viii, 3 (P.L., LXXXIII, 877): "Gentilium libros vel haereticorum volumina monachus legere caveat."

having drawn therefrom valuable material for the elucidation of the sacred Books.

Isidore was born in the year 570 of a family belonging originally to Carthage, who had migrated to Seville, doubtless after the destruction of Carthage in 552. He was brought up by his brother Leander, one or two of whose works we have,[1] and who became Bishop of Seville, the chief city of Betica, in 576. Isidore succeeded him twenty-five years later and died on the 4th April 636. His biographers highly praise his character and piety. He also held a certain place in the religious history of his time. It was he who presided at the fourth national Council at Toledo held in December 633. He read continuously, pen in hand, extending his investigations far beyond the circle of Christian authors to profane writers and scholiasts, and copied out everything that seemed to him worthy of interest, without troubling himself to indicate the sources upon which he had drawn.[2]

His master work was the *Etymologiae* or *Origines*, a veritable encyclopædia of human knowledge, which his friend Braulio, the Bishop of Saragossa,[3] received from his hands unfinished, and divided it into twenty books, after having made perhaps a few corrections : I. Grammar ; II. Rhetoric and Dialectic ; III. The four mathematical disciplines (Arithmetic, Geometry, Music, Astronomy) ; IV. Medicine ; V. The Laws and the Times ; VI. The Ecclesiastical Books and Offices ; VII. God, the Angels, the Faithful ; VIII. The Church and the Sects ; IX. Tongues, Nations, Kingdoms, the Army, the Citizens, and Parents ; X. Etymological Lists ; XI. Men and Monsters ; XII. The Animals ; XIII. The Universe and its Divisions ; XIV. The Earth and its Parts ; XV. Buildings and the Fields ; XVI. Stones and Metals ; XVII. Rural Matters ; XVIII. War and Games ; XIX. Ships, Buildings and Clothes ; XX. Food and Domestic and Agricultural Utensils. Isidore himself confesses that

---

[1] A *De Institutione Virginum et Contemptu Mundi* and a *Homilia de Triumpho Ecclesiae ob Conversionem Gothorum :* P.L., LXXII, 873–898.

[2] There have been numerous works in recent years on the sources used by Isidore : Manitius, G.L.L.M., p. 62 et s. ; H. Philipp, *die histor. u. geogr. Quellen n den Etymologiae des Is. v. Sev.*, Berlin, 1913 ; O. Probst, *Isidors Schrift de medicina,* taken from the *Archiv. fur Geschichte der Medizin*, VIII, i (1916) ; P. Lehmann, *Kassiodorstudien* (*Philologus*, vol. 71 [1912] and 72 [1913]) ; P. Wessner, *Isidor und Sueton* (*Hermes*, 1917, pp. 201–300).

[3] Some writings of Braulio are included in Migne, vol. LXXX.

he has hardly done more than put together notes which he had culled from the " Ancients " : " En tibi, sicut pollicitus sum, misi opus de origine quarundam rerum *ex veteris lectionis recordatione collectum* atque ita in quibusdam adnotatum *sicut extat conscriptum stilo majorum.*" [1] But a twofold purpose dominates this collection of extracts which are sometimes lengthened to prolixity, but more often are condensed to the extent of dryness. The leading idea is that in order to study deeply any science, the etymology of the words used must be understood accurately : " Etymology," he declares, " is the knowledge of the origin of words when we explain by the reason the value of a verb or a noun. Aristotle called this σύμβολον, Cicero *annotatio*. Thus the word *flumen* takes its form from *fluendo*, because the *fluvius* increases by flowing. The very name of this science makes us realise its utility and necessity. For when we see whence a noun has issued, we can more quickly understand its value." [2] The greater part of the etymology advanced by Isidore is arbitrary,[3] but not more so than that furnished by Plato in the *Cratyle* or the learned Varro in his works on grammar. The other purpose animating Isidore was to turn into edification details which at first sight seem the least capable of lending themselves to it. He even speculates on the letters of the alphabet and gives them a mystic sense. In this, too, he was only continuing a far more ancient tradition.

In addition to the *Etymologiae*, we must mention the *De Natura Rerum* dedicated to King Sisefuth. It is a kind of cosmography in which theology has its place. Thus at the end of § xxvii Isidore asks himself what will happen to the stars at the Resurrection if they really have souls. Already in his dialectical arguments there is that imperturbable confidence which was to encourage the Middle Ages to discuss minutely the most inaccessible questions. The *Chronicle*, in two parts, goes from the beginning of the world to the year

---

[1] *Ep.* vi ad Braulionem.
[2] *Etym.* I, xxviii.
[3] *Segnis*, without spirit, without fire, according to him should come from *sine igne ; amicus*, from *hamus* a clamp, a friend being one on to whom one clamps oneself ; *pectus* is the part covered with hairs (*pexus*) between the two breasts ; *avis* from *avia*, because the bird flies hither and thither where there is no road, etc. Isidore fairly often uses Greek words. Certain blunders make one think that he could not have been very familiar with that language (*e.g.* III, xxi, 6).

615; following the example of St Augustine, he divides the history of the universe into six periods, corresponding to the six days of the Creation. The *De Viris Illustribus*, in which probably he was not the only one to have a hand, provides a useful supplement to similar works by St Jerome and Gennadius. His *Historiae* open with a eulogy of Spain which is celebrated.

This great worker of no critical ability or method exercised an immense influence. To form some idea of the prodigious and widespread diffusion of the *Etymologiae* in the Middle Ages, one must read the *Isidor Studien* by Ch. H. Beeson,[1] in which he has grouped together all the *non-Spanish* manuscripts up to the IXth century which he could trace, and gives a list of them by their countries. This simple list is instructive by itself and gives evidence of Isidore's brilliant reputation. It was in France that his knowledge was first received with special acclamation; but a great number of manuscripts of his works also came from Ireland, and we know the important *rôle* played by Ireland in the development of education in the Middle Ages.

VII

AFTER Boethius, Cassiodorus and Isidore of Seville, the framework of the intellectual life of the Middle Ages was established for a long time. A natural line of demarcation at this point closes the history of Latin Christian Literature.

I believe I have not over-estimated its merits. I have not concealed the fact that really finished literary authors are rare. With his vibrating sensibility and warm imagination St Augustine possessed that quality : a life of practical action held him at an early stage, and it is only occasionally that we find in his polemical or exegetic writings pages to equal certain wonderful chapters in his *Confessions*. St Jerome too could have been a master of style had he so wished, as is sufficiently shown by his letters; but he subjected and

---

[1] In the *Quellen und Unters. zur lat. Philologie des Mittelalters*, IV, 2 (1913). At the end of his work, basing them on some fifteen manuscripts Beeson published several *tituli* in verse which he is inclined to attribute to Isidore on the formal testimony of the written tradition, in spite of the contrary opinion of Ebert and the doubts of Manitius. These short pieces have otherwise very slight interest.

sacrificed himself to his labours on the Scriptures. We must not forget Tertullian when stirred by passion, although he is half spoilt by his own subtilty. In the case of all of them, rhetorical phraseology did their works much harm in the sense that their efforts to write cleverly were satisfied by the traditional methods it enjoined on them, and, owing to religious scruples, or to errors of taste, it too rarely sought after a choicer originality. The Christian poetry cannot bear comparison with the pagan. It produced no epic poet of any great breadth of vision, no dramatic poet, not even a fabulist ; a few passably happy lyrical poems and a few beautiful church hymns form the only productions which will really live.

But let us guard ourselves against a certain rather rigid type of " humanism " which would only judge the Christian writings from the point of view of the classic ideal. When we recognise in the profane writers a more marked diversity of tone and subject, and a more sustained perfection, ought this concession in any way to militate against the admiration with which the Christian writers inspire us ? [1]

Whatever be its defects, this vivid Latin Christian Literature deserves to be more carefully studied than appears to be generally the case, and whoever is interested in the history of ideas will not regret having made the effort. There are numerous historical and literary problems which can only be grasped fully after we have seen their factors coming to light during the period we have just traversed. And again, how many strong personalities are revealed, how many magnificent minds and pathetic souls anxious for the destiny of mankind, each one preserving, in spite of the community of their faith and the identity of its theoretic solutions, their original action upon this eternal enigma ! On the day when our Higher Course of Studies shall have taken a more generous interest in some of their masterpieces, scholarly research will again turn in the direction of patristic study, and we shall then be on the road to win back our former hegemony in this domain of which a prolonged lack of interest has dispossessed us.

[1] Remy de Gourmont, who does not shrink from giving a paradoxical form to ideas that are otherwise correct, writes : " The Latin Church is, we think, rather more attractive than that of Horace, and the soul of the ascetics more rich in ideals than that of the *egotistical and sly* (sic) *old victim to gout.*" (*Le Latin Mystique,* 1913, p. 5.)

TABLES REPRESENTING
LATIN CHRISTIAN LITERATURE

N.B.—Table I will enable the reader to obtain a synoptic view of Latin Christian Literature and to appraise (1) the contribution of each province in the Roman West; and (2) side by side, the contribution of contemporary Greek Christian Literature, and Latin and Greek Profane Literature. In the tables following, the classification of the works varies with the authors. In cases where the chronological order is sufficiently established and has special value (as for instance as regards St Augustine) this order has been adhered to. In other cases, I have preferred to classify by the matter, or even alphabetically.

TABLE I

General View of Latin Christian Literature

Roman Emperors	Latin Christian Literature					Principal Contemporary Greek Christian Writers	Contemporary Profane Literature	
	Italy	Africa	Spain	Gaul	Illyria		Greek	Latin
100 Trajan (98-117)						Ignatius of Antioch, Polycarp of Smyrna	Plutarch (c. 46-125)	Pliny the Younger, Tacitus (c. 55-120) Juvenal (c. 60-130) Suetonius (c. 75-160) Justin Gaius (110-180 ?) Frontonius (c. 90-168)
117. Hadrian								
138. Antoninus Pius						Papias of Hierapolis	Arrianus	Apuleius (c. 125 ?)
161. Marcus Aurelius 161-9. Lucius Verus		First Latin versions of the Bible (?)				Aristides, Hegesippus, Aristo of Pella, St Justin		
180. Commodus		Acta of the condemnation of the martyrs of Scillium				Tatian, Athenagoras, the letter concerning the martyrs of Lyons (177), Theophilus of Antioch, St Irenaeus	Lucian (c. 125-190)	
193. Pertinax								
193. Julianus 193. Septimus Severus		First writings of Tertullian : the Apologeticum (197)				Epistle to Diognetes (?) Pantaenus, Clement of Alexandria (c. 160-215)		
200	Fragment of Muratori					Homilies of Clément		

Emperors	Latin writers				Greek writers		Historia Augusta
211. Caracalla					Origen (185-254), Inscription of Abercius, Julius the African	Philostratus, Dion Cassius	
217. Macrinus 218. Heliogabalus 222. Alexander Severus 238. Maximin Military Anarchy	Death of Tertullian (?) Minucius Felix						Spartianus, Capitolinus, Vulcatius Gallicanus Trebellius Pollio
250 Decius (249-251)	Novatian						
251. Gallus 253. Æmilianus	St Cyprian, Firmilian of Cesarea, Commodian (?)				St Gregory Thaumaturgus	Plotinus (204-270)	
253. Valerian and Gallienus 268. Claudius II.					Denys of Alexandria Oracula Sibyllina Theognostis	Longinus (c. 220-273)	
270. Aurelian 275. Tacitus 276. Florianus 276. Probus 282. Carus						Porphyry (233-c. 301/5)	
283. Carinus and Numerianus 284. Diocletian (286) Maximian	Arnobius Lactantius			Victorinus de Pettau		Heliodorus	
305. Constantius 306. Constantine					Pierius S. Pamphilius, S. Methodius of Olympia		Vopiscus, Lampadius
313. (Edict of Milan) Constantine (306)-337	Donatus the Great	Juvencus	Reticius of Autun, Itinerarium Burdigalense		Eusebius of Cesarea	Philostratus	Compilation of the History of Augustus

TABLE I—*contd.*
General View of Latin Christian Literature

ROMAN EMPERORS	LATIN CHRISTIAN LITERATURE					PRINCIPAL CONTEMPORARY GREEK CHRISTIAN WRITERS	CONTEMPORARY PROFANE LITERATURE	
	ITALY	AFRICA	SPAIN	GAUL	ILLYRIA		GREEK	LATIN
337. Constans, Constantius II	Firmicus Maternus (Sicily), Proba, Lucifer of Calaris (Sardinia), Eusebius of Vercelli		Hosius of Cordova			Saint Athanasius		
361. Julian		Marius Victorinus	Pacian of Barcelona, Gregory of Elvira	St Hilary of Poitiers, Phebadius of Agen		Saint Gregory of Nazianzen (c. 330-c. 390)	Libanius, Themistius	Aurelius Victor, Eutropius
363. Jovian		Zéno Bishop of Verona				Apollinaris of Laodicea	Himerius	
423. John								
425. Valentinian III				Orientius, Hilary of Arles, Evagrius, Prosper of Aquitaine		S. Cyril of Alexandria (c. 380-444), Socrates, Sozomenes	Proclus	Nicomachus Flavianus
455. Petronius	Sedulius, Leo the Great, Arnobius the Younger			Faustus of Riez, Vincent of Lerins, Salvianus		Theodoret (386-c. 458), Basil of Seleucia		Nicomachus Dexter
455. Avitus . . 457. Majorianus . 461. Libius Severus . 467. Anthemius .				Gennadius of Marseilles, Claudianus Mamertus, Sidonius Apollinaris				
472. Olybrius . .								

Date / Rulers							
473. Glycerius		Stobaeus	Gelasius of Cyzicus				Asterius
474. Julius Nepos							
475. Romulus Augustulus							
Goth Kings							
476. Odoacer	Dracontius Victor of Vita						
493. Theodoric	Boethius, Cassiodorus, St Benedict			Denys the Little	Avitus of Vienne		Priscian
500		Procopius of Gaza			The poet Cyprian, Ennodius, St Cesarius of Arles	Eugippius Fulgentius of Ruspa	
526. Athalaric		Closing of the schools of Athens (529)	Justinian, Denys the Areopagite				Vettius Agorius Mavortius
534. Theodahad	Victor of Capua Arator						
536. Vitiges							
541. Totila				Jordanis		Facundus of Hermianum	
550.			Cyril of Scythopolis				Maximianus
560.	Collectio Avellana, Venantius Fortunatus		John Malalas		S. Gregory of Tours		
570.							
580.							
590.	St Gregory the Great		Evagrius the Scholiast		St Isidore of Seville		
600							

TABLE II

TERTULLIAN	DATES [1]	EDITIONS			FRENCH TRANSLATIONS
		MIGNE	CORPUS SCR. ECCL. LAT.	VARIOUS	
1. de Anima	208/211	2, 687-798	20, 298	OEHLER, L., 1851/4	DE GENOUDE, Paris, 1852; 2, 2
2. Apologeticum	end of 197	1, 305-604	"	2, 553; 1, 111; RAUSCHEN, in F.P. (1916); MAYOR, Camb. 1917	2, 1 — 251; WALTZING, Liége, 1919
3. de Baptismo	200/206	1, 1305-1334	20, 201	1, 619; RAUSCHEN, in F.P. (1912); LUPTON, in C P. T. (1908)	3, 239
4. de Corona	211	2, 93-122	"	1, 415	2, 130
5. de Carne Christi	208/211	2, 797-838	"	2, 423	1, 389
6. de Cultu feminarum lib. II	200/206	1, 1417-1448	"	1, 701	3, 305
7. de Exhortatione Castitatis	208/211	2, 963-978	"	1, 737	-, 357
8. de Fuga	213	2, 123-142	"	1, 461	2, 423
9. adversus Hermogenem	200/206	2, 219-264	47, 126	2, 337	3, 51
10. de Idololatria	211/212	1, 737-774	20, 30	1, 67	3, 217
11. de Jejunio	after 213	2, 1003-1030	—, 274	1, 851	3, 377
12. adversus Judaeos	200/206	2, 633-682	"	2, 699	-, 1
13. adversus Marcionem l. V	207/8 [3]	2, 263-556	"	2, 45	1, 1
14. ad Martyras	Jan.-Feb. 197	1, 691-702	"	1, 3	2, 449
15. de Monogamia	after 213	2, 979-1004	"	1, 761	3, 409
16. ad Nationes l. II	after Feb. 197	1, 629-680	20, 59	1, 306	3, 465
17. de Oratione	200/206	1, 1243-1304	—, 180	1, 553	3, 263
18. de Pallio	209	2, 1083-1106	"	1, 913	2, 153
19. de Poenitentia	200/206	1, 1333-1360	"	1, 643	2, 197; P. de Labriolle, in H.L. (1906)

20. de Patientia	do.	1, 1359-1386	47, 1	1, 587	2, 173
21. de Praescriptione . . .	about 200	2, 9-92	"	2, 1	2, 343; P. de Labriolle in H.L. (1907)
22. adversus Praxean . . .	after 213	2, 175-220	—, 227	2, 651	3, 177
23. de Pudicitia	217/222	2, 1029-1084	20, 219	1, 791	3, 443; P. de Labriolle, in H.L. (1906)
24. de Resurrectione carnis .	208/211	2, 837-934	47, 25	2, 465	1, 435
25. ad Scapulam	212	1, 773-784	—, "	1, 539	3, 457
26. Scorpiace	221/2	2, 143-176	20, 144	1, 495	3, 137
27. de Spectaculis . . .	about 200	1, 701-738	—, 1	1, 17	2, 391
28. de Testimonio animae .	197/200	1, 681-692	—, 134	1, 399	—, 117
29. ad Uxorem	200/206	1, 1385-1418		1, 669	3, 333
30. adversus Valentinianos .	208/211	2, 559-632	47, 177	1, 381	—, 103
31. de Virginibus velandis (4)	208/211	2, 935-962	"	1, 883	—, 277

(1) The dates given above are taken from Monceaux's *Rev. de Philologie*, XXII (1893), p. 77-92 (cf. *Hist. Litt. de l'Afrique chrét.*, I, 256-296). We may compare those suggested in Harnack's *Chronol.*, II (1904), 256-296, and by K. Adam in *Der Katholik*, XXXVII (1908), 341-370, 416-434. There are no important divergences except in the case of No. 10 (Harnack giving 198-202/3); No. 11 (Harnack, shortly after 217/18; Adam, after 217); No. 15 (Harnack, 217-221; Adam, about 220); No. 27 (Adam, shortly before 197).

(2) Many portions are translated in Turmel's *Tertullian* (1905).

(3) This work has appeared in several editions. See page 86.

(4) Treatises lost: adv. Apelleiacos (cf. de Carne Christi, 8); de Aaron Vestibus (cf. saint Jerome, *Ep.*, 64, 23); de Aaron Submissione (mentioned in the index to the *Agobardinus*); de Carne et Anima (*ibid.*); de Censu animae adv. Hermogenem (cf. de Anima, I; II; 21); de Ecstasi (in Greek); de Fato (cf. de Anima, 20); Liber ad Amicum philosophum (cf. Saint Jerome, *Ep.* 22, 22; adv. Jovinianum 1, 13); de Paradiso (cf. adv. Marcionem V, 12; de Anima, 55); de Spe fidelium (cf. adv. Marc. III, 24; Saint Jerome in Ezech. 36 [P.L., 25, 339]); de Superstitione Saeculi (mentioned in the index to the *Agobardinus*).

TABLE III

SAINT CYPRIAN	DATES	EDITIONS			FRENCH TRANSLATIONS
		MIGNE	CORPUS SCR. ECCL. LAT.	VARIOUS	
1. Epistulae	248/9-258	4, 191-438	3, 2, p. 465	"	DE GENOUDE (1) 5bis, p. 30-334
2. ad Donatum . . .	246	—, 192-223	—, 1, p. 3	LÉONARD (2); KRABINGER (3)	— 19
3. de Habitu Virginum .	249	—, 440-464	—, 187	KRABINGER (4)	— 337
4. de Lapsis . . .	251	—, 465-494	—, 237		— 353
5. de catholicae Ecclesiae unitate	2nd half 251	—, 495-520	—, 209	ID. (ibid.)	— 378
6. de dominica Oratione .	251/2	—, 519-544	—, 267		— 397
7. ad Demetrianum . .	251/2	—, 544-564	—, 351	LÉONARD (2)	— 422
8. de Mortalitate . .	252/6	—, 583-602	—, 297	ID.; KRABINGER (5)	— 447
9. de Opere et Eleemosynis	252/6	—, 601-622	—, 373	KRABINGER (3)	— 463
10. de Bono patientiae .	begun 256	—, 622-638	—, 397	ID.	— 483
11. de Zelo et livore . .	256/7	—, 638-652	—, 419		— 501
12. ad Fortunatum . .	257	—, 651-676	—, 317	D.; GASSNER (6)	— 513
13. ad Quirinum (Testimoniorum libri III)	before 249	—, 675-780	—, 35	"	— 538
14. Quod idola dii non sint .	date uncertain	—, 564-582	—, 19	"	— 440
APOCRYPHA					
1. de laude Martyrii . .	252/3 (7)	—, 787-804	—, 3, p. 26	"	— 685
2. adversus Judaeos . .	249/250 (8)	—, 919-926	—, 133	"	— "
3. de Montibus Sina et Sion .	III Cent. 210/240 (9)	—, 909-918	—, 104	"	— "
4. ad Vigilium Episcopum de Judaica Incredulitate	end of II Cent. (10) 235/260 (11)	6, 49-58	—, 119	"	— "

	Date				
5. de Spectaculis	III Cent.	4, 779-788	3, 3	A. L. L., 8 (1892)1-22 (WOLFFLIN)	— 660 THIBAUT, 1868, 2, 86
6. de Bono pudicitiae	id.	", 819-828	", 13		"
7. ad Novatianum	middle III Cent. [12]	3, 1205-1218	", 52		"
8. adversus Aleatores	260/300 [12]	4, 827-836	", 92	T. U. V. I, p. 11 (HARNACK); MIODONSKI [14]; HILGENFELD [15]	"
9. Liber de rebaptismate	middle III Cent. [13]	3, 1185-1204	", 69	F.P. fasc. XI (1916, RAUSCHEN)	"
10. de Pascha computus	243 before Easter	", 939-972	", 248	"	"
11. de Singularitate clericorum	2nd half IV Cent.	4, 835-870	", 173	MIODONSKI (Cracow, 1893)	"
12. Exhortatio de paenitentia	middle VII Cent. [16]	", 869-882	", ,,	T.U., XXXIV, 1 (1909, HELLMANN)	"
13. de duodecim Abusivis saeculi	VII Cent. [17]		", 152		
14. de duplici martyrio ad Fortunatum [20]	1530	", 881-906	", 220	"	GUILLON, 1837, 1, 272
15. Oratio I	V Cent. [18]	", 905-906	", 144	"	"
16. Oratio II	id. [18]	", 905-910	", 146	"	"
17. Epistulae I	date uncertain	"	", 272	"	"
18. — II	id.	"	", 272	"	"
19. — III	IV Cent. [19]	"	", 273	"	"
20. — IV	date uncertain	"	", 274	"	"
21. Caena Cypriani	V Cent. [18]	", 925-932	"	HAGEN in Z. f. wiss. Theol., 27 (1884), 164; HARNACK in T.U. N.F. IV, 3b (1899)	"

[1] Les Pères de l'Eglise, Paris, 1842.
[2] Namur, 1887.
[3] Tubingen, 1859.
[4] Ibid. 1853.
[5] Ibid. 1859.
[6] Salzburg, 1882.
[7] Monceaux, II, 104.
[8] A.C.L., II, 2, 406.
[9] Ibid. 384.
[10] Corssen, Z.N.W. 1911, p. 1-36.
[11] A.C.L., II, 2, 393.

[12] A.C.L., III, 2, 380.
[13] A.K.L., II, 500.
[14] Erlangen et Leipzig, 1889.
[15] Fribourg-i-B., 1889.
[16] Monceaux, II, 87.   The work was edited in 1751 by Trombelli.
[17] Hellmann, op. cit.
[18] T.U. xix, 3b (1899, Harnack).
[19] Mercati, in Rendiconti del R. Instituto Lombardo, di sc. e. l. Ser. II, XXXII (1899), p. 986 et s.
[20] The work of Erasmus.

TABLE IV

SAINT HILARY OF POITIERS	DATES	EDITIONS			FRENCH TRANSLATIONS
		MIGNE	CORPUS SCR. ECCL. LAT.	VARIOUS	
1. Commentarii in Matthaeum · ·	about 355	**9**, 917-1078	**65**, 180		GUILLON, 1837, 1, 272
2. Liber I ad Constantium · ·	356	**10**, 557-564	"	"	Chefs-d'œuvre des Pères de l'Eglise, 1838 ; Vol. V, p. 33.
3. de Trinitate · · · ·	356/359	—, 25-472	"	"	"
4. de Synodis · · · ·	begun 359	—, 479-546	"	"	"
5. Liber II ad Constantium ·	Jan. 360	", 563-572	—, 196	"	"
6. contra Constantium Imperat	361	—, 577-603	"	"	"
7. Tractatus super Psalmos ·	360/367	**9**, 231-908	**12**	"	Ibid. V, p. 5-19.
8. contra Auxentium · ·	364/5	**10**, 609-618	**65**, 3	"	
9. Tractatus Mysteriorum ·	364/6	"	—, 208	J.-F. GAMURRINI, Rome, 1887.	
10. Hymni (1) · · · ·	"	—, 551	—, 245	K. T. No. 47/49 (1910).	CLÉMENT, Les Poètes chrétiens, 1857.
11. id. (2) · · ·	"	"	"	BLUME et DREVES, Anal. Hymn. L.1908; Z. K. T. 13 (1889) 737	
12. Tractatus in Job (3) · ·	"	—, 723-4	—, 229	"	LARGENT, Saint Hilary, 1902, p. 55.
13. Epistula ad Abram filiam (4) ·	"	—, 549-552	—, 236	"	
14. Fragmenta historica · ·	359 et s.				
Fragmentum I · · ·	"	—, 627	—, 98	"	"
— II · · ·	"	—, 632	—, 103	"	"

III	658,	49	"
IV	678,	155	"
V	681,	89	"
VI	686,	164	"
VII	695,	93	"
VIII	699,	78	"
IX	703,	87	"
X	705,	174	"
XI	710,	43	"
XII	714,	156	"
XIII	717,	47	"
XIV	718,	159	"
XV	719,	160	"

(1) Contained in the Arezzo manuscript.
(2) Ascribed to Hilary.
(3) Two fragments.
(4) Of doubtful authenticity.

TABLE V

SAINT AMBROSE	DATES	Migne	Corpus Scr. Eccl. Lat.	Various	French Translations
		Editions			
1. de Officiis ministrorum libri tres	386	**16**, 25-184		Krabinger, Tüb. 1857	Abbé de Bellegarde, 1689.
2. de Virginibus libri tres	v. 377	187-232	,,	,,	Duranti de Bonrecueil, 1729.
3. de Viduis l. unus	do.	233-262	,,	,,	do.
4. de Virginitate l. unus	392	265-302	,,	,,	do.
5. de Institutione Virginis l. unus	387	305-334	,,	,,	do.
6. de Mysteriis liber		389-410	,,	Rauschen, F. P., fasc. VII, 1909	P. de Labriolle, Saint Ambroise, 1908, p. 273.
7. Exhortatio virginitatis	393	335-364	,,	,,	,,
8. de Sacramentis libri sex (1)	date uncertain	417-462	,,	,,	,,
9. de Paenitentia l. duo	about 384	465-524	,,	,,	,,
10. de Fide l. quinque	379/381	527-698	,,	,,	,,
11. de S. Spiritu libri tres	381	703-816	,,	,,	,,
12. de Incarnationis dominicae sacramento l. unus	379/383	817-846	,,	,,	,,
13. Fragmentum Ambrosianum ex Theodoreto desumptum	,,	847-850	,,	A. E. Burn, Nicela of Remesiana, Camb. 1905, p. 112	,,
14. de lapsu virginis consecratae (2)	date uncertain	367-384	,,	Schenkl, in Ambrosiana, Milan, 1897, ch. V	,,
15. de Excessu fratris sui Satyri l. duo.	Sept. 375	1289-1354	,,		,,
16. Hymni nonnulli	,,	1409-1412	,,	Blume et Dreves, Anal. hymnica medii aevi, L. 1907	,,
17. de Obitu Valentiniani consolatio	July 392	1357-1384	,,	,,	,,
18. de Obitu Theodosii oratio	26 Feb. 395	1385-1406	,,	,,	anon. 1876.
19. Sermo contra Auxentium de basilicis tradendis	386	1007-1018	,,	,,	,,

				P. DE LABRIOLLE, *Saint Ambroise*, 1908.
20. Epistulae	379/396	—, 875-1286	"	"
21. Hexaemeron l. VI	after 388	14, 123-274	32, 1, 3	"
22. de Paradiso l. I	375/378	—, 275-314	", 265	"
23. de Cain et Abel l. II	id.	—, 315-360	", 339	"
24. de Noe l. I	378	—, 361-416	", 413	"
25. de Abraham l. II	after 388	—, 419-500	", 501	"
26. de Isaac et Anima l. I	id.	—, 501-534	", 641	"
27. de bono mortis l. I	id.	—, 539-568	", 703	"
28. de Fuga saeculi l. I	after 391	—, 569-596	", II, 163	"
29. de Jacob et vita beata l. II	after 388	—, 597-638	", 2	"
30. de Joseph patriarcha l. I	do.	—, 641-672	", 73	"
31. de benedictionibus patriarcharum l. II	do.	—, 675-694	", 125	"
32. de Helia et Jejunio l. I	after 386	—, 697-728	", 411	"
33. de Nabutha . II	date uncertain	—, 751-756	", 469	"
34. de Tobia l. I	do.	—, 759-794	", 519	"
35. de Interpellatione Job et David l. IV	about 383	—, 797-850	", 211	"
36. Apologia prophetae David	383/386-7	—, 851-884	", 299	"
37. — altera prophetae David (4)	do.	—, 887-916	", 359	"
38. Enarrationes in XII Psalmos Davidicos	384-5/397	15, 921-1180		"
39. Expositio in Ps. CXVIII	after 387	—, 1197-1526	62, 1	"
40. Expositio Evangelii secundum Lucam	386/388	—, 1527-1850	32, IV, 1	"
41. de Excidio urbis Hierosolymitanae l. V (5)	date uncertain	—, 1961-2205	"	C. F. WAEBER et J. CAESAR, Marburg, 1864
42. Commentarius in Cantica Canticorum (6)	XII Cent.	—, 1851-1962	"	"

(1) Authenticity disputed.
(2) Authenticity doubtful.
(3) Numerous letters translated in P. de Labriolle, *op. cit.* p. 37-161.
(4) Unauthenticated.
(5) Authenticity doubtful.

(6) Drawn up in the XII Cent. from various passages in the writings of St Ambrose.

N.B.—Various *apocrypha* are included in Vol. XVII of the *Patr. Lat.* col. 9 to 1160. It is quite possible that the *Explanatio Symboli ad Initiandos* (17, 1155-1190) may have been by St Ambrose.

TABLE VI

THE SHORT POEMS OF THE IV CENT.	DATES	EDITIONS			FRENCH TRANSLATIONS
		MIGNE	CORPUS SCR. ECCL. LAT.	VARIOUS	
1. de Ave Phoenice	2nd half IV Cent.	7, 277-284	27, 2, 1,135	A. L., No. 731; P. L. M., III, 247	GAMBER (1), p. 119.
2. Cento (the poetess Proba)	”	19, 803-818	16, 1,568	”	”
3. de Cruce	”	2, 1113-1114	3, 305	S.S., I, 166	”
4. de Evangelio	”	”	23, 270	”	”
5. de Ecclesia	”	”	16, 1,621	A.L., I, 1, No. 16; P.L.M., IV, 214	”
6. de Fratribus septem Maccabaeis	”	50, 1275-1286	23, 240 et 255	”	”
7. in Genesin fragmentum (2)	end of IV Cent.	2, 1097-1102	3, 283 et	J. E. B. MAYOR, Lon. 1889	”
8. Geneseos liber	”	19, 345-380	23, 1		”
9. de Judicio Domini	date uncertain	”	3, 308-325	OEHLER, Opp. Tertulliani, II, 776. Ibid, p. 769.	”
10. de Jona	”	”	23, 221	RIVINUS, Sanctae reliquiae duum Victorinorum, Gothae 1652.	”
11. de Jesu Christo Deo et Homine	”	”	”		”
12. Laudes Domini	316/323	19, 379-386	”	BRANDES, progr. Braunschweig, 1887.	”
13. de Ligno Vitae (3)	”	51, 1091-1094	”		”
14. Marcionem (adversus)	see p. 319	2, 1051-1090	”	OEHLER, op. cit. II, 781	”

	Date				
15. de Mortibus boum	end of IV Cent.	**19**, 797-800	,,	A.L., I, 2, No. 893.	CLÉMENT, op. cit. p. 82.
16. de Naturis rerum	,,	,,	,,	A.S.C., I, 121	DOBBELSTEIN, diss. Louvain, 1879, p. 49.
17. Nicomachum (contra Flavianum) (4)	394/5	,,	,,	P.L.M., III, 286; A.L. No. 4; HERMES, IV (1870) 354.	,,
18. de Pascha (or de Resurrectione) (5)	,,	,,	**3**, 289 et **23**, 212	CEHLER, op. cit. II, 769.	,,
19. de Sodoma	,,	**2**, 1101-1106	**3**, 302 et **23**, 227	,,	,,
20. Senatorem (ad quemdam) . .	,,	—, 1105-1108	,,	,,	,,
21. de Ternarii numeri excellentia .	,,	**125**, 821-2	,,	MERCATI, Studi e Testi, 12 (1904) p. 23	,,
22. Tityrus (6)	,,	**19**, 773-780	**16**, 1,609 —, 1,615 et	A.L., I, 2, No. 719a	,,
23. de Verbi incarnatione (6) . .	,,	,,			,,
24. Versus ad gratiam Domini (7) .	,,	,,	**10**, 310		,,

(1) *Le livre de la Genèse dans la Poésie Latine du Ve S.* 1899.
(2) Forms the beginning of the *Geneseos Liber*.
(3) See *de Cruce*.
(4) See Ch. Morel's commentary, *Revue Archéol.*, XVIII (1868), p. 51-55.

(5) See *de Cruce* (No. 3).
(6) Centos.
(7) See *Tityrus* (No. 22).

TABLE VII

SAINT JEROME	DATES	EDITIONS			FRENCH TRANSLATIONS
		MIGNE	CORPUS SCR. ECCL. LAT.	VARIOUS	BAREILLE, P. 1878-1885 (?); P. DE LABRIOLLE, 1907
Treatises, Opuscula, various, Sermons					
1. Vita Pauli	374/9	23, 17-28	"	TAMETTI, Turin, 1903.	2, 408
2. Altercatio Luciferiani et Orthodoxi	382/5	—, 155-182	"	"	—, 450
3. adversus Helvidium	382/4	—, 183-206	"	"	—, 477
4. Liber hebraicarum quaestionum in Genesin	386/391	—, 935-1010	"	"	3, 507
5. Liber de situ et nominibus locorum hebraicorum	id.	—, 859-928	"	"	—, 501
6. Liber de nominibus hebraïcis	id.	—, 771-858	"	"	—, 438
7. Vita Hilarionis	id.	—, 29-54	"	id.	2, 417 ; id.
8. Vita Malchi	id.	—, 53-60	"	id.	—, 441
9. de Viris illustribus	392	—, 601-720	"	S. Q. fasc. XI (1895)	3, 270
10. contra Jovinianum (²)	392/3	—, 211-338	"	"	2, 500
11. contra Johannem Jerosolymitanum	395/6 (¹)	—, 355-396	"	"	3, 15
12. contra Rufinum l. II	402	—, 397-456	"	"	3, 60
13. contra Rufinum liber III	c. 403	—, 457-492	"	"	3, 60
14. contra Vigilantium	406	—, 339-352	"	"	3, 1
15. Tractatus in Psalmos	392/401	"	"	A.M. III, 2 (1897) I	"
16. — in Marci Evangelium	id.	"	"	— 319	"
17. — varii	id.	"	"	— 373	"
18. Tractatuum in Psalmos series altera				— III, 3 (1903) I	"
19. Dialogus adv. Pelagianos	415	23, 495-590	"	"	3, 163

Commentaries

	Date			
20. On the Epistle to Philemon	386/7	**26**, 599-618	,,	**11**, 50; P. DE LABRIOLLE
21. the Galatians	id.	—, 307-438	,,	**10**, 221
22. the Ephesians	id.	—, 439-554	,,	—, 374
23. Titus	386/7	**26**, 555-600	,,	**11**, 1
24. Ecclesiastes	389/390	**23**, 1009-1116	,,	**4**, 1
25. Nahum	c. 392	**25**, 1231-1272	,,	**9**, 92
26. Micheas	id.	—, 1151-1230	,,	—, 1
27. Sophonias	id.	—, 1337-1388	,,	—, 214
28. Aggeus	id.	—, 1387-1416	,,	—, 272
29. Habacuc	id.	—, 1273-1338	,,	—, 139
30. Jonas	395/6	—, 1117-1152	,,	**8**, 509
31. Abdias	id.	—, 1097-1118	,,	**8**, 487
32. Isaias (13-23)	before 398	**24**, 901-942	,,	**5**, 4
33. Saint Matthew	398	**26**, 15-218	,,	**9**, 524
34. The Psalms	392/402	,,	A. M. III. I (1895)	,,
35. Osee	406	**25**, 815-946	,,	**8**, 166
36. Joel	id.	—, 947-988	,,	**3**, 317
37. Amos	id.	—, 989-1096	,,	—, 365
38. Daniel	406/8	**24**, 491-584	,,	**7**, 390
39. Isaias	408/410	**24**, 17-678	,,	**5**, 1 et **6**, 1
40. Zacharias	406	**25**, 1415-1542	,,	**9**, 305
41. Malachias	406	—, 1541-1578	,,	—, 451
42. Ezechiel	410/5	—, 15-490	,,	**6**, 422 et **7**, 1
43. Jeremias	415/20	**24**, 679-900	**59**, REITER (1913)	**6**, 161

Revision of the Bible

	Date			
44. Revision of the Latin Versions of the Gospels	384	**29**, 541-726	,,	,,
45. Revision of the Epistles of St Paul	before 385	—, 727-822	,,	,,

---

(1) According to Holl, S.B.B., 1916, No. viii/ix.
(2) Bickel's *Diatribe in Senecae phil. fragmenta*, I (L. 1915), p. 382 et s. edits critically § I, 41-46; II, 5-14; 28.
(3) Fairly numerous pieces translated in Turmel's *Saint Jerome*, 6, 1906 (P. C.).
N.B.—For the Commentary on the *Apocalypse*, see Victorinus of Pettau, p. 221.

2 M

TABLE VII—*contd.*

SAINT JEROME	DATES	EDITIONS			FRENCH TRANSLATIONS
		MIGNE	CORPUS SCR. ECCL. LAT.	VARIOUS	
46. Revision of the rest of the New Testament	before 398	—, 823-872	,,	,,	P. DE LABRIOLLE
47. 1st Revision of the Psalms (*Psalt. Romanum*)	384	29, 120-398	,,	,,	,,
48. 2nd Revision of the Psalms (**from the Greek**) (*Psalt. Gallicanum*)	386/391	—, 119-397	,,	,,	,,
49. Revision (**from the Greek**) of the Book of Job	386/391	—, 61-114	,,	,,	,,
50. Revision (**from the Hebrew**): Pentateuch	398/404	28, 163-462	,,	,,	,,
51. Josue	404/5	,, 461-504	,,	,,	,,
52. Judges	id.	,, 503-542	,,	,,	,,
53. Ruth	id.	,, 543-548	,,	,,	,,
54. Samuel	before 392	,, 547-664	,,	,,	,,
55. Kings	before 392	,, 663-672	,,	,,	,,
56. Malachias	id.	,, 673-772	,,	,,	,,
57. Isaias	id.	,, 771-848	,,	,,	,,
58. Jeremias	id.	,, 847-938	,,	,,	,,
59. Ezechiel	id.	,, 937-1014	,,	,,	,,
60. 12 Prophets	id.	,, 1013-1075	,,	,,	,,
61. Job	393	,, 1083-1122	,,	,,	,,
62. Psalms	before 392	,, 1123-1240	,,	,,	,,
63. Esdras	before 395	,, 1404-1434	,,	,,	,,
64. Books of Solomon	398	—, 1241-1292	,,	,,	,,
65. Paralipomena	396	—, 1323-1402	,,	,,	,,

No.		Date				
66.	(from the Chaldee) Esther	before 404 (?)	—, 1433-1450	"	"	"
67.	— Judith	date uncertain	29, 37-60	"	"	"
68.	— Tobias	id.	—, 23-38	"	"	"
	Various Translations					
69.	Chronicle of Eusebius	379/381	27, 33-702	"	"	7, 543 et 8, 1"
70.	Origen's Homilies on Jeremias	id.	25, 583-692	"	"	8, 48
71.	— — Ezechiel	id.	—, 691-786	"	"	4, 554
72.	— — Isaias	id.	24, 901-936	"	"	
73.	— — the Canticle of Canticles		23, 1117-1144	"	"	—, 105
74.	de Spiritu Sancto, by Didymus	382/4	—, 101-154	"	"	
75.	Origen's Homilies on St Luke	386/391	26, 219-306	"	"	10, 114
76.	Monastic Rule of Pachomius, Theodore, and Orsenius	388/391	23, 65-100	"	"	"
77.	**Letters**	end of 404	22	54, (*Ep.* I à LXX); 55, (*Ep.* LXXI to CXX), 56 (*Ep.* CXXI à CLIV) (¹)	"	1 et 2 "
		370 to 419				

(¹) The *Indices* of this edition, given by Hilberg, are still wanting.

TABLE VIII

SAINT AUGUSTINE (1)	DATES	EDITIONS			FRENCH TRANSLATIONS
		Migne	Corpus Scr. Eccl. Lat.	Various	Peronne, Ecalle, Vincent, etc. Paris (Vivès) 1869 et s.
1. de Pulchro et Apto (2)	about 380	"	"	"	"
2. Panegyric on Bauton et Valentinian (3)	385	"	"	"	"
3. contra Academicos l. III	386	32, 905-958	"	"	2, 400
4. de Vita beata	id.	959-976	"	"	", 476
5. de Ordine l. II	id.	977-1020	"	"	", 502
6. Soliloquiorum l. II	386/7	869-904	"	"	", 565
7. de Immortalitate animae	id.	1021-1034	"	"	3, 1
8. de Grammatica (4)	id.	1385-1408	"	Keil, G. L. 5,496	4, 1
9. de Musica l. VI (5)	387/391	1081-1194	"	"	3, 93
10. Principia rhetorices	id.	1439-1448	"	R. L. M., 137	4, 104
11. Principia dialecticae (6)	id.	1409-1420	"	W. Crecelius, Elherfeld, 1857	", 52
12. Categoriae X ex Aristotele decerptae (7)	id.	1419-1440	"	"	", 71
13. de Quantitate Animae	387/8	1035-1080	"	"	3, 24
14. de Moribus eccl. cathol. et de moribus Manichaeorum	388/9	1309-1378	"	"	", 493
15. de Genesi c. Manichaeos l. II	388/390	34, 173-220	"	"	", 423
16. de libero Arbitrio l. III	388/395	32, 1221-1310	"	"	", 292
17. de Magistro	389/	", 1193-1220	"	"	", 253
18. de Vera religione	389/390	34, 121-172	"	"	", 596
19. de diversis quaestionibus LXXXXIII liber unus	389/396	40, 11-100	"	"	21, 1

No. / Work	Date				
20. de Utilitate credendi ad Honoratum	391/2	42, 65-92	25, I, p. 3	25, 271	"
21. de duabus Animabus contra Manichaeos	id.	—, 93-112	—, I, 51	—, 315	"
22. contra Fortunatum disputatio	392	—, 111-130	—, I, 83	—, 343	"
23. de Fide et symbolo	Oct. 393	40, 181-196	41, 1	21, 223	"
24. de Genesi ad litteram liber imperfectus	393/4	34, 219-246	28, 1	3, 490	"
25. Psalmus abecedarius c. partem Donati	id.	43, 23-32	51, 3	28, 24	"
26. Epist. ad Galatas Expositio	id.	35, 2105-2148	"	11, 60	"
27. Ep. XXVIII ad Hieronymum (de nova Vet. Test. versione)	about 393	33, 111-114	34, 103	4, 320	"
28. de Sermone Dei in monte l. II	about 394	35, 1229-1308	"	9, 19	"
29. Expositio quarundam propositionum ex. Epist. ad Romanos		—, 2063-2088		11, 1	"
30. contra Adimantum	394/5	42, 129-172	35, 1, 115	25, 365	"
31. de Mendacio	id.	40, 487-518	41, 411	22, 1	"
32. de Continentia	id.	—, 348-372	—, 139	21, 444	"
33. de diversis quaestionibus ad Simplicianum l. II.	396/7	—, 101-148	"	—, 117	"
34. de Agone christiano	id.	—, 289-310	—, 99	—, 364	"
35. contra epistulam quam vocant Fundamenti l. I	id.	42, 173-206	25, I, 193	25, 431	Gibb and Montgomery, C.1908
36. Confessionum l. XIII	397/8 [8]	32, 659-866	33, 1	2, 103	"
37. de Doctrina Christiana	397/427 [9]	34, 15-122	"	6, 439	"
38. Quaestionum Evangeliorum l. II	397/400	35, 1321-1364		9, 135	"
39. Annotationes in Job	397/400	34, 825-886	28, III, 509	8, 110	"
40. de Trinitate l. XV	398/416	42, 819-1098	"	29, 595	"

(1) For lost or unauthenticated works, cf. Teuffel, *Röm. Litter.*, III (1913), p. 364 et s.

(2) Lost. See *Conf.* IV, xiii.

(3) Lost. See *ibid.* VI, vi et *Contra Litter. Petil.*, III, xxv, 30.

(4) A fragment in Mai, N. P.B., I, 2, 165 ; re-edit. by C. W. Weber, Marburg, 1861. It is not in Migne.

(5) A fragment in Mai, C. V. S., 3, 116.

(6) Authenticity disputed. See Zurek, *De S. Aug. princ. rhetoricis* Diss. Vindob. 1905, p. 73.

(7) Authenticity doubtful.

(8) According to Monceaux, *C. R. de l'Acad. des Inscr.*, 1908, p. 53.

(9) See p. 416, N. 1.

TABLE VIII—*contd.*

SAINT AUGUSTINE	DATES	EDITIONS			FRENCH TRANSLATIONS
		MIGNE	CORPUS SCR. ECCL. LAT.	VARIOUS	
41. de Catechizandis Rudibus . .	400	**40**, 309-348	,,	FAUSSET, Lon. 1896 KRUGER, S. Q., Heft IV (1909)	**21**, 393
42. contra Faustum Manichaeum l. XXXIII . .	id.	**42**, 207-518	**25**, 1, 251	,,	**25**, 480
43. de Consensu evangelistarum l. IV .	id.	**34**, 1041-1230	**43**, 1	,,	**8**, 422
44. ad inquisitiones Januari l. I II (Ep. LIV-LV)	id.	**33**, 199-223			**4**, 449
45. de Opere monachorum . .	id.	**40**, 547-582	**41**, 529	,,	**22**, 84
46. de Fide rerum quae non videntur .	id.	—, 171-180	—, ,,	,,	**21**, 209
47. contra Epistulam Parmeniani l. III	id.	**43**, 33-108	**51**, 19	,,	**28**, 40
48. de Baptismo c. Donatistas . .	id.	**40**, 107-244	**41**, 185	,,	—, 142
49. de Bono coniugali . . .	400-401	**40**, 373-396	—, ,,	,,	**21**, 476
50. de Sancta Virginitate . . .	400-401	—, 397-428	—, 233	,,	—, 511
51. contra litteras Petiliani l. III .	401/403	**43**, 245-388	**52**, 3	,,	**28**, 350
52. ad catholicos epistula de secta Donatistarum (de Unitate Ecclesiae) .	end of 401	—, 391-446			**29**, 4
53. de Genesi ad litteram l. XII .	401/415	**34**, 245-486	**28**, I, 3	,,	**7**, 39
54. de actis cum Felice Manichaeo l. II .	404 (?)	**42**, 519-552	**25**, 1, 801	,,	**26**, 331
55. de Natura boni	405	—, 551-572	—, 1, 855	,,	—, 379
56. contra Secundinum Manichaeum l. I	405/6	—, 577-602	—, 1, 905	,,	—, 411
57. contra Cresconium grammaticum partis Donati l. IV . .	406/7	**43**, 445-594	**52**, 325	,,	**29**, 81
58. de Divinatione daemonum l. I .	406/411	**40**, 581-592	**41**, 597	,,	**22**, 130
59. Ep. XCIII ad Vincentium (de haereticis vi coercendis) . .	408	**33**, 321-347	**34**, 445	,,	**4**, 628

60. Ep. LII ad Deogratiam (Sex Quaestiones c. Paganos)	408/9	—, 370-386	—, 544	„	—, 702
61. Ep. CVIII ad Macrobium (de non iterando baptismo)	409	**33**, 405-417	**34**, 612	„	**5**, 2
62. Ep. CXVIII ad Dioscorum (de philosophiae erroribus)	410	—, 439-449	—, 665	„	—, 40
63. Ep. CXX ad Consentium (de Trinitate)	id.	**43**, 452-462	—, 704	„	—, 70
64. de Unico baptismo c. Petilianum	id.	**43**, 595-614	**53**, 3	„	**29**, 286
65. Breviculus conlationis cum Donatistis	411	—, 613-650	—, 29	„	—, 309
66. contra partem Donati post gesta	412	—, 651-690	—, 97	„	—, 362
67. Ep. CXXXVII ad Volusianum (de Incarnatione)	id.	**33**, 515-525	**44**, 96	„	**5**, 160
68. Ep. CXXXVIII ad Marcellinum (id.)	id.	—, 524-535	—, 126	„	—, 174
69. Ep. CXL ad Honoratum (de gratia)	id.	—, 538-577	—, 155	„	—, 191
70. de peccatorum Meritis et Remissione et de baptismo parvulorum l. III.	id.	**44**, 109-200	**60**, 3	„	**30**, 3
71. de Spiritu et littera ad Marcellinum	end of 412	**40**, 201-246	—, 155-229	„	—, 126
72. de Fide et operibus	413	**33**, 197-230	**41**, 3	„	**21**, 242
73. Ep. CXLVII ad Paulinam (de videndo Deo)	id.	**33**, 596-622	**44**, 274	„	**5**, 273
74. de Civitate Dei	413-426	**41**, 11-804	**40**, I et II	DOMBART, dans B. T., t. I (1909), t. II (1905)	**23**, 442
75. Ep. ad Julianam (de bono viduitatis)	414	**40**, 429-450	**41**, 303	„	**21**, 587
76. Ep. CLVII ad Hilarium Siculum (de Pelagianismo)	id.	**33**, 674-693	**44**, 449	„	**5**, 315
77. de Natura et gratia liber I	415	**44**, 247-290	**60**, 233	„	**30**, 193
78. ad episcopos Eutropium et Paulum de perfectione Justitiae hominis	id.	—, 291-318	**42**, 3	„	**30**, 253
79. Ep. CLXVI ad Hieronymum (de origine animae)	id.	**33**, 720-733	**44**, 545	„	**5**, 450
80. Ep. CLXVII ad Hier. (de sententia Jacobi)	id.	**33**, 733-741	**44**, 586	„	**5**, 469

(1) December 398, according to Monceaux, *C. R. de l'Acad. des Inscr.*, 1908, p. 58.   (2) Authenticity disputed. See Batiffol, *Le Cathol. de S. Aug.*, 1920, t. I, p. 132.

TABLE VIII—*contd.*

SAINT AUGUSTINE	DATES	EDITIONS			FRENCH TRANSLATIONS
		MIGNE	CORPUS SCR. ECCL. LAT.	VARIOUS	
81. ad Orosium presbyterum contra Priscillianistas et Origenistas .	id.	42, 669-678	,,	,,	26, 555
82. Enarrationes in Psalmos .	415	36, 66-1906	,,	,,	11, 15
83. in Joannis Evangelium tr. cxxiv .	416/7	35, 1379-1976	,,	,,	9, 10
84. in Epist. Joannis ad Parthos .	416	—, 1977-2062	,,	,,	10, 450
85. de gestis Pelagii ad Aurelium episcopum l. I	beginning of 417	44, 319-360	42, 51	,,	30, 292
86. Ep. CLXXXV ad Bonifacium (de correctione Donatistarum)	417	33, 792-815	57, 1	,,	5, 547
87. Ep. CLXXXVI ad Paulinum Nol. (de Pelagianismo)	id.	—, 815-831	—, 45	,,	—, 579
88. Ep. CLXXXVII ad Dardanum (de praesentia Dei)	id.	—, 832-848	—, 81	,,	—, 603
89. de Gratia Dei et de peccato originali l. II	418	44, 359-410	42, 125	,,	30, 343
90. Sermo ad Caesareensis ecclesiae plebem	Sept. 418	43, 689-698	53, 167	,,	29, 414
91. Gesta cum Emerito Caesareensi Donatistarum episcopo	id.	—, 697-706	—, 181	,,	—, 426
92. contra sermonem Arianorum l. I. .	418	42, 677-708	,,	,,	26, 566
93. de Patientia .	about 418	40, 611-626	,,	,,	22, 170
94. de adulterinis Coniugiis l. II	419	40, 451-486	41, 345	,,	21, 588
95. Locutionum in Heptateuchum l. VII	id.	34, 485-546	28, I, 507	,,	7, 383
96. Quaestionum in Heptateuchum l. VII	id.	—, 547-824	—, III, 3	,,	—, 469
97. Ep. CXCIX ad Hesychium (de fine saeculi)	id.	33, 904-925	57, 243	,,	6, 68

	Date	P.L.		Notes	
98. de Nuptiis et concupiscentia l. II · ·	419/420	44, 413-474	42, 211	"	30, 421
99. de Natura et origine animae l. IV ·	end of 419	—, 475-548	60, 303	"	20, 508
100. contra duas epistulas Pelagian. ad Bonifacium	420	44, 549-638	—, 423	"	31, 4
101. contra mendacium liber ad Consentium	id.	40, 517-548	41, 467	"	22, 40
102. contra Gaudentium Donatistarum episc. l. II	id.	43, 707-752	53, 201	"	29, 440
103. contra adversarium Legis et Prophetarum l. II	id.	42, 604-666	"	"	26, 458
104. contra Julianum haeresis pelagianae defens., l. VI	421	44, 641-874	"	KRABINGER, Tübingen, 1861, S.	31, 123
105. Enchiridium ad Laurentium	id.	40, 231-290	"	Q, 2, 4	21, 287
106. de Cura pro mortuis gerenda	421	40, 591-610	41, 619	"	22, 143
107. de octo Dulcitii quaestionibus liber	422 (or 425)	—, 147-170	"	"	21, 179
108. de Gratia et libero arbitrio l. I	426/427	44, 881-912	"	"	31, 465
109. de correptione et gratia	id.	—, 915-946	"	"	—, 515
110. Retractationum l. II	id.	32, 583-656	36, 1	"	2, 1
111. Speculum de Scriptura (1)	427	34, 887-1040	12, 3	"	8, 203
112. Collatio cum Maximiano Arianorum episc.	428	42, 709-742	"	"	27, 3
113. contra Maximinum ·	id.	—, 743-814	"	"	—, 47
114. de Haeresibus ad Quodvultdeum l. I	id.	—, 21-50	"	WELCHMANN, Oxford, 1871; OEHLER, Corpus Haereseologicum I, 187 (B. 1856)	25, 211
115. Tractatus adv. Judaeos	id.	—, 51-64	"	"	—, 248
116. de Praedestinatione Sanctorum liber ad Prosperum et Hilarium	428/429	44, 959-992	"	"	31, 578
117. de dono perseverantiae liber	id.	45, 993-1034	"	"	—, 627
118. Opus imperfectum contra Julianum (2)	429/430	—, 1049-1608	"	"	—, 704

(1) The two *Speculum Peccatoris* (P.L., 40, 967, and 983) are unauthenticated. The *Speculum audi Israel* is not in Migne, but only in C. V. 12, 287. Leop. Delisle defended its authenticity, 1884.

(2) For the letters see p. 418; for the sermons and the fresh *tractatus* published by Dom Morin, *ibid.* p. 420.

INDEX

PRINTED IN GREAT BRITAIN BY
THE EDINBURGH PRESS, 9 AND 11 YOUNG STREET, EDINBURGH

The History of Civilization . .

Editor : C. K. OGDEN, M.A.

Magdalene College, Cambridge.

This series, which will eventually comprise upwards of 200 volumes, is designed to form a complete Library of Social Evolution. The field has been carefully mapped out, both as regards subjects and periods ; and, though the first instalments will be published as they are ready, the necessary degree of chronological sequence will be secured by the fact that the volumes of " L'Evolution de l'Humanité " will be used as a nucleus and translated as they appear.

A. Pre-History and Antiquity

I. Introduction and Pre-History

* An asterisk indicates that the volume does not form part of the French collection " L'Evolution de l'Humanité ".

i

II. The Early Empires

III. Greece

IV. Rome

V. Beyond the Roman Empire

B. Christianity and the Middle Ages

I. The Origins of Christianity

II. The Break-up of the Empire

III. Religious Imperialism

IV. The Art of the Middle Ages

V. Reconstitution of Monarchic Power

VI. Social and Economic Evolution

VII. Intellectual Evolution

EDUCATION IN THE MIDDLE AGES	. . .	G. Huisman
PHILOSOPHY IN THE MIDDLE AGES	. .	E. Bréhier
SCIENCE IN THE MIDDLE AGES		Abel Rey and P. Boutroux

VIII. From the Middle Ages to Modern Times

NATIONS OF WESTERN AND CENTRAL EUROPE	P. Lorquet
RUSSIANS, BYZANTINES, AND MONGOLS . .	(Ed.) P. Boyer
THE BIRTH OF THE BOOK	G. Renaudet
*THE INFLUENCE OF SCANDINAVIA ON ENGLAND	M. E. Seaton
*THE PHILOSOPHY OF CAPITALISM . . .	T. E. Gregory
*THE PRELUDE TO THE MACHINE AGE . .	D. Russell
*LIFE AND LABOUR : XV TO XVIII CENTURY	G. Renard

A special group of volumes will be devoted to

(i) Subject Histories

*THE HISTORY OF MEDICINE	C. Singer
*THE HISTORY OF MONEY . . .	T. E. Gregory
*THE HISTORY OF COSTUME . . .	M. Hiler
*THE HISTORY OF WITCHCRAFT . . .	M. Summers

(ii) Historical Ethnology

*THE ETHNOLOGY OF INDIA	T. C. Hodson
*THE PEOPLES OF ASIA . . .	L. H. Dudley Buxton
*THE THRESHOLD OF THE PACIFIC . . .	C. E. Fox

In the Sections devoted to MODERN HISTORY *the majority of titles will be announced later. Many volumes are, however, in active preparation, and of these the first to be published will be*

*THE RESTORATION STAGE . . .	M. Summers
*LONDON LIFE IN THE XVIII CENTURY	M. Dorothy George
*THE INFLUENCE OF CHINA ON EUROPE IN THE XVIII CENTURY	A. Reichwein

---

LONDON :
KEGAN PAUL, TRENCH, TRUBNER & CO., LTD.
NEW YORK : ALFRED A. KNOPF, INC.

Printed in Great Britain by Stephen Austin & Sons, Ltd., Hertford.

UNIVERSITY LIBRARY NOTTINGHAM

KV-025-411

AC 0011299 2

WITHDRAWN

EGG NUTRITION AND BIOTECHNOLOGY

TO

DARRELL B. BRAGG,
A GREAT MENTOR AND FRIEND
WHO LED US TO EGG RESEARCH

Egg Nutrition and Biotechnology

Edited by

J.S. Sim

Department of Agricultural, Food and Nutritional Science
University of Alberta
Canada

S. Nakai

Faculty of Agricultural Sciences
University of British Columbia
Canada

and

W. Guenter

Department of Animal Science
University of Manitoba
Canada

CABI *Publishing*

CABI *Publishing* **is a division of CAB** *International*

CABI Publishing
CAB International
Wallingford
Oxon OX10 8DE
UK

CABI Publishing
10E 40th Street
Suite 3203
New York, NY 10016
USA

Tel: +44 (0)1491 832111
Fax: +44 (0)1491 833508
Email: cabi@cabi.org

Tel: +1 212 481 7018
Fax: +1 212 686 7993
Email: cabi-nao@cabi.org

© CAB *International* 2000 except Chapter 34. All rights reserved. No part of
this publication may be reproduced in any form or by any means, electronically,
mechanically, by photocopying, recording or otherwise, without the prior permission
of the copyright owners.

A catalogue record for this book is available from the British Library, London, UK.

Library of Congress Cataloging-in-Publication Data
Egg nutrition and biotechnology / edited by J.S. Sim, S. Nakai, and W.
    Guenter.
        p.   cm.
    Includes bibliographical references and index.
    ISBN 0-85199-330-3 (alk. paper)
    1. Eggs--Biotechnology.   I. Sim, J. S. (Jeong S.)   II. Nakai,
Shuryo.   III. Guenter, W. (Wilhelm)
TP248.65.E35E34   1999
641.3'75--dc21   99-29719
                                                                             CIP

ISBN 0 85199 330 3

Typeset by AMA DataSet Ltd, UK
Printed and bound in the UK by Biddles Ltd, Guildford and King's Lynn

Contents

Contributors

J.R. Abril, *Omega Tech Inc., Boulder, CO 80301, USA*

P.G. Abril, *Omega Tech Inc., Boulder, CO 80301, USA*

E.M. Akita, *Faculty of Agricultural Sciences, University of British Columbia, Vancouver, British Columbia, V6T 1Z4, Canada*

K.E. Anderson, *Department of Poultry Science, North Carolina State University, Raleigh, NC 27695-7624, USA*

M.M. Bain, *Glasgow University Veterinary School, Poultry Research Group, Glasgow, UK*

G.V. Barbosa-Cánovas, *Department of Biological Systems Engineering, Washington State University, Pullman, WA 99164-6120, USA*

W.R. Barclay, *Omega Tech Inc., Boulder, CO 80301, USA*

F. Baron, *Laboratoire de Technologie Alimentaire, Ecole Nationale Supérieure Agronomique, 35042 Rennes, France*

M.M. Bryant, *Poultry Science Department, Auburn University, Auburn, AL 36849-5416, USA*

A.H. Cantor, *Department of Animal Sciences, University of Kentucky, Lexington, Kentucky, USA*

D. Carlander, *Department of Medicine, Cystic Fibrosis Centre, University Hospital, 75185, Uppsala, Sweden*

F.J. Chang, *Department of Biological Systems Engineering, Washington State University, Pullman, WA 99164-6210, USA*

G. Cherian, *Department of Agricultural, Food and Nutritional Science, 410 AG/FOR Centre, University of Alberta, Edmonton, T6G 2P5, Canada*

M. Coleman, *MAC Associates, Columbus, OH 43221, USA*

C.W. Comer, *Alltech Inc., Guelph, Ontario, Canada*

P.A. Curtis, *Department of Food Science, North Carolina State University, Raleigh, NC 27695-7624, USA*

A.A. Devitt, *Lipid Chemistry and Molecular Biology Laboratory, Department of Food Science, Purdue University, West Lafayette, IN 47907-1160, USA*

M.K. Dunlap, *Department of Animal Sciences, University of Kentucky, Lexington, Kentucky, USA*

A. Fabisz-Kijowska, *Department of Biochemistry and Biotechnology, Agricultural University of A. Cieszkowski, Poznan, Poland*

D.J. Farrell, *School of Land and Food, The University of Queensland, St Lucia, Queensland 4072, Australia*

S. Fauvel, *Laboratoire de Technologie Alimentaire, Ecole Nationale Supérieure Agronomique, 35042 Rennes, France*

M.J. Ford, *Department of Animal Sciences, University of Kentucky, Lexington, Kentucky, USA*

G.W. Froning, *Department of Food Science and Technology, University of Nebraska, Lincoln, Nebraska, USA*

R.K. Gast, *US Department of Agriculture, Agricultural Research Service, Southeast Poultry Research Laboratory, Athens, GA 30605, USA*

M. Gautier, *Laboratoire de Technologie Alimentaire, Ecole Nationale Supérieure Agronomique, 35042 Rennes, France*

J. Gautron, *INRA, Station de Recherches Avicoles, Nouzilly, France*

M.M. Góngora-Nieto, *Department of Biological Systems Engineering, Washington State University, Pullman, WA 99164-6120, USA*

W. Guenter, *Department of Animal Science, University of Manitoba, Winnipeg, Manitoba, R3T 2N2, Canada*

C.M. Hasler, *Functional Foods for Health Program, Department of Food Science and Human Nutrition, University of Illinois, Urbana, IL 61801, USA*

S.D. Hatch, *Faculty of Nutrition, Departments of Poultry and Animal Science, Texas A&M University, College Station, TX 77843-2472, USA*

M.T. Hincke, *Department of Cellular and Molecular Medicine, Faculty of Medicine, University of Ottawa, Ottawa, Ontario, K1H 8N5, Canada*

S. Horiike, *R & D Division of Q.P. Corporation, Tokyo, 183-0034, Japan*

L.A. Horrocks, *Docosa Foods Ltd, 1275 Kinnear Road, Columbus, OH 43212-1155, USA*

W.H. Howell, *Department of Nutritional Sciences, University of Arizona, Tucson, AZ 85721, USA*

D.R. Jones, *Department of Food Science, North Carolina State University, Raleigh, NC 27695-7624, USA*

F.T. Jones, *Department of Poultry Science, University of Arkansas, Fayetteville, AR 72701, USA*

L.R. Juneja, *Nutritional Foods Division, Taiyo Kagaku Co., 9–5 Akabori-Shinmachi, Yokkaichi, Mie 510 0825, Japan*

M.V. Kaminski, Jr, *Finch University of Health Sciences, The Chicago Medical School, North Chicago, IL 60714, USA*

J.X. Kang, *Department of Medicine, Massachusetts General Hospital, Boston, MA 02129, USA*

K.R. Kang, *Department of Agricultural, Food and Nutritional Science, University of Alberta, Edmonton, Alberta, T6G 2P5, Canada*

A. Kennedy, *Canadian Egg Marketing Agency, Ottawa, Ontario, K1R 5A3, Canada*

J. Kijowski, *Food Technology Department, Agricultural University of A. Cieszkowski, Poznan, Poland*

Y.K. Kim, *National Livestock Research Institute, RDA, Korea*

T. Kokubu, *R & D Division of Q.P. Corporation, Tokyo, 183-0034, Japan*

H. Kollberg, *Department of Paediatrics, Cystic Fibrosis Centre, University Hospital 75185, Uppsala, Sweden*

D. Kritchevsky, *The Wistar Institute, Philadelphia, PA 19104, USA*

K.S. Kubena, *Faculty of Nutrition, Departments of Poultry and Animal Science, Texas A&M University, College Station, TX 77843-2472, USA*

M. Kunou, *R & D Division of Q.P. Corporation, Tokyo, 183-0034, Japan*

W.E.M. Lands, *National Institute on Alcohol Abuse and Alcoholism, Bethesda, MD 20892-7003, USA*

A. Larsson, *Department of Medicine, Cystic Fibrosis Centre, University Hospital 75185, Uppsala, Sweden*

M.A. Latour, *Department of Animal Science, Purdue University, West Lafayette, IN 47907-1160, USA*

A. Leaf, *Department of Medicine, Massachusetts General Hospital, Boston, MA 02129, USA*

E.N. Lee, *Department of Agricultural, Food and Nutritional Science, University of Alberta, Edmonton, Alberta, T6G 2P5, Canada*

S.B. Lee, *Department of Food Science, University of Guelph, Guelph, Ontario, N1G 2W1, Canada*

G. Lesnierowski, *Food Technology Department, Agricultural University of A. Cieszkowski, Poznan, Poland*

X. Li, *Department of Agricultural, Food and Nutritional Science, University of Alberta, Edmonton, Alberta, T6G 2P5, Canada*

E.C.Y. Li-Chan, *Faculty of Agricultural Sciences, University of British Columbia, Vancouver, British Columiba, V6T 1Z4, Canada*

L.T. Lim, *Department of Food Science, University of Guelph, Guelph, Ontario, N1G 2W1, Canada*

L. Ma, *500 N. McDonald Ave. A-7, Douglas, GA 31533, USA*

R.R. Marquardt, *Department of Animal Science, University of Manitoba, Winnipeg, Manitoba, R3T 2N2, Canada*

Y. Masuda, *R & D Division of Q.P. Corporation, Tokyo, 183-0034, Japan*

P.K. Mayo, *Faculty of Nutrition, Departments of Poultry and Animal Science, Texas A&M University, College Station, TX 77843-2472, USA*

M.D. McKee, *Faculty of Dentistry, McGill University, Montreal, Quebec, Canada*

D.J. McNamara, *Egg Nutrition Center, Washington, DC 20006, USA*

R.D. Miles, *University of Florida, Gainesville, FL 32611, USA*

Y. Mine, *Department of Food Science, University of Guelph, Guelph, Ontario, N1G 2W1, Canada*

K. Montoya, *Department of Food Science, University of Guelph, Guelph, Ontario, N1G 2W1, Canada*

S. Nakai, *Faculty of Agricultural Sciences, University of British Columbia, Vancouver, British Columbia, V6T 1Z4, Canada*

Y. Nys, *INRA, Station de Recherches Avicoles, Nouzilly, France*

M. Panheleux, *INRA, Station de Recherches Avicoles, Nouzilly, France*

A.J. Pescatore, *Department of Animal Sciences, University of Kentucky, Lexington, Kentucky, USA*

D.L. Peters, *Department of Food Science and Technology, University of Nebraska, Lincoln, Nebraska, USA*

D.A. Roland Jr, *Poultry Science Department, Auburn University, Auburn, AL 36849-5416, USA*

D.A. Roland Sr, *Poultry Science Department, Auburn University, Auburn, AL 36849-5416, USA*

A.E. Sefton, *Alltech Inc., Guelph, Ontario, Canada*

J. Self, *Cal-Maine Foods Inc., Jackson, MS 39207, USA*

J.S. Sim, *Department of Agricultural, Food and Nutritional Science, University of Alberta, Edmonton, Alberta, T6G 2P5, Canada*

S.E. Solomon, *Glasgow University Veterinary School, Poultry Research Group, Glasgow, UK*

M. St Maurice, *Department of Cellular and Molecular Medicine, Faculty of Medicine, University of Ottawa, Ottawa, Ontario, K1H 8N5, Canada*

V.G. Stanley, *Prairie View A&M University, Prairie View, Texas, USA*

G.G. Stella, *Faculty of Nutrition, Departments of Poultry and Animal Science, Texas A&M University, College Station, TX 77843-2472, USA*

R.M.W. Stevenson, *Department of Microbiology, University of Guelph, Guelph, Ontario, N1G 2W1, Canada*

M.L. Straw, *Department of Animal Sciences, University of Kentucky, Lexington, Kentucky, USA*

N. Suguro, *R & D Division of Q.P. Corporation, Tokyo, 183-0034, Japan*

S.S. Sumner, *Department of Food Science, Virginia Tech University, Blacksburg, Virginia, USA*

H.H. Sunwoo, *Department of Agricultural, Food and Nutritional Science, University of Alberta, Edmonton, Alberta, T6G 2P5, Canada*

B.G. Swanson, *Department of Food Science and Human Nutrition, Washington State University, Pullman, WA 99164-6120, USA*

J.B. Tharrington, *Department of Food Science, North Carolina State University, Raleigh, NC 27695-7624, USA*

C.P.W. Tsang, *Agriculture Canada, Central Experimental Farm, Ottawa, Canada*

M.A. Tung, *Department of Food Science, University of Guelph, Guelph, Ontario, N1G 2W1, Canada*

M.E. Van Elswyk, *Omega Tech Inc., Boulder, CO 80301, USA*

B.A. Watkins, *Lipid Chemistry and Molecular Biology Laboratory, Department of Food Science, Purdue University, West Lafayette, IN 47907-1160, USA*

P.E. Wejåker, *Department of Medicine, Cystic Fibrosis Centre, University Hospital 75185, Uppsala, Sweden*

Y.-F. Xiao, *Beth Israel Deaconess Medical Center and Harvard Medical School, Boston, MA 02129, USA*

Y.K. Yeo, *Lipid Chemistry Laboratory, Kyungpook National University, Taegu, Korea*

L. Yu, *Lipid Chemistry and Molecular Biology Laboratory, Department of Food Science, Purdue University, West Lafayette, IN 47907-1160, USA*

G. Zeidler, *Department of Animal Sciences, University of California, Riverside, CA 92521, USA*

J.X. Zhang, *Poultry Science Department, Auburn University, Auburn, AL 36849-5416, USA*

Preface

The egg has been an important food throughout human civilization. Consuming eggs, however, has been associated with both negative and positive perceptions. The rapidly declining per capita consumption of eggs over the past three decades is a major challenge faced by the egg industry. To meet this challenge, researchers around the world have begun to look at the egg beyond its traditional food value, focusing on economically viable biomedical, nutraceutical and ovo-biotechnology.

Leading researchers around the world from many different disciplines began to meet and share their findings at the First International Egg Symposium in 1992. The Second International Egg Symposium was held in Banff, Alberta, Canada, 5–8 April 1998. The theme of the symposium was Egg Nutrition and Newly Emerging Ovo-Biotechnologies. The meeting attracted an internationally diverse group of people from the business sector, researchers, health professionals, egg farmers and processors, government regulators, marketers and consumers. This symposium highlighted three different themes: (i) food fats and chronic diseases, misconception of food cholesterol and egg consumption; (ii) eggs as life-supporting chemicals, functional nutraceuticals and emerging new biotechnologies; and (iii) food safety, and newly emerging pasteurization technologies for egg products.

Thirty-nine excellent pieces of work presented at the symposium have been reviewed, edited and published in the form of a symposium monograph. The purpose of this book is to expand utilization of this valuable resource beyond the symposium participants. This book will serve as a key reference not only for egg researchers and the egg industry, but also more broadly, for researchers in related disciplines including agriculture, nutrition, medicine, pharmacology and biotechnology. Concurrently it will be a good resource for students at the graduate and undergraduate level of poultry science studies.

The editors wish to express their sincere thanks to members of the organizing committee for their commitment and for making the symposium a most memorable experience. Thanks are also due to many referees for their enormous effort and expert advice; without them peer-review would not have been possible. Last but not least, we would like to thank the authors, each distinguished in the field to which he or she has contributed. We are grateful to CAB *International* for publishing *Egg Nutrition and Biotechnology* with their customary excellence. This monograph is the result of a special team effort, of which all involved should be proud.

Last, but not least, we wish to express hearty thanks to our own hosting members, Linda Callen, Judy Carss, Martin Zuidhof, Ruth McGovern, Hoon Sunwoo and other members for their unselfish services toward the organization and flawless operation of the symposium.

Jeong S. Sim
Shuryo Nakai
Wilhelm Guenter

Acknowledgements

We gratefully acknowledge the following agencies and industry patrons who generously donated funds to support the symposium:

- Agriculture & Agri-Food Canada
- Alberta Agricultural Research Institute
- Alltech Inc.
- Burnbrae Farms Ltd
- Canadian Egg Marketing Agency
- Canadian Inovatech Inc.
- Designer Egg Producers Association International
- Egg Nutrition Centre
- Faculty of Agriculture, Forestry & Home Economics, University of Alberta
- Flax Council of Canada
- Korea–Canada Scientists and Engineers Association
- Lohmann Tierzucht GmbH
- M.G. Wallbaum Co.
- Manitoba Egg Producers
- OmegaTech Inc.
- Ovo-Biotechnica Inc.
- Taiyo Kagaku Co. Ltd (Japan)
- Villetard Eggs Ltd
- Western Margarine

Foreword

The egg industry is unique in that a single product is used to supply two distinct and mutually exclusive markets. Shell eggs have traditionally been used for breakfast preparation in many countries, as well as being used in home meal preparation, baking and other foods in many cultures. The egg products industry, using eggs removed from the shell, is more recent in origin and is targeted at the industrial production of food, often on a very large scale. As such, it has largely been restricted to developed countries with large industries involved in food processing. As the 20th century draws to a close, both of these markets are undergoing rapid change, for quite different reasons.

The shell egg industry was built on the egg's reputation as a perfectly packaged, portion controlled, and highly nutritious food item. The egg's fall from grace can be traced largely to the discovery that serum cholesterol in human subjects was one of the (many) risk factors in cardiovascular disease. This information was given great publicity, and demonstrated, not for the first or the last time, how easy it is to instil fear into the average consumer. Never mind that no direct evidence was ever produced linking egg consumption with heart disease. The belief became accepted as fact by many commentators, and not a few physicians. The nadir for the shell egg industry was probably the infamous *Time* magazine cover produced in 1983 depicting bacon and eggs on a platter in the shape of a human face with a distinctly unhappy expression.

The egg industry, since that event, has invested millions of dollars in research and in promotional efforts to publicize the real relationship, or rather the lack of it, between egg consumption and human heart and cardiovascular disease. The research has confirmed what egg industry people believed all along – that the egg is nature's perfect food and is a benefit to consumers' health. But convincing consumers continues to be an expensive and time-consuming goal. Nevertheless, progress is being made and the industry is developing new initiatives, such as the production of novel eggs enriched with nutrients such as ω-3 fatty acids and vitamins.

The egg products industry developed first as a salvage operation designed to remove unwanted and surplus eggs from the shell market. But in the past 20 years, this market has emerged as a major component of the food industry, as innovative products have been developed for a huge variety of applications both within the food industry and, increasingly, outside it. For many food applications, liquid egg is mainly a convenience: it's much easier for a pasta manufacturer to order several thousand litres of liquid egg than to purchase them in the shell. In addition, however, the liquid egg will be pasteurized, which lends the assurance of safety and freedom from most potentially pathogenic bacteria. Liquid eggs are widely used in sauces, salad dressings, puddings, cakes, etc. Separated yolks and/or whites are also widely used to impart texture, and for their functional properties like emulsifying and foaming. Additives such as salt and sugar provide further enhancement and variation of properties. The extraction of some of the egg's chemical components such as lysozyme, lecithin and avidin provide examples of the diversity now found in the egg processing industry.

In the 1990s, two important symposia dealing with egg utilization and technology have been organized by Dr Jeong Sim, of the University of Alberta in Edmonton, Canada. The First Symposium, on Non-conventional Egg Uses and Newly Emerging Processing Technologies was held in Banff, Canada, in April 1992. The Proceedings were published by CAB *International* in 1994 as *Egg Uses and Processing Technologies: New Developments*. Building on the success of the 1992 meeting, the Second Symposium was held in Banff in April 1998, and this book represents an edited version of its proceedings. The 1998 Symposium covers new developments in familiar areas, but also covers some exciting new ground.

There is plenty of 'good news' about eggs delivered by many highly respected scientists. David Kritchevsky's work on dietary fat and disease is world renowned and demonstrates that the egg has an important part to play in human nutrition. Similarly, other work on metabolism shows how important the egg and its components can be.

A large scale 'meta-analysis' reviewing many hundreds of studies of the effects of dietary cholesterol on serum cholesterol was undertaken in the 1990s. It included many hundreds of individual comparisons of the effects on humans of varying their intake of fats, cholesterol and other components present in eggs. The egg industry must wonder how many dollars it would take to bring this information to the wider audience necessary before the egg can be truly rehabilitated as a valued part of people's daily diet.

The importance of specific groups of fatty acids has also been studied in some detail. This knowledge gives further encouragement to the use of eggs in prudent diets.

A huge amount of data are available to encourage people to consume eggs, and there is progress to report. Data now being presented to and by physicians should eventually result in better acceptance by a public driven to scepticism by repeated episodes of food scares and exaggerations.

In Part III of this book, egg lipids and their nutritional values are discussed in detail. The unique chemistry of the egg yolk can be harnessed for the benefit of the consumer, and contemporary production systems are available to modify fatty acid profiles.

The functional characteristics of eggs are the object of intense study, as is the utilization of some of the components previously considered as waste. Modification of egg proteins, the use of eggs or egg components as 'functional foods', and the value of egg shells and egg shell membranes are relatively new applications. A truly impressive volume of research is now available for the egg industry to harness in the development of new uses for eggs, both within and out of the shell.

At the First Symposium, some time was devoted to the production of foreign immunoglobulins in egg yolks and their extraction for medical use. This science has developed very rapidly and the Second Symposium contains a whole section devoted to this area. The ease and non-invasive nature of the method for immunizing hens has resulted in a plethora of applications of this technology. Methods are now emerging in which immunoglobulins from egg yolks (IgY) can be applied to the prevention and/or diagnosis of a wide variety of animal diseases. This will soon be extended to the field of human medicine.

The safety of eggs for human consumption was taken for granted until the mid 1980s, when it became known that *Salmonella enteritidis* could infect the ovaries of laying hens and be transmitted *in ovo*. This knowledge was another detriment to the shell egg industry, and again the effect was made dramatically worse by a combination of exaggeration and poor understanding by the media and the consumers who relied on them for information. While the true incidence of *S. enteritidis* in shell eggs offered for sale may be in the range of 1 in 10^4 to 1 in 10^6, people sometimes believe that they may find a contaminated egg in every carton.

As with the cholesterol issue, the egg industry responded to safety concerns by intensifying research, and also by creating pro-active programmes which have greatly reduced the risk of a consumer buying a shell egg containing *S. enteritidis*. Technology is now available for rapid cooling of shell eggs, thus reducing the multiplication of any bacterial contamination. It is also possible to pasteurize eggs in the shell, but both these strategies assume that some eggs will be contaminated. Great strides have also been taken in reducing to very low levels the actual rate of contamination. Elimination of infected breeder flocks, and testing of the environment and eggs from commercial stocks are among these schemes.

A continuing problem of shell egg production has traditionally been the fragility of the egg shell itself. Research in the 1980s and 1990s has greatly improved our knowledge of the structure of this unique biological system, and there is a good prospect that improvements may result. Certainly, as hens become ever more efficient and productive, their capacity to put a sound shell on each egg is increasingly threatened. A variety of adjustments to feeding and nutrition, and the better understanding of shell structure, will surely provide industry with the needed security.

The Second Symposium was a great success, and Dr Sim is to be congratu-lated on maintaining such a high standard. This book is a lasting testament to the hard work of all those involved, and should become an essential resource for all those involved in the world's egg industries.

Peter Hunton
President
The World Poultry Congress 2000
Ontario Egg Producers

Food Fats and Health

Dietary Fat and Disease: What Do We Know and Where Do We Stand?

D. Kritchevsky

The Wistar Institute, Philadelphia, Pennsylvania, USA

The major killer diseases of the developed world are coronary artery disease (CAD) and cancer. Both are characterized as 'life style' diseases of multiple aetiology, but once that has been said emphasis goes back to specific single factors, among which fat occupies a prominent position. Many of the effects and involvements of dietary fat have been reviewed exhaustively, but these fields are not static and new data keep intruding on the old comfortable assumptions. In the CAD area, the enhancing role of saturated fat is well established. The possible deleterious effects of *trans*-unsaturated fats have been debated for over four decades, and the topic has not really been resolved. Specific effects of triglyceride structure are now emerging as an atherogenic entity.

In the cancer–fat area, one issue now is whether it is fat *per se* or calories derived from fat. Caloric restriction inhibits experimental carcinogenesis regardless of the fat content of the diet. A new fat that spans both CAD and cancer is conjugated linoleic acid (CLA). CLA is present mainly in dairy foods (especially cheeses) and in the meat of ruminants. CLA has been shown to inhibit carcinogenesis in carcinogen-treated rats or in immunodeficient mice injected with human tumour cells. It also inhibits cholesterol-induced atherosclerosis in rabbits. The mechanisms of CLA action are unresolved. The effects of fat on CAD and cancer are still areas open to research and speculation.

Introduction

In the face of all of the negative publicity concerning dietary fat, it is important to remember that fat is an essential nutrient. Because of its high caloric density, fat may contribute towards obesity which is a risk factor for cancer, coronary disease and diabetes, but obesity is due more to overconsumption than to any intrinsic structural or biological property of fat. In general, fat represents about

© CAB *International* 2000. *Egg Nutrition and Biotechnology*
(eds J.S. Sim, S. Nakai and W. Guenter)

20% of an individual's body weight. Fat is a source of energy and may serve as an insulator of vital organs. Fat is the source of essential fatty acids and serves to transport vitamins A, D, E and F. Cell membranes contain lipids – phospholipids and cholesterol. Cholesterol, in addition to its role in membrane structure, is also the precursor of corticosteroids, bile acids and sex hormones (Box 1.1).

Cardiovascular Disease

Discussion of fat and cardiovascular disease usually begins with cholesterol. This is because of the early studies of Anitschkow (1913) who showed that feeding cholesterol to rabbits led to deposition of this sterol in their arteries. We know now that there are a number of risk factors for cardiovascular disease – among them elevated blood cholesterol levels, elevated blood pressure, cigarette smoking and obesity. It should be pointed out that risk factors represent statistical rather than medical diagnoses. They tell us the odds for or against succumbing to heart disease and are useful guidelines for populations, but of much less value in assessing individual risk. Hopkins and Williams (1981) described over 200 risk factors for coronary disease. A single measurement of cholesterol may be misleading, since plasma cholesterol levels tend to fluctuate diurnally and seasonally (Kritchevsky, 1985; Hegsted and Nicolosi, 1987). A study of plasma cholesterol fluctuations in the ten American Lipid Research Clinics showed a definite seasonal variation and suggested that total and low-density lipoprotein (LDL) cholesterol levels fluctuated inversely with length of day (Gordon *et al.*, 1988).

Since Gofman and his colleagues (1950) demonstrated fractionation of plasma lipoproteins by ultracentrifugation, we have turned our attention to these fractions (which are defined by their hydrated densities), and the roles of LDL and high-density lipoprotein (HDL) are evaluated. LDL and HDL are known popularly as the 'bad' and 'good' cholesterol, but recent findings by Krauss and Burke (1982) have shown that LDL can be subfractionated into small dense or large particles and the former are the more atherogenic. Thus, we now have the 'good–bad' and the 'bad–bad' cholesterol. Berg (1963) described lipoprotein (a), another form of LDL which interferes with fibrinolysis and is associated with a high risk of coronary disease (Kostner *et al.*, 1981; Rhoades *et al.*, 1986).

Box 1.1.   Biological roles of fat.

Source of energy
Insulation of important organs
Transport of vitamins A, E, D and K
Source of essential fatty acids
Source of steroids
Presence in membranes

As we learn more about the pathophysiology of coronary disease, more variables enter the picture. Several decades ago, the description was simple: dietary cholesterol was assumed to contribute to circulating cholesterol which was then deposited in the arterial wall. Today we must consider the role(s) of the initial endothelial injury, platelet aggregation, smooth muscle cell proliferation and migration, chemoattractants and eicosanoids as well as LDL and, what is currently of great interest, oxidized LDL. Elevated cholesterol levels are still important, but cholesterol is no longer the only actor on the stage. However, it is still the centre of diagnostic attention. Accumulating data suggest that dietary cholesterol *per se* does not contribute greatly to circulating cholesterol. Gertler *et al.* (1950) showed that while the blood cholesterol levels of men with coronary disease were significantly higher than those of controls, in no case did they reflect the level of cholesterol in the diet (Table 1.1). It is of interest to note that in the subgroups with heart disease as well as in the controls there was no significant difference in serum cholesterol level between the men who ate the most cholesterol and those who ate the least. Thirty years later, Dawber *et al.* (1982) made a similar observation regarding egg intake and cholesterolaemia. Gordon *et al.* (1981) analysed daily dietary intake of men in three large heart studies, Hawaii, Puerto Rico and Framingham. Comparing diets of men who had coronary disease with those who did not, they found significant differences in caloric intake, carbohydrate intake and alcohol intake – all lower in the subjects who had coronary disease. There were no differences in total fat or cholesterol intake or in level of fat saturation. The level of saturation of fat is a strong determinant of blood cholesterol level (McNamara *et al.*, 1987) (Table 1.2). For instance, when the diet contained saturated fat, the difference in plasma cholesterol level between the low cholesterol (288 mg) and high

Table 1.1. Dietary and serum cholesterol in subjects with or without coronary heart disease (CHD) (ten men per subgroup).

Subgroup	Group		
	CHD	Control	$P<$
Lowest serum cholesterol			
Serum cholesterol (mm l^{-1})	5.07 ± 0.13	4.19 ± 0.05	0.001
Dietary cholesterol (g week^{-1})	3.30 ± 0.5	3.80 ± 0.3	NS
Highest serum cholesterol			
Serum cholesterol (mm l^{-1})	10.16 ± 0.44	8.09 ± 0.08	0.001
Dietary cholesterol (g week^{-1})	4.10 ± 0.6	4.30 ± 0.4	NS
Lowest cholesterol intake			
Serum cholesterol (mm l^{-1})	7.01 ± 0.36	5.74 ± 0.41	0.05
Dietary cholesterol (g week^{-1})	1.30 ± 0.1	1.40 ± 0.1	NS
Highest cholesterol intake			
Serum cholesterol (mm l^{-1})	7.45 ± 0.57	5.51 ± 0.26	0.01
Dietary cholesterol (g week^{-1})	5.70 ± 0.2	7.00 ± 0.3	0.01

NS, not significant.
From: Gertler *et al.*, 1950.

Table 1.2.   Plasma cholesterol levels in subjects fed high or low levels of cholesterol with saturated or unsaturated fat.

Group	Cholesterol	
	Dietary (mg)	Plasma (mm l⁻¹)
Low cholesterol		
Saturated fat	288 ± 64	6.28 ± 1.29
Unsaturated fat	192 ± 60	5.63 ± 1.19
High cholesterol		
Saturated fat	863 ± 161	6.41 ± 1.32
Unsaturated fat	820 ± 102	5.79 ± 1.19

Thirty-nine subjects in the unsaturated fat group, 36 subjects in the saturated fat group.
From: McNamara *et al.*, 1987.

cholesterol (863 mg) diets was 2.1%. When the fat was unsaturated, the difference in plasma cholesterol level between low cholesterol (192 mg) and high cholesterol diets (820 mg) was 2.3%. However, on low cholesterol intake, plasma cholesterol on unsaturated fat was 10.4% lower than on saturated fat; on the high cholesterol, the difference was 9.7%. Generally speaking, for every 100 mg of cholesterol ingested, the mean increase in plasma cholesterol is 2.3 ± 0.2 mg dl⁻¹ (McNamara, 1990).

Keys *et al.* (1965) formulated an equation that could predict changes in plasma cholesterol from changes in type of dietary fat and level of dietary cholesterol. Hegsted *et al.* (1965) devised a similar equation. Both sets of investigators found stearic acid to exert a smaller than predicted effect. Dietary experiments using fats rich in stearic acid have shown them not to be cholesterolaemic in humans (Grande *et al.*, 1970; Bonanome and Grundy, 1988). Stearic acid-rich fats (such as cocoa butter) are less atherogenic than expected in rabbits (Kritchevsky and Tepper, 1965; Kritchevsky *et al.*, 1982). Hayes and Khosla (1992) suggest that dietary myristic acid is hypercholesterolaemic in a dose-related manner, linoleic acid is hypocholesterolaemic up to a dietary content of about 6% of calories, and palmitic acid is neutral except in cholesterol-rich regimens. Triglyceride structure may be a determinant of atherogenicity even if it does not affect plasma cholesterol (Kritchevsky, 1988). Results obtained using native or randomized tallow and lard are a case in point (Kritchevsky *et al.*, 1998) (Table 1.3).

It is now becoming evident that a cholesterol level that is too low may also predispose to risk. A review of a large number of trials (yielding 68,406 deaths) found that cholesterol levels below 160 mg dl⁻¹ (4.14 mm l⁻¹) were associated with increased mortality (Jacobs *et al.*, 1992). Persons with low cholesterol had 20% more cancer deaths, 40% more cardiovascular, no-cancer deaths, 35% more deaths from injury and 50% more deaths due to problems of the digestive system. A review of the association between low cholesterol levels and risk of cancer found that risk surfaced in the course of the

Table 1.3.　Influence of native or randomized tallow or lard on atherosclerosis in rabbits fed 0.5% cholesterol.

	Group			
	Tallow	Randomized tallow	Lard	Randomized lard
% of total 16 : 0 at SN2 position	3.8	8.5	21.3	7.6
% of total 16 : 0	15.3	34.3	99.5	35.5
Average atherosclerosis[a]				
Aortic arch	1.29 ± 0.24	1.50 ± 0.53	2.69 ± 0.28	1.50 ± 0.28
Thoracic aorta	0.79 ± 0.29	0.79 ± 0.28	1.75 ± 0.28	0.69 ± 0.19

[a]Graded visually on a 0–4 scale.
From: Kritchevsky *et al.*, 1998.

hypocholesterolaemic regimen, suggesting that abnormalities arose in the course of clinical trials (Kritchevsky and Kritchevsky, 1992).

A new development in the area of lipids and atherosclerosis is the observation by Lee *et al.* (1994) that conjugated linoleic acid (*cis*9, *trans*11 octadecadienoic acid) can reduce the severity of experimental atherosclerosis produced in rabbits fed a cholesterol-containing diet. Conjugated linoleic acid (CLA) is actually a family of positional and geometric isomers of linoleic acid, but the one most prevalent in food is the *cis*9, *trans*11 modification. CLA has long been known to be a component of milk, but its biological roles have been discovered only recently.

Cancer

Watson and Mellanby (1930) showed that fat augmentation of the diet fed to rats being treated with coal tar caused a 68% increase in skin tumours. The dietary fat content was increased from 3 to 12.5–25.0% by addition of butter. In rats, diets high in fat enhanced the yield of epitheliomas produced by UV radiation (Baumann *et al.*, 1939). A later study (Jacobi and Baumann, 1940) showed that the yield of chemically induced skin tumours was increased when the level of dietary fat was increased. Highly saturated fats were less co-carcinogenic than corn oil (Miller *et al.*, 1944). Carroll and Khor (1971) found that rats fed saturated fat developed fewer chemically induced mammary tumours than did rats fed unsaturated fats. Ip *et al.* (1985) showed that the tumour-enhancing effect of unsaturated fat was due to the presence of linoleic acid, which is essential for tumour growth.

In humans, risk for development of cancer is clearly correlated with being overweight (Lew and Garfinkel, 1979; Garfinkel, 1985), but excess weight can be due to dietary factors other than fat. Goodwin and Boyd (1987) summarized data from a number of studies relating to dietary fat and the risk of breast cancer. While most international comparisons (seven of nine) found an association between fat intake and breast cancer, only one of 14 case–control studies showed a correlation. Studies from Japan (Hirohata *et al.*, 1985) and Hawaii

(Hirohata *et al.*, 1987) found little correlation between dietary fat and breast cancer. Rogers and Longnecker (1988) summarized data from 14 epidemiological studies of fat intake and breast cancer and concluded that there was either a weak correlation or none at all. Willett *et al.* (1987) studied more than 89,000 American women whose fat intake ranged from 32 to 44% of calories and found no correlation between risk of mammary cancer and fat intake.

In colon cancer, as in breast cancer, the international comparisons show a positive correlation between cancer incidence and fat intake (Armstrong and Doll, 1975; Knox, 1977; Higginson and Sheridan, 1991), but this is not borne out in case–control studies (Higginson, 1966; Graham *et al.*, 1978; Bingham *et al.*, 1979). Studies from France (Marquart-Moulin *et al.*, 1986) and Belgium (Tuyns *et al.*, 1987) have not found dietary fat to be a risk factor for colon cancer. Jensen *et al.* (1982) found a negative correlation between saturated fat intake and colon cancer in Finland and Denmark. Stemmermann *et al.* (1984) studied a group of 7074 Japanese Hawaiians of whom 106 (1.5%) had colon cancer, 59 (0.8%) had rectal cancer and 406 (5.7%) other cancers. The fat intake of the controls and of the subjects with rectal or colon cancer was virtually the same. Rogers and Longnecker (1988) summarized data from 24 studies and found a weak association between fat intake (g day^{-1}) and colon cancer risk, but overall the various findings were inconsistent.

The fat effect may be due principally to the caloric contribution rather than fat *per se*. Seventy years ago, Hoffman (1927) suggested that cancer incidence could be correlated with overnutrition. Moreschi (1909) demonstrated that the growth of transplanted tumours was inhibited in underfed mice. Rous (1914) showed that food restriction inhibited the growth of both spontaneous and transplanted tumours in rats. In the 1940s, the laboratories of Tannenbaum (Michael Reese Hospital, Chicago) and Baumann (University of Wisconsin, Madison) began investigation into the effect of food restriction and tumorigenesis. Tannenbaum (1942) showed that the effect was not limited to one strain of mouse and that caloric restriction was most effective when instituted during the progression phase of tumorigenesis (Tannenbaum, 1944). Lavik and Baumann (1943) examined the separate effects of fat and calories in mice treated topically with methylcholanthrene. When the diet was low in both calories and fat, no skin tumours were observed. A diet low in fat but high in calories led to a 93% higher incidence of tumours than did a diet high in fat but low in calories. The low fat–high caloric diet was only 18% less promoting than one high in both calories and fat (Table 1.4).

We (Kritchevsky *et al.*, 1984) tested the effects of caloric restriction (by 40%) and fat saturation in rats given 7,12-dimethylbenz(*a*)anthracene. When the fat was coconut oil, no tumours were observed in the restricted rats; when the fat was corn oil, tumorigenesis was suppressed by 75% in the calorically restricted rats (Table 1.5). A later study showed that at 10% caloric restriction, tumour incidence was unaffected, but tumour multiplicity (tumours/tumour-bearing rat) and tumour burden (weight of all tumours) were reduced by 36 and 47%, respectively. At 30% restriction, tumour incidence had fallen by 42% and tumour multiplicity and tumour burden by 72 and 91%, respectively (Klurfeld *et al.*, 1989a). Caloric restriction was shown to be an effective inhibitor of carcinogenicity even in the face of high fat (20 or 26.7%) diets (Klurfeld *et al.*, 1989b) (Table 1.6). There is a positive correlation between feed efficiency and tumour incidence in calorically restricted rats (Kritchevsky *et al.*, 1989). Caloric restriction was effective by inhibiting spontaneous tumour formation in mice even when the regimen was instituted when the mice were 1 year old (Weindruch and Walford, 1982). In a review of international data, Albanes (1987) found that common human cancers were associated positively with body weight or caloric intake. Total caloric intake is correlated positively with risk of colon cancer (Jain *et al.*, 1980; Lyon *et al.*, 1987). Regular exercise

Table 1.4.   Influence of fat and calories on methylcholanthrene-induced skin tumours in mice.

	Regimen	
Fat	Calories	Tumour incidence (%)
High	High	66
High	Low	28
Low	High	54
Low	Low	0

From: Lavik and Baumann, 1943.

Table 1.5.   Influence of fat type and caloric restriction (by 40%) on DMBA-induced mammary tumours in rats.

Regimen	Fat (%)	Tumour incidence (%)
Ad libitum	Coconut oil (3.9)	58
Restricted	Coconut oil (8.4)	0
Ad libitum	Corn oil (3.9)	80
Restricted	Corn oil (8.4)	20

Coconut oil contained 1% corn oil.
From: Kritchevsky *et al.*, 1984.

Table 1.6.   Effect of fat level and 25% caloric restriction on DMBA-induced mammary tumours in rats.

Regimen	Tumour incidence (%)	Multiplicity	Tumour burden (g)
Ad libitum			
5% Corn oil	65	1.9 ± 0.3	4.2 ± 1.9
15% Corn oil	85	3.0 ± 0.6	6.6 ± 2.7
20% Corn oil	80	4.1 ± 0.6	11.8 ± 3.2
Restricted			
20% Corn oil	60	1.9 ± 0.4	1.5 ± 0.5
26.7% Corn oil	30	1.5 ± 0.3	2.3 ± 1.6
P	< 0.005	< 0.0001	< 0.05

From: Klurfeld *et al.*, 1989b.

(Paffenbarger *et al.*, 1987) or vigorous occupational activity may reduce colon cancer risk (Garabrant *et al.*, 1984; Vena *et al.*, 1985).

The accumulated data suggest that the best nutritional advice for the average, healthy person is moderation, variety and balance. The effects of nutrition on gene expression are being investigated, and we may find eventually that fat, as well as other nutrients, plays a more fundamental role in life processes than we are now aware of. It is probably most healthy to eat a little of everything and not too much of anything.

Acknowledgement

Supported, in part, by a Research Career Award (HL00734) from the National Institute of Health.

References

Albanes, D. (1987) Total calories, body weight and tumour incidence in mice. *Cancer Research* 47, 1987–1992.

Anitschkow, N. (1913) Über die Veränderung der Kaninchenaorta bei experimenteller cholesterin steatose. *Beitrag Pathologische Anatomie und Allgemeine Pathologie* 56, 379–404.

Armstrong, B. and Doll, R. (1975) Environmental factors and cancer incidence and mortality in different countries, with special reference to dietary practice. *International Journal of Cancer* 15, 617–631.

Baumann, C.A., Jacobi, H.P. and Rusch, H.P. (1939) The effect of diet on artificial tumour production. *American Journal of Hygiene* 30, 1–6.

Berg, K. (1963) A new serum type system in man: the Lp(a) system. *Acta Pathologica et Microbiologia Scandinavica* 59, 369–382.

Bingham, S., Williams, D.R., Cole, T.J. and James, W.P.T. (1979) Dietary fibre and regional large bowel mortality in Europe. *British Journal of Cancer* 40, 456–463.

Bonanome, A. and Grundy, S.M. (1988) Effect of dietary stearic acid on plasma cholesterol and lipoprotein levels. *New England Journal of Medicine* 319, 1244–1248.

Carroll, K.K. and Khor, H.T. (1971) Effect of level and type of dietary fat on incidence of mammary tumours induced in female Sprague–Dawley rats by 7,12-dimethylbenz-(*a*)anthracene. *Lipids* 6, 415–420.

Dawber, T.R., Nickerson, R.J., Brand, F.N. and Pool, J. (1982) Eggs, serum cholesterol and coronary heart disease. *American Journal of Clinical Nutrition* 36, 617–625.

Garabrant, D.H., Peters, J.M., Mack, T.M. and Bernstein, L. (1984) Job activity and colon cancer risk. *American Journal of Epidemiology* 119, 1005–1014.

Garfinkel, L. (1985) Overweight and cancer. *Annals of International Medicine* 103, 1034–1036.

Gertler, M.M., Garn, S.M. and White, D.D. (1950) Serum cholesterol and coronary artery disease. *Circulation* 2, 696–702.

Gofman, J.W., Lindgren, F., Elliott, H., Mantz, W., Hewitt, J., Strisower, B., Herring, V. and Lyon, T.P. (1950) The role of lipids and lipoproteins in atherosclerosis. *Science* 111, 166–171.

Goodwin, P.J. and Boyd, N.F. (1987) Critical appraisal of the evidence that dietary fat is related to breast cancer risk in humans. *Journal of the National Cancer Institute* 79, 473–485.

Gordon, D.J., Hyde, J., Trost, D.C., Whaley, F.S., Hannan, P.J., Jacobs, D.R. and Ekelund, L.G. (1988) Cyclic seasonal variation in plasma lipid and lipoprotein levels: the lipid research clinics coronary primary prevention trial placebo group. *Journal of Clinical Epidemiology* 41, 679–689.

Gordon, T., Kagan, A., Garcia-Palmieri, M., Kannel, W.B., Zukel, W.J., Tillotson, J., Sorlie, P. and Hjortland, M. (1981) Diet and its relation to coronary heart disease in three populations. *Circulation* 63, 500–515.

Graham, S., Dayal, H., Swanson, M., Mittelman, A. and Wilkinson, G. (1978) Diet in the epidemiology of cancer of the colon and rectum. *Journal of the National Cancer Institute* 61, 709–714.

Grande, F., Anderson, J.T. and Keys, A. (1970) Comparison of effects of palmitic and stearic acids in the diet on serum cholesterol in man. *American Journal of Clinical Nutrition* 23, 1184–1193.

Hayes, K.C. and Khosla, P.R. (1992) Dietary fatty acid thresholds and cholesterolemia. *FASEB Journal* 6, 2600–2607.

Hegsted, D.M. and Nicolosi, R.J. (1987) Individual variation in serum cholesterol levels. *Proceedings of the National Academy of Sciences of the United States of America* 84, 6259–6261.

Hegsted, D.M., McGandy, R.B., Myers, M.L. and Stare, F.J. (1965) Quantitative effects of dietary fat on serum cholesterol in man. *American Journal of Clinical Nutrition* 17, 281–295.

Higginson, J. (1966) Etiological factors in gastrointestinal cancer in man. *Journal of the National Cancer Institute* 37, 527–545.

Higginson, J. and Sheridan, M.J. (1991) Nutrition and human cancer. In: Alfin-Slater, R.B. and Kritchevsky, D. (eds) *Human Nutrition: A Comprehensive Treatise*, Vol. 7 *Cancer and Nutrition*. Plenum Press, New York, pp. 1–50.

Hirohata, T., Shigematsu, T., Nomura, A.M.Y., Nomura, Y., Horie, A. and Hirohata, T. (1985) Occurrence of breast cancer in relation to diet and reproductive history: a case–control study in Fukuoka, Japan. *National Cancer Institute Monographs* 69, 187–190.

Hirohata, T., Nomura, A.M.Y., Hankin, J.H., Kolonel, L.N. and Lee, J. (1987) An epidemiologic study on the association between diet and breast cancer. *Journal of the National Cancer Institute* 78, 595–600.

Hoffman, F.L. (1927) *Cancer Increase and Overnutrition*. Prudential Insurance Company, Newark, New Jersey, USA.

Hopkins, P.N. and Williams, R.R. (1981) A survey of 246 suggested coronary risk factors. *Atherosclerosis* 40, 1–52.

Ip, C., Carter, C.A. and Ip, M.M. (1985) Requirement of essential fatty acid for mammary tumorigenesis in the rat. *Cancer Research* 45, 1997–2001.

Jacobi, H.P. and Baumann, C.A. (1940) The effect of fat on tumour formation. *American Journal of Cancer* 39, 338–342.

Jacobs, D., Blackburn, H., Higgins, M., Reed, D., Iso, H., McMillan, G., Neaton, J., Nelson, J., Potter, F., Rifkind, B., Rossousu, J., Shekelle, R. and Yusuf, S. (1992) Report of the conference on low blood cholesterol: mortality associations. *Circulation* 86, 1046–1060.

Jain, M., Cook, G.M., Davis, F.G., Grace, M.G., Howe, G.R. and Miller, A.B. (1980) A case–control study of diet and colorectal cancer. *International Journal of Cancer* 26, 57–768.

Jensen, O.M., MacLennan, R. and Wahrendorf, J. (1982) Diet, bowel function, fecal characteristics and large bowel cancer in Denmark and Finland. *Nutrition and Cancer* 4, 5–19.

Keys, A., Anderson, J.T. and Grande, F. (1965) Serum cholesterol response to changes in the diet. IV. Particular saturated fatty acids in the diet. *Metabolism* 14, 776–787.

Klurfeld, D.M., Welch, C.B., Davis, M.J. and Kritchevsky, D. (1989a) Determination of the degree of energy restriction necessary to reduce DMBA-induced mammary tumorigenesis in rats during the promotion phase. *Journal of Nutrition* 119, 286–291.

Klurfeld, D.M., Welch, C.B., Lloyd, L.M. and Kritchevsky, D. (1989b) Inhibition of DMBA-induced mammary tumorigenesis by caloric restriction in rats fed high fat diets. *International Journal of Cancer* 43, 922–925.

Knox, E.G. (1977) Foods and disease. *British Journal of Preventive and Social Medicine* 31, 71–80.

Kostner, G.M., Avogaro, P., Cazzolati, G., Marth, E., Bittolo-Bon, G. and Quinci, G.B. (1981) Lipoprotein Lp(a) and the risk of myocardial infarction. *Atherosclerosis* 38, 51–61.

Krauss, R.M. and Burke, J. (1982) Identification of multiple classes of plasma low density lipoproteins in humans. *Journal of Lipid Research* 23, 97–104.

Kritchevsky, D. (1985) Variation in serum cholesterol levels. In: Weininger, J. and Briggs, G.M. (eds), *Nutrition Update Volume 2*. John Wiley and Sons, New York, pp. 91–103.

Kritchevsky, D. (1988) Effects of triglyceride structure on lipid metabolism. *Nutrition Reviews* 46, 177–181.

Kritchevsky, D. and Tepper, S.A. (1965) Cholesterol vehicle in experimental atherosclerosis. 7. Influence of naturally occurring saturated fats. *Medicine et Pharmacologica Experimentalis* 12, 315–320.

Kritchevsky, D., Weber, M.M. and Klurfeld, D.M. (1984) Dietary fat versus caloric content in initiation and promotion of 7,12-dimethylbenz(*a*)anthracene induced mammary tumorigenesis in rats. *Cancer Research* 44, 3174–3177.

Kritchevsky, D., Welch, C.B. and Klurfeld, D.M. (1989) Response of mammary tumors to caloric restriction for different time periods during the promotion phase. *Nutrition and Cancer* 12, 259–269.

Kritchevsky, D., Tepper, S.A., Bises, G. and Klurfeld, D.M. (1982) Experimental atherosclerosis in rabbits fed cholesterol-free diets. 10. Cocoa butter and palm oil. *Atherosclerosis* 41, 279–284.

Kritchevsky, D., Tepper, S.A., Kuksis, A., Eghtedary, K. and Klurfeld, D.M. (1998) Cholesterol vehicle in experimental atherosclerosis. 21. Native and randomized lard and tallow. *Journal of Nutritional Biochemistry* 9, 582–585.

Kritchevsky, S.B. and Kritchevsky, D. (1992) Serum cholesterol and cancer risk. An epidemiological perspective. *Annual Review of Nutrition* 12, 391–416.

Lavik, P.S. and Baumann, C.A. (1943) Further studies on the tumour-promoting action of fat. *Cancer Research* 3, 749–756.

Lee, K.N., Kritchevsky, D. and Pariza, M.W. (1994) Conjugated linoleic acid and atherosclerosis in rabbits. *Atherosclerosis* 108, 19–25.

Lew, E.A. and Garfinkel, L. (1979) Variations in mortality by weight among 750,000 men and women. *Journal of Chronic Disease* 32, 563–576.

Lyon, J.L., Mahoney, A.W., West, D.W., Gardner, J.W., Smith, K.R., Sorenson, A.W. and Stanish, W. (1987) Energy intake: its relation to colon cancer. *Journal of the National Cancer Institute* 78, 853–861.

Marquart-Moulin, G., Riboli, E., Cornee, J., Charnay, B., Berthezene, P. and Day, N. (1986) Case–control study on colorectal cancer and diet in Marseilles. *International Journal of Cancer* 38, 183–191.

McNamara, D.J. (1990) Effects of dietary cholesterol on serum cholesterol. In: Pearson, A.M. and Dutson, T.R. (eds), *Advances in Meat Research*, Vol. 6. Elsevier Applied Science, London, pp. 63–87.

McNamara, D.J., Kolb, R., Parker, T.S., Batwin, H., Samuel, P., Brown, C.D. and Ahrens, E.H., Jr (1987) Heterogeneity of cholesterol homeostasis in man: responses to changes in dietary fat quality and cholesterol quantity. *Journal of Clinical Investigation* 79, 1729–1739.

Miller, J.A., Kline, B.E., Rusch, H.P. and Baumann, C.A. (1944) The effect of certain lipids on the carcinogenicity of *p*-dimethyamino-azobenzene. *Cancer Research* 4, 756–761.

Moreschi, C. (1909) Beziehungen zwischen Ernährung und Tumourwachstum. *Zeitschrift für Immunitätsforschung* 2, 651–675.

Paffenbarger, R.S., Jr, Hyde, R.T. and Wing, A.L. (1987) Physical activity and incidence of cancer in diverse populations: a preliminary report. *American Journal of Clinical Nutrition* 45, 312–317.

Rhoades, G.G., Dahlen, G., Berg, K. and Morton, N.E. (1986) Lp(a) lipoprotein as a risk factor for myocardial infarction. *Journal of the American Medical Association* 256, 2540–2544.

Rogers, A.E. and Longnecker, M.P. (1988) Dietary and nutritional influences on cancer. A review of epidemiologic and experimental data. *Laboratory Investigation* 59, 729–759.

Rous, P. (1914) The influence of diet on transplanted and spontaneous tumours. *Journal of Experimental Medicine* 20, 433–451.

Stemmermann, G.N., Nomura, A.M.Y. and Heilbrun, K.L. (1984) Dietary fat and the risk of colorectal cancer. *Cancer Research* 44, 4633–4637.

Tannenbaum, A. (1942) The genesis and growth of tumours. II. Effects of caloric restriction *per se*. *Cancer Research* 2, 460–467.

Tannenbaum, A. (1944) The dependence of the genesis of induced skin tumours on the caloric intake during different stages of carcinogenesis. *Cancer Research* 4, 463–477.

Tuyns, A.J., Halterman, M. and Kaaks, R. (1987) Colorectal cancer and the intake of nutrients: oligosaccharides are a risk factor, fats are not. A case–control study in Belgium. *Nutrition and Cancer* 10, 181–196.

Vena, J.E., Graham, S., Zielezny, M., Swanson, M.K., Barnes, R.E. and Nolan, J. (1985) Lifetime occupational exercise and colon cancer. *American Journal of Epidemiology* 122, 357–365.

Watson, A.F. and Mellanby, E. (1930) Tar cancer in mice. II. The condition of the skin when modified by external treatment or diet, as a factor in influencing the cancerous reaction. *British Journal of Experimental Pathology* 11, 311–322.

Weindruch, R. and Walford, R.L. (1982) Dietary restriction in mice beginning at one year of life: effect on life span and cancer incidence. *Science* 215, 1415–1418.

Willett, W.C., Stampfer, M.J., Colditz, G.A., Rosner, B.A., Hennekens, C.H. and Speizer, F.E. (1987) Dietary fat and the risk of breast cancer. *New England Journal of Medicine* 316, 22–28.

Food Cholesterol and its Plasma Lipid and Lipoprotein Response: Is Food Cholesterol Still a Problem or Overstated?

2

W.H. Howell

Department of Nutritional Sciences, University of Arizona,
Tucson, Arizona, USA

A meta-analytical investigation was designed to determine if the findings of past reviews could be generalized to broader experimental settings. This meta-analysis also allowed determination of the extent to which study and subject characteristics influenced the predictive models of lipid and lipoprotein response to dietary change. The intention was to develop a broadly applicable model, to predict more appropriately the extent to which meeting the United States National Cholesterol Education Program (NCEP) Steps I and II national dietary guidelines could be expected to affect changes in blood lipid levels of the American population.

A computer-assisted search was conducted to locate diet intervention studies between January 1966 and February 1994. The searches identified 224 studies that met our criteria. Data from these studies on 8143 subjects in 366 independent groups with 878 diet–blood lipid comparisons were subjected to weighted multiple regression analysis. The regression models developed for serum total cholesterol, triacylglycerol and low-density (LDL), high-density and very low-density lipoprotein cholesterol have multiple correlations of 0.74, 0.34, 0.65, 0.41 and 0.14, respectively. The average effects of dietary changes on serum lipids found in this broad set of studies are consistent with those found in most previous investigations. Predictions indicate compliance with current dietary recommendations (30% of energy from fat, < 10% from saturated fat and < 300 mg dl^{-1} cholesterol) would reduce plasma total and LDL cholesterol levels by approximately 5% compared with levels associated with the average American diet.

Introduction

The quantitative relationships among dietary fat and cholesterol and plasma lipid levels have been the subject of much study and some controversy over the past 40 years. Because previous quantitative reviews in this area focused on the most tightly controlled, highest quality experiments, our research group conducted a meta-analytical investigation designed to determine if the findings of these past reviews could be generalized to broader experimental settings. This meta-analysis also allowed determination of the extent to which study and subject characteristics, initial serum lipid levels, interactions of dietary manipulations and/or duration of treatment influenced the predictive models of lipid and lipoprotein response to dietary change. Our intention was to develop a more broadly applicable model, spanning a diversity of study designs and types of subjects. As a result, it may be able to predict more appropriately the extent to which meeting the United States National Cholesterol Education Program (NCEP) Steps I and II dietary guidelines could affect changes in blood lipid levels of the American population.

Computer and archival (manual) search strategies were used to locate diet intervention studies published in English between February 1994 and January 1966. The data included changes in dietary cholesterol and fat, i.e. total, saturated (SFA), monounsaturated (MUFA) and polyunsaturated (PUFA) fatty acids, as well as corresponding changes in serum total cholesterol, triacylglycerol and high-density (HDL), low-density (LDL) and very low-density (VLDL) lipoprotein cholesterol levels in adult subjects. The searches identified 224 studies (Howell *et al.*, 1997) that met the above-listed inclusion criteria. Data from these studies on 8143 subjects in 366 independent groups with 878 diet–blood lipid comparisons were subjected to weighted multiple regression analyses to construct prediction models for the blood lipid variables (Howell *et al.*, 1997).

Serum Lipid Prediction Models

Serum total cholesterol

As indicated in Table 2.1, the best-fitting model for change in serum total cholesterol included changes in SFA (% of total energy), PUFA (% of total energy) and dietary cholesterol (mg). This prediction model explained 74% of the variance in change in serum total cholesterol. These relationships indicate that a 1% alteration in total energy from SFA will result in a 49.1 mM (1.9 mg dl^{-1}) change in serum total cholesterol. Likewise, a change in PUFA of 1% of total energy will produce a 23.3 mM (0.90 mg dl^{-1}) change (in the opposite direction) in serum total cholesterol. Finally, a change of 1 mg dl^{-1} in dietary cholesterol will produce a change of 0.57 mM (0.022 mg dl^{-1}) in serum total cholesterol. Neither a change in total fat as a percentage of total energy nor a change in MUFA added significant predictive power to this model.

LDL cholesterol

Changes in SFA and PUFA were the best predictors of change in LDL cholesterol and explained a combined total of 65% of its variance. The model indicates that for every 1% change in SFA (% of total energy), a change in LDL cholesterol of 46.5 mM (1.8 mg dl^{-1}) was predicted, and an increase of 1% PUFA (% of total energy) was expected to decrease LDL cholesterol by

Table 2.1. Prediction models for changes in serum total and lipoprotein cholesterol and triacylglycerol.

Serum lipid (mg dl⁻¹) and dietary factor	B	SE	95% CI
ΔSerum total cholesterol ($n = 177$, $R^2 = 0.736$)			
ΔSFA	1.918	0.141	1.656–2.200
ΔPUFA	−0.900	0.163	−1.226– −0.574
ΔCholesterol	0.0222	0.0037	0.0146–0.0294
ΔLDL ($n = 115$, $R^2 = 0.649$)			
ΔSFA	1.808	0.156	1.496–2.120
ΔPUFA	−0.495	0.209	−0.913– −0.077
ΔHDL ($n = 167$, $R^2 = 0.410$)			
ΔSFA	0.287	0.065	0.157–0.417
ΔFat	0.192	0.054	0.084–0.300
Δtriacylglygerol ($n = 124$, $R^2 = 0.337$)			
ΔPUFA	−1.066	0.225	−1.516– −0.616
ΔFat	−0.919	0.175	−1.269– −0.569
ΔCholesterol	0.0144	0.0067	0.0010–0.0278

n, number of independent study groups; R^2, percentage of response variance accounted for; B, unstandardized regression coefficient; SE, standard error of B; 95% CI, confidence interval of B; Δ, change; SFA, saturated fatty acids; PUFA, polyunsaturated fatty acids; LDL, low-density lipoprotein; HDL, high-density lipoprotein.

12.93 mM (0.50 mg dl⁻¹). Of particular note in this model is the absence of change in dietary cholesterol. Although change in dietary cholesterol had a significant bivariate relationship to change in LDL-cholesterol, it did not reach a sufficient level of significance ($P = 0.067$) to enter the equation. This suggests that it was its joint relationship with SFA and PUFA that affected the change in LDL cholesterol rather than any independent effect it might have had.

HDL cholesterol

The best-fitting model for change in HDL cholesterol included changes in SFA and total fat. The predictive model for HDL cholesterol explained 41% of the variance associated with dietary change. The model indicates that for every 1% change in total energy from SFA, a change in HDL cholesterol of 7.4 mM (0.3 mg dl⁻¹) was predicted. A 1% change in energy from total fat will produce a 5.0 mM (0.2 mg dl⁻¹) change in HDL cholesterol.

Triacylglycerol

The prediction model for triacylglycerol presented in Table 2.1 accounts for 36% of the variance associated with modifications in diet. Changes in dietary cholesterol, PUFA and total fat as a percentage of total calories entered the prediction equation. It is of interest that in this model, change in total fat enters with a negative coefficient, i.e. a decrease in total fat in the diet will lead to an increase in triacylglycerol, other things being equal. This finding is consistent with previous observations of the effects of substituting simple carbohydrate for fat in isoenergetic diets.

Effects of other factors

After the prediction models were identified, sensitivity analyses were performed to assess the effects of subject and design characteristics, such as dietary variable interactions, initial dietary and serum lipid levels and treatment duration. These analyses do not assess the independent effects of these factors but rather their influence on the effects of dietary change on serum lipid levels.

The only dietary interaction term that added predictive power to the models was PUFA×FAT (total fat as a percentage of total energy), which increased the multiple regression coefficient by 5% in the triacylglycerol model. This indicates that the effect of changes in total fat is a linear function of changes in PUFA. Specifically, a decrease in total fat energy will increase triacylglycerol only if the change in PUFA is less than 9.4% of total energy. For positive changes in PUFA of more than 9.4% of total energy, a decrease in fat will result in a reduction in triacylglycerol.

Interactions of initial dietary intake variables and initial serum lipid concentrations with dietary changes did not add substantially to the prediction models, i.e. pre-treatment diet levels and pre-treatment serum lipid concentrations did not have a substantial independent effect on post-dietary treatment response.

Of the other subject and study design characteristics considered, only the location of subjects had a significant interaction with PUFA dietary change. Specifically, the results indicated that the effects of changes in PUFA intake for subjects confined to hospitals or metabolic wards were significantly less than those for free-living subjects.

Comparison of Prediction Models

Other models have been published that allow the prediction of changes in serum total cholesterol from changes in diet. Most notable are those of Keys (Keys *et al.*, 1957; Keys and Paulin, 1966) and Hegsted (Hegsted *et al.*, 1965, 1993; Hegsted, 1986). A comparison of these and other models is given in Table 2.2. The first six equations listed in Table 2.2 are multivariate models predicting a change in serum total cholesterol from changes in dietary fat and cholesterol. All of these models include terms for change in both SFA and PUFA, and their regression coefficients are quite similar, all falling within the range of overlapping confidence intervals. Four of the models also include linear terms for change in dietary cholesterol, which are consistent, with one exception.

Specifically, the data of Hegsted *et al.* (1965) showed a comparatively high coefficient for dietary cholesterol, whereas the cholesterol coefficients estimated in metabolic ward (Hegsted *et al.*, 1993) and free-living models were more similar to those of Howell *et al.* (1997). It is noteworthy that in all published models, blood lipid reductions by dietary changes are mediated

Table 2.2.   Prediction equations for diet-mediated change in serum total cholesterol concentrations.

Source[a]	Equation[b]
Keys *et al.* (1957)	2.74 ΔSFA – 1.31 ΔPUFA
Hegsted *et al.* (1965)	2.16 ΔSFA – 1.65 ΔPUFA + 0.677 ΔCholesterol
Keys and Parlin (1966)	2.6 ΔSFA – 1.3 ΔPUFA + 0.95 $(Cholesterol_2^{1/2} - Cholesterol_1^{1/2})$
Hegsted *et al.* (1993)	
Metabolic ward	2.10 ΔSFA – 1.16 ΔPUFA + 0.670 ΔCholesterol
Free-living	2.75 ΔSFA – 1.03 ΔPUFA + 0.400 ΔCholesterol
Howell *et al.* (1997)	1.92 ΔSFA – 0.90 ΔPUFA + 0.022 ΔCholesterol
Hegsted (1986)	
Exponential	$93.27 - 93.07\ e^{-0.000484\ \Delta Cholesterol}$
Linear	0.039 ΔCholesterol
McNamara (1990)	0.023 ΔCholesterol
Hopkins (1992)[c]	$47.2\ e^{-0.00384\ Cholesterol_i} \cdot (1 - e^{-0.00136\ \Delta Cholesterol})$

SFA, saturated fatty acids; PUFA, polyunsaturated fatty acids.
[a] When there were multiple models, the particular equation is identified.
[b] The coefficients in the equations have been re-scaled for application to the measurement units used in this study (mg dl^{-1} for serum lipids, % of total energy for dietary fats and mg dl^{-1} for dietary cholesterol).
[c] $Cholesterol_i$, initial serum cholesterol level.

primarily by reductions in SFA. Increases in PUFA account for about one-half of the effect of SFA. Compared with these influences, the contribution of dietary cholesterol manipulation to change in serum lipids is minimal.

Predicted Serum Lipid Response to Dietary Guidelines

A useful application of any serum lipid response model is to determine the extent to which compliance with population-based dietary guidelines can be expected to influence population-wide serum lipid levels. Using the models of Howell *et al.* (Table 2.1) and comparing the NCEP Step I and II dietary recommendations (Expert Panel, 1993) with the average American diet (AAD) (DHHS, 1986), an estimate of the expected change in serum lipid levels can be determined. As presented in Table 2.3, the serum total cholesterol model predicts that changing from the AAD to the NCEP Step I and Step II diets would reduce serum total cholesterol levels by an average of 4.2 and 7.6%, respectively (assuming an initial serum cholesterol level of 240 mg dl^{-1}).

The predicted reductions in LDL cholesterol levels are 4.5 and 7.7%, respectively (assuming an initial LDL level of 160 mg dl^{-1}). HDL cholesterol levels would be expected to fall by an average 6 and 9%, respectively (assuming an initial HDL cholesterol level of 35 mg dl^{-1}). This predicted decrease in HDL cholesterol levels is particularly important in the management of post-menopausal women at risk of heart disease. Low HDL cholesterol levels have been associated with a higher risk in women than in men.

Table 2.3.   Predicted shifts in serum total and LDL cholesterol changing from the AAD to the NCEP Step I and Step II diets.

	AAD[a]	NCEP I[b]	NCEP II[b]	ΔADD to NCEP I	ΔADD to NCEP II
Cholesterol (mg dl⁻¹)	385	300	200	−85.0	−185.0
Total fat (% kcal)	37	30	30	−7.0	−7.0
SFA (% kcal)	13	10	7	−3.0	−6.0
PUFA (% kcal)	7	10	10	3.0	3.0
MUFA (% kcal)	17	10	13	−7.0	−4.0
Predicted serum cholesterol Δ (mg dl⁻¹)[c]				−10.2	−18.3
Predicted LDL Δ (mg dl⁻¹)[c]				−6.9	−12.3
Predicted HDL Δ (mg dl⁻¹)[c]				−2.2	−3.1

AAD, average American diet; NCEP, National Cholesterol Education Program; Δ, change; SFA, saturated fatty acids; PUFA, polyunsaturated fatty acids; MUFA, monounsaturated fatty acids; LDL, low-density lipoprotein; HDL, high-density lipoprotein.
[a]National Health and Nutrition Examination Survey data.
[b]NCEP Adult Treatment Panel Step I and Step II Diet Guidelines.
[c]Based on equations to estimate changes in serum total, LDL and HDL cholesterol levels resulting from modifications in dietary fat and cholesterol (Howell *et al.*, 1997):

$$\Delta \text{Serum total cholesterol (mg dl}^{-1}) = 1.918\ \Delta SFA - 0.900\ \Delta PUFA + 0.022\ \Delta Cholesterol$$
$$\Delta LDL\ (\text{mg dl}^{-1}) = 1.808\ \Delta SFA - 0.495\ \Delta PUFA$$
$$\Delta HDL\ (\text{mg dl}^{-1}) = 0.287\ \Delta SFA + 0.192\ \Delta FAT.$$

Influence of Other Dietary Components

The dietary determinants of serum lipid levels identified in the published prediction models focus on the percentage of total energy from total fat, SFA, PUFA and the amount of dietary cholesterol. Findings from recent research, however, indicate that alternative dietary factors, such as specific fatty acids, antioxidants and fibre, may explain some of the variance in serum lipid response unaccounted for by changes in the traditional dietary components.

Linoleic and α-linolenic fatty acids

PUFAs are universally considered antiatherogenic in that dietary increases in these fatty acids are associated with decreases in serum lipids. The effect of PUFA on thrombogenicity, i.e. platelet aggregation potential, is less clearly defined and, in this regard, it is important to distinguish between the major PUFA classes: the ω-6 PUFA, whose parent member is linoleic acid (18 : 2*n*-6); and the ω-3 PUFA, whose parent member is α-linolenic acid (18 : 3*n*-3). Figure 2.1 summarizes the comparative effects of these PUFAs on eicosanoid metabolism and thrombogenicity. The interest in ω-3 fatty acids centres on their competitive inhibition of the production of the thrombogenic eicosanoid thromboxane A from the 2-series (TXA₂) (Lagarde, 1990). TXA₂ is derived from arachidonic acid, the chief metabolite of linoleic acid. Dietary increases in ω-3 fatty acids, principally α-linolenic acid, inhibit TXA₂ production, whereas the

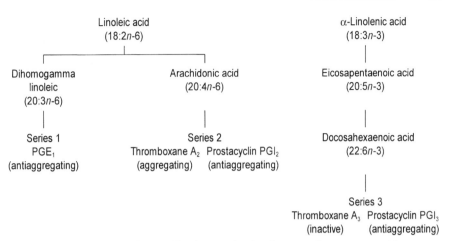

Fig. 2.1.   Comparative effects of linoleic and α-linolenic acids on eicosanoid metabolism.

availability of the prostanoid PGI_3, a potent platelet antiaggregator, increases. PGI_3 is derived from eicosapentaenoic (EPA) and docosahexaenoic (DHA) acids, metabolites of α-linolenic acid. By competing for desaturation and elongation, increases in dietary α-linolenic acid relative to linoleic acid may decrease thrombogenicity and consequently the risk of heart disease.

Monounsaturated fatty acids

Oleic acid is the primary *cis*-MUFA in the diet. Olive oil, canola oil and high-oleic forms of sunflower and safflower oils are the main dietary sources. Most studies report that oleic acid is a neutral atherogenic factor, neither raising nor lowering serum lipids (Kris-Etherton and Yu, 1997). The antithrombogenic activity of *cis*-MUFA has been studied much less than that of PUFA. In some animal models, MUFA-rich diets have been shown to inhibit platelet aggregation as well as to generate LDL particles resistant to oxidation (Sirtori *et al.*, 1992). A potential disadvantage of a diet very high in oleic acid (20–25% of total energy) is an increase in total calorie intake, resulting in weight gain. Replacement of SFA with MUFA would avoid a net increase in total energy intake.

Another category of MUFA is the *trans*-isomers. The most common *trans*-isomer is elaidic acid. There are important differences in the *cis*- and *trans*-MUFAs. *Trans*-MUFAs are released by the hydrogenation of PUFA vegetable oils to produce margarines and shortenings used in many processed foods. Primarily from these sources, *trans*-MUFAs constitute about 3% of total energy in the AAD. The atherogenic potential of *trans*-MUFA is similar to that of SFA although, when substituted for the short chain SFAs, *trans*-MUFA reduces both LDL and HDL cholesterol levels (Judd *et al.*, 1994). The most consistent finding is that when compared with either SFA or PUFA, *trans*-MUFA appreciably lowers HDL cholesterol (Zock and Katan, 1992).

Complex carbohydrates

In contrast to the lipid-lowering effect of *cis*-MUFA, replacement of SFA with starches results in an increase in triacylglycerol and VLDL concentrations, a fall in HDL levels and minimal change in LDL cholesterol (Grundy, 1986). This effect is of particular concern in overweight individuals who may already have high triacylglycerol levels and low HDL levels. Reduction in total energy intake is the goal, rather than a low-fat, high-carbohydrate diet.

The non-absorbable complex carbohydrates are categorized as either water-soluble or insoluble dietary fibres. Water-soluble dietary fibre has been shown to reduce LDL cholesterol levels in hypercholesterolaemic men (Anderson *et al.*, 1990). This effect, however, was demonstrated at very high intakes of oat bran fibre (15–30 g day^{-1}), which limits its application to recommendations for the general population.

Fruit, vegetables and some cereals are the primary dietary sources of water-insoluble fibre. The effect of these foods on reducing coronary heart disease risk is considered to be independent of their influence on serum lipids. Recent evidence indicates that there may be an interaction effect between fibre intake and SFA. Specifically, increased fibre intake may moderate the atherogenicity of SFA intake (Ascherio *et al.*, 1996).

Antioxidants

The protective effect of a diet rich in fruit and vegetables may also be related to its increased vitamin and flavonoid antioxidant composition. Considerable evidence indicates that free radical oxidation of LDL particles plays an important role in atherogenesis. Vitamins E and C, the carotenoids and the flavonoids have been identified as free radical scavengers and, consequently, as potential mediators of LDL oxidation. In addition, results of clinical trials suggest that vitamin E reduces platelet aggregation and, thus, is antithrombogenic (Salonen, 1989). The protective effects of the dietary antioxidants on heart disease risk also appear to be independent of their effects on serum lipids. This characteristic may help to explain some of the anomalies in the epidemiologic data on heart disease incidence. For example, the Mediterranean populations have high intakes of fruit and vegetables, which correspond to relatively lower incidences of heart disease. In contrast, northern European populations consume less fruit and vegetables and have higher incidences of heart disease. These population differences in heart disease incidence correlate poorly with serum lipid levels (Ulbricht and Southgate, 1991).

Conclusions

One clear conclusion from this review is that coronary artery disease risk cannot be attributed to any single dietary component. Given the complex and interactive nature of the effects of diverse dietary factors on both serum lipids and heart disease risk, a new approach to nutrition counselling is warranted. Nutrition guidelines for the US population remain focused on reducing total fat, SFAs and dietary cholesterol, while increasing PUFAs in the diet. This traditional approach may be too simplistic, especially with regard to dietary cholesterol. Alternative diet–lipid hypotheses merit consideration. More emphasis on the antithrombogenic ω-3 fatty acids, dietary fibre and the dietary antioxidants, along with weight control and regular physical activity, is needed. Less emphasis on single dietary components such as cholesterol and its primary food source, eggs, is the informed approach.

References

Anderson, J.W., Spencer, D.B., Hamilton, C.C., Smith, S.F., Tietyen, J., Bryant, C.A. and Oeltgen, P. (1990) Oat-bran cereal lowers serum total and LDL cholesterol in hypercholesterolemic men. *American Journal of Clinical Nutrition* 52, 495–499.

Ascherio, A., Rimm, E.B., Giovannucci, E.L., Spiegelman, D., Stampfer, M. and Willett, W.C. (1996) Dietary fat and risk of coronary heart disease in men: cohort follow up study in the United States. *British Medical Journal* 313, 84–90.

Department of Health and Human Services, US Department of Agriculture (1986) Nutrition monitoring in the United States – a progress report from the Joint Nutrition Monitoring Evaluation Committee. Hyattsville, MD. National Center for Health Statistics, 1986. [DHHS publication no. (PHS) 86–1255.]

Expert Panel on Detection, Evaluation, and Treatment of High Blood Cholesterol in Adults (1993) Summary of the second report of the National Cholesterol Education Program (NCEP) Expert Panel on Detection, Evaluation, and Treatment of High Blood Cholesterol in Adults (Adult Treatment Panel II). *Journal of the American Medical Association* 269, 3015–3023.

Grundy, S.M. (1986) Comparison of monounsaturated fatty acids and carbohydrates for lowering plasma cholesterol. *New England Journal of Medicine* 314, 745–748.

Hegsted, D.M. (1986) Serum-cholesterol response to dietary cholesterol: a re-evaluation. *American Journal of Clinical Nutrition* 44, 299–305.

Hegsted, D.M., McGandy, R.B., Myers, M.L. and Stare, F.J. (1965) Quantitative effects of dietary fat on serum cholesterol in man. *American Journal of Clinical Nutrition* 17, 281–295.

Hegsted, D.M., Ausman, L.M., Johnson, J.A. and Dallal, G.E. (1993) Dietary fat and serum lipids: an evaluation of the experimental data. *American Journal of Clinical Nutrition* 57, 875–883.

Hopkins, P.N. (1992) Effects of dietary cholesterol on serum cholesterol: a meta-analysis and review. *American Journal of Clinical Nutrition* 55, 1060–1070.

Howell, W.H., McNamara, D.J., Tosca, M.A., Smith, B.T. and Gaines, J.A. (1997) Plasma lipid and lipoprotein responses to dietary fat and cholesterol: a meta-analysis. *American Journal of Clinical Nutrition* 65, 1747–1764.

Judd, J.T., Clevidence, B.A., Muesing, R.A., Wittes, J., Sunkin, M.E. and Podczasy, J.J. (1994) Dietary *trans* fatty acids: effects on plasma lipids and lipoproteins of healthy men and women. *American Journal of Clinical Nutrition* 59, 861–868.

Keys, A. and Parlin, R.W. (1966) Serum cholesterol response to changes in dietary lipids. *American Journal of Clinical Nutrition* 19, 175–181.

Keys, A., Anderson, J.T. and Grande, F. (1957) Prediction of serum-cholesterol responses of man to changes in the diet. *Lancet* ii, 959–966.

Kris-Etherton, P.M. and Yu, S. (1997) Individual fatty acid effects on plasma lipids and lipoproteins: human studies. *American Journal of Clinical Nutrition* 65 (5 Suppl.), 1628S–1644S.

Lagarde, M. (1990) Metabolism of *n*-3/*n*-6 fatty acids in blood and vascular cells. *Biochemical Society Transactions* 18, 770–772.

McNamara, D.J. (1990) Relationship between blood and dietary cholesterol. *Advances in Meat Research: Meat and Health* 6, 63–87.

Salonen, J.T. (1989) Antioxidants and platelets. *Annals of Medicine* 21, 59–62.

Sirtori, C.R., Gatti, E., Tremoli, E., Galli, C., Gianfranceschi, G., Franceschini, G., Colli, S., Maderna, P., Marangoni, F., Perego, P. and Stragliotto, E. (1992) Olive oil, corn oil and *n*-3 fatty acids differently affect lipids, lipoproteins, platelets, and superoxide formation in type II hypercholesterolemia. *American Journal of Clinical Nutrition* 56, 113–122.

Ulbricht, T.L.V. and Southgate, D.A.T. (1991) Coronary heart disease: seven dietary factors. *Lancet* 338, 985–992.

Zock, P.L. and Katan, M.B. (1992) Hydrogenation alternatives: effects of *trans* fatty acids and stearic acid versus linoleic acid on serum lipids and lipoproteins in humans. *Journal of Lipid Research* 33, 399–410.

Antiarrhythmic Effects of *n*-3 Polyunsaturated Fatty Acids

A. Leaf[1], J.X. Kang[1] and Y.-F. Xiao[2]

[1]*Department of Medicine, Massachusetts General Hospital Boston, Maryland, USA;* [2]*Beth Israel Deaconess Medical Center and Harvard Medical School, Boston, Maryland, USA*

It has been shown in animals, and probably in humans, that *n*-3 polyunsaturated fatty acids (PUFAs) are antiarrhythmic. We report recent studies on the cardiac antiarrhythmic actions of *n*-3 PUFAs. These PUFAs have been reported to prevent cardiac ischaemia-induced fatal ventricular arrhythmias in several animal species, and we have studied the mechanism of their antiarrhythmic effects. The PUFAs stabilize the electrical activity of isolated cardiac myocytes by inhibiting sarcolemmal ion channels, so that a stronger electrical stimulus is required to elicit an action potential and the relative refractory period (RRP) is markedly prolonged. The RRP is the time taken following one action potential before the heart cell can respond again to another stimulus with an action potential. These appear at present to be the probable major antiarrhythmic actions of the PUFAs. These actions in turn result from potent modulating effects on the ionic membrane currents, which constitute the signalling mechanism of all excitable tissues.

Introduction

Earlier, Gudbjarnason and Hallgrimsson (1975) and Murnaghan (1981) had suggested that unsaturated fatty acids may have antiarrhythmic effects. Based on this suggestion, McLennan *et al.* (McLennan, 1993; McLennan *et al.*, 1988) reported that feeding rats a diet with the fat containing largely saturated or monounsaturated fatty acids (MUFAs) resulted in a high incidence of irreversible ventricular fibrillation when their coronary arteries were subsequently ligated experimentally. When vegetable oils were the major source of the dietary fat, there was a reduction in arrhythmic mortality by some 70%. With tuna fish oil, however, they reported irreversible ventricular arrhythmias to be completely prevented with or without reflow to the ischaemic myocardium. They confirmed their findings in marmosets (McLennan *et al.*, 1992). These striking observations led us to pursue the possible mechanism(s) for such an antiarrhythmic action of the fish oil.

Results of Animal Feeding Trials

First, we wanted to see if we could confirm their findings. Together with Professor George E. Billman, The Ohio State University School of Medicine, Columbus, Ohio, we studied a reliable canine model of sudden cardiac death. Ligating the left main coronary artery produced a surgically induced myocardial infarction, and an inflatable cuff was placed around the left circumflex artery. The dogs were allowed about a month to recover from the surgery and their myocardial infarction, during which they were trained to run on a treadmill. The animals were then screened for susceptibility to a fatal ventricular arrhythmia (VF) when the left circumflex artery was occluded while they were running on a treadmill. Some 60% of animals were found to be susceptible, and these were the dogs studied. Once an animal is 'susceptible', it remains susceptible on further exercise–ischaemia trials. In ten of the 13 such dogs, an emulsion of a concentrate of fish oil free fatty acids (polyunsaturated fatty acids; PUFAs) infused intravenously just prior to the exercise–ischaemia test significantly ($P < 0.005$) prevented the fatal VF (Billman *et al.*, 1997). In the control exercise–ischaemia tests 1 week prior to the test and 1 week following the tests with the infusion of the PUFAs, all animals promptly developed fatal ventricular arrhythmias requiring prompt defibrillation to save the dogs.

In additional studies, we found that pure eicosapentaenoic acid (C20 : 5*n*-3, EPA), docosahexaenoic acid (C22 : 6*n*-3, DHA) or α-linolenic acid (C18 : 3*n*-3, LNA) are apparently equally antiarrhythmic in this dog preparation (G.E. Billman *et al.*, personal communication). We purposely infused the *n*-3 fatty acids rather than fed the dogs fish oil to be certain exactly what ingredient(s) of the fish oil prevented the fatal VF. In dietary studies, invariably several things must change and confound the interpretation; however, when the free fatty acids are infused intravenously just prior to producing the ischaemia and the fatal VF is prevented, then we think that the effect results from what has just been infused.

Having thus confirmed directly the findings of the earlier workers, we set out to determine the mechanism by which the *n*-3 PUFAs produced their antiarrhythmic effect. To have a simple, available model to study in which we could visualize the production of arrhythmias and possible prevention of the arrhythmias by the PUFAs, we studied cultured neonatal rat cardiac myocytes (Kang and Leaf, 1994). Hearts were quickly removed from 1- to 2-day-old decapitated rat pups. The cardiac cells were separated with trypsin digestion and the cells were plated on microscope coverslips. By the second day of culture, we saw clumps of growing myocytes of a few to several hundred cells. Each group of cells was contracting spontaneously, rhythmically and synchronously. With a microscope, a video camera and an edge monitor, we could focus on a single myocyte in a clump of cells and see and record the rate and amplitude of contractions. With this *in vitro* model, we produced arrhythmias with a number of chemicals known to produce fatal VF in humans. Other agents tested were elevated extracellular $[Ca^{2+}]$, toxic levels of the cardiac glycoside ouabain (Kang and Leaf 1994), and excessive β-adrenergic agonist isoproterenol (Kang and Leaf, 1995a), lysophosphatidyl-choline, acyl carnitine and even the calcium inophore A23187 (Kang and Leaf, 1996a). With each agent a tachyrhythmia was induced.

If the PUFAs were added to the fluid perfusing the isolated myocytes before the arrhythmogenic toxins were administered, they would in every instance prevent the expected arrhythmia. If the toxin first induced the arrhythmia and the PUFAs were then added to the superfusate in the continued presence of the toxin, within a few minutes the arrhythmia would be terminated and the cells would commence beating regularly again. Then, in the continued presence of the toxin, the PUFA can be extracted from the cells with delipidated bovine serum albumin (BSA) and the arrhythmia promptly resumes. These results indicated that it was only the free PUFAs partitioning into the membrane phospholipids that prevented the arrhythmias. If the fatty acids had been covalently bound to any constituent in the membrane, they would not have been extracted from the cell membrane by the fatty-acid-free albumin. When the ethyl ester or the triglyceride of the PUFAs were tested, they were not antiarrhythmic in this model; the free carboxylic acid group is essential for this antiarrhythmic action.

We then tested which PUFAs were antiarrhythmic (Kang and Leaf, 1994). Both the *n*-3 and *n*-6 classes of PUFAs are antiarrhythmic, but arachidonic acid (C20:4*n*-6, AA) was anomalous. Cyclooxygenase metabolites of AA (except prostacyclin I_2) cause arrhythmias (Li *et al.*, 1997). For this reason, we have recommended that only the *n*-3 PUFAs should be tested in clinical trials as antiarrhythmic agents.

The structural requirements for an antiarrhythmic compound that acts in the manner of these PUFAs are a long acyl or hydrocarbon chain with two or more C=C unsaturated bonds and a free carboxyl group at one end. With this guideline, we found all-*trans*-retinoic acid also to be specifically anti-arrhythmic (Kang and Leaf, 1995b).

Electrostabilizing Effects on Heart Cells

The antiarrhythmic action of the PUFAs results from their effects on the electrophysiology of cardiac myocytes (Kang *et al.*, 1995). They cause slight hyperpolarization of the resting or diastolic membrane potential and an increase in the threshold voltage for the opening of the Na^+ channel. This results in an increased depolarizing stimulus of about 50% required to induce an action potential. In addition, the relative refractory period of the cardiac cycle is prolonged by around threefold. These two effects on every myocyte in the heart could account for the increased electrical stability and resistance of the heart to lethal arrhythmias.

A simple demonstration of this electrical stabilizing effect by the *n*-3 fatty acids on every individual heart cell *in vitro* was made in the absence of humoral or neural effects. We placed two small platinum electrodes on opposite sides of the coverslip on which perfused cultured neonatal rat cardiac myocytes were beating regularly. The cells were observed with a video recorder and displayed on a monitor screen. With an edge detector, we could focus on one cell in a clump of cells and record the rate and amplitude of its contractions, as shown in Fig. 3.1. The two platinum electrodes were connected to an external voltage source so that we could stimulate the cells with the resulting external electric field. It was easy to double the beating rate with electrical current pulses imposed from the external electrical field. When the external current source was turned off, the cells resumed their previous beating rate. The second line of the continuous tracing was conducted. After addition of EPA (15 µM) to the superfusate of the same cell, the beating rate became slower but, in the presence of the *n*-3 PUFA, the cell paid no attention

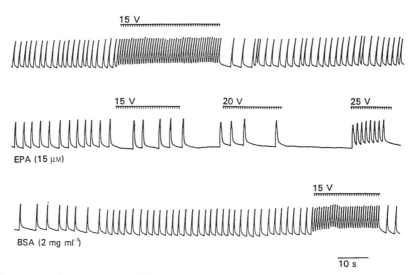

Fig. 3.1. A demonstration of the direct electrical stabilizing effect of the *n*-3 fatty acids on each heart cell *in vitro* in the absence of humoral or neural influences. Two platinum electrodes connected to a voltage source were placed across the microscope coverslip on which cultured heart cells were beating regularly while being perfused in a chamber. The top tracing shows the effect on the beating rate of the single heart cell in a clump of cultured cells adherent to the microscope coverslip when the external field was turned on and current impulses emitted from the electrodes to stimulate the cultured cells. At 15 V applied to the external field, the cells doubled their beating rate in response to the stimuli. When the external current source was turned off, the cells resumed their previous beating rate. The second line of the continuous tracing shows that after addition of EPA (15 µM) to the superfusate of the same cell, the beating rate became slower but, in the presence of the *n*-3 PUFA, the cell paid no attention to the stimuli from the external electrical field of 15 or 20 V, and at 25 V the myocyte began to respond to the external stimuli but only to every third stimulus. The third line of the continuous tracing is again of the same cell but after delipidated bovine serum albumin (BSA) had been added to the superfusate to extract all the free fatty acids from the cultured heart cells. With this, the beating rate of the myocytes returned to the control rate and again the cells responded to the external electrical stimuli delivered at 15 V (Kang and Leaf, 1996a).

to the stimuli from the external electrical field of 15 or 20 V. Then at 25 V, the myocyte began to respond to the external stimuli but only to every third stimulus. The third line of the continuous tracing was again of the same cell but after delipidated BSA had been added to the superfusate. Serum albumin is the normal vehicle for transporting hydrophobic fatty acids through the aqueous medium of body fluids. It has several binding sites per molecule, and the first three binding sites have very high affinity for binding the free fatty acids so they can reverse the normal traffic of fatty acids between the albumin and the phospholipid cell membranes and extract the fatty acids from the heart cells. With this, the beating rate of the myocytes returned to the control rate and again the cells responded to the external electrical stimuli delivered at 15 V (Kang and Leaf, 1996a).

These electrical stabilizing effects in turn result from an action of the PUFAs modulating the conductance of ion channels in the plasma membranes of the heart cells. By whole-cell voltage clamp measurements, we have found that the PUFAs inhibit the voltage-dependent Na$^+$, i.e. I_{Na} (Xiao *et al.*, 1995), K$^+$ which is the transient outward current, I_{to}, and the delayed rectifier current, I_K, but not the inward rectifying current, I_{K1} (Y.-F. Xiao *et al.*, unpublished results), as well as the L-type Ca^{2+} current, $I_{Ca,L}$, (Xiao *et al.*, 1997). In the case of the Na$^+$ channels, we have shown that only the antiarrhythmic PUFAs displace [^{3}H]batrachotoxinin-20-α-benzoate bound to the sodium channel pore protein non-competitively (Kang and Leaf, 1996b). This is similar to our finding that PUFAs non-competitively displaced [^{3}H]nitrendipine (a specific L-type calcium channel antagonist) from its binding site at the external pore of the calcium channel protein (Hallaq *et al.*, 1992). Because the displacement in each case, though specific, was non-competitive, we cannot resolve the important question of whether the PUFAs bind specifically and primarily to ion channel proteins directly or interact primarily with the phospholipid of the cell membranes to change the conformation of transmembrane protein channels allosterically.

In the cultured neonatal rat heart cells, the PUFAs were shown to shift the steady-state potential for inactivation of the Na$^+$ channels to more hyperpolarized potentials. This means that it requires a more negative resting membrane potential to prepare the cell to be responsive to another normal depolarizing stimulus and initiate another action potential (Xiao *et al.*, 1995). A recent study of the effects of the PUFAs on the Na$^+$ currents in α-subunits of the human myocardial Na$^+$ channel expressed in stable human embryonic kidney cells (Xiao *et al.*, 1998) showed no effect on the activated opening of the Na$^+$ channel. The only effect seen was a large shift in the hyperpolarization of the membrane potential necessary to close the Na$^+$ channel. Attaining a closed resting, but activatable state is required before the channel is again susceptible to initiation of a new action potential. This makes the I_{Na} voltage-dependent in the presence of the PUFAs, as we have found (Xiao *et al.*, 1995, 1998). Myocytes apparently must maintain their normal resting membrane potentials in order to avoid the inhibitory actions of the PUFAs on I_{Na}.

These effects, primarily on inhibition of the Na$^+$ and Ca^{2+} currents, we now think, may account for the potent antiarrhythmic effects of these PUFAs.

In the ischaemic myocardium, myocytes become slightly depolarized due to functional reduction of the Na, K-ATPase sodium pump and the accumulation of potassium in the interstitial fluid. These cells then are 'hyperexcitable' and subject to induction of premature action potentials and arrhythmias because they may be activated by any minimal stray depolarizing stimuli. Their resting membrane potential is more positive and closer to the threshold for the gating of the I_{Na} so that a smaller than normal depolarizing current may elicit a premature action potential and initiate an arrhythmia. Because they have a reduced resting membrane potential, it is just these ischaemic 'hyperexcitable' myocytes that are eliminated quickly from the further effects of the PUFAs. After their first activation, the necessity for a more negative resting potential in order to revert the channels to an activatable resting state makes the channel unresponsive and eliminates these partially depolarized myocytes as arrhythmogenic risks.

The potent inhibitory action of the PUFAs on L-type Ca^{2+} currents, $I_{Ca,L}$ (Xiao *et al.*, 1997), complements this action on I_{Na}. Significant inhibition of $I_{Ca,L}$ is observed at 20 nM Ca^{2+} in the medium bathing the cultured rat myocytes. This effect prevents triggered arrhythmias induced by overload of cytosolic Ca^{2+} and increased cytosolic Ca^{2+} fluctuations. Most arrhythmogenic cardiotoxins may induce fatal ventricular tachyrhythmia (VT) or VF by triggered after-potentials from excessive cytosolic Ca^{2+} fluctuations which are prevented by the PUFAs, e.g. cardiac glycosides, lysophosphatidylcholine, excessive catecholamines, thromboxane A_2, etc.

At present, we cannot say whether the PUFAs will prevent lethal arrhythmias in patients, but two secondary prevention trials, which unexpectedly showed prevention of ischaemia-induced sudden cardiac death, are encouraging. One dietary study (de Logeril *et al.*, 1994) was a prospective, randomized, single-blind, secondary prevention trial which compared the effect of a Mediterranean α-linolenic acid (C18:3*n*-3, LNA)-rich diet with the usual post-infarct prudent diet. The subjects on the more fat-restricted experimental diet receiving the α-linolenic acid (C18:3*n*-3, LNA) showed a remarkable reduction in mortality and morbidity of some 70%, including prevention of sudden death (Fig. 3.2). Because of other dietary changes, the possibility of confounding effects cannot be eliminated in this study. The other study (Burr *et al.*, 1989) was also a randomized, prospective, secondary prevention trial in which advice to eat oily fish two or three times weekly was compared with no such advice. This study did not record arrhythmic deaths. However, it found no reduction in new events but a 29% reduction in mortality, suggesting a reduction in sudden deaths which comprise 50–60% of the acute mortality from heart attacks (American Heart Association, 1997). In both studies the survival curves showed a very early beneficial separation of the experimental versus control groups (Fig. 3.3), quite unlike the 2 years required in the cholesterol-lowering trial (Lipids Research Council Program, 1984) before the lower mortality was significant, and no reductions in cholesterol concentrations occurred. A recent case–control study (Siscovick *et al.*, 1995) reported an inverse relationship between fish consumption and sudden cardiac death, suggesting an antiarrhythmic effect from ingestion of fish.

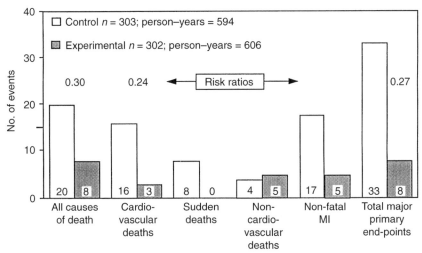

Fig. 3.2. The Mediterranean α-linolenic acid-rich diet in the secondary prevention of coronary heart disease (de Lorgeril *et al.*, 1994). The 605 patients who had just had a heart attack and, therefore, were at high risk of a second heart attack were randomized to either a control 'prudent diet' or an experimental diet in which saturated fats were reduced and olive oil and a soft margarine made from canola oil (10% α-linolenic acid) were added. Increased fruit and vegetables were encouraged in the diet. The study was stopped at a mean folllow-up time of 27 months because of the striking beneficial outcomes in the experimental group. The risk ratios for the experimental versus the control group show a 70% reduction of all causes of death, which was accounted for by the reduction in cardiovascular deaths. Of interest in the context of our hypothesis is the complete suppression of sudden death in the experimental group. These benefits occurred without any changes in serum cholesterol levels. Prepared with permission of the authors (de Lorgeril *et al.*, 1994).

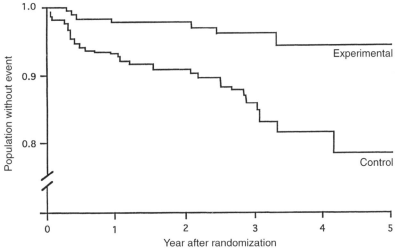

Fig. 3.3. Survival curves of combined cardiac deaths and non-fatal heart attacks from the study shown in Fig. 3.2 (de Lorgeril *et al.*, 1994). Note the very early separation of the experimental and control survival curves. This early response is consistent with the rapidity of the electrophysiological effects of the PUFAs on the cardiac ion channels.

Conclusion

It is apparent that there exists a basic control of cardiac function by common dietary fatty acids, which has been largely overlooked. The *n*-3 PUFAs have been part of the human diet for some 2–4 million years (Leaf and Weber, 1987) and are safe. With some 250,000 sudden cardiac deaths annually largely due to VF in the USA alone, there may be a potential large public health benefit from the practical application of this recent understanding. Carefully planned and executed clinical trials are now needed to determine the antiarrhythmic effectiveness of these fatty acids in humans at high risk of fatal arrhythmias.

Acknowledgements

Studies from the authors' laboratory have been supported in part by research grant DK38165 from the NIDDK of the National Institutes of Health of the US Public Health Service, the American Heart Association, Ohio affiliate (GEB) and American Heart Association Grant-In-Aid (Y-FX).

References

American Heart Association (1997) *Heart and Stroke Facts: Statistical Supplement.* American Heart Association, Dallas, Texas, USA.

Billman, G.E., Kang, J.X. and Leaf, A. (1997) Prevention of ischemia-induced cardiac sudden death by *n*-3 polyunsaturated fatty acids. *Lipids* 32, 1161–1168.

Burr, M.L., Gilbert, J.F., Holliday, R.M., Elwood, P.C., Fehily, A.M., Rogers, S., Sweetnam, P.M. and Deadman, N.M. (1989) Effects of changes in fat, fish, and fibre intakes on death and myocardial reinfarction: diet and reinfarction trial (DART). *Lancet* 334, 757–761.

de Lorgeril, M., Renaud, S., Mamelle, N., Salen, P., Martin, J.L., Monjaud, J.G., Guidollet, J., Touboul, P. and Delaye, J. (1994) Mediterranean alpha-linolenic acid-rich diet in secondary prevention of coronary heart disease. *Lancet* 343, 1454–1459.

Gudbjarnason, S. and Hallgrimsson, J. (1975) The role of myocardial membrane lipids in the development of cardiac necrosis. *Acta Medica Scandinavic* 587 (Suppl.), 17–26.

Hallaq, H., Smith, T.W. and Leaf, A. (1992) Modulation of dihydropyridine-sensitive calcium channels of heart cells by fish oil fatty acids. *Proceedings of the National Academy of Sciences of the United States of America* 89, 1760–1764.

Kang, J.X. and Leaf, A. (1994) Effects of long-chain polyunsaturated fatty acids on the contraction of neonatal rat cardiac myocytes. *Proceedings of the National Academy of Sciences of the United States of America* 91, 9886–9890.

Kang, J.X. and Leaf, A. (1995a) Prevention and termination of the β-adrenergic agonist-induced arrhythmias by free polyunsaturated fatty acids in neonatal rat cardiac myocytes. *Biochemical and Biophysical Research Communications* 208, 629–636.

Kang, J.X. and Leaf, A. (1995b) Protective effect of all-*trans*-retinoic acid against cardiac arrhythmias induced by isoproterenol, lysophosphatidylcholine or ischemia and reperfusion. *Journal of Cardiovascular Pharmacology* 297, 87–106.

Kang, J.X. and Leaf, A. (1996a) Prevention and termination of arrhythmias induced by lysophosphatidyl choline and acylcarnitine in neonatal rat cardiac myocytes by free omega-3 polyunsaturated fatty acids. *European Journal of Pharmacology* 297, 97–106.

Kang, J.X. and Leaf, A. (1996b) Evidence that free polyunsaturated fatty acids modify Na⁺ channels by directly binding to the channel proteins. *Proceedings of the National Academy of Sciences of the United States of America* 93, 3542–3546.

Kang, J.X., Xiao, Y.F. and Leaf, A. (1995) Free long-chain polyunsaturated fatty acids reduce membrane electrical excitability in neonatal rat cardiac myocytes. *Proceedings of the National Academy of Sciences of the United States of America* 92, 3997–4001.

Leaf, A. and Weber, P.C. (1987) A new era for science in nutrition. *American Journal of Clinical Nutrition* 45, 1048–1053.

Lipids Research Clinics Program (1994) The lipid research clinics coronary primary prevention trial results: I. Reduction in incidence of coronary heart disease. *Journal of the American Medical Association* 251, 351–364.

Li, Y., Kang, J.X. and Leaf, A. (1997) Differential effects of various eicosanoids on the production or prevention of arrhythmias in cultured neonatal rat cardiac myocytes. *Prostaglandins* 54, 511–530.

McLennan, P.L. (1993) Relative effects of dietary saturated, monounsaturated, and polyunsaturated fatty acids on cardiac arrhythmias in rats. *American Journal of Clinical Nutrition* 57, 207–212.

McLennan, P.L., Abeywardena, M.Y. and Charnock, J.S. (1988) Dietary fish oil prevent ventricular fibrillation following coronary artery occlusion and reperfusion. *American Heart Journal* 116, 709–717.

McLennan, P.L., Bridle, T.M., Abeywardena, M.Y. and Charnock, J.S. (1992) Dietary lipid modulation of ventricular fibrillation threshold in the marmoset monkey. *American Heart Journal* 123, 1555–1561.

Murnaghan, M.F. (1981) Effects of fatty acids on the ventricular arrhythmia threshold in the isolated heart of the rabbit. *British Journal of Pharmacology* 73, 909–915.

Siscovick, D.S., Raghunathan, T.E., King, I., Weinmann, S., Wicklund, K.G., Albright, J., Bovbjerg, V., Arbogast, P., Smith, H. and Kushi, L.H. (1995) Dietary intake and cell membrane levels of long-chain n-3 polyunsaturated fatty acids and the risk of primary cardiac arrest. *Journal of the American Medical Association* 274, 1363–1367.

Xiao, Y.-F., Kang, J.X., Morgan, J.P. and Leaf, A. (1995) Blocking effects of polyunsaturated fatty acids on Na⁺ channels of neonatal rat ventricular myocytes. *Proceedings of the National Academy of Sciences of the United States of America* 921, 1000–1004.

Xiao, Y.-F., Gomez, A.M., Morgan, J.P., Lederer, W.J. and Leaf, A. (1997) Suppression of voltage-gated L-type Ca²⁺ currents by polyunsaturated fatty acids in adult and neonatal rat cardiac myocytes. *Proceedings of the National Academy of Sciences of the United States of America* 94, 4182–4187.

Xiao, Y.-F., Wright, S.N., Wang, G.K., Morgan, J.P. and Leaf, A. (1998) N-3 fatty acids suppress voltage-gated Na⁺ currents in HEK293t cells transfected with the α-subunit of the human cardiac Na⁺ channel. *Proceedings of the National Academy of Sciences of the United States of America* 95, 2680–2685.

Lipid Mediators in a Paradigm Shift: Balance Between ω-6 and ω-3

4

W.E.M. Lands
National Institute on Alcohol Abuse and Alcoholism,
Bethesda, Maryland, USA

There are two contrasting hypotheses regarding cardiovascular mortality: one concerns excessive molecules circulating in the plasma and the other concerns excessive inflammatory, proliferative signals in the vascular wall. Some lipids mediate cellular actions, whereas other lipids serve as surrogate indices of pathology. Successful intervention in decreasing myocardial infarctions by low-dose aspirin suggests that a prostaglandin-related *n*-6 eicosanoid (thromboxane A_2?) mediates fatal thrombotic events. Also, successful intervention in decreasing cardiovascular death by 3-hydroxy-3-methylglutaryl coenzyme A (HMG-CoA) reductase inhibitors suggests that an isoprenoid derivative (prenylated oncogene?) mediates inflammatory/proliferative processes in atherosclerotic plaques. Inflammatory, proliferative events are also mediated by excessive formation and function of *n*-6 eicosanoids associated with release of cytokines, platelet-activating factor (PAF) and PAF mimics, as well as reactive oxygen species (ROS), all of which cause further pathophysiology.

In this context, two hydrolytic enzymes carried on high-density lipoproteins (HDLs), PAF-acetylhydrolase and paraoxonase, diminish the pathological effects of PAF mimics carried on oxidized low-density lipoproteins (LDLs). We reported 25 years ago that the formation of *n*-6 eicosanoids is diminished competitively by the ω-3 type of highly unsaturated fatty acid (HUFA) released from tissue phospholipids when 20 : 4*n*-6 is released. In this way, dietary *n*-3 fats diminish *n*-6 eicosanoid-mediated risks of thrombosis, leucocyte adhesion, vascular wall inflammation and myocardial arrhythmia. Future progress may come from carefully interpreting known metabolic patterns that maintain HUFA precursors of *n*-6 eicosanoids in tissue lipids. Clinical targets for healthy humans are 20–26 kg m^{-2} for body mass index, 70–110 mg dl^{-1} for blood glucose, less than 200 mg dl^{-1} for cholesterol, and it seems likely that another useful clinical target will be more than 45% for the proportion of *n*-3 HUFA in plasma phospholipid HUFA.

Recognizing Cellular Signals

The past 50 years witnessed two contrasting hypotheses regarding major causes of cardiovascular mortality: one attributing the cause to excessive cholesterol and triglyceride circulating in the easily obtained plasma and the other attributing it to excessive inflammatory, proliferative signals among cells in the vascular wall (Ross, 1995). Biomedical research has provided an enormous amount of information on many circulating plasma lipoprotein components, and it is now giving even more productive insights into inflammatory interactions among cells of the vessel walls. Some lipids cause signalling that mediates cellular pathology, whereas other lipids serve as surrogate indices of that pathology. Lipid mediators produce signals during three important types of pathology: thrombotic, ischaemic events in the vascular lumen; arrhythmia of the myocardial muscle; and inflammatory, progressive stenosis of vascular walls. As the disease mechanisms become clear, we can separate causes from consequences and develop interpretations that lead to more effective new therapeutic interventions.

Past successes

Successful intervention by low-dose aspirin in decreasing myocardial infarctions suggests that a prostaglandin-related derivative (thromboxane A_2?) may mediate fatal thrombotic events. Also, successful intervention by 3-hydroxy-3-methylglutaryl coenzyme A (HMG-CoA) reductase inhibitors in decreasing cardiovascular death suggests that an isoprenoid derivative (prenylated oncogene?) may mediate inflammatory/proliferative processes in developing atherosclerotic plaques. Such inflammatory, proliferative events may also be mediated by excessive formation and function of n-6 eicosanoids associated with increased release of cytokines, platelet-activating factor (PAF) and reactive oxygen species (ROS), all of which cause further pathophysiology. We now know that inflammatory oxidant stress also forms oxidized phospholipids that act as PAF mimics, further amplifying cell adhesion and local inflammatory events. In this context, two hydrolytic enzymes carried on high-density lipoproteins (HDLs), PAF-acetylhydrolase and paraoxonase, diminish the levels and pathological actions of PAF mimics that are carried on oxidized low-density lipoproteins (LDLs). Those anti-inflammatory enzymes carried on HDL can play an important role in preventing excessive inflammatory signalling. Increased awareness of inflammatory and proliferative signals in many clinical disorders is directing attention toward regulating the formation and function of the n-6 eicosanoids known to exacerbate those disorders. Thus, all of the above lipid mediators are functional alternatives to the surrogate role historically assigned to circulating levels of cholesterol as a risk factor.

We reported long ago (Lands *et al.*, 1973) that the rate of formation of n-6 eicosanoids was diminished competitively by the ω-3 type of highly unsaturated fatty acid (HUFA) which is released from tissue phospholipids when 20 : 4n-6 is released. To obtain evidence that dietary ω-3 fats decrease stroke morbidity, we studied cats (Black *et al.*, 1979), and to show that ω-3 fats decrease myocardial infarctions, we studied dogs (Culp *et al.*, 1980). Such nutritional tactics diminish risks of *n-6* eicosanoid-mediated thrombosis, leucocyte adhesion, vascular wall inflammation and myocardial arrhythmia. Now, the biomedical community is at a cross-roads – recognizing that proportions of eicosanoid precursors in the average diet probably should be changed, but unsure of choosing how much change or for how long and unsure of how much benefit might be obtained from a specified change.

Future understanding

In summarizing their pioneering research, Brown and Goldstein (1997) indicated that a major role for free cholesterol is to stabilize a steroid regulatory element-binding protein (SREBP) at endoplasmic reticular membranes. By doing this, cholesterol provides a desirable suppression of a coordinated proteolytic release of the SREBP N-terminal peptide that translocates to the nucleus and activates transcription of a wide range of lipid-metabolizing genes (HMG-CoA synthase, HMG-CoA reductase, squalene synthase, acetyl-CoA carboxylase, fatty acid synthase, LDL receptor, lipoprotein lipase). When all of the protease-related factors cooperate with cholesterol in suppressing the cleavage and transfer of the signalling peptide, the expression of this broad set of genes controlling lipid-mediated events will be restrained. Inadequate feedback suppression of HMG-CoA reductase may permit excessive signalling with farnesyl and geranylgeranyl derivatives while also providing excessive formation of a product further downstream, cholesterol. Thus, elevated plasma cholesterol is a very distant consequence (surrogate index) of inadequate restraint in SREBP-based signalling that seems exacerbated in response to excessive intakes of dietary saturated fat. Identifying and correcting the inadequately restrained steps will become an exciting new area of therapeutics.

Successful therapeutic intervention with inhibitors of HMG-CoA reductase suggests that an isoprenoid derivative may mediate the inflammatory/proliferative processes of atherogenesis. Essential roles for prenylated proteins in intracellular signalling (G-proteins, proto-oncogenes, etc.) are increasingly evident, leading to still newer therapeutic agents that block proliferative signals by preventing transfer of a prenyl group (farnesyl or geranylgeranyl) to proteins that require it to be attached for full activity. Perhaps prenylated proteins (Kawata *et al.*, 1994) mediate cytokine-enhanced events in arterial plaque formation (Corsini *et al.*, 1995). For example, prenylation of p21RAS by a farnesyl transferase is an essential step in *ras*-mediated signalling through protein kinase pathways (Wang *et al.*, 1996). The function of prenylated proteins is strongly linked to responses by immune/inflammatory systems (Terkeltaub *et al.*, 1994; Fields *et al.*, 1996; Gronroos *et al.*, 1996; Williams, 1996) and platelets (Huzoor-Akbar, 1993). These functions should be considered when interpreting the consequences of agents inhibiting HMG-CoA reductase (Waters *et al.*, 1994), because such agents influence the availability of many isoprene intermediates as well as the end-product, cholesterol (Fig. 4.1).

Forty years ago, the ease of cholesterol measurement led investigators to focus on convenient associations of disease state with plasma cholesterol

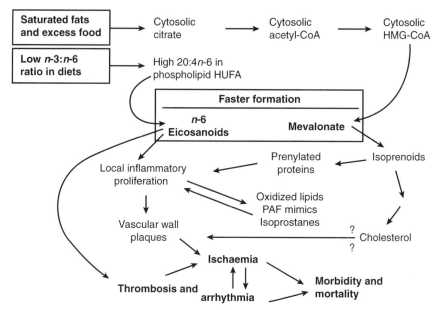

Fig. 4.1. Mediators and markers in cardiovascular disease. The figure is adapted from one presented at the Third International Conference on Nutrition in Cardio-cerebrovascular Diseases (Lands, 1993).

levels. Clearly, diets with excess saturated fat were associated both with cardiovascular mortality and with elevated plasma cholesterol. Less clear at that time was whether the associated risk factor, elevated plasma cholesterol, was a causal mediator or a distal surrogate index for cardiovascular disease. Meanwhile, public health efforts to decrease perceived risk factors led people to add dietary polyunsaturated fats by using vigorously marketed products such as corn oil and soybean oil that contain large amounts of *n*-6 fatty acids.

Retrospective examination of the known actions of *n*-6 eicosanoids (Fig. 4.1) suggests that a more balanced dietary intake of *n*-3 and *n*-6 polyunsaturated acids may be preferable to the current dominance of *n*-6 fats. Quantitative competition among the *n*-3/*n*-6 acids for storage in and release from tissue phospholipids is now well defined (Lands *et al.*, 1992), and a relative *n*-6 eicosanoid synthetic potential can be estimated from known dietary intakes or from tissue lipid analyses (Lands, 1996). Such data should be used in designing future clinical nutrition studies. For example, reasonable clinical targets for healthy humans are 20–26 kg m^{-2} for body mass index, 70–110 mg dl^{-1} for blood glucose, less than 200 mg dl^{-1} for cholesterol, and it seems likely that another useful clinical target could be more than 45% for the proportion of *n*-3 HUFA in the plasma phospholipid HUFA.

Eicosanoid Formation from HUFA

Eicosanoids are a diverse family of very active derivatives of 20-carbon essential fatty acids. They are not stored in tissues, but they are formed quickly during tissue stimulation, they act quickly upon nearby cellular receptors, and they are inactivated quickly by metabolic enzymes. The transitory nature of these lipid mediators fits them to an important role in modulating rapid physiological responses, with most tissues not forming eicosanoids most of the time. Both prostaglandin and leukotriene types of *n*-6 eicosanoids now have well-documented roles in exacerbating inflammatory, proliferative conditions, as well as in enhancing thrombosis and vasospasm. As a result, therapeutic interventions to decrease the formation and signalling by *n*-6 eicosanoids are useful approaches to the treatment of many different disorders.

The fact that *n*-3 fatty acid homologues of the *n*-6 fatty acids act as competitive antagonists of the formation of *n*-6 eicosanoids (Lands *et al.*, 1973) led to evaluating the natural occurrence of these competing *n*-3 acids in cellular lipids. They are released along with the *n*-6 eicosanoid precursors during cellular responses. More *n*-6 eicosanoid mediators of pathology (especially thromboxane and leukotriene) were discovered (Samuelsson, 1983), and their *n*-3 homologues were found to be less active. A need then became apparent to develop better documented rationales and recommendations for maintaining a healthy balance between *n*-3 and *n*-6 eicosanoid precursors in tissue lipids (Lands, 1986). The major dietary source of *n*-6 eicosanoids is linoleate, whereas arachidonate is the major immediate *n*-6 eicosanoid precursor maintained in tissues. Alternatively, dietary sources of *n*-3 eicosanoids are linolenate, eicosapentaenoate and docosahexaenoate.

Eicosapentaenoate is the major immediate *n*-3 eicosanoid precursor maintained in tissues, whereas docosahexaenoate is a major competitive antagonist of eicosanoid formation (Lands *et al.*, 1973), and it also seems important in forming essential membrane components (Lands, 1997). Some quantitative aspects of the dynamics of the 'housekeeping' metabolic steps involved in maintaining these acids in membrane phospholipids are noted in the section on dietary influences.

Thrombosis and vasospasm

Successful diminution of mortality from myocardial infarction by low-dose aspirin (Ridker *et al.*, 1991) confirmed an important role for thrombosis and its mediating *n*-6 eicosanoid, thromboxane A_2, in the fatal event. Thrombosis is a platelet-mediated process in which the lipid mediator, thromboxane, is formed by sequential actions of the enzymes, phospholipase, prostaglandin synthase and thromboxane synthase. Thromboxane activates thromboxane receptors, inducing intracellular signalling that permits calcium entry associated with platelet aggregation and vascular muscle contraction. The potent eicosanoid, thromboxane A_2, gives maximal *in vitro* aggregation of platelets at about 40 ng ml^{-1} plasma and 50% aggregation at about 3–5 ng ml^{-1} (Lands *et al.*, 1985), whereas the *n*-3 homologue is inactive (Needleman *et al.*, 1979).

Wide diversity among healthy individuals included a tendency of platelets from many individuals to over-respond (producing > 40 ng ml^{-1}) to the aggregating stimulus. The responses distributed along a curvilinear relationship for aggregation (from 20 to 80%) and thromboxane biosynthesis (from 20 to 130 ng ml^{-1} plasma). Following dietary supplementation with an n-3 fatty acid, the downward shift in values (Lands *et al.*, 1985) indicated a significant diet-suppressed tendency for thrombosis. More physiological measures of early changes in platelet shape (Schoene *et al.*, 1992) and calcium flux (Podczasy *et al.*, 1995) that approximate *in vivo* conditions provide clear evidence of the ability of dietary n-3 fats to suppress thrombotic tendency relative to platelets rich in n-6 acids. Thus, increasing the n-3 : n-6 ratio of nutrients remains a valuable dietary tactic to accompany low-dose aspirin for diminishing the risk of thrombotic events mediated by n-6 eicosanoids (Ridker *et al.*, 1991).

Myocardial arrhythmias

Possibly one-half of deaths from coronary heart disease have detectable thrombi, but the other half may be due to unstable electrical patterns of the heart leading to ventricular fibrillation, as reviewed by Nair *et al.* (1997). Dietary fish oil (but not corn oil) significantly reduced myocardial ischaemic damage (Hock *et al.*, 1987) and decreased cardiac inotropic response to α- (but not β-) adrenergic agonists (Reibel *et al.*, 1987). Also, treatment with a variety of lipoxygenase inhibitors prevented a significant ischaemia-induced ventricular fibrillation (Cooper *et al.*, 1988), suggesting that dietary n-3 fatty acids might decrease the formation and function of the n-6 leukotriene eicosanoids. Although fish oil significantly reduced ventricular fibrillation, sheep fat increased the severity of arrhythmias (McLennan *et al.*, 1988), and a dietary cross-over study showed that the arrhythmic effect of the saturated diet was reduced after shifting to a diet rich in n-3 fats (McLennan *et al.*, 1990).

Confirming evidence for n-3 fatty acid benefits (Hock *et al.*, 1990) included an improved relaxation response to acetylcholine (Malis *et al.*, 1991), decreased inositol trisphosphate release (Anderson *et al.*, 1996) and diminished ouabain-induced entry of calcium associated with L-type calcium channel action (Hallaq *et al.*, 1992). Many non-esterified unsaturated acids (both n-3 and n-6 types) can be antiarrhythmic by inhibiting channel conduction of voltage-dependent L-type Ca^{2+} currents (Kang and Leaf, 1994; Xiao *et al.*, 1997), although the n-6 acid, arachidonate, is arrhythmogenic. However, following inhibition of eicosanoid-forming enzymes, arachidonate consistently reduced beating rates and was antiarrhythmic like other unsaturated acids (Kang and Leaf, 1994). Thus, n-6 eicosanoids (but not n-3 eicosanoids) exacerbate arrhythmogenic events.

Appreciable amounts of non-esterified fatty acids and long chain acylcarnitines accumulate in myocytes during ischaemic conditions (Heathers *et al.*, 1987). A 70-fold increase in long chain acylcarnitines was regarded as mediating the hypoxia-induced increase in $α_1$-adrenergic receptors on myocytes (Heathers *et al.*, 1987) as well as tissue injury, ventricular tachycardia and fibrillation following ischaemia *in vivo* (DaTorre *et al.*, 1991). Perhaps these effects were derived from not only suppressing the voltage-dependent L-type calcium channels and inducing afterdepolarizations (Wu *et al.*, 1993) but also decreasing cellular coupling by gap junction conductance (Zimmerman *et al.*, 1995). Important questions regarding dietary benefits are: (i) whether increased *n*-3 acids in tissue lipids *in vivo* diminish either acylcarnitine accumulation or α_1-receptor signalling; (ii) whether non-esterified *n*-3 acids released *in vivo* selectively antagonize some ion conduction process; or (iii) whether the *n*-3 acids diminished the *in vivo* formation and function of *n*-6 eicosanoids.

Inflammatory Signals

An important discovery was that atherosclerotic plaque formation occurs at arterial wall regions of low shear stress where turbulent flow and eddy currents lengthen the residence time (Moore *et al.*, 1994). In such regions, local accumulations of inflammatory signals and mediators may contribute significantly to leucocyte adhesion, vascular wall inflammation and atherogenesis.

Isoprostanes

The discovery of isoprostanes, a series of prostaglandin-like lipids that are produced by non-enzymatic free radical-catalysed oxidation of arachidonate (Morrow *et al.*, 1990), led to valuable insights into the occurrence and consequences of *in vivo* oxidant stress, as reviewed by Roberts and Morrow (1997). The oxidation occurs with polyunsaturated acids esterified at the 2-position of phospholipids, and hydrolysis then produces non-esterified isoprostanes in plasma and urine. Isoprostanes cause increased vascular tone (in part by acting at thromboxane-like receptors), and they are also sensitive surrogate markers for oxidative, inflammatory events *in vivo* (Morrow *et al.*, 1992). Ischaemia-reperfusion events (such as reperfusion following coronary by-pass operations) generate isoprostanes and extend the pathology to the surrounding vasculature as well as serving as markers of the regional oxidant stress (Delanty *et al.*, 1997). Reports of increased urinary isoprostanes during activities commonly regarded as innocuous, such as smoking (Bachi *et al.*, 1996; Reilly *et al.*, 1996) and alcohol intake comparable with social drinking (Meagher *et al.*, 1996), illustrate both the sensitivity of isoprostanes as markers and the ease of initiating oxidant stress.

Recognition that isoprostane produced *in vivo* can cause a dose-dependent release of endothelin (Fukunaga *et al.*, 1995) by acting through tissue receptors similar to (but distinct from) those for thromboxane helps interpret the aetiology of hepatorenal syndrome (Moore *et al.*, 1992; Morrow *et al.*, 1993). Also, alcohol-induced oxidant stress in the liver may now be linked aetiologically to isoprostane release (Nanji *et al.*, 1994) and a subsequent increased hepatic vascular resistance (Luca *et al.*, 1997), probable precursors of portal hypertension and oesophageal varices in chronic alcoholics. The ability of thromboxane receptor antagonists to block alcohol-induced increases in portal pressure turns attention to the nature and selectivity of thromboxane-like receptors that respond also to isoprostanes (Marley *et al.*, 1997) in ways that seriously amplify the consequences of oxidant stress in the liver.

Platelet-activating factor (PAF) and PAF mimics

PAF, like the eicosanoids, is a potent biological signalling agent that is not accumulated in tissues, but is synthesized upon activation of a set of closely regulated enzyme reactions. The process begins with activated phospholipase-catalysed release of the highly unsaturated fatty acid at the 2-position of 1-O-alkyl-2-acyl-sn-glycero-3-phosphorylcholine. The resulting lyso-PAF is then acetylated by transfer of the acetyl group from acetyl-CoA by a specific acetyltransferase to form the biologically active lipid, PAF, as reviewed by Snyder (1995). This potent lipid mediator is not an oxidized phospholipid, but it promotes inflammatory conditions, which can oxidize other phospholipids. Inflammatory processes are amplified by signal transduction from PAF receptors through pathways that increase cytosolic calcium and activate intracellular signalling by the α- and β-forms of protein kinase C (Bussolino et al., 1994). This mechanism would then increase the transcription of inflammatory mediators, prostaglandin synthase-2 (Bazan et al., 1994), c-Fos, c-Jun and NF-κB (Tan et al., 1994).

Because inflammatory conditions also produce increased amounts of oxidants, it is important to note that phospholipids with oxidized 2-acyl esters derived from cellular (Patel et al., 1992; Tanaka et al., 1993) or plasma (Heery et al., 1995) phosphatidylcholines can activate inflammatory cells through PAF receptors. This would result in further enhancing cell adhesion and local inflammatory events. Thus, an important consequence of oxidant stress is non-enzymatic formation of oxidized phospholipids that have potent biological actions either as PAF mimics (Zimmerman et al., 1995) or as the hydrolysed isoprostane derivatives noted above. For instance, oxidized phospholipids in mildly oxidized LDL (Watson et al., 1997) increased monocyte adhesion and transmigration (Navab et al., 1996, 1997). Action of the oxidized lipid mediators through PAF receptors was confirmed by the ability of a synthetic PAF receptor antagonist to block the lipid-stimulated secretion of interleukin-8 (IL-8) and macrophage inflammatory protein-1α as well as to block leucocyte adhesion and aggregation in the microcirculation.

Inactivation of PAF by PAF acetylhydrolase-catalysed cleavage of the 2-acyl substituent is paralleled by a similar hydrolytic inactivation of the PAF mimic-oxidized phospholipids (Patel et al., 1992; Heery et al., 1995). Also, PAF acetylhydrolase prevents the in vitro accumulation of minimally modified LDL with its pathophysiological properties (Watson et al., 1995b). The availability of PAF acetylhydrolase from liver, tissue macrophages, platelets and neutrophils, as reviewed by Snyder (1995) and Stafforini et al. (1997), provides an important counterbalance to the pathophysiological roles of both the enzymatically formed PAF and the non-enzymatically formed PAF mimics. Oxidant stress can both generate PAF mimics and also inactivate the human plasma acetylhydrolase (Ambrosio et al., 1994), thereby potentiating and prolonging pro-inflammatory effects of PAF and PAF mimics. Such PAF mimics can induce monocyte–endothelial interactions similar to those implicated in the pathogenesis of atherosclerosis, rheumatoid arthritis, inflammatory bowel disease or multiple sclerosis (Watson et al., 1997).

Anti-inflammatory enzymes carried by HDL

HDLs constitute a family of diverse particulate complexes in plasma with densities in a specified range. Some particles contain PAF acetylhydrolase in association with apolipoprotein E (apoE), which may facilitate movement from HDL to LDL where the hydrolase can cleave and inactivate oxidized phospholipids (Van Lenten *et al.*, 1995; Watson *et al.*, 1995b). Lecithin–cholesterol acyltransferase (LCAT) is another HDL-associated enzyme that can hydrolyse and inactivate oxidized PAF mimics, although it apparently could not hydrolyse PAF (Goyal *et al.,* 1997).

Paraoxonase is another hydrolase associated with HDL particles, and it may move from HDL to LDL where it can prevent accumulation of PAF mimics in oxidized LDL. It then diminishes the pathological actions of oxidized LDL (Watson *et al.*, 1995a; Shih *et al.*, 1996), and reduces the risks for atherosclerosis (Wu and Corr, 1992). Also, paraoxonase carried by HDL can protect LDL from accumulating oxidized products during sustained oxidant stress (Mackness *et al.*, 1993), although paraoxonase activity was much less for the BB genotype than the AA or AB genotype (Mackness *et al.*, 1997). Such results extend the earlier observation of higher abundance of the BB genotype in patients with angiographically documented coronary artery disease (Serrato and Marian, 1995). Association of paraoxonase with different fractions of plasma HDL suggests that paraoxonase may not be an integral component, but it is carried as an HDL complex form, particularly associated with apoJ (Kelso *et al.*, 1994).

Generalized oxidant stress in rabbits eating an atherogenic diet lowered paraoxonase activity and decreased paraoxonase mRNA 2.7-fold while it increased apoJ mRNA 2.4-fold. Similarly, when oxidized LDL was injected into C57BL/6 mice, it lowered paraoxonase activity 59% and raised apoJ levels 3.6-fold (Navab *et al.*, 1997). This shift in the apoJ : paraoxonase ratio did not occur with the C3H strain of mice, which dramatically differs from the C57BL/6 strain in that it does not develop inflammatory responses to an atherogenic diet (Liao *et al.*, 1994). ApoJ is a positive acute phase protein that is elevated in tissues undergoing wound repair and in atherosclerotic lesions, and its elevation in plasma is associated with progression of atherosclerosis. Because apoJ forms a tight complex with paraoxonase that is carried in HDL particles, more research is needed to determine whether apoJ facilitates or hinders the hydrolytic removal of lipid oxidation products that are carried on oxidized LDL (Witztum and Steinberg, 1991).

Dietary Effects on Lipid Mediators

All of the progress noted above has not changed the four carefully phrased points of advice provided long ago by the American Heart Association, which remain appropriate for Americans even today: (i) eat less calories; (ii) eat a smaller percentage of calories as fat; (iii) substitute unsaturated fats for saturated fats; and (iv) include some polyunsaturated fats. The current challenge is to paraphrase and interpret those points in ways that build upon our growing awareness of the lipid mediators participating in mechanisms of cardiovascular disease.

Much evidence indicates that dietary n-3 acids may decrease cardio-vascular morbidity and mortality by shifting lipid mediators toward beneficial effects in all three pathological processes: inflammatory, progressive stenosis of vascular walls; thrombotic, ischaemic events in the vascular lumen; and arrhythmia of the myocardial muscle (Fig. 4.1). To help design and interpret new clinical trials with n-3 dietary fats, we developed empirical equations that summarize 30 years of accumulated metabolic information and describe quantitatively the competitive metabolism of essential fatty acids (Lands et al., 1990b, 1992). Those empirical equations predict probable patterns in tissue fatty acid composition (Equation 4.1) and indicate the probable intensity of evoked responses to eicosanoid lipid mediators in processes noted on the left side of Fig. 4.1.

$$
\begin{aligned}
\frac{20:3n\text{-}3 + 20:4n\text{-}6}{\text{as \% Plipid HUFA}} =\ & \frac{100}{1 + \dfrac{PC6}{en\%P6}\left(1 + \dfrac{en\%P3}{PC3} + \dfrac{en\%H3}{HI3} + \dfrac{en\%O}{CO} + \dfrac{en\%P6}{KS}\right)} + \ldots \\
\ldots +\ & \frac{100}{1 + \dfrac{HC6}{en\%H6}\left(1 + \dfrac{en\%H3}{HC3}\right)}
\end{aligned}
\qquad 4.1
$$

Quantitative relationships among essential fatty acids in maintaining a proportion of n-6 eicosanoid precursors within the HUFAs of tissue phospholipids (Plipid) based upon the average daily energy percentage (en%) of ingested nutrient. The symbols are defined and interpreted by Lands et al. (1992). Thus, they provide a functional alternative to the equations developed by Keys and others to predict changes in levels of plasma cholesterol (Equation 4.2), as reviewed recently by Howell et al. (1997), which reflect processes driven by dietary saturated fats as noted on the right side of Fig. 4.1.

$$
\begin{array}{lll}
\Delta\text{cholesterol} = 70.8 \times \Delta\text{SFA} - 33.9 \times \Delta\text{PUFA} \\
(\mu\text{mol l}^{-1}) \qquad\quad (\text{en\%}) \qquad\qquad (\text{en\%})
\end{array}
\qquad 4.2
$$

Quantitative relationship for the probable change in plasma cholesterol (μmol l^{-1}) that would follow changes in the average daily energy percentage (en%) of dietary saturated or polyunsaturated fatty acids.

Application of both empirical Equations 4.1 and 4.2 is probably limited to diets within two standard deviations of aggregate averages of the populations from which they were derived, and further refinements might be made with carefully controlled, quantitative long-term diet studies with humans. Nevertheless, extensive similarities in lipid metabolism between rats and humans permit results from dietary studies with rats (Lands et al., 1990b) to help refine and interpret the more expensive and logistically difficult studies with humans (Lands et al., 1992; Lands, 1995).

Overall metabolic discrimination between the n-3 and n-6 types of essential fatty acid is slight when forming tissue esters (Lands et al., 1982). Therefore, the almost complete dominance of n-6 fatty acids in plasma lipids of individuals in Chicago (Lands et al., 1992) primarily reflected voluntary food choices made by those individuals (consciously or subconsciously). A dilemma evolves in agreeing to decrease *n*-6 intakes to levels that would be only a few times (rather than 50 times) that needed for an appropriate growth response, because benefits and losses are difficult for consumers and marketers to assess equally. Most adult Americans already have more than 3 kg of 18 : 2*n*-6, with about 20–40% of human body mass being fat and 15–20% of body fat being 18 : 2*n*-6. This large reservoir needs 3 years to equilibrate with dietary lipids (Dayton *et al.*, 1966).

During the past decades, dietary recommendations have emphasized replacing saturated fats with unsaturated fats, ingesting less than 10% of daily calories (10 en%) as saturated fat, and even regarding monounsaturated fat (18 : 1*n*-9) as being useful for displacing saturated fat from the diet. Now, there is a clear public health need to address the imbalance in *n*-3 and *n*-6 essential fatty acids (Lands *et al.*, 1990a; Lands, 1993, 1994). Reasonable clinical targets for healthy humans have been 20–26 kg m^{-2} for body mass index, 70–110 mg dl^{-1} for blood glucose, less than 200 mg dl^{-1} for cholesterol, and it seems likely that another useful clinical target will be more than 45% for the proportion of *n*-3 HUFA in plasma phospholipid HUFA.

Medical researchers attempt various interventions to decrease eicosanoid-mediated disorders, and Enders *et al.* (1995) reviewed clinical efforts to use supplemental dietary *n*-3 acids. Unfortunately, many studies in that review appeared to examine clinical consequences, with little attention to the amount of dietary and adipose linoleate against which the *n*-3 supplements were competing. The current heavy 'pressure' of dietary linoleate (18 : 2*n*-6) in the USA seems likely to diminish the success of expensive and time-consuming clinical studies by competing with supplemental *n*-3 fats. Investment of increasingly scarce clinical research funds needs more careful prospective estimates of the consequence of specifically defined proportions of dietary essential fatty acids (Lands, 1994, 1996). For example, in approaching the clinical problems of rheumatoid arthritis and coronary heart disease, a research team in Adelaide (Mantzioris *et al.*, 1995; James and Cleland, 1997) employed a simple tactic. They replaced salad oils rich in 18 : 2*n*-6 with olive or flaxseed oil, resulting in modest amounts of dietary *n*-3 HUFA, giving significant benefits. Further careful dietary planning that employs known diet–tissue relationships (Lands *et al.*, 1992; Lands, 1996) will permit much more to be done to diminish the impact of various inflammatory lipid mediators on cardiovascular integrity.

To aid in designing clinical studies, a spreadsheet (Table 4.1) uses Equation 4 and the associated constants described by Lands *et al.* (1992) to predict levels of fatty acids maintained in plasma lipids. The predicted proportions of *n*-3 and *n*-6 among the HUFAs of plasma phospholipids reflect many competitive metabolic interactions of the 18-carbon UFA and the 20- and 22-carbon HUFAs. Because fatty acid metabolism produces similar patterns in humans and rodents, much of the experience with laboratory animals assists interpretation of metabolic selectivities in humans, and a large amount of data on lipid metabolism can be evaluated collectively.

In addition, the relative proportions of acids maintained in the phospholipids and triacylglycerols of plasma tend to be very similar to the

Table 4.1.   Predicted maintenance of fatty acids in plasma lipids. A spreadsheet for predicting the probable n-6 eicosanoid response intensity. The proportion of 20 : 3n-6 + 20 : 4n-6 in the phospholipid HUFA serves as a surrogate index of the relative abundance of precursors for rapidly forming potent n-6 eicosanoids. Researchers requiring more information about the spreadsheet can contact the author at the address given or at wlands@willco.niaaa.nih.gov.

Diet identifier	1	2	3	4	5	5A	2A	2B	Japan	USA
Average daily dietary intakes										
en% 18 : 3n-3	1.50	1.00	0.70	0.60	0.30	0.30	1.00	1.00	0.90	1.00
en% 18 : 2n-6	0.50	1.00	1.30	1.40	1.70	1.70	1.00	1.00	6.30	6.50
en% n-3 HUFA	0.03	0.03	0.03	0.03	0.03	0.20	0.20	0.40	1.30	0.03
en% n-6 HUFA	0.05	0.05	0.05	0.05	0.05	0.05	0.05	0.05	0.05	0.05
Plasma TG: predicted UFA proportions										
18 : 3n-3 % in TG	2.0	1.3	0.9	0.8	0.4	0.4	1.3	1.3	1.2	1.3
18 : 3n-6 % in TG	1.4	2.8	3.7	4.0	4.8	4.8	2.8	2.8	17.9	18.5
Plasma PL: predicted 20 : 3n-6 + 20 : 4 n-6 in PL-HUFA										
n-6 %HUFA in PL	31	49	58	61	69	54	38	31	47	78
(probable eicosanoid reponse intensity)										

Constants: V_{max} = 100.0; PC6 = 0.0441; PC3 = 0.0555; CO = 5.000; K_s = 0.175; HI6 = 0.040; HI3 = 0.008; HC6 = 0.5; HC3 = 8.8; Factor 3 = 1.31; Factor 6 = 2.84.

proportions in other tissues (Lands *et al.*, 1990b). This fact makes plasma maintenance levels useful indicators of the probable internal exposure of tissues to the *n*-3 and *n*-6 precursors of eicosanoids. This spreadsheet permits the use of known average daily dietary intakes to predict the *n*-6 as %HUFA, which is a surrogate index for the *n*-6 eicosanoid response intensity. Another spreadsheet was developed to use Equations 3 and 4 described by Lands *et al.* (1992) in a 'reverse' mode to employ gas chromatographic analyses of triglycerides and phospholipids from 100 µl sample of fasting blood (Ohta *et al.*, 1990) to predict average dietary intakes of the *n*-3 and *n*-6 fatty acids. Such estimates based on biomarkers may be more reliable and valid than estimates based upon questionnaires and interviews.

Interactions of *n*-3 and *n*-6 HUFAs and eicosanoids, as well as the prenylated proteins with inflammatory leukotrienes (Gronroos *et al.*, 1996), represent important new insights into disease mechanisms. Better understanding of how such lipid mediators influence the pathological processes noted in Fig. 4.1 seems likely to help researchers, nutritionists, and health educators clarify for the public which agents are causal and what balance in dietary essential fatty acids is appropriate.

References

Ambrosio, G., Oriente, A., Napoli, C., Palumbo, G., Chiarello, P., Marone, G., Condorelli, M., Chiariello, M. and Triggiani, M. (1994) Oxygen radicals inhibit human plasma acetylhydrolase, the enzyme that catabolizes platelet-activating factor. *Journal of Clinical Investigation* 93, 2408–2416.

Anderson, K.E., Du, J.-X., Sinclair, A. J., Woodcock, E.A. and Dart, A.M. (1996) Dietary fish oil prevents reperfusion Ins(1,4,5)P$_3$ release in rat heart: possible anti-arrhythmic mechanism. *American Journal of Physiology* 271, H1483–H1490.

Bachi, A., Zuccato, E., Baraldi, M., Fanelli, R. and Chiabrando, C. (1996) Measurement of urinary 8-epi-prostaglandin F2alpha, a novel index of lipid peroxidation *in vivo*, by immunoaffinity extraction/gas chromatography-mass spectrometry. Basal levels in smokers and non-smokers. *Free Radical Biology and Medicine* 20, 619–624.

Bazan, N.G., Fletcher, B.S., Herschman, H.R. and Mukherjee, P.K. (1994) Platelet-activating factor and retinoic acid synergistically activate the inducible prostaglandin synthase gene. *Proceedings of the National Academy of Sciences of the United States of America* 91, 5252–5256.

Black, K.L., Culp, B.R., Randall, O.S. and Lands, W.E.M. (1979) The protective effects of dietary fish oil and focal cerebral infarction. *Prostaglandins and Medicine* 3, 257–268.

Brown, M.S. and Goldstein, J.L. (1997) The SREBP pathway: regulation of cholesterol metabolism by proteolysis of a membrane-bound transcription factor. *Cell* 89, 331–340.

Bussolino, F., Silvagno, F., Garbarino, G., Costamagna, C., Sanavio, F., Arese, M., Soldi, R., Aglietta, M., Pescarmoa, G., Camussi, G. and Bosia, A. (1994) Human endothelial cells are targets for platelet-activating factor (PAF). *Journal of Biological Chemistry* 269, 2877–2886.

Cooper, D.R., Keliher, G.J. and Kowey, P.R. (1988) Modulation of arachidonic acid metabolites and vulnerability to ventricular fibrillation during myocardial ischemia in the cat. *American Heart Journal* 116, 1194–1200.

Corsini, A., Raiteri, M., Soma, M.R., Bernini, F., Fumagalli, R. and Paoletti, R. (1995) Pathogenesis of atherosclerosis and the role of 3-hydroxy-3-methylglutaryl coenzyme A reductase inhibitors. *American Journal of Cardiology* 76(2), 21A–28A.

Culp, B.R., Lands, W.E.M., Lucchesi, B.R., Pitt, B. and Romson, J. (1980) The effect of dietary supplementation of fish oil on experimental myocardial infarction. *Prostaglandins* 20, 1021–1031.

DaTorre, S.D., Creer, M.H., Pogwizd, S.M. and Corr, P.B. (1991) Amphipathic lipid metabolites and their relation to arrhythmogenesis in the ischaemic heart. *Journal of Molecular and Cellular Cardiology* 23 (Suppl. I), 11–22.

Dayton, S., Hashimoto, S., Dixon, W. and Pearce, M.L. (1966) Composition of lipids in human serum and adipose tissue during prolonged feeding of a diet high in unsaturated fat. *Journal of Lipid Research* 7, 103–111.

Delanty, N., Reilly, M.P., Pratico, D., Lawson, J.A., McCarthy, J.F., Wood, A.E., Ohnishi, S.T., Fitzgerald, D.J. and FitzGerald, G.A. (1997) 8-Epi PGF$_{2\alpha}$ generation during coronary reperfusion. A potential quantitative marker of oxidant stress *in vivo*. *Circulation* 95, 2492–2499.

Enders, S., DeCaterina, R., Schmidt, E.B. and Kristensen, S.D. (1995) n-3 Polyunsaturated fatty acids: update. *European Journal of Clinical Investigation* 25, 629–638.

Fields, P.E., Gajewski, T.F. and Fitch, F.W. (1996) Blocked Ras activation in anergic CD4$^+$ T cells. *Science* 271, 1276–1278.

Fukunaga, M., Yura, T. and Badr, K.F. (1995) Stimulatory effect of 8-epi-PGF2α, an F2-isoprostane, on endothelin release. *Journal of Cardiology and Pharmacology* 26 (Suppl. 3), S51–S52.

Goyal, J., Wang, K., Liu, M. and Subbaiah, P.V. (1997) Novel function of lecithin-cholesterol acyltransferase. Hydrolysis of oxidized polar phospholipids generated during lipoprotein oxidation. *Journal of Biological Chemistry* 272, 6231–6239.

Gronroos, E., Andersson, T., Schippert, A., Zheng, L. and Sjolander, A. (1996) Leukotriene D_4-induced mobilization of intracellular Ca^{2+} in epithelial cells is critically dependent on activation of the small GTP-binding protein Rho. *Biochemical Journal* 316, 239–245.

Hallaq, H., Smith, T.W. and Leaf, A. (1992) Modulation of dihydropyridine-sensitive calcium channels in heart cells by fish oil fatty acids. *Proceedings of the National Academy of Sciences of the United States of America* 89, 1760–1764.

Heathers, G.P., Yamada, K.A., Kanter, E.M. and Corr, P.B. (1987) Long-chain acylcarnitines mediate the hypoxia-induced increase in α_1-adrenergic receptors on adult canine myocytes. *Circulation Research* 61, 735–746.

Heery, J.M., Kozak, M., Stafforini, D.M., Jones, D.A., Zimmerman, G.A., McIntyre, T.M. and Prescott, S.M. (1995) Oxidatively modified LDL contains phospholipids with platelet-activating factor-like activity and stimulates the growth of smooth muscle cells. *Journal of Clinical Investigation* 96, 2322–2330.

Hock, C.E., Holahan, M.A. and Reibel, D.K. (1987) Effect of dietary fish oil on myocardial phospholipids and myocardial ischemic damage. *American Journal of Physiology* 252, H554–H560.

Hock, C.E., Beck, L.D., Bodine, R.C. and Reibel, D.K. (1990) Influence of dietary *n*-3 fatty acids on myocardial ischemia and reperfusion. *American Journal of Physiology* 259, H1518–H1525.

Howell, W.H., McNamara, D.J., Tosca, M.A., Smith, B.T. and Gaines, J.A. (1997) Plasma lipid and lipoprotein responses to dietary fat and cholesterol: a meta-analysis. *American Journal of Clinical Nutrition* 65, 1747–1764.

Huzoor-Akbar, Wang, W., Kornhauser, R., Volker, C. and Stock, J.B. (1993) Protein prenylcysteine analog inhibits agonist-receptor-mediated signal transduction in human platelets. *Proceedings of the National Academy of Sciences of the United States of America* 90, 868–872.

James, M.J. and Cleland, L.G. (1997) Dietary *n*-3 fatty acids and therapy for rheumatoid arthritis. *Seminars in Arthritis and Rheumatism* 27, 85–97.

Kang, J.X. and Leaf, A. (1994) Effects of long-chain polyunsaturated fatty acids on the contraction of neonatal rat cardiac myocytes. *Proceedings of the National Academy of Sciences of the United States of America* 91, 9886–9890.

Kawata, S., Nagase, T., Yamasaki, E., Ishiguro, H. and Matsuzawa, Y. (1994) Modulation of the mevalonate pathway and cell growth by pravastatin and D-limonene in a human hepatoma cell line (Hep G2). *British Journal of Cancer* 69, 1015–1020.

Kelso, G.J., Stuart, W.D., Richter, R.J., Furlong, C.E., Jordan-Starck, T.C. and Harmony, J.A. (1994) Apolipoprotein J is associated with paraoxonase in human plasma. *Biochemistry* 33, 832–839.

Lands, W.E.M. (1986) *Fish and Human Health*. Academic Press, Orlando

Lands, W.E.M. (1993) Eicosanoids and health. *Annals of the New York Academy of Science* 676, 46–59.

Lands, W.E.M. (1994) State of the art: where are we and where are we going? In: *Proceedings of the American Heart Association Scientific Conference on Omega-3 Fatty Acids in Nutrition, Vascular Biology and Medicine*. American Heart Association, Houston, pp. 1–8.

Lands, W.E.M. (1995) Long-term fat intake and biomarkers. *American Journal of Clinical Nutrition* 61 (Suppl.), 721S–725S.

Lands, W.E.M. (1996) Control of eicosanoid response intensity. In: Vanderhoek, J.Y. (ed.), *Frontiers in Bioactive Lipids*. Plenum Press, New York, pp. 23–30.

Lands, W.E.M. (1997) Two faces of essential fatty acids. *INFORM* 8, 1141–1147.

Lands, W.E.M., LeTellier, P.R., Rome, L.H. and Vanderhoek, J.Y. (1973) Inhibition of prostaglandin biosynthesis. *Advances in Bioscience* 9, 15–28.

Lands, W.E.M., Inoue, M., Sugiura, Y. and Okuyama, H. (1982) Selective incorporation of polyunsaturated fatty acids into phosphatidylcholine by rat liver microsomes. *Journal of Biological Chemistry* 257, 14968–14972.

Lands, W.E.M., Culp, B.R., Hirai, A. and Gorman, R. (1985) Relationship of thromboxane generation to the aggregation of platelets from humans: effects of eicosapentaenoic acid. *Prostaglandins* 30, 819–825.

Lands, W.E.M., Hamazaki, T., Yamazaki, K., Okuyama, H., Sakai, K., Goto, Y. and Hubbard, V.S. (1990a) Changing dietary patterns. *American Journal of Clinical Nutrition* 51, 991–993.

Lands, W.E.M., Morris, A.J. and Libelt, B. (1990b) The influence of dietary polyunsaturated fats on the composition of fatty acids in rat tissues. *Lipids* 25, 505–516.

Lands, W.E.M., Libelt, B., Morris, A.J., Kramer, N.C., Prewitt, T.E., Bowen, P., Schmeisser, D., Davidson, M.H. and Burns, J.H. (1992) Maintenance of lower proportions of n-6 eicosanoid precursors in phospholipids of human plasma in response to added dietary n-3 fatty acids. *Biochimica et Biophysica Acta* 1180, 147–162.

Liao, F., Andalibi, A., Qiao, J., Allayee, H., Fogelman, A.M. and Lusis, A.J. (1994) Genetic evidence for a common pathway mediating oxidative stress, inflammatory gene induction, and aortic fatty streak formation in mice. *Journal of Clinical Investigation* 94, 877–884.

Luca, A., Pagan-Garcia, J.C., Bosch, J., Feu, F., Caballeria, J., Groszmann R.J. and Rodes, J. (1997) Effects of ethanol consumption on hepatic hemodynamics in patients with alcoholic cirrhosis. *Gastroenterology* 112, 1284–1289.

Mackness, M.I., Arrol, S., Abbott, C.A. and Durrington, P.N. (1993) Is paraoxonase related to atherosclerosis? *Chemico-Biological Interactions* 87, 161–171.

Mackness, M.I., Arrol, S., Mackness, B. and Durrington, P.N. (1997) Alloenzymes of paraoxonase and effectiveness of high-density lipoproteins in protecting low-density lipoprotein against lipid peroxidation. *Lancet* 349, 851–852.

Malis, C.D., Leaf, A., Varadarajan, G.S., Newell, J.B., Weber, P.C., Force, T. and Bonventre, J.V. (1991) Effects of dietary omega-3 fatty acids on vascular contractility in preanoxic and postanoxic aortic rings. *Circulation* 84, 1393–1401.

Mantzioris, E., James, M.J., Gibson, R.A. and Cleland, L.G. (1995) Differences exist in the relationships between dietary linoleic and alpha-linolenic acids and their respective long-chain metabolites. *American Journal of Clinical Nutrition* 61, 320–324.

Marley, R., Harry, D.H., Anand, R., Fernado, B., Davies, S. and Moore, K. (1997) 8-Isoprostaglandin $F_{2\alpha}$, a product of lipid peroxidatin, increases portal pressure in normal and cirrhotic rats. *Gastroenterology* 112, 208–213.

McLennan, P.L., Abseywardena, M.Y. and Charnock, J.S. (1988) Dietary fish oil prevents ventricular fibrillation following coronary artery occlusion and reperfusion. *American Heart Journal* 116, 709–716.

McLennan, P.L., Abeywardena, M.Y. and Charnock, J.S. (1990) Reversal of the arrhythmogenic effects of long-term saturated fatty acid intake by dietary n-3 and n-6 polyunsaturated fatty acids. *American Journal of Clinical Nutrition* 51, 53–58.

Meagher, E.A., Lucey, M.R. and FitzGerald, G.A. (1996) Oxidant injury in social drinking and alcoholic cirrhosis. *Hepatology* 24, 444A.

Moore, J.E., Jr, Xu, C., Glagov, S., Zarins, C.K. and Ku, D.N. (1994) Fluid wall shear stress measurements in a model of the human abdominal aorta: oscillatory behavior and relationship to atherosclerosis. *Atherosclerosis* 110, 225–240.

Moore, K., Wendon, J., Frazer, M., Karani, J., Williams, R. and Badr, K. (1992) Plasma endothelin immunoreactivity in liver disease and the hepatorenal syndrome. *New England Journal of Medicine* 327, 1774–1778.

Morrow, J.D., Hill, K.E., Burk, R.F., Nammour, T.M., Badr, K.F. and Roberts, L.J. (1990) A series of prostaglandin F2-like compounds are produced *in vivo* in humans by a non-cyclooxygenase, free radical-catalyzed mechanism. *Proceedings of the National Academy of Sciences of the United States of America* 87, 9383–9387.

Morrow, J.D., Awad, J.A., Boss, H.J., Blair, I.A. and Roberts, L.J. (1992) Non-cyclooxygenase-derived prostanoids (F2-isoprostanes) are formed *in situ* on phospholipids. *Proceedings of the National Academy of Sciences of the United States of America* 89, 10721–10725.

Morrow, J.D., Moore, K.P., Awad, J.A., Ravenscraft, M.D., Marini, G., Badr, K.F., Williams, R. and Roberts, L.J. (1993) Marked overproduction of non-cyclooxygenase derived prostanoids (F2-isoprostanes) in the hepatorenal syndrome. *Journal of Lipid Mediators* 6, 417–420.

Nair, S.S.D., Leitch, J.W., Falconer, J. and Garg, M.L. (1997) Prevention of cardiac arrhythmia by dietary (*n*-3) polyunsaturated fatty acids and their mechanism of action. *Journal of Nutrition* 127, 383–393.

Nanji, A.A., Khwaja, S., Tahan, S.R. and Sadrzadeh, H.S.M. (1994) Plasma levels of a novel noncyclooxgenase-derived prostanoid (8-isoprostane) correlate with severity of liver injury in experimental alcoholic liver disease. *Journal of Pharmacology and Experimental Therapy* 269, 1280–1285.

Navab, M., Berliner, J.A., Watson, A.D., Hama, S.Y., Territo, M.C., Lusis, A.J., Shih, D.M., Van Lenten, B.J., Frank, J.S., Demer, L.L., Edwards, P.A. and Fogelman, A.M. (1996) The Yin and Yang of oxidation in the development of the fatty streak. A review based on the 1994 George Lyman Duff Memorial Lecture. *Arteriosclerosis, Thrombosis and Vascular Biology* 16, 831–842.

Navab, M., Levy-Hama, S., Van Lenten, B.J., Fonarow, G.C., Carninez, C.J., Castellani, L.W., Brennan, M.-L., Lusis, A.J. and Fogelman, A.M. (1997) Mildly oxidized LDL induces an increased apolipoprotein J/paraoxonase ratio. *Journal of Clinical Investigation* 99, 2005–2019.

Needleman, P., Raz, A., Minkes, M.S., Ferendelli, J.A. and Sprecher, H. (1979) Triene prostaglandins: prostacyclin and thromboxane biosynthesis and unique biological properties. *Proceedings of the National Academy of Sciences of the United States of America* 76, 944–948.

Ohta, A., Mayo, M.C., Kramer, N. and Lands, W.E.M. (1990) Rapid analysis of fatty acids in plasma lipids. *Lipids* 25, 742–747.

Patel, K.D., Zimmerman, G.A., Prescott, S.M. and McIntyre, T.M. (1992) Novel leukocyte agonists are released by endothelial cells exposed to peroxide. *Journal of Biological Chemistry* 267, 15168–15175.

Podczasy, J.J., Church, J.P. and Schoene, N.W. (1995) Effects of dietary fish oil on calcium homeostasis in rat platelets. *Nutritional Biochemistry* 6, 327–333.

Reibel, D.K., Holahan, M.A. and Hock, C.E. (1987) Effects of dietary fish oil on cardiac responsiveness to adrenoceptor stimulation. *American Journal of Physiology* 254, H494–H499.

Reilly, M., Delanty, N., Lawson, J.A. and FitzGerald, G.A. (1996) Modulation of oxidant stress *in vivo* in chronic cigarette smokers. *Circulation* 94, 19–25.

Ridker, P.M., Manson, J.E., Buring, J.E., Goldhaber, S.Z. and Hennekens, C.H. (1991) The effect of chronic platelet inhibition with low-dose aspirin on atherosclerotic progression and acute thrombosis: clinical evidence from the Physicians' Health Study. *American Heart Journal* 122, 1588–1592.

Roberts, J.L., II, and Morrow, J.D. (1997) The generation and actions of isoprostanes *Biochimica et Biophysica Acta* 1345, 121–135.

Ross, R. (1995) Cell biology of atherosclerosis. *Annual Review of Physiology* 57, 791–804.

Samuelsson, B. (1983) From studies of biochemical mechanism to novel biological mediators: prostaglandin endoperoxides, thromboxanes, and leukotrienes. Nobel Lecture. *Bioscience Reports* 3, 791–813.

Schoene, N.W., Allman, M.A., Dougherty, R.M., Denvir, E. and Iacono, J.M. (1992) Diverse effects of dietary stearic and palmitic acids on platelet morphology. In: Sinclair, A. and Gibson, R. (eds), *Proceedings of the Third International Congress on Essential Fatty Acids and Eicosanoids*. American Oil Chemists Society, Champaign, Illinois, pp. 290–292.

Serrato, M. and Marian, A.J. (1995) A variant of human paraoxonase/arylesterase (HUMPONA) gene is a risk factor for coronary artery disease. *Journal of Clinical Investigation* 96, 3005–3008.

Shih, D.M., Gu, L., Hama, S., Xia, Y.-R., Navbi, M., Fogelman, A.M. and Lusis, A.J. (1996) Genetic–dietary regulation of serum paraoxonase expression and its role in atherogenesis in a mouse model. *Journal of Clinical Investigation* 97, 1630–1639.

Snyder, F. (1995) Platelet-activating factor and its analogs: metabolic pathways and related intracellular processes. *Biochimica et Biophysica Acta* 1254, 231–240.

Stafforini, D.M., Prescott, S.M., Zimmerman, G.A. and McIntyre, T.M. (1997) Mammalian platelet-activating factor acetylhydrolases. *Biochimica et Biophysica Acta* 1301, 161–173.

Tan, X.D., Sun, X., Crussi-Gonzalez, F.X., Crussi-Gonzalez, F. and Hsueh, W. (1994) PAF and TNF increase the precursor of NF-kappa B p50 mRNA in mouse intestine: quantitative analysis by competive PCR. *Biochimica et Biophysica Acta* 1215, 157–162.

Tanaka, T., Minamino, H., Unezaki, S., Tsukatani, H. and Tomura, A. (1993) Formation of platelet activating factor-like phospholipids by Fe^{2+}/ascorbate/EDTA-induced lipid peroxidation. *Biochimica et Biophysica Acta* 1166, 264–274.

Terkeltaub, R., Solan, J., Barry, M., Jr, Santoro, D. and Bokoch, G.M. (1994) Role of the mevalonate pathway of isoprenoid synthesis in IL-8 generation by activated monocytic cells. *Journal of Leukocyte Biology* 55, 749–755.

Van Lenten B.J., Hama, S.Y., de Beer, F.C., Stafforini, D.M., McIntyre, T.M., Prescott, S.M., La Du, B.N., Fogelman, A.M. and Navab, M. (1995) Anti-inflammatory HDL becomes pro-inflammatory during the acute phase response. Loss of protective effect of HDL against LDL oxidation in aortic wall cell cocultures. *Journal of Clinical Investigation* 6, 2758–2767.

Wang, T., Danielson, P.D., Li, B., Shah, P.C., Kim, S.D. and Donahoe, P.K. (1996) The p21 farnesyltransferase α subunit in TGF-β and activin signalling. *Science* 271, 1120–1122.

Waters, D., Higginson, L., Gladstone, P., Kimball, B., Le May, M., Boccuzzi, S.J. and Lesperance, J. (1994) Effects of monotherapy with an HMG-CoA reductase inhibitor on the progression of coronary atherosclerosis as assessed by serial quantitative arteriography. The Canadian Coronary Atherosclerosis Intervention Trial. *Circulation* 89, 959–968.

Watson, A.D., Berliner, J.A., Hama, S.Y., La Du, B.N., Faull, K.F., Fogelman, A.M. and Navab, M. (1995a) Protective effect of high density lipoprotein associated paraoxonase. Inhibition of the biological activity of minimally oxidized low density lipoprotein. *Journal of Clinical Investigation* 96, 2882–2891.

Watson, A.D., Navab, M., Hama, S.Y., Sevanian, A., Prescott, S.M., Stafforini, D.M., McIntyre, T.M., La Du, B.N., Fogelman, A.M. and Berliner, J.A. (1995b) Effect of platelet activating factor-acetylhydrolase on the formation and action of minimally oxidized low density lipoprotein. *Journal of Clinical Investigation* 95, 774–782.

Watson, A.D., Leitinger, N., Navab, M., Faull, K.F., Horkko, S., Witztum, J.L., Palinski, W., Schwenke, D., Salomon, R.G., Sha, W., Subbanagounder, G., Fogelman, A.M. and Berliner, J.A. (1997) Structural identification by mass spectrometry of oxidized phospholipids in minimally oxidized low density lipoprotein that induce monocyte/endothelial interactions and evidence for their presence *in vivo*. *Journal of Biological Chemistry* 272, 13587–13607.

Williams N.T. (1996) Cell inactivation linked to Ras block. *Science* 27, 1234.

Witztum, J.L. and Steinberg, D. (1991) Role of oxidized low density lipoprotein in atherogenesis. *Journal of Clinical Investigation* 88, 1785–1792.

Wu, J. and Corr, P.B. (1992) Influence of long-chain acylcarnitines on voltage-dependent calcium current in adult ventricular myocytes. *American Journal of Physiology* 263, H410–H417.

Wu, J., McHowat, J., Saffitz, J.E., Yamada, K.A. and Corr, P.B. (1993) Inhibition of gap junctional conductance by long-chain acylcarnitines and their preferential accumulation in junctional sarcolemma during hypoxia. *Circulation Research* 72, 879–889.

Xiao, Y.-F., Gomez, A.M., Morgan, J.P., Lederer, W.J. and Leaf, A. (1997) Suppression of voltage-gated L-type Ca^{2+} currents by polyunsaturated fatty acids in adult and neonatal rat ventricular myocytes. *Proceedings of the National Academy of Sciences of the United States of America* 94, 4182–4187.

Zimmerman, G.A., Prescott, S.M. and McIntyre, T.M. (1995) Oxidatively fragmented phospholipids as inflammatory mediators: the dark side of polyunsaturated lipids. *Journal of Nutrition* 1256 (Suppl,), 1661S–1665S.

Egg Consumption

Eggs, Dietary Cholesterol and Heart Disease Risk: an International Perspective

5

D.J. McNamara

Egg Nutrition Center, Washington DC, USA

During the past 5 years, there have been a number of reports from epidemiological studies on the relationships between dietary factors and coronary heart disease (CHD) morbidity and mortality. The results from these studies indicated no significant relationship between dietary cholesterol intake and CHD incidence when multivariate analysis of the data included dietary fat and fibre. Two of the larger studies have involved analysis of data from over 43,000 male health professionals which indicated that dietary cholesterol (0.1 mg kcal^{-1}) did not contribute to the risk of either a myocardial infarction (relative risk 1.03) or fatal CHD (relative risk 1.06). In the Nurses' Health Study of over 80,000 nurses, dietary cholesterol was not a significant contributor to CHD incidence.

One additional piece of evidence against the 'cholesterol-independent effect' is the observation that across cultures there is a negative relationship between per capita egg consumption and CHD mortality. The countries with the highest per capita egg consumption (Japan, Mexico, Spain and France) are the countries with the lowest rates of CHD mortality. These data argue against an independent effect of dietary cholesterol on CHD risk and, in part, can explain the observations of Stamler and colleagues. In groups with extremely high dietary cholesterol intakes, greater than 750 mg day^{-1}, there is a correspondingly lower intake of fruit and vegetables, and higher intake of animal products. The lower intakes of fruit and vegetables result in a lower intake of dietary fibre, antioxidant vitamins, B vitamins and polyunsaturated fat. This dietary pattern would be predicted to lead to a higher incidence of hyperlipidaemia, increased oxidative stress and hyperhomocysteinaemia, all defined risk factors for CHD. The increased risk associated with an extremely high dietary cholesterol intake may not be due to the dietary cholesterol but rather the multiple nutrients, which are absent from a diet high in animal products. These confounding variables were never considered in the 'cholesterol-independent effect' hypothesis proposed by Stamler, yet are consistent with the most recent

© CAB *International* 2000. *Egg Nutrition and Biotechnology*
(eds J.S. Sim, S. Nakai and W. Guenter)

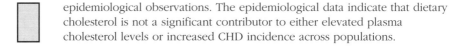
epidemiological observations. The epidemiological data indicate that dietary cholesterol is not a significant contributor to either elevated plasma cholesterol levels or increased CHD incidence across populations.

Dietary Cholesterol and Egg Restrictions

In 1972, the American Heart Association published an update on its dietary recommendations, which included a numerical restriction in dietary cholesterol intake to less than 300 mg day^{-1}. The recommendations also included the statement that the public should limit their egg consumption to no more than three eggs per week. To date, this is the only food-specific restriction listed in the American Heart Association's dietary guidelines. Since that time, numerous health promotion agencies in the USA have included quantitative limits on dietary cholesterol intakes as part of their overall dietary recommendations. These agencies are the US Department of Agriculture/US Department of Health and Human Services and National Research Council, Committee on Diet and Health, Food and Nutrition Board, Commission on Life Sciences. However, other dietary recommendations have not included specific limits on any single food item. Interestingly, on an international basis, the majority of countries which have developed national dietary guidelines have not included dietary cholesterol restrictions as part of the general population recommendation (Truswell, 1994). The 1995 version of Dietary Guidelines for Americans (US Department of Agriculture/US Department of Health and Human Services, 1995) included numerical limits on dietary cholesterol intakes. An effort was made to assure consistency with the Food and Drug Administration Nutrition Facts Label and dietary recommendations from the National Cholesterol Education Program (Expert Panel on Detection, Evaluation, and Treatment of High Blood Cholesterol in Adults reported by Adult Treatment Panel II, 1994).

Dietary Cholesterol, Plasma Cholesterol and CHD Risk

Howell (Chapter 2) has presented the results of clinical studies investigating the relationship between dietary cholesterol and plasma cholesterol levels. These data indicate that dietary cholesterol, when consumed within physiological ranges, has only a limited effect on the plasma cholesterol level of most individuals. Data also indicate that between 15 and 20% of the population have hypersensitivity to dietary cholesterol whereas the majority of the population have little if any plasma cholesterol response to changes in the amount of cholesterol in the diet (McNamara, 1995).

Over the past 10 years, a second argument has been developed regarding the role of dietary cholesterol in determining coronary heart disease (CHD) risk based on a hypothesis suggesting that dietary cholesterol can increase CHD risk independently of any effect on plasma cholesterol concentrations. Shekelle and Stamler (1989) used data from the Western Electric Study to propose that dietary cholesterol could be related to increased CHD incidence even after adjustment for plasma cholesterol levels. This hypothesis is now being used as an adjunct argument for population-wide dietary cholesterol restrictions (Krauss *et al.*, 1996). However, evidence from a number of recently reported epidemiological studies, as well as international data on per capita egg consumption patterns, all contradict the hypothesis that dietary cholesterol has an 'independent effect' on CHD risk.

Shekelle and Stamler (1989) reported that those individuals in the upper-most quintile of dietary cholesterol intakes had an increased relative risk for CHD (Fig. 5.1). The level of cholesterol intake in this top quintile was more than 1079 mg day^{-1}; the fourth quintile, with an average cholesterol intake of 827 mg day^{-1}, was not significantly different from the lowest quintile. These data would seem to suggest that the overall dietary pattern of the study sub-jects in the top quintile were substantially more different than just having a high cholesterol intake. These extreme dietary cholesterol intakes also suggest that these individuals had very high overall intakes of animal products and, correspondingly, very low intakes of grains, fruit and vegetables. Thus, the question must be raised of whether the higher CHD incidence in this group was due to what was excessive in the diet or, perhaps, what was inadequate in the diet. With today's understanding of the role of antioxidants and the B vita-mins in CHD risk, it is clear that increased relative risk can occur not only from nutrient excesses but also from nutrient deficiencies. The potential importance of such confounding dietary variables, which in theory could make a major contribution to the higher CHD incidence in this quintile, was not evaluated by Stamler and colleagues and raises serious questions regarding the validity of their 'independent effect' hypothesis.

In contrast, studies reported by Connor and co-workers (Artaud-Wild *et al.*, 1993) indicated that different populations could consume diets with sim-ilar cholesterol–saturated fat index (CSI) values yet have significantly different CHD incidence rates (Fig. 5.2). France and the UK have similar dietary CSI

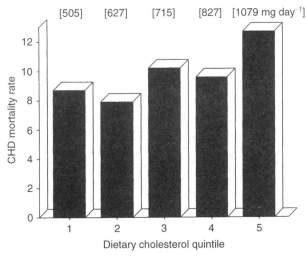

Fig. 5.1. CHD mortality rates by dietary cholesterol quintiles from the Western Electric Study (Shekelle and Stamler, 1989). The data suggest that very high intakes of dietary cholesterol are related to increased CHD incidence.

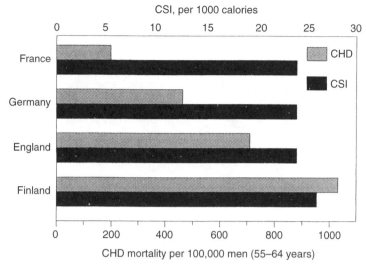

Fig. 5.2. Rates of CHD mortality in four countries relative to the cholesterol–saturated fat index (CSI) dietary patterns for each country. Data from Artaud-Wild *et al.* (1993).

patterns and yet differ almost fivefold in CHD mortality rates. These investigators concluded that a high CSI value was not a contributor to CHD risk if the diet contained large amounts of fruit and vegetables and vegetable oils. In a similar manner, in the Ireland–Boston Study, the CHD cases had a lower vegetable-food score (–0.44 versus 0.06) and a higher animal-food score (0.24 versus –0.04) than controls (Kushi *et al.*, 1985). These data are consistent with the concept that the diet–heart disease relationship is a function of both what is in the diet and what is missing from the diet.

Stamler and Shekelle (1988) also used data from a selective number of clinical studies to add additional support to the dietary cholesterol 'independent effect' hypothesis. While the data suggest that dietary cholesterol is related to increased CHD risk, it should be noted that the difference in dietary cholesterol intakes between cases and controls was only 16 mg day^{-1} 1000 kcal^{-1}. Given an average intake of 400–500 mg day^{-1} and an average endogenous cholesterol synthesis of 1000 mg day^{-1}, it is clear that this difference can hardly provide a plausible explanation for the differences in CHD incidence. In contrast, Ravnskov (1995) compiled a much larger number of clinical studies and presented evidence that there were no differences in dietary cholesterol intakes between cases and controls. Based on the available data, Ravnskov (1995) concluded that there was no evidence for an 'independent effect' of dietary cholesterol on CHD relative risk (Fig. 5.3).

The epidemiological evidence from cross-cultural and within-population studies has been unable to document a significant relationship between dietary cholesterol intakes and CHD incidence. The results of an analysis of the Twenty Countries database by Hegsted and Ausman (1988) found that dietary cholesterol was not a contributing factor to CHD incidence. Data from the

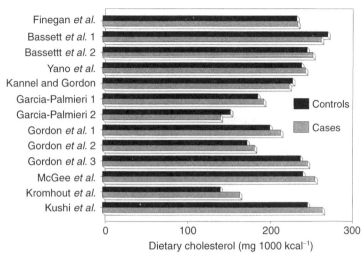

Fig. 5.3. Comparison of dietary cholesterol intakes in CHD cases and controls from 13 epidemiological trials as reported by Ravnskov (1995). See original text for specific study references.

Framingham Heart Study have also failed to document any relationship between dietary cholesterol intakes and either plasma cholesterol levels or CHD incidence (Dawber *et al.*, 1982; Millen *et al.*, 1996). Esrey *et al.* (1996) reported data from the Lipid Research Clinic's Prevalence Study of 4546 men showing that dietary cholesterol was not related to either plasma lipid levels or CHD incidence either with or without adjustment for plasma cholesterol levels. Two recently published epidemiological studies have found similar results. Data from a study in over 43,000 male health professionals indicated that saturated fat calories were related to CHD incidence while dietary cholesterol had no significant effect on relative risk of CHD, as shown in Table 5.1 (Ascherio *et al.*, 1996). In a similar manner, data from a study of 80,000 nurses indicated that dietary cholesterol did not contribute to CHD incidence, as indicated in Table 5.1 (Hu *et al.*, 1997).

From these data sets, it is clear that across cultures and within populations, dietary cholesterol is not a significant contributor either to the average plasma cholesterol level of a population or to CHD morbidity or mortality. The hypothesis that dietary cholesterol contributes to CHD risk independently of its effects on plasma cholesterol is not supported by the existing body of evidence and, therefore, should be considered an invalid argument for population-wide restrictions in dietary cholesterol intake or in egg consumption.

Eggs and CHD Mortality Rates

Figure 5.4 illustrates the relationship between per capita egg consumption and CHD mortality rates per 100,000 men age 35–74 years in 24 industrialized countries. There is a negative relationship between per capita egg

Table 5.1. Relationship between dietary lipids and relative risk for CHD in men and women.

Dietary lipid	Relative risk: males[a]	
	Myocardial Infarction	Fatal CHD
Cholesterol (100 mg 1000 kcal⁻¹)	1.03	1.06
18 : 3 (1% kcal)	0.41	0.57
Trans-fatty acids (2% kcal)	1.13	0.93
18 : 2 (5% kcal)	0.97	0.69
Saturated fatty acids (5% kcal)	0.86	1.34

Dietary lipid	Relative risk of CHD: females[b]
Cholesterol (200 mg 1000 kcal⁻¹)	1.12
Monounsaturated fatty acids (5% kcal)	0.81
Trans-fatty acids (2% kcal)	1.93
Polyunsaturated fatty acids (5% kcal)	0.62
Saturated fatty acids (5% kcal)	1.17

From: [a]Ascherio *et al.*, 1996; [b]Hu *et al.*, 1997.

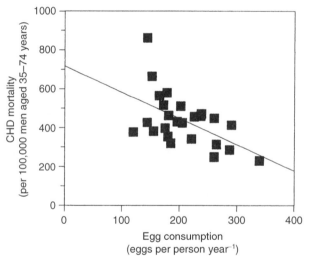

Fig. 5.4. Relationship between national CHD mortality rates and per capita egg consumption of 24 industrialized countries.

consumption and CHD mortality rates. In fact, the highest per capita egg-consuming countries are Japan, Mexico, Spain and France, which also happen to be the countries with the lowest CHD mortality rates of any of the industrialized countries (American Heart Association, 1998). The data indicate that egg consumption *per se* is not related to CHD mortality and, in fact, appears to be negatively related to CHD deaths. It has been suggested that egg consumption has no relationship to CHD risk when included in diets high in fruit and vegetables (Kushi *et al.*, 1985).

Changes in Egg Consumption and Plasma Cholesterol Levels

It has been suggested that the decrease in per capita egg consumption from 405 eggs in 1945 to 235 eggs in 1995 explain in part the decrease in plasma cholesterol observed in the population (Stamler *et al.*, 1998). It is calculated that this 170 eggs per year decrease resulted in a 2.2 mg dl^{-1} decrease in the average plasma cholesterol level (0.46 eggs day^{-1} × 215 mg cholesterol per egg × 0.022 mg dl^{-1} mg^{-1} day^{-1} change in dietary cholesterol) (Howell *et al.*, 1997; McNamara, 1998). Thus, a 46% decrease in per capita egg consumption contributed to only a 1% decrease in the average plasma cholesterol level of the American population.

Eggs, Nutrition and Nutrient Density

Eggs contribute one-third of the cholesterol in the American diet (Federation of American Societies for Experimental Biology, 1995) yet its contributions to other nutrients in the diet are substantially greater than its contribution to the total caloric content. As shown in Table 5.2, eggs contribute only 1.3% of the total calories but substantial amounts of high-quality protein, folate and riboflavin, as well as a number of other nutrients in excess of its caloric contributions. The nutrient density of eggs make them a valuable contributor to the overall nutritional balance of the diet (Table 5.3) and, as an economical source of high-quality protein, an important component in the diets of the elderly, low-income families and growing children. High nutrient value at low economical and caloric expense are important considerations in the diets of many

Table 5.2. Contributions of eggs to the nutritional quality of the American diet.

Nutrient	Daily value (%)	Nutrient	Daily value (%)
kcal	1.3	Protein	3.9
Riboflavin	6.4	Vitamin A	4.3
Vitamin E	4.3	Folate	5.1
Vitamin B$_6$	2.1	Vitamin B$_{12}$	3.7
Zinc	2.8	Iron	2.4

From: NHANES III (Federation of American Societies for Experimental Biology, 1995).

Table 5.3. Recommended daily values of major nutrients from two large eggs (140 kcal).

Nutrient	Daily value (%)	Nutrient	Daily value (%)
Food energy	6	Protein	20
Riboflavin	30	Folate	12
Vitamin B$_{12}$	16	Iron	8
Vitamin D	12	Phosphorus	16
Vitamin A	12	Selenium	34
Vitamin E	6	Zinc	8
Vitamin B$_6$	8		

segments of the population, and undue restrictions on inclusion of such items in the diet are unfounded, unnecessary and potentially harmful.

Conclusions

Most industrialized countries do not recommend specific restrictions in dietary cholesterol intakes for their populations. The findings from clinical trials and epidemiological surveys indicate that dietary cholesterol is not a significant contributor to either an elevated plasma cholesterol level or an increased risk for CHD. In contrast, the dietary recommendations in the USA have resulted in eggs being considered a 'bad food' and an item to be restricted rigorously in the diet. For many segments of the population, such restrictions only result in a reduction in the nutritional value of the diet. The value of eggs as an afford-able, nutrient-dense, convenient commodity is far in excess of its potential contribution to changes in plasma cholesterol. Rather than a constant over-emphasis of the dietary cholesterol content of eggs, consumers need to under-stand better the value of eggs in the diet and the importance of nutritional balance, variety and moderation.

References

American Heart Association (1998) *1998 Heart and Stroke Statistical Update*. American Heart Association, Dallas, Texas, USA.

Artaud-Wild, S.M., Connor, S.I., Sexton, G. and Connor, W.E. (1993) Differences in coronary mortality can be explained by differences in cholesterol and saturated fat intakes in 40 countries but not in France and Finland. A paradox. *Circulation* 88, 2771–2779.

Ascherio, A., Rimm, E.B., Giovannucci, E.L., Spiegelman, D., Stampfer, M. and Willett, W.C. (1996) Dietary fat and risk of coronary heart disease in men: cohort follow up study in the United States. *British Medical Journal* 313, 84–90.

Dawber, T.R., Nickerson, R.J., Brand, F.N. and Pool, J. (1982) Eggs, serum cholesterol, and coronary heart disease. *American Journal of Clinical Nutrition* 36, 617–625.

Esrey, K.L., Joseph, L. and Grover, S.A. (1996) Relationship between dietary intake and coronary heart disease mortality: lipid research clinics prevalence follow-up study. *Journal of Clinical Epidemiology* 49, 211–216.

Expert Panel on Detection, Evaluation, and Treatment of High Blood Cholesterol in Adults (Adult Treatment Panel II) (1994) National Cholesterol Education Program. Second report of the expert panel on detection, evaluation, and treatment of high blood cholesterol in adults (Adult Treatment panel II). *Circulation* 89, 1333–1445.

Federation of American Societies for Experimental Biology (1995) *Report on Nutrition Monitoring in the United States*. US Government Printing Office, Washington, DC.

Hegsted, D.M. and Ausman, L.M. (1988) Diet, alcohol and coronary heart disease in men. *Journal of Nutrition* 118, 1184–1189.

Howell, W.H., McNamara, D.J., Tosca, M.A., Smith, B.T. and Gaines, J.A. (1997) Plasma lipid and lipoprotein responses to dietary fat and cholesterol: a meta-analysis. *American Journal of Clinical Nutrition* 65, 1747–1764.

Hu, F.B., Stampfer, M.J., Manson, J.E., Rimm, E., Colditz, G.A., Rosner, B.A., Hennekens, C.H. and Willett, W.C. (1997) Dietary fat intake and the risk of coronary heart disease in women. *New England Journal of Medicine* 337, 1491–1499.

Krauss, R.M., Deckelbaum, R.J., Ernst, N., Fisher, E., Howard, B.V., Knopp, R.H., Kotchen, T., Lichtenstein, A.H., McGill, H.C., Pearson, T.A., Prewitt, T.E., Stone, N.J., Van Horn, L. and Weinberg, R. (1996) Dietary guidelines for healthy American adults – a statement for health professionals from the Nutrition Committee, American Heart Association. *Circulation* 94, 1795–1800.

Kushi, L.H., Lew, R.A., Stare, F.J., Ellison, C.R., el Lozy, M., Bourke, G., Daly, L., Graham, I., Hickey, N., Mulcahy, R. and Kevaney, J. (1985) Diet and 20-year mortality from coronary heart disease. *New England Journal of Medicine* 312, 811–818.

McNamara, D.J. (1995) Dietary cholesterol and the optimal diet for reducing risk of atherosclerosis. *Canadian Journal of Cardiology* 11 (Suppl. G), 123G–126G.

McNamara, D.J. (1998) Dietary cholesterol, serum cholesterol, and risks of cardiovascular and noncardiovascular diseases – reply. *American Journal of Clinical Nutrition* 67, 491–492.

Millen, B.E., Franz, M.M., Quatromoni, P.A., Gagnon, D.R., Sonnenberg, L.M., Ordovas, J.M., Wilson, P.W.F., Schaefer, E.J. and Cupples, L.A. (1996) Diet and plasma lipids in women. 1. Macronutrients and plasma total and low-density lipoprotein cholesterol in women: the Framingham nutrition studies. *Journal of Clinical Epidemiology* 49, 657–663.

National Research Council, Committee on Diet and Health, Food and Nutrition Board, Commission on Life Sciences (1989) *Diet and Health: Implications for Reducing Chronic Disease Risk.* National Academy Press, Washington, DC.

Ravnskov, U. (1995) Quotation bias in reviews of the diet–heart idea. *Journal of Clinical Epidemiology* 48, 713–719.

Shekelle, R.B. and Stamler, J. (1989) Dietary cholesterol and ischaemic heart disease. *Lancet* i, 1177–1178.

Stamler, J. and Shekelle, R. (1988) Dietary cholesterol and human coronary heart disease. The epidemiological evidence. *Archives of Pathology and Laboratory Medicine* 112, 1032–1040.

Stamler, J., Greenland, P., Van Horn, L. and Grundy, S.M. (1998) Dietary cholesterol, serum cholesterol, and risks of cardiovascular and noncardiovascular diseases. *American Journal of Clinical Nutrition* 67, 488–489.

Truswell, A.S. (1994) Dietary goals and guidelines: national and international perspectives. In: Shills, M.E., Olson, J.A. and Shike, M. (eds), *Modern Nutrition in Health and Disease.* Lea & Febiger, Philadelphia, pp. 1612–1625.

US Department of Agriculture and US Department of Health and Human Services (1995) *Nutrition and Your Health: Dietary Guidelines for Americans.* US Government Printing Office, Washington, DC.

Egg Products Around the World: Today and Tomorrow

6

G. Zeidler

Department of Animal Sciences, University of California, Riverside, California, USA

In the 21st century, the way in which eggs will be produced and the characteristics of the finished products will be strongly affected by the increasing economic pressures for higher profit margins and consumers' demand for products which better fit their changing lifestyle. The lack of a significant number of high profit margin products and the inability to control egg surpluses resulted in chronic low profitability for the egg industry, especially in countries where eggs are not protected. The phenomenal improvement in production efficiency and the dramatic increase in production unit size was not enough to reverse the trend and to improve profit margins. Unfortunately, it is well known that increasing market share does not solve profitability problems; however, bringing in new customers who are eager to pay a premiun for their chosen new product will. Not providing the consumer with meaningful product choices and the low priority given to retail egg product development strongly affected egg consumption in many countries, as consumers moved to alternatives.

Aggressive product development, improving the convenience and palatability of shell eggs and egg products, expanding the utilization of eggs as food ingredients and elevating their food safety and nutritional profile will remain the key to improving egg consumption, with higher profit margins. The success of home meal replacements (HMRs) which will benefit producers and retailers opens up a great opportunity for egg products if they follow the lead of poultry meats.

Introduction

In many parts of the world, shell eggs are produced and traded as a commodity. They are produced at the lowest price possible and carry a low profit margin for the average producer. Profitability fluctuates strongly due to uncontrolled egg surpluses. As profit margins have eroded slowly over the years, increasing egg production and packaging operation size have become common practice. Consolidation of the egg business will continue at a fast pace, as well as adding breaking operations and further processing units to the emerging mega farms and cooperatives. Shell egg consumption will continue to decline in developed countries where egg product consumption will continue to increase.

Developing countries will continue to promote egg consumption due to its great nutritional price/value, and to increase self-sufficiency where possible. Many developing countries experienced a significant improvement in the standard of living as personal income doubled and averaged US$1200 per capita in 1996 (Burns *et al.*, 1996). Purchasing more meats and eggs was one of the immediate reactions to the extra income. World diets have improved and in 1996 included 34 kg of meat per person per year. The advantages of poultry are better feed conversion and efficient production, but production relies heavily on the international grain and energy costs. In contrast, red meat animals can be fed by grazing and on locally grown feed supplementation, and are less dependent on global grain prices and availability of hard currency.

The growing demand for meat and eggs pressured the world grain supply. In the USA, grain prices reached a record high at US$5 bushel^{-1} of maize and US$3 bushel^{-1} of wheat in May 1996. Prices have dropped subsequently as grain producers increased their production. However, the financial crisis in the Pacific Basin and in Russia in the following years was devastating to local growers who could not pay for imported feed as well as to feed and egg and poultry meat exporters. Similarly to developed countries, many developing countries are facing the loss of prime agricultural land and water to more profitable uses such as housing, industrial parks, roads, recreation and others. China has only 8% of its land as prime agricultural land. It is expected that up to 50% of the land could be lost by 2025 if the current trend is not altered. On the other hand, China is the largest total meat and egg producer in the world, and consumption is skyrocketing, from 12.5 kg of meat and 48 eggs per capita in 1980 to 53 kg of meat and 289 eggs in the year 2000. Therefore, the pressure on the grain, meat and egg exporters is expected to increase substantially in the years to come.

Countries which are able to develop low cost feed supply in addition to low cost labour will become a major players in egg and egg product exports. As trade barriers for agricultural products are expected to be lifted, a significant portion of egg production will move to these countries, similarly to the fate of many other low profit margin products. Countries where strong animal welfare legislation is in force will be more vulnerable as the legislation leads to higher production costs (Evans, 1995).

In recent years, more emphasis has been placed on further processing of eggs and egg products. Yet, the egg industry is far behind most food categories such as poultry meat and dairy which emphasize a large variety of products for all occasions, partly because of the greater technical difficulties in achieving similar goals for eggs.

Future egg products will improve the existing product concepts and new products will also emerge. Extended shelf life, improved food safety and nutritional profile, highly defined sensory quality and improved convenience will be the major developmental routes, as well as expanding the utilization of eggs as an ingredient in processed foods.

Extended shelf life liquid egg products produced according to Swartzel *et al.* (1989) are currently the most successful egg product on the market. They are sold mainly to a variety of food manufacturers, food services, mass feeding operations and to a few retail establishments, mostly in Europe, the USA and Australia. The high cost of the legal consequences arising from food poisoning have turned major corporations, hospitals and mass feeders away from shell eggs and towards pasteurized liquid and dry egg products. Marketing shell egg fortified with nutraceuticals such as ω-3-fatty acids and vitamin E, as well as promoting specific production and handling methods such as free range or organic, captured about 5% of the shell egg market in numerous countries. However, the high price charged for many of these products (up to $6 dozen^{-1} in the USA) can harm these products in the long run.

The new generation of home meal replacement (HMR) products is currently one of the most successful new food products in the USA. Poultry meat is most active in this new category where eggs have hardly started. The concept is based on moderately extending the shelf life of highly perishable, chilled, ready to eat or ready to cook products protected by refrigeration and multilayer barrier packaging. An efficient short to medium range distribution system is essential, as many products are frequently delivered to individual stores rather than to a central warehouse. Freshly made home cooking characteristics, a tailored nutritional profile, preserved sensory characteristics and lower portion price make HMR highly popular. The HMR concept can help egg product developers to overcome many of the technical difficulties that have haunted egg products in the past and to retain fresh egg characteristics in retail and food service egg products.

In Search of High Profit Margins

In the last decade and into the 21st century, high profit margins connected to increasing market share has become the formula for company success in developed countries. Manufacturing facilities of low profit margin products are often transferred to lower labour costs, lower taxation and lesser environmental and labour regulation regions or to one of the developing countries.

In California, the largest producer of many fruits and vegetables, all the intensive labour frozen vegetable manufacturing plants and some of the fresh produce have been moved to Mexico. Until 1996, California was also the largest US egg producer. It lost the title to Ohio after the majority of the new facilities were built out of state and some in Mexico.

High profit margins do not last forever as they attract extensive competition. Therefore, to remain successful in a fast changing world, an industry and the individual company must reinvent itself regularly. As time goes on, products and markets become more commodity-like and less profitable. Watches, radios and calculators are a few examples. The dramatic increase in competition in the last two decades, greatly supported by the global economy and by the exploding advances in computers and telecommunication, have changed the way in which business is conducted. As a result, many companies lost their ability to increase prices at will on many of their products. The profitability slowly deteriorated due to unmatched rising costs and accumulated inflation. Technical breakthroughs also turned many expensive products into low cost, low profit margin items. In the USA if egg producers in one region decide to raise the prices of shell eggs beyond a certain level, the price discovery system and the network of egg handlers will react immediately, and truckloads of lower cost eggs could be at a retailer's door within 48 h. Furthermore, today's consumers are more knowledgeable and sophisticated and, with the help of efficient information systems, can find alternatives to unpopular price-hiked foods. When the major cereal manufacturers doubled the price of their products in 1995, consumers moved quickly to muffins and bagels and to emerging low cost cereal products. After a delayed rolling back of prices, the cereal giants did not completely overcome the situation as many consumers enjoyed the new products and their improved convenience.

In the past, the major corporate effort to retain high profitability focused on increasing the market share. 'Grow and profits will follow' was the popular motto. However, in the late 1980s and early 1990s, it was found the hard way that a large market share does not protect against profitability problems. Numerous giant companies with a leading market share in their field, such as Intel, IBM, K-Mart, Sears, US Airways and others, were shaken to the core as a result of profitability loss of their major products and services which threatened their existence. The classical market share theory was then modified.

The new theory states that high profitability can be secured if increased market share is associated with increasing company value (stockholder equity in public corporation). Figure 6.1 demonstrates that increasing revenues from successful products and services can achieve high profitability, more than cost cutting (which is more limited). Box 6.1 lists the parameters which can help achieve or retain high profitability. 'Expanding business concept' can also be a powerful tool to turn profits around. Disney started mainly as a theme park

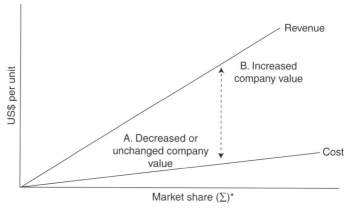

Fig. 6.1. The reinvention process to high profitability. $(\Sigma)^*$ – summation of corporate individual products and its various operations.

Box 6.1. Factors affecting profitability.

- Brand name
- Reputation for products and services
- Ability to increase prices
- Subsidies and trade barriers (without severe quotas and price restrictions)
- Ability to meet today's consumer needs and desires
- Innovative and well-financed R & D Department
- New products and product concepts
- Patents and licences
- Mergers, acquisitions and cooperatives
- Expanding business concepts
- Selling low profit margin units
- Efficient manufacturing and efficient operations
- Effective and innovative management
- Focusing on core business

---

and an animated films company. Today, it is a vacation–entertainment company, having hotels, cruise ships, movies and TV programmes, sports teams, toys and more, capturing a larger percentage of consumers' free time expenditure. In the food arena, several seafood retailers and chicken and turkey growers have expanded into restaurants. In California, several restaurants which specialized in poultry are manufacturing HMR products and gourmet poultry snacks for supermarkets.

In order to succeed in the reinvention process, the company should carefully define the following:

1. What really is important to today's customers?
2. What type of products and services will bring higher profit without a tangible customer resistance?
3. Why should consumers buy from them and not from the competitors?

High customer enthusiasm is a must for any successful new product, as price becomes of lesser importance when consumers really want a product. Therefore, many corporations add consumer research units to their operations. However, forecasting an exceptionally successful product or service is tricky and hard to predict.

The reinvention process is illustrated in Fig. 6.1 as a transition from low profit area A to high profit area B. The borderline between the areas differs for different industries and for different company goals and philosophies. Therefore, business decisions are frequently different for the same situation. For example, should a company distribute dividends (which are taxed twice) or instead let investors (owners) enjoy the increase in stockholder equity which is reflected in elevated company financial strength and stock price. The common ground for all reinvention processes is that very large amounts of profits are needed to make the transition. Therefore, severe and often painful measures should be taken to achieve it, together with a strong and talented leader who

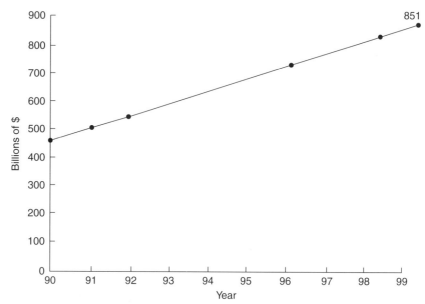

Fig. 6.2. Retained earnings of corporate America adjusted for inventories and depreciation in the second quarter of 1999. Source: Standard and poor.

can execute the programme. In the last decade, the corporate profit margin and retained earnings in the USA grew to a record high (Figs 6.2 and 6.3). The availability of huge amounts of cash enabled the investment in advanced technology which further improved efficiency and productivity, keeping labour costs and inflation down and retained the stock bull market high.

An Economic Profile of Shell Egg Production with Limited or No Further Processing

For many years, the egg industry was, and still is, commodity oriented in most parts of the world. There, uncontrolled surpluses frequently consumed previously earned profits. Historically, at the turn of the century, chickens were an integrated part of rural living, providing eggs and meat for the household as well as supplementary income from selling products locally. Getting into the egg business was relatively easy: rural land was cheap and capital investment for constructing the facility and purchasing equipment was relatively small. Cages, computers and automation did not exist and the farmer could build the structure. Three hundred hens were enough to register a farmer as an egg producer. No wonder there were 5 million registered poultry farmers in the USA in 1900.

Table 6.1 summarizes the growth and profitability of Southern Californian egg producers since 1925 (data were available on a monthly basis and were accumulated by D. Bell). The analysis is for production only, and egg packaging is not included. In 1997, packaged eggs receive about 15 cents more than farm eggs (the cost of packaging is not deducted). Southern California has

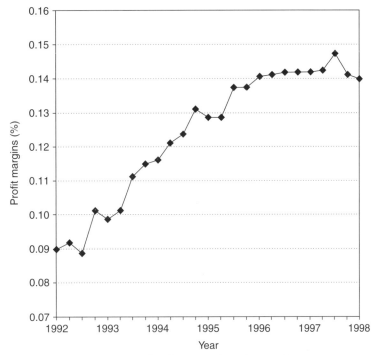

Fig. 6.3. Profit margins per unit of real output of nonfinancial US corporations (1992–1998). Source: US Commerce Department.

Table 6.1. Southern California egg industry profitability (1925–1997).

Year	Eggs laid per hen	No. of hens per flock	Feed cost per cwt	Egg farm price (dozen)	Profitability (5 year average)	
					US$ hen^{-1} year^{-1}	¢ dozen^{-1} year^{-1}
1925–1929	144	1,196	2.54	31.2	0.47	3.92
1930–1934	148	1,219	1.74	21.0	−0.06	−0.49[a]
1935–1939	164	1,278	1.81	23.3	0.47	3.43
1940–1944	177	1,953	2.25	33.8	1.37	9.26[b]
1945–1949	183	2,123	3.81	50.2	1.43	9.35
1950–1954	209	2,469	4.00	47.0	1.82	10.46[c]
1955–1959	232	4,357	3.51	37.3	0.87	4.51
1960–1964	238	13,053	3.12	30.3	1.20	6.06[d]
1965–1969	239	37,008	2.93	28.5	0.72	3.62
1970–1974	233	56,000	4.04	32.6	−0.30	−1.55
1975–1979	234	67,000[e]	5.82	45.1	0.51	2.62
1980–1984	n/a	n/a	8.30	51.0	−0.19	−0.96[f]
1985–1989	n/a	n/a	7.38	48.7	0.26	1.26[f]
1990–1994	n/a	n/a	7.63	49.9	0.44	2.09[f]
1995–1997	260[f]	300,000[g]	8.82	55.7	0.70	3.32[h]

[a]Great Depression; [b]World War II; [c]Korean War; [d]Vietnam War; [e]estimated; [f]extrapolated from eggs per hen; [g]US average; [h]economic boom.

been for many years the largest egg production region in the USA. Most of the Southern Californian production is represented by shell eggs, with a relatively small amount of egg products. Table 6.1 demonstrates that the growth of the average egg farm until 1959 was modest, and the average farm contained several thousand hens. Rapid expansion started in 1960 and reached an average of 300,000 hens per farm in 1997. (Since 1980, the number of hens and laying records have been kept confidential.) In that period, major investment loans were needed to finance the expansion in equipment, facilities and hired labour needed to run a large operation.

Structure life span is generally 20 years and equipment life is 10 years. Common commercial loans range from 10 to 20 years. Shorter loan periods and extending the usage of facilities beyond their useful life gave many farmers a period of financial relief by retaining higher egg profits. The majority of family farms were commonly under-capitalized and, therefore, constantly in debt. This made them vulnerable to long periods of a depressed egg market or high interest rates. Furthermore, depreciation expenses, which should be put aside to finance future expansion, were commonly used to offset unexpected losses, resulting in larger future loans.

The interest and depreciation expenses strongly reduce profitability, which is expressed as cents per dozen eggs per year or US$ per chicken per year in Table 6.1. Furthermore, the tight financial conditions and the unpredicted strong fluctuation in egg revenue due to uncontrolled egg surpluses often resulted in investment decision errors by inexperienced farmers which could dry up their cash flow and eliminate their equity. The low profitability and higher financial risks led to a record number of egg farms disappearing due to bankruptcies, quitting the business, producing other farm products or consolidating with larger operations. The inability to attract the next generation into the family farming business also caused many farms to cease production. The enormous appreciation of land prices since 1965 sweetened the transition. In the last century, most US egg producers disappeared, and their number was reduced from 5 million in 1900 to 10,000 farms in 1976, to 2310 in 1986 and to 341 farms in 1997, many of them with over 1,000,000 hens. US consolidation is still strong at about 5–10% per year. In the year 2000, it is expected that 300 farms will remain active, where 25 of them will control 80% of all the eggs produced. This phenomenon is common to many other agricultural sections, and farmers still top the list of disappearing occupations (Table 6.2). Similar trends exist in many countries.

Science and technology dramatically improve operation efficiency. Hens laid 81% more eggs in 1997 than in 1925. Feed cost rose 247%, but hens became much lighter in weight and ate much less feed. Hen mortality is also down. However, as with many other agricultural commodities, the inability of egg producers to increase prices of shell eggs reverses many of these benefits. The agricultural product price increase index is lagging behind that of processed food and most manufacturing sections, as demonstrated by the producer price index for 1975–1996 (Table 6.3). During this period, agricultural products rose by 49% compared with 89.4% for processed foods and feed,

Table 6.2. Growing and declining occupations in the USA (1994–2005).

Occupations	Growth/decline
Computer scientist and systems analyst	+755,000
Sales force	+441,000
Security	+415,000
Restaurant and food service managers	+192,000
Bank tellers	−152,000
Typists and word processors	−221,000
Farmers	−273,000

Table 6.3. US producers price index (1982 = 100).

	1975	1980	1985	1990	1995	1996	Total change (%)
Agricultural products	77.0	102.9	95.1	112.2	107.4	114.8	49.0
Textiles	67.4	89.7	102.9	114.9	120.8	122.7	82.0
Processed food and feed	72.6	95.9	103.5	121.9	127.0	134.2	84.8
Metals and metal products	61.5	95.0	104.4	123.0	134.5	124.9	111.2
Machinery	57.9	86.0	107.2	120.7	126.6	126.2	118.0
Chemicals	62.0	89.0	103.7	123.6	142.5	143.2	131.0
Wood products	62.1	101.5	106.6	129.7	178.1	179.7	189.4

Source: US Department of Labor, Bureau of Labor Statistics, 1997.

118% for machinery and 131% for chemicals. Southern California egg price increases are far below the agricultural product average.

The inability to increase prices and to control chronic egg surpluses strongly affected profit margins. The profitability of shell eggs has deteriorated greatly since 1965 as compared with the previous 40 years. In the last 15 years (1983–1997) the average annual profitability for a dozen eggs in Southern California stood at 2 cents dozen^{-1} year^{-1}. Strong annual profit fluctuations are also characteristic of shell eggs, ranging from +11.7 to −6.7 cents dozen^{-1} year^{-1}. This profit average can be converted to 42 cents hen^{-1} year^{-1}.

However, according to Chilson and associates, Rancho Cucamonga, California, an almost constant gap in profitability of about 6–8 cents dozen^{-1} year^{-1} exists between the top third and bottom third egg producers. As a result, in 1994, top producers made on average 5-6 cents dozen^{-1} year^{-1} (or US$1.26 hen^{-1} year^{-1}) which is considered to be a good income, whereas many inefficient producers lost money. The burden of borrowing money accounts for up to 5 cents dozen^{-1} year^{-1}, however, the average loan expenses are already incorporated into the profitability figures. The combination of efficiency and debt has a strong effect on the profitability of an individual company.

An example of a shell egg company with limited products can be illustrated by Cal-Main Foods Inc., the largest shell egg company in the USA. This company has over 15 million birds and a market share of 7.5% of all eggs sold in the USA. Shell eggs account for 92% of sales and egg products for 6%.

In the 9 months ending on 28 February, 1998, sales grew by US$8.5 million to US$232.5 million but profits dropped from US$14 million to US$6.2 million. The company pursues a strong acquisition programme, which was responsible for the increase in revenue but was strongly criticized by analysts for not being able to improve its profit margins. The company issued about 13 million shares in late 1986 at US$8 per share (NASDAQ CALM). However, without high profit margins and no future change in sight, the stock is constantly underperforming at US$6.25 in April 1998 (Fig. 6.4). In September 1999 the stock dropped further to 4³⁄₁₆ while sales grew to 10% of all US eggs.

The picture of shell egg production drawn by this analysis can easily be misleading, appearing to show that shell eggs are low profit products. On the contrary, dairy Delis and eggs are the most profitable profit centres in many supermarkets today. However, egg producers do not earn much out of it, in 1995, egg producers in California had net profits of US$6 million. The same eggs brought US$300 million to retail outlets. In many other states, egg producers earn more for their shell eggs and supermarkets share is less of the huge egg profits, depending on the different supermarket philosophies and the bargaining strength of local producers. However, most shell eggs are still a commodity and egg producers are still at a disadvantage in obtaining a reasonable share of the egg profits. In countries with a controlled economy, producers are much better off but have to yield to quotas on hens and price caps on eggs, which limit their total revenue. These economics are generally protected by trade barriers, many of which are supposed to decline or be removed within 5 years.

Effect of egg products on the bottom line

Egg consumption has declined in most developed countries. In the last 4 years, egg consumption stabilized in the USA and even increased by four eggs per

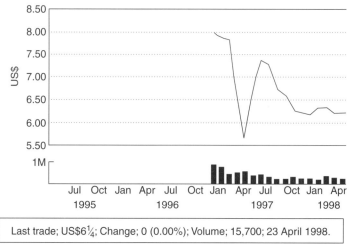

Last trade; US$6¼; Change; 0 (0.00%); Volume; 15,700; 23 April 1998.

Fig. 6.4.   Stock performance of Cal-Main Foods Inc. (CALM, NASDAQ).
Source: Iverson Financial Systems, Inc. (www.cnnfn.com).

Table 6.4. Per capita consumption of shell eggs and egg products in the USA (1945–1997).

Year	Shell eggs	Eggs products	Total
1945	379	23	402
1950	364	25	389
1955	346	25	371
1960	292	29	321
1965	286	29	315
1970	277	34	311
1975	247	30	277
1980	237	36	273
1985	218	38	256
1990	187	48	235
1995	172	64	236
1996	171	66	237
1997	169	70	239

Source: USDA, ERS, Poultry Yearbook and Livestock, Dairy and Poultry, 1997.

capita to 239 in 1997. However, as Table 6.4 indicates, shell egg consumption continued to decline to 169 in 1997, and stabilization was achieved by a constant increase in egg products to 70 eggs per capita in 1997. A similar trend can be observed in numerous EEC countries. Shell eggs are a premium product for the egg producer, whereas egg products used to be an avenue for disposing of small, irregular, cracked and surplus eggs at much lower price. However, the egg product market has expanded rapidly as it overcomes the major disadvantages of shell eggs.

1. Shell eggs are less convenient to handle, transport and for use in meal preparation. Yaffee *et al.* (1991) found that young adults and students see shell egg preparation as messy and time consuming, with a need to clean up afterwards. They consume fewer eggs than the national average, and many prefer to eat them away from home in food service outlets.
2. Shell eggs are associated with food safety problems resulting from *Salmonella enteritidis*. *S. enteritidis* can penetrate the egg through ovarian transmittance, through cracks in the shell or by surviving in the shell pores attached to the membrane where they are protected from sanitizers. The egg content can be contaminated by a significant number of *S. enteritidis* when the shell is broken during meal preparation (Zeidler *et al.*, 1999). Many food service and mass feeding operations such as hospitals, old peoples homes and schools, voluntarily or by law, have turned to liquid egg products which are pasteurized and safe.
3. Shell eggs are used mainly for breakfast, and the disappearance of the traditional home breakfast has strongly affected shell egg consumption. On the other hand, a large proportion of egg products are used for bakery, confectionery, salad dressing, surimi sauces and desserts, which are consumed at meals other than breakfast.

The development of ultrapasteurized extended shelf life chilled liquid egg products has enabled long range shipment as well as improved convenience, mainly to food service and mass feeding operations which prefer chilled rather than frozen egg products. This innovation has had a major effect on the increased utilization of liquid egg products.

Numerous egg products were introduced into the retail market in recent years where egg substitutes currently have the largest niche. Total volume is still small compared with shell eggs, but profit margins are much higher. Egg substitutes are sold on average at 102% of the price of large shell eggs. Furthermore, egg substitutes are made from lower cost egg whites and successfully compete with shell eggs despite low palatability and inferior egg characteristics. Here again, egg producers are at a disadvantage, as food companies and supermarkets share most of the profits from retail egg products whereas egg producers receive a tiny fraction of them.

A potential problem for the highly capitalized low profit margin shell egg companies is the possibility of being taken over by food companies which have the technical ability and the financial resources to transform shell eggs into high profit margin products and market them successfully. The cost of an average new shell egg farm with packaging capability is US$10–15 million, and the emerging mega farms make this possibility a reality. Michael Foods Inc. was an insignificant potato and dairy company, which entered the egg business by purchasing three large egg companies which were active in further processing. It also bought patented key technologies and started a strong product development programme. Within a few years, it became an almost US$1 billion food/egg company, controlling about 50% of all US liquid egg products. Wall Street loved the idea, and by 1997 their stock more than tripled to US$29 (MIKL, NASDAQ, 22 million shares, US$1.51 EPS) (Fig. 6.5), on September 1999 the stock kept its price level and was traded around $28 million.

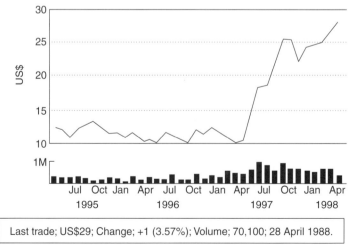

Fig. 6.5. Stock performance of Michael Foods Inc. (MIKL, NASDAQ).
Source: Iverson Financial Systems, Inc. (www.cnnfn.com).

The example of Michael Foods triggered strong product development programmes in many US companies and around the world.

Egg products also became an integrated part of the egg industry in countries that can develop sufficient low cost poultry feed, such as India, Thailand,
Brazil, Argentina and Venezuela. These countries are emerging as producers of
low cost shell eggs, and liquid, frozen and dry egg products which are already
causing major problems for traditional egg exporters such as The Netherlands
and, in the future, will cause problems for the USA. A large proportion of their
production is marketed in the Pacific Basin and, more recently, in the EEC.
Other potential countries such as the Ukraine will follow after the necessary
infrastructure is developed. On the other hand, China, the largest egg producer
in the world (40% of all eggs), will not become a major exporter as it is
increasingly dependent on grain imports. However, after the Hong Kong
take-over in 1997, China started to provide Hong Kong, the worlds largest shell
egg importer, with a large proportion of its needs and reduced most imports.

Consumer Needs and Wants in an Era of Rapid Economic, Social and Lifestyle Changes

Many US economic practices and associated life style changes are watched
carefully around the world. The principles of a free market became recognized
worldwide, and most countries started to tailor it to their own specific situation
and to the external pressures resulting from global economy and international
trade. The desire to preserve local cultural, tradition and life style has a strong
effect on the specifics and speed of a country's transformation.

Many changes, which were initiated in the USA after World War II or even
since the beginning of the 20th century, are accelerating toward the 21st
century. The average life expectancy, which stood at 46 years in 1900, almost
doubled and will pass 80 years in the near future. Soon, newly retiring people
will have about 20 years to live beyond their official retirement. Older people
are now healthier, more financially secure, and many remain active profession-
ally, socially and in leisure. Over 60% of those over 100 years old live an
independent life alone, with their family or in an active elderly community.
Currently, the elderly have the lowest poverty segment among all age groups,
whereas in the 1950s and 1960s they had the largest poverty segment. Most
importantly, those over 65 years of age are the fastest growing age group in
America, predicted to make up more than 20% of the population by the year
2025 (Table 6.5). The baby boomers, the best-educated and well to do generation, who were born between 1946 and 1964 are turning 50 and will soon start
to retire. The USA being a major economic and political power assures that the
rights and financial interest of the elderly are well secured. Strongly depending
on the medical profession, the mature and the elderly are dictating to the
market many of the healthy nutritional specifications for new products. As they
are able to pay, these strong requests turn into multibillion product lines.

Women entered the work force in large numbers during World War II
and are now an irreplaceable part of the two-salary household (only 16%
of married couples live on one income). Their fight for equal opportunity,

Table 6.5.   Projected changes in age segments in the USA (in millions).

Age group	1995	2005	Ten year change (%)
Total population	263.4	288.3	9.5
5–17 years	48.9	53.7	9.8
25–34 years	41.7	36.8	−11.8
45–64 years	51.4	70.1	36.4
75+ years	15.7	18.4	20.0

Source: Census Bureau, 1997 (www.census.gov).

income and job satisfaction has resulted in their being employed in almost every profession. The salary gap between men and women is closing, and in 1997 it stood at a 20% difference for the same job. Currently, women head about 65% of all entrepreneurial new businesses, and 46% of potential senior executives are women (currently only 4% of women are in senior executive positions). That is bad news for home cooking as more and more women do not have the time or the desire to prepare meals from scratch except for special events. Furthermore, more and more women do not know how to cook and depend on food prepared by others.

The computer and telecommunication revolution has brought more wealth to the USA than all other industries combined, and they affect every aspect of business and personal life. As a result, the demand for skilled workers dramatically increases where machines are constantly replacing low skilled workers. Productivity and profitability are being pushed to the extreme in the name of a stable and prosperous economy (low inflation rate) and successful global competition. Since 1990, corporate America spent more than one trillion dollars on high technology systems. Together with the continuous down sizing and labour force reduction, productivity was greatly improved. Productivity soared in 1997 to a record 5.6% in the manufacturing sector and 2% for the whole of the USA. At the same time, 80,000 employees lost their job in the first quarter of 1998, 35,000 of them in high tech, where 230,000 new jobs were created. The push for higher productivity pressures all employees to a longer workday, less weekend and vacation time (Table 6.6), and more time for upgrading skills. A total of 70% of all Americans are spending a part of their weekend in work-related activities. On the positive side, the gross domestic product (GDP) (Fig. 6.6) and per capita income are soaring (Table 6.7). Americans enjoy the highest standard of living (Table 6.8), per capita income and the best food buying power in the world (Fig. 6.7). They own more cars, computers, TVs, stereos, appliances and other electronic wonders than the population of any other industrial country.

However, part of the social cost is less leisure time, less sleep time than needed (just over 5 h per night) and a lower life expectancy than other industrial nations (Table 6.9). Long working hours, high divorce rates and the break up of families affect children who are left without sufficient supervision after school hours (≈55% of them) while parents are at work. Most teenage pregnancies and juvenile crimes occur between 3 and 7 p.m. The gap between

Table 6.6.   Paid holidays and vacations in various countries.

Countries	No. of days
Germany	40
Belgium	38.5
Austria	38
Spain	38
Luxembourg	37
France	36.5
Sweden	36
Greece	35
Italy	33.5
USA	20

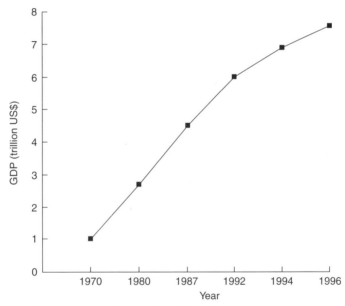

Fig. 6.6.   US Gross Domestic Product (in trillions).

Table 6.7.   Personal and household income in the USA (1935–1996).

Year	1935	1945	1955	1965	1970	1975	1980	1985	1990	1995	1996
Per capita income (US$)	474	1223	1881	2773	3893	5,851	9,910	13,896	18,636	23,196	24,231
Per four person family (US$)						15,848	24,332	32,777	41,151	49,687	

Source: US Department of Commerce, 1997 (www.doc.gov).

corporate highest and lowest salaries and that between rich and poor keep expanding. The number of poor in the USA rose to over 30 million, whereas the upper 10% now own over 60% of the wealth (up from 45% in 1980). Lower quality education and medical services, higher infant mortality rates, shorter

Table 6.8. Standard of living in seven major industrial democracies. (Gross domestic product per capita, 1991.)

Country	Percentage of USA
USA	100
Germany	87.2
Canada	87.1
Japan	85.8
France	82.7
Italy	76.4
Great Britain	72.5

Table 6.9. Life expectancy in various industrialized nations. (Calculated from birth, 1991.)

Country	Years
Japan	78.8
Iceland	78.0
Switzerland	78.0
Sweden	77.6
Canada	77.4
The Netherlands	77.1
France	76.8
Australia	76.7
Germany	76.2
USA	76.0

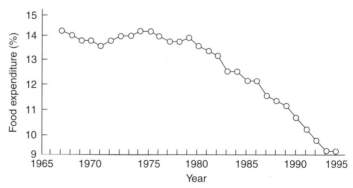

Fig. 6.7. Food expenditures in the USA as a percentage of disposable income (1967–1995). Source: US Department of Agriculture (www.USDA.gov).

life expectancy, lack of needed professional skills, weak family structure and a higher crime rate are associated more with the less fortunate. As a result, America became a more polar 'angry' and less patient society, with significantly less happiness and life satisfaction than other industrialized nations (Table 6.10). Some of these trends are also beginning to develop in other countries.

Major changes in the economy and in life style strongly influenced eating habits. The average American family has about 1 h per day for dinner, which includes purchasing, preparing, eating and cleaning up. Ordinary poultry meat and, in particular, red meat, takes too long to cook and prepare and, therefore, does not fit into this tight regime. Unfortunately, eggs, which can easily fit these requirements, do not feature as an item for lunch or dinner. The new generation of food products is better adapted to the new eating trends. These include time-saving meal preparation, such as microwaving and other rapid cooking methods, and the use of ready-to-eat and ready-to-cook meal components or whole meal replacements. Time saving on cleaning up has been achieved by use of disposable and multipurpose packages which can be used for cooking in, warming up in and eating from, also significantly reducing time spent in the kitchen. An attractive nutritional profile and ease of preparation successfully satisfy the needs of different age groups and genders. An extensive product variety for ethnic, religious and various income levels further expanded the use of these products (Friedman *et al.*, 1996).

Eating away from home and carry-out of prepared food to eat at home is constantly increasing, and in 1994 passed retail store sales. About 60% of all meats and 25% of all eggs are consumed away from home. The cost of food in the USA is the lowest in the world, and stood at 9.3% of the GDP in 1995 (Fig. 6.7). This enables the average consumer to have almost a free choice in selecting his/her foods and their degree of preparation. Furthermore, this dramatic reduction in expenses on food since the 1950s, where 33% of the GDP was spent on food, left the American people in 1996 with US$336 billion of net income to spend on whatever they like. Since the 1950s, US$23 trillion of net income was saved. Unfortunately, the low food cost is associated with a large

Table 6.10. Life satisfaction and happiness in various industralized countries (1991).

Country	Life satisfaction	Happiness	Overall index
Iceland	82	95	89
Sweden	80	92	86
The Netherlands	82	88	85
Denmark	81	88	85
Northern Ireland	78	86	82
Norway	74	88	81
Ireland	74	86	80
Belgium	72	82	77
USA	73	80	77
Finland	71	80	76

amount of waste. Twenty-five per cent of the food produced in the USA (96.7 billion pounds) is spoiled or wasted (harvest losses are not included) (Table 6.11). This includes 31% of all eggs and 16% of all meat and fish. A major effort is being made to salvage part of this food, which could feed about 85 million people year round. The modern consumer is interested in convenience, food safety, improved nutritional profile, a variety of products for every occasion and, lately, 'home cooking' taste and more gourmet and luxury items. For many segments of the population, price is not a top priority any more for the products of their choice. A ready-to-cook package with two chicken breasts, for example, costs more than a whole chicken. This opened up a golden opportunity for the food industry to develop many high profit margin products and to improve their overall profitability.

Present and Future Egg Products

In developed countries, the processed food market is a dynamic but saturated market as population growth is very small. A great opportunity to increase profit margins was opened up to the food industry when many in all segments of the population were able to pay for better-tailored, more expensive food products of their choice. The immense benefits from successful new products resulted in extensive new product development which reached almost 17,000 in 1995 up from 7000 ten years earlier (Fig. 6.8). Egg products are more active in food service than in retail. However, the number of new products in both categories has significantly increased in the last 7 years, but it still lags behind most food categories. Tyson Co., the world's largest poultry meat company which processes 70 million hens per week, places top priority on new product development, and introduces over 300 new products each year. It has also constructed plants specifically for further processing, one of which is dedicated solely to McDonald's products. Product development is expensive

Table 6.11.   Food production and food wasted[a] in the USA.

Commodity	Food supply (million lbs)	Food waste (million lbs)	% Waste
Grain products	45,606	14,546	32
Fruit	48,338	11,310	23
Vegetables	63,077	15,946	25
Dairy products	76,276	25,408	32
Red meat, poultry and fish	51,466	8,235	16
Eggs	7,918	2,486	31
Dry beans, peas and lentils	2,263	359	16
Nuts	1,861	295	16
Sweeteners	38,827	11,861	31
Fat, oils	20,250	6,767	33
Total	355,882	96,267	27

[a]Harvest losses not included.
Source: Economic Research Service, USDA, 1996.

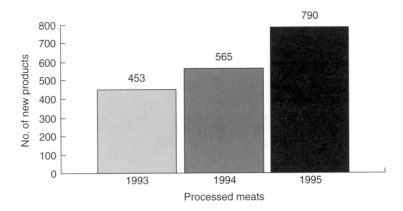

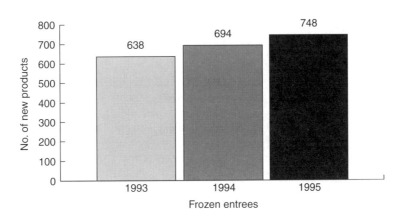

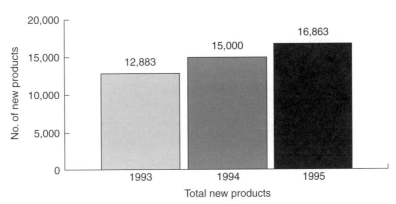

Fig. 6.8. New food product introductions in the USA.

as about 85% of all new products fail or cannibalize and disappear within a few years. Acquiring new successful products through mergers and acquisitions is cheaper and, therefore, mergers and acquisitions in the food processing business have reached record heights in the last few years.

Several processed food categories are now in high demand:

1. Home meal replacements (HMRs)
2. Nutraceuticals fortified food products
3. Safe foods
4. Low/no fat and cholesterol foods.

Eggs have some representatives in these categories. However, most effort is still made in the traditional products for industrial and food service use. As a result, retail outlets handle a limited amount of egg products and specialty shell eggs.

Home meal replacements (HMR)

In 1994, supermarket chains around the USA were shaken by the news that sales from eating away from home surpassed retail outlet sales. Sixty per cent of meats were also consumed away from home. In the drive to regain customers and lost sales, HMR became an effective measure. In 1996 and 1997, purchases of HMRs from supermarkets and specialty stores rose at the expense of take out from food service and restaurants. It is expected that HMR will become a US$100 billion niche. HMR uses the fact that in general consumers prefer to eat their main meal of the day at home, but do not have the time or the energy to prepare it from scratch. They visit the supermarket 2.2 times a week and prefer to purchase HMRs if a variety of desired products is available. For many, the time saving is more important than the price.

The nine factors which make HMR a success are: (i) convenience; (ii) taste; (iii) price/value; (iv) Nutrition; (v) safety; (vi) point of differentiation; (vii) appearance; (viii) suitable portion size; and (ix) clear preparation instructions.

HMRs fall into in several major categories:

1. ready to eat – sold hot or cold for immediate consumption
2. ready to heat – takes less than 5 min to reheat
3. ready to cook
    - cooked in less than 10 min: stir-fry or grilled products
    - cooked in 30 min or less: stuffed breasts, roast chops, etc.

In order to provide a taste similar to that of home cooking and an authentic flavour, many HMRs are prepared as short shelf life and minimally processed products. The shelf life of the better tasting products ranges from several days to 2 weeks. They are protected by precise chilling temperatures and multilayer barrier packaging, but hardly at all with preservatives. A modified/controlled atmosphere is frequently used. Short range and efficient distribution directly to stores is essential for the short shelf life products. In some cases, products are prepared during the night, are on the shelf the next morning and are gone in 1 or 2 days. HMR in many cases is placed in the Deli section – the highest profit centre for the supermarket – and therefore they provide a high profit margin to producers and supermarkets alike. Under these conditions, supermarkets are more than willing to accommodate unique products by reducing or eliminating various fees, providing an opportunity for small local producers.

A variety of HMR products are available currently in the market (Farquhar, 1997). Poultry meats are one of the most active in this category (Fig. 6.9). Hot and cold red meats, fish, salads, soups, cut vegetables and fruit, party trays and ethnic foods are some of the other HMR categories. Egg products are currently lightly represented in the form of quiche and sliced hard boiled eggs, but have a great potential. Processing easily destroys egg texture and authentic flavour, which has limited the number of successful processed egg products in the past. The new technology will enable the production of egg products, which preserve fresh egg characteristics which consumers appreciate highly. Various products can be made in cooperation with chefs and caterers in modern processing lines but also in low volume commissary kitchens. Mallard is an up-scaled Californian restaurant which started to manufacture poultry meat HMRs ready to eat in 7 min. In a short time, sales reached US$40 million before the operations were sold to Tyson. It is now foreseen that HMRs will be one of the more important supermarket categories to bring back consumers and to improve profit margins.

Reducing fat and cholesterol

Reduced fat and cholesterol products are now a mature US$15 billion category in the USA. In other countries, there is less interest in the topic, which is reflected in the number of available products. Fat and cholesterol reduction level generally range from none to moderate. In the USA, fat content (but not saturated fat) is the most read information on the product nutritional label. On the contrary, interest in cholesterol has fallen for consumers in the same way as salt and sugar, as they became tired and confused by conflicting information. Numerous research works indicate that food cholesterol does not significantly increase serum cholesterol in healthy young people. Nevertheless, the American Heart Association (AHA) did not relax the four eggs per week (208 eggs year^{-1}) limit on egg consumption, and many physicians further imposed stricter restrictions on their patients. The AHA also believe that food cholesterol plays a part in artherosclerosis which affects all segments of the population and even children 8–10 years old. Therefore, the cholesterol issue could return to the headlines in the future.

Like eggs, poultry meat and dairy products also supply the food system with a large amount of fat and cholesterol (Table 6.12). To address the issue, a huge array of products were developed ranging from none to extremely high levels of fat and cholesterol, enabling consumers to choose the products that fit their needs, and eliminating the negative comments and restrictions that eggs received. Furthermore, they succeeded in receiving the endorsement of the AHA for major fat-free products sold in restaurants and in retail stores. Non-fat milk is one of these products. In addition to the AHA purple-heart

Fig. 6.9. Up to 2 weeks shelf life home meal replacement (HMR) new products. Portion sizes are from individual meal to party tray size. Chicken cordon bleu (top); Turkey, mash potatoes and green beans dinner (middle); shrimp and krab louie salad with surimi and hard boiled eggs (bottom).

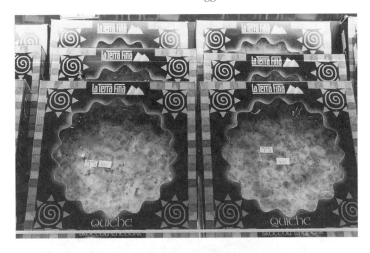

Fig. 6.9. *Continued.* Quiche with eggs (top); cut vegetables party tray (middle); turkey and swiss cheese tortillas roller – a California sandwich (bottom).

Fig. 6.9. *Continued.* Chicken salad (top); various sushi and sahimi party tray (bottom).

endorsement, a statement on the new non-fat milk carton reads 'may help to reduce serum triglycerides and cholesterol'. Egg substitutes are the only fat- and cholesterol-free product in this category. Growth is currently small due to low egg flavour and characteristics, but sales have reached about US$200 million. Recently, an edible film technology was used to create a whole egg substitute by producing a yolk look-alike, which is attached to egg white. This product is packaged in a small tub and enables the consumer to prepare 'sunny side up' and poached eggs.

The enormous low fat and cholesterol campaign and the huge number of available products did not help the American public to reduce their average weight (it increased). This failure triggered a new trend to relax fat restrictions and to try to achieve better results through improved eating quality, dietary variety and moderation, which will improve quality of life. Some products are already in the market, such as egg substitute, which includes 20% yolk (Fig. 6.10).

Table 6.12.   Fat, saturated fat and cholesterol contribution of certain animal products to the US diet in 1996.

	US annual production (billions)	Cholesterol (mg per 1.0 kg food)	Fat (%)	Saturated fats (%)	Total cholesterol (tonnes)	Total fat (million tonnes)	Total saturated fat (million tonnes)
Fresh milk	154.331 lbs	175	3.7	2.4	12,276	2.60	1.68
Broilers	26.823 lbs	527	6.0	1.6	6,425	0.74	0.20
Shell eggs	76.184 eggs	3707	7.0	2.3	16,370	0.31	0.10
Eggs consumed	61.360 eggs	3707	7.0	2.3	13,192	0.25	0.082

Fig. 6.10.   Relaxed fat and cholesterol attitudes resulted in egg substitute with 20% yolk.

Food safety

The eruption of more virulent and sometimes deadly pathogens in the mid 1980s resulted in the implementation of various Hazard Analysis of Critical Control Points (HACCP) programmes along the food chain in many countries. Shell eggs became vulnerable, as sanitizing did not completely destroy *S. enteritidis*, which could get into the egg through transovarian transmittance or cracks in the shell, or could find shelter inside the shell pores. Several egg products were introduced claiming safer eggs for a large premium (Fig. 6.11). However, some of these products attracted strong resistance as high product safety is regarded as the responsibility of the producer and not a justification for high profits is regarded as the duty of the producer. Therefore, emphasis is now being placed on improving safety through processing technology. Improving cooling rates of shell eggs in order to bring the internal temperature to less than 45°F in the shortest time possible, thus suppressing microbial growth, was developed using cryogenic cooling of loose eggs in North Carolina State University (Anderson *et al.*, 1992) and by forced air cooling of packaged eggs was developed in University of California (Zeidler *et al.*, 1998).

The first system, which pasteurized shell eggs, is now being tested. The FPS Hydro-175 pasteurizes 175 cases h^{-1} of shell eggs through three water baths at varying temperatures between 130 and 140°F and then chilling them to 45°F internal yolk temperature in a fourth water bath. The manufacturer claims a five log reduction of *Salmonella* without thermally affecting the egg content. The major drawback is the high price paid for the low output machine. Other systems, which use different concepts, are also being developed.

Numerous European poultry meat and egg companies have integrated HACCP in ISO 9002 registration, which stands for high quality and safe operations. The majority of consumers are not aware of HACCP or ISO 9000, which are used mainly in trade. Good and continual educational programmes can increase brand loyalty for HACCP and ISO 9000 users, thus improving profit margins.

Fig. 6.11.   Health eggs – ozone treated eggs. A very high premium Israeli product.

Fortification of shell eggs and egg products

Fortification with nutraceuticals is currently a rapidly expanding category in the USA, which had already reached sales of US$16–17 billion in 1997. Nutraceuticals are food components, which also provide health benefits for better well-being and disease prevention. Shell eggs were one of the first products to be fortified after experience was gained in the effort to reduce cholesterol by nutritional means. It was found that the profile of fatty acids, fat-soluble vitamins and minerals, such as iodine, fluorine, manganese and B vitamins, of the egg could be altered easily. Designer eggs were the commercial shell egg products, which were enriched in ω-3 fatty acids, ω-6 fatty acids or vitamin E. Iodine is allowed to be used in Japan but is prohibited in the USA. Dr Sim's Canadian Designer Eggs (Alberta, Canada) (Fig. 6.12) were one of the first ω-3 commercial products, and today this product can be found in many countries. Extensive literature and review articles justify the benefits from the supplementation (Van Elswyk, 1993, 1997; Scheideler and Froning, 1996, Scheideler and Froning *et al.*, 1997; Miles, 1998). In most cases, designer eggs as well as other specialty eggs such as organic and vegetarian diets are charging and getting a high premium, and are capturing up to 5% of the shell egg market.

The major disadvantages of designer eggs are a low enrichment level and almost worldwide prohibition on making medical or physiological claims. Eggs can be enriched with about 2 mg g^{-1} of ω-3 fatty acids, whereas wild salmon or tuna can reach up to 14 mg g^{-1}. Specifically, farm-grown salmon (Sal Omega Salmon) can reach 30 mg g^{-1}. The fish industry is preparing a strong campaign with ω-3, especially the ailing tuna industry. No major price hiking is planned. Fish products could use claims, as most research was conducted using deep-sea fish meals as part of the treatment. ω-3 Fatty acids can also be consumed in the form of gelatin capsules, which contain 200 mg and cost a fraction of the fortified egg price. A large-scale production of these acids by Hoffman/LaRoche makes fortification of any food an easy task.

ω-3 Fatty acids have been found to have many health benefits such as 70% reduction of death due to heart attack. However, most consumers are not

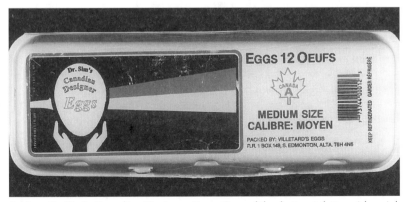

Fig. 6.12.   Dr Sim's Canadian Designer Eggs. One of the first ω-3 fatty acid enriched shell eggs.

aware of these benefits. A continuous education programme about the benefits of ω-3 fatty acids does not exist, running the risk that these products will become a fad. Eggs can be enriched with vitamin E up to sixfold, to 6 IU up from the normal level in eggs of 1 IU which count as 12% of the daily RDA. However, many consumers are routinely taking 400–1000 IU vitamin E in the form of capsules daily which make this fortification meaningless for them. Under the current situation, major growth of this egg category is not forecast.

References

Anderson, K.E., Jones F.T. and Curtis, P.A. (1992) *Heat Loss from Commercially Packaged Eggs in Past-Processing Coolers.* Extension Report in Poultry Science, North Carolina Cooperation Extension Service.

Burns, G., Lindorff, D., Carey, J. and Mandel, M.J. (1996) *The New Economics of Food Business Week,* May 20, pp. 78–84.

Evans, T. (1995) Broiler production costs around the world. *Broiler Industry* 58 (12), 38–44.

Farquhar, J.W. (1997) *Home Meal Replacement.* Proceedings of the 50th Annual Reciprocal Meat Conference, American Meat Science Association, 29 June–2 July, Ames, Iowa, pp. 19–20.

Friedman, M., Dornblaser, L. and Blaesing, D. (1996) New products come alive in '95. *Prepared Foods* 165 (5), 29–90.

Miles, R.D. (1998) Designer eggs: altering mother nature's most perfect food. In: Lyons, T.P. and Jacques, K.A. (eds), *Proceedings of Alltech's 19th Annual Symposium on Bio-technology in The Food Industry.* Nottingham, Nottingham University Press, pp. 423–435.

Scheideler, S.E. and Froning, G.W. (1996) The combined influence of dietary flaxseed variety, level, form and storage conditions on egg production and composition among vitamin E supplemented hens. *Poultry Science* 75, 1221–1226.

Scheidler, S.E., Froning, G.W. and Cuppett, S. (1997) Studies of consumer acceptance of high omega-3 fatty acid-enriched eggs. *Journal of Applied Poultry Research* 6, 137–146.

Swartzel, K.R., Ball H.R., Jr and Samimi, M. (1989) Method for ulltrapasteurization of liquid whole egg products. US Patent 4,808,425.

Van Elswyk, M.E. (1993) Designer foods: manipulating the fatty acid composition of meat and eggs for the health conscious consumer. *Nutrition Today* (Mar/Apr), 21–27.

Van Elswyk, M.E. (1997) Nutritional and physiological effects of flax seed in diets for laying fowl. *World's Poultry Science Journal* 53, 253–264.

Yaffee, M.H., Schutz, H., Stone, A., Bakhary, S. and Zeidler, G. (199 l) Consumer perception and utilization of eggs and egg products. *Poultry Science* 70 (Suppl. 1), 188.

Young, D. (1998) Food frontiers: multi-dimentional retail trends. *Meat and Poultry* 44 (3), 28–30.

Zeidler, G. (1995) ANUGA the crystal ball for worldwide poultry products. *Turkey World* 71 (5), 22–26.

Zeidler, G., Thompson, J., Kuney, D., Ernst, R. and Riemann, H. (1999) Low cost rapid cooling system of packaged shell eggs. *Proceedings of the 14th European Symposium on the Quality of Eggs and Egg Products,* 19–23 September, Bologna, Italy.

Giving Eggs a Bad Rap: What Physicians Should Know and Tell Their Patients About Cholesterol

7

M.V. Kaminski, Jr

Finch University of Health Sciences, The Chicago Medical School, North Chicago, Illinois, USA

The human body requires cholesterol. The liver manufactures approximately 3000 mg day^{-1}. This is equivalent to the cholesterol contained in one dozen eggs. Experts in human fat requirements state 'Cholesterol must not be avoided' in the diet. It is the base molecule, which is converted into steroid hormones, oestrogen, progesterone, testosterone and cortisol. If cholesterol is too low, brain- and nerve-related problems could develop.

Two recent studies have discredited the notion that eating eggs will increase cholesterol to dangerous levels (Schnohr *et al.*, 1994; Hu *et al.*, 1999. Further, it is now well accepted that high-density lipoproteins (HDL), the so-called 'good' cholesterol, is beneficial. HDL is elevated by activities such as exercise and modest consumption of alcohol. Low-density lipoprotein on the other hand is called the 'bad' cholesterol. When it is elevated, there is an association with increased arteriosclerosis, heart attack and stroke. New research indicates that the over-consumption of sugar and refined carbohydrates, not eggs, is strongly associated with obesity and elevation of bad cholesterol. Further, bad cholesterol does not enter the lining of a blood vessel to form an obstructing plaque unless it is oxidized. Thus the total mechanism must include activities or diseases associated with free radical generation and excess. These mechanisms include factors such as smoking and poorly controlled diabetes. These variables must then be balanced against the consumption of free radical scavengers such as vitamin A, C and E, selenium and others.

Good fats need to be eaten to maintain and promote healthy brain and nerves. Myelin is 75% fat, a quarter of which is cholesterol. Cholesterol is required for brain cell membrane stability. Two other very important fats are docosahexaenoic acid (DHA) and phosphatidylcholine. Eggs are a good source of these critical molecules. The brain is 70% fat, most of which is DHA. In the healthy brain, phospholipids are usually attached to DHA as the unsaturated fatty acid. Phospholipids also protect the nerves from injury and deterioration due to ingestion of toxins and endogenous free radical production. DHA deficiency has been implicated in attention deficit disorder and hyperactivity in children. Research has shown that supplementation with these fats has been used successfully to treat disorders such as schizophrenia, Alzheimer's disease and others. Therefore, high level use of eggs in the diet is recommended.

Cholesterol: Essential for Life

For the most part, physicians never tell their patients what we are about to review concerning the true role of dietary cholesterol in arteriovascular disease. In fact, some physicians themselves are initially unaware that cholesterol, a molecule essential for life, is by itself unrelated to coronary artery disease (Granner, 1998).

Seventy-five per cent of circulating cholesterol within the body is actually synthesized by the liver, and not directly eaten. Why does the body produce so much cholesterol on its own? Because cholesterol plays an essential role in fuelling metabolism and shaping the body's physical characteristics as the precursor of all steroid hormones, i.e. cortisol, male, female and mineral hormones (Fig. 7.1). Furthermore, cholesterol is a critical component of healthy brain and nerve cells (Fielding and Fielding, 1985). In fact, I become uneasy when a patient's serum cholesterol drops below 100 mg dl^{-1}. A cholesterol reading at this level in a patient in the intensive care unit is actually a sign that the patient is likely to die.

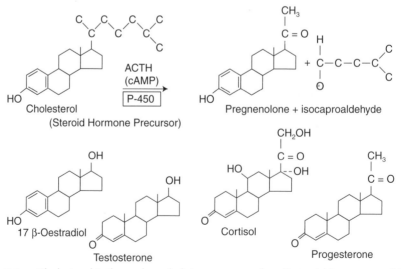

Basic Steroid Hormone Structures

Fig. 7.1. Cholesterol is the carbon skeleton precursor for all steroid hormones which are essential for life.

Total Cholesterol: Not the Villain of Vascular Disease

Total cholesterol, *per se*, does not cause atherosclerosis (Gibbons and Dzau, 1996). To understand the real molecular triggers behind vascular disease, one needs to explore the specific components and actions of cholesterol.

Most physicians are aware that, based on the size and density of the particle, cholesterol can be classified as high- or low-density lipoprotein (HDL or LDL). HDL is the 'good cholesterol'. In fact, an elevated HDL is protective; the higher the HDL, the lower the incidence of coronary artery disease. Several strategies can be used to raise HDL cholesterol. These include losing weight, drinking two glasses of red wine or grape juice a day, exercising and eating tofu.

In contrast, LDL cholesterol, the 'bad cholesterol', has been associated with an increased risk of systemic occlusive vascular disease, or 'hardening of the arteries'. Elevated LDL cholesterol is closely linked with obesity, a sedentary lifestyle, hyperglycaemia and hyperinsulinaemia, and the consumption of *trans*-fatty acids (found in margarine) and/or saturated fats (found in many fried foods). However, despite these negative associations, it is important to remember that LDL cholesterol by itself neither causes blood vessel injury nor induces plaque formation. The true villain in this vascular melodrama is oxidized LDL (Liao *et al.*, 1995).

This distinction is crucial because it allows us to protect the body against the specific agents that damage the arteries, by preventing the oxidation of LDL cholesterol. One approach is to utilize powerful antioxidants such as vitamins A, E and C, and selenium. In addition, certain phytochemicals found in foods, such as soy protein and ω-3-rich foods, can also down-regulate pro-oxidant activity.

Both ω-3 and ω-6 fatty acids are called 'essential' because they cannot be synthesized by the body. However, ω-3 serves as the precursor for anti-inflammatory prostaglandins, leukotrienes and thromboxanes, while ω-6 fatty acids produce mediators that are pro-inflammatory (Blok *et al.*, 1996). Since inflammation produces oxidizing free radicals, ω-3s are considered the most beneficial.

The Beginnings of Cholesterol 'Paranoia'

How we physicians got started down the road of paranoia about dietary cholesterol is a story well worth relating (Prior *et al.*, 1961). Over 20 years ago, an experiment was conducted on rabbits that involved feeding them high-fat diets and then administering cholesterol to them directly. Lo and behold, the rabbits soon developed fatty lesions in their arteries – and the 'scientific' link between cholesterol and arterial plaque was forever established.

As the results of this experiment quickly spread among the medical community, however, there was one important detail about the experiment that was commonly overlooked. The cholesterol that was administered to the rabbits came from a can that had been sitting open upon a shelf. Thus, the contents of the can had been oxidized by their contact with the open air. When the same experiment was repeated much later, using purified cholesterol, no arterial plaque was produced. That is because oxidized LDL was (and is) the culprit, not total cholesterol, whether HDL or LDL. Nevertheless, a nutritional obsession was born, and, as with any obsession based on a half-truth, it caused its own, often worse, set of problems.

A New Culprit: Excessively Refined Carbohydrates

The food industry responded to the public demand to reduce cholesterol and fat in the diet by creating fat-free food of all varieties. Foods that were always fat-free, such as pretzels, suddenly carried a label boasting that they were 'cholesterol-free'. Unfortunately, these and other fat-free snacks contained refined carbohydrate, including sugar and flour. Easily digested and absorbed, these carbohydrates quickly elevate the body's levels of blood glucose. That is why 'fat-free' does not mean calorie free.

It is now apparent that a general public crazed by the words 'no-' and 'low-fat' over-consumed these foods and, in the process, became much fatter. In fact, since fat-free products came on the market approximately 10 years ago, the average person has gained 10 lbs in weight (Steward *et al.*, 1995). Even worse, the over-consumption of refined carbohydrate appears to be causally linked to syndrome X (Fig. 7.2).

Syndrome X is a condition characterized by obesity, hypertension, insulin resistance, hyperinsulinaemia and hyperglycaemia (DeFronzo and Ferrannini, 1991). This metabolic derangement is fuelled by a poor diet and also produces hypercholesterolaemia, particularly elevation of LDL. Moreover, hyperglycaemia increases oxidative stress when glucose combines with proteins via a non-enzymatic process called 'the Maillard reaction'. In this process, glycosylated proteins lose their ability to guard against oxidation. Free radical-quenching defence proteins such as superoxide dismutase are rendered ineffective, and free radical formation escalates. We will examine this process in more detail below.

For now, the important point to remember is that free radicals oxidize LDL cholesterol. This oxidized LDL cholesterol, in turn, damages the vascular surface. Monocytes, a type of white cell, are attracted to the injury, and migrate beneath the surface to consume oxidized LDL cholesterol. These white cells then become the characteristic foam cell of arterial plaque, which causes narrowing of the blood vessel wall. Later they calcify and are occluded easily by a thrombus or blood clot, particularly during times of stress.

Glycosylation, Oxidative Stress and Ageing

Glycosylation is a process familiar to most physicians. In common practice, a physician assesses compliance of a diabetic patient by checking levels of both blood glucose and haemoglobin A1-C (Wolffenbuttel *et al.*, 1996). Haemoglobin A1-C is the glycosylated product of haemoglobin exposed to higher blood glucose levels over time. If the patient is 'well behaved' in following dietary guidelines during the inter-office visit period and blood sugar levels are kept in check, there will be little haemoglobin A1-C. If, on the other hand, the patient 'misbehaves' and becomes hyperglycaemic due to an undisciplined diet,

Glucose Regulation and Functional Physiology

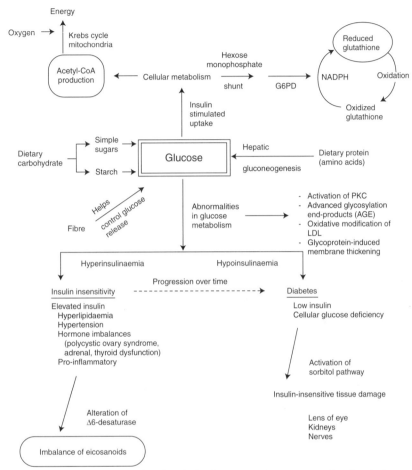

Fig. 7.2. A diet dominated by refined carbohydrate, simple sugar or other foods that result in a rapid rise in glucose and insulin is potentially lethal. The combination of excess calories with hyperinsulinaemia and hyperglycaemia results in disease as detailed in this figure. (Reprinted with permission of Jeffrey Bland, Healthcomm International, Gig Harbor, Washington.)

simply taking insulin before the office visit to lower blood sugar and 'masquerade' as a compliant patient will not work. In general, elevated haemoglobin A1-C confirms over-consumption of refined carbohydrate.

Protein glycosylation contributes directly to the accelerated ageing process seen in diabetics and indirectly accelerates ageing by increasing free radical activity. Unquenched free radical or reactive oxygen species (ROS) released through glycosylation not only oxidize LDL cholesterol, they can cause extensive damage to cells as well, thereby mediating the process of premature ageing, as well as the progression of many chronic diseases, including cancer. This mechanism of the ageing process, then, is not simply the passage of time (Harman, 1994). Rather, it is a loss of function that occurs as a direct result of degeneration triggered by ROS damage. Free radicals thus play a significant role in the formation of cataracts, advancing arthritis and renal insufficiency frequently associated with hypercholesterolaemia, especially in diabetics (Porte and Schwartz, 1996).

The Role of Saturated Fat and *Trans*-Fatty Acids

Saturated fat and *trans*-fatty acids are also causally related to coronary artery disease. Unfortunately, in a misguided effort to satisfy the public's growing demand for lower dietary cholesterol, these 'cholesterol-free' fats were heavily advocated by the food industry, and this just compounded the problem. If fried foods such as French fries and doughnuts are prepared in shortening, they become loaded with saturated fats. By substituting margarine for butter, an individual has simply elected to consume *trans*-fatty acids instead. In either case, an independent negative impact is sustained by increasing the formation of arterial plaque (Simopoulos, 1996). On the other hand, diets rich in olive oil (which contains monosaturated fats) and low in saturated and *trans*-fatty acids are associated with a decreased incidence of both heart disease and cancer.

Fighting Chronic Inflammation: ω-3 versus ω-6

In addition to quenching free radical activity, there are other anti-inflammatory dietary strategies that can lower the likelihood of developing coronary artery disease. Foods or supplements that provide a rich supply of antioxidants can be taken with ω-3 fatty acids. ω-3 down-regulates the conversion of ω-6/ arachidonic acid into pro-inflammatory prostaglandins, leukotrienes and thromboxanes, and it does not need much. The consumption of as little as three cold seawater fish meals a week has been associated with these benefits (Fig. 7.3).

The pro-inflammatory nature of ω-6 fatty acids is well established (Blok *et al.*, 1996), thus it is unfortunate that oils rich in ω-6 fatty acids, such as corn oil and safflower oil, are such commonly used vegetable oils for cooking today. Never before in the history of the world have humans been exposed to such high levels of dietary ω-6 and low levels of ω-3 fatty acids in the food supply. Ideally, optimal consumption would follow a 1 : 1 ratio, which is the natural ratio reflected in the composition of the cell membrane. Safflower oil is 70% ω-6 while corn oil is 40% ω-6. Thus, regular consumption of either of these oils quickly overwhelms the very modest ω-3 content in the diet of most people.

When a stressful event occurs, essential fatty acids are mobilized from cell membranes and converted to prostaglandins, leukotrienes and thromboxane mediators. However, if these mediators are derived predominantly from ω-6, the subsequent physiological response is 'over the top'. For example, prosta-glandin E_2, derived from ω-6, exaggerates a fever reaction, whereas prosta-glandin PGE_3, derived from ω-3, does not. As you might expect, thromboxane A_2, which causes extreme smooth muscle contraction and hypercoagulation, is synthesized from ω-6. Thromboxane A_3, derived from ω-3, has very nearly the opposite effect, and this may explain why Eskimos on very high-fat diets have a very low incidence of coronary artery disease and asthma. The same relationship holds true for the leukotrienes. While ω-3 produces leukotrienes of the five series which are generally anti-inflammatory, some of the leukotrienes of the four series formed from ω-6 produce an inflammatory response more than 1000 times that of histamine (Murakami *et al.*, 1994).

Therefore, avoiding oils high in ω-6 and consuming more oils rich in ω-3 is a very good idea. Flaxseed oil and canola oil both have very favourable essential fatty acid profiles. Switching to oils richer in ω-3, however, is just the first step. The second step is to understand what your body needs to process these beneficial fatty acids.

Unfortunately, during times of stress, not everyone is genetically equipped to process dietary ω-3 fatty acids into the functioning downstream fatty acids eicosapentaenoic acid (EPA) and docosahexaenoic acid (DHA) (Fig. 7.3). EPA is the precursor for anti-inflammatory prostaglandins, leukotrienes and thromboxanes. DHA is an essential component of healthy nerves and brain. Some individuals occasionally have inefficient activity of Δ5 and Δ6 desaturase. These enzymes convert ω-3 to EPA and DHA. Because fish and chicken have excellent Δ5 and Δ6 desaturase activity, fish oil and egg yolk are superior sources of EPA and DHA.

Knowing these key sources is important, because DHA deficiency can lead to serious neurological malfunction. Rats fed exclusively ω-6 fatty acids for three generations can no longer find their way out of a maze. It is disconcerting to know that in the USA we are into the third generation of children fed infant formula rich in ω-6 and deficient in ω-3 fatty acids. In Europe, infant formula has been supplemented with DHA for nearly a decade (Yokota, 1993). This is a critical infant nutritional issue for the USA, still undergoing consideration by the FDA.

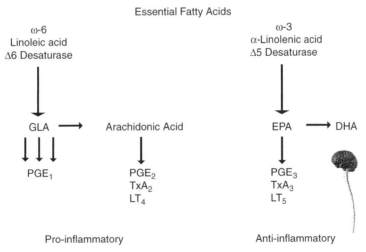

Fig. 7.3. Unlike some humans, fish and chickens have an uncompromised ability to convert α-linolenic acid (ω-3) into the anti-inflammatory products of EPA. Eating eggs and fish is, therefore, important to provide these nutrients beyond the Δ5-desaturase step.

A New Focus: Other Independent Agents that Cause Artery Disease

When one-half of all those who suffer a myocardial infarction do not have high cholesterol, it becomes prudent to stop focusing on simply avoiding the dietary cholesterol found in eggs and other foods. What then, are the other molecular agents underlying coronary infarction that we need to focus more attention on? These are relatively newly discovered independent risk factors, such as triglycerides, lipoprotein (a) (Lp(a)), apolipoprotein A-1 (apoA-1), apoB, C-reactive protein (CRP) and fibrinogen. The latter two are indicators of pro-clotting response to inflammatory stress, while some of the others, such as Lp(a) and the apolipoproteins, are heavily influenced by heredity. The good news is that all of these risk factors for coronary and peripheral vascular occlusion can be modified through lifestyle, diet and exercise.

Homocysteine

In a healthy artery, the endothelial cells form a continuous protective layer that regulates the passage of substances from the plasma to the underlying artery wall. If the endothelial cells are damaged, however, their permeability may be altered, allowing direct interaction between elements from the blood and the artery wall. Homocysteine can actually act like a powerful molecular abrasive, 'scraping' the inner layer of blood vessels. Thus, high levels of this amino acid have been correlated with damaged endothelium, increased platelet utilization and the formation of atherosclerotic lesions (Ross, 1990). One study found that men with extremely high homocysteine levels were three times more likely to have an associated myocardial infarction, even when adjustments for other factors such as blood lipids were considered (Stampfer *et al.*, 1992).

Homocysteine is fast becoming an important functional marker for other reasons too. Homocysteine is an intermediate in the biosynthesis of cysteine from methionine, via cystathionine. That means that it occupies an extremely pivotal metabolic juncture in the body. Deficiency of vitamin B_{12}, folic acid and/or vitamin B_6 can affect the enzyme pathways involved in cysteine formation, resulting in increased circulating homocysteine levels in the blood.

In fact, homocysteine is located in such a critical metabolic pathway that it affects methyl and sulphur group metabolism throughout the entire body. For this reason, it can serve as an important functional marker for assessing the status of the skeletal and nervous systems. It might be appropriate to label homocysteine's position in the metabolic process 'dysfunction junction', because of the wide array of health conditions associated with elevated levels of this important amino acid. These include depression, multiple sclerosis, diabetes, birth defects, Alzheimer's disease, rheumatoid arthritis and osteoporosis (Miller and Kelly, 1997). High homocysteine, then, represents a metabolic 'traffic jam' that signals possible danger to heart, bone, brain and the nervous system.

Triglycerides

Triglycerides are esterified fatty oils found primarily in the core of chylo-microns and very low-density lipoprotein (VLDL). Elevated blood levels of triglycerides, but not cholesterol, have been associated with an impaired fibrinolytic system (Hiraga *et al.*, 1996), potentially impairing the body's pro-clotting response to inflammatory stress and thus accounting for another possible aetiology in the development of cardiovascular disease. In fact, recent angiographic studies have implicated triglycerides in the progression of both coronary and peripheral atherosclerosis, independently of LDL (Davignon and Cohn, 1996; Drexel *et al.*, 1996).

A diet high in fried food and saturated fats can increase serum trigly-cerides. Since triglycerides are also derived from excess glucose in the blood-stream, excess refined carbohydrates, including the 'fat-free' products high in sugar and flour, may also result in elevated serum triglycerides.

In a recent study, researchers noted the powerful role of triglycerides as predictors of myocardial infarction (Koren *et al.*, 1996). In fact, triglycerides do not just increase the likelihood of developing cardiovascular disease; they also reflect the severity of coronary artery disease in those who already have it (Hachinski *et al.*, 1996). In addition, elevated serum triglycerides have been linked specifically to the occurrence of atherothrombotic stroke and transient ischaemic attacks (Stampfer *et al.*, 1996).

Lipoprotein(a)

A friend or relative, let us call him 'Uncle Nick', does everything he is not supposed to do. He consumes a diet high in saturated fats, regularly over-indulges in alcohol and tobacco, leads a high-stress lifestyle, becomes obese and yet, somehow, Uncle Nick miraculously manages to 'beat the odds' and avoid suffering any of the major complications of cardiovascular disease well into old age. At the same time, we learn of another individual, let us dub him 'Uncle Leroy', who exercises regularly, watches his diet, avoids alcohol and tobacco, remains fit and healthy, and bang, suddenly one day in his early 50s, he suffers his first heart attack, seemingly from 'out of the blue'. Does this defiance of the odds mean that life style risk factors ultimately are not that important? The answer is absolutely negative. It simply means that there is much more to cardiovascular health than meets the eye, and what we might think of as 'bad luck' or 'fate' may actually be the work of microscopic particles in the blood such as Lp(a).

Lipoproteins are heavy particles that transport fats that are not soluble in water (primarily triglycerides and cholesterol esters) through the bloodstream. One type of lipoprotein, or Lp(a), is formed by an LDL cholesterol molecule attached to a protein component called apolipoprotein (a).

Research over the last 20 years has uncovered a critical relationship between Lp(a) and coronary artery disease, establishing its causative role in atherothrombogenesis and its strong association with a wide range of cardiac events (Kostner *et al.*, 1981; Rhoads *et al.*, 1986; Loscaizo, 1990; Frohlich, 1995; Sauer *et al.*, 1996).

As many as 50% of individuals who suffer myocardial infarction do not display conventional factors of concern such as fatty diets, lack of exercise, hypertension, smoking and high cholesterol (Futterman and Lemberg, 1998). Lp(a) can serve as the 'missing link' of information in many of these cases. Lp(a) is determined largely by an individual's genetic background, and remains unaffected by many of the external influences associated with heart disease (Armstrong *et al.*, 1986; Schreiner, 1993). Thus high levels of this lipoprotein can help explain why a seemingly 'healthy' patient may experience a heart attack, while an 'unhealthy' patient, with a preponderance of various other biochemical and life style risk factors, may not.

In fact, Lp(a) has been cited as a better predictor of coronary disease severity than most other lipid parameters (Merz, 1989; Hearn *et al.*, 1990). Doetsch *et al.* (1991) called it the most important genetic factor associated with early atherosclerosis and coronary artery disease. Scientists have still not fully determined the precise function of Lp(a) within the human body. However, there are a variety of ways in which Lp(a) could promote the development of atherosclerosis and thrombosis.

Lp(a) binds to endothelial and macrophage cells, fibrinogen and fibrin, promoting the deposition of cholesterol and other fatty waste in blood vessel walls. Lp(a) also prevents clot lysis, adding fibrin and other debris to athero-sclerotic plaque. Some scientists have suggested that Lp(a), by inhibiting plasminogen activity, indirectly suppresses smooth muscle cell growth, encouraging the proliferation of the muscle cells commonly seen in athero-sclerotic lesions (Grainger and Metcalfe, 1995).

Lp(a) is also an important tool for assessing the extent of carotid athero-sclerosis. Also, elevated serum levels of Lp(a) can serve as the most significant warning indicator for patients with a high risk of stroke (Jaurgens *et al.*, 1985; Költringer and Jurgens, 1985; Murai *et al.*, 1986; Watts *et al.*, 1995).

Apolipoprotein A-1 (apoA-1)

We have already seen how over-generalizing about 'fats' and 'oils' and 'cholesterol' leads to some serious misconceptions about what really constitutes a healthy diet. As I mentioned before, knowing the percentage breakdown of ω-3s and ω-6s in various oils is a critical factor for making the right dietary choices. Similarly, to understand better the impact of HDL and LDL cholesterol in the body we need to examine some of their important components.

A protein found in many lipoprotein complexes, apoA-1, is the major component of HDL, the 'good cholesterol', apoA-1 provides more insight into the potential benefit provided by HDL; higher levels of this protein are thus predictive of a decreased incidence of cardiovascular disease. In a controlled study of adolescents with a history of coronary heart disease, French research-ers found that in young men, apoA-1 was the best negative predictor of a family history of early myocardial infarction, while in young women it was HDL cholesterol (Amouyel *et al.*, 1993). In a Mayo Clinic study, cardiovascular specialists argued that plasma apolipoprotein levels, particularly A-1 and A-2, may be considerably better indicators of favourable cardiovascular disease status than levels of traditional lipid determinants (Kottke *et al.*, 1986).

Apolipoprotein B

To obtain a better indication of how LDL, the bad cholesterol, may be impacting the cardiovascular system, we need to examine another protein component of lipoproteins called apoB. ApoB is the primary substance in LDL, and high levels are associated with significantly increased incidence of coronary artery disease (Cremer amd Muche, 1990). Reinhart *et al.* (1990) concluded that both apolipoproteins A-1 and B provide important information about the presence of coronary artery disease. Researchers at Johns Hopkins went even further, asserting that the 'non-traditional' markers apoA-1 and apoB were better indicators of premature coronary atherosclerosis than plasma lipoproteins (Kwiterovich *et al.*, 1992).

Ratio of apoB to apoA-1

Not only do the apolipoproteins provide a clearer perspective for evaluating HDL and LDL levels, the specific ratio of apoB to apoA-1 gives us even more detailed insight into how the relative effects of HDL and LDL 'stack up'.

One study on 225 patients with angiographic evidence of coronary artery disease concluded that the strongest association between coronary artery disease and blood analytes was found in the ratio apoB : apoA-1 (Sahi *et al.*, 1993). This powerful ratio has far-reaching applications over a wide range of ages and cardiovascular conditions. Van Stiphout and his colleagues (1986) compared lipid levels in two groups: children of fathers with severe coronary atherosclerosis and children whose fathers were free of atherosclerosis. They found a higher ratio of apoB to apoA-1 in sons of fathers with severe coronary atherosclerosis, and suggested that the ratio be used to detect children who have an increased probability of developing atherosclerosis in later life. These findings were supported by another study that found apoB : apoA-1 the best predictor of a family history of coronary artery disease in children, and an important consideration in their cardiovascular health (Beigel *et al.*, 1993).

Is there any bottom line? ApoA-1, apoB and the apoB : apoA-1 ratio provide physicians with a more complete and accurate indication of just how HDL and LDL are influencing an individual's overall cardiovascular environment – in the present, the past and the future.

Fibrinogen

Another crucial piece of the cardiovascular puzzle is fibrinogen. A globulin synthesized in the liver, fibrinogen strongly affects various blood-clotting factors, including the aggregation of blood platelets. It has direct effects on the vascular wall and is a prominent acute-phase reactant. Fibrinogen plays a key role in arterial occlusion by promoting atherosclerotic plaque, thrombus formation, endothelial injury and hyperviscosity (Caen *et al.*, 1993; Lau *et al.*, 1993; Giannasi *et al.*, 1995; Levenson *et al.*, 1995; Juhan-Vague *et al.*, 1996).

Recently, researchers discovered fibrinogen involvement in the subclinical phase of extracoronary and coronary atherosclerosis. They postulated that a synergistic effect existed between the total cholesterol : HDL ratio and fibrinogen, with fibrinogen acting as the potential trigger for spurring the atherogenic effect associated with elevated lipids in the bloodstream (Levenson *et al.*, 1997). Another study on over 200 stroke patients established a link between plasma levels of fibrinogen and brain infarction mortality (Suarez *et al.*, 1996).

Fibrinogen can be increased by smoking, obesity, inflammation, stress, oral contraceptives and ageing (Ernst, 1992, 1993a,b; Laharrague *et al.*, 1993; Ernst and Resch, 1995). As we discussed earlier, ageing does not simply mean the mere passage of time, but the cumulative, degenerative effect of ROS on the human body. In fact, with the exception of oral contraceptives, ROS are associated with all of the fibrinogen-raising agents listed above.

C-reactive protein

One of the most exciting recent discoveries concerning the molecular milieu associated with cardiovascular disease is CRP. It is believed that chronic subclinical inflammation may be a crucial factor in the pathogenesis of athero-thrombosis. CRP is a marker specifically associated with the production of inflammatory cytokines. These cytokines appear to encourage coagulation and damage to the vascular endothelium, increasing the potential threat to cardiovascular health (Grau *et al.*, 1996).

A recent study published in the *New England Journal of Medicine* found that plasma CRP is a strong predictor of myocardial infarction and stroke. Men with CRP values in the highest quartile had three times the incidence of myocardial infarction and twice the incidence of ischaemic stroke. Significantly, these relationships remained steady over long periods, and were independent of other lipid and non-lipid factors, including smoking.

Interestingly, evidence suggests that previous infection with pathogens such as *Chlamydia pneumoniae* or *Helicobacter pylori* may initially trigger the chronic inflammation detected by CRP (Ridker *et al.*, 1997). Researchers thus theorize that one way in which aspirin improves cardiovascular function is through its anti-inflammatory effect, and the subsequent lowering of CRP levels.

Diagnosis and Treatment

Hopefully you can now better understand that dietary cholesterol is not the only factor to consider in an individual confronted with a family or personal history of vascular occlusive disease. Proper testing needs to incorporate the wide range of specific molecular triggers influencing cardiovascular health, and a composite analysis of these factors is crucial to understanding the full implication of test results. Figure 7.4 shows the report form of just such a multifactorial analysis, available from a commercial laboratory.

Many of the test markers exert a more powerful impact on coronary status in concert with one another. Studies have shown, for example, that the combination of high LDL cholesterol, elevated triglycerides and low HDL is a greater

Comprehensive Cardiovascular Risk Profile

Great Smokies Diagnostic Laboratory ^SM

63 Zillicoa Street
Asheville, NC 28801-1074

Patient:

ID#:   Age: 68   Sex: Female

Collected: 7/10/98   Received:7/13/98   Completed: 7/14/98

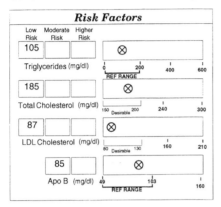

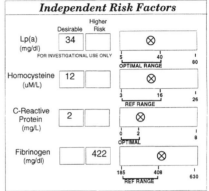

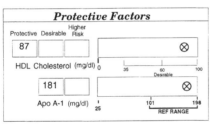

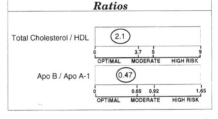

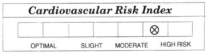

The cardiovascular risk reported here is based only on the markers
presented. Evaluation of other factors (e.g., genetics, blood pressure,
and smoking status) are essential for overall patient risk assessment.

© GSDL • *College of American Pathologists #31722-01* • *CLIA Lic.#34D0655571* • *Medicare Lic. #34-8475* • *m,rp,crd,061698*

Fig. 7.4. This single report form details risk and protective factors for arteriosclerosis. In this patient, C-reactive protein and fibrinogen are elevated indcating the presence of an inflammatory focus. Inflammation is associated with oxidative stress, the oxidation of LDL and plaque formation.

concern than elevated LDL alone (Assman and Schulte, 1991). Similarly, a recent follow-up study on CRP revealed that although it is an independent risk factor, its risk is additive when high levels occur with elevated blood lipid scores. Thus, this cardiovascular assessment contains a composite cardiovascular index, determined by a multivariate analysis of all of the individual lipid scores and independent cardiovascular factors.

Once test results have been evaluated carefully, numerous therapeutic interventions can be implemented to improve cardiovascular health significantly. Conditions such as hypertriglyceridaemia and low HDL cholesterol, for example, can often be managed through a treatment programme that addresses diet, weight control, exercise and smoking cessation (NIH, 1993). Homocysteine is a modifiable cardiovascular risk factor that can often be treated effectively with vitamin supplements such as B_6, B_{12}, and folic acid (Noma *et al.*, 1990). Niacin and neomycin have been shown to reduce serum Lp(a) levels in patients with hyperlipidaemia (Gurakar *et al.*, 1985; Carlson *et al.*, 1989; Stampfer *et al.*, 1992), and combined hormone therapy using progesterone and oestradiol effectively can also lower Lp(a) (Haines *et al.*, 1996).

A Review of Dietary Guidelines

Dietary changes should take into consideration the 'big picture' concerning cholesterols and should not be aimed simply at avoiding all fats. Given the oversaturation of our diet and cell membranes with ω-6 fatty acids, a deliberate effort must be made to replace ω-6 with ω-3 fat. Thus, oils rich in ω-6, such as corn or safflower oil, are out. Saturated and *trans*-fatty acids found in lard and margarine should be avoided in favour of monosaturated fatty acids, such as those found in olive oil. Canola and flaxseed oils are also good choices due to their favourable ω-3 to ω-6 ratios. Direct consumption of foods rich in EPA and DHA, including fish, fish oil and, yes, even egg yolk (especially eggs from hens raised on feeds containing flaxseed, DHA or other ω-3s), is very desirable. Repeat: eggs are good for you – especially the fatty component in the yolk – as they represent our only land source of EPA and DHA.

Foods containing high amounts of simple sugars and refined carbohydrates that are absorbed into the bloodstream too quickly (table sugar, refined flour, rice, etc.) should be excluded from the diet. They should be replaced with foods that register a low glycaemic index, i.e. foods that do not raise blood sugar levels dramatically after they are consumed. Glucose- and sucrose-containing foods, especially soft drinks, candy and other confectionery, are out. Fructose can substitute as a sweetener since it does not raise blood glucose levels. Potato products and all baked goods made from refined flour or rice need to be avoided. Pumpernickel and rye provide good substitutes for white bread. Finally, fruit and fresh vegetables should replace snacks that register a high glycaemic index (potato chips).

Antioxidant and vitamin supplements are also powerful components of this comprehensive approach. When vitamins are added to the DHA diet fed to chickens, the cardiovascular benefit derived from eating their eggs increases significantly (van Elswyk *et al.*, 1998). Moreover, therapeutic doses of vitamins B_6 and B_{12} and folic acid are critical in patients who carry the homocysteinaemic gene. However, no vitamin or antioxidant works effectively on its own. That is why a recent Finnish study found that taking β-carotene by itself increased the risk of lung cancer in smokers (Heinonen and Albanes, 1994). It is always prudent to administer a multivitamin with a full profile of antioxidants.

Summing it Up – In an Eggshell

There is really no compelling reason to avoid eggs in the diet. Remember it is mainly oxidized or rancid cholesterol that causes arterial plaque. Also remember that hypercholesterolaemia is not a 'disease', but a laboratory finding that requires further evaluation. If accompanied by a genetic condition such as hyperhomocysteinaemia, targeted therapy with specific vitamin supplements is necessary to correct the imbalance.

In my own clinical experience, if an elevated lipid profile stems from excess consumption of refined carbohydrates, it is usually not as easy to correct, due to the patient's psychological dependence on these foods. Indeed, the craving for soft drinks, French fries and snacks exhibiting a high glycaemic index can approach the level of an addiction in some patients. These are the true 'carbohydrataholics'.

If their diet is brought under control, however, the signs and symptoms of cardiovascular disease begin to abate in a week or two despite continued morbid obesity. Since the cardiovascular disease was triggered by the overconsumption of glucose-stimulating foods, the proper treatment for hypertension and hyperglycaemia of this type is not another pill. I frequently admonish these patients by telling them: 'Your problem is not a lack of pills', nor does their hypercholesterolaemia stem from eating eggs or other sources of dietary cholesterol. The use of cholesterol-lowering agents should be discouraged until the proper dietary and life style changes outlined here have been strictly applied.

In fact, with the proper interventions, the outlook is quite hopeful. Evidence from randomized, controlled trials confirms that comprehensive life style changes may be able to induce regression of even severe coronary atherosclerosis after 1 year, without the use of lipid-lowering drugs (Omish *et al.*, 1990).

References

Amouyel, P., Isorez, D., Bard, J.M., Goldman, M., Lebel, P., Zylberberg, G. and Fruchart, J.C. (1993) Parental history of early myocardial infarction is associated with decreased levels of lipoparticle A1 in adolescents. *Arteriosclerosis and Thrombosis* 13(11), 1640–1644.

Armstrong, V.W., Cremer, P., Eberie, E., Manke, A., Schulze, F., Wieland, H. *et al.* (1986) The association between serum Lp(a) concentrations and angiographically assessed coronary atherosclerosis. *Atherosclerosis* 62, 249–257.

Assman, G. and Schulte, H. (1991) Triglycerides and atherosclerosis: results from the prospective cardiovascular Münster study. *Atherosclerosis Reviews* 22, 51–63.

Beigel, Y., Georg, J., Leibovici, L., Mattiyahu, A., Sclarovsky, S. and Bieden, L. (1993) Coronary risk factors in children of parents with premature coronary artery disease. *Acta Paediatrica* 82(2), 162–165.

Blok, W.L., Katan, M.V. and van der Meer, J.W. (1996) Modulation of inflammation and cytokine production by dietary (*n*-3) fatty acids. *Journal of Nutrition* 126, 1515–1533.

Caen, J.P., Soria, J., Collet, J.P. and Soria, C. (1993) Fibrinogen, a vascular risk factor. *Bulletin de l'Académie Nationale de Medécine* 177(8), 1433–1441.

Carlson, L.A., Hamsten, A. and Asplund, A. (1989) Pronounced lowering of serum levels of lipoprotein Lp(a) in hyperlipidaemic subjects treated with nicotinic acid. *Journal of International Medicine* 226, 271–276.

Cremer, P. and Muche, R. (1990) The Göttingen risk, incidence, and prevalence (GRIPS) study. Recommendations for the prevention of coronary heart disease. *Therapeutische Umschau* 47(6), 482–491.

Davignon, J. and Cohn, J.S. (1996) Triglycerides: a risk factor for coronary heart disease. *Atherosclerosis* 124, S57–S64.

DeFronzo, R.A. and Ferrannini, E. (1991) Insulin resistance. A multifaceted syndrome responsible for NIDDM, obesity, hypertension, dyslipidemia, and atherosclerotic cardiovascular disease. *Diabetes Care* 14(3), 173–194.

Doetsch, K., Roheim, P.S. and Thompson, J.J. (1991) Human lipoprotein(a) quantified by 'capture' ELISA. *Annals of Clinical Laboratory Science* 21(3), 216–218.

Drexel, H., Steurer, J., Muntwyler, J., Meienberg, S., Schmid, H.R. and Schneider, E. (1996) *Circulation* 94(9), 199–205.

Ernst, E. (1992) Oral contraceptives, fibrinogen, and cardiovascular risk. *Atherosclerosis* 93, 1–5.

Ernst, E. (1993a) Regular exercise reduces fibrinogen levels: a review of longitudinal studies. *British Journal of Sports Medicine* 27(3), 175–176.

Ernst, E. (1993b) Fibrinogen as a cadiovascular risk factor – interrelationship with infections and inflammation. *European Heart Journal* 14 (Suppl. K), 82–87.

Ernst, E. and Resch, K.L. (1995) Therapeutic interventions to lower plasma fibrinogen concentration. *European Heart Journal* 47–52 (Suppl. A), 52–53.

Fielding, C.J. and Fielding, P.E. (1985) Metabolism of cholesterol and lipoproteins. In: Vance, D.E. and Vance, J.E. (eds), *Biochemistry of Lipids and Membranes.* Benjamin/Cummings, p. 94.

Frohlich, J.J. (1995) Lipoproteins and homocysteine as risk factors for atherosclerosis: assessment and treatment. *Canadian Journal of Cardiology* 11 (Suppl. C), 18C–23C.

Futterman, L.G. and Lemberg, L. (1998) Fifty percent of patients with coronary artery disease do not have any of the conventional risk factors. *American Journal of Critical Care* 7(3), 240–244.

Giannasi, G., Ferrari, S. and Galetta, F. (1995) Fibrinogen as a cardiovascular risk factor. *Minerva Cardioangiologica* 43(5), 169–175.

Gibbons, G.H. and Dzau, V.J. (1996) Molecular therapies for vascular diseases. *Science* 272,: 689–693.

Granner, D.K. (1998) Hormones of the adrenal cortex. In: Murray, R.K. *et al.* (eds), *Harper Biochemistry*, Vol. 48. pp. 547–559.

Grainger, D.J. and Metcalfe, J.C. (1995) Transforming growth factor-beta: the key to understanding lipoprotein(a)? *Current Opinions on Lipidology* 6(2), 81–85.

Grainger, D.J., Kirschenlohr, H.L., Metcalfe, J.C., Weissberg, P.L., Wade, D.P. and Lawn, R.M. (1993) Proliferation of human smooth muscle cells promoted by lipoprotein(a). *Science* 260(5114), 1655–1658.

Grau, A.J., Buggle, F., Beeher, H. *et al.* (1996) The association of leukocyte count, fibrinogen, and C-reactive protein with vascular risk factors and ischaemic vascular diseases. *Thrombosis Research* 82(3), 245–255.

Gurakar, A., Hoeg, J.M., Kostner, G., Papadopoulos, N.M. and Brewer, H.B., Jr (1985) Levels of lipoprotein Lp(a) decline with neomycin and niacin treatment. *Atherosclerosis* 57, 293–301.

Hachinski, V., Graffagnino, C., Beaudry, M., Berneir, G., Buck, C., Donner, A. *et al.* (1996) Lipids and stroke: a paradox resolved. *Archives of Neurology* 53(4), 303–308.

Haines, C.J., Chung, T.K., Masarei, J.R., Tomlinson, B. and Lau, J.T. (1996) An examination of the effect of combined cyclical hormone replacement therapy on lipoprotein(a) and other lipoproteins. *Atherosclerosis* 119(2), 215–222.

Harman, D. (1994) Free-radical theory of aging. *Annals of the New York Academy of Science* 717, 1–15.

Hearn, J.A., DeMaio, S.J., Roubin, G.S., Hammarstrom, M. and Sgoutas, D. (1990) Predictive value of lipoprotein(a) and other serum lipoproteins in the angiographic diagnosis of coronary artery disease. *American Journal of Cardiology* 66(17), 1176–1180.

Heinonen, O. and Albanes, D. (1994) The alpha tocopherol β carotene cancer prevention study group. The effect of vitamin E and β carotene on the incidence of lung cancer and other cancers in male smokers. *New England Journal of Medicine* 330(15), 1029–1035.

Hiraga, T., Shimada, M., Tsukada, T. and Murase, T. (1996) Hypertriglyceridemia, but not hypercholesterolemia, is associated with alterations of the fibrinolytic system. *Hormone and Metabolic Research* 28(11), 603–606.

Hu, F.B., Stampfer, M.J., Rimm, E.B., Manson, J.F., Ascherio, A., Colditz, G.A., Rosner, B.A., Spiegelman, D., Speizer, F.E., Sacks, F.M., Hennekens, C.H. and Willett, W.C. (1999) A prospective study of egg consumption and risk of cardiovascular disease in men and women. *Journal of the American Medical Association* 281, 1387.

Jaurgens, G., Taddei-Peters, W.C., Költringer, P., Petek, W., Chen, Q., Greilberger, J. *et al.* (1985) Lipoprotein(a) serum concentration and apolipoprotein(a) phenotype correlate with severity and presence of ischaemic cerebrovascular disease. *Stroke* 26(10), 1841–1848.

Juhan-Vague, I., Pyke, S.D., Alessi, M.C., Jespersen, J., Haverkate, F. and Thompson, S.G. (1996) Fibrinolytic factors and the risk of myocardial infarction or sudden death in patients with angina pectoris. *Circulation* 94(9), 2057–2063.

Költringer, P. and Jurgens, G. (1985) A dominant role of lipoprotein(a) in the investigation an evaluation of parameters indicating the development of cervical atherosclerosis. *Atherosclerosis* 58, 187–198.

Koren, E., Corder, C., Mueller, G., Centurion, H., Hallum, G., Fesmire, J., McConathy, W.D. and Alaupovic, P. (1996) Triglyceride enriched lipoprotein particles correlate with the severity of coronary artery disease. *Atherosclerosis* 122(1), 105–115.

Kostner, G.M., Avogaro, P., Cazzolato, G., Marth, E., Bittolo-bon, G. and Qunici, G.B. (1981) Lipoprotein Lp(a) and the risk for myocardial infarction. *Atherosclerosis* 38, 51–61.

Kottke, B.A., Zinsmeister, A.R., Holmes, D.R., Jr, Kneller, R.W., Hallaway, B.J. and Mao, S.J. (1986) Apolipoproteins and coronary artery disease. *Mayo Clinic Proceedings* 61, 1.

Kwiterovich, P.O., Jr, Coresh, J., Smith, H.H., Bachorik, P.S., Derby, C.A. and Pearson, T.A. (1992) Comparison of the plasma levels of apolipoproteins B and A-1, and other risk factors in men and women with premature coronary artery disease. *American Journal of Cardiology* 69(12), 1015–1021.

Laharrague, P.F., Cambus, J.P., Fillola, G. and Corberant, J.X. (1993) Plasma fibrinogen and physiological aging. *Aging* 5, 445–449.

Lau, C.S., McLaren, M., Mackay, I. and Belch, J.J. (1993) Baseline plasma fibrinolysis and its correlation with clinical manifestations in patients with Raynaud's phenomenon. *Annals of the Rheumatic Diseases* 52(6), 443–448.

Levenson, J., Giral, P., Razavian, M., Gariepy, J. and Simon, A. (1995) Fibrinogen and silent atherosclerosis in subjects with cardiovascular risk factors. *Arteriosclerosis, Thrombosis and Vascular Biology* 15(9), 1263–1268.

Levenson, J., Giral, P., Megnien, J.L., Gariepy, J., Plainfosse, M.C. and Simon, A. (1997) Fibrinogen and its relation to subclinical extracoronary and coronary athero-sclerosis in hypercholesterolemic men. *Arteriosclerosis, Thrombosis and Vascular Biology* 17(1), 45–50.

Liao, F., Andalibi, A., Lusis, A.J. and Fogelman, A.M. (1995) Genetic control of the inflammatory response induced by oxidized lipids. *American Journal of Cardiology* 75, 65B–66B.

Loscaizo, J. (1990) Lipoprotein(a): a unique risk factor for atherothrombotic disease. *Atherosclerosis* 10(5), 672–679.

Merz, B. (1989) Is it time to include lipoprotein analysis in cholesterol screening? Medical news and perspectives. *Journal of the American Medical Association* 261(4), 496–497.

Miller, A.L. and Kelly, G.S. (1997) Homocysteine metabolism: nutritional modulation and impact on health and disease. *Alternative Medicine Review* 2(4), 234–254.

Murai, A., Miyahara, T., Fujimoto, N., Matsuda, M. and Kameyama, M. (1986) Lp(a) lipoprotein as a risk factor for coronary heart disease and cerebral infarction. *Atherosclerosis* 59, 199–204.

Murakami, M., Arm, J.P. and Austen, K.F. (1994) Cytokine regulation of mast call protease phenotype and arachidonic acid metabolism. *Annals of the New York Academy of Science* 744, 84–98.

National Institutes of Health; Conference Statement (1993) Triglyceride high density lipoprotein and coronary heart disease. *Journal of the American Medical Association* 269, 505 510.

Noma, A., Maeda, S., Okuno, M., Abe, A. and Muto, Y. (1990) Reduction of serum lipoprotein(a) levels in hyperlipidaemic patients with α-tocopheryl nicotinate. *Atherosclerosis* 84, 217–231.

Ornish, D., Brown, S.E., Scherwitz, L.W., Billings, J.H., Armstrong, W.T., Ports, T.A., McLanahan, S.M., Kirkeeide, R.L., Brand, R.J. and Gould, K.L. (1990) Can lifestyle changes reverse coronary heart disease? *Lancet* 336, 129–133.

Prior, J.T., Kurtz, D.M. and Ziegler, D.O. (1961) The hypercholesterolemic rabbit: an aid to understanding arteriosclerosis in man? *Archives of Pathology* 71, 672–684.

Porte, D. and Schwartz, M.W. (1996) Diabetes complications: why is glucose potentially toxic? *Science* 272(5262), 699–700.

Reinhart, R.A., Gani, K., Arndt, M.R. and Broste, S.K. (1990) Apolipoproteins A-1 and B as predictors of angiographically defined coronary artery disease. *Archives of International Medicine* 150(8), 1629–1633.

Rhoads, G.G., Dahlen, G., Berg, K., Morton, N.E. and Dannenberg, A.L. (1986) Lp(a) as a risk factor for myocardial infarction. *Journal of the American Medical Association* 256, 2540–2544.

Ridker, P.M., Cushman, M., Stampfer, M.J., Tracy, R.P. and Hennekens, C.H. (1997) Inflammation, aspirin, and the risk of cardiovascular disease in apparently healthy men. *New England Journal of Medicine* 336(14), 973–979.

Ross, R. (1990) Factors influencing atherogenesis. In: Hurst, J.W., Schlant, R.C., Rackley, C.E., Sonnenblick, E.H. and Wenger, N.K. (eds), *The Heart, Arteries and Veins.* McGraw-Hill, New York, pp. 877–923.

Sahi, N., Pahlajani, D.B. and Sainani, G.S. (1993) Apolipoproteins A-1 and B as predictors of angiographically assessed coronary artery disease. *Journal of the Association of Physicians in India* 41(11), 713–715.

Sauer, S., Ulutin, T., Sanommmz, H., Koakoaglu, E., Uaciasik, N., Bayram, C. and Sultuybek, G. (1996) Plasma Lp(a) and t-PA–PA1-1 complex levels in coronary heart disease. *Thrombosis Research* 83(1), 77–85.

Schnohr, P., Thomsen, O.O., Hansen, P.R., Boberg-Ans, G., Lawaetz, H. and Weeke, T. (1994) Egg consumption and high-density-lipoprotein cholesterol. *Journal of Internal Medicine* 235, 249–251.

Schreiner, P.J. (1993) Lipoprotein(a) as a risk factor for preclinical atherosclerosis. *Arteriosclerosis and Thrombosis* 13(6), 826–833.

Simopoulos, A.T. (1996) *Trans* fatty acids. In: Spiller, G.E. (ed.), *Handbook of Lipids in Human Nutrition*. CRC Press, Boca Raton, Florida, p. 98.

Stampfer, M.J., Malinow, M.R., Willet, W.C., Newcomer, L.M., Upson, B., Ullmann, D. *et al.* (1992) A prospective study of plasma homocyst(e)ine and risk of myocardial infarction in US physicians. *Journal of the American Medical Association* 268, 877–881.

Stampfer, M.J., Krauss, R.M., Ma, J., Blanche, P.J., Hall, L.G., Sacks, F.M. and Hennekens, C.H. (1996) A prospective study of triglyceride level, low-density lipoprotein particle diameter, and risk of myocardial infarction. *Journal of the American Medical Assocociation* 276, 882–888.

Steward, H.L., Andrews, S.S., Morrison, B. and Balart, L.A. (eds) (1995) *Sugar Busters – Cut Sugar to Trim Fat*. Sugar Buster, LLC, USA.

Suarez, C., Castillo, J., Suarez, P., Navieiro, J. and Lema, M. (1996) The prognostic value of analytical hemorheological factors in stroke. *Revue Neurologique* 24, 190–192.

van Elswyk, M.E., Hatch, S.D., Stella, G.G., Mayo, P.K. and Kubena, K.S. (1998) Poultry-based alternatives for enhancing the Ω3 fatty acid content of American diets. *World Review on Nutrition and Diet* 83, 102–115.

van Stiphout, W.A., Hofman, A., Kruijssen, H.A., Vermeeren, R. and Groot, P.H. (1986) Is the ratio of apo B/apo A-1 an early predictor of coronary atherosclerosis? *Atherosclerosis* 62, 179–182.

Watts, G.F., Mazurkiewicz, J.C., Tonge, K., Nelson, V., Warburton, F.G. and Slavin, B.M. (1995) Lipoprotein(a) as a determinant of the severity of angiographically defined carotid atherosclersis. *Quarterly Journal of Medicine* 88, 321–326.

Wolffenbuttel, B.H., Giordano, D., Founds, H.W. and Bucaoa, R. (1996) Long-term assessment of glucose control by haemoglobin–AGE measurement. *Lancet* 347, 513–515.

Yokota, A. (1993) Relationship of polyunsaturated fatty acid composition and learning ability in rat. *Nippon Sanfujinka Gakkaishii* (in Japanese) 45, 15–22.

Producer's Perspective on Egg Consumption: How Does the Market React?

8

A. Kennedy
Canadian Egg Marketing Agency, Ottawa, Ontario, Canada

The Canadian Egg Marketing Agency (CEMA) is a not-for-profit organization representing 1300 egg producers from coast to coast. While our industry generates over C$1 billion into the economy, it is vulnerable to shifts in consumer attitudes and perceptions about eggs. Consumption patterns plummeted during the 1980s mainly as a result of health concerns. Scientific findings linking dietary cholesterol to heart disease, combined with a *Salmonella* outbreak in the UK, posed a serious threat to the egg industry. Consumers were able to abandon a food staple because the expanding food choices, particularly at breakfast, offered a novel and convenient alternative that fits into busier lifestyles. The egg industry has spent the past two decades trying to woo consumers back. Understanding our consumer was essential in order to increase egg consumption. The industry develops its marketing strategy based on extensive research. Information gained from tracking studies, focus groups, telephone interviews and mailed surveys has contributed to a successful marketing plan that, last year, resulted in the first per capita increase in consumption since 1979. Research provides valuable insights for the positioning of eggs within the context of a healthy diet. Also, partnerships with credible organizations have benefited the agency. Not only do they provide a cost-efficient means of collecting additional data, they also provide new opportunities for positioning our product and ourselves with consumers and with health professionals. CEMA strives to ensure that health professionals, the media and consumers have access to up-to-date, relevant and credible information on nutrition and food. We recognize that one nutrition discovery, quickly taken out of context or blown out of perspective, could be equally, if not more damaging than the cholesterol scare.

© CAB *International* 2000. *Egg Nutrition and Biotechnology*
(eds J.S. Sim, S. Nakai and W. Guenter)

Introduction

Canadian Egg Marketing Agency

The Canadian Egg Marketing Agency (CEMA) is a national producer organization, celebrating its 25th anniversary this year. Over 1300 egg producers are involved in egg production in Canada. Laying operations have an average flock size of 13,600. The provincial range is 6500–25,000. Canada produces almost half a billion eggs each year. Since our creation in 1972, CEMA has had, as part of its mandate, the promotion of eggs in Canada. This is accomplished with a coordinated, national effort geared towards advertising, promotion, research and nutrition education. At the Agency and at provincial levels, our focus is on increasing the total market for eggs by encouraging new consumption habits.

Quality assurance

Consumers in Canada value Canadian-produced food for its quality, nutritional value and record of safety. They expect the government and food producers to ensure that they have access to the best quality of food available. This is aided by labelling eggs with the Grade 'A' symbol and 'best before' date.

Egg Consumption Trends

Confidence in the food supply enabled egg consumption to increase gradually over several decades. However, in the late 1980s, consumption patterns changed (Figs 8.1, 8.2 and 8.3). Our industry was threatened by two prominent factors: research linking dietary cholesterol to heart disease and a *Salmonella* outbreak in the UK. CEMA and egg producers around the world rallied

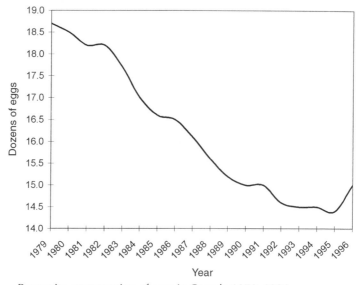

Fig. 8.1.   Per capita consumption of eggs in Canada 1979–1996.

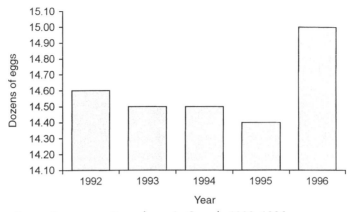

Fig. 8.2.   Per capita consumption of eggs in Canada 1992–1996.

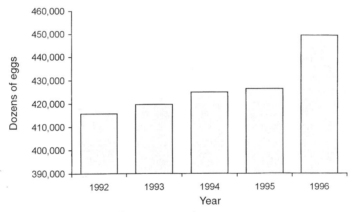

Fig. 8.3.   Total consumption of eggs in Canada 1992–1996.

to address these issues. Each in its own way contributed to public chaos, confusion and panic, thereby resulting in a rapid drop in egg consumption.

In response to the *S. enteritidis* outbreak, the UK required eggs to be destroyed, culled birds and established new regulations to stabilize the situation. Unfortunately, these measures occurred after the public had lost confidence in the egg supply.

Salmonella Control Programme

Negative publicity caused Canada to respond by developing and implementing a *S. enteritidis* control programme. To establish a bench mark and dispel any concerns we had about the safety of eggs from Canadian flocks, Agriculture Canada conducted a random survey of 10% of all Canadian flocks that existed at that time. Our concerns were dispelled when the results of the survey and risk factor study showed the chance of having a Grade A egg infected with *S. enteritidis* is one in a million or once in 82 lifetimes.

CEMA remains committed to keeping eggs safe. The 'Start Clean, Stay Clean' programme introduced biosecurity measures to control *S. enteritidis* to producers. Annual on-site inspections, educational support and a compensation programme that is now linked to the strengths and weaknesses of a producer's operation are incentives used to ensure that Canadian egg producers are leaders in *S. enteritidis* control programmes.

Educational resources were also developed providing background information as well as decals or stickers to constantly remind food service workers to follow safe food-handling practices. CEMA continues to promote safe food-handling practices by participating in consumer food safety programmes. Recently, CEMA committed both financial and staff resources towards a multi-agency educational campaign on food safety called 'Fight BAC'.

Cholesterol Concerns

Addressing the cholesterol concerns associated with egg consumption was equally challenging. By the mid 1980s, the media had ensured that consumers, even those with very little interest in nutrition, could associate eggs with cholesterol. For a while it appeared that not eating eggs was a cure for heart disease.

Addressing public concern for heart disease has been an uphill struggle. At times, the egg industry has had some formidable opponents. The American Heart Association and the American Surgeon General advised consumers, up until recently, to limit egg consumption. While the Canadian government chose to focus on saturated fat rather than cholesterol, many health professionals continued to identify eggs as a food that should be consumed less frequently. How do you market a product in such a negative environment?

Consumer Studies

Understanding your consumer becomes essential. The first step involves routine market surveillance or a situational analysis. CEMA has been fortunate to have a board that values research and measurement. Since the early 1980s, CEMA has commissioned national Consumer Usage and Attitude studies (U & A). The primary objective of the study is to gather information about Canadian shoppers. We want to understand how and when they eat eggs, and why.

The research identifies personal egg consumption by the primary grocery shopper, household egg consumption, egg usage, purchasing patterns, health concerns, attitudes towards eggs and advertising recall. Information is collected from more than 1200 telephone interviews.

In 1997, the U & A provided some very positive news for CEMA:

- Although cholesterol continues to be of concern, it is having less of an effect on people's egg eating behaviours.
- Eggs are perceived as an excellent source of protein, and a good source for many vitamins and minerals.
- Eggs are identified as one of their top three staples.

Clearly the scientific findings being generated and that CEMA is promoting have started to reach the consumer.

CEMA has gone beyond looking at light, medium and heavy egg consumers. Research was used to determine quantitatively who in the household is eating eggs, how many eggs each member is consuming in what form, who prepares them and when. Detailed information based on extensive record-keeping assists us in developing secondary target audiences. For the first time in CEMA's history, we are now considering developing targeted messages to individual household members, specifically teenagers.

Another tool used to monitor consumer habits is the National Institute of Nutrition's Tracking Nutrition Trends Study. CEMA has been one of the founding sponsors for this research. Three reports have been produced to date: 1989, 1994 and 1997.

Two conclusions from the most recent report impact on CEMA's strategy:

- 'Nutrition should continue to play a significant role in food product development and marketing activities of the agri-food industry. Special focus should be placed on quick and easy solutions in healthy eating, which provide convenience in conjunction with nutrition value'.
- 'Education efforts should continue to maximize consumer understanding of the nutritional information that is provided and to put nutrition in some type of meaningful context for Canadian consumers'.

New Egg Marketing Strategies

As a result of these combined findings, CEMA has developed our most recent marketing strategy to promote 'It's okay to eat eggs more often'. Our goal is to build on the shifting attitudes towards eggs. We will do this by promoting quick and easy egg recipes that portray eggs in a healthy way. The same messages will be incorporated into our integrated marketing plan. TV advertisements, retail promotions, magazine inserts and educational resource material will focus on promoting nutritional value, versatility and convenience.

While consumers have responded favourably to our current marketing campaign, it is not enough. The egg industry must work with health professionals to add credibility and strength to our message that eggs are part of a healthy diet.

By establishing a Resourceful Partner theme, CEMA has entered into an important dialogue with health professionals.

Through conference sponsorships and exhibits, CEMA enjoys one on one dialogue with health professionals. We learn which resources are recognized and used, how best to distribute them and what new material is needed.

Our scientific fact sheets and newsletters provide professionals with current findings in order to update their knowledge on dietary fat. A scientific advisory group assists in the identification of new topics as well as in the development of new resources. Our material is seen as excellent, with minimum industry bias.

Our biggest compliment came when CEMA resource materials were advertised to Canadian physicians using the Physicians' Hotline catalogue. The orders for the first month of the programme exceeded the 6 month projections. CEMA has entered into partnership with the Dieticians of Canada as a sponsor of their National Nutrition Month Campaign. The campaign profiles the dietician as a source of reliable nutrition information and provides CEMA with an opportunity to promote our message that eggs are part of a healthy eating pattern to both health professionals and consumers.

Our most recent partnership is with the Canadian Heart and Stroke Foundation. Our goal is to move the focus away from cholesterol and onto risk factors, such as activity and healthy body weight, that have a greater impact. CEMA will assist with the development of new resource material as well as participating in community events.

CEMA strives to ensure that health professionals, the media and consumers have access to up to date, relevant and credible information on the nutritional and food safety aspects of eggs. We value partnerships and look for initiatives to build on a foundation of scientific knowledge.

While we are confident that we have turned the corner on *Salmonella* and cholesterol, CEMA also recognizes that a new nutrition discovery, quickly taken out of context or blown out of proportion, could damage the egg market. Maintaining confidence in the food supply is essential. Working collectively, I am confident that egg producers, scientists and government officials can respond to future issues in a constructive and timely manner. Eggs offer Canadian consumers a convenient and versatile source of nourishment. They have a place in a healthy eating pattern.

Egg Lipids and Nutrition

Eggs as a Functional Food Alternative to Fish and Supplements for the Consumption of DHA

9

M.E. Van Elswyk[1], S.D. Hatch[2], G.G. Stella[2],
P.K. Mayo[2] and K.S. Kubena[2]

[1]Omega Tech Inc., Boulder, Colorado, USA; [2]Faculty of
Nutrition, Departments of Poultry and Animal Science, Texas
A&M University, College Station, Texas, USA

Docosahexaenoic acid (DHA) can be incorporated easily into egg yolk through manipulation of the laying hen diet. Given this ability, the egg has been proposed as an alternative food source to fish for this important fatty acid. While the nutritional profile of these eggs is comparable with fish and functionality identical to typical eggs, the specific health benefits of consuming these eggs must be identified. The first study investigated the influence of consuming four DHA-rich or four typical eggs per week for 6 weeks on the plasma lipids and platelet aggregation of male and female volunteers ($n = 40$). Neither egg significantly influenced plasma cholesterol or triglycerol. DHA-rich egg consumption significantly reduced collagen-induced platelet aggregation and enhanced the plasma phospholipid content of DHA. In a second study, male volunteers ($n = 40$) with elevated triacylglycerol and depressed high-density lipoprotein (HDL) levels were selected to consume two DHA-rich or two typical eggs daily, 5 days a week, for 12 weeks. None of the men were involved in drug or diet therapies and all consumed a semi-controlled diet providing 36% of calories from fat. Plasma cholesterol levels were unaffected by either egg. Consuming either egg significantly increased HDL. The low-density lipoprotein particle density was negatively effected by typical eggs but improved by DHA-rich egg consumption. The final study involved providing 8–14 eggs weekly to women ($n = 25$) in their final trimester of pregnancy. DHA-rich eggs positively influenced pregnancy outcome by significantly increasing placental weights and reducing the occurrence of low birth weight infants. These studies suggest that when DHA is provided in the diet in a form other than through fish or supplements, the health benefits of DHA are duplicated.

Introduction

The opportunity to enhance cardiovascular health through dietary *n*-3 fatty acids (FAs) may be furthered by the modification of poultry rations to include a source of *n*-3 FA for the promotion of *n*-3 FA deposition in poultry meat and eggs. The concept of nutritionally modifying foods to provide health benefits beyond the nutrients they traditionally contain has been referred to as *designer* or *functional food* production. The growing role of such foods in improving the nutritional quality of our food supply has been endorsed by nutrition professionals (American Dietetics Association, 1995). Researchers have been actively pursuing the design of a commercially viable *n*-3 FA-rich shell egg for the past decade (Hargis *et al.*, 1991; Hargis and Van Elswyk, 1993; Aymond and Van Elswyk, 1995; Herber and Van Elswyk, 1996). Such efforts have yielded a shell egg containing a minimum of 150 mg of docosahexaenoic acid (DHA) and 120 mg of the essential *n*-3 FA and DHA precursor, linolenic acid (LNA; 18 : 3*n*-3). The palatability of these *n*-3 FA-enhanced eggs has been verified using both trained and consumer panellists (Van Elswyk *et al.*, 1992, 1995). Studies designed to mimic typical egg storage by consumers have found the shelf life of these highly unsaturated eggs to be comparable with that of typical eggs (Marshall *et al.*, 1994a). The introduction of a commercially available, nutritionally enhanced shell egg can increase the *n*-3 FA intake of US consumers. Per capita shell egg consumption averages three eggs per week, and replacement of typical eggs with *n*-3 FA-rich eggs would result in consumption of the equivalent of one 3 ounce fatty fish meal weekly. This would increase the US *n*-3 FA intake to what epidemiologic data suggest as useful for promoting cardiovascular health.

Studies designed to evaluate the potential for health promotion through *n*-3 FA-rich shell eggs have produced promising results. Hargis and Van Elswyk (1991) investigated the influence of consuming three *n*-3 FA-rich shell eggs or three typical eggs daily for 6 weeks in 20 free-living, normolipidaemic men in a crossover study. Consumption of three enriched eggs supplied 750 mg of total *n*-3 FA daily, predominantly as DHA, or the equivalent of one fatty fish meal per day. Typical eggs, which naturally contain negligible amounts of DHA, contributed less than 100 mg of DHA per three eggs day^{-1}. Apart from avoiding other eggs or egg-rich products, no dietary restrictions were placed on the participants. Plasma total, low-density lipoprotein (LDL), and high-density lipoprotein (HDL) cholesterol levels did not vary significantly following consumption of either egg in this crossover study. Consistent with the well-documented hypotriglyceridaemic effect of dietary *n*-3 FA, individuals consuming enriched eggs realized a significant reduction (−16%) in plasma triacylglycerol following just 3 weeks of enriched egg consumption. The authors noted, however, that the ability to sustain this effect was questionable and that the potential antithrombotic effects of *n*-3 FA-rich eggs warranted investigation.

In another crossover study of free-living, normolipidaemic individuals (12 per treatment), Oh and co-workers (1991) noted the influence of consuming four *n*-3 FA-rich or typical eggs daily during 4-week intervals. Individuals consumed approximately 1 g of total *n*-3 FA per day from four enriched eggs or the equivalent of one fatty fish meal daily. The authors reported significant reductions in systolic blood pressure (−3 to 7 mmHg), a reduction in plasma triacylglycerol and a blunting of the increase in plasma total cholesterol (+10%) observed when typical eggs were consumed.

More recently, Ferrier and co-workers (1995) have reported the results of a crossover study of 28 free-living males consuming four eggs daily from hens fed on flaxseed. Unlike the eggs in the above studies, which were produced by supplementing laying rations with fish oil, flaxseed feeding results in LNA-rich yolks. Eggs from hens fed two levels of flaxseed were utilized, with one egg treatment providing 397 mg of total *n*-3 FA per day (261 mg of LNA; 80 mg of DHA) and the other providing 667 mg of total *n*-3 FA (527 mg of LNA; 87 mg of DHA). No significant changes were reported for plasma total, LDL or HDL cholesterol, or triacylglycerol in this normolipidaemic population. The authors did report, however, significant increases (+33%) in the DHA content of blood platelet phospholipids of individuals consuming either of the two types of *n*-3 FA-rich eggs. These authors speculated that this increase would be sufficient to reduce blood platelet reactivity and consequently the risk of myocardial infarction and thrombosis. In summary, these studies provide compelling evidence to support the role of *n*-3 FA-rich eggs in promoting cardiovascular health. These studies are limited in their practicality, however, as all have investigated egg consumption far in excess of that of the typical consumer. Furthermore, data linking *n*-3 FA with improved cardiovascular health focus not only on disease protection but also on therapy. Several studies have reported the therapeutic benefits of dietary *n*-3 FA to individuals with existing heart disease (O'Keefe *et al.*, 1995; Eritsland *et al.*, 1996; Kang and Leaf, 1996). The ability of *n*-3 FA-rich eggs to provide such therapeutic benefits to dyslipid-aemic individuals therefore warrants investigation, especially considering the likelihood that these fatty acid-modified eggs will appeal to this segment of the population. The following are data from two recent *n*-3 FA-rich egg feeding trials, one involving normolipidaemic individuals and one involving dyslipidaemic participants.

Normolipidaemic Subjects and Methods

Subjects

Male and female volunteers were recruited from the Texas A&M University faculty and graduate student body. Initial screening, via questionnaire, was designed to exclude smokers, individuals with a family history of premature heart disease, a body mass index (BMI) of more than 29 for men and more than 28 for women, chronic use of anti-inflammatory drugs, or previous diagnosis of hypertension or other chronic disease associated with impaired cardiovascular health. Volunteers also completed a questionnaire concerning their typical intake of several classifications of fish (e.g. catfish, salmon, shrimp and clams), eggs and alcoholic beverages. Individuals reporting a typical fish intake of more than once a week, egg consumption less than twice a month and alcohol intake (1 oz) more than once a day were not recruited. Volunteers who successfully completed the initial recruitment phase provided a blood sample, collected from the antecubital vein into siliconized evacuated tubes containing 0.5 ml of 0.129 M buffered sodium citrate (13 mm × 100 mm, No. 369705, Becton Dickinson Vacutainer Systems, Franklin Lakes, New Jersey) by a phlebotomist following an overnight fast. Whole blood and plasma preparations were kept at physiological temperature (37°C) until use for platelet activity studies or frozen at −75°C until further analysis. For screening and throughout the remainder of the study, fasting total serum cholesterol and triglycerides were determined enzymatically (Cholesterol 50, No. 353-50, and Triglyceride (INT) 20, No. 336-20, Sigma Diagnostics, St Louis, Missouri). For screening purposes only, plasma HDL cholesterol was determined by magnesium precipitation followed by an enzymatic assay (HDL Cholesterol, No. 352-3, Sigma Diagnostics). Individuals exhibiting total cholesterol of more than 6.21 mM or HDL cholesterol of less than 0.339 mM were not recruited. A final study population of 44 participants (male and female) began the study following informed consent. The study protocol and consent form were approved by the Texas A&M University Institutional Review Board.

Experimental design

The study was designed to be 26 weeks long, divided into three 6-week periods of egg consumption separated by two 4-week periods of egg abstinence to represent 'washout' periods. Blood lipids were determined at baseline and week 6 of each test period. Subjects were instructed to abstain from fish or flaxseed products for 2 weeks prior to initiation of the study and throughout the washout periods. During the initial treatment period, individuals were assigned randomly to treatment groups which included those consuming typical (control) eggs ($n = 14$), those consuming LNA-rich eggs ($n = 15$) and those consuming DHA-rich eggs ($n = 15$). Eggs were produced continuously during the study by feeding hens either typical diets virtually devoid of n-3 FA or diets containing 5% whole omega flaxseed (LNA source) or 1.5% menhaden oil (DHA source).

In an effort to reflect the egg consumption of typical consumers, volunteers were asked to consume four n-3 FA-rich or control eggs weekly, based on current American Heart Association guidelines. The egg yolk FA profile was monitored during each test period and is provided in Table 9.1. Subjects consuming LNA-rich eggs in test period 1 consumed 1100 mg of total n-3 FA weekly from eggs, those consuming DHA-rich eggs received 840 mg weekly, while those consuming control eggs received 300 mg weekly. Egg n-3 FA content varied with hen feed consumption as influenced by climate changes. The study was initiated in April and completed in October. Hens consumed less feed (data not shown) in the summer months, causing a modest decline in yolk n-3 FA during the study. For test periods 2 and 3, the mean total n-3 FA intake from LNA-rich eggs was 880 mg, 590 mg from DHA-rich eggs and 230 mg from control eggs. Importantly, LNA-rich eggs consistently resulted in greater egg yolk n-3 FA consumption than DHA-rich eggs. The LNA-rich eggs

Table 9.1.   Fatty acid profile of experimental eggs.

	SFA[1]	MUFA[2]	18:2n-6	18:3n-3	20:4n-6	20:5n-3	22:6n-3	Total n-3[3]
				Fatty acids (mg yolk^{-1})				
Test period 1								
Control	1915±35[a]	2526±50[a]	797±12[a]	32.6±8[b]	98.3±1[a]	4.4±4[a]	41.6±0.9[c]	78.6±10[c]
LNA-rich	1723±34[b]	2452±46[a]	794±18[a]	167±4[a]	66.5±1[b]	19.5±6[c]	89.0±3[b]	276±13[a]
DHA-rich	1914±27[a]	2507±37[a]	755±11[a]	41.0±5[b]	46.9±0.8[c]	14.5±5[a]	153±2[a]	209±8[b]
Test period 2								
Control	2151±98[a]	2470±48[a]	776±8[a]	33.1±9[b]	85.8±2[a]	0	47.2±4[b]	80.3±14[c]
LNA-rich	2117±121[a]	2650±108[a]	868±40[a]	144±7[a]	68.0±4[ab]	4.2±4[a]	80.3±14[ab]	229±19[a]
DHA-rich	2299±151[a]	2499±90[a]	811±39[a]	24.0±1[b]	56.4±11[b]	5.25±5[a]	119±16[a]	150±13[b]
Test period 3								
Control	1476±53[b]	2071±73[b]	545±33[b]	17.8±5[b]	98.8±4[a]	1.4±1	15.5±4[c]	34.7±5[c]
LNA-rich	1647±26[a]	2347±41[a]	639±14[a]	136±6[a]	86.9±4[b]	0	76.1±4[b]	212±10[a]
DHA-rich	1465±38[b]	1992±46[b]	533±12[b]	28.9±5[b]	58.8±1[c]	0	115±3[a]	145±8[b]

Means ± SEM differ significantly (*P* < 0.05) if superscripts [(abc)] differ within a period.
[1]Total SFA = 16:0 + 18:0;
[2]Total MUFA = 16:1 + 18:1;
[3]Total n-3 = LNA + EPA + DHA.

maintained a 1.8:1 LNA:DHA ratio and DHA-rich eggs maintained a 0.2:1 LNA:DHA ratio throughout the entire experiment.

Subjects were not informed of their assigned egg treatment group. Subjects were instructed to consume their usual diets, with the exception of eliminating aspirin and non-steroidal anti-inflammatories, all fish and flaxseed products and eggs other than those provided or occurring in typical baked goods throughout the entire study. Study eggs were to be eaten throughout the week, with no more than two eggs per 3-day period and by not eating any eggs 24 h prior to a scheduled blood collection. Cooking methods were not specified because the cooking method does not appear to alter the egg FA profile or FA functionality (Van Elswyk *et al.*, 1992). Participants were also provided with egg recipes to support compliance further. Participants were instructed to restrict excess alcohol consumption (> 2 oz day^{-1}) and not consume alcohol 48 h prior to blood draw.

Participants were further advised to maintain their body weight and physical activity throughout the study. Participants were trained by a registered dietician to keep 3-day food records (blank forms were provided) and instructed to report consumption of non-restricted medications and supplements as well. Two-dimensional food models (photo-mechanical transfers) were provided to aid subjects in accurate estimation of portion size. Food records were collected at baseline and twice during each treatment period. Additionally, random 24-h recalls were conducted during the study to assess the reliability of reported and actual nutrient intakes. Reported foods were analysed for key nutrients using the Minnesota Nutrition Data System software

(Food Database Version 7A, Nutrient Database Version 22, Nutrition Coordinating Center, Minneapolis, Minnesota).

Platelet aggregation

A subset of the population (n = 21; 7 per treatment) was selected randomly to be followed for platelet aggregation each time blood was collected. Immediately following collection, citrated blood was centrifuged at 37°C and 180 g for 12 min to obtain platelet-rich plasma (PRP) then transferred via siliconized pipettes to a polypropylene conical tube and incubated in a 37°C shaking water bath. Remaining blood was centrifuged again at 37°C and 1040 g for 15 min to obtain platelet-poor plasma (PPP). Platelets in PRP were counted using a Coulter Counter Model ZM (Coulter Electronics, Luton, Beds, UK) and adjusted to 2.5×10^8 platelets ml^{-1} using autologous PPP. PRP was prepared from three tubes per subject and combined into polypropylene conical tubes via a siliconized pipette to be maintained at 37°C in a shaking H_2O bath until assay. All samples were stimulated within 2 h of collection. Aggregation was measured using a dual-channel aggregometer (No. DP247E, Sienco Inc., Morrison, Colorado) and aggregation curves were recorded on a chart recorder (No. 20230-050990, Spectra/Chrom, Australia). For each subject, curves were recorded following 2 µg ml^{-1} collagen (Hormone Chemie, No. 10500, Nycomed Arzmiemittel, Munich, Germany) stimulation. At the end of the study, slopes were calculated and evaluated for the desired response. A desirable response was defined as a 10% or greater decrease in the slope of the aggregation curve from baseline, compared with an undesirable response being no change or an increase from baseline.

Statistical analysis

Data are presented as means ± SEM. Only data from subjects completing the entire trial (n = 30) were analysed. During the initial test period, three subjects were dismissed due to non-compliance, two subjects were excused due to scheduling conflicts, and one subject withdrew due to relocation. The additional eight subjects were deleted from the data set as their plasma fatty acid profiles were indicative of non-compliance. Body weight, nutrient intake and plasma lipids were evaluated by ANOVA using SAS (SAS System for Windows, Rel 6.11, SAS Institute, Cary, North Carolina). Statistically different means were separated further using Duncan's Multiple Range Test. Carry-over from one egg treatment to the next was evaluated and found to be non-significant. Aggregation curve slopes calculated from platelet aggregation studies were categorized, as previously described, and the data analysed by the χ^2 goodness of fit test.

Results

The average age and body weight of those completing the study was 24.7 ± 0.4 years and 72.5 ± 1.8 kg, respectively. These parameters were not statistically different between treatment groups, and body weight did not change significantly during the study. Self-selected nutrient intake is presented in Table 9.2. As expected, those consuming the LNA- or DHA-rich eggs consumed significantly greater amounts of those FAs, respectively. Due to the apparently high amount of LNA contributed by the background diet, total *n*-3 FA intake was not statistically different between those consuming typical versus enriched eggs. Although obscured by background diet variation, LNA-rich eggs provided approximately 200 mg more total *n*-3 FA weekly as compared with DHA-rich eggs (Table 9.1).

Plasma lipid values were not significantly different between treatment groups prior to egg consumption. Egg treatment did not significantly influence plasma lipids in either gender. However, a significant treatment × gender × sequence of egg consumption interaction was noted for plasma cholesterol. Male plasma cholesterol values were unchanged regardless of egg treatment or the order in which egg treatments were consumed. Females, however, exhibited a significant treatment × egg consumption sequence interaction such that women who consumed enriched eggs during the last two 6-week periods had significantly lower plasma cholesterol than those completing the study on control eggs (Table 9.3). In either gender, no significant influence of yolk FA on plasma triglycerides were observed.

In vitro platelet aggregation was significantly influenced by egg yolk *n*-3 FA but not by gender. Platelet responsiveness to 2 μg ml^{-1} collagen at baseline, as well as reductions in response to yolk *n*-3 FA, varied among individuals. Owing to the variation among individuals, data were analysed non-parametrically following categorization of responsiveness into desired (decreased aggregation) or undesired as described above. χ^2 analysis indicated that responsiveness to low-dose collagen stimulation was significantly reduced following consumption of either LNA- or DHA-rich eggs (Table 9.4).

Table 9.2.　Self-selected nutrient intake of individuals consuming experimental eggs.

	Egg treatment		
	Control	LNA-rich	DHA-rich
Energy (kJ)	8986 ± 634[a]	9218 ± 820[a]	8961 ± 774[a]
Protein (%)	15.4 ± 0.8[a]	15.6 ± 0.7[a]	15.7 ± 0.6[a]
Fat (%)	34.6 ± 1.5[a]	33.9 ± 2[a]	33.8 ± 2[a]
Carbohydrate (%)	50.0 ± 2[a]	50.5 ± 2[a]	50.5 ± 2[a]
Cholesterol (g)	318.5 ± 25[a]	320.0 ± 28[a]	304.5 ± 19[a]
P : S ratio[1]	0.59 ± 0.05[a]	0.64 ± 0.05[a]	0.61 ± 0.04[a]
DHA (g)	0.037 ± 0.01[c]	0.07 ± 0.006[b]	0.10 ± 0.004[a]
EPA (g)	0.00[a]	0.01 ± 0.001[a]	0.01 ± 0.9[a]
LNA (g)	1.22 ± 0.1[b]	1.36 ± 0.2[a]	1.23 ± 0.2[b]
Total *n*-3 FA(g)	1.26 ± 0.1[a]	1.44 ± 0.2[a]	1.34 ± 0.2[a]
Fibre (g)	15.5 ± 1[a]	16.7 ± 2[a]	15.1 ± 2[a]

χ ± pooled SEM per day differ significantly within a row if superscripts[abc] differ.
[1]Polyunsaturated : saturated fat ratio.

Table 9.4.   Influence of LNA- or DHA-rich eggs on plasma total cholesterol and triacylglycerol.

	Control (mmol^{-1})	LNA-rich (mmol^{-1})	DHA-rich (mmol^{-1})
Cholesterol			
Week 0	3.58 ± 0.12	3.59 ± 0.15	3.56 ± 0.18
Week 6	3.57 ± 0.10	3.57 ± 0.10	3.46 ± 0.10
Triacylglycerol			
Week 0	1.26 ± 0.06	1.37 ± 0.10	1.31 ± 0.08
Week 6	1.27 ± 0.10	1.24 ± 0.08	1.21 ± 0.08

Mean ± SEM; n = 30 per treatment. No significant differences.

Table 9.3.   Categorization of platelet responsiveness following n-3 FA-rich egg consumption.

Egg treatment	Percentage decreased	Percentage increased/not changed
Control	0 (0)	100 (6)
DHA-rich	56 (5)	44 (9)
LNA-rich	71 (5)	29 (7)
χ^2	66.1[a]	48.6[a]

Values in parentheses represent subject number per group.
[a]P < 0.001.

Discussion

The mechanism by which n-3 FA-rich diets reduce cardiovascular disease mortality remains controversial. Current literature suggests a relationship between dietary n-3 FA and cellular membrane functions as well as with plasma lipids. In the current study, plasma cholesterol response of females to egg consumption depended upon the order in which they consumed the experimental eggs. Completing the study with typical eggs elevated plasma cholesterol while completing with DHA-rich eggs resulted in comparatively lower cholesterol levels. Gender differences in response to dietary cholesterol have been reported. Ginsberg and co-workers (1995) reported that the slope of the mean response of total plasma cholesterol in women was almost twice that observed in men, specifically 0.073 versus 0.038 mM per 100 mg of additional dietary cholesterol. Participants in the current study were consuming an average of 100 mg of cholesterol per day above their baseline intake by the addition of four eggs weekly. The apparent ability of n-3 FA to offset this response to dietary cholesterol in women warrants further investigation.

The physiological significance of increased dietary n-3 FA in the current study is evident in the reduction of platelet activity in response to egg yolk n-3 FA. In a review of studies investigating the influence of DHA on human platelet reactivity, Gaudette and Holub (1991) proposed several mechanisms for DHA-mediated changes in platelet aggregation following oral administration. They proposed that DHA release from plasma lipid (PL) may interfere with arachidonic acid (AA) metabolism or that DHA may alter membrane properties and subsequent enzyme activities. However, as the amount of DHA released following agonist stimulation is limited, the authors emphasized the latter mechanism. Recent results from Ferretti *et al.* (1995) support this mechanism. These authors reported that DHA, independently of eicosapentaenoic acid (EPA), reduced the thromboxane/prostacyclin synthetic ratio in men consuming 6 g of DHA daily. Alternatively, since LNA-rich eggs also reduced platelet aggregation, a mechanism for dietary LNA-induced reduction of platelet aggregation, independently of DHA, is possible.

The most striking aspect of this study is the demonstration of significant changes in platelet reactivity with a relatively minute amount of *n*-3 fatty acid supplementation. Importantly, however, the amount of FA provided by LNA- and DHA-rich eggs in the current study was approximately 140 and 100 mg daily, respectively, similar to that demonstrated to reduce cardiovascular disease mortality in Dutch men (Kromhout, 1992). The current data demonstrate that when *n*-3 FA are incorporated into a food source other than fish, the biochemical changes attributed to fish consumption are duplicated. Furthermore, the biopotency of egg yolk DHA versus LNA for mediating physiological changes attributed to *n*-3 FA consumption was demonstrated. Despite provision of less total *n*-3 FA by DHA-rich eggs as compared with LNA-rich eggs, the effects of both eggs on platelet aggregation were statistically similar. This observation suggests the importance of consuming pre-formed dietary DHA rather than depending on LNA for DHA derivation. This study demonstrated, for the first time, that moderate consumption of *n*-3 FA-enriched eggs in amounts consistent with a heart healthy diet provides an economical, convenient vehicle for increasing the limited *n*-3 FA consumption of Americans while promoting the health benefits of fish consumption.

Dyslipidaemic Subjects and Methods

Subjects

In an effort to accumulate data concerning the usefulness of these eggs in the diets of individuals at increased risk of heart disease, our laboratory conducted a study involving males with moderately elevated total cholesterol (200–240 mg dl^{-1}), depressed HDL cholesterol (< 35 mg dl^{-1}) and elevated triacylglycerol (> 150 mg dl^{-1}). Plasma lipids were determined as described previously. It is believed that a significant portion of the responsiveness to various dietary fat interventions is associated with genetic factors. Therefore, plasma samples were sent to Dr Ronald Krauss, University of California at Berkeley, for the identification of participant LDL subclass patterns and their categorization into either the pattern A, AB or B phenotype. The B phenotype is associated with elevated triacylglycerol and apolipoprotein B, reduced HDL and features of insulin resistance syndrome, making this pattern the most atherogenic lipoprotein phenotype (Krauss and Dreon, 1995). Lipoprotein patterns were determined using non-denaturing polyacrylamide gradient gel electrophoresis to separate LDL particles by size and shape. Densitometry was used to calculate peak particle diameters. The pattern B phenotype is characterized by a major peak of small, dense LDL particles ≤ 255 Å (Krauss and Dreon, 1995). The A pattern phenotype is characterized by the majority of large, more buoyant LDL particles typically ≥ 264 Å. The pattern A lipoprotein subclass is the least atherogenic lipoprotein phenotype and the AB pattern carries an intermediate risk. Participants were selected from a population of company employees between the ages of 25 and 50 years, who did not smoke or have a family history of premature heart disease mortality, and were not involved in diet or pharmacological therapies for lipid disorders. Additionally, individuals with diabetes and medically treated hypertension were not recruited.

Diets

Three-day diet records were collected from the selected population to determine the average fat and caloric intake of the population using the Minnesota Nutrient Database Version 2.8. Based on the calculated average fat consumption of the selected population, participants were provided with breakfast and lunch meals designed to supply 36% of calories from fat, but free from concentrated sources of n-3 FA, 5 days per week during a 10-week study. The distribution of dietary fatty acids was also designed to match reported intakes. Specifically, 13% of calories were supplied as saturated fatty acids, 13% as monounsaturates and 10% as polyunsaturated fatty acids.

Experimental design

A 2-week lead-in period, free from eggs, preceded the 8-week period of egg consumption. Following the lead-in, a baseline blood sample was collected to determine plasma total cholesterol, triacylglycerol and LDL particle size. During the experimental period, participants consumed breakfast and lunch on Monday to Friday in a communal dining facility and self-selected evening and weekend meals. Participants were provided fat gram allowances designed to maintain a distribution of fat calories at 36% of total calories. During breakfast and lunch, individuals were assigned to one of two calorie levels based upon reported average caloric intake in an effort to maintain body weight $\pm 2\%$ from baseline throughout the study. In self-selecting meals, individuals were not expected to calculate calories but simply to follow a recommendation for fat intake. Importantly, participants were instructed to avoid all abundant sources of n-3 FA including fish, seafood and flaxseed.

Results

Baseline values for any of the parameters reported did not differ statistically between the egg treatment groups. The average body weight of those completing the study was 85.9 ± 3 kg. Individuals consuming the higher calorie level (3300 kcal) weighed significantly ($P < 0.001$) more than those consuming the lower calorie level (2500 kcal). Self-selected nutrient intakes, determined from evening and weekend meal selections, did not vary significantly between treatment groups. Participants consumed an average of 34.5% of calories from fat, 12% as saturated fatty acids, 13.4% as monounsaturated fatty acids and

6.0% as polyunsaturated fatty acids. Consuming two *n-3* FA-modified eggs daily contributed 244 mg of LNA, 7.0 mg of EPA and 192 mg of DHA for a total of 2.2 g of total *n-3* FA on a weekly basis. Typical eggs contributed 54 mg of LNA, 54 mg of DHA and a negligible amount of EPA for a total of 270 mg of total *n-3* FA on a weekly basis.

In our study, 15 of the 23 participants were of the B subclass pattern. Actual LDL particle size was not significantly different between egg treatment groups at baseline (initial) or at the conclusion (final) of the study (Table 9.5). However, when the percentage change in LDL particle size from initial to final was calculated within each egg treatment group, a significant ($P < 0.03$) difference was noted between the percentage change for typical versus enriched shell egg consumers. The negative percentage change (–0.38%) in LDL particle size among B pattern individuals consuming typical eggs represented a further decrease in particle size and subsequently an enhanced density. Conversely, the positive percentage change in LDL particle size among B pattern (+1.88%) individuals consuming *n-3* FA-rich eggs represented an increase in particle size and, therefore, a shift toward a more buoyant, less atherogenic particle. Evidence suggests that triacylglycerol metabolism plays a critical role in the production of small, dense LDL particles (Krauss, 1987; Krauss *et al.*, 1988). Although the metabolic basis for this interaction is not known, it is suggested that changes in LDL subfraction profiles may be amplified by factors that decrease plasma triacylglycerol concentrations. Although not statistically significant, individuals consuming enriched eggs in the current study realized a 5% decline in plasma triacylglycerol, while those consuming typical eggs experienced a 15% increase in circulating triacylglycerol (data not shown).

Table 9.5.   Initial and final LDL particle subclass distribution of study participants.

ID no.	Egg treatment	Initial particle size (Å)	Final particle size (Å)	Percentage change
1	FAM	248.8	247.9	–0.036
2	FAM	249.7	261[a]	+4.5
3	FAM	241	241.8	+0.3
4	FAM	243	251.7	+3.6
6	Control	249.3	245	–1.7
8	FAM	246.9	247	+0.04
10	Control	248.6	252.3	+1.5
12	Control	249.5	248.3	–0.5
13	FAM	247	246.3	–0.3
14	FAM	248.7	262.6[a]	+5.6
15	Control	249.2	247.1	–0.8
16	FAM	245.7	250	+1.7
18	Control	247.8	247.5	–0.1
22	Control	251.8	248.5	–1.3
23	Control	249.1	249.6	+0.2

ID no. = participant identification number; FAM = fatty acid-modified.
[a]Change from pattern B classification to pattern AB.

Potentially then, the increase in n-3 FA intake from enriched eggs may provide a decline in plasma triacylglycerol and consequently an improved LDL subclass profile among dyslipidaemic individuals consuming *n*-3 FA-rich shell eggs.

Conclusion

Poultry-based functional foods represent an effective means of enhancing the availability of dietary DHA. While supplements are useful for providing concentrated amounts of DHA for a finite time period, the introduction of DHA from whole foods may represent a more sustainable and consistent supply of dietary DHA.

References

American Dietetic Association (1995) Position of the American Dietetic Association: phytochemicals and functional foods. *Journal of the American Dietetic Association* 95, 493–496.

Aymond, W.M. and Van Elswyk, M.E. (1995) Yolk thiobarbituric acid reactive substances and *n*-3 FA in response to whole and ground flaxseed. *Poultry Science* 74, 1388–1394.

Bang, H.O. and Dyerberg, J. (1972) Plasma lipids and lipoproteins in Greenlandic west coast Eskimos. *Acta Medica Scandinavica* 192, 85–89.

Burchfiel, C.M., Reed, D.M., Strong, J.P., Sharp, D.S., Chyou PoHuang and Rodriguez, B.L. (1996) Predictors of myocardial lesions in men with minimal coronary atherosclerosis at autopsy: the Honolulu Heart Program. *Annals of Epidemiology* 6, 37–146.

Eritsland, J., Arnesen, H., Gronseth, K., Fjeld, N.B. and Abdelnoor, M. (1996) Effect of dietary supplementation with *n*-3 fatty acids on coronary artery bypass graft patency. *American Journal of Cardiology* 77, 31–36.

Ferretti, A., Nelson, G.J., Schmidt, P.C., Bartolini, G., Kelby, D.S. and Flanagon, V.P. (1998) Dietary docosahexaenoic acid reduces the thromboxane/prostacyclin synthetic ratio in humans. *Journal of Nutritional Biochemistry* 9, 88–92.

Ferrier, L.K., Caston, L.J., Leeson, S. *et al.* (1997) α-Linolenic acid and docosahexaenoic acid-enriched eggs from hens fed flaxseed: influence on blood lipids and platelet phospholipid fatty acids in humans. *American Journal of Clinical Nutrition* 55, 411–414.

Gaudette, D.C. and Holub, B.J. (1991) Docosahexaenoic acid (DHA) and human platelet reactivity. *Journal of Nutritional Biochemistry* 2, 116–121.

Ginsberg, H.N., Karmally, W., Siddiqui, M. *et al.* (1995) Increases in dietary cholesterol are associated with modest increases in both LDL and HDL cholesterol in healthy women. *Arteriosclerosis, Thrombosis and Vascular Biology* 15, 169–178.

Hargis, P.S. and Van Elswyk, M.E. (1991) Modifying yolk fatty acid composition to improve the health quality of shell eggs. In: Habarstroh, C. and Morris, C.E. (eds), *Fat and Cholesterol Reduced Foods: Technologies and Strategies*. The Portfolio Publishing Co., Woodlands, Texas, pp. 249–260.

Hargis, P.S. and Van Elswyk, M.E. (1993) Manipulating the fatty acid composition of poultry meat and eggs for the health conscious consumer. *World's Poultry Science* 49, 251–264.

Hargis, P.S., Van Elswyk, M.E. and Hargis, B.M. (1991) Dietary modification of yolk lipid with menhaden oil. *Poultry Science* 70, 874–883.

Herber-McNeill, S.M. and Van Elswyk, M.E. (1996) Dietary marine algae promotes efficient deposition of *n*-3 FA for the production of enriched shell eggs. *Poultry Science* 75, 1501–1507.

Kang, J.X. and Leaf, A. (1996) The cardiac antiarrhymthic effects of polyunsaturated fatty acid. *Lipids* 31, S41–S44.

Krauss, R.M. (1987) Relationship of intermediate and low-density lipoprotein subspecies to risk of coronary artery disease. *American Heart Journal* 113, 578–582.

Krauss, R.M. and Dreon, D.M. (1995) Low-density-lipoprotein subclasses and response to a low-fat diet in healthy men. *American Journal of Clinical Nutrition* 62, 478S–487S.

Krauss, R.M., Williams, P.T., Lindgren, F.T. *et al.* (1988) Coordinate changes in levels of human serum low and high density lipoprotein subclasses in healthy men. *Arteriosclerosis* 8, 155–162.

Kromhout, D. (1992) Dietary fats: long-term implications for health. *Nutrition Reviews* 50, 49–53.

Marshall, A.C., Sams, A.R. and Van Elswyk, M.E. (1994a) Oxidative stability and sensory quality of stored eggs from hens fed 1.5% menhaden oil. *Journal of Food Science* 59, 561–563.

Marshall, A.C., Kubena, K.S., Hinton, K.R. *et al.* (1994b) N-3 fatty acid enriched table eggs: a survey of consumer acceptability. *Poultry Science* 73, 1334–1340.

Mayo, P.K., Van Elswyk, M.E. and Kubena, K.S. (1995) Shell eggs as a vehicle for dietary omega-3 fatty acids: influence on serum lipids and platelet aggregation in humans. *Journal of the American Dietetic Association* 95S, A10.

Oh, S.Y., Rye, J., Hsieh, C. *et al.* (1991) Eggs enriched in *n*-3 FA and alterations in lipid concentrations in plasma and lipoproteins and in blood pressure. *American Journal of Clinical Nutrition* 54, 689–695.

O'Keefe, J.H. *et al.* (1995) Potential beneficial effects of monounsaturated and polyunsaturated fats in elderly patients with or at risk of coronary artery disease. *Cardiology in the Elderly* 3, 5–10.

Van Elswyk, M.E., Sams, A.R. and Hargis, P.S. (1992) Composition, functionality, and sensory evaluation of eggs from hens fed dietary menhaden oil. *Journal of Food Science* 57, 342–344, 349.

Van Elswyk, M.E., Dawson, P.L. and Sams, A.R. (1995) Dietary menhaden oil influences sensory characteristics and headspace volatiles of shell eggs. *Journal of Food Science* 60, 85–89.

Designer Egg Concept: Perfecting Egg Through Diet Enrichment with ω-3 PUFA and Cholesterol Stability

10

J.S. Sim

*Department of Agricultural, Food and Nutritional Science,
University of Alberta, Edmonton, Alberta, Canada*

The health-promoting effects of dietary ω-3 fatty acids have provoked considerable effort to enrich animal products using various sources of ω-3 fatty acids, such as flaxseed, canola, algae or fish oils. The egg industry in particular has been very responsive in seeking new technology to exploit products beyond their traditional food value. One such technology is the designer egg, which retains the functional, nutritional and sensory qualities, but has a significantly altered lipid composition.

An increased level of long chain polyunsaturated fatty acid (PUFA) foods, however, poses a potential risk. Auto-oxidation of PUFAs may occur in animal products. Cholesterol also undergoes auto-oxidation in the presence of light and molecular oxygen, through a free radical reaction. Great care therefore is required in scaling up the production of ω-3 PUFA-enriched animal products, because of the susceptibility of animal products to peroxidation. Little information about the stability of egg cholesterol in ω-3 PUFA-enriched eggs is currently available. I would like to introduce the designer egg concept and its nutritional and health implications, and to present data pertaining to egg lipids and cholesterol stability in ω-3 PUFA-enriched egg yolk and the ways of preventing auto-oxidation.

Introduction

In the industrialized world, animal products contribute more than 60% of total lipids, 70% of saturated fats and 100% of cholesterol of the diet. Consumer preference for animal products will probably continue. Thus, it would be of national strategic importance in the fight against heart disease to design/ modify animal products in such a way that dietary risks are minimized. Both epidemiological and clinical intervention studies have demonstrated a decrease in coronary heart disease mortality in people consuming relatively small amounts of ω-3 fatty acids (0.5 g day^{-1}) over a long period of time. One large designer egg supplies more than 600 mg of most needed ω-3 poly-unsaturated fatty acids (PUFAs) and 6 mg of tocopherols; it would still have additional beneficial effects for egg consumers due to its balanced ratios of PUFA to saturated fatty acid (SFA) (1 : 1) and ω-6 : ω-3 PUFAs (1 : 1). There-fore, designer eggs may offer an alternative choice of food product to today's nutrition–health conscious egg consumers around the world.

Similar efforts should be made to design other animal products to achieve the ultimate goal of minimizing the dietary risk of coronary heart disease. Con-sumers have begun to take control of their own health. They are driving the market for a new category of foods with the potential for health promotion well beyond the traditionally recognized benefits. It is clear that this rapidly emerging area of designer egg production has enormous market potential. An increasingly competitive world market environment requires that the industry concentrates on producing what the market needs rather than simply supply-ing what they produce. The egg industry has been very responsive in seeking new technology to improve the consumers' negative perception of the egg associated with cholesterol, *Salmonella* and even allergy problems attached to egg products. I would like to introduce the designer egg concept and its nutritional and health implications, and to present data pertaining to egg lipids and cholesterol stability in ω-3 PUFA-enriched egg yolk and the ways of preventing auto-oxidation.

Food Lipids and the Egg Industry

The rapid decline in per capita consumption of eggs over the past 30 years (Fig. 10.1) is a most challenging problem facing the egg industry in many parts

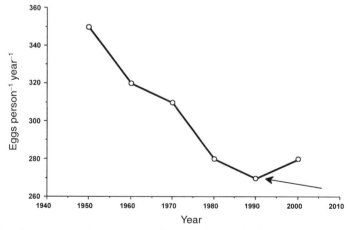

Fig. 10.1. Egg consumption pattern in the USA during the last 50 years. Now, the declining trend in egg consumption has been reversed in North America, and has begun to rise since 1996 (arrow). This change was attributed to a new market surge of specialty eggs, such as designer eggs.

of the world. The negative perception related to the high cholesterol content, 195–250 mg per egg (Yaffee *et al.*, 1991) is undoubtedly one of the major contributing factors. Consumers' attitudes towards lipid in general have changed their attitude towards egg consumption because of the fear that egg cholesterol will raise their blood cholesterol levels. Eggs therefore have been singled out by diet–heart advocates as a food to be avoided (Connor and Connor, 1983), even though the egg contains the best and least expensive high quality protein and balanced distribution of minerals and vitamins, except vitamin C (Shrimpton, 1987).

The first response to 'cholesterol phobia' was the extensive investigation into factors, genetic, dietary and pharmacological in nature, that would reduce the cholesterol content of eggs. However, various attempts to reduce the cholesterol content (Waldroup *et al.*, 1986; Hargis, 1988) or produce cholesterol-free products have met with no success. Due to the failure of attempts to reduce cholesterol levels significantly in eggs, researchers began to investigate alternative manipulation to improve the nutritional quality of the egg and to re-establish its position as a healthy and safe food item.

According to the diet–heart hypothesis, the amount and type of dietary lipids influence plasma and lipoprotein lipid levels, which in turn increase the risk of coronary heart disease (US Department of Health and Human Services, 1988). The principal nutrient-related health problems in North America arise from the over-consumption of lipid, mainly of animal origin (57–75%). The National Institutes of Health (1984) and Health Canada (1990) have adopted recommendations and target dietary guideline to limit lipid intake and modify the type of lipid consumption (Fig. 10.2). Thus, animal agriculture must respond to the perceived needs of consumers by producing foods that are more healthy and which reflect the national nutritional guidelines. The egg

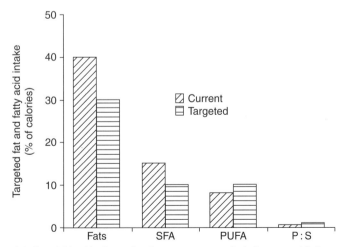

Fig. 10.2. National Health Organizations recommended dietary guidelines or target levels of dietary fats by reducing total fat intake to less than 30%, SFA (saturated fatty acid) intake to less than 10% and PUFA (polyunsaturated fatty acid) intake to 10% of total caloric intake.

industry in particular has been greatly encouraged to intensify efforts in developing and marketing products that would facilitate adherence to the dietary guidelines or national recommended target levels for fat and cholesterol.

ω-3 Fatty Acids

The pioneering discovery that ω-3 fatty acids protect against coronary heart disease in Greenland Eskimos consuming fish (Dyerberg and Bang, 1979) has generated much research over the past decades on the various health benefits of dietary ω-3 fatty acid from fish oils. Researchers around the world have focused on the health effects of the dietary supply of ω-3 fatty acids. This is partly because those fatty acids have been reported to protect against cardiovascular and inflammatory diseases, as well as certain types of cancer (Kinsella *et al.*, 1990; Simopooulos, 1991). Also, it has been shown that ω-3 fatty acids are essential nutients for adults and children (Holman *et al.*, 1982; Bjerve, 1991). The benefits of dietary ω-3 PUFA include, among others, reductions in plasma triglycerides, blood pressure, platelet aggregation, thrombosis and atherosclerosis, particularly in diabetics, tumour growth, skin disease and enhanced immunity. Health Canada (1990) adopted a recommendation that ω-3 PUFAs are essential nutrients, thus recommending that the dietary supply should be at least 0.5% of the energy intake as linolenic acid (LNA). When the diet of infants contains no eicosapentaenoic acid (EPA) and docosahexaenoic acid (DHA), then LNA should be supplied as 1% of energy intake. This recommendation was made on the basis of the fact that North American diets are deficient in the ω-3 fatty acids.

The egg industry has stepped in to fill this gap and has begun to return the ω-3 fatty acids into the food supply. The ratio of ω-6 to ω-3 fatty acids is important, and the current high ratio should be reduced to less than 4 : 1 (Beare-Rogers, 1991). To date, the main supply of ω-3 fatty acids in the human diet has been fish and fish oil. The major ω-6 and ω-3 PUFAs are summarized in Box 10.1.

Canadian Designer Eggs™

The fatty acid composition of yolk fat can readily be modified by diet (Cruickshank, 1934; Sim *et al.*, 1973). In recent years, several researchers have investigated the ability of the hen to enrich the egg with ω-3 fatty acids. The

---

Box 10.1.   Major ω-6 and ω-3 fatty acids.

Linoleic acid (LA)	C18 : 2ω-6
Arachidonic acid (AA)	C20 : 4ω-6
Linolenic acid (LNA)	C18 : 3ω-3
Eicosapentaenoic acid (EPA)	C20 : 5ω-3
Docosapentaenoic acid (DPA)	C22 : 5ω-3
Docosahexaenoic acid (DHA)	C22 : 6ω-3

incorporation of ω-3 PUFAs into egg yolk fat was accomplished easily by feed-ing laying hens diets containing flaxseed (Nwokolo and Sim, 1989; Caston and Leeson, 1990; Sim, 1990; Jiang *et al.*, 1992) and fish oils (Yu and Sim, 1987; Hargis *et al.*, 1991). The egg lipid composition is the result of a combination of *de novo* lipogenesis and incorporation of lipid components from the diet. Another factor regulating the quantity and the type of fatty acid deposition is the feedback inhibition of dietary long chain PUFAs (Reiser *et al.*, 1963). Therefore, it is feasible to alter the fatty acid composition of poultry products through dietary manipulation of long chain PUFAs and to design food prod-ucts reflecting the nutritional guidelines, supplying ω-3 fatty acids while having optimal PUFA : SFA and ω-6 : ω-3 fatty acid ratios.

Sim *et al.* (1992), Jiang and Sim (1992) and Sim (1993) have carried out a series of studies to enhance the value of chicken eggs enriched in ω-3 fatty acids (500-600 mg per egg) with a significantly elevated PUFA : SFA ratio (from 0.6 to 1.02), and lowering the ω-6 : ω-3 fatty acid ratio (from 10 : 1 to 1 : 1). One large egg can supply about 600 mg of total ω-3 fatty acids (balanced with DHA, docosapentaenoic acid (DPA) and EPA) equivalent to an approximately 100 g serving of fish (Fig. 10.3). A consumer survey indicated the public's interest in ω-3 fatty acid-enriched eggs as a dietary alternative to fish (Marshall *et al.*, 1994).

Although LNA was the major ω-3 fatty acid deposited in the egg yolk, a considerable amount of longer chain ω-3 fatty acids was also incorporated into the phospholipid fractions of the yolk lipids. The hens fed flaxseed produced eggs enriched with ω-3 fatty acids (7–12% of yolk lipids) in the following order: LNA > DHA > DPA > EPA (Sim and Qi, 1995). This indicates that laying hens can convert dietary LNA to EPA, DPA and DHA via the desaturase and elongase enzyme systems (Garg *et al.*, 1988). Arachidonic acid (AA), the metabolite of linoleic acid (LA; ω-6 fatty acid), was significantly reduced. Con-sequently, the ratio of ω-6 to ω-3 fatty acids was significantly decreased in the ω-3 fatty acid-enriched eggs (from 10 : 1 to 1 : 1).

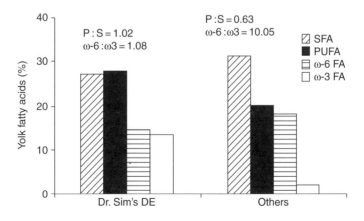

Fatty acid profile of designer eggs

Fig. 10.3.   Fatty acid profile comparison of an ω-3 fatty acid-enriched egg (DE) and a regular egg (others). P : S = polyunsaturated : saturated.

Nutritional Significance

A series of studies was carried out to examine the influence, if any, that ω-3 PUFA-enriched eggs have on plasma cholesterol and tissue fatty acid modification in animals and humans. Plasma and liver tissue cholesterol levels and fatty acid composition were analysed after feeding ω-3 fatty acid-enriched eggs to rats (Jiang and Sim, 1992), as an animal model, and humans (Jiang and Sim, 1993), as egg consumers.

Plasma cholesterol profile

The eggs were hard-boiled and the yolks were removed, pulverized and dried. Dry yolk powders were incorporated into a semi-synthetic diet at a 15% level and fed to weaning female Sprague–Dawley rats for 4 weeks. The blood and liver cholesterol levels and fatty acid composition were determined at the end of the feeding period. Feeding ω-3 PUFA-enriched eggs reduced both plasma and liver total cholesterol contents by 20 and 38%, respectively (Fig. 10.4).

Twenty-four healthy male students aged 18–32 years were recruited and divided randomly into two groups of 12 each. Each subject had two eggs at breakfast. Before the start and at the termination of the 18-day study, subjects fasted for more than 12 h prior to blood samples being taken at the University Health Clinic. There are clear patterns to state that consumption of designer eggs does not provoke plasma cholesterol despite their high inherent cholesterol content, increases HDL cholesterol, suppresses LDL cholesterol and produces a marked reduction of plasma triglyceride levels (Fig. 10.5). Consuming designer eggs also enriches body tissue lipids with ω-3 fatty acids, in particular phospholipids. Other researchers also reported similar results. Ferrier *et al.* (1992) found that human consumption of LNA-enriched eggs

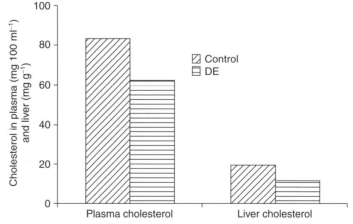

Fig. 10.4. Plasma and liver cholesterol levels of rats at the end of 28 days of being fed yolk powder with and without ω-3 PUFA enrichment. Source: Jiang and Sim (1992).

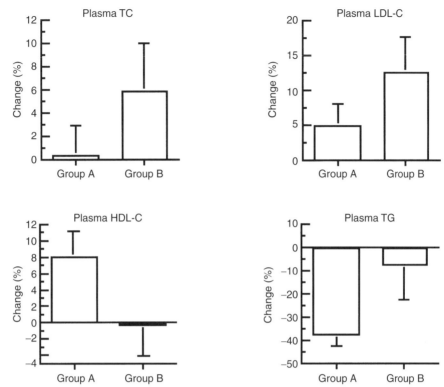

Fig. 10.5. Percentage change in plasma total cholesterol (TC), low-density lipo-protein cholesterol (LDL-C), high-density lipoprotein cholesterol (HDL-C) and plasma triglyceride (TG) levels in human subjects after consuming two ω-3 PUFA-enriched designer eggs (A) or regular eggs (B) with their habitual diets for a period of 3 weeks. Source: Jiang and Sim (1993).

decreased serum triglycerides and increased ω-3 fatty acids, particularly DHA, which accumulated in platelet phospholipids.

The results demonstrate that designing the fatty acid composition of egg yolk lipids through chicken diets can modify the cholesterolaemic and lipidaemic properties of chicken eggs. The designer egg concept offers an alternative choice of food production to today's nutrition–health conscious consumers around the world. Eggs, which have been considered an athero-genic food, are now consumed safely if enriched with ω-3 fatty acids.

Nursing mother's milk

Aware of the importance of ω-3 PUFA to infants (Carlson *et al.*, 1992), the mag-nitude of changes in the fatty acid composition of breast milk and plasma fatty acids of eight nursing women were studied upon consumption of two designer eggs for a period of 6 weeks. Consuming two eggs as a part of their normal daily meal for 6 weeks resulted in a significant deposition of total ω-3 fatty acids at 3.6% compared with 1.9% for the pre-test milk and a reduction in the ω-6 : ω-3 fatty acid ratio from 6.7 to 3.0. The longer chain EPA and DHA comprised 1.2% compared with 0.4% in the pre-test milk. Consuming ω-3-enriched eggs did not alter the AA content in the milk. This phenomenon made the milk fat more favourable by increasing the DHA : AA ratio from 0.75 to 1.2 (Fig. 10.6). Total plasma cholesterol and triglyceride levels were not affected (Cherian and Sim, 1996). The ω-3 PUFA-enriched eggs (designer eggs) contained about 690 mg of total ω-3 fatty acid with 165 mg of long chain *n*-3 fatty acids (EPA, DPA and DHA). Assuming the intake of a 1-month old infant to be 794 ml, infants nursed from women consuming designer eggs could have over 300 mg of long chain ω-3 fatty acids such as EPA, DPA and DHA. Thus, a diet supplemented with designer eggs or their egg oils should provide an alternative way of supplying ω-3 fatty acids for breast-fed infants. These differences in the ω-3 fatty acid content of breast milk could have implications for the development of suckling infants.

Infant foods

The egg yolk consists of lipids and protein. More than 66% of the total dry yolk mass is fats. An average egg provides about 6 g of lipids, which are contained exclusively in the yolk. One designer egg can supply about 600 mg of total ω-3 PUFA to the human diet with an elevated level of DHA and AA in the eggs. Both the DHA and AA are essential for proper brain development in infants (Cherian *et al.*, 1997). The designer egg is a potential vehicle to provide the much-needed DHA and AA, which more closely mimics the fatty acid composition of human breast milk (Fig. 10.7). Compared with human milk, most commercial infant formulas are based on soybean oil and contain about

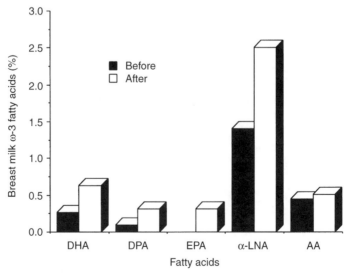

Fig. 10.6.   Fatty acid composition of breast milk from nursing mothers before (basal) and after (6th week) consuming two designer eggs daily for a period of 6 weeks.

53% LA and 7% LNA. Most infant formulas contain LA and LNA in amounts comparable with those in human milk, but they lack long chain ω-3 PUFA contents, DHA and AA in particular (Simopoulos and Salem, 1992). It is crucially important to supply the pre-formed essential long chain PUFAs, both ω-3 DHA and ω-6 AA, in an adequate balance (Carlson *et al.*, 1992). Currently available infant formulas do not contain fatty acids above 18 carbons (Table 10.1).

The primary goal of infant formulas is to mimic the growth and development of the breast-fed infant (Simopoulos and Salem, 1992). One approach to improving a milk formula is to match the composition of human breast milk, which contains both DHA and AA (Fig. 10.7). Designed egg yolk oils provide an adequate amount of ω-3 and ω-6 precursors and long chain PUFAs, including DHA, while still sustaining a significant level of AA in the egg with various ratios of ω-6 : ω-3 ranging from 20 to 1. Industry and the scientific community alike are searching for a new oil source supplying both long chain ω-6 and ω-3 PUFAs. Since the fatty acid make-up of designer eggs resembles that of human

Table 10.1. Essential fatty acid profile of commercial infant formulas (survey conducted).

%	Commercial infant formulas					DE oils	HBM
LA	13.9	22.0	23.6	31.2	31.1	13.0	9.9
LNA	1.9	3.1	3.5	4.4	4.1	9.3	2.4
AA	—	—	—	—	—	1.6	0.4
DHA	—	—	—	—	—	2.2	0.3

LA, 18 : 2ω-6; LNA, 18 : 3ω-3; AA, 20 : 4ω-6; DHA, 22 : 6ω-3; DE, designer egg; HBM, human breast milk.

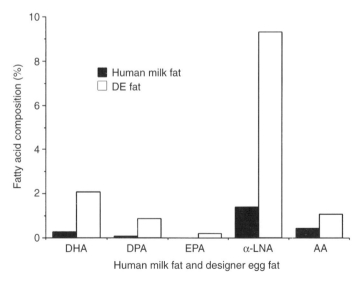

Fig. 10.7. Long chain *n*-6 and *n*-3 fatty acid concentrations in human milk and designer egg oil.

milk fat, yolk oil may be regarded as an essential oil base for the infant food industry.

Designer egg oil

An average egg also provides about 6 g of lipids, which are contained exclusively in the yolk. More than 66% of the total yolk mass is fats, thus the yolk from these n-3 PUFA-enriched eggs can be regarded as a potential oil crop rich in long chain PUFAs, both DHA and AA being essential for infants. Designer egg yolk oil may be regarded as an essential oil base for infant formula because it resembles the fatty acid composition of human milk. Designed egg yolk oils provide an adequate amount of n-3 and n-6 precursors and long chain PUFAs including DHA while still sustaining a significant level of AA in the egg with various ratios of n-6 : n-3 in a range of 22.1–1.4.

There is an excellent possibility and a unique opportunity to diversify egg uses. Egg oil extraction–purification technologies developed at the University of Alberta are presently available to be exploited for an industrial application. A bench-top model of egg oil extracting technology directly from fresh egg yolk using an aqueous solvent system and subsequently partitioning into the neutral oil and lecithin fractions by a cold precipitation technique was devised and patented as a potential technology to be exploited (Fig. 10.8). Subsequently, a scaled-up process has been undertaken jointly in collaboration with food industry partners. Technology of egg oil extraction and fractionation of lecithin from fresh egg yolk (Canadian Patent Application No. 612,411, 21 September, 1989, European Patents, Japan, South Korea, Finland under patent cooperation treaty, PCT No. 8150, 10 July, 1990) is an outcome from this research.

Food Safety

There are potential risks associated with a high level of long chain PUFAs in foods. Auto-oxidation of long chain PUFAs occurs in feeds and egg products. Caution is needed in scaling up the production of ω-3 PUFA-enriched eggs, egg oils and their infant food applications, since the susceptibility of food lipids to oxidation is closely associated with the degree of unsaturation. A series of experiments to investigate the lipid stability from lipid oxidation and ways of preventing auto-oxidation have been conducted.

Flaxseed in chicken feed

In our earlier study, feeds containing a large amount of flaxseed have been associated with a fish flavour or lower sensory quality of egg products during storage. This was attributed to a combination of lipid rancidity in the feed and lipid peroxidation in the chicken tissues and eggs (Jiang et al., 1992). Therefore, we conducted an experiment to monitor the chemical changes in the flaxseed, the very source of dietary ω-3 fatty acid in the poultry feed, under various storage conditions. The changes in the content and stability of α-LNA were found to be negligible in the early stage of storage, but oxidation

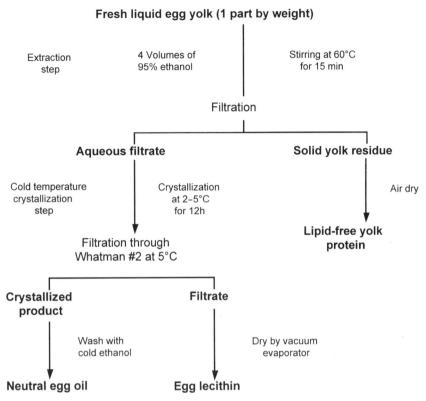

Fig. 10.8.   Schematic flow chart of a sequential extraction, fractionation and purification procedure for egg oil and lecithin from fresh yolk.

potential markedly increased after a period of 60 days. The results indicated that the intact flaxseed (whole) is well protected from lipid oxidation by the presence of its intrinsic tocopherol content, and further supplementation of tocopherol significantly extends its stability even when flaxseeds are physically broken open for feed compounding and storage. This study confirmed that flaxseed contains a sufficient amount of natural antioxidants as tocopherols, and protects dietary ω-3 fatty acids in the chicken feed from auto-oxidation within 60 days (Gopalakrishman *et al.*, 1996).

Tocopherols

In the early development stage of the designer egg, an off-flavour (fish-taint) from eggs enriched with ω-3 PUFAs was experienced. We suspect that the fish flavour generation could be the result of rancidity of ω-3 fatty acids in feeds and/or animal products. This problem was dealt with by stabilizing the dietary source of ω-3 PUFA with a natural form of tocopherols before incorporation into chicken feeds (Qi and Sim, 1998). A significant reduction in off-flavour, volatile compounds, cholesterol oxidation products and thiobarbituric acid-reacting substances was achieved in both feed and egg products by stabilizing the dietary fats with a natural form of tocopherols as antioxidants (Cherian *et al.*, 1996a,b; Li *et al.*, 1996). Supplementing antioxidants into chicken feed not only effectively eliminates the off-flavour problem, but also greatly improves the stability of egg products. The tocopherol concentrations in egg yolk increased linearly with increasing levels of dietary tocopherol levels (Fig. 10.9).

With increasing levels of dietary tocopherol supplementation in laying hen diets, malondialdehyde contents in the egg yolk decreased from 41 to 18 nmol g^{-1} of egg yolk (Fig. 10.10). This proves that lipid stability could be improved by increasing the tocopherol contents of eggs. Reduction of the oxidation products and increasing the tocopherol concentration (antioxidants) in the yolk were major technological breakthroughs eliminating the preceding sensory and off-flavour problems. Thus, designer eggs not only supply a stable form of essential ω-3 PUFAs, but also a natural form of tocopherols including vitamin E, to today's most health conscious consumers.

Cholesterol oxidation

Cholesterol undergoes auto-oxidation in the presence of light and molecular oxygen, through a free radical reaction, and forms cholesterol oxide products which are considered potent atherogens and carcinogens to humans (Ames, 1983; Hubbard *et al.*, 1989). The presence of several cholesterol oxide products in commercial egg products has been reported, but little information about cholesterol stability in ω-3 fatty acid-enriched eggs and methods to prevent oxidation is available. Considering the importance of PUFAs and tocopherols as antioxidants in lipid oxidation, the effect on oxidative stability of

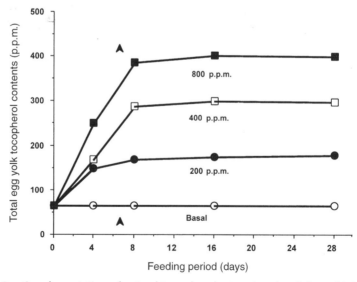

Fig. 10.9. Supplementation of natural tocopherols at various levels into chicken feed reaches a plateau on the eighth day of feeding. Tocopherol deposition into egg yolk is proportional to the dietary levels.

cholesterol in the egg yolk of feeding flax, sunflower, palm and fish oils, with and without tocopherols, to laying hens was investigated. Results show that cholesterol oxidation is accelerated by the presence of long chain PUFAs in the order fish oil > flaxseed oil > sunflower seed oil > palm oil. The initial levels of cholesterol oxides were 7–10 p.p.m. and reached over 200 p.p.m. within a 4-month storage period. Cholesterol oxide formation was accelerated further

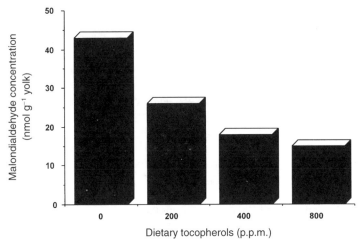

Fig. 10.10. Effect of tocopherol supplementation on lipoperoxide level in the egg yolk. Egg yolk lipid stability was greatly improved by increasing the tocopherol contents of eggs.

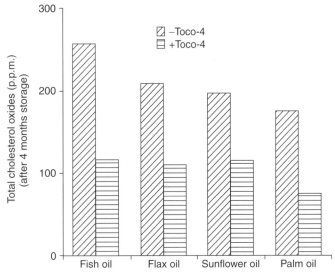

Fig. 10.11. Effects of dietary fatty acids and tocopherol supplementation on cholesterol oxidation in egg yolk. The cholesterol oxidation was significantly reduced in the presence of tocopherol. Egg yolk cholesterol oxidizes during storage. Tocopherol protects cholesterol from oxidation.

by heat at 110°C for 22 h. Feeding tocopherol supplements to laying hens increased the intrinsic tocopherol content of eggs (Fig. 10.9), and the presence of increased tocopherols significantly reduced the formation of cholesterol oxides in the egg yolk regardless of its fatty acid profile (Fig. 10.11). Feeding laying hens with tocopherol-supplemented diets can delay or prevent the cholesterol oxidation potential of ω-3 PUFA-enriched eggs during storage and processing. This study suggests that adding vitamin E or a natural form of toco pherols, which would benefit the food industry and human health, can prevent cholesterol oxide formation in ω-3 PUFA-enriched eggs.

Acknowledgements

This work has been supported by Grants from Natural Sciences Engineering, Research Council of Canada (NSERC), University of Alberta, Alberta Agricultural Research Institute (AARI), Flax Council of Canada and Designer Egg Producers Association International (DEPAI).

References

Ames, B.N. (1983) Dietary carcinogens and anticarcinogens. *Science* 221, 1256–1264.

Beare-Rogers, J. (1991) *Nutrition Recommendations in Canada*. Bureau of Nutritional Sciences Food Directorate, Health Protection Branch, Health and Welfare Canada. Inform 2 (No. 4), 326, AOCS Annual Meeting at Chicago.

Bjerve, K.S. (1991) Omega-3 fatty acid deficiency in man: implications for requirement of alpha-linolenic acid and long chain omega-3 fatty acids. *World Review on Nutrition and Diet* 65, 133–142.

Carlson, S.E., Cooke, R.J., Werkman, S.H. and Tolley, E.A. (1992) First year growth of infants fed standard compared to marine oil *n*-3 supplemented formula. *Lipids* 27, 901–907.

Caston, L. and Leeson, S. (1990) Research note: dietary flaxseed and egg composition. *Poultry Science* 69, 1617–1620.

Cherian, G. and Sim, J.S. (1996) Changes in the breast milk fatty acids and plasma lipids of nursing mothers following consumption of *n*-3 polyunsaturated fatty acid enriched eggs. *Nutrition* 12, 8–12.

Cherian, G., Wolfe, F.W. and Sim, J.S. (1996a) Dietary oils with added tocopherols: effects on egg or tissue tocopherols, fatty acids and oxidative stability. *Poultry Science* 75, 423–432.

Cherian, G., Wolfe, F.W. and Sim, J.S. (1996b) Feeding dietary oils with tocopherols: effects on internal qualities of eggs during storage. *Journal of Food Science* 61, 15–18.

Cherian, G., Gopalarkrishnan, N., Akiba, Y. and Sim, J.S. (1997) Effect of maternal dietary *n*-3 fatty acids on the accretion of long chain polyunsaturated fatty acids in the tissues of developing chick embryo. *Biology of the Neonate* 72, 165–174.

Connor, S.L. and Connor, W.E. (1983) The importance of dietary cholesterol in coronary heart disease. *Preventive Medicine* 12, 115.

Cruickshank, E.M. (1934) Studies in fat metabolism in the fowl. I. The composition of the egg fat and depot fat of the fowl as affected by the ingestion of large amounts of fats. *Biochemical Journal* 28, 965–971.

Dyerberg J. and Bang, H.O. (1979) Haemostic function and platelet polyunsaturated fatty acids in Eskimos. *Lancet* ii, 433–435.

Ferrier, L.K., Caston, L., Leeson, S., Squires, E.J., Celi, B., Thomas, L. and Holub, B. (1992) Changes in serum lipids and platelet fatty acid composition following consumption of eggs enriched in alpha-linolenic acid (LnA). *Food Research International* 25, 263–268.

Garg, M.L., Sebokova, E., Wierzbicki, E., Thompson, A.B.R. and Clandinin, M.T. (1988) Differential effects of dietary linoleic and linolenic acid on lipid metabolism in rat tissues. *Lipids* 23, 847–852.

Gopalakrishnan, N., Cherian, G. and Sim, J.S. (1996) Chemical changes in the lipids of canola and flax seeds during storage. *Fett (Lipid)* 98 (Suppl. 5), 168–171.

Hargis, P.S. (1988) Modifying egg cholesterol in the domestic fowl: a review. *World's Poultry Science Journal* 44, 17–29.

Hargis, P.S., Van Elswyk, M.E. and Harris, M.M. (1991) Dietary modification of yolk lipid with menhaden oil. *Poultry Science* 70, 874–883.

Health Canada (1990) *Nutritional Recommendations.* Canadian Government Publishing Centre, Ottawa, 24, 57.

Holman, R.T., Johnson, S.B. and Hatch, T. (1982) A case of human linolenic acid deficiency involving neurological abnormalities. *American Journal of Clinical Nutrition* 35, 617–623.

Hubbard, R.W., Ono, Y. and Sanchez, A. (1989) Atherogenic effect of oxidized products of cholesterol. *Progress in Food and Nutrition Science* 13, 17–44.

Jiang, Z. and Sim, J.S. (1992) Effects of dietary *n*-3 fatty acid-enriched chicken eggs on plasma and tissue cholesterol and fatty acid compositions of rats. *Lipids* 27, 279–284.

Jiang, Z. and Sim, J.S. (1993) Consumption of *n*-3 fatty acid enriched eggs and changes in plasma lipids of human subjects. *Nutrition* 9, 513–518.

Jiang, Z., Ahn, D.U., Ladner, L. and Sim, J.S. (1992) Influence of feeding full-fat flax and sunflower seeds on internal and sensory qualities of eggs. *Poultry Science* 71, 378–382.

Kinsella, J.E., Lokesh, B. and Stone, R.A. (1990) Dietary *n*-3 polyunsaturated fatty acids and amelioration of cardiovascular disease: possible mechanisms. *American Journal of Clinical Nutrition* 52, 1–28.

Li, S.X., Cherian, G. and Sim, J.S. (1996) Cholesterol oxidation in egg yolk powder during storage and heating as affected by dietary oils and tocopherol. *Journal of Food Science* 61, 721–725.

Marshall, A.C., Kubena, K.S., Hinton, K.R., Hargis, P.S. and Van Elswyk, M.E. (1994) *n*-3 Fatty acid enriched table eggs: a survey of consumer acceptability. *Poultry Science* 73, 1334–1340.

National Institutes of Health (1984) *NIH Consensus Development Statement on Lowering Blood Cholesterol to Prevent Heart Disease.* Vol. 5, No. 7. National Institutes of Health, Washington, DC.

Nwokolo, E. and Sim, J.S. (1989) Barley and full-fat canola seed in layer diets. *Poultry Science* 68, 1485–1489.

Qi, G.H. and Sim, J.S. (1998) Natural tocopherol enrichment and its effect in *n*-3 fatty acid modified chicken eggs. *Journal of Agricultural and Food Chemistry* 46, 1920–1926.

Reiser, R., Williams, M.C., Sorrels, M.F. and Murty, N.L. (1963) Biosynthesis of fatty acids and cholesterol as related to diet fat. *Archives of Biochemistry and Biophysics* 102, 276–285.

Shrimpton, D.H. (1987) The nutritive value of eggs and their dietary significance. In: Wells, R.G. and Beljavin, C.J. (eds), *Egg Quality – Current Problems and Recent Advances.* Butterworth and Co., London, pp. 11–25.

Sim, J.S. (1990) Flaxseed as a high energy/protein/omega-3 fatty acid ingredient for poultry. In: Carter J.R. (ed.), *Proceedings of the 53rd Flax Institute of the United States.* NDSU, Fargo, North Dakota, pp. 65–71.

Sim, J.S. (1993) Designing eggs and health/nutritional implication for egg consumers. In: *Proceedings of 54th Minnesota Nutrition Conference & National Renders Technical Symposium.* Bloomington, Minnesota, pp. 275–286.

Sim, J.S. and Qi, G.-H. (1995) Designing poultry products using flaxseed. In: Thompson, L.U. and Cunnane, S. (eds), *Flaxseed in Human Nutrition.* American Oil Chemist's Society Press, pp. 315–333.

Sim, J.S., Hudgson, G.S. and Bragg, D.B. (1973) Effect of dietary animal tallow and vegetable oil on fatty acid composition of egg yolk, adipose tissue and liver of laying hens. *Poultry Science* 52, 51–57.

Sim, J.S., Cherian, G. and Jiang, Z. (1992) Alpha-linolenic acid metabolism: the chicken and the egg. *International Journal of Applied and Basic Nutritional Science (Nutrition)* 8, 221–222.

Simopoulos, A.P. (1991) Omega-3 fatty acids in health and disease and in growth and development. *American Journal of Clinical Nutrition* 54, 438–463.

Simopoulos, A.P. and Salem, N. (1992) Egg yolk as a source of long chain polyunsaturated fatty acids in infant feeding. *American Journal of Clinical Nutrition* 55, 411–415.

US Department of Health and Human Services (1988) *The Surgeon General's Report on Nutrition and Health.* US Government Printing Office, Washington, DC.

Waldroup P.W., Ndife, L.I., Hellwig, H.M., Herbert, J.A. and Berrio, L. (1986) Influence of probuccal on egg cholesterol concentration. *Poultry Science* 64, 205–211.

Yaffee, M., Schultz, H., Stone, J., Brokhari, S. and Zeidler, G. (1991) Consumer perception and utilization of eggs and egg products. *Poultry Science* 70, 188–192.

Yu, M.M. and Sim, J.S. (1987) Biological incorporation of *n*-polyunsaturated fatty acids into chicken eggs. *Poultry Science* 66, 195 (abstract).

Not All ω-3-Enriched Eggs are the Same

11

D.J. Farrell

School of Land and Food, The University of Queensland,
St Lucia, Queensland 4072, Australia

ω (*n*)-3-enriched eggs can be produced by feeding hens on diets containing seed oils or microalgae. These will result in eggs containing different proportions and concentration of the long chain *n*-3 free fatty acids (FFAs). The physiological effects of these FFAs are different. α-Linolenic acid (LNA) (18 : 3*n*-3) is of no benefit until converted in a body to the active forms, eicosapentaenoic acid (EPA) (20 : 5*n*-3), docosapentaenoic acid (DPA) (22 : 5*n*-3) and docosahexaenoic acid (DHA) (22 : 6*n*-3). It is clear that oil seeds rich in LNA result in eggs that contain predominantly LNA and lesser concentrations of DHA + DPA, while eggs from hens fed marine algae contain DPA + DHA almost exclusively. In order to enrich eggs with a significant amount of EPA, it is necessary to provide the hens with fish meal or fish oil. It is recognized that EPA is the most important *n*-3 FFA in reducing the incidence of heart disease and some forms of cancer. The British Nutrition Foundation recommends human consumption of 1.4 g of EPA + DHA per adult per week, but makes no mention of LNA, perhaps because of poor conversion.

Introduction

Broadhurst *et al.* (1998) argued convincingly that the successful evolution of *Homo habilis* to *Homo sapiens*, approximately 2 million years ago, coincided with increased accessibility to fish. These authors suggest that for the expansion of the brain to have occurred, there was the need for man to consume diets rich in arachidonic acid (AA, 20 : 4*n*-6) and docosahexaenoic acid (DHA, 22 : 6*n*-3). Freshwater fish lipid has a DHA : AA ratio which is closer to that in our brain phospholipids than any other food source. Furthermore, a recent survey by Petridou *et al.* (1998) in the Greater Athens area provides some evidence that a maternal diet rich in fish may reduce the risk of cerebral palsy in the offspring.

The purpose of this chapter is to highlight the fact that the three important n-3 polyunsaturated fatty acids (PUFAs) are not always interchangeable in their beneficial effects. Foods rich in α-linolenic acid (LNA, 18 : 3n-3) may not be as effective in human health as the long chain PUFAs such as eicosapenta-enoic acid (EPA, 20 : 5n-3) and DHA. Tinoco (1982) reviewed many aspects of LNA in different species.

It is widely accepted that the diet of western man is usually deficient in n-3 PUFAs, particularly the long chain PUFAs (Barlow and Pike, 1991; Simopoulos, 1991; Sinclair, 1991). Our main source of long chain PUFAs is fish, the consumption of which has declined substantially (Barlow and Pike, 1991). In the USA, the current estimated annual per capita fish consumption is about 6.5 kg or one serving (125 g) of fish per week. This has not always been the case. Crawford *et al.* (1970) compared the fatty acid profile of ruminant livestock in the wild and those domesticated, and found that the meat in the former group had much higher amounts of both n-6 and n-3 PUFAs than the latter. Eggs from wild pheasants, partridge and grouse contained significant amounts of LNA of 7, 10 and 30%, respectively, of total FFAs (Leskanich and Noble, 1997). Simopolous and Salem (1989) showed that hens with access to free-range foraging produced eggs with significant enrichment of PUFAs compared with conventionally housed hens. This was due to the range of foods available to the hens when out of doors, particularly the weed, purslane, rich in LNA (3–4 mg g^{-1} fresh weight). The reason why many western diets do not have sufficient amounts of n-3 PUFAs is not only because of recent changes in food habits but also because management and feeding practices of our domestic livestock have changed.

There have been numerous reviews on the enrichment of the hen's diet to produce n-3 PUFA eggs (Hargis and Van Elswyk, 1993; Leskanich and Noble, 1997). Although the importance of the n-3 PUFAs has been emphasized, it is generally recognized that it is the balance of the n-3 and n-6 PUFAs that is most important. Although there is some disagreement regarding the ideal balance (Sinclair, 1991), it is generally agreed that the dietary intake of n-6 and n-3 PUFAs should be less than 6 : 1 (British Nutrition Foundation, 1992); others feel that it should be closer to 1 : 1 (Simopoulos, 1991).

There are three recognized areas in which n-3 PUFAs are important to human health; these are in coronary heart disease (Leaf and Weber, 1988), particularly atherosclerosis, arrhythmias and thrombosis, inflammatory diseases and infant development. It is also recognized that the three major n-3 PUFAs, i.e. LNA, EPA and DHA, may not have the same beneficial effects in reducing the incidence of these diseases. It is important to examine more closely this last point because n-3 PUFA-enriched eggs vary with different concentrations and mixtures of these, and may, therefore, be of greater or lesser value in human health.

It is generally recognized that the health benefits of LNA are limited until they are converted to EPA or DHA in the human body through desaturation and chain elongation. There is competition between n-6 and n-3 and n-9 PUFAs for the enzymes for desaturation and chain elongation (Simopulos, 1991; Broadhurst *et al.*, 1998). High levels of linoleic acid (LA, 18 : 2n-6) can slow down the rate of conversion of LNA to EPA and DHA (Sinclair, 1991). Broadhurst *et al.* (1998) pointed out that LNA may not be converted to DHA or EPA in any significant amounts unless there has been a long-term deficiency of PUFA, or if LNA is consistently low.

As pointed out by Simopoulos (1991), there is some evidence that elderly people, hypertensive individuals and some diabetics have a limited capacity to synthesize EPA and DHA from LNA. Much of the research supporting the beneficial effects of *n*-3 PUFA has centred largely on EPA and DHA, with little on LNA (Sanders, 1993). Gaudete and Holub (1991) concluded that DHA could contribute significantly to the inhibition of platelet aggregation important in coronary atherosclerosis (Fox and Di Corleto, 1988). It was unclear whether this was because of retroconversion via docosapentaenoic acid (DPA, $22 : 5n$-3) to EPA or to DHA *per se*. However, Siscovick *et al.* (1995) considered only EPA and DHA in seafood in their assessment of *n*-3 PUFAs in reducing the incidence of primary cardiac arrest in humans.

Ferrier *et al.* (1995) measured the fatty acid composition of subjects who consumed 28 enriched eggs per week from hens on diets with 0, 10 and 20% flaxseed. The increases in DHA, EPA and total *n*-3 PUFAs, although statistically significant, were relatively small given the large number of eggs consumed.

It is now widely accepted that DHA is essential for fetal and infant development (Nettleton, 1993) and is found in significant amounts in breast milk. It has also been suggested that infants, and particularly those born pre-term, cannot convert LNA to DHA in sufficient quantities to meet requirements (Broadhurst *et al.*, 1998). Some milk powders used in infant formula are currently being fortified with fish oil in order to overcome this uncertainty and to provide the infant with EPA and DHA. This is in keeping with the proposal by Nettleton (1995).

There is little information on the role of LNA in inflammatory and auto-immune disorders. Most of the research has centred on the use of marine oils (Simopoulos, 1991). Since hormone-like substances, such as the prostaglandins and leukotrienes, are synthesized from the 20-carbon chain long chain PUFAs, it follows that LNA has no biological activity in this respect until converted to a long chain PUFA.

In summary, because there is considerable uncertainty about the biological effects of LNA in human health and the inefficiency with which LNA is converted to a long chain PUFA, particularly in infants, it is important that ω (*n*)-3-enriched eggs should contain a significant proportion of PUFA as long chain PUFAs. Over the past 10 years, there has been great interest in the production of *n*-3-enriched eggs (Hargis and Van Elswyk, 1993; Leskanich and Noble, 1997).

Methods of Enrichment

Flaxseed

Although the technology is relatively simple, there are considerable differences in the balance of the *n*-3 PUFAs in enriched eggs produced by various means. In Canada alone, there are at least 13 producers of *n*-3-enriched eggs

(Anonymous, 1998); the vast majority of these are produced by hens given flaxseed in their diet (for reviews, see Sim and Qi, 1997; Van Elswyk, 1997). The consequence of this is that the majority of the *n*-3 PUFAs are in the form of LNA since flaxseeds contain about 42% oil of which 53% is LNA. This can lead to increased fatty livers, a reduction in egg quality and organoleptic problems. Although it is now recognized that the latter problem has improved considerably, it has not been overcome completely (Caston *et al.*, 1994).

Scheideler *et al.* (1997) reported some negative effects on appearance and flavour of eggs from hens fed diets with 10 and 15% flaxseed. One effect is a change in yolk colour and another is consumer perception of scrambled eggs.

Incremental amounts of flaxseed in the diet do not always give a corresponding increase in enrichment of *n*-3 PUFAs in egg yolk. Van Elswyk (1997) showed that when results of several workers were combined, feeding flaxseed at 5, 10, 15, 20 and 30% of the diet gave corresponding enrichments of LNA in egg yolk (mg g^{-1}) of 8.5, 16.3, 19.0, 30.0 and 38.0.

Although some authors have reported a small increase in the EPA content of egg yolk as a result of feeding hens diets with flaxseed, others do not report values for EPA in yolk (Ahn *et al.*, 1995; Scheideler *et al.*, 1998). Most workers have shown no significant enrichment in EPA of eggs modified by feeding hens diets rich in flaxseed (Aymond and Van Elswyk, 1995; Ferrier *et al.*, 1995). Thus, eggs enriched with *n*-3 PUFAs through the feeding of flaxseed to hens are characterized by high relative amounts of LNA, significant amounts of DPA + DHA and almost no increase in EPA. The amount of DHA that is incorporated into egg yolk is important from a health point of view, as already discussed. The conversion of LNA to DHA by the hen is relatively poor. For example, Ferrier *et al.* (1995) reported that of the total *n*-3 PUFA in egg yolk, 16% was in the form of DPA + DHA when hens were given a diet with 20% flaxseed; the corresponding value was 24% for a diet with 10% flaxseed. Cherian and Sim (1994) reported that the long chain PUFA content of enriched eggs when given to lactating mothers was 163 mg out of a total of 690 mg, i.e. 24%. However, the major *n*-3 fatty acid in breast milk was LNA. The proportion of *n*-3 long chain PUFAs relative to total *n*-3 PUFAs varies not only with amount of flaxseed in the diet but also with the strain of hen (Ahn *et al.*, 1995; Scheideler *et al.*, 1998). It also depends on whether flaxseed was given to hens in whole or ground form (Aymond and Van Elswyk, 1995). A recent paper by Scheideler *et al.* (1998) showed a substantial increase in LNA and DHA in eggs from the same strain of hen on diets with 10% flaxseed at 58 compared with 36 weeks of age.

Rapeseed

Rapeseed, or canola seed, contains about 42% oil, of which about 11% is LNA. Brettschneider *et al.* (1995) found a step-wise decline in egg production and egg mass when hens were fed graded levels of rapeseed (0–30%) over 40 weeks of lay. Sinapine is found in rapeseed and can be converted to trimethylamine (TMA) through the action of internal bacterial enzymes. Brown layers in particular accumulate TMA in yolk through a reduction in their ability to synthesize TMA oxidase (Brettschneider *et al.*, 1995). These workers treated rapeseed using a hydrothermal procedure, and showed a substantial rise in TMA in egg yolk in untreated compared with treated rapeseed. Untreated seed showed significant increases in TMA in yolk, with increasing inclusion. Increases in the heat-treated seed were small. Hydrothermal treatment resulted in a decline in sinapine and glucosinolates in rapeseed from 615 and 50 mg kg^{-1} to 13.8 and 1.9 mg kg^{-1}, respectively.

There have been few reports on the enrichment of *n*-3 PUFAs using rapeseed. J. S. Sim (unpublished data) reported total *n*-3 PUFA of 200 mg in eggs from hens after 15 days on diets with 16% canola seed. On the other hand, Brettschneider *et al.* (1995) found only 127 mg in eggs from hens on a diet with 15% rapeseed and 159 mg on a diet with 30% rapeseed. Of these total amounts, only 29 and 32 mg, respectively, were *n*-3 long chain PUFAs.

Pearl millet

Collins *et al.* (1997) have reported recently on the enrichment of eggs from hens on 68% pearl millet. This grain contains 5% oil, of which 4% of the total PUFA is LNA. The total enrichment of *n*-3 PUFA was 5.7 mg g^{-1} yolk compared with 5.1 mg in ordinary eggs. The DHA was 2.7 mg compared with 1.8 mg. The total amounts were only 103 mg in the enriched egg compared with 98 mg in an ordinary egg. Because the increase in DHA is very small, pearl millet can hardly be considered to be a suitable enrichment source.

Fish oils

Fish oils, unlike vegetable oils, do have high levels of the important long chain PUFAs, EPA and DHA. Much of the research on fish oils as a method of enriching the hen's egg with *n*-3 PUFA has focused on menhaden oil. While fish vary greatly in their fat content and PUFA profile, freshwater fish are generally not as good a source of long chain PUFAs as marine fish (Chetty *et al.*, 1989).

Much of the research on menhaden oil has been undertaken by Van Elswyk and colleagues at Texas A&M University. Hargis *et al.* (1991) demonstrated only small increases in LNA in egg yolk from hens given 3% menhaden oil in the diet. The largest increase in egg yolk was observed as DHA (180 mg), but only about 30 mg as EPA as well as LNA. Menhaden oil contains about 16% of total FFA as EPA (Huang *et al.*, 1990).

Oh *et al.* (1991) fed white leghorn hens a diet containing 10% blended fish oils (Max EPA). The eggs (60 g) contained about 660 mg of DPA + DHA and about 100 mg of EPA; total PUFA was calculated to be almost 1 g egg^{-1}. Farrell *et al.* (1994) reported that hens fed on diets with 6% cod liver oil or 6% mackerel oil produced eggs with 0.9 and 1.1% EPA of total FFA, respectively, and 5.2 and 6.9% as DPA + DHA.

Huang *et al.* (1990) showed that the content (% FFA) of EPA in the hen's egg after 4 weeks increased from 0.03% to 0.25, 0.40 and 0.50% on diets containing 0, 1, 2 and 3% menhaden oil, respectively. There was virtually no LNA deposited in the egg, mainly because most marine fish oils contain only small amounts.

Marine algae

Yongmanitchai and Ward (1989, 1991) showed that some marine micro-organisms, particularly some strains of freshwater algae, were capable of synthesizing significant amounts of *n*-3 PUFA, particularly EPA and DHA. Recently, the microalga *Schizocpytrium* sp. has been produced commercially by heterotrophic fermentation and drum-dried to give a product that can be mixed into poultry diets (Abril and Barclay, 1998). The product has been evaluated by Herber and Van Elswyk (1996). The marine algae contain only one *n*-3 long chain PUFA, DHA at 7.4% of the total FFA. Production data, although highly variable, indicated reduced egg output on diets containing 4.8% algae, and at 2.4% when compared with a diet containing 1.5% menhaden oil after 4 weeks of lay. Egg weight was not different between treatments; again there was much variation between and within treatments. Incorporation of total *n*-3 PUFAs in eggs (175 mg in 60 g of egg) was similar on diets with 1.5% menhaden oil or 2.4% algae. Increasing algae to 4.8% of the diet gave a value of 225 mg. Most (93%) of the *n*-3 PUFA incorporated was in the form of DHA in the eggs from hens on the algae diet. For menhaden oil, DHA was 86% but some EPA would also be present, although this was not reported.

Recently, Abril and Barclay (1998) reported no adverse effects of the algae on any production parameter when measured over 4 months using 256 hens. The authors stated that the marine algae contained 17.5% DHA by weight. This is not in agreement with the analysis of Herber and Van Elswyk (1996). Abril and Barclay (1998) also reported egg enrichment of DHA of 134, 170 and 220 mg per egg from hens on diets with 0.87, 2.87 and 4.11% of the marine algae, respectively. If a hen consumes 100 g of feed per day, then the efficiency of capture of DHA from the algae will be 92, 33 and 30%, respectively.

Enrichment with vegetable oils

There are very few publications in which pure sources of vegetable oils high in LNA have been used to enrich the hen's egg. Farrell (1994) and D. J. Farrell (unpublished results) reported effects of feeding hens on diets containing 6% cod liver oil, 6% canola oil or 6% linseed oil over 12 weeks. At the end of this time, the birds were starved for 12 h and a blood sample was then withdrawn. Generally speaking, the PUFA composition of plasma was reflected in the make up of the egg yolk (Table 11.1). Only in the case of the fish oil was there any significant capture of EPA in egg yolk, even though there were measurable concentrations of EPA in blood plasma on all diets. Interestingly, the mean cholesterol concentration of eggs from hens on the two vegetable oil diets was lower ($P < 0.05$) than those from hens on the control and fish oil-based diets. Compared with the controls, decreased cholesterol levels were 0% (fish), 9% (canola) and 11% (linseed).

Although hen's blood plasma and egg yolk levels of LNA were elevated substantially on the two vegetable oil-based diets, LNA concentrations in plasma from fasted humans consuming these egg types were low and similar (Farrell, 1994). Despite the much higher levels of total *n*-3 PUFA in eggs from hens given the diet with linseed oil, the concentrations in human plasma as DHA and total *n*-3 PUFA were, if anything, lower in the linseed eggs than the canola eggs. Much higher levels of DHA and total *n*-3 PUFA were observed in the plasma of those humans consuming eggs from hens fed the diet with cod liver oil.

Oil mixtures

Farrell (1998) has published the results of an extensive study with humans consuming *n*-3 PUFA eggs from hens on four diets with a mixture of oils. The results are shown in Table 11.2.

It can be seen that the three diets containing fish oil showed declining enrichment of the eggs with EPA as the fish oil was reduced from 5 to 2% of inclusion. In all three diets, well over half of the *n*-3 PUFAs was in the form of long chain PUFAs. Even when the diet contained a mixture of 2% fish oil, 1% linseed and 1% canola oil, the eggs contained 4.25% long chain PUFA out of a total of 6.6%.

Table 11.1.   The *n*-3 content (% free fatty acids) of hen plasma (P, *n* = 6) and egg yolk (Y, *n* = 5) from the same group given diets with 7% sunflower oil, 7% cod liver oil, 7% canola oil or 7% linseed oil.

	Control		Cod liver oil		Canola oil		Linseed oil	
	P	Y	P	Y	P	Y	P	Y
18 : 3*n*-3	0.07	0.14	0.47	0.60	1.52	1.31	7.41	8.96
20 : 5*n*-3	0.23	0	0.73	0.73	0.28	0	0.36	0.16
22 : 6*n*-3	0.83	0.44	4.52	4.15	1.98	1.21	2.23	1.64
Total *n*-3	1.17	0.7	6.09	5.82	3.92	2.76	10.52	10.65

Source: Farrell, 1994; D.J. Farrell, unpublished results.

Table 11.2.   The *n*-3 PUFA (% FA) content of eggs (*n* = 6) from hens on different dietary treatments and used in the experiment with human volunteers.

	Egg type[1]				
	F	FL	FLR	C	SD
LNA (18 : 3)	0.36[a]	2.26[b]	2.32[b]	0.20[a]	0.128
EPA (20 : 5)	1.00[a]	0.58[b]	0.45[b]	0.20[c]	0.187
DPA (22 : 5)	0.63[a]	0.52[a]	0.42[b]	0.06[c]	0.104
DHA (22 : 6)	5.27[a]	3.80[b]	3.38[b]	0.44[c]	0.751
Total	7.34[a]	7.24[a]	6.60[a]	0.94[b]	0.938
n-6 : *n*-3 ratio	1.25[a]	1.52[a]	1.80[a]	25.75[b]	2.297

[1]Treatment F = 50 g of fish oil kg^{-1}; FL = 30 g of fish oil + 10 g of linseed oil kg^{-1}; FLR = 20 g of fish oil + 10 g of linseed oil + 10 g of canola oil kg^{-1}; C = control diet 40 g of sunflower oil kg^{-1}.
Values in the same row not sharing a common superscript are significantly different (*P* < 0.05).
From: Farrell, 1998.

Table 11.3.   Combined fasting plasma *n*-3 PUFA values (% of total) measured in volunteers (14 per treatment) at 16 and 22 weeks on the experimental treatments.

| Fatty acid (*n*-3) | Dietary treatment[1] | | | | |
	F	FL	FLR	C	SD
LNA (18 : 3)	1.22	1.27	1.36	0.83	0.981
EPA (20 : 5)	0.91[a]	0.78[ab]	0.93[a]	0.60[b]	0.411
DPA (22 : 5)	0.57[ab]	0.71[a]	0.58[ab]	0.42[b]	0.304
DHA (22 : 6)	2.15[a]	2.14[a]	1.85[ab]	1.26[b]	0.858
Total	5.03[ab]	5.11[a]	4.93[a]	3.28[b]	1.547
n-6 : *n*-3 ratio	6.51[a]	7.06[a]	7.70[a]	12.20[b]	3.496

[1]F = 50 g of fish oil kg^{-1}; FL = 30 g of fish oil + 10 g linseed oil kg^{-1}; FLR = 20 g of fish oil + 10 g of linseed oil + 10 g of canola oil kg^{-1}; C = control diet 40 g of sunflower oil kg^{-1}.
Values not sharing a common letter are significantly different (*P* < 0.05).
From: Farrell, 1998.

When humans consumed seven eggs per week of these same egg types, fasting blood plasma levels were higher for most *n*-3 PUFAs than in the controls consuming seven ordinary eggs per week (Table 11.3). EPA and DHA were higher on two out of three of the treatments. In order to enrich eggs with significant amounts of the *n*-3 long chain PUFAs, the enrichment mixture must also be high in these fatty acids.

Concluding Remarks

The purpose of this chapter was to review the different approaches used to produce *n*-3-enriched eggs. It is clear that several of the enrichment mixtures rely on the use of flaxseed, which contains only LNA. There is virtually no additional EPA deposited in egg yolk, but significant amounts (≈ 33%) may be converted to DPA + DHA from flaxseed. To increase EPA and DHA contents of egg yolk substantially, it is necessary to feed hens on diets rich in these long chain PUFAs. This is particularly important because of the uncertainty of the efficacy of LNA in human health and the inability of the more vulnerable groups in society (the elderly and the very young) to convert LNA to the long chain PUFAs effectively (Sinclair, 1991). Oh *et al.* (1991) fed hens on a diet containing 10% blended fish oil (Max EPA). The eggs contained (% FFA) about 2% EPA and 11% DHA.

Shown in Table 11.4 are typical analyses (FFA, mg) of a 60 g *n*-3-enriched egg using different enrichment products. In some cases, it was necessary to assume that a 62 g egg contains 6.2 g of lipid; of this 85% is FFA.

Several international organizations such as BNF, NATO, COMA and ISSFAL (Anonymous, 1997) make dietary recommendations for humans only for EPA and DHA, recognizing the uncertainty as to the usefulness of LNA in the reduction in the incidence of several metabolic disorders associated with a dietary deficiency of the *n*-3 PUFAs.

Table 11.4.   Enrichment products used to fortify the hen's egg (60 g) with *n*-3 fatty acids.

Product	Inclusion (%)	LNA	EPA	DHA + DPA	Total
Flaxseed[1]	10	292	6	132	430
Can alna[2]	17	290	—	163	454
Canola seed[3]	15	100	4	33	137
Marine algae[4]	2.4	—	—	163	176
Menhaden oil[5]	3	26	30	185	241
Mackerel oil[6]	4	23	40	251	343
Millet[7]	68	23	—	49	103

From: [1]Van Elswyk (1997); [2]Ahn *et al.* (1995); [3]Brettschneider *et al.* (1995); [4]Herber and Van Elswyk (1996); [5]Hargis *et al.* (1991); [6]Farrell *et al.* (1991); [7]Collins *et al.* (1997).

References

Abril, J.R. and Barclay, W.R. (1998) Safe use of microalgae (DHA Gold™) in laying-hen feed supplement in the production of DHA enriched eggs. In: *2nd International Symposium on Egg Nutrition and Newly Emerging Ova-Technologies.* 5–8 April, Banff, Alberta, p. 49 (poster abstract).

Ahn, D.U., Sunwoo, H.H., Wolfe, E.H. and Sim, J.S. (1995) Effects of dietary α-linolenic acid and strain of hen on the fatty acid composition, storage stability and flavour characteristics of chicken eggs. *Poultry Science* 74, 1540–1574.

Anonymous (1997) Summary of international organisations with established recommended values for omega-3 fatty acids. *Research Communiqué.* Omega Tech. Inc., Boulder, Colorado.

Anonymous (1998) *Omega-3 Enriched Eggs.* Flax Council of Canada.

Aymond, W.M. and Van Elswyk, M.E. (1995) Yolk thiobarbituric acid reactive substances and *n*-3 fatty acids in response to whole and ground flaxseed. *Poultry Science* 74, 1388–1394.

Barlow, S. and Pike, I.H. (1991) Humans and animals benefit from omega-3 polyunsaturated fatty acids. *Feedstuffs* 63(18), 18–26.

Brettschneider, S. Dänicke, S. and Jeroch, H. (1995) The influence of graded levels of rapeseed in laying hen diets on egg quality and special consideration of hydrothermal treatment of rapeseed. In: Briz, R.C. (ed.), *Egg and Egg Products Quality. Proceedings of the VI European Symposium on the Quality of Egg and Egg Products.* Zaragoza, Spain, pp. 227–232.

British Nutrition Foundation (1992) *Unsaturated Fatty Acids: Nutritional and Physiological Significance.* The Report of the British Nutrition Foundation's Task Force, Chapman and Hall, London.

Broadhurst, C.L., Cunnane, S.C. and Crawford, M.A. (1998) Rift Valley lake fish and shell fish provide brain-specific nutrition for early homo. *British Journal of Nutrition* 79, 3–21.

Caston, L.J., Squires, E.J. and Leeson, S. (1994) Hen performance, egg quality, and the sensory evaluation of eggs from SCWL hens fed dietary flax. *Canadian Journal of Animal Science* 74, 347–353.

Cherian, G. and Sim, J.S. (1994) Omega-3 fatty acid enriched eggs as a source of long-chain ω-3 fatty acids for developing infants. In: Sim, J.S. and Nakai, S. (eds), *Egg Uses and Processing Technologies: New Developments.* CAB International, Wallingford, UK, pp. 402–411.

Chetty, N., Reavis, S.C., Immelman, A.R., Atkinson, P.M. and van As, J.G. (1989) Fatty acid composition of some South African fresh-water fish. *South African Medical Journal* 76, 368–370.

Collins, V.P., Cantor, A.H., Pescatore, A.J., Straw, M.L. and Ford, M.J. (1997) Pearl millet in layer diets enhances egg yolk *n*-3 fatty acids. *Poultry Science* 76, 326–330.

Crawford, M.A., Gale, M.M., Woodford, M.H. and Casperd, N.M. (1970) Comparative studies of fatty acid composition of wild and domestic meats. *International Journal of Biochemistry* 1, 295–305.

Farrell, D.J. (1994) The fortification of hens' eggs with ω-3 long chain fatty acids and their effects in humans. In: Sim, J.S. and Nakoi, S. (eds), *Egg Uses and Processing Technologies: New Developments.* CAB International, Wallingford, UK, pp. 386–401.

Farrell, D.J. (1998). Enrichment of hen eggs with *n*-3 long chain fatty acids and evaluation of enriched eggs in humans. *American Journal of Clinical Nutrition* 68, 538–544.

Farrell, D.J., Dombusch, M. and Thomson, E. (1994) The feeding of diets with various fish and vegetable oils to hens and the enrichment of eggs with *n*-3 fatty acids. *Proceedings of the Nutrition Society of Australia* 16, 130.

Ferrier, L.K., Caston, L., Leeson, S., Squires, J., Weaver, B.J. and Holub, B.J. (1995) α-Linolenic acid and docosahexaenoic acid-enriched eggs from hens fed flaxseed: influence on blood lipids and platelet phospholipid fatty acids in humans. *American Journal of Clinical Nutrition* 62, 81–86.

Fox, P.L. and Di Corleto, P.E. (1988) Fish oils inhibit endothelial cell production of platelet-derived factor-like protein. *Science* 41, 453–456.

Gaudette, D.C. and Holub, B.J. (1991) Docosahexaenoic acid (DHA) and human platelet reactivity. *Journal of Nutritional Biochemistry* 2, 116–121.

Hargis, P.S. and Van Elswyk, M.E. (1993) Manipulating the fatty acid composition of poultry meat and eggs for the health conscious consumer. *World's Poultry Science Journal* 49, 251–264.

Hargis, P.S., Van Elswyk, M.E. and Hargis, B.M. (1991) Diet modification of yolk lipid with menhaden oil. *Poultry Science* 70, 874–883.

Herber, S.M. and Van Elswyk, M.E. (1996) Dietary marine algae promotes efficient deposition of *n*-3 fatty acids for the production of enriched shell eggs. *Poultry Science* 75, 1501–1507.

Huang, Z.-B., Leibovitz, H., Lee, C.M. and Millar, R. (1990) Effects of dietary fish oil on ω-3 fatty acid levels in chicken eggs and thigh flesh. *Journal of Agricultural and Food Chemistry* 38, 743–747.

Leaf, A. and Weber, P.C. (1988) Medical progress: cardiovascular effects of *n*-3 fatty acids. *New England Journal of Medicine* 318, 549–557.

Leskanich, C.D. and Noble, R.C. (1997) Manipulation of the *n*-3 polyunsaturated fatty acid composition of avian eggs and meat. *World's Poultry Science Journal* 53, 155–181.

Nettleton, J.A. (1993) Are *n*-3 fatty acids essential nutrients for foetal and infant development? *Journal of the American Dietetic Association* 93, 58–64.

Oh, S., Ryue, J., Hsieh, C.-H. and Bell, D.E. (1991) Eggs enriched in ω-3 fatty acids and alterations in lipid concentrations in plasma and lipoproteins and in blood pressure. *American Journal of Clinical Nutrition* 54, 689–695.

Petridou, E. Koussoriu, M., Toupakdi, N., Youronkos, S.M., Papavassilou, A., Pentekalis, S., Olsen, J. and Trichopoulos, D. (1998) Diet during pregnancy and the risk of cerebral palsy. *British Journal of Nutrition* 79, 407–412.

Sanders, T.A.B. (1993) Marine oils: metabolic effects and role in human nutrition. *Proceedings of the Nutrition Society* 52, 457–472.

Scheideler, S.E., Fronning, G. and Cuppett, S. (1997) Studies of consumer acceptance of high omega-3 fatty acid enriched eggs. *Journal of Applied Poultry Research* 6, 137–146.

Scheideler, S.E., Jaroni, D. and Froning, G. (1998) Strain and age effects of an egg consumption from hens fed diets rich in *n*-3 fatty acids. *Poultry Science* 77, 192–196.

Sim, J.S. and Qi, G.-H. (1995) Designing poultry products using flaxseed. In: Thompson, L.U. and Cunnane, L.U. (eds), *Flaxseed in Human Nutrition*. American Oil Chemists' Society Press, pp. 315–333.

Simopoulos, A.R. (1991) Omega-3 fatty acids in health and disease and in growth and development. *American Journal of Clinical Nutrition* 54, 438–463.

Simopoulos, A.P. and Salem, N. (1989) *N*-3 fatty acids in eggs from range-fed Greek chickens. *New England Journal of Medicine* 321, 1412.

Sinclair, A.J. (1991) The good oil: omega 3 polyunsaturated fatty acids. *Today's Life Science* 3(8), 18–27.

Siscovick, D.S., Raghunathan, T.E., King, I., Weinmann, S., Wicklund, K.G., Albright, J., Bvrbjerg, V., Arbogast, P., Smith, H., Kushi, L.H., Cobb, L.A., Copass, M.K., Psaty, M., Lemaitre, R., Retzlaff, B., Childs, M. and Knopp, R.H. (1995) Dietary intake and cell membrane levels of long-chain *n*-3 polyunsaturated fatty acids and risk of primary cardiac arrest. *Journal of the American Medical Association* 274, 1363–1367.

Tinoco, J. (1982) Dietary requirements and functions of α-linolenic acid in animals. *Progress in Lipid Research* 21, 1–45.

Van Elswyk, M.E. (1997) Nutritional and physiological effects of flax seed in diets for laying fowl. *World's Poultry Science Journal* 53, 253–264.

Yongmanitchai, W. and Ward, O.P. (1989) Omega-3 fatty acids: alternative sources of production. *Process Biochemistry* 24, 117–125.

Yongmanitchai, W. and Ward, O.P. (1991) Screening of algae for potential alternative sources of eicosapentaenoic acid. *Phytochemistry* 30, 2963–2967.

Tocopherols, Retinol and Carotenes in Eggs and Hatched Chick Tissues as Influenced by Dietary Palm Oil

12

G. Cherian, K.R. Kang and J.S. Sim

Department of Agricultural, Food and Nutritional Science, University of Alberta, Edmonton, Alberta, Canada

Incorporation of palm oil (PO) increased the tocotrienol content of eggs, liver, meat and adipose tissue. Total tocotrienols were higher in eggs of hens fed 1.5% PO than those fed 3.5% PO. An increase in retinol was observed in the eggs, liver and dark meat of hens fed as PO diet. Feeding diets containing 1.5 or 3.5% PO increased the carotenes in eggs and liver tissue. However, carotenoids were not detected in white meat, dark meat or adipose tissue. Dark meat incorporated higher levels of tocopherols than white meat. The diets had no effect on egg or yolk weight. Egg yolks from hens fed PO had a darker yolk colour than those without PO. Inclusion of tocopherols resulted in lower ($P < 0.05$) thiobarbituric acid (TBA) values in the eggs, white and dark meat. Among the PO diets, eggs from the 3.5% PO diet had the lowest TBA value ($P < 0.05$). Addition of tocopherol mix in the control diet increased total tocopherol content in liver tissue of hens and hatched chicks.

Introduction

Improving the nutritional and health-enhancing properties of chicken eggs by altering the monounsaturated and polyunsaturated fatty acid (PUFA) composition has been well documented. Other efforts were aimed at increasing antioxidant vitamins (tocopherols, β-carotene, retinol), vitamin B_{12} and trace minerals such as iodine and selenium. Poultry products contain low levels of natural antioxidants. Therefore, altering the PUFA composition of eggs may enhance susceptibility to lipid oxidation, resulting in lower quality (Jiang *et al.*, 1992; Van Elswyk *et al.*, 1995) and may indicate a need for antioxidants (Cherian *et al.*, 1996). Vitamin E compounds (tocopherols and tocotrienols) are well recognized for their effective inhibition of lipid oxidation in food and biological systems (Kamal-Eldin and Appelqvist, 1996). Vitamin E is synthesized by plants and is present in oil seeds and leaves. Palm oil (PO) contains about 600–1000 p.p.m. of carotenoids, tocotrienols, tocopherols and sterols. The antioxidant activity of tocotrienols has been reported to be higher than that of α-tocopherol (Watkins *et al.*, 1993). In addition to the potential benefits of tocopherols, tocotrienols and carotenoids as free radical scavengers; such antioxidant nutrients may also exhibit health benefits in certain diseases such as cancer, coronary heart disease and immune functions (Bendich, 1990).

Some adverse health effects have been associated with certain synthetic antioxidants and they increase the cost of feeding. Alternative natural antioxidant sources for stabilizing feed and food products are needed. Therefore, incorporation of natural antioxidants by dietary means may be more effective and economical in controlling post-slaughter lipid peroxidation. In this context, our objectives were to determine the effectiveness of tocopherols, tocotrienols, retinol and carotenoids in poultry products by incorporating a tocopherol mix or PO with a high *n*-3 PUFA diet. Poultry products such as eggs and muscle (white, dark) were examined.

The tissues of newly hatched chicks are rich in longer chain PUFAs (Noble and Cocchi, 1990; Cherian and Sim, 1992). The content of tocopherols in the hatched chick tissues has been reported to be affected by yolk vitamin E levels. (Cherian and Sim, 1997; Surai *et al.*, 1997). As tocols are involved in providing immunity to hatched chicks and protection against lipid peroxidation, the content of liver tocols as influenced by PO supplementation to laying hens was also examined.

Materials and Methods

Birds and diets

These experiments were reviewed by the University of Alberta Animal Care Committee to ensure adherence to Canadian Council on Animal Care guidelines.

A total of 240 Single Comb White Leghorn laying hens were housed in two double-deck cage batteries with two birds in each cage. The birds were allotted to one of the four dietary treatments, with each treatment replicated three times randomly among the batteries. The diets were wheat–soybean meal–ground flax–fish meal-based with added oils at 3.5% to provide a high PUFA content (Table 12.1). The control diet had 2% fish oil + 1.5% animal tallow + tocopherol mix. The tocopherol mix contained 17.3, 36.3 and 7.3% of δ-, γ- and α-tocopherols. Previous tests (Cherian *et al.*, 1996) with added fish oil in hens' diets reported the need for additional antioxidant. Thus, tocopherol mix was included in the control diet. To test the antioxidant potency of PO in a high PUFA environment in the three experimental diets (lower (L), medium (M), higher (H)), PO was included at 0, 1.5 or 3.5%. The dietary oils included fish oil, animal tallow or crude PO.

Table 12.1. Composition and calculated analysis of the laying hen diets.

Ingredients	Dietary treatments[a]			
	Control	L	M	H
Wheat	59.0	59.0	59.0	59.0
Soybean meal	5.5	5.5	5.5	5.5
Limestone	7.5	7.5	7.5	7.5
Dical phos	3.0	3.0	3.0	3.0
Layer pre-mix[b]	1.5	1.5	1.5	1.5
Flax	17.0	17.0	17.0	17.0
Fishmeal	3.0	3.0	3.0	3.0
Animal tallow	1.5	1.5	0.0	0.0
Fish oil	2.0	2.0	2.0	0.0
Palm oil	0.0	0.0	1.5	3.5
Analyses				
Crude protein	16.2	16.2	16.2	16.2
ME[c] (kcal kg^{-1})	2937.5	2937.5	2937.5	2937.5
Ether extracts	9.9	9.9	9.9	9.9
Calcium	3.7	3.7	3.7	3.7
Available phosphorus	0.8	0.8	0.8	0.8

Values are given in μg g^{-1}.
[a]Control, and diets L, M and H represent laying hen diets containing palm oil at 0, 1.5 or 3.5%. The control diet contained animal tallow, fish oil and 0.07% tocopherol mix. The tocopherol mix contained 17.3, 36.3 and 7.3% of δ-, γ- and α-tocopherols.
[b]Supplied per kilogram of the diet: vitamin A, 8000 IU; cholecalciferol, 1200 ICU; vitamin E, 5 IU; riboflavin, 4 mg; calcium pantothenate, 6 mg; niacin, 15 mg; vitamin B$_{12}$, 10 μg; choline chloride, 100 mg; biotin, 100 μg; selenium, 0.1 mg; DL-methionine, 500 mg; manganese sulphate, 0.4 g; zinc oxide, 0.1 g.
[c]Metabolizable energy.

Sample collection

On day 20 of feeding, two eggs from each replicate, totalling six per treatment, were selected randomly. The birds (six per treatment) were killed and tissues (liver, white meat and dark meat) were removed. A total of 60 fertile eggs were collected after 4 weeks on experimental diet and incubated. On the day of hatching, the liver tissue of newly hatched chicks ($n = 8$) was collected.

Tocotrienol, tocopherol, carotene and retinol analysis

The egg and tissue samples were weighed into a test tube with 8 ml of ethanol containing 0.1% pyrogallol, followed by adding 0.2 ml of vitamin E internal standard and 2 ml of potassium hydroxide solution (50%, w/v) under nitrogen. The contents of test tubes were saponified for 30 min at 70°C. The mixtures were then extracted with 8 ml of hexane : ethyl acetate (9 : 1, v/v). After adding 10 ml of 1% sodium chloride solution, solvents were allowed to separate. The extracts were dried under nitrogen. The residues were reconstituted with ethanol and the aliquots of samples were injected directly into the high-performance liquid chromatography (HPLC) system.

A Varian 5000 liquid chromatograph system was used with a Shimadzu SIL-9A model autosampler. A Supelcosil, 3 μm RP LC-18 column with a guard column (5 cm, 20–40 μm LC-18 packing) was used for chromatographic separations. A Waters TUV486 detector set at 450 nm was connected in series with a Varian UV50 variable wavelength detector at 326 nm to enable the simultaneous detection of carotenes and retinol. Tocotrienols and tocopherols were detected with a Shimadzu RF-535 fluorescence detector at an excitation wavelength of 298 nm and an emission wavelength of 328 nm. The isocratic mobile phases used for the separation of carotenes, retinol, tocotrienols and tocopherols were acetonitrile : tetrahydrofuran (THF) : methanol : 1% ammonium acetate (65 : 25 : 6 : 4, by vol.) containing 0.05% triethylamine (TEA) and methanol : acetonitrile (50 : 50, v/v), respectively, at 1.5 ml min^{-1}.

Thiobarbituric acid (TBA) analyses

Tissue (2 g) or egg samples were homogenized in 18 ml of perchloric acid. The homogenate was filtered and was mixed with 2 ml of 20 mM TBA in distilled water and incubated in a boiling water bath for 30 min (Cherian *et al.*, 1996). Absorbance was determined at 531 nm. The TBA values are reported as mg of malondialdehyde per kg of egg or tissue.

Statistics

A one-way ANOVA was carried out to analyse the effects of dietary crude PO on tocotrienols, tocopherols, carotenes and retinol content of egg yolk and tissues, and TBA values. Observations within treatments were used as the error term. Significant differences among treatment means were analysed by a Student–Newman–Keuls multiple range test at $P < 0.05$ (Steel and Torrie, 1980). Computations were done using the General Linear Models procedure of the SAS Institute (1985).

Results and Discussion

The composition and the tocopherol content of the hens' diet are shown in Tables 12.1 and 12.2. The diets differing in vitamin E had no effect on egg weight or yolk weight (data not shown). The egg yolks from hens fed PO had a darker ($P < 0.05$) yolk colour. The crude PO contained high amounts of carotenoids at 500–700 mg l^{-1}, comprised of α- and β-carotenes at 36 and 54%, respectively. This resulted in an increase of α- and β-carotene contents in the H eggs (0.9 versus 0.0 μg g^{-1}) when compared with L eggs, resulting in darker yellow yolk (Table 12.3). Although a minor component, carotenoid enhancement may provide beneficial effects as reported, and darker yolks might be more aesthetically appealing to consumers. Incorporation of PO also resulted in significant incorporation of retinol in the eggs (Table 12.3). There was no difference in retinol content of the diets, and the increase in retinol in eggs from hens fed PO suggested that β-carotene was converted to retinol by the hens and thus deposited into the ovum. Although the content of retinol and carotene could be enhanced by dietary means, for economic reasons, that may not be commercially feasible. Incorporating PO in the laying hen diet seemed

Table 12.2. Tocotrienols, tocopherols, carotenes and retinol content of laying hen diets.

	Experimental diets			
	Control	L	M	H
δ-Tocotrienol	0.2	0	1.8	3.2
γ-Tocotrienol	32.8	30.5	47.3	57.2
α-Tocotrienol	5.9	4.5	9.3	13.3
Σ-Tocotrienol	38.9	35.0	58.4	73.8
δ-Tocopherol	131.7	0.8	1.6	2.0
γ-Tocopherol	307.0	27.4	35.1	39.4
α-Tocopherol	91.7	34.6	42.5	45.0
Σ-Tocopherol	530.4	62.8	79.1	86.3
Σ-Tocopherol + tocotrienol	569.3	97.6	137.5	160.1
α-Carotene	0.0	0	2.1	4.2
β-Carotene	0.2	0.2	4.2	8.1
Retinol	3.3	3.2	3.8	4.4

Values are given in $\mu g \, g^{-1}$.
All diets contain wheat, soybean meal, ground flaxseed, fish meal with added fish oil + 1.5% tallow (L), +1.5% palm oil (M) and 3.5% palm oil (H).

Table 12.3. Effect of dietary crude palm oil on the tocotrienols, tocopherols, carotenes and retinol content of egg yolk.[1]

	Experimental diets			
	Control	L	M	H
γ-Tocotrienol	31[b]	2.4[b]	5.2[a]	4.7[a]
α-Tocotrienol	2.8[c]	1.1[c]	10.8[a]	6.2[b]
Σ-Tocotrienol	5.8[c]	3.5[c]	16.0[a]	10.9[b]
δ-Tocopherol	57.4[c]	2.3[a]	8.8[b]	10.9[b]
γ-Tocopherol	176.2[b]	11.4[a]	14.8[b]	16.9[b]
α-Tocopherol	314.1[c]	33.6[a]	165.2[b]	156.1[b]
Σ-Tocopherol	547.7[c]	147.2[a]	188.7[b]	183.9[b]
Σ-Tocopherol + tocotrienol	553.5[c]	150.1[a]	204.7[b]	194.8[b]
α-Carotene	0.0	0.0	2.1	4.2
β-Carotene	0.2	0.2	4.2	8.1
Retinol	5.1[c]	4.7[bc]	5.3[ab]	5.6[a]

Values are given in $\mu g \, g^{-1}$.
All diets contain wheat, soybean meal, ground flaxseed, fish meal with added fish oil + 1.5% tallow (L), +1.5% palm oil (M) and 3.5% palm oil (H).
[1]The eggs were collected after 20 days of feeding the experimental diet.
[abc]Means within a row with no common superscript differ significantly ($P < 0.05$).

to be an alternative, economically feasible and natural means for enriching egg lipids with carotenes and retinol. Incorporation ($P < 0.05$) of tocols was achieved by inclusion of PO in the diet. A plateau in the incorporation of tocols was observed by day 20 of feeding. Although the diet content of tocotrienol was higher in H, the content of α-tocopherol in eggs was higher in hens fed M, suggesting that intake of one fat-soluble vitamin can interfere with the utilization of other fat-soluble vitamins. Supplementation of tocopherol mix increased the tocopherol content in eggs.

Apart from eggs, the adipose tissue incorporated the highest level of tocopherols at 7.5, 11.4 and 7.9 µg g^{-1} for L, M and H diets, respectively (Table 12.4). The incorporation of tocotrienols in liver was much lower at 0.6, 2.2 and 1.4 µg g^{-1} for L, M and H diets, respectively. α- and β-carotenes were not detected in the adipose tissue. Supplementation increased the tocopherol content more in the dark meat than in white meat (Table 12.5). Similarly, tocotrienol levels were higher ($P < 0.05$) in white meat when compared with

Table 12.4.   Tocotrienols, tocopherols and retinol concentration of liver and adipose tissue as influenced by hens' diets containing different oils.[1]

	Experimental diets			
	Control	L	M	H
Liver				
γ-Tocotrienol	1.3[a]	0.6[b]	1.2[a]	0.8[b]
α-Tocotrienol	ND	ND	1.0[a]	0.6[b]
Σ-Tocotrienol	1.3[b]	0.6[c]	2.2[a]	1.4[b]
δ-Tocopherol	4.5[a]	0.1[b]	0.2[b]	0.1[b]
γ-Tocopherol	40.4[a]	1.2[b]	1.9[b]	1.7[b]
α-Tocopherol	50.2[a]	18.4[b]	21.7[b]	17.4[b]
Σ-Tocopherol	95.1[a]	19.8[b]	23.8[b]	19.2[b]
Retinol	187.6[b]	156.7[a]	1363.6[ab]	1499.1[a]
α-Carotene	0.2[b]	3.7[a]	3.5[a]	ND
β-Carotene	ND	5.7[a]	5.0[a]	0.4[b]
Adipose tissue				
γ-Tocotrienol	7.8[b]	5.9[c]	8.8[a]	6.2[c]
α-Tocotrienol	2.1	1.6[c]	2.6[a]	1.7[c]
Σ-Tocotrienol	9.9[b]	7.5[c]	11.4[a]	7.9[c]
δ-Tocopherol	7.9[a]	1.6[b]	0.8[b]	1.0[b]
γ-Tocopherol	20.3[a]	4.9[b]	3.3[c]	2.4[c]
α-Tocopherol	53.1[a]	29.2[c]	38.0[b]	26.7[c]
Σ-Tocopherol	81.2[a]	35.7[c]	42.1[b]	30.1[c]
Retinol	9.5	8.0	10.2	9.7

Values are given in µg g^{-1}.
All diets contain wheat, soybean meal, ground flaxseed, fish meal with added fish oil + 1.5% tallow (L), +1.5% palm oil (M) and 3.5% palm oil (H).
[1]The eggs were collected after 20 days of feeding the experimental diet.
[abc]Means within a row with no common superscript differ significantly ($P < 0.05$).

Table 12.5. Tocotrienols, tocopherols and retinol concentration in white and dark meat as influenced by hens' diets containing different oils.[1]

	Experimental diets			
	Control	L	M	H
White meat				
γ-Tocotrienol	0.1[b]	0.1[b]	0.2[a]	0.4[a]
α-Tocotrienol	0.2[a]	0.1[c]	0.0[b]	0.2[b]
Σ-Tocotrienol	0.3[b]	0.4[a]	0.4[a]	0.4[a]
δ-Tocopherol	0.4[a]	0.2[a]	0.1[b]	0.1[b]
γ-Tocopherol	1.1[a]	0.2[b]	0.2[b]	0.2[b]
α-Tocopherol	2.0	1.7	1.8	1.8
Σ-Tocopherol	3.3	2.0[b]	2.3[b]	2.1[b]
Σ-Tocopherol + tocotrienol	3.7[a]	2.3	2.7[b]	2.5[b]
Retinol	0.3	0.2	0.3	0.3
Dark meat				
γ-Tocotrienol	0.3[b]	5.9[c]	8.8[a]	6.2[c]
α-Tocotrienol	ND	1.6[c]	2.6[a]	1.7[c]
Σ-Tocotrienol	0.3[c]	7.5[c]	11.4[a]	7.9[c]
δ-Tocopherol	0.7[a]	1.6[b]	0.8[b]	1.0[b]
γ-Tocopherol	3.1[a]	4.9[b]	3.3[c]	2.4[c]
α-Tocopherol	3.5[a]	29.2[c]	38.0[b]	26.7[c]
Σ-Tocopherol	7.3[a]	35.7[c]	42.1[b]	30.1[c]
Σ-Tocopherol + tocotrienols	7.7[a]	3.2[c]	3.8[c]	4.8[b]
Retinol	0.8[b]	0.8[b]	1.2[a]	1.1[a]

Values are given in µg g^{-1}.
All diets contain wheat, soybean meal, ground flaxseed, fish meal with added fish oil + 1.5% tallow (L), +1.5% palm oil (M) and 3.5% palm oil (H).
[1]The eggs were collected after 20 days of feeding the experimental diet.
[abc]Means within a row with no common superscript differ significantly ($P < 0.05$).

dark meat. This discrepancy in α-tocopherol incorporation between white and dark meat has been reported previously (Lin *et al.*, 1989). Oxidative changes were reported to be greater in dark meat than white meat (Lin *et al.*, 1989). Therefore, the highest content of tocopherols and tocotrienols in the dark meat may provide protection to the higher PUFA-containing lipids in the dark meat.

Inclusion of tocopherols resulted in lower ($P < 0.05$) TBA values in the eggs and tissues of the control group (Table 12.6). Eggs from those fed the H diet had the lowest TBA value. Thus, the lower ($P < 0.05$) TBA values for M and H coincide with the content of intrinsic antioxidants available to the bird. Although, the diet content of tocols was higher in the H group, no difference was observed in the TBA value of white meat. The dark meat of chicken contains higher levels of PUFA-rich phospholipids (Cherian *et al.*, 1996). Oxidative changes are reported to be greater in dark meat than in white meat. (Lin *et al.*, 1989). The lower TBA value of dark meat from H-fed birds may suggest that an added protection of dark meat lipids was provided by dietary PO.

Table 12.6.   Effect of dietary palm oil on the thiobarbituric acid values of egg or tissues.

	Experimental diets			
	Control	L	M	H
Egg	0.30 ± 0.00[d]	0.40 ± 0.01[a]	0.36 ± 0.0[b]	0.32 ± 0.01[c]
White meat	0.99 ± 0.02[c]	1.26 ± 0.03[a]	1.13 ± 0.02[b]	1.10 ± 0.02[b]
Dark meat	0.83 ± 0.02[c]	1.41 ± 0.02[a]	1.34 ± 0.03[a]	1.17 ± 0.04[b]
Liver	0.99 ± 0.02[b]	1.15 ± 0.03[a]	0.90 ± 0.05[b]	0.96 ± 0.05[b]

All diets contain wheat, soybean meal, ground flax seed, fish meal with added fish oil + 1.5% tallow (L), +1.5% palm oil (M) and 3.5% palm oil (H).
[abc]Means within a row with no common superscript differ significantly ($P < 0.05$).
Data are presented as means ± SE ($n = 6$).

Egg tocopherol content increased the tocopherol content in hatched chick liver. Chicks from the control group had significantly higher levels of toco-pherols (653 µg g^{-1}) when compared with 285.6, 338.4 and 410.5 µg g^{-1} for L, M and H group chicks. Alpha-tocopherol was the major form of tocopherol in hatched chick liver. This result suggests that the amount of tocopherol present in the yolk and therefore potentially available to the chicks depends on the maternal supply. The liver is the major site of α-tocopherol deposition during chick embryo development. The hepatic sequestration of yolk-derived tocols may act as a reservoir and supplier of tocopherols to other PUFA-rich tissues during the early developmental period. Thus, altering the tocopherol content of a hen's diet may ultimately enhance the antioxidant capacity and the resis-tance to lipid peroxidation of other PUFA-rich tissues of the hatched chick.

Conclusion

Supplemental PO when fed with a high PUFA diet enhanced tocopherol, toco-tienol, α- and β-carotene and retinol contents of chicken eggs, white and dark meat. This appears to be an effective means of increasing the content of such health-enhancing vitamins in eggs and poultry products. Due to the increased health concern of using synthetic food additives, PO supplementation in the birds' diet may be a novel way of minimizing lipid oxidation and may help in providing a quality product acceptable to consumers.

References

Bendich, A. (1990) Antioxidant nutrients and immune function. *Advances in Experi-mental Medicine and Biology* 262, 35–36.

Cherian, G. and Sim, J.S. (1992) Preferential accumulation of *n*-3 fatty acids in the brain of chicks from eggs enriched with *n*-3 fatty acids. *Poultry Science* 71, 1658–1668.

Cherian, G. and Sim, J.S. (1997) Egg yolk polyunsaturated fatty acids and vitamin E content alters the tocopherol status of hatched chicks. *Poultry Science* 76, 1753–1759.

Cherian, G., Wolfe, F.H. and Sim, J.S. (1996) Dietary oils with added tocopherols: effects on egg or tissue tocopherols, fatty acids, and oxidative stability. *Poultry Science* 75, 423–431.

Jiang, Z., Ahn, D.U., Ladner, L. and Sim, J.S. (1992) Influence of full fat flax and sunflower seeds on internal and sensory quality of yolk. *Poultry Science* 71, 378–382.

Kamal-Eldin, A. and Appelqvist, L.A. (1996) The chemistry and antioxidant properties of tocopherols and tocotrienols. *Lipids* 31, 671–701.

Lin, C.F., Gray, J.I., Asghar, A., Buckley, D.J., Booren, A.M. and Flegal, C.J. (1989) Effect of dietary oils and α-tocopherol supplementation on lipid composition and stability of broiler meat. *Journal of Food Science* 54, 1457–1461.

Noble, R.C. and Cocchi, M. (1990) Lipid metabolism and the neonatal chicken. *Progress in Lipid Research* 29, 107–140.

Steel, R.G.D. and Torrie, J.H. (1980) *Principles and Procedures of Statistics: A Biometrical Approach*. 2nd edn. McGraw-Hill Book Co., Toronto, Ontario, Canada.

Surai, P.F., Gaal, T., Noble, R.C. and Speake, B.K. (1997) The relationship between the α-tocopherol content of the yolk and its accumulation in the tissues of the newly hatched chick. *Journal of the Science of Food and Agriculture* 75, 212–216.

Van Elswyk, M.E., Dawson, P.L. and Sams, A.R. (1995) Dietary menhaden oil influences sensory characteristics and headspace volatiles of shell eggs. *Journal of Food Science* 60, 85–89.

Watkins, T., Lenz, P., Gapor, A., Struck, M., Tomeo, A. and Bierenbaum, M. (1993) γ-Tocotrienol as a hypocholesterolemic and antioxidant agent in rats fed atherogenic diets. *Lipids* 28, 1113–1118.

Docosahexaenoic Acid-Enriched Foods: Production of Eggs and Health Benefits

13

L.A. Horrocks[1] and Y.K. Yeo[2]

[1]*Docosa Foods Ltd, Columbus, Ohio, USA;* [2]*Lipid Chemistry Laboratory, Kyungpook National University, Taegu, Korea*

Healthy human volunteers in Taegu, Korea consumed animal products enriched in *n*-3 polyunsaturated fatty acids, primarily in docosahexaenoic acid (DHA), for 4 weeks. Women, aged 20 years, consumed three eggs, 200 g of chicken or 200 g of pork per day. Compared with control subjects or values obtained before consuming the food, the subjects consuming DHA-enriched foods had significantly lower values for platelet aggregation, plasma total cholesterol and plasma low-density lipoprotein cholesterol. They had no change in high-density lipoprotein cholesterol. The levels of plasma triacylglycerols were also lower by 30%. Boys, aged 14 years, consumed 585 ml of milk for 4 weeks. The boys drinking DHA-enriched milk had significantly lower values for platelet aggregation, but not for plasma total cholesterol. The proportions of DHA in plasma neutral and polar lipids were much higher after consuming the DHA-enriched foods than before for all subjects.

Introduction

The leading cause of death in western nations is cardiovascular disease (Nair *et al.*, 1997). The increase in deaths due to coronary heart disease in these nations has been blamed on the increased consumption of saturated fats. Hypolipidaemic pharmaceutical agents are effective to various degrees in reducing serum triacylglycerols and low-density lipoprotein (LDL) cholesterol, and in increasing high-density lipoprotein (HDL) cholesterol. However, these drugs also have significant side effects. Many billions of dollars are spent annually on these drugs. Better nutrition with more long chain ω-3 fatty acids, especially docosahexaenoic acid (DHA), may produce the same lipid changes and positive effects on cardiovascular risk factors with no side effects and much less expense.

At least half of the deaths from coronary artery disease are sudden cardiac deaths with fatal arrhythmia due to ventricular fibrillation. Epidemiological studies have shown decreased cardiovascular disease with greater fish oil consumption. Fish oil not only reduces triglycerides in the blood and decreases thrombosis, but also prevents cardiac arrhythmias. A monthly intake of 5500 mg of ω-3 fatty acids from fish was associated with a 50% reduction in the risk of primary cardiac arrest (Siscovick *et al.*, 1995). In a 30-year study of middle-aged men, there was an inverse association between fish consumption and death from coronary heart disease, particularly for non-sudden deaths (Daviglus *et al.*, 1997).

Fish oil, containing eicosapentaenoic acid (EPA) and DHA, is known to reduce human plasma triacylglycerol levels, but has little effect on HDL or LDL cholesterol levels (Layne *et al.*, 1996). These changes were seen within 3 months of beginning supplementation. The study included 26 subjects, including 15 with a low ratio of polyunsaturated to saturated fatty acids as is typical in western diets. In this study, animal products enriched in *n*-3 poly-unsaturated fatty acids (PUFAs), primarily in DHA, were tested to determine if they have the same effects as fatty fish.

Materials and Methods

Milk study

The 250 and 280 human subjects (males aged 14 years) were fed with either 585 ml of regular milk (three times a day, 195 ml each time) or 585 ml of *n*-3 PUFA-enriched milk (Einstein milk™) for 4 weeks. After 4 weeks of feeding, blood samples were drawn from fasting subjects. Platelet aggregation was determined with a platelet aggregometer after preparing platelet-rich plasma (PRP) according to the method of Gaudette and Holub (1990). Lipoprotein cholesterol was measured with the LDX system (Cholestech Co., Hayward, California).

Egg, chicken and pork studies

Female subjects, aged 20 years, were divided into four groups. Eggs, chicken and pork were enriched with *n*-3 fatty acids to obtain ratios of 2.1, 2.0 and 3.3 for *n*-6 : *n*-3 fatty acids. Two groups of 100 subjects consumed three eggs (60 g each) daily. One group ate generic eggs, whilst the other group ate Edison eggs™. A group of 20 subjects consumed 200 g of Edison chicken™ meat daily, and another group of 20 consumed 200 g of Edison pork™ daily. After 4 weeks, blood samples were drawn from fasting subjects to measure the platelet aggregation, lipoprotein cholesterol and plasma fatty acid composi-tion. The experimental procedures were the same as used for the milk study.

Results

Edison 300® eggs containing at least 300 mg of DHA per 100 g of egg are now being produced in Korea by Woobang Science Co., Taegu, Korea. From them, we obtained a feed supplement for laying hens containing fish oil, flaxseed and ingredients that stimulate the conversion of *n*-3 PUFAs to DHA. The level of the supplement correlated positively with feed consumed and egg production, and negatively with egg weight.

Eggs were produced with relatively low increases in most ω-3 fatty acids but with more than a fivefold increase in DHA (Table 13.1). The DHA enrichment technology gave eggs at Ohio State with 2.9–3.3 mol% DHA, quite similar to the level in Edison 300 eggs in Korea. Only the PUFAs are given for the latter. The Edison 300 eggs were used for studies in healthy women.

A marked decrease in platelet aggregation was found (Table 13.2). Platelet aggregation (thrombus formation) is part of the blood-clotting cascade. The total cholesterol content of the plasma was 174.4±11.3 with generic eggs and 141.1±9.1 with Edison 300 eggs. The Korean college women on the regular egg diet had a plasma cholesterol level much higher than that of the women on the Edison egg diet. The cholesterol level at the beginning of the diet was

Table 13.1. Fatty acid composition of control and DHA-enriched eggs from Ohio State and Edison 300 eggs from Korea.

Fatty acid	Control	DHA-enriched	Edison 300
14 : 0	0.5	0.6	
16 : 0	25.6	25.7	
16 : 1	1.9	2.5	
18 : 0	10.3	7.1	
18 : 1*n*-9	40.9	41.9	
18 : 2*n*-6	17.0	15.3	12.3
18 : 3*n*-6	0.1	0.1	
18 : 3*n*-3	0.4	1.4	1.9
20 : 0	0.1	0.1	
20 : 1*n*-9	0.2	0.3	
20 : 3*n*-6	0.2	0.2	
20 : 4*n*-6	1.7	1.1	0.6
20 : 5*n*-3	0.0	0.2	0.5–3.0
22 : 4*n*-6	0.1	0.1	
22 : 5*n*-6	0.5	0.1	
22 : 5*n*-3	0.1	0.3	
22 : 6*n*-3	0.6	3.3	3.6

Table 13.2. Degree of platelet aggregation in females consuming generic eggs or DHA-enriched Edison 300 eggs.

Aggregant	Generic eggs	Edison 300 eggs
Collagen, 5 µl	26.3±7.9	9.0±4.3[a]
Collagen, 10 µl	32.7±6.5	11.7±6.9[a]

The values are mean percentages ± SE for 100 subjects, females, age 20 years, per group. Each subject consumed three eggs daily for 4 weeks.
[a]Values for the two groups are significantly different ($P < 0.05$).

not reported. It was probably between 155 and 180, as was found for the women in other studies.

The consumption of eggs enriched with α-linolenic acid and DHA caused marked increases in the levels of those two PUFAs in the plasma (Table 13.3). The ratio of ω-6 to ω-3 fatty acids was also markedly decreased.

The composition of Einstein milk includes 0.2% EPA and 0.2% DHA (Table 13.4). Human breast milk in North America contains from 0.14 to 0.2% DHA, depending on diet (Chen *et al.*, 1995), but normal cow's milk contains only traces of these fatty acids. EPA is converted to DHA by human liver at a rather slow rate.

Platelet aggregation was significantly decreased in boys drinking Einstein milk daily for 4 weeks (Table 13.5). This decrease was found with only 0.7

Table 13.3. Polyunsaturated fatty acids in plasma from females consuming generic eggs or DHA-enriched Edison 300 eggs.

Fatty acid	Generic eggs	Edison 300 eggs
18 : 2n-6	35.9 ± 2.1	33.7 ± 2.3
18 : 3n-3	0.4 ± 0.0	0.6 ± 0.1[a]
20 : 4n-6	6.0 ± 1.0	6.6 ± 0.5
20 : 5n-3	0.5 ± 0.1	0.8 ± 0.1
22 : 6n-3	2.8 ± 0.4	4.8 ± 0.4[a]
n-6 : n-3	11.5 ± 2.2	6.5 ± 1.3

The values are mean percentages (mol%) ± SE for 100 subjects, females, age 20 years, per group. Each subject consumed three eggs daily for 4 weeks.
[a]Values for the two groups are significantly different (*P* < 0.05).

Table 13.4. Polyunsaturated fatty acids in generic milk and in DHA-enriched Einstein milk.

Fatty acid	Generic milk	Einstein milk
18 : 2n-6	2.7	3.5
18 : 3n-3	0.2	0.3
20 : 4n-6	0.7	0.1
20 : 5n-3	Tr	0.2
22 : 6n-3	Tr	0.2
n-6 : n-3	8.2	2.7

Table 13.5. Degree of platelet aggregation in males consuming generic milk or DHA-enriched Einstein milk.

Aggregant	Generic milk	Einstein milk
Collagen, 5 µl	22.4 ± 2.1	17.1 ± 1.8[a]

The values are mean percentages ± SE for 250 subjects for generic milk and 280 subjects for Einstein milk, males, age 14 years. Each subject consumed 585 ml of milk daily for 4 weeks.
[a]Values for the two groups are significantly different (*P* < 0.05).

mol% of ω-3 fatty acids in the DHA-enriched Einstein milk. These boys had low plasma cholesterol levels that were not affected by the type of milk consumed.

The plasma fatty acids of these boys differed according to the type of milk consumed (Table 13.6). This explains the differences in Table 13.5. Note that the plasma fatty acids of Korean boys consuming regular milk include 2.6 mol% of DHA. In American boys, this value is less than 2 mol% (Stevens *et al.*, 1995).

Similar results for platelet aggregation and total plasma cholesterol were obtained with women, age 20 years, consuming chicken or pork. The women consuming Edison chicken for 4 weeks had lower levels of plasma cholesterol and triglycerides than at the beginning of the diet (Table 13.7). There was no change in the high level of HDL. All of the decrease was from the LDL. The plasma glucose level decreased slightly after consuming the Edison chicken.

The women consuming Edison pork for 4 weeks had lower levels of plasma cholesterol and triglycerides than at the beginning of the diet (Table 13.8). There was no change in the high level of HDL. All of the decrease was from the LDL.

Table 13.6. Polyunsaturated fatty acids in plasma from males consuming generic milk or DHA-enriched Einstein milk.

Fatty acid	Generic milk	Einstein milk
18 : 2n-6	29.1 ± 0.3	26.1 ± 0.5
18 : 3n-3	0.4 ± 0.0	0.4 ± 0.0
20 : 4n-6	8.1 ± 0.2	8.2 ± 0.2
20 : 5n-3	0.6 ± 0.0	0.9 ± 0.1[a]
22 : 6n-3	2.6 ± 0.1	5.5 ± 0.2[a]
n-6 : n-3	10.4 ± 1.2	5.1 ± 0.5

The values are mean percentages (mol%) ± SE for 250 subjects for generic milk and 280 subjects for Einstein milk, males, age 14 years. Each subject consumed 585 ml of milk daily for 4 weeks.
[a]Values for the two groups are significantly different ($P < 0.05$).

Table 13.7. Plasma lipids and glucose in women, before and after eating DHA-enriched chicken.

Component	Before	After
Total cholesterol	155.2 ± 8.8	132.1 ± 8.6[a]
Triacylglycerol	100.3 ± 13.9	73.1 ± 7.4
Glucose	94.0 ± 1.3	88.7 ± 1.9[a]
HDL cholesterol	49.9 ± 4.4	49.4 ± 4.7
LDL cholesterol	85.2 ± 6.4	68.1 ± 4.4[a]
Total : HDL cholesterol	3.2 ± 0.2	2.8 ± 0.2

The values are mg dl^{-1}, means ± SE, for 20 female subjects, age 20 years, before and after consuming 200 g of chicken daily for 4 weeks.
[a]Values for the two groups are significantly different ($P < 0.05$).

The women consuming Edison chicken or Edison pork, 200 g daily, had decreased platelet aggregation (Table 13.9).

Discussion

EPA and DHA are both present in fish oils. Fish oils generally contain more EPA than DHA, and EPA is known to be a substrate for cyclooxygenase. Thus, EPA was presumed to be the active component of fish oils for cardiovascular protection. Purified ethyl esters of these two fatty acids were tested for their ability to suppress arrhythmias induced by ischaemia, and to retard development of hypertension in rats genetically predisposed to hypertension. The purposes of the test were also to offset the constriction caused by thromboxane in isolated blood vessels, and to reduce the excretion of protein in the urine in a model of kidney failure caused by hypertension. DHA was more effective than EPA in all of these tests. The results imply that DHA is the principal active component in fish oil for cardiovascular protection (McLennan *et al.*, 1996).

A long-term study in Copenhagen, Denmark has examined the risks of ischaemic heart disease as a function of serum lipid parameters. The combination of high triglyceride and low HDL cholesterol was at least as powerful a predictor of ischaemic heart disease as high LDL cholesterol. The former is characteristic of insulin-resistant subjects. They concluded that efforts to prevent ischaemic heart disease should include intervention against high triglycerides and not just against hypercholesterolaemia (Jeppesen *et al.*, 1997).

Table 13.8.   Plasma lipids and glucose from women before and after eating DHA-enriched pork.

Component	Before	After
Total cholesterol	180.8 ± 11.4	157.1 ± 10.3[a]
Triacylglycerol	96.0 ± 16.5	72.1 ± 11.4
Glucose	93.3 ± 1.9	89.0 ± 1.7
HDL cholesterol	52.6 ± 4.7	50.9 ± 5.2
LDL cholesterol	110.0 ± 8.0	91.8 ± 7.3[a]
Total : HDL cholesterol	3.8 ± 0.3	3.3 ± 0.2

The values are mg dl^{-1}, means $\pm$ SE, for 20 female subjects, age 20 years, before and after consuming 200 g of pork daily for 4 weeks.
[a]Values for the two groups are significantly different ($P < 0.05$).

Table 13.9.   Degree of platelet aggregation with collagen in females consuming Edison chicken or Edison pork.

Diet	Before	After
Edison chicken	61.7 ± 1.9	47.3 ± 2.5[a]
Edison pork	67.5 ± 2.5	43.7 ± 1.8[a]

The values are mean percentages $\pm$ SE for 20 subjects, females, age 20 years, for platelet aggregation with collagen. Each subject consumed 200 g of chicken or pork daily for 4 weeks.
[a]Values for the two groups are significantly different ($P < 0.05$).

Platelet function and blood coagulation play important roles in coronary artery disease. Several studies with fish diets or fish oil supplements have demonstrated decreased platelet aggregation and thromboxane production, and prolonged bleeding time. The effects of α-linolenic acid from flaxseed oil were compared with EPA plus DHA from fish oil in healthy human subjects. The fish oil decreased serum total cholesterol and triacylglycerols, but flaxseed oil had no effect. No differences in effects on collagen-induced platelet aggregation and thromboxane production were observed (Freese and Mutanen, 1997). Thus, the 18-carbon ω-3 fatty acid was as effective as fish oil for haemostatic factors, but not for changes in serum lipid cardiovascular risk factors.

The effects of fish oil and flaxseed oil, 35 mg kg^{-1} daily for 3 months, were compared in 26 subjects. A typical western diet with a low ratio of PUFAs to saturated fatty acids was consumed by 15 of the subjects. For the latter subjects, fish oil reduced the plasma triacylglycerol levels by between 24 and 27%. In both groups of subjects, neither fish oil nor flaxseed oil affected the concentrations of LDL or HDL cholesterol. This intake of fish oil may have some protective value in healthy individuals by reducing atherogenic risk factors, especially in those persons consuming the typical western diet (Layne *et al.*, 1996).

In some patients with elevated serum triacylglycerol levels, supplements containing EPA and DHA have increased serum levels of LDL cholesterol. A group of 26 subjects with combined hyperlipidaemia, LDL cholesterol greater than 130 mg dl^{-1} and triacylglycerols greater than 150 mg dl^{-1}, received DHA at dosages of 1.25 or 2.5 g daily for 6 weeks. Reductions of serum triacylglycerols were 20.9 and 17.6%, respectively, with no change in a placebo group. Small increases in HDL cholesterol with no change in LDL cholesterol were seen in all groups. Low fat, high carbohydrate diets are often recommended for patients with combined hyperlipidaemia. This diet usually exacerbates the lipid abnormalities, whereas supplementation of the diet with DHA may be useful clinically.

In addition to the cardiovascular effects, DHA-enriched foods are beneficial because DHA is essential for brain functioning. Inclusion of plentiful DHA in the diet improves learning ability and the development of the brain. DHA is good for the eyes and is helpful in recovery from certain visual dysfunctions. DHA has been reported to prevent and treat senile dementia. DHA has a positive effect on diseases such as hypertension, arthritis, depression, diabetes mellitus and some cancers.

References

Chen, Z., Pelletier, G., Hollywood, R. and Ratnayake, W. (1995) Trans fatty acid isomers in Canadian human milk. *Lipids* 30, 15–21.

Davidson, M.H., Maki, K.C., Kalkowski, J., Schaefer, E.J., Torri, S.A. and Drennan, K.B. (1997) Effects of docosahexaenoic acid on serum lipoproteins in patients with combined hyperlipidemia: a randomized, double-blind, placebo-controlled trial. *Journal of the American College of Nutrition* 16, 236–243.

Daviglus, M.L., Stamler, J., Orencia, A.J., Dyer, A.R., Liu, K., Greenland, P., Walsh, M.K., Morris, D. and Shekelle, R.B. (1997) Fish consumption and the 30-year risk of fatal myocardial infarction. *New England Journal of Medicine* 336, 1046–1053.

Freese, R. and Mutanen, M. (1997) Alpha-linolenic acid and marine long-chain *n*-3 fatty acids differ only slightly in their effects on hemostatic factors in healthy subjects. *American Journal of Clinical Nutrition* 66, 591–598.

Gaudette, D.C. and Holub, B.J. (1990) Effect of albumin-bound DHA on phospho-inositide phosphorylation in collagen stimulated human platelets. *Thrombosis Research* 58, 435–444.

Jeppesen, J., Hein, H.O., Suadicani, P. and Gyntelberg, F. (1997) Relation of high TG, low HDL cholesterol and LDL cholesterol to the incidence of ischaemic heart disease – an 8-year follow-up in the Copenhagen Male Study. *Arteriosclerosis, Thrombosis and Vascular Biology* 17, 1114–1120.

Layne, K.S., Goh, Y.K., Jumpsen, J.A., Ryan, E.A., Chow, P. and Clandinin, M.T. (1996) Normal subjects consuming physiological levels of 18 : 3(*n*-3) and 20 : 5(*n*-3) from flaxseed or fish oils have characteristic differences in plasma lipid and lipoprotein fatty acid levels. *Journal of Nutrition* 126, 2130–2140.

McLennan, P.L., Howe, P., Abeywardena, M., Muggli, R., Raederstorff, D., Mano, M., Rayner, T. and Head, R. (1996) The cardiovascular protective role of docosa-hexaenoic acid. *European Journal of Pharmacology* 300, 83–89.

Nair, S.S.D., Leitch, J.W., Falconer, J. and Garg, M.L. (1997) Prevention of cardiac arrhythmia by dietary (*n*-3) polyunsaturated fatty acids and their mechanism of action. *Journal of Nutrition* 127, 383–393.

Siscovick, D.S., Raghunathan, T.E., King, I., Weinmann, S., Wicklund, K.G., Albright, J., Bovbjerg, V., Arbogast, P., Smith, H., Kushi, L.H., Cobb, LA., Copass, M.K., Psaty, B. M., Lemaitre, R., Retzlaff, B., Childs, M. and Knopp, R.H. (1995) Dietary intake and cell membrane levels of long-chain *n*-3 polyunsaturated fatty acids and the risk of primary cardiac arrest. *Journal of the American Medical Association* 274, 1363–1367.

Stevens, L.J., Zentall, S.S., Deck, J.L., Abate, M.L., Watkins, B.A., Lipp, S.R. and Burgess, J.R. (1995) Essential fatty acid metabolism in boys with attention-deficit hyperactivity disorder. *American Journal of Clinical Nutrition* 62, 761–768.

Biological Activities of Conjugated Linoleic Acids and Designer Eggs

14

B.A. Watkins[1], A.A. Devitt[1], L. Yu[1] and M.A. Latour[2]

[1]Lipid Chemistry and Molecular Biology Laboratory, Department of Food Science, and [2]Department of Animal Science, Purdue University, West Lafayette, Indiana, USA

Recent investigations suggest that conjugated linoleic acid (CLA) isomers possess anticarcinogenic properties, including inhibition of forestomach cancer in mice, suppression of mammary tumours in rats and inhibition of cancer cell proliferation. CLA may also function as a repartition agent in growing animals. For example, when young rodents, pigs and broiler chicks were fed CLA, they demonstrated improved feed efficiency and reduced body fat. Few studies, however, describe the effects of CLA on egg production and fatty acid composition of yolk lipids.

The purpose of the present investigation was to measure the effects of CLA supplementation on egg yolk composition in laying hens. Forty Single Comb White Leghorn hens were divided into four groups of ten hens, and egg production and yolk fatty acid composition measured over 4 months. Group 1 served as the control (not supplemented with oil), group 2 received 1 g of CLA every other day, group 3 received 1 g of CLA every fourth day, and group 4 was sham-supplemented (given 1 g of safflower oil) every other day. Hen egg and yolk weights increased during the supplementation period but were not significantly affected by the oral lipid treatments. The results of the gas chromatographic analysis indicated that CLA was incorporated successfully into the yolk lipids. Egg yolks contained all of the CLA isomers present in the human supplement [9,11 (*trans*-, *cis*- and *cis*-, *trans*-), 10,12 (*trans*-, *cis*-) and 9,11 and 10,12 both *cis*-, *trans*-isomers]. Upon analysis, hen blood lipids showed no changes in very low-density lipoprotein, triglyceride, phospholipid, cholesterol ester and free cholesterol levels due to the lipid treatments. The CLA concentration in egg yolk was positively correlated with the frequency of supplementation. Although egg yolk fatty acid composition was altered by supplementation, blood lipids and egg production were not influenced by CLA.

© CAB *International* 2000. *Egg Nutrition and Biotechnology*
(eds J.S. Sim, S. Nakai and W. Guenter)

Introduction

Chemistry of conjugated linoleic acids (CLAs)

CLAs are positional and geometric isomers of conjugated octadecadienoic acids that occur naturally in several foods, but their concentration is highest in dairy and beef products. The CLA isomers lack a methylene group separating the double bonds located at the Δ-9 and Δ-12 positions of the essential fatty acid linoleic acid. The growing body of literature on CLAs suggests that these isomeric conjugated fatty acids promote beneficial health and biological effects (Ip *et al.*, 1994, 1996; Lee *et al.*, 1994; Decker, 1995).

The positional isomers of CLA include 7,9-, 8,10-, 9,11-, 10,12- and 11,13-conjugated octadecadienoic acids (counting from the carboxyl end of the molecule). Each of the aforementioned positional conjugated diene isomers can occur in the following geometric configurations: *cis-*, *trans-*; *trans-*, *cis-*; *cis-*, *cis-*; and *trans-*, *trans-* (Haumann, 1996; Sehat *et al.*, 1998). The most common CLA isomer found in natural products is *cis*-9, *trans*-11-octadecadienoic acid, which is now proposed to be named 'rumenic acid' (Kramer *et al.*, 1998a).

CLA isomers possess many unique biological activities compared with linoleic acid. The research on CLAs indicates anticarcinogenic, antiatherosclerotic, antioxidative, immunomodulative and antibacterial effects (Scimeca *et al.*, 1994; Decker, 1995; Haumann, 1996; Parodi, 1996; Sugano *et al.*, 1998). One of the earliest experiments on CLAs indicated that these fatty acids, isolated from extracts of grilled ground beef, exhibited anticarcinogenic activity against chemically induced skin cancer in mice (Ha *et al.*, 1987). Recent experiments on prostate cancer cell lines demonstrated that CLA isomers are incorporated into cell lipids and that CLAs compared with linoleic acid decreased cell proliferation (Cornell *et al.*, 1997). Furthermore, CLAs were found to reduce prostaglandin E_2 concentrations in rat serum, spleen (Sugano *et al.*, 1997) and *ex vivo* bone organ culture (Li and Watkins, 1998).

Sources of CLAs

CLAs are found naturally in a wide variety of food products. Some of the foods are beef, lamb, poultry, seafood, cheese, butter, milk and vegetable oils (Ip, 1994). Fats and meats from ruminant species are the richest natural sources of CLAs. Lamb, veal and beef contain from 2.7 to 5.6 mg of CLA g^{-1} of fat (Haumann, 1996). Cheese and milk fat have about 3–6 mg of CLA g^{-1} of fat (Ip, 1994). The linoleic acid present in the diets of grazing animals is converted to CLA by an isomerase which is released by ruminal bacteria (*Butyrivibrio fibrisolvens*) (Chin *et al.*, 1992) as a part of the biohydrogenation process (Bartlet and Chapman, 1961). CLA may also be produced from linoleic acid in the colon by microorganisms of conventional rats since no CLA was detected in the faeces of germ-free rats given the same diet (Chin *et al.*, 1994a). In most cases, the *cis*-9, *trans*-11 isomer is the predominant isomeric form of CLA found naturally, except for vegetable oils which can contain several other isomers. Estimates of CLA intake range from 1.5 to 0.3 g per person day^{-1} and appear to be dependent on gender and the intake of animal and vegetable foods (Fritsche and Steinhart, 1998).

Besides the natural sources, CLAs are produced synthetically by alkali isomerization of linoleic acid (Haumann, 1996). The synthetic sources of CLA are prepared from linoleic acid or vegetable oils (sunflower and safflower) which are rich in linoleic acid (Ha *et al.*, 1990; Christie *et al.*, 1997). Many commercial CLA products are available as supplements, but their composition may be variable (Christie *et al.*, 1997).

Biological activities of CLA

Growth

Several investigators have documented that feeding CLAs improved feed efficiency and reduced body fat deposition in growing pigs, rats, mice, rabbits and chickens (Cook *et al.*, 1993; Chin *et al.*, 1994b; Haumann, 1996; Parodi, 1996; Park *et al.*, 1997; Sugano *et al.*, 1997; Li and Watkins, 1998). Nutritional studies with CLA isomers showed that these fatty acids are incorporated into different organs, and that both neutral and polar lipid fractions of animal (Belury and Kempa-Steczko, 1997; Sebedio *et al.*, 1997; Sugano *et al.*, 1997; Kramer *et al.*, 1998b; Li and Watkins, 1998) and human tissues (Fritsche *et al.*, 1997) were enriched. Moreover, CLAs may affect the fatty acid composition and content of rodent tissues and cultured cells (Li and Watkins, 1998). These experiments suggest that the incorporation of CLAs may be dose and time dependent in animals, humans and cell culture models. For example, Huang *et al.* (1994) gave healthy men CLA in cheese and found that the plasma CLA concentration increased significantly with cheese consumption. Although the data are limited on the toxicity of CLA, a recent study by Scimeca (1998) indicated no treatment-related effects of CLA on histopathological and haematological analyses of blood from rats.

Carcinogenesis

Potential anticarcinogenic effects of CLA have been demonstrated by both *in vivo* and *in vitro* studies. Pariza *et al.* (1983) tested the inhibitory effects of crude CLA extracts from fried ground beef against two mutagens, 2-amino-3-methylimidazo[4,5-*f*]quinoline and 2-aminofluorene mediated by rat liver S-9, in normal, phenobarbital- or aroclor-treated rats. In this study, the CLA extract showed an inhibitory effect on chemically induced mutagenesis.

Shultz *et al.* (1992a) investigated the effect of CLA on human MCF-7 breast cancer cell growth. Cancer cells were enriched with varying concentrations of linoleic acid and CLA ($1.7–7.1 \times 10^{-5}$ M) for 12 days. While linoleic acid initially stimulated cancer cell growth at concentrations of $3.5–7.1 \times 10^{-5}$ M, CLA inhibited cell growth after 8–12 days of incubation at the same linoleic acid concentrations. In addition, cytotoxicity for MCF-7 cells was greater with CLA than that with linoleic acid. Shultz *et al.* (1992b) also observed that CLA inhibited the growth of HT29 colon cancer cells; however, conflicting results on the effects of C18 fatty acid isomers on cancer cells have been reported (DesBordes and Lea, 1995). In 1997, Liu and Belury reported that CLA significantly decreased ornithine decarboxylase activity, which is a hallmark event of tumour promotion, in the cultured keratinocyte cell line HEL-30.

There is convincing evidence that CLA isomers inhibit carcinogenesis in animal models (Haumann, 1996). Ip and co-workers (1991, 1994, 1995, 1996) showed that dietary supplementation with CLA (free acid at 1% by weight) resulted in protective effects against mammary carcinogenesis in rats. Moreover, Ip *et al.* (1991) found that CLA inhibited the development of mammary tumours induced by a high dose of dimethylbenz(*a*)anthracene in rats fed synthetically prepared CLA (0.5, 1.0 and 1.5% of the diet) for 24 weeks. The number of mammary adenocarcinomas was reduced by 32, 56 and 60%, respectively, compared with the controls given the AIN-76A basal diet. The final tumour incidence and cumulative tumour weight also decreased in rats fed the diet containing CLA. The response observed in these experiments might be dose dependent at levels of 0.5–1% CLA. The *cis*-9, *trans*-11 isomer of CLA was detected in the phospholipid fraction of liver and mammary tumours of rats, and the incorporation of *cis*-9, *trans*-11 increased with dietary intake. In addition, CLA was observed to inhibit lipid peroxidation in the mammary gland but not in the liver.

Rats at a similar age were given lower doses of dietary CLA (0.05, 0.1, 0.25 and 0.5%) for 5 weeks, and a dose-dependent inhibitory effect in chemically induced mammary tumour formation was observed for all doses (Ip *et al.*, 1994). The anticarcinogenic activity of CLA in the methylnitrosourea model suggests that CLA may have a direct modulating effect on susceptibility of the target organ to neoplastic transformation. However, CLA also showed inhibitory effects on proliferative activity of the mammary gland. More recent studies indicate that the free acid and triacylglycerol forms are essentially identical in providing anticancer activity in rats (Ip *et al.*, 1995). Furthermore, a continuous dietary supplementation with CLA was required for maximal inhibition of tumour formation.

The anticarcinogenic activity of CLA has been confirmed in other animal models. For example, CLA was reported to suppress initiation of skin carcinogenesis induced by 7,12-dimethylbenz(*a*)anthracene (Parodi, 1996) and phorbol ester skin promotion in mice (Liu and Belury, 1997). Inhibition of benzo(*a*)pyrene-induced forestomach neoplasia was observed in mice given synthetic CLA by gavage (Ha *et al.*, 1990). Four and two days before administration of benzo(*a*)pyrene, mice were given one of the treatments four times (0.1 ml of CLA, 0.1 ml of linoleic acid or 0.1 ml of 0.85% saline as a sham control). Compared with the control, a 50% reduction in the neoplasms was observed in animals given CLA. Only the *cis*-9, *trans*-11 isomer of CLA was detected in forestomach phospholipids in this study.

Protective effects of CLA on colon carcinogenesis induced by 2-amino-3-methylimidazo[4,5-*f*]quinoline were investigated using male F344 rats (Liew *et al.*, 1995). The 2-amino-3-methylimidazo[4,5-*f*]quinoline is a mutagenic heterocyclic amine that develops naturally in cooked meat and fish but requires metabolic activation to be carcinogenic. CLA resulted in a significant inhibition of DNA–IQ formation at a dietary level of 0.5% by weight.

Ip *et al.* (1996) and Ip and Scimeca (1997) also investigated the anti-carcinogenic mechanism of CLA by studying the interactions between CLA and other fat sources. The anticarcinogenic activity of CLA was evaluated in diets containing fat levels of 10, 13.3, 16.7 and 20% by weight, and 20% fat from either corn oil or lard (Ip *et al.*, 1996). The results indicated that mammary cancer prevention produced by 1% CLA was not influenced by the level or type of fat in the diet. Unfortunately, these studies did not consider the influence of *n*-3 polyunsaturated fatty acids which are known to be protective against carcinogenesis (Rose, 1997). Ip *et al.* (1997) further reported that the efficacy of the anticarcinogenic activity of CLA was not altered by dietary linoleic acid intake. Interestingly, the accumulation of CLA in mammary tissue was found to be dose dependent for certain dietary CLA levels, and that the dietary linoleic acid level did not affect incorporation of CLA into either neutral or polar lipids.

Atherosclerosis

CLA has also exhibited antiatherosclerotic activity in both the rabbit and hamster (Lee *et al.*, 1994; Nicolosi *et al.*, 1997). Hamsters were given a hyper-cholesterolaemic diet and a supplement of 0.06, 0.11 and 1.1% CLA (Nicolosi *et al.*, 1997). CLA significantly reduced signs of early atherosclerosis, and reduced the total serum cholesterol, low-density lipoprotein (LDL) cholesterol and triacylglycerols without influencing high-density lipoprotein (HDL) cholesterol. Cholesterol-lowering effects of CLA were observed and confirmed in a rabbit feeding study by Lee *et al.* (1994). Rabbits were given a semi-synthetic diet containing 14% fat and 0.1% cholesterol with a supplement of 0.5 g of CLA day^{-1} over 12 weeks. The CLA-supplemented rabbits had markedly lower levels of total serum cholesterol, LDL cholesterol, and triacylglycerols compared with those not given CLA. Moreover, the cholesterol ratios of LDL to HDL and the total serum to HDL were significantly reduced in the CLA-supplemented group. Examination of the aorta revealed less atherosclerotic plaque formation in rabbits given CLA. The antiatherosclerotic property of CLA was comparable with that of linoleic acid in hamsters (Haumann, 1996). Reductions in cholesterol levels by either linoleic acid or CLA were similar, i.e. about 20%, when linoleic acid or CLA was provided at 2% of dietary calories. The reduction in symptoms of early atherogenesis, however, was approximately three times greater with the CLA diet compared with the linoleic acid diet. Although antiatherosclerotic activity of CLA has been reported, and despite a possible relationship to antioxidant properties, the exact mechanism for its action has not been elucidated.

Antibacterial

The potassium salts of CLA were found to have antibacterial activity against *Listeria monocytogenes* at a concentration of 50 µg ml^{-1} (Wang and Johnson, 1992). CLA showed higher bactericidal activity in brain–heart infusion broth at pH 5 than at pH 6. Potassium salts of CLA exhibited a bacteriostatic activity, thereby prolonging the lag phase in both whole milk and skimmed milk at 4°C. The length of the lag phase was proportional to the concentration of the CLA salts in skimmed milk at 25°C. Other fatty acids tested were not as effective in skimmed or whole milk, although some of them were bactericidal in brain–heart infusion broth.

Antioxidant

Ha *et al.* (1990) reported that CLA acted as an antioxidant *in vitro*. The antioxidant activity of CLA isomers was evaluated using the thiocyanate method and compared with known antioxidants, including α-tocopherol, ascorbic acid and butylated hydroxytoluene (BHT). The experiment was conducted by adding ferrous ammonium sulphate and thiocyanate into an aqueous linoleic acid solution, followed by measuring the degree of linoleic acid oxidation (peroxide value). CLA showed more powerful antioxidative activity than α-tocopherol, comparable with that for BHT. The above observation was supported by Ip *et al.* (1991). The lipid peroxidation products in rats fed CLA were quantified by measuring endogenous thiobarbituric acid-reactive substances in liver and mammary gland. The results showed that CLA reduced lipid oxidation in mammary gland but not in liver. Maximal antioxidant activity was observed with only 0.25% CLA in the diet, while the greatest anticarcinogenic effect was obtained at a dietary CLA level of 1%. In understanding the metabolism of CLA, one recent study (Yurawecz *et al.*, 1995) suggests that CLA is converted into furan fatty acids during oxidation and should be considered as an endogenous source of furan fatty acids in biological systems.

The effects of CLA on the activities of protein kinase C (Benjamin *et al.*, 1992) and phospholipase C (Bonordon *et al.*, 1993) might aid in understanding other biological actions of these fatty acids that relate to antioxidant properties. These experiments suggest that CLA may alter signal transduction and, since the redox (oxidation–reduction) state has been related to signal transduction in biological systems, CLA may reduce messenger molecules (reactive oxygen species or cytokines) involved in cell–cell signalling. Oxidative stress is associated with many degenerative diseases, and the present knowledge might support a role for CLA in protection against this condition.

Immunomodulation

CLA isomers appear to act as immunomodulating agents and they may protect against pathogenic microorganisms to aid in reducing allergic reactions (Parodi, 1996; Sugano *et al.*, 1998). In an investigation on immune cell function, Turek *et al.* (1998) found that CLA could influence cytokine production by peritoneal macrophages in rats given diets varying in *n*-6 and *n*-3 fatty acids. The study revealed that CLA reduced basal and lipopolysaccharide-induced levels of interleukin-6 by macrophages in rats given soybean oil, and reduced basal levels of tumour necrosis factor production by macrophages in rats given a high *n*-6 or *n*-3 fatty acid diet.

Besides the effects on cytokines, CLA isomers were found to reduce tissue prostaglandin E_2 (PGE_2) levels in rats (Sugano *et al.*, 1997; Li and Watkins, 1998). Other studies suggest that CLA can influence immune cell function. For example, Wong *et al.* (1997) reported that CLA might modulate immune defence, including lymphocyte proliferation in mice, and Sugano *et al.* (1998) observed that CLA altered chemical mediators and immunoglobulins (Igs) in rats. Although these experiments showed that CLA did not influence histamine release, it did reduce the amount of leukotriene B_4 from peritoneal exudate cells, spleen and lung. Furthermore, the levels of IgA, IgG and IgM increased in spleen and mesenteric lymph node lymphocytes, but the IgE level decreased in rats given a 1% dietary level of CLA. Some research suggests that CLA may stimulate porcine lymphocyte blastogenesis and, in a study with rats, Cook *et al.* (1993) observed that CLA increased mitogen response and macrophage phagocytosis in rats. In support of the previous investigation, Miller *et al.* (1994) reported that spleen lymphocyte blastogenesis was enhanced in rats given CLA.

Bone

In a recent investigation on bone modelling, Watkins *et al.* (1997) reported that milk fat stimulated bone formation rate in growing chicks possibly by modulating *ex vivo* PGE_2 production in bone. Since milk fat is a primary dietary source of CLA, having a concentration up to 30 mg of CLA g^{-1} fat (Parodi, 1996), the positive effect of milk fat on bone formation might be related to modulating PGE_2 production. With regard to bone metabolism, PGE_2 is recognized to be a mediator of both bone formation and bone resorption *in vivo* (Marks and Miller, 1993), and moderate levels of this prostanoid favour bone formation. The recent work of Li and Watkins (1998) demonstrated that CLA at 1% of the diet reduced *ex vivo* PGE_2 production in bone of rats independently of the amount of dietary *n*-6 or *n*-3 fatty acids. At present, no study has been published that describes how CLA supplements affect bone modelling or remodelling in animals or humans.

Designer Eggs

For years, scientists and health professionals have been investigating and debating the effects of foods, nutrients and diet on promoting health and reducing disease. Many nutritionists support and recommend a low fat, high fibre diet to healthy people interested in dietary prevention of chronic disease. As the press disseminates information from nutrition/health studies, often the results are inadequately presented and difficult for the general public to interpret. Once scientific criteria are established for developing health claims for functional/ designed foods, the relationships between nutrients and disease will become clear (Clydesdale, 1997). Moreover, the curiosity in self-medication, the explosion in the elderly population and rising health care costs fuel the interest in foods and their potential health benefits. Because of the intense interest in the relationship between diet and health, much attention has been paid to manipulating foods to promote health. The term 'designer foods' emerged some years ago to describe a food tailored to contain specific concentrations and proportions of nutrients critical to good health. Other similar terms have been used such as functional foods, nutraceuticals and phytochemical sources. The public interest in new foods that offer health benefits will stimulate opportunities for developing designer foods from poultry products. Although many designer egg products have been marketed around the world, the continued growth and acceptance of these products will depend on nutritional and health labelling laws.

In January 1993, the Food and Drug Administration (FDA) published regulations implementing the Nutrition Labeling and Education Act of 1990 in the USA. This law requires nutritional labelling information for processed foods, fresh fruit, vegetables and seafood. The Food Safety and Inspection Service published similar regulations pertaining to meat and poultry products. Labels for retail foods contain information on total calories, calories from fat, total fat, saturated fat, cholesterol, sodium, total carbohydrates, dietary fibre, sugars, protein, vitamin A, vitamin C, calcium and iron. Optional nutritional information can include calories from saturated, polyunsaturated and monounsaturated fats, potassium, soluble fibre, insoluble fibre and other vitamins and minerals. These laws bring greater relevance to the issue of linking nutrient composition to health problems since the FDA now allows specific health claims for certain nutrients (Box 14.1). It is not clear yet as to how the public will perceive and utilize this information; however, consumers may respond by making more informed decisions before purchasing foods. As nutrition/ health-related research continues, the FDA may allow more health claims for other nutrients.

Cruickshank (1934) was the first to suggest and demonstrate that dietary fats could change the composition of lipids in poultry. More recent attention given to modifying the fatty acid composition of poultry meat and eggs has focused on elevating *n*-3 polyunsaturated fatty acids (PUFAs) because of the health benefits associated with these fatty acids. Since the chicken is a monogastric, much of the dietary fat is assimilated directly with minimal modification (Watkins, 1995). Furthermore, it is well documented that when fishmeal, menhaden oil and flaxseed products are fed, the *n*-3 PUFAs contained in these products are readily incorporated into tissue lipids of broilers and turkeys. In addition, broiler chickens can chain elongate and desaturate dietary sources of α-linolenic acid (18 : 3*n*-3) to form eicosapentaenoic acid (20 : 5*n*-3); however, this process is limited (Watkins, 1995).

The chicken can modulate its tissue concentrations of PUFAs by the types and amounts of fatty acids it consumes (Watkins, 1995) because liver contains desaturation/elongation enzymes to facilitate the formation of PUFAs. In most

---

Box 14.1.   Health claims now allowed by the FDA.

- Calcium's link in preventing osteoporosis
- Reduced fat content to reduce the risk of cancer
- Saturated fatty acids and cholesterol links to coronary heart disease
- Fibre in certain fruits and vegetables and cancer prevention and reduced risk of coronary heart disease
- Sodium link to hypertension
- Low fat intakes from diets of fruit and vegetables link to a reduced risk of cancer

practical poultry diets, the essential fatty acid linoleic acid is at a higher concentration than α-linolenic acid. In this case, greater amounts of *n*-6 PUFAs are formed compared with the amounts of *n*-3 PUFAs. When the dietary concentration of 18 : 3*n*-3 increases relative to 18 : 2*n*-6, an elevation of *n*-3 PUFA formation occurs. Feeding sources of *n*-3 PUFAs to poultry increases the carcass concentration of 20 : 5*n*-3 but lowers that of 20 : 4*n*-6. Appreciable amounts of *n*-3 PUFAs also accumulate in egg yolk of hens fed menhaden oil. Commercial interest in feeding flaxseed and flaxseed oil has been exploited to elevate the concentrations of *n*-3 PUFAs in poultry meat and eggs to produce designer foods.

Feeding *trans*-fatty acids from hydrogenated oils can lead to accumulatium in broiler tissues and in egg yolk (Watkins, 1995). Consumption of hydrogenated oil is under intense scrutiny because of its negative effect on blood cholesterol levels which increases the risk of coronary heart disease in humans (Lichtenstein, 1993).

Several common chronic diseases are affected by imbalances in fatty acid metabolism in humans (Watkins *et al.*, 1996). An excess of saturated fats is conducive to coronary heart disease and atherosclerosis. Uncontrolled lipid peroxidation causes inflammation, and oxidative damage leading to free radical formation in tissues is believed to contribute to many life-threatening diseases in humans (Ames, 1989). Free radicals are believed to be involved in the development of cardiovascular disease, stroke and certain cancers. The free radicals attack DNA, proteins and PUFAs in cell membranes, and attack on DNA is hypothesized to cause mutagenesis and carcinogenesis. Although the body maintains enzyme systems and levels of natural antioxidants to terminate free radical formation, components of these enzymes and the antioxidants must be supplied continually in the diet. Interest in foods derived from plants has arisen because of their concentrations of phytochemicals that may reduce lipid peroxidation and protect the body from free radical damage (Caragay, 1992). Phytochemicals are abundant in a variety of plants, but those present in soybeans, garlic, cabbage, ginger, liquorice, umbelliferae (carrots and celery) and flax have received a great amount of research attention. Carotenoids, tocopherols, phenolics and flavonoids are examples of plant phytochemicals. Future studies on enriching poultry meat and eggs with antioxidant vitamins and phytochemicals could provide additional opportunities for developing designer foods.

Enrichment of Layer Egg Yolk Lipids with CLA

Substantial progress has been made in understanding lipoprotein metabolism in the hen and lipid deposition in the developing egg yolk. Furthermore, the deposition of dietary fatty acids into yolk lipids has been studied extensively. Attention given to modifying the fatty acid composition of egg yolks has focused on elevating *n*-3 PUFAs because of the healthy effects associated with these fatty acids. More recently, interest has shifted to research on the health benefits of CLA and their applications to food systems. Since numerous investigations suggest that CLAs possess antiatherosclerotic and anticarcinogenic properties in addition to reducing body fat in animals, an experiment was conducted to evaluate the effect of feeding CLAs to chicken. The purpose of this study was to measure the effects of CLA supplementation to laying hens on egg yolk lipid composition. Hens were supplemented with a commercial grade soft gel capsule (PharmaNutrients, Tonalin™) containing either CLA or safflower oil. The CLA mixture was a human grade dietary supplement that contained 1 g of CLA isomers encapsulated in the soft gel. CLA capsules contained several isomers of CLA ($\approx$ 55–56% CLA) as free fatty acids.

Forty Single Comb White Leghorn hens (35 weeks of age) were divided into four groups of ten hens, and egg production was observed for 13 weeks. Egg collection continued for another 4 weeks past the supplementation period to monitor CLA content in egg yolk after withdrawal of the treatments. Group 1 served as the control, group 2 received 1 g of CLA every other day, group 3 received 1 g of CLA every fourth day and group 4 was given safflower oil every other day as a sham control. Hens were housed two per cage, and a single cage housing two roosters was utilized for treatment group separation. The laying hens were identified with wingbands and placed in numbered cages.

Ten randomly selected eggs from each group were collected from bi-weekly laying periods throughout the study to determine egg weights and obtain egg yolk samples. The sample shell egg was weighed, shelled and the yolk separated from albumen to determine the yolk weight. Two yolks were combined, mixed thoroughly and an aliquot of 1 g used for lipid extraction. The yolk samples were extracted with chloroform/methanol (2 : 1, v/v) and fatty acid methyl esters (FAME) prepared according to Li and Watkins (1998) for capillary gas chromatographic analysis.

Initial hen weight and egg samples were determined at the onset and completion of the feeding trial, and no significant difference was found between the treatment groups. Egg production averaged seven eggs hen^{-1} week^{-1} and was not altered by the dietary inclusion of CLA. However, hen feed consumption did appear to decrease with increasing CLA supplementation without influencing egg production, thus confirming that CLA could improve feed efficiency. Shell egg weights were greater in hens given CLA; however, yolk weights were unchanged (15–16 g for all groups). Although our results indicate that CLA did not influence yolk consistency, it is not clear if higher levels of supplementation would affect the egg quality.

The results indicated that CLA was incorporated successfully into the yolk lipids. Egg yolks contained the following CLA isomers: 9,11(*trans*-, *cis*- and *cis*-, *trans*-); *trans*-10, *cis*-12; *cis*-, *cis*- (9,11 and 10,12). Total CLA ranged from 0.7 to 1.2% of total fatty acids in the supplemented groups. Upon analysis, hen blood lipids showed no changes in very low-density lipoprotein, triglyceride, phospholipid, cholesterol ester and free cholesterol across the treatment groups. The concentration of CLA in egg yolk was positively correlated with the frequency of supplementation, and CLA content peaked at 5 weeks of dietary supplementation. From these data, it appeared that the *cis*-9, *trans*-11 isomer was incorporated into the yolk lipids more readily, based on the FAME analysis. This result is consistent with the analysis of CLA isomers in foods that naturally contain CLA such as milk, cheese, butter and steak (Fritsche and

Steinheart, 1998; O'Shea *et al.*, 1998; Yurawecz *et al.*, 1998). The fatty acid profile of the enriched yolks exhibited a decrease in the amount of monounsaturates, similar to the findings of reduced tissue monounsaturates in rabbits fed CLA (Lee *et al.*, 1995). The current experiment also revealed that supplementing with CLA and safflower oil elevated the *n*-6 fatty acid content in yolks, which corroborates the findings of March and MacMillan (1989) that linoleic acid feeding to hens elevated the *n*-6 fatty acid content in egg. The total amount of PUFAs was greater in egg yolk of hens given CLA compared with the control, which might suggest that CLA may have been desaturated and elongated (unpublished observations in rat liver; Belury and Kempa-Steczko, 1997). Upon analysis of fatty acids in yolk of stored eggs (4–6°C), the total amount of CLA diminished with increased storage time (6 months). This phenomenon was reported in CLA-containing products such as cheese and milk (Shantha *et al.*, 1995). Eggs from this study contained more CLA (1.25% of the total fatty acids) than other foods such as dairy and beef products (0.29–0.89% of the total fatty acids). This study demonstrated that CLA could be enriched in egg yolk for the development of new designer eggs for the consumer.

Conclusions

The current popularity of nutrition and interest in the relationships between diet and health provide opportunities for developing designer foods from poultry egg products. As food labelling laws become established, some consumers will respond by making more informed decisions about diet and the foods they select. Their decisions will be influenced by the health claims for nutrients allowed by government agencies. As the list of nutrients grows and as congressional action occurs for nutraceuticals, new designer food products and markets will open for the progressive food industries. Food scientists working with nutritionists should be looking for alternative means to modify the egg to deliver selected nutrients such as *n*-3 PUFAs and CLAs to the consumer.

References

Ames, B.N. (1989) Endogenous oxidative DNA damage, aging, and cancer. *Free Radical Research Communications* 7, 121–127.

Bartlet, J.C. and Chapman, D.G. (1961) Detection of hydrogenated fats in butter fat by measurement of *cis–trans* conjugated unsaturation. *Journal of Agricultural and Food Chemistry* 9, 50–53.

Belury, M.A. and Kempa-Steczko, A. (1997) Conjugated linoleic acid modulates hepatic lipid composition in mice. *Lipids* 32, 199–204.

Benjamin, H., Storkson, W., Liu, W. and Pariza, M.W. (1992) The effect of conjugated dienoic derivatives of linoleic acid (CLA) on mouse forestomach protein kinase C (PKC)-like activity. *Federation of the American Societies of Experimental Biology Journal* 6, A1396.

Bonordon, W.J., Storkson, W., Liu, W., Albright, K. and Pariza, M. (1993) Fatty acid inhibition of 12-*O*-tetradecanoyl-phorbol 13-acetate (TPA)-induced phospholipase

C activity. *Federation of the American Societies of Experimental Biology Journal* 7, A618.

Caragay, A.B. (1992) Cancer preventive foods and ingredients. *Food Technology* 46, 65–68.

Clydesdale, F.M. (1997) A proposal for the establishment of scientific criteria for health claims for functional foods. *Nutrition Reviews* 55, 413–422.

Chin, S.F., Storkson, J.M., Lui, W., Albright, K.J. and Pariza, M.W. (1994a) Conjugated linoleic acid (9,11- and 10,12-octadecadienoic acid) is produced in conventional but not germ-free rats fed linoleic acid. *Journal of Nutrition* 124, 694–701.

Chin, S.F., Storkson, J.M., Albright, K.J., Cook, M.E. and Pariza, M.W. (1994b) Conjugated linoleic acid is a growth factor for rats as shown by enhanced weight gain and improved feed efficiency. *Journal of Nutrition* 124, 2344–2349.

Chin, S.F., Liu, W., Storkson, J.M., Ha, Y.L. and Pariza, M.W. (1992) Dietary sources of conjugated dienoic isomers of linoleic acid, a newly recognized class of anti-carcinogens. *Journal of Food Component Analysis* 5, 185–197.

Christie, W.W., Dobson, G. and Gunstone, F.D. (1997) Isomers in commercial samples of conjugated linoleic acid. *Lipids* 32, 1231.

Cook, M.C., Miller, C.C., Park, Y. and Pariza, M. (1993) Immune modulation by altered nutrient metabolism: nutritional control of immune-induced growth depression. *Poultry Science* 72, 1301–1305.

Cornell, K.K., Waters, D.J., Coffman, K.T., Robinson, J.P. and Watkins, B.A. (1997) Conjugated linoleic acid inhibited the *in vitro* proliferation of canine prostate cancer cells. *Federation of the American Societies for Experimental Biology Journal* 11, A579 (abstract).

Cruickshank, E.M. (1934) Studies in the fat metabolism in the fowl. I. The composition of the egg fat and depot fat of the fowl as affected by the ingestion of large amounts of different fats. *Biochemical Journal* 28, 965–977.

Decker, E.A. (1995) The role of phenolics, conjugated linoleic acid, carnosine, and pyrroloquinoline quinone as nonessential dietary antioxidants. *Nutrition Reviews* 53, 49–58.

DesBordes, C. and Lea, M.A. (1995) Effects of C18 fatty acid isomers on DNA synthesis in hepatoma and breast cancer cells. *Anticancer Research* 15, 2017–2022.

Fritsche, J. and Steinhart, H. (1998) Amounts of conjugated linoleic acid (CLA) in German foods and evaluation of daily intake. *Zeitschrift für Lebensmittel-Untersuchung und -Forschung* A-206, 77–82.

Fritsche, J., Mossoba, M.M., Yurawecz, M.P., Roach, J.A.G., Sehat, N., Ku, Y. and Steinhart, H. (1997) Conjugated linoleic acid (CLA) isomers in human adipose tissue. *Zeitschrift für Lebensmittel-Untersuchung und -Forschung* A-205, 415–418.

Ha, Y.L., Grimm, N.K. and Pariza, M.W. (1987) Anticarcinogens from fried ground beef: heat-altered derivatives of linoleic acid. *Carcinogenesis* 8, 1881–1887.

Ha, Y.L., Storkson, J. and Pariza, M.W. (1990) Inhibition of benzo(*a*)pyrene-induced mouse forestomach neoplasia by conjugated dienoic derivatives of linoleic acid. *Cancer Research* 50, 1097–1101.

Haumann, B.F. (1996) Conjugated linoleic acid offers research promise. *INFORM* 7, 152–159.

Huang, Y., Luedecke, L.O. and Shultz, T.D. (1994) Effect of cheddar cheese consumption on plasma conjugated linoleic acid concentrations in men. *Nutrition Research* 14, 373–386.

Ip, C. (1994) Conjugated linoleic acid in cancer prevention research: a report of current status and issues. *Special Report Prepared for the National Live and Meat Board.* Report No. 100–104.

Ip, C. and Scimeca, J.A. (1997) Conjugated linoleic acid and linoleic acid are distinctive modulators of mammary carcinogenesis. *Nutrition and Cancer* 27, 131–135.

Ip, C., Chin, S.F., Scimeca, J.A. and Pariza, M.W. (1991) Mammary cancer prevention by conjugated dienoic derivative of linoleic acid. *Cancer Research* 51, 6118–6124.

Ip, C., Singh, M., Thompson, H.J. and Scimeca, J.A. (1994) Conjugated linoleic acid suppresses mammary carcinogenesis and proliferative activity of the mammary gland in the rat. *Cancer Research* 54, 1212–1215.

Ip, C., Scimeca, J.A. and Thompson, H. (1995) Effect of timing and duration of dietary conjugated linoleic acid on mammary cancer prevention. *Nutrition and Cancer* 24, 241–247.

Ip, C., Briggs, S.P., Haegele, A.D., Thompson, H.J., Storkson, J. and Scimeca, J.A. (1996) The efficacy of conjugated linoleic acid in mammary cancer prevention is independent of the level or type of fat in the diet. *Carcinogenesis* 17, 1045–1050.

Ip, C., Jiang, C., Thompson, H.J. and Scimeca, J.A. (1997) Retention of conjugated linoleic acid in the mammary gland is associated with tumour inhibition during the post-initiation phase of carcinogenesis. *Carcinogenesis* 18, 755–759.

Kramer, J.K.G., Parodi, P.W., Jensen, R.G., Mossoba, M.M., Yurawecz, M.P. and Adlof, R.O. (1998a) Ruminic acid: a proposed common name for the major conjugated linoleic acid isomer found in natural products. *Lipids* 33, 835.

Kramer, J.K.G., Sehat, N., Dugan, M.E.R., Mossoba, M.M., Yurawecz, M.P., Roach, J.A.G., Eulitz, K., Aalhus, J.L., Schaefer, A.L. and Ku, Y. (1998b) Distributions of conjugated linoleic acid (CLA) isomers in tissue lipid classes of pigs fed a commercial CLA mixture determined by gas chromatography and silver ion-high-performance liquid chromatography. *Lipids* 33, 549–558.

Lee, K.N., Kritchevsky, D. and Pariza, M.W. (1994) Conjugated linoleic acid in rabbits.*Atherosclerosis* 108, 19–25.

Lee, K.N., Storkson, J.M. and Pariza, M.W. (1995) Dietary conjugated linoleic acid changes fatty acid composition in different tissues by decreasing monounsaturated fatty acids. Institute of Food Technologists, Annual Meeting: Abstracts 183.

Li, Y. and Watkins, B.A. (1998) Conjugated linoleic acids alter bone fatty acid composition and reduce *ex vivo* prostaglandin E_2 biosynthesis in rats fed *n*-6 or *n*-3 fatty acids. *Lipids* 33, 417–425.

Lichtenstein, A. (1993) Trans fatty acids, blood lipids, and cardiovascular risk: Where do we stand? *Nutrition Reviews* 51, 340–343.

Liew, C., Schut, H.A.J., Chin, S.F., Pariza, M.W. and Dashwood, R.H. (1995) Protection of conjugated linoleic acids against 2-amino-3-methylimidazo[4,5-*f*]quinoline-induced colon carcinogenesis in the F-334 rat: a study of inhibitory mechanism. *Carcinogenesis* 15, 3037–3043.

Liu, K. and Belury, M.A. (1997) Conjugated linoleic acid modulation of phorbol ester-induced events in murine keratinocytes. *Lipids* 32, 725–730.

March, B.E. and MacMillan, C. (1990) Linoleic acid as a mediator of egg size. *Poultry Science* 69, 634–639.

Marks, S.C. and Miller, S.C. (1993) Prostaglandins and the skeleton: the legacy and challenges of two decades of research. *Endocrine Journal* 1, 337–344.

Nicolosi, R.J., Rogers, E.J., Kritchevsky, D., Scimeca, J.A. and Huth, P.J. (1997) Dietary conjugated linoleic acid reduces plasma lipoproteins and early aortic atherosclerosis in hypercholesterolemic hamsters. *Artery* 22, 266–277.

O'Shea, M., Lawless, F., Stanton, C. and Devery, R. (1998) Conjugated linoleic acid in bovine milk fat: a food-based approach to cancer chemoprevention. *Trends in Food Science and Technology* 9, 192–196.

Pariza, M.W., Loretz, L.J., Storkson, J.M. and Holland, N.C. (1983) Mutagens and modulators of mutagenesis in fried ground beef. *Cancer Research* 43, 2444s–2446s.

Park, Y., Albright, K.J., Lui, W., Storkson, J.M., Cook, M.E. and Pariza, M.W. (1997) Effect of conjugated linoleic acid on body composition in mice. *Lipids* 32, 853–857.

Parodi, P.W. (1996) Milk fat components: possible chemopreventive agents for cancer and other diseases. *Australian Journal of Dairy Technology* 51, 24–32.

Rose, D.P. (1997) Dietary fatty acids and prevention of hormone-responsive cancer. *Proceedings of the Society of Experimental Biology and Medicine* 216, 224–233.

Scimeca, J.A. (1998) Toxicological evaluation of dietary conjugated linoleic acid in male Fisher 344 rats. *Food and Chemical Toxicology* 36, 391–395.

Scimeca, J.A., Thompson, H.J. and Ip, C. (1994) Effects of conjugated linoleic acid on carcinogenesis. In: Weisburger, E.K. (ed.), *Diet and Breast Cancer*. Plenum Press, New York, pp. 59–65.

Sebedio, J.L., Juaneda, P., Dobson, G., Ramilison, I., Martin, J.C., Chardigny, J.M. and Christie, W.W. (1997) Metabolites of conjugated isomers of linoleic acid (CLA) in the rat. *Biochimica et Biophysica Acta* 1345, 5–10.

Sehat, N., Yurawecz, M.P., Roach, J.A.G., Mossoba, M.M., Kramer, J.K.G. and Ku, Y. (1998) Silver-ion high-performance liquid chromatographic separation and identification of conjugated linoleic acid isomers. *Lipids* 33, 217–221.

Shantha, N.C., Ram, L., O'Leary, J., Hicks, C. and Dechder, E. (1995) Conjugated linoleic acid concentration in dairy products as affected by processing and storage. *Journal of Food Science* 60, 695–697.

Shultz, T.D., Chew, B.P. and Seaman, W.R. (1992a) Differential stimulatory and inhibitory responses of human MCF-7 breast cancer cells to linoleic acid and conjugated linoleic acid in culture. *Anticancer Research* 12, 2143–2146.

Shultz, T.D., Chew, B.P., Seaman, W.R. and Luedecke, L.O. (1992b) Inhibitory effect of conjugated dienoic derivatives of linoleic acid and β-carotene on the *in vitro* growth of human cancer cells. *Cancer Letters* 63, 125–133.

Sugano, M., Tsujita, A., Yamasaki, M., Yamada, K., Ikeda, I. and Kritchevsky, D. (1997) Lymphatic recovery, tissue distribution, and metabolic effects of conjugated linoleic acid in rats. *Journal of Nutritional Biochemistry* 8, 38–43.

Sugano, M., Tsujita, A., Yamasaki, M., Noguchi, M. and Yamada, K. (1998) Conjugated linoleic acid modulates tissue levels of chemical mediators and immunoglobulins in rats. *Lipids* 33, 521–527.

Turek, J.J., Li, Y., Schoenlein, I.A., Allen, K.G.D. and Watkins, B.A. (1998) Modulation of macrophage cytokine production by conjugated linoleic acids is influenced by the dietary *n*-6 : *n*-3 fatty acid ratio. *Journal of Nutritional Biochemistry* 9, 258–266.

Wang, L. and Johnson, E.A. (1992) Inhibition of *Listeria monocytogenes* by fatty acids and monoglycerides. *Applied Environmental Microbiology* 58, 624–629.

Watkins, B.A. (1995) Biochemical and physiological aspects of polyunsaturates. *Poultry and Avian Biological Reviews* 6, 1–18.

Watkins, B.A., Toborek, M. and Hennig, B. (1996) Dietary fat and health. In: Hui, Y.H. (ed.), *Bailey's Industrial Oil and Fat Products*, 5th edn, Vol. 1. John Wiley & Sons, Inc., New York, pp. 159–214.

Watkins, B.A., Shen, C.-L., McMurtry, J.P., Xu, H., Bain, S.D., Allen, K.G.D. and Seifert, M.F. (1997) Dietary lipids modulate bone prostaglandin E_2 production, insulin-like growth factor-I concentration and formation rate in chicks. *Journal of Nutrition* 127, 1084–1091.

Wong, M.W., Chew, B.P., Wong, T.S., Hosick, H.L., Boylston, T.D. and Shultz, T.D. (1997) Effects of dietary conjugated linoleic acid on lymphocyte function and growth of mammary tumours in mice. *Anticancer Research* 17, 987–993.

Yurawecz, M., Hood, J.K., Mossoba, M.M., Roach J.A.G. and Ku, Y. (1995) Furan fatty acids determined as oxidation products of conjugated octadecadienoic acid. *Lipids* 30, 595–598.

Yurawecz, M.P., Roach, J.A.G., Sehat, N., Mossoba, M.M., Kramer, J.K.G., Fritsche, J., Steinhart, H. and Ku, Y. (1998) A new conjugated linoleic acid isomer 7 *trans*, 9 *cis*-octadecadienoic acid, in cow milk, cheese, beef, and human milk and adipose tissue. *Lipids* 33, 803–809.

Safe Use of Microalgae (DHA GOLD™) in Laying Hen Feed for the Production of DHA-Enriched Eggs

15

J.R. Abril, W.R. Barclay and P.G. Abril
Omega Tech Inc., Boulder, Colorado, USA

Dried *Schizochytrium* sp. microalgae produced by fermentation (DHA GOLD™) was evaluated for its safe use in the production of docosahexaenoic acid (DHA)-enriched eggs by laying hens. Eggs containing 2.5–5.0 times the DHA content of regular market eggs can be produced when 165 mg of DHA per hen day^{-1} is included in laying hen rations. In the present study, three concentrations of microalgae (0.86, 2.57 and 4.29% of ration) were fed to laying hens over a 4-month period. These concentrations provided 165, 495 and 825 mg of DHA per hen day^{-1}, respectively.

The results of the study indicated that increasing levels of DHA from 165 to 825 mg as DHA GOLD™ had no negative effects on any of the measured production parameters except for egg weight. At the highest level of DHA, eggs averaged about 1 g less in weight (56.6 versus 57.7 g) than control eggs. This was an expected result due to reduction in n-6 fatty acids, which positively influence egg size. Increasing concentrations of DHA in the form of DHA GOLD™ had positive effects on egg production (%), feed conversion (feed consumed per dozen eggs) and mean body weights. There were no significant differences between treatments in hen organ weights, haematological parameters or feathering scores. Histopathological examination of the hens at the end of the trial also indicated that no alterations could be observed in the tissues, which differentiated between treatment groups.

Overall, the results of the study indicated that DHA in the form of DHA GOLD™ is safe as a feed supplement for laying hens at up to 4.3% of feed rations.

Introduction

Over the past several years, numerous attempts have been made to produce docosahexaenoic acid (DHA)-enriched poultry eggs using feed ingredients such as flaxseed or fish oil per meal. Use of flaxseed, while relatively inexpensive, results primarily in enrichment of eggs with linolenic acid (18 : 3n-3), and DHA levels above 80 mg per egg are rarely observed (Van Elswyk, 1997). Use of fish oil and fish meal can result in higher DHA enrichment levels, but it has proven very difficult to produce eggs commercially with over 100 mg of DHA per egg without periodically running into significant sensory problems (Leskanich and Nobel, 1997). These observations have pointed to the need for a more stable source of ω-3 fatty acids for use in laying hen feed that is also specifically rich in DHA.

We developed a pure fermentation process for producing a DHA-rich microalgae-like microorganism, *Schizochytrium* sp., which can be used as a feed supplement (Barclay, 1992; Barclay *et al.*, 1994). Microalgae are the original source of DHA in the marine food chain. Previous research studies with DHA GOLD™ have indicated that this microalgal form of DHA is very stable in feed environments. It can be used readily to produce eggs with DHA levels at least up to 175 mg of DHA per egg without any organoleptic compromise (Abril and Barclay, 1998; Barclay *et al.*, 1998).

A study was conducted to demonstrate that this microalgal source of DHA is safe for use as a supplement in laying hen feed. Laying hens were fed the dried DHA-rich microalgae at approximately 1×, 3× and 5× the expected commercial dosage for 4 months, and egg production and fatty acid composition were monitored. Histopathological examinations and haematological analyses were conducted on the hens at the end of the feeding trial. The results of this safety trial are outlined below.

Materials and Methods

In this study, three levels of dried DHA-rich algae (DHA GOLD™), 0.86, 2.57 and 4.29% of ration, were used providing 165, 495 and 825 mg of DHA per hen day^{-1}. A control treatment was also included. The DHA content of the algae was 17.5% by weight (Table 15.1). The laying hens were fed these rations for a period of 4 months. All diets were made to meet NRC (National Research

Table 15.1. Fatty acid composition (% by weight of the algae) of DHA GOLD™ used in the safety trial.

Fatty acid	Average	SD
C14 : 0	4.22	0.26
C16 : 0	15.09	0.42
C16 : 1	0.14	0.05
C18 : 0	0.09	0.09
C18 : 1	0.05	0.10
C20 : 3	0.54	0.07
C20 : 5n-3	0.38	0.02
C22 : 5n-6	5.97	0.03
C22 : 6n-3	17.5	0.07

Council) requirements for poultry diets. The study was conducted at the PARC Institute (Easton, Maryland), following Food and Drug Administration (FDA) guidelines for both Redbook and GLC (Good Laboratory Practices).

Each treatment consisted of 64 laying hens divided into eight replicates (cages) per group for a total of 256 animals in the study (Table 15.2). As required by the FDA laying hen target animal safety protocols, all of the hens were pre-conditioned for 1 month prior to the start of the dosing period by feeding a basal commercial type layer feed. Body weights, food conversion, egg production, egg weight, shell thickness and interior quality were measured at the end of each of the 4 months during the dosing period. Eggs were also collected and analysed at the end of months 2 and 4 for their weight, shell thickness, interior egg quality and fatty acid profile.

At the end of the 4-month dosing period, terminal sacrifices were conducted and two randomly selected hens from each dose level and replicate were evaluated for haematological and histopathological changes. Haematological analyses included the following: red blood cell count, haematocrit, differential leucocyte count and haemoglobin. As dietary ω-3 fatty acids are known to decrease platelet reactivity, blood-clotting time was also determined. Gross necropsy was completed on all layers found dead during the trial or killed for scheduled evaluation. Weights were determined for the following organs: liver, kidney, heart, bursa of Fabricus, brain, spleen, thymus, bone marrow and ovaries. These tissues were also collected and preserved for histopathological examination. Feed samples, eggs and laying hen breast tissue samples were evaluated for fatty acid composition by gas chromatography. The consequences of the experimental diets were determined via statistical analysis of feed consumption/efficiency, egg production, egg weight, egg quality, body weight, organ weight and histopathology.

Results and Discussion

Analysis of the DHA content of the laying hen rations confirmed that the hens were fed a consistent, accurate dose of DHA in the form of DHA GOLD™ throughout the trial (Table 15.3).

The results also indicate that, in general, increasing additions (165–825 mg of DHA per hen day^{-1}) in the form of dried *Schizochytrium* sp. microalgae had no negative effects on any of the egg production parameters measured except

Table 15.2. Laying hen experimental design.

Treatment	Dose[a]	No. of replicates	No. of hens per replicate	Total
Control	0	8	8	64
Level 1	165	8	8	64
Level 2	495	8	8	64
Level 3	825	8	8	64
Total				256

[a]Dose in mg DHA hen^{-1} day^{-1}.

for egg weight. Eggs from hens in the highest treatment group were significantly different from those from the other three treatments, averaging about 1 g less in weight (56.6 versus 57.7 g). This is an expected effect on the basis of influence of long chain ω-3 fatty acids on the ω-6 fatty acid (arachidonic acid) content in the hens and eggs. In some instances poultry farmers increase the size of eggs produced by a flock by increasing the linoleic acid (C18 : 2*n*-6) content of the laying hen ration. March and MacMillan (1990) demonstrated that increasing dietary linoleic acid from 0.6 to 4.3% increased egg weight during the first 14 weeks of production. Increasing the DHA + eicosapentaenoic acid (EPA) content of laying hen rations leads to a linear decrease in the long chain ω-6 fatty acid content of the birds and their eggs through preferential incorporation into membrane phospholipids (Cossignani *et al.*, 1994; Damiani *et al.*, 1994). Therefore, it would be expected that egg size would be reduced. However, this effect was only observed at the highest DHA dose (825 mg per hen day^{-1}) evaluated in the present study.

On the other hand, increasing the concentration of DHA in the form of dried *Schizochytrium* sp. microalgae in the hens' rations had a positive effect on several egg production parameters (Table 15.4):

1. Egg production (%) was highest in the treatment group receiving the highest dose of DHA.
2. Feed conversion (feed consumed per dozen eggs) was lowest in the two treatment groups receiving the highest doses of DHA.

Table 15.3. Analysis of DHA content (% DHA GOLD™) of test feeds, for the 4-month duration of test and allowable tolerances.

Test	Average[a]	SD	HCL[b]	Expected	LCL[c]
Control	0	0	0	0	0
Level 1	0.87	0.04	1.16	0.93	0.7
Level 2	2.87	0.33	3.41	2.74	2.06
Level 3	4.11	0.41	5.70	4.57	3.44

[a]Average 4 months; [b]high control limit; [c]low control limit.

Table 15.4. Laying hen egg production parameters.

Treatment	Egg production (%)	Feed conversion
Control	78.96 ± 2.52[a]	2.76 ± 0.07[a]
Level 1	79.36 ± 2.07[a]	2.74 ± 0.03[ab]
Level 2	80.09 ± 1.61[ab]	2.69 ± 0.04[ab]
Level 3	81.84 ± 1.80[b]	2.69 ± 0.05[b]

Feed consumed (lbs) to produce one dozen eggs.
[a,b]Values bearing the same superscripts are not significantly different (*P* < 0.05).

3. The mean body weights of the hens measured on days 56 and 84 indicated that the hens in all treatment groups receiving DHA in the form of dried microalgae weighed significantly more (≈ 50 g) than the control hens.

4. Hens from all three treatment groups receiving DHA in the form of dried microalgae produced eggs that were significantly higher on the Minolta redness colour scale than the control treatment.

There was no significant negative effect of DHA in the form of dried *Schizochytrium* sp. microalgae on any of the other egg production and egg quality parameters measured (Table 15.5). Additionally, there were neither significant differences in any of the organ weights measured nor significant differences in the feathering score between any of the treatments. The results of the histopathological examination also indicated that no alterations could be observed in the tissues examined, which would differentiate between treatment groups. Interestingly, no development of fatty liver syndrome was noted in the hens fed the microalgal DHA. Hens fed elevated levels of fish oil do develop fatty livers (Van Elswyk *et al.*, 1994).

There were also no significant differences between treatments for any of the haematological analyses conducted. The average DHA concentrations in the eggs produced by the control, low, mid and high dose treatment groups (on day 55 of the study) were 27, 34, 170 and 220 mg per egg, respectively (Table 15.6). There were also no differences in the organoleptic quality of the eggs between any of the treatments.

The results of this safety trial indicate that dried *Schizochytrium* sp. microalgae produced by fermentation (DHA GOLD™) is safe for use as a supplement in laying hen feed when used at levels up to 4.3% of the feed. High

Table 15.5. Egg quality parameters.

Treatment	Egg shell thickness (in)	Albumen height (mm)	Roche colour fan	L/a/b[a]
Control	0.017	73.35	5.77	59.6/2.9/42.4
Level 1	0.017	72.32	5.90	58.1/3.1/41.4
Level 2	0.017	72.29	5.84	57.9/3.1/41.6
Level 3	0.017	72.14	5.83	59.3/3.1/42.1

[a]L, lightness; a, redness; b, yellowness.

Table 15.6. Egg DHA content.[a]

Treatment	mg of DHA egg[-1]
Control	26.6 ± 1.05
Level 1	134.4 ± 21.90
Level 2	170.3 ± 10.03
Level 3	220.0 ± 14.80

[a]Data are two replicate analyses for each set of pooled eggs from replicates 1–4 and from replicates 5–8.

quality, DHA-enriched eggs containing up to 220 mg of DHA per egg can be produced readily with this feed supplement without any of the sensory problems associated with other sources of ω-3 fatty acids.

References

Abril, R. and Barclay, W. (1998) Production of DHA enriched poultry eggs and meat using an algae-based feed ingredient. *World Review on Nutrition and Dietetics* 83, 77–88.

Barclay, W.R. (1992) Process for the heterotrophic production of microbial products with high concentrations of omega-3 highly unsaturated fatty acids. US Patent 5,130,242.

Barclay, W.R., Meager, K.M. and Abril, J.R. (1994) Heterotrophic production of long chain omega-3 fatty acids utilizing algae and algae-like microorganisms. *Journal of Applied Phycology* 6, 123–129.

Barclay, W., Abril, R., Abril, P., Weaver, C. and Ashford, A. (1998) Production of DHA from microalgae and its benefits for use in animal feeds. *World Review on Nutrition and Dietetics* 83, 61–76.

Cossignani, L., Santinclli, F., Rosi, M., Simonetti, M.S., Valfre, F. and Damiani, P. (1994) Incorporation of n-3 PUFA into hen egg yolk lipids. II: Structural analysis of triacylglycerols, phosphatidylcholines and phosphatidylethanolamines. *Italian Journal of Food Science* 3, 293–305.

Damiani, P., Cossignani, L., Simonetti, M.S., Santinelli, F., Castellini, M. and Valfre, F. (1994) Incorporation of n-3 PUFA into hen egg yolk lipids. I: Effect of fish oil on the lipid fractions of egg yolk and hen plasma. *Italian Journal of Food Science* 3, 275–292.

Leskanich, C.O. and Nobel, R.C. (1997) Manipulation of the *n*-3 polyunsaturated fatty acid composition of avian eggs and meat. *World's Poultry Science Journal* 53, 155–183.

March, B.E. and MacMillan, C. (1990) Linoleic acid as a mediator of egg size. *Poultry Science* 69, 634.

Van Elswyk M.E. (1997) Comparison of *n*-3 fatty acid sources in laying hen rations for improvement of whole egg nutritional quality: a review. *British Journal of Nutrition* 78 (Suppl. 1), S61–S69.

Van Elswyk, M.E., Hargis, B.M., Williams, J.D. and Hargis, P.S. (1994) Dietary menhaden oil contribution to hepatic lipidosis. *Poultry Science* 73, 653–662.

Ovo-Technologies

Molecular Modification of Egg Proteins for Functional Improvement

16

S. Nakai

Faculty of Agricultural Sciences, University of British Columbia, Vancouver, British Columbia, Canada

Modification of egg proteins conducted in our laboratory since 1992 and its related techniques are reviewed. A controlled Maillard reaction under atmospheric pressure to make a phosvitin–galactomannan conjugate improved antioxidant activity and emulsification properties. A high-pressure Maillard reaction to make a lysozyme–dextran conjugate was a new approach in obtaining the conjugate more quickly while maintaining high enzymatic activity. A simpler semi-continuous ultrafiltration than previously reported was proposed to isolate IgY from egg yolk on a pilot plant scale. Disulphide-reduced IgY was immobilized on a chitosan column through thioether linkages that enabled elution of adsorbed antigens under milder conditions than before and repeated use of the same immunoaffinity column. High level expression of cystatin C was feasible in *Pichia pastoris* resulting in oligomannosylation of the cystatin with increased thermostability and antimicrobial activity. Fabrication of cost-effective recombinant cystatin with high activity and stability with minimum allergenicity or side effects may be feasible by applying a novel computer-aided optimization technique to site-directed mutagenesis.

Introduction

We have previously reported the separation of IgY by filtration (Nakai *et al.*, 1994) and ion exchange (Fichtali *et al.*, 1994), as well as the preparation of phosvitin using salt extraction of delipidated granules (Losso and Nakai, 1994). Furthermore, the preparation of an antigen-binding Fab' fragment from IgY using a fungal proteinase was also reported (Akita and Nakai, 1994). In this chapter, we discuss the recent progress made in our laboratory. The topics covered in this chapter are all related to the modification of egg proteins to improve their functional properties. The discussion can be categorized into three groups, namely (i) glycosylation of ovalbumin, lysozyme and phosvitin by the Maillard reaction; (ii) separation and utilization of IgY, specifically in immunoaffinity chromatography; and (iii) maximum expression of cystatin in yeast and possible optimization of its functional properties by site-directed mutagenesis.

The major objective of this chapter was to discuss the recent advancement in modifying egg proteins and the prospect of potential technological development in the future. However, this review may be restricted as it is based mainly on the work conducted in our laboratory; therefore, it cannot avoid criticisms from researchers in different aspects of egg science. It is intended to stimulate arguments on the direction of egg research in the 21st century.

Glycosylation of Proteins by the Maillard Reaction

Glycosylation of proteins using a controlled Maillard reaction has become an important tool for improving the stability of protein molecules without affecting, or indeed even improving, the original functional properties of protein molecules. An advantage of glycosylation of proteins using the Maillard reaction is the mildness of the reaction without the need to use any coupling agents. The first most useful review work on the Maillard glycosylation may be that of Kato and Kobayashi (1991). Ovalbumin–dextran conjugate formation was compared using cyanogen bromide (CNBr)-activated dextran and the Maillard reaction. The resultant heat-stable conjugate demonstrated emulsifying properties superior to any commercial synthetic emulsifiers. This approach was also reported by Kato *et al.* (1994). Improvements not only in emulsifying properties, but also in gelling and foaming properties were observed. One remarkable discovery was the reactivity of the glycosylated lysozyme that was extended to Gram-negative bacteria.

Recently, phosvitin was also glycosylated in our laboratory, thereby improving its antioxidant activity (Nakamura *et al.*, 1998a), as shown in Fig. 16.1. Antioxidant activity was measured using a model system of linoleic acid exposed to air over the maximum at the surface area with and without ferrous ions. The phosvitin–galactomannan conjugate was shown to have slightly better antioxidant activity than a powder mixture in the absence of ferrous ions (Fig. 16.1A). However, the difference between mixture and conjugate is almost negligible in the presence of ferrous ions (Fig. 16.1B). An interesting finding was that upon autoclaving, phosvitin in the mixture decreased the antioxidant activity probably due to heat denaturation of the protein, whereas autoclaving did not affect the activity of the conjugate. Apparently, the glycosylation protected the phosvitin from heat denaturation, which could not be expected by simply blending phosvitin with galactomannan in powder form. A more remarkable discovery was the effect on emulsifying properties (Fig. 16.1C), when they were measured by the method of Pearce and Kinsella (1978). The mixture yielded less dispersed, less stable emulsions than those of the conjugate.

A new interpretation of the mechanism of enhanced protection and improved functionalities was introduced by Nakamura *et al.* (1998a). Based on

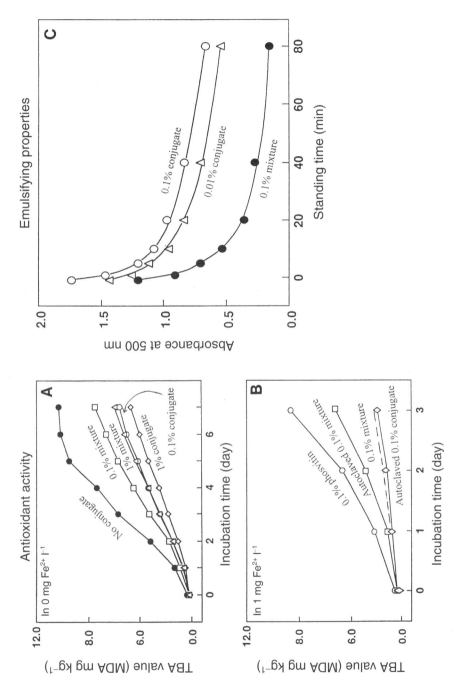

Fig. 16.1. Antioxidant and emulsifying properties of a phosvitin–galactomannan conjugate.

the 'polar paradox' theory of Porter *et al.* (1989), the powdered model system represents a bulk oil system; thus hydrophilic antioxidants, such as phosvitin, would locate at the air–oil interface, thereby preventing oxidation. As a result, there was not much difference in the antioxidant activity of phosvitin by mixing or conjugation. However, autoclaving of the mixture should have denatured the unprotected phosvitin, thus reducing the antioxidant activity of the mixture, while the conjugate was stable. In the case of emulsifying properties, not all of the mixture can remain at the water–oil interface because galactomannan is dispersible in water. However, in the case of conjugate, it is possible that the whole molecule would stay in the interface, thereby attracting more water molecules surrounding the oil droplets due to the hydrophilic properties of the galactomannan moiety. Furthermore, due to the long chain glycosidic groups in the conjugate, the surface viscosity may increase, thus resulting in further stabilization of the emulsion.

Despite a considerable improvement in the functional properties of proteins glycosylated by a controlled Maillard reaction, there is a drawback, which is the slow reaction requiring 1–2 weeks. Promotion of the Maillard reaction was achieved successfully by using high-pressure heating (Nakamura *et al.*, 1997). The remarkable increase in lysozyme activity to 200% was due to a decrease in the extent of heat denaturation, thereby maintaining high solubility of lysozyme. However, it has been reported that promotion of covalent bond formation under the conditions used in this study (60°C, 150 MPa, 1 h) cannot be expected (Balny and Masson, 1993). It is thus possible that the solubility increase caused by high-pressure treatment may be the main cause of the increase in activity, rather than solely glycosylation. If this approach is successful, immobilization of proteins on polysaccharide columns to use in affinity chromatography may be a potential application of this treatment as a new tool for separation techniques.

Isolation and Utilization of IgY

Every effort which has been made in our laboratory in the past was in order to reduce as much as possible the costs of isolation and utilization of IgY. This is especially important considering the application of the antibody for animal feeding. An ultrafiltration process for isolating IgY from egg yolk may constitute the simplest semi-continuous method, thus being most economical for IgY isolation. Based on the proposal that a sequential filtration system may be the most logical approach (Nakai *et al.*, 1994), we have developed an ultrafiltration (UF) system (Kim and Nakai, 1996). A scale-up of this method (Kim and Nakai, 1998) was conducted after the hydrophobic paper filtration was replaced with a solid-phase column and the tedious freeze–thaw process was discontinued. Briefly, the finally recommended process was: $10 \times$ diluted yolk (pH 5.0) $\rightarrow$ UF (250 kDa) $\rightarrow$ cellulose/C_{18} column $\rightarrow$ UF (30 kDa, pH 9.0, 1.5 M NaCl). Although it should depend on the combination of different UF membranes and systems, higher than 80% recovery with more than 90% purity can be expected using the new filtration system.

Immunoaffinity chromatography is one of the most powerful separation techniques, being capable of purifying up to 10,000-fold in a single pass process (Labrou and Clonis, 1994). However, the greatest obstacles in large-scale use of this chromatography with extremely high specificity are the costs of the affinity ligand as well as problems associated with elution of strongly bound antigens from the columns. Coupling of a disulphide-reduced IgY with chitosan gel through a thioether linkage was employed in our laboratory to construct an immobilized IgY column (Losso *et al.*, 1998). It was found that the extent of reducing IgY to create new SH groups was most critical in maintaining the highest antibody-binding activity during immobilization. Use of 2-mercaptoethylamine, which is milder than 2-mercaptoethanol, to yield a pair of single arms from the Y-shaped two arms of IgY was critical. More or less extensive reduction immediately affected the antigen-binding activity of the affinity column. Mild conditions (0.5 M glycine–HCl with 2 M NaCl at pH 4.6) required to elute antigens adsorbed to the column throughout repeated use of the same column could be a great advantage.

Bovine serum albumin (BSA) in cow's milk was eliminated using IgY affinity chromatography as it may be a cause of juvenile diabetes (Losso *et al.*, 1998). Over 97% of the BSA present originally was removed almost specifically from milk. The column could be regenerated more than 20 times with minimal loss of the affinity purification capacity.

Utilization of IgY for immunosupplementation has made obvious progress in animal feeding, as discussed in other chapters of this book, but it has not yet been fully established for human consumption. In order to promote its utilization for human diet supplementation, two problems may have to be solved, i.e. prevention of degradation in the stomach and possible allergenicity. For the former, Shimizu *et al.* (1993) developed an effective preventative method using liposome. We proposed a simpler gelatin–cellulose derivative coating for preventing degradation of IgY in the stomach (see Chapter 23). In terms of allergenicity, Akita *et al.* (1999) reported that the allergenicity of IgY was far below that of egg white proteins based on the passive cutaneous anaphylaxis reaction on rat skin.

Potential Utilization of Cystatins

High level expression of recombinant cystatins

Cystatin, an inhibitor of sulphydryl proteinases, was first isolated from egg white by Fossum and Whitaker (1968). Contrary to the general recognition of proteinase inhibitors as antinutrient factors, beneficial effects of these inhibitors have been reported after their long-term feeding (Kennedy, 1993). Since most proteases in muscles are sulphydryl proteinases, such as cathepsins B, H, L, M, S and N, involvement of cystatins in the function and malfunction of muscles is highly probable. The potential of their broad application in medical/biological treatments has been reported in the literature, such as antimicrobial (Bjorck *et al.*, 1990), antiviral (Ebina and Tsukada, 1991) and insecticidal effects (Koiwa *et al.*, 1998), and prevention of cerebral haemorrhage (Abrahamson *et al.*, 1988) and cancer cell metastasis (Colella *et al.*, 1993).

An advantage of cystatins compared with synthetic protease inhibitors currently in use in medical treatments is their less intensive side effects, as exemplified in treatments of human immunodeficiency virus (HIV)-positive patients. The greatest problem in utilizing cystatins for medical treatments is their high cost (US$140 egg cystatin mg^{-1}). Many papers have been published on the utilization of inhibitors for seryl-, aspartyl- and metallo-proteases in medical treatments; all of those are relatively inexpensive. In contrast, reports on cystatins are less frequent in the literature, probably because of extremely low contents of cystatins in natural resources despite their ubiquitous presence in both the animal and plant kingdoms. This fact makes the broad use of cystatins as chemopreventive agents prohibitive.

The first report of efficient production of human cystatin C from *Escherichia coli* was by Dalbøg *et al.* (1989). By fusing cystatin C complementary DNA (cDNA) to a DNA fragment encoding the signal peptide of the *E. coli* outer membrane protein A, it was possible to produce 180 mg of cystatin C l^{-1} in the periplasm during experiments carried out in 1.5–10 l fermentations. Yields higher than 1 g cystatin C l^{-1} were then obtained by initiating the product formation at 40°C for a couple of hours late in an optimized fermentation process.

We have compared mouse cystatin production between *Saccharomyces cerevisiae* and methylotrophic yeast *Pichia pastoris* (Nakamura *et al.*, 1998b), with yields of 1.3 and 110 mg l^{-1}, respectively. Table 16.1 shows the degree of polymerization (DP) of sugars in glycosylation obtained during fermentation. The DP of glycosylation of cystatin C from *S. cerevisiae* is much higher than that from *P. pastoris*, 310 versus 90, respectively. These results of high level expression of recombinant proteins are essential for broad utilization of this multifunctional protease inhibitor. Based on the fact that the cost of 1 l of culture media is less than US$1, it is reasonable to consider that the time is ripe for a large-scale commercial production of bioactive peptides and proteins by genetic engineering. This is frequently much cheaper than extraction from natural sources such as eggs.

The heat stability of differently glycosylated cystatin C was compared in Fig. 16.2 based on papain-inhibiting activity (Nakamura *et al.*, 1998b). Unglycosylated control with 100% activity is the least stable upon heating to 95°C, resulting in 97.5% destruction. In contrast, the cystatin glycosylated with

Table 16.1. Carbohydrate composition of oligo- and polymannosylated cystatins expressed in *S. cerevisiae* and *P. pastoris*.

		Degree of polymerization	
Glycosylation	Host yeast	*N*-acetylglucosamine	Mannose
Oligomannosylation	*S. cerevisiae*	2	13
	P. pastoris	2	13
Polymannosylation	*S. cerevisiae*	2	310
	P. pastoris	2	90

a DP of 310 (Cyst310) is most heat resistant, with a destruction of only 18%. However, this high polymannosylation simultaneously reduced the inhibitory activity by 81.5%. The best result was obtained with Cyst90 yielded from *P. pastoris*, maintaining 83.7% activity after 29% heat destruction.

Figure 16.3 shows our unpublished data on the antimicrobial activity of cystatins. Three cystatins, from human, egg white and rat, all equally prevented the growth of *Salmonella typhimurium*. However, glycosylation

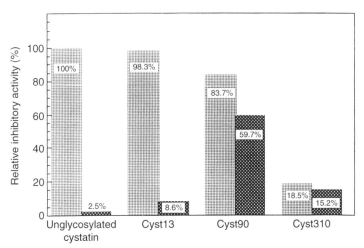

Fig. 16.2. Papain-inhibiting activity of recombinant mouse cystatin C before and after heating. The heating process was performed for a 0.1% solution in 50 mM sodium phosphate buffer, pH 7.5, by heating to 95°C at a rate of 1°C min^{-1} from 30°C. ▨ , unheated sample; ■ , heated sample.

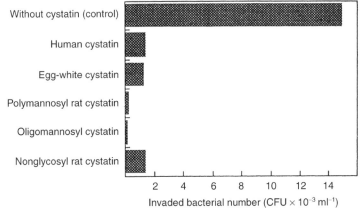

Fig. 16.3. Protective effect of cystatins on *Salmonella typhimuriun* invasion in the cultured epithelial cell line, CV-1. A total of 1×10^6 cells ml^{-1} of *S. typhimurium* were exposed to 1×10^5 cells ml^{-1} of CV-1 cells with 10 µg ml^{-1} cystatin. After a 2 h incubation at 37°C, the number of bacteria which had invaded the CV-1 cells was determined by the plate-MPN technique.

induced during production of cystatins from yeast further intensified the prevention of the *Salmonella* growth. Also, when we assessed the antiviral effect of cystatins against rotavirus, the viability of CV-1 cells infected with rotavirus was 10% of that without rotavirus. This reduced viability value was restored to 80% by adding cystatins after a 48-h incubation. However, the glycosylation of these cystatins did not affect their viability.

Figure 16.4 shows a comparison of the amino acid sequence of cystatins from egg white and human. All cystatins belong to family II of the cystatin superfamily consisting of approximately 115 amino acid residues with disulphide linkages and without glycosylation. Three parts of the inhibitor molecules are in close contact with the active cleft of papain: the N terminus containing a conserved glycine residue, the first hairpin containing the conserved active motif QXVXG, and a second hairpin loop at the C terminus containing a conserved tryptophan residue.

Cystatin M was reported for the first time by Sotiropoulou *et al.* (1997). Its loss of expression is probably associated with progression of a primary tumour to a metastatic phenotype. An inverse correlation between stefin A and malignant progression was observed by Calkins and Sloane (1995). Stefin A belongs to family I of the cystatin superfamily, with the shortest amino acid sequence of about 100 residues without any disulphide linkage and glycosidic chain. It is still unclear whether it is cystatin A (stefin), C (Colella *et al.*, 1993) or M which plays the major role in the mechanism of cancer cell metastasis.

Computer-aided optimization of site-directed mutagenesis

By combining a regulated random design, centroid search and mapping as a cycle, we have developed a new experimental global optimization technique for site-directed mutagenesis (Nakai *et al.*, 1998a). As the menu in Fig. 16.5 demonstrates, repeating the cycles will guide the search toward the optimum. The mapping plays an important role in finding the global optimum among local optima, if any. Table 16.2 shows a comparison of our random-centroid optimization (RCO) for experimental optimization with the computational optimization using the currently most advanced global optimization algorithms. Iterations, that are the number of times an experiment needs to be repeated in order to reach the optimum, are very different between our RCO and the computational optimization. Whenever working equations or response values of the experiments are unavailable, computers will provide the relationships between factor level and response, from which the optimum can be located very rapidly, even if it takes 10,000–50,000 iterations. However, this approach is prohibitive for slow, expensive experiments in the life sciences.

The RCO may, therefore, be useful in expensive, time-consuming biological experiments, such as site-directed mutagenesis. The RCO was modified for application to site-directed mutagenesis and named RCG, i.e. the RCO for genetic study (Nakai *et al.*, 1998b). For mutation of one site in the sequence each time, two factors are needed, i.e. the location of the mutation site in the sequence and the amino acid to replace the amino acid residue at the site selected. The optimum T_{50} (half-survival temperature) found was derived from

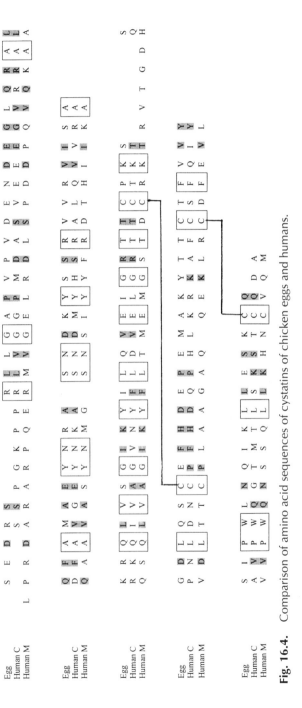

Fig. 16.4. Comparison of amino acid sequences of cystatins of chicken eggs and humans.

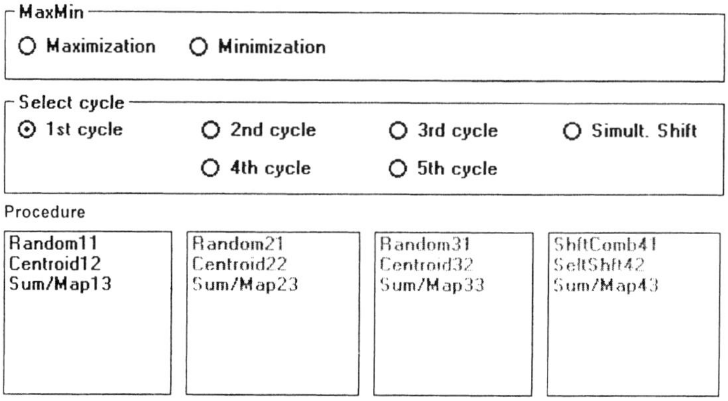

```
┌─ MaxMin ──────────────────────────────────────────────────────────┐
│  ⊙ Maximization    ○ Minimization                                  │
└────────────────────────────────────────────────────────────────────┘

┌─ Select cycle ────────────────────────────────────────────────────┐
│  ⊙ 1st cycle       ○ 2nd cycle      ○ 3rd cycle      ○ Simult. Shift│
│                    ○ 4th cycle      ○ 5th cycle                     │
└────────────────────────────────────────────────────────────────────┘

Procedure
┌──────────────┐ ┌──────────────┐ ┌──────────────┐ ┌──────────────┐
│ Random11     │ │ Random21     │ │ Random31     │ │ ShftComb41   │
│ Centroid12   │ │ Centroid22   │ │ Centroid32   │ │ SeltShft42   │
│ Sum/Map13    │ │ Sum/Map23    │ │ Sum/Map33    │ │ Sum/Map43    │
│              │ │              │ │              │ │              │
│              │ │              │ │              │ │              │
└──────────────┘ └──────────────┘ └──────────────┘ └──────────────┘
```

Fig. 16.5.   Menu of random-centroid optimization.

Table 16.2.   Optimization efficiency for multimodal functions.

	Random-centroid optimization[a]	Global optimization algorithms (level-set program[b], simulated annealing, genetic algorithm)
Class	Experimental	Computational
Working equation	No need	Need
Iterations required:		

Wood's function: $y = [100(x_2 - x_1^2)^2 + (1 - x_1)^2 + 90(x_4 - x_3^2)^2 + (1 - x_3)^2 + 10.1\{(x_2 - 1)^2 + (x_4 - 1)^2\}$
$+ 19.8(x_2 - 1)(x_4 - 1)] / 100 + 10$ (at least two minima)

	< 50	$50,824^b$

Heese's function: $y = -25(x_1 - 2)^2 - (x_2 - 2)^2 - (x_3 - 1)^2 - (x_4 - 4)^2 - (x_5 - 1)^2 - (x_6 - 4)^2 + 320$
(18 minima)

	< 50	$14,064^b$

From: [a]Nakai *et al.* (1998a); [b]Yassien (1993).

site-directed mutagenesis at the active site helix of *Bacillus stearothermophilus* neutral protease. Although it was still an incomplete optimization, we found an optimum after only 13 mutations (Nakai *et al.*, 1998b). Since a significant change in molecular structure cannot be expected from a one-site mutation, simultaneous two-site mutation experiments are under way in our laboratory.

It is possible, therefore, that the original function of peptides or proteins can be optimized or new functions can even be created in mutants using RCG. Examples of genetic optimization are the minimization of allergenicity or side effects and the maximization of preventative activity of cell invasion. An increase in the stability of protein molecules under extreme temperatures or pH may also be an important example of genetic optimization.

Introduction of efficient optimization techniques to improve functions of proteins, which can be produced cost-effectively using modern biotechnology, could certainly be the beginning of the new era of 'Biotechnological Invasions in Chemical Synthesis' (van Balken, 1997) in the next century. This would endorse the production of peptides or proteins of human origin to avoid allergenicity or side effects. Human lysozyme and cystatins could be new nutraceuticals in an attempt to prevent diseases through diet.

References

Abrahamson, M., Dalbøg, H., Olafsson, I., Carlsen, S. and Grugg, A. (1988) Efficient production of native, biologically active human cystatin C by *Escherichia coli*. *FEBS Letters* 236, 14–18.

Akita, E.M. and Nakai, S. (1994) Preparation and purification of Fab' immunoactive fragments from chicken egg immunoglobulin using pepsin and *Aspergillus saitoi* protease. In: Sim, J.S. and Nakai, S. (eds), *Egg Uses and Processing Technologies*. CAB International, Wallingford, UK, pp. 228–240.

Akita, E.M., Jang, C.B., Kitts, D.D. and Nakai, S. (1999) Evaluation of allergenicity of egg yolk immunoglobulin Y and other egg proteins by passive cutaneous anaphylaxis. *Food and Agricultural Immunology* 11, 191–201.

Balny, C. and Masson, P. (1993) Effects of high pressure on proteins. *Food Review International* 9, 611–628.

Bjorck, L., Akesson, P., Bohus, M., Trojnar, J., Abrahamson, M., Olafsson, I. and Gribb, A. (1990) Bacterial growth blocked by a synthetic peptide based on the structure of a human protease inhibitor. *Nature* 337, 385–386.

Calkins, C.C. and Sloane, B. (1995) Mammalian cysteine proteases inhibitor: biochemical properties and possible roles in tumor progression. *Biological Chemistry, Hoppe-Seyler* 376, 71–80.

Colella, R., Chambers, A.N. and Denhardt, D.T. (1993) Anticarcinogenic activities of naturally occurring cysteine proteinase inhibitors. In: Troll, W. and Kennedy, A.R. (eds), *Protease Inhibitors as Cancer Chemopreventive Agents*. Plenum Press, New York, pp. 199–216.

Dalbøg, H., Jensen, E.B., Tøttrup, H., Grubb, A., Abrahamson, M., Olafsson, I. and Carlsen, S. (1989) High-level expression of active human cystatin C in *Escherichia coli*. *Gene* 79, 325–332.

Ebina, T. and Tsukada, K. (1991) Protease inhibitors prevent the development of human rotavirus-induced diarrhea in suckling mice. *Microbiology and Immunology* 35, 583–588.

Fichtali, J., Charter, E.A., Lo, K.V. and Nakai, S. (1994) A new process for IgY isolation from industrially separated egg yolk including automation and scale-up. In: Sim, J.S. and Nakai, S. (eds), *Egg Uses and Processing Technologies*. CAB International, Wallingford, UK, pp. 213–227.

Fossum, K. and Whitaker, J.R. (1968) Ficin and papain inhibitor from chicken egg white. *Archives of Biochemistry and Biophysics* 125, 367–375.

Kato, A., Ibrahim, H.R., Nakamura, S. and Kobayashi, K. (1994) New methods for improving the functionality of egg white proteins. In: Sim, J.S. and Nakai, S. (eds), *Egg Uses and Processing Technologies*. CAB International, Wallingford, UK, pp. 250–268.

Kato, A. and Kobayashi, K. (1991) Excellent emulsifying properties of protein-dextran conjugates. In: El-Nokaly, M. and Cornell, D. (eds), *Microemulsions and Emulsions in Foods*. American Chemical Society, Washington, DC, pp. 213–229.

Kennedy, A.R. (1993) Anticarcinogenic activity of protease inhibitors. In: Troll, W. and Kennedy, A.R. (eds), *Protease Inhibitors as Cancer Chemopreventive Agents*. Plenum Press, New York, pp. 9–64.

Kim, H. and Nakai, S. (1996) Immunoglobulin separation from egg yolk: a serial filtration system. *Journal of Food Science* 61, 510–512, 523.

Kim, H. and Nakai, S. (1998) Simple separation of immunoglobulin from egg yolk by ultrafiltration. *Journal of Food Science* 63, 485–490.

Koiwa, H., Shade, R.E., Zhu-Salzman, K., Subramanian, L., Murdock, L.L., Nielsen, S.S., Bressan, R.A. and Hasegawa, P.M. (1998) Phage display selection can differentiate insecticidal activity of soybean cystatins. *Plant Journal* 14, 371–379.

Labrou, N. and Clonis, Y.D. (1994) The affinity technology in downstream processing. *Journal of Biotechnology* 36, 95–119.

Losso, J.N. and Nakai, S. (1994) A simple procedure for the isolation of phosvitin from chicken egg yolk. In: Sim, J.S. and Nakai, S. (eds), *Egg Uses and Processing Technologies*. CAB International, Wallingford, UK, pp. 150–157.

Losso, J.N., Vanderstoep, J. and Nakai, S. (1998) Removal of bovine serum albumin from cow's milk using chicken egg-yolk antibodies immobilized on chitosan gel. *Food and Agricultural Immunology* 10, 47–56.

Nakai, S., Li-Chan, E. and Lo, K.V. (1994) Separation of immunoglobulin from egg yolk. In: Sim, J.S. and Nakai, S. (eds), *Egg Uses and Processing Technologies*. CAB International, Wallingford, UK, pp. 94–105.

Nakai, S., Dou, J., Lo, K.V. and Scaman, C.H. (1998a) Optimization of site-directed mutagenesis. 1. A new random-centroid optimization program for Windows useful in research and development. *Journal of Agricultural and Food Chemistry* 46, 1642–1654.

Nakai, S., Nakamura, S. and Scaman, C.H. (1998b) Optimization of site-directed mutagenesis. 2. Application of random-centroid optimization to one-site mutation of *B. stearothermophilus* neutral protease to improve thermostability. *Journal of Agricultural and Food Chemistry* 46, 1655–1661.

Nakamura, S., Kato, A. and Kobayashi, K. (1991). New anitmicrobial characteristics of lysozyme–dextran conjugate. *Journal of Agricultural and Food Chemistry* 39, 647–650.

Nakamura, K., Furukawa, N., Matsuoka, A., Takahashi, T. and Yamanaka, Y. (1997) Enzyme activity of lysozyme–dextran complex prepared by high-pressure treatment. *Food Science and Technology International, Tokyo* 3, 235–238.

Nakamura, S., Ogawa, M., Nakai, S., Kato, A. and Kitts, D.D. (1998a) Antioxidant activity of a Maillard-type phosvitin–galactomannan conjugate with high emulsifying activity and heat stability. *Journal of Agricultural and Food Chemistry* 46, 3958–3963.

Nakamura, S., Ogawa, M. and Nakai, S. (1998b) Effects of polymannosylation of recombinant cystatin C in yeast on its stability and activity. *Journal of Agricultural and Food Chemistry* 46, 2882–2887.

Pearce, K.M. and Kinsella, J.E. (1978) Emulsifying properties of proteins: evaluation of a turbidimetric technique. *Journal of Agricultural and Food Chemistry* 26, 716–723.

Porter, W.L., Black, E.D. and Drolet, A.M. (1989) Use of polyamide oxidative fluorescence test on lipid emulsion: contrast in relative effectiveness of antioxidants in bulk versus dispersed systems. *Journal of Agricultural and Food Chemistry* 37, 615–624.

Shimizu, M., Miwa, Y., Hashimoto, K. and Goto, A. (1993) Encapsulation of chicken egg yolk immunoglobulin G (IgY) by liposomes. *Bioscience, Biotechnology and Biochemistry* 57, 1445–1449.

Sotiropoulou, G. Anisowicz, A. and Sager, R. (1997) Identification, cloning, and characterization of cystatin M, a novel cysteine proteinase inhibitor, down-regulated in breast cancer. *Journal of Biological Chemistry* 272, 903–910.

van Balken, J.A.M. (ed.) (1997) *Biotechnology Invades Chemistry*. Butterworth Heinemann, UK.

Yassien, H.A. (1993) A level set global optimization method for nonlinear engineering problems. PhD Thesis, University of British Columbia, Vancouver, British Columbia, Canada.

Bioavailability and Commercial Use of Eggshell Calcium, Membrane Proteins and Yolk Lecithin Products

17

N. Suguro, S. Horiike, Y. Masuda, M. Kunou
and T. Kokubu
R & D Division of Q.P. Corporation, Tokyo, Japan

We have investigated the use of eggshells as a dietary source of calcium and developed eggshell powders refined hygienically and ground into edible, microfine powders. Eggshell calcium (i.e. powdered eggshell) was shown to have higher absorptivity and availability in mature male rats than those of calcium carbonate. Also, eggshell calcium was more effective in increasing bone mineral density in ovariectomized osteoporotic rats. In addition, eggshell calcium was investigated for use as an oral phosphate binder (OPB). Thus far, calcium carbonate has been the most widely used OPB for the treatment of hyperphosphataemia in haemodialysis patients. We found that eggshell calcium was more efficient as an OPB when compared with calcium carbonate. The advantage of eggshell calcium is probably due to the porous structure and trace proteins found in eggshells. We have found that egg membrane protein adheres to and grows human skin fibroblasts and increases their production of type III collagen, which is rich in the skin of infants, presumably softening the skin. This egg membrane protein is being used as an ingredient of many cosmetics. Furthermore, egg yolk lecithin is a rich source of phosphatidylcholine (PC), which is a major phospholipid component of the cellular membrane. PC also serves as a precursor of acetylcholine, a neurotransmitter. We have found that egg PC in conjunction with vitamin B_{12} may slow the progress of or even prevent Alzheimer's disease.

Introduction

Approximately 2,500,000 tons of eggs per year are used in Japan, 44% of which (1,100,000 tons) are consumed by the industry and restaurants. At Q.P. Corporation and its subsidiaries, about 190,000 tons of eggs per year are processed, i.e. more than 7.5% of the eggs used in Japan (without including imported eggs). Although Q.P. Corporation produces and markets mainly mayonnaise,

© CAB *International* 2000. *Egg Nutrition and Biotechnology*
(eds J.S. Sim, S. Nakai and W. Guenter)

dressings and other condiments, it also manufactures a wide variety of canned foods and health foods as well as bulk egg products and fine chemicals. Q.P. Corporation has also investigated effective uses of egg by-products and waste.

The objectives of this chapter are to discuss our investigation and utilization of egg by-products, eggshell and egg membrane, and to report the results of our recent study on the effect of egg yolk lecithin in conjunction with vitamin B_{12} on Alzheimer's disease.

Utilization of Eggshell Calcium

Eggshell production

As the food industry uses large quantities of eggs, eggshell disposal poses a significant challenge to the industry in this time of increasing awareness of environmental safety. At Q.P. Corporation, the majority of egg waste comes from eggshells, and more than 17,000 tons of eggshells are produced every year. Rather than disposal, practical utilization of eggshells has been investigated, particularly as a dietary source of calcium (Ca). At Q.P. Corporation, about 10% of eggshells are processed for food, 60% are used as fertilizer or feed, while the rest ($\approx 30\%$) are disposed of.

Eggshell powders

Eggshells are processed for food as eggshell powders, refined hygienically and ground into edible, fine powders. Figure 17.1 shows the manufacturing process for eggshell powders. After whole eggs are washed and cracked, the egg yolk and white are separated from them. The eggshell and eggshell membrane are collected, further ground, and washed with water to remove the membrane. The eggshells are then dried and ground again into fine powders. This process yields eggshell powders, which are referred to as eggshell Ca.

Table 17.1 shows the chemical composition of eggshell Ca. There is as much as 37.7% Ca in eggshell Ca. Therefore, the addition of only a small amount of eggshell Ca is sufficient to fortify foods with Ca. Further, eggshell Ca has a low phosphorus (P) content. The ideal Ca : P intake ratio in daily foods is thought to be 1 : 1. However, studies have shown that while P intake is currently sufficient, Ca deficiency prevails, and the excessive intake of P is undesirable (Ministry of Health and Welfare, 1994). Furthermore, Ca-fortifying agents from fish or animal bone contain large quantities of P as well as Ca, but eggshell Ca contains only approximately 100 mg% P. The major component of eggshell Ca is Ca carbonate. In addition, eggshell Ca contains other minerals, such as potassium, sodium and magnesium, and some protein.

Figure 17.2 shows electron micrographs of both Ca carbonate and eggshell Ca. While chemically synthetic Ca carbonate has a flat surface, eggshell Ca has a porous structure.

Calcium intake in Japan

In Japan, insufficient Ca intake is a serious nutritional problem, which may be closely related to the frequent incidence of osteoporosis among the elderly.

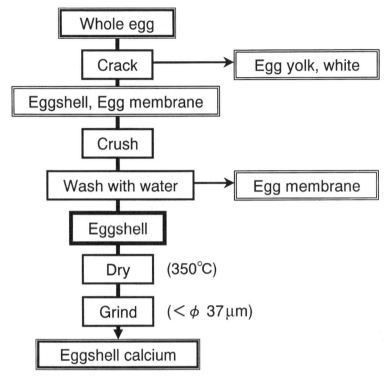

Fig. 17.1. Manufacturing process for eggshell powders (eggshell calcium).

Table 17.1. Chemical composition of eggshell calcium.

Water	0.5%
Protein	3.2%
Ash	95.3%
Ca	37.7%
K	41.4 mg%
Na	96.4 mg%
P	106.0 mg%
Fe	1.6 mg%
Mg	376.0 mg%
Pb	< 0.07 p.p.m.

Whereas the intake of most nutrients has been sufficient in Japan, the Ca intake has never been adequate. According to the National Nutrition Survey (Ministry of Health and Welfare, 1997), Ca intake in the latest survey in 1995 was approximately 585 mg per capita day^{-1}, which has not changed since 1970. The Japanese Recommended Dietary Allowance (RDA) of Ca for adults (above 19 years old, either male or female) is 600 mg (Ministry of Health and Welfare, 1994). Therefore, Ca intake still remains below the daily require-ments. It is worth noting that the RDA of Ca in Japan is lower than those of

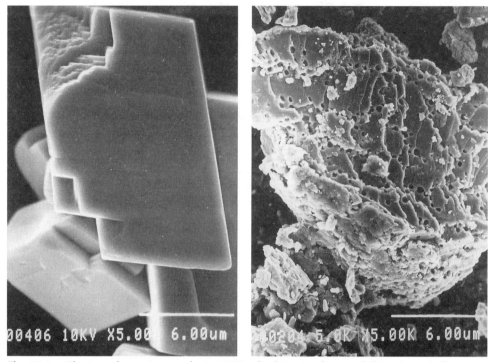

Fig. 17.2.   Electron photomicrographs (× 5000) of calcium carbonate (left) and eggshell calcium (right).

other countries. For example, while the RDA of Ca for an adult male is 600 mg in Japan, it is 800 and 1000 mg in Canada and the USA, respectively. Recently, it is suggested that the RDA of Ca be increased above 600 mg to prevent osteoporosis in Japan. These results may suggest that an adequate intake of Ca from the ordinary Japanese diet is extremely difficult. Therefore, it is recommended to add foods fortified with eggshell Ca to the Japanese diet.

Absorptivity of eggshell calcium

As a nutraceutical, eggshell Ca has shown a higher absorptivity than Ca carbonate in mature male rats (Goto *et al.*, 1981). Figure 17.3 shows the results of rat-based comparisons of absorptivity between eggshell powder and Ca carbonate. Three sources of Ca, namely Ca carbonate, coarse eggshell powder (retained by 5-mesh sieve) and fine eggshell powder (eggshell Ca) were tested for absorptivity in Wistar rats during the growth or maturation period. Although there were no differences in absorptivity during the growth period, during maturation, when absorptivity declines, eggshell powders were superior to Ca carbonate in absorptivity. Other studies in pregnant rats also showed similar results, with the absorption rate of eggshell Ca being higher than that of Ca carbonate (Niiyama and Sakamoto, 1984).

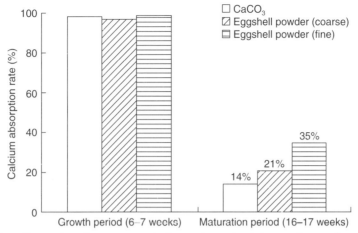

Fig. 17.3. Comparison between eggshell powder and calcium carbonate for absorptivity in male rats. (From Goto *et al.*, 1981.)

Effect of eggshell calcium on bone mineral density in ovariectomized rats

It was reported recently that eggshell Ca was effective in increasing bone mineral density (BMD) in ovariectomized osteoporotic rats (Omi and Ezawa, 1998). Those experiments were performed as follows: 6-week-old Sprague–Dawley female rats were ovariectomized, and then divided into two groups: a Ca carbonate group and an eggshell Ca group. Both diets contained 0.3% Ca from either Ca carbonate or eggshell Ca as the Ca source. The duration of the experiment was 57 days. At the end of the experiment, the serum samples, the lumbar spine, the tibiae and the femurs were collected. The BMD of both proximal metaphysis and diaphysis of the tibia as well as the lumbar spine were measured using dual-energy X-ray absorptiometry. Breaking force and energy for the extracted femur were examined using a dynagraph of bone strength.

There were no significant differences in body weight gain, food intake or food efficiency between the two groups. The biochemical data of serum, such as Ca and P, were also normal for both groups. However, significant differences were observed between the two groups in the BMD. The BMD of the lumbar spine for the eggshell Ca group was significantly greater than that of the Ca carbonate group (Fig. 17.4). The BMD of the tibial proximal metaphysis was also significantly higher in the eggshell Ca group. A tendency towards a higher BMD of the tibial diaphysis was also observed for the eggshell Ca group. These data suggest that eggshell Ca could be effective in preventing bone loss.

Nutraceutical effects of eggshell calcium

The nutraceutical uses of eggshell Ca and its perception as a natural source of Ca have been exploited in fortification of a variety of food products including breads and confectioneries. Q.P. Corporation has manufactured eggshell

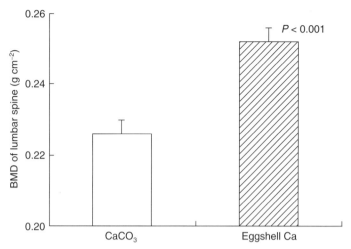

Fig. 17.4. The effect of eggshell calcium in bone mineral density of extracted lumbar spine in ovariectomized rats. (From Omi and Ezawa, 1998.)

Ca-enriched products, e.g. Ca condiments for rice, Ca-fortified rice crackers, confectioneries and fruit juice drinks. We also market eggshell Ca as a raw material to other food processing companies, with steadily increasing sales.

Use of eggshell calcium as an oral phosphate binder

Another use for eggshell Ca that has been investigated recently is as an oral phosphate binder (OPB). Patients suffering from renal failure often require haemodialysis. However, this is insufficient to remove serum P properly. As a result, hyperphosphataemia often occurs. One way to prevent hyperphosphataemia is the intake of low phosphate diets. However, proper regulation is difficult, and OPBs are used to obstruct the intestinal absorption of phosphate in diets. Thus far, Ca carbonate has been the most widely used OPB (Slatopolsky *et al.*, 1986). However, when compared with Ca carbonate, recent studies have shown a greater efficiency of eggshell Ca in lowering the serum P level without causing the serum Ca concentrations to increase (Ogihara *et al.*, 1996).

For some patients, Ca carbonate administration is insufficient to lower serum P, particularly those patients using gastric inhibitory agents, e.g. H_2-blockers (Takahashi *et al.*, 1995). On the other hand, improvements were observed in serum P concentration when the patients were administered eggshell Ca. Table 17.2 shows the effects of eggshell Ca as the OPB in H_2-blocker-treated patients (Ogihara *et al.*, 1996). In non-H_2-blocker patients, both Ca carbonate and eggshell Ca were equally effective in decreasing serum P. However, in H_2-blocker-treated patients, Ca carbonate produced only a slight decrease in serum P concentrations while eggshell Ca decreased them to levels seen in non-H_2-blocker-treated patients. Currently, studies are under way to replicate these findings on a larger scale.

Table 17.2.   The effects of eggshell calcium as a phosphate binder under H_2-blocker administration.

	Non-H_2-blocker patients		H_2-blocker patients	
	$CaCO_3$ (%)	Eggshell Ca (%)	$CaCO_3$ (%)	Eggshell Ca (%)
Change of serum P	−15.6	−18.5	−5.3	−17.7
Change of serum Ca	+4.3	+2.1	+6.3	+3.4

Patients: non-H_2-blocker ($n = 14$), H_2-blocker ($n = 24$). Phosphate binder: $CaCO_3$ or eggshell Ca (3.0 g day^{-1}). Experimental period: 4 weeks.
From: Ogihara *et al.*, 1996.

Mechanisms underlying the effects of eggshell calcium

Although the mechanisms underlying the beneficial effects of eggshell Ca are unclear, they may be related to the porous structure and trace proteins found in eggshells. Research is being undertaken to help elucidate the mechanisms and function of eggshell Ca.

Utilization of Egg Membrane Proteins

Egg membrane is also generally considered an egg waste. Egg membrane has been thought to be beneficial in the treatment of some injuries. For example, in Japan, when Sumo wrestlers get flesh abrasions, they will often peel the egg membrane from the eggshell and cover their injuries. They believe that this facilitates their recovery.

Protein products have been prepared from hydrolysed egg membrane, which is stable in water for easy industrial use. The effects of this egg membrane protein have been studied on cell growth. Egg membrane protein-coated dishes were first prepared by pouring the egg membrane protein solution into cell suspension culture dishes, which were then allowed to dry. Normal human skin fibroblasts were then cultured in these dishes. Untreated dishes (i.e. cell suspension culture dishes) were insufficient for human skin fibroblast growth. However, human skin fibroblasts did grow in tissue culture dishes. The dishes coated with soluble egg membrane protein at 0.1, 1, 10 and 100 µg cm^{-2} also allowed the cells to grow similarly to or more than tissue culture dishes (Fig. 17.5).

The effects of egg membrane protein on cell growth were also assessed over time. Compared with untreated dishes (i.e. cell suspension culture dishes), tissue culture dishes and egg membrane protein-coated dishes promoted growth of human skin fibroblasts. With egg membrane protein-coated dishes, this effect appeared to be related to the egg membrane protein concentration, with greater cell growth at higher concentrations (Fig. 17.6).

The quantities of collagen were compared in the egg membrane protein-coated dishes and tissue culture dishes. Human skin fibroblasts produce collagen, and type III collagen is rich in the skin of infants, being considered to soften skin (Hata, 1986). Table 17.3 shows that the type III collagen ratio

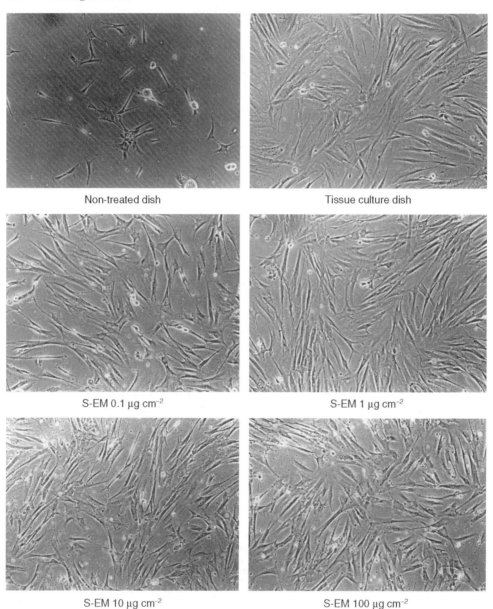

Non-treated dish

Tissue culture dish

S-EM 0.1 µg cm^{-2}

S-EM 1 µg cm^{-2}

S-EM 10 µg cm^{-2}

S-EM 100 µg cm^{-2}

Fig. 17.5. Cell culture on dishes coated with various amounts of soluble egg membrane (S-EM) protein (× 120).

using egg membrane protein-coated dishes was around 9.3%, while the ratio using tissue culture dishes was only about 7.6%. These results suggest that egg membrane protein tends to allow growth of human skin fibroblasts and may facilitate their production of type III collagen.

This egg membrane protein is currently being used as a raw material in many cosmetics and toiletries for its emollient properties.

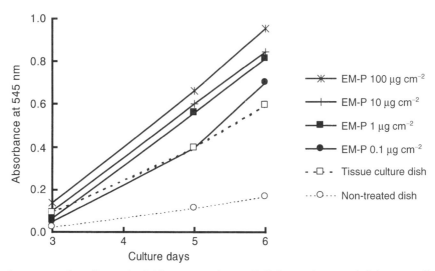

Fig. 17.6. The effects of soluble egg membrane (S-EM) protein-coated dishes on cell growth over time. Cell: human skin fibroblasts. Medium: DMEM + 10% FCS. Beginning cell number: 1×10^3 per well. Stain: crystal violet method.

Table 17.3. Amount of collagen produced by human fibroblasts.

Dishes	Total collagen (I + III) (c.p.m. 10^{-5} cells)	Type III collagen ratio (III : I + III) (%)
Egg membrane-coated dish	4039 ± 209	9.28 ± 0.65
Tissue culture dish	3932 ± 25	7.59 ± 0.26

Utilization of Yolk Lecithin

Egg phosphatidylcholine and its neuronal involvement in the brain

The lipid portion of the egg contains 30% phospholipids (PL), known as egg yolk lecithin. Phosphatidylcholine (PC) accounts for approximately 84% of these PL. A number of lecithin products have been developed after extracting from egg yolk.

Choline derived from PC by breakdown is a precursor of acetylcholine (AC), which has neuronal involvement in the brain (Canty and Zeisel, 1994). Choline thus produced is then taken up into the neurons. There, AC is synthesized from choline by the action of choline acetyltransferase. It has been suggested that vitamin B_{12} catalyses the synthesis of AC (Nadeau and Roberge, 1988). AC is released as a neurotransmitter and binds to the postsynaptic receptor. One important function of AC is concerned with learning and memory. Alzheimer's disease (AD) is a progressive neurodegenerative disease which is the major cause of severe dementia and is now one of the leading causes of death. It is characterized by a number of structural as well as neuropharmacological changes, some of which include a reduction of AC, cholinergic neuronal loss and a decrease in the activity of choline acetyl-transferase.

A number of studies have investigated the therapeutic effect of PC in AD, but have met with little success (Bartus *et al.*, 1982; Dysken, 1987). These studies administered soybean PL, however, which has a different fatty acid composition from that of egg yolk PL (Sanada *et al.*, 1997). As mentioned earlier, vitamin B_{12} may promote the synthesis of AC from choline. Therefore, the effects of egg PC in conjunction with vitamin B_{12} on performance have been investigated in an animal model with memory impairment.

Memory improvement in rats

Rats with nucleus basalis magnocellularis (NBM) lesions have been used as an animal model with memory impairment. These lesions induce memory deficits in the Morris water maze task. The effects of egg PC in conjunction with vitamin B_{12} were investigated on the performance of those rats in the Morris water maze task, and on AC concentrations in the brain (Masuda *et al.*, 1998). Male Wistar rats, 13 weeks old at the time of surgery, were given NBM lesions by the injection of 30 nmol of ibotenic acid neurotoxin. Sham-operated controls were injected with phosphate-buffered saline.

Each day, rats received intragastric administration of 10 g kg^{-1} of egg yolk PC, 1 mg kg^{-1} of vitamin B_{12}, or the combination of 2.5 g kg^{-1} of egg yolk PC and 0.025 mg kg^{-1} of vitamin B_{12} for 18 days following surgery. The Morris water maze is a behavioural test thought to assess spatial learning and memory and consists of a circular pool divided into four equal quadrants. During training, rats were placed in the pool and required to swim to locate a submerged platform. Following training, a spatial probe test was given in which the platform was removed and the rats were allowed to swim for 60 s. The amount of time that the rat spent swimming in the quadrant where the platform had been located during training was measured.

Memory retention was significantly impaired in NBM-lesioned control rats compared with sham-operated controls (Fig. 17.7). Neither vitamin B_{12} nor egg PC alone was sufficient to influence memory impairment. However, egg PC in conjunction with vitamin B_{12} significantly improved memory retention in NBM-lesioned rats. Figure 17.8 shows AC concentrations in the frontal cortex from each experimental group. The NBM-lesioned group had lower AC levels than sham-operated controls. Similar to the results of behavioural testing, the combination treatment of egg PC and vitamin B_{12} significantly increased AC levels in the frontal cortex of NBM-lesioned rats. Although the mechanisms are unclear, these results suggest that egg PC in conjunction with vitamin B_{12} improves the memory deficits of NBM-lesioned rats through its action on the cholinergic neurons.

Alzheimer's disease improvement in humans

The clinical benefits of this new combination therapy have been assessed in patients with AD (Sanada *et al.*, 1997). Seventeen patients (Box 17.1) with mild to moderate AD were orally administered supplements containing 10 g of egg

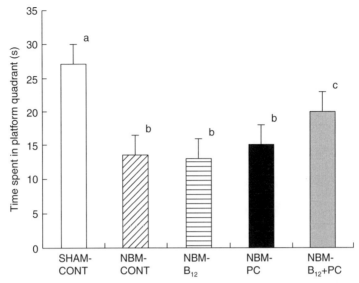

Fig. 17.7. Effect of egg phosphatidylcholine in conjunction with vitamin B_{12} on memory retention in NBM-lesioned rat. Different superscripts indicate significant differences. (From Masuda *et al.*, 1998.)

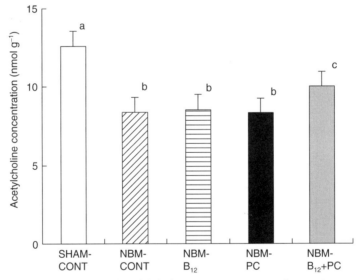

Fig. 17.8. Effect of egg phosphatidylcholine in conjunction with vitamin B_{12} on acetylcholine concentrations in frontal cortex in NBM-lesioned rat. Different superscripts indicate significant differences. (From Masuda *et al.*, 1998.)

PC and 100 μg of vitamin B_{12} daily for 12 weeks. To examine intellectual and mental function, subjects were administered a variety of examinations. Mental function impairment scale (MENFIS) is the test established in Japan to assess cognitive and mental function in clinical experiments. Serum choline and vitamin B_{12} levels were also measured.

The serum choline and vitamin B_{12} concentrations significantly increased after 4 weeks (Fig. 17.9). With regard to mental examinations, the revised Hasegawa's dementia scale (HDSR) score, mini-mental state examination (MMSE) score and Alzheimer's disease assessment scale (ADAS) did not change significantly; however, the MENFIS total score was significantly improved after 8 and 12 weeks (Fig. 17.10). Although modest, these

---

Box 17.1.   Experimental design of egg phosphatidylcholine in conjunction with vitamin B_{12} on patients with dementia of Alzheimer type: patient data and methods.

Baseline data of patients: $n = 17$ (male 4, female 13)
   Mean age 74.0 ± 2.4 years
   Severity of dementia, FAST stage
      Stage 4 $n = 12$
      Stage 5 $n = 4$
      Stage 6 $n = 1$
Supplement: 10 g of egg PC and 100 μg of vitamin B_{12} per day
Experimental period: 12 weeks
Test to examine intellectual and mental function
   HDSR: revised Hasegawa's dementia scale
   MMSE: mini-mental state examination
   ADAS: Alzheimer's disease assessment scale
   MENFIS: mental function impairment scale
Biochemical analysis: serum choline, vitamin B_{12} (pre- and every 4 weeks)

Source: Sanada *et al.*, 1997.

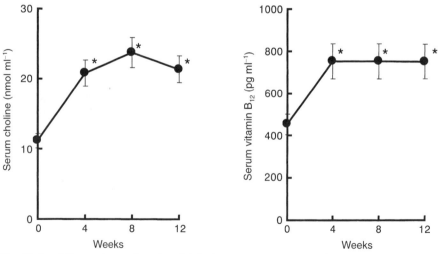

Fig. 17.9.   Effects of egg phosphatidylcholine in conjunction with vitamin B_{12} on patients with dementia of Alzheimer type: serum choline and vitamin B_{12} concentrations. *$P < 0.01$ versus week 0. (From Sanada *et al.*, 1997.)

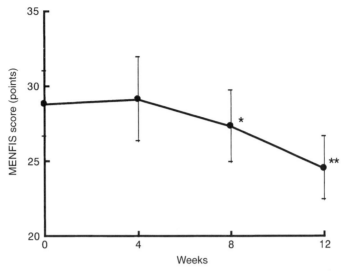

Fig. 17.10.   Effects of egg phosphatidylcholine in conjunction with vitamin B_{12} on patients with dementia of Alzheimer type: changes in MENFIS. *$P < 0.05$, **$P < 0.01$ versus week 0. (From Sanada *et al.*, 1997.)

preliminary results suggest that a combination therapy of egg PC and vitamin B_{12} may have a certain clinical value for AD, thus suggesting the requirement for clinical trials of this therapy on a large scale with appropriate controls. Further study is needed to clarify the precise mechanism underlying these benefits.

Although some drugs, which have been approved by the Food and Drug Administration in the USA, have been partially beneficial in AD, they have some side effects. On the other hand, substances extracted from ordinary foods seem to be the safest candidates. Both egg PC and vitamin B_{12} are derived from ordinary foods and, in our study, produced no obvious side effects (Masuda *et al.*, 1998), and did not seem to be harmful for extended use. Q.P. Corporation now has a food supplement containing egg PC and vitamin B_{12} on the retail market.

Conclusions

Through the research and development of various egg nutraceuticals, we are firmly committed to the promotion and maintenance of health. Furthermore, the utilization of these egg by-products contributes to environmental responsibility and the reduction of waste materials.

Acknowledgement

We thank Dr Stephen L. Irish of Q.P. Corporation for useful discussions and advice given during preparation for presenting the symposium paper and of this manuscript.

References

Bartus, R.T., Dean, R.L., Beer, B. and Lippa, A.S. (1982) The cholinergic hypothesis of geriatric memory dysfunction. *Science* 217, 408–417.

Canty, D.J. and Zeisel, S.H. (1994) Lecithin and choline in human health and disease. *Nutrition Reviews* 52, 327–339.

Dysken, M. (1987) A review of recent clinical trials in the treatment of Alzheimer's dementia. *Psychiatric Annals* 17, 178–191.

Goto, S., Suzuki, K., Kanke, Y., Kokubu, T. and Kurokawa, T. (1981) The utilization of egg shell as calcium source. In: *Abstract of the 35th Annual Meeting of Japanese Society of Food and Nutrition*, Tokushima, p. 124.

Hata, R. (1986) Collagen – its function and metabolism. *Protein, Nucleic Acid and Enzyme* 31, 29–52.

Masuda, Y., Kokubu, T., Yamashita, M., Ikeda, H. and Inoue, S. (1998) Egg phosphatidylcholine combined with vitamin B_{12} improved memory impairment following lesioning of nucleus basalis in rats. *Life Sciences* 62, 813–822.

Ministry of Health and Welfare (1994) *Recommended Dietary Allowances for the Japanese*. Daiichi Publication, Tokyo, pp. 93–97, 105.

Ministry of Health and Welfare (1997) *The Present Condition of National Nutrition – Results of the National Nutrition Survey in 1995*. Daiichi Publication, Tokyo, pp. 29–30.

Nadeau, A. and Roberge, A.G. (1988) Effects of vitamin B_{12} supplementation on choline acetyltransferase activity in cat brain. *International Journal for Vitamin and Nutrition Research* 58, 402–406.

Niiyama, Y. and Sakamoto, S. (1984) Calcium utilization in pregnant rats fed soy protein isolate. *Nutritional Science of Soy Protein (Japan)* 5, 53–58.

Ogihara, M., Suzuki, T., Umeda, H., Nakamura, T., Ishibashi, K., Nomiya, M., Yamaguchi, O., Shiraiwa, Y. and Sasaki, S. (1996) Change of effects of phosphate binder under histamine H_2-receptor antagonist administration; comparative study between calcium carbonate and egg shell calcium. *Kidney and Dialysis* 41, 695–698.

Omi, N. and Ezawa, I. (1998) Effect of egg-shell Ca on preventing of bone loss after ovariectomy. *Journal of Home Economics of Japan* 49, 277–282.

Sanada, J., Masuda, Y., Kamimura, N., Takahashi, M., Kitamura, Y., Yamashita, M. and Inoue, S. (1997) Clinical benefit of egg phosphatidylcholine combined with vitamin B_{12} on patients with dementia of Alzheimer type. *Geriatric Medicine* 35, 363–368.

Slatopolsky, E., Weerts, C., Lopez-Hilker, S., Norwood, K., Zink, M., Windus, D. and Delmez, J. (1986) Calcium carbonate as a phosphate binder in patients with chronic renal failure undergoing dialysis. *New England Journal of Medicine* 315, 157–161.

Takahashi, N., Shoji, T., Hirohata, M., Ishizu, T., Miki, S., Ono, S., Kaifu, Y., Yuasa, S. and Matsuo, H. (1995) The effects of histamine H_2-receptor antagonists on the phosphorus binding ability of calcium carbonate in hemodialysis patients. *Journal of Japanese Society for Dialysis Therapy* 28, 1069–1074.

Biological Characteristics of Egg Components, Specifically Sialyloligosaccharides in Egg Yolk

18

L.R. Juneja
*Nutritional Foods Division, Taiyo Kagaku Co.,
9–5 Akahori-Shinmachi, Yokkaichi, Mie, Japan*

In addition to manufacturing many bioactive compounds including antigen-specific immunoglobulin (IgY) from eggs, we have investigated the functional carbohydrate moieties in hen's egg yolk. Sialic acid (*N*-acetylneuraminic acid) and sialyloligosaccharides have been isolated successfully on an industrial scale. These sialyloligosaccharides are present mainly in glycoprotein form in eggs. The chemical structure of the major sialyloligosaccharides of egg yolk was determined by hydrazinolysis–reacetylation treatment to be an *N*-linked disialyl-biantennary glycan chain.

It has been reported that the level of sialyloligosaccharides is very high in mother's milk at the time of parturition, and is likely to be an important part of the defence mechanism against pathogens, viruses and toxins. Rotavirus is a major pathogen of infectious gastroenteritis and kills a large number of infants a year. A preparation of egg yolk sialyloligosaccharides (Sunsial™) was found to inhibit rotavirus both *in vitro* and *in vivo*. A suckling mice group administered sialyloligosaccharides showed significantly lower diarrhoeal incidences compared with the Sunsial-free control group. Sialyloligosaccharides also showed a strong inhibition of *Helicobacter pylori* which causes gastric ulcers.

Sunsial was administered to infant rats during the lactation period to investigate its effect on learning performance using the maze test. The test group administered Sunsial had a higher success rate in reaching the goal, and goal-reaching time was shorter than that of the Sunsial-free control group. These results suggest that these carbohydrates may play an important role in improving learning ability in infants. The compounds were safe when tested by acute, subacute and mutagenicity tests and when used in infant formula and baby food.

Introduction

Hen eggs are considered to be a chemical storehouse composed of various important chemical compounds that form the basis of life. We have studied extensively the characteristics and physiological functions of egg components. Egg yolk contains a wide variety of nutrients.

Yamamoto *et al.* (1997) have developed a unique technology for commercial-scale production of antigen-specific yolk immunoglobulins (IgY) from eggs for food, feed, cosmetics, diagnostics and affinity chromatography applications. Passive immunization by oral administration of IgY was effective in preventing dental caries, rotaviral diarrhoea, etc. Some food products, e.g. candies, chocolates and gums containing anti-*Streptococcus mutans* (a cause of tooth decay) IgY, produced at our facilities, have been launched in the Japanese market for oral care.

The other components isolated from egg yolk, e.g. oligosaccharides attached to terminal sugar sialic acid, have been shown to have unique functionality. Sialic acid as a component of glycoconjugates (mainly glycoproteins and glycolipids) exists in many biological materials. The terminal glycosylation sequences, in particular sialyloligosaccharides, are responsible for a variety of complex biological events such as cell adhesion, virus infections and the neutralization of toxins.

It has been reported that the level of sialyloligosaccharides in mother's milk is very high at the time of parturition. Sialyloligosaccharides are likely to play their most important role in the defence mechanisms against diseases caused by pathogenic microorganisms including pneumonia, diarrhoea, gastritis and ulcers. Sialic acid derivatives (gangliosides) are known to be involved in brain (neuron) functions and are also important in protecting infants from various diseases. Recently, sialic acid and sialyloligosaccharides have attracted attention from pharmacological and food chemical industries because of their potential biological functions. As an example, sialylglycoconjugates on the cell surface are known to serve as receptors for microorganisms, virus and toxins (Fishman and Brady, 1976; Paulson *et al.*, 1984; Smith *et al.*, 1984; Morschhauser *et al.*, 1990).

Sialyloligosaccharides such as sialyl-LeX and sialyl-LeA have been characterized as carbohydrate ligands of the inflammatory response (Phillips *et al.*, 1990) and cancer metastasis (Kannagi *et al.*, 1988).

We have investigated the functional carbohydrates in hen eggs, resulting in development of a variety of industrial preparations. We have also isolated and characterized the major sialyloligosaccharide moieties of egg yolk as a step toward the elucidation of their biological and physiological functions. In addition, we have supplied various grades of the products to use in infant formulas, health foods and nutritional supplements (Koketsu *et al.*, 1993, 1995a, 1996; Seko *et al.*, 1997).

Sialyloligosaccharides from Egg Yolk

Several sialyloligosaccharides in egg yolk have been isolated and their structures determined (Koketsu *et al.*, 1993, 1995b). The supernatant of water extract of delipidated egg yolk (DEY) was dialysed using a ultrafiltration membrane with cut-off molecular weights of less than about 1000 Da. The asparagine-linked oligosaccharides in the concentrate were liberated by hydrazinolysis/re-*N*-acetylation, and the reducing ends of the resulting oligosaccharides were labelled with *p*-aminobenzoic ethyl ester (ABEE) to make them UV sensitive (Matsuura and Imaoka, 1988; Ohta *et al.*, 1990). The ABEE-derivatized oligosaccharides were fractionated using an anion-exchange column (Fig. 18.1) and reversed-phase high-performance liquid chromatography (HPLC) (Matsuura *et al.*, 1992) (Fig. 18.2). Of the total sialyloligosaccharides obtained from the water extract of DEY, mono-sialyl (SI) and di-sialyloligosaccharides (SII) were found to be present at 47.7 and 50.6%,

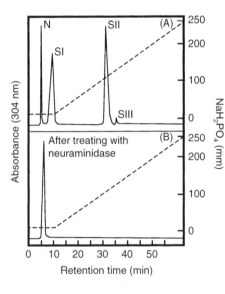

Fig. 18.1.   Separation of ABEE-sialyloligosaccharides from the delipidated egg yolk on a DEAE-5PW anion-exchange column (0.75 × 7.5 cm) with a linear gradient of NaH_2PO_4 from 10 to 250 mM NaH_2PO_4. Flow rate, 0.5 ml min^{-1}; detection, 304 nm. (A) The elution profile of acidic oligosaccharides; (B) the neuraminidase digest of (A). (N, SI, SII and SIII indicate the elution position of standard neutral oligosaccharide, mono-, di- and tri-sialyloligosaccharides). (From: Koketsu *et al.*, 1993, with permission from *Journal of Food Science* (1993), Institute of Food Technologists, Chicago.)

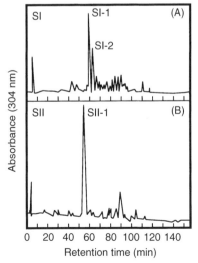

Fig. 18.2.   Separation of SI (mono-) and SII (di-sialyloligosaccharides) from the delipidated egg yolk on a Wakosil 5C18-200 column (0.4 × 25 cm). Eluant, NaH_2PO_4 acetonitrile (92 : 8, v/v); flow rate, 0.5 ml min^{-1}; detection, 304 nm. (A) and (B) show the elution profiles of SI and SII, respectively. (From: Koketsu *et al.*, 1993, with permission from *Journal of Food Science* (1993), Institute of Food Technologists, Chicago.)

respectively. The quantities of SI-1, SI-2 and SII-1 in Fig. 18.2 were calculated to be 9.6, 6.5 and 17.5%, respectively, on the basis of their UV absorbance at 304 nm. The structures of isolated sialyloligosaccharides were determined by analysis with HPLC and ^{1}H nuclear magnetic resonance (NMR) (Vliegenthart *et al.*, 1983). The major sialyloligosaccharides isolated from DEY were of the *N*-acetyllactosamine type (Fig. 18.3).

Biological Activities of Egg Yolk Sialyloligosaccharides

Sialylglycoconjugates, such as gangliosides, sialyloligosaccharides and sialylglycoproteins, have been reported to play various important roles in animal tissue cells and in humans. For example, they act as a receptor for viruses such as Sendai virus (Holmgren *et al.*, 1980), influenza virus (Suzuki *et al.*, 1992; Von Itzstein *et al.*, 1993), corona virus (Schultze and Herrler *et al.*, 1994), etc. We studied hen egg sialylglycoconjugates to apply to functional foods or pharmaceuticals (Koketsu *et al.*, 1991, 1995c).

Rotavirus inhibition effect of egg yolk sialyloligosaccharides

Rotavirus is known as a major pathogen of infectious gastroenteritis in infants. Also, every year a large number of children worldwide suffer from diarrhoea and vomiting caused by rotavirus infection (Kaspikian *et al.*, 1991; Gouvea *et al.*, 1994; Kaga *et al.*, 1994; Noel *et al.*, 1994; Tabassum *et al.*, 1994).

Clinical study of vaccines for prevention of rotavirus infections has been conducted (Forrest, 1993; Greenberg, 1993); however, the vaccination has remained unsuccessful because of difficulty in inducing a specific antibody in

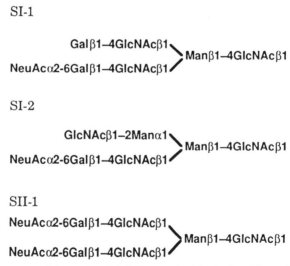

SI-1

Galβ1–4GlcNAcβ1
NeuAcα2-6Galβ1–4GlcNAcβ1 ⟩ Manβ1–4GlcNAcβ1

SI-2

GlcNAcβ1–2Manα1
NeuAcα2-6Galβ1–4GlcNAcβ1 ⟩ Manβ1–4GlcNAcβ1

SII-1

NeuAcα2-6Galβ1–4GlcNAcβ1
NeuAcα2-6Galβ1–4GlcNAcβ1 ⟩ Manβ1–4GlcNAcβ1

Fig. 18.3. Structure of the major sialyloligosaccharides isolated from delipidated egg yolk. (From: Koketsu *et al.*, 1993, with permission from *Journal of Food Science* (1993), Institute of Food Technologists, Chicago.)

the intestinal tract of infants who have not yet developed general immunity (DeMol *et al.*, 1986). A solution for the prevention of rotavirus infection is thus overdue.

A suspension of DEY was incubated with *Bacillus* neutral proteinase to release the peptides bearing oligosaccharides from glycoproteins. The peptidyl oligosaccharides appeared in the supernatant of the suspension, and its concentrate was found to inhibit rotaviral infection *in vitro* (Fukudome *et al.*, 1989; Svensson, 1992). The IC_{50} of this fraction was 60 mg ml^{-1} (Fig. 18.4). The fraction was subjected to chromatography to separate sialyloligosaccharides (acidic oligosaccharides) and neutral oligosaccharides on an anion exchanger. The sialyloligosaccharide fraction inhibited rotaviral replication, and its IC_{50} (50% inhibitory concentration) was 31.9 mg ml^{-1}, while the neutral oligo-saccharide fraction showed no inhibition (Fig. 18.4). The peptidyl sialyl-oligosaccharide and sialyloligosaccharide fractions were incubated with neuraminidase. However, the asialo products showed no inhibitory effect on rotavirus propagation. These results clearly indicate that the difference in the rotavirus inhibition shown by the peptide-linked oligosaccharide fraction and the sialyloligosaccharide fraction is due to sialic acid.

The inhibitory effect of the sialyloligosaccharide fraction on rotavirus was investigated *in vivo* using suckling mice (Hatta *et al.*, 1993) which were previously infected with rotavirus SA-11 (4.4×10^5 fluorescent colony-forming units per mouse) 3 h before administration of the sialyloligosaccharide fraction. The incidence of diarrhoea was assessed 1, 3 and 5 days after oral administration of 2.5 mg of sialyloligosaccharide fraction per mouse. The group administrated with the sialyloligosaccharide fraction showed a significantly lower incidence of rotaviral diarrhoea by (24 and 43% on the third and fifth day, respectively) as compared with the control group (Fig. 18.5). The egg yolk sialyl-oligosaccharides can be prepared by the method mentioned above, and the oral administration of sialyloligosaccharides isolated from hen eggs, which are one of the most popular foods, may be useful for prevention of rotaviral infection.

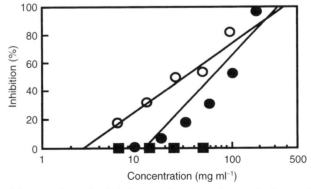

Fig. 18.4.   Inhibitory effect of sialyloligosaccharide and neutral oligosaccharide fractions on rotavirus (SA-11) infection. ○, Sialyloligosaccharide fraction; ●, oligo-saccharide fraction; ■, neutral oligosaccharide fraction.

Learning performance of sialyloligosaccharides

In order to confirm the effect of administration of sialyloligosaccharides on infant rats during the lactation period, their learning performance with or without intake of sialyloligosaccharides was investigated using the maze test (Fig. 18.6). The egg yolk sialyloligosaccharides was administrated to rats of age 14–21 days, and the goal-reaching time and success rate in reaching the goal were monitored for 42 to 49-day-old rats by applying the maze test. The results revealed that the group administrated the egg yolk sialyloligosaccharide fraction had a higher success rate in reaching the goal with a significantly shorter goal-reaching time than the control group who were not fed sialyloligosaccharide (Fig. 18.6). This result suggests that the sialyloligosaccharides play an important role in improving the learning performance of infant rats. However, the administration of sialyloligosaccharides should begin during the lactation

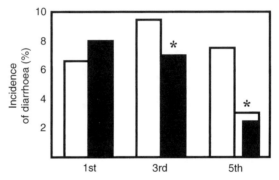

Fig. 18.5.   Effect of administration of the sialyloligosaccharide fraction to suckling mice previously inoculated with rotavirus (SA-11, 4.4×10^5 fluorescent colony-forming units per mouse). Left bar, saline; right bar, sialyloligosaccharide fraction (2.5 mg dose per head). *$P < 0.05$.

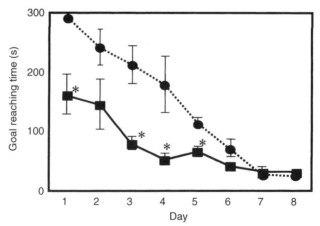

Fig. 18.6.   Effect of oral administration of the sialyloligosaccharide fraction on goal-reaching time of rats examined by the maze test. ■, Sialyloligosaccharide fraction; ●, saline.

period, thereby not only improving the learning performance but also protecting the rats from various infectious diseases during their growth.

Stability and safety of egg yolk sialyloligosaccharides

We have prepared a product (Sunsial™) enriched with sialyloligosaccharides using a unique enzymatic and purification technique. Sunsial is stable at low pH, high temperatures and high salt concentrations. It is stable at room temperature for 12 months. For better shelf life, storage in cool, dry and dark conditions is recommended. The acute, subacute and mutagenicity tests performed with Sunsial showed no toxicity.

Innovative and Unique Characteristics of Sunsial

Sunsial containing sialyloligosaccharides has different physiological effects such as the inhibition of virus and bacterial infection. The absorption, excretion and effect on learning ability of sialyloligosaccharides was investigated. Sialic acid is a component of glycoprotein and ganglioside, which exists mainly in the cell membrane, conspicuously concentrated in the central nervous systems and brain, and is considered to play an important role in expression and development functions in those tissues (Reutter *et al.*, 1982; Karpiak *et al.*, 1984). Therefore, it was presumed that sialic acid and its derivatives were closely associated with the improvement in learning performance.

It is reported that the early events of virus attachment and entry into cells are critical for rotaviral replication (Bass *et al.*, 1992). Together with the above finding, the prevention of rotaviral inhibition by certain food ingredients could be a good option to solve this global problem. Sunsial has been found to inhibit rotavirus *in vitro* and *in vivo* (Koketsu *et al.*, 1995c).

Sunsial was incubated with neuraminidase, but the asialo products showed no inhibitory effect on rotaviral propagation. These results clearly indicated that the rotaviral inhibition shown by Sunsial is attributable to sialic acid.

During the last two decades, interest in the structure and function of oligosaccharides has increased rapidly. It is possible that the oligosaccharides, especially sialyloligosaccharides, are involved in several important biological functions.

These compounds are safe and non-immunogenic and have been used in infant formula and baby food. Sunsial, containing sialyloligosaccharides, which are natural and safe, may offer the food industry a great opportunity of designing foods, especially medicinal foods for targeting nutrition improvement as well as disease prevention.

References

Bass, D.M., Baylor, M.R., Chen, C., Meng, L. and Greenberg, H.B. (1992) Liposome-mediated transfection of intact viral particles reveals that plasma membrane penetration determines permissivity of tissue culture cells to rotavirus. *Journal of Clinical Investigation* 90, 2313–2320.

DeMol, P., Zissis, G., Butzler, J.P., Mutwewingabo, A. and André, F.E. (1986) Failure of live, attenuated oral rotavirus vaccine. *Lancet* 2(8498), 108.

Fishman, P.H. and Brady, R.O. (1976) Biosynthesis and function of gangliosides. *Science* 194, 906–915.

Forrest, B.D. (1993) Diarrhoeal disease: current concepts and future challenges. Diarrhoeal disease and vaccine development. *Transactions of he Royal Society of Tropical Medicine and Hygiene* 87, 39–41.

Fukudome, K., Yoshie, O. and Konno, T. (1989) Comparison of human, simian, and bovine rotaviruses for requirement of sialic acid in hemagglutination and cell adsorption. *Virology* 172, 196–205.

Gouvea, V., Decastro, L., Timenetsky, M.D., Greenberg, H. and Santos, N. (1994) Rotavirus serotype G5 associated with diarrhea in Brazilian children. *Journal of Clinical Microbiology* 32, 1408–1409.

Greenberg, H.B. (1993) Rotavirus vaccination – current status – a brief summary. In: Tzotzos, G.T. (ed.), *Biotechnology R&D Trends, Vol. 700*. New York Academy of Sciences, New York p. 32.

Hatta, H., Tsuda, K., Akachi, S., Kim, M., Yamamoto, T. and Ebina, T. (1993) Oral passive immunization effect of anti-human rotavirus IgY and its behavior against proteolytic enzymes. *Bioscience, Biotechnology and Biochemistry* 57, 1077–1081.

Holmgren, J., Svennerholm, L., Elwing, H., Fredman, P. and Strannegard, Ö. (1980) Sendai virus receptor: proposed recognition structure based on binding to plastic-adsorbed gangliosides. *Proceedings of the National Academy of Sciences of the United States of America* 77, 1947–1950.

Kaga, E., Iizuka, M., Nakagomi, T. and Nakagomi, O. (1994) The distribution of G (Vp7) and P (Vp4) serotypes among human rotaviruses recovered from Japanese children with diarrhea. *Microbiology and Immunology* 38, 317–320.

Kannagi, R., Fukusi, Y., Tachikawa, T., Noda, A., Shin, S., Kitahara, A., Itai, S., Arii, S., Shigeta, K., Hiraiwa, N., Fukuda, Y., Hakomori, S. and Imura, H. (1988) Quantitative and qualitative characterization of human cancer-associated serum glycoprotein antigens expressing epitopes consisting of sialyl or sialyl-fucosyl type 1 chain. *Cancer Research* 48, 3856–3863.

Kaspikian, A.Z., Flores, J., Vesikari, T., Ruuska, T., Madore, H.P., Green, K.Y., Gorziglia, M., Hoshino, Y., Chanock, R.M., Midthun, K. and Perez-Schael, I. (1991) Recent advances in development of a rotavirus vaccine for prevention of severe diarrheal illness of infants and young children. In: Whistler, R.L. and Wolfrom, M.L. (eds), *Advances in Experimental Medical Biology Vol. 310*. Academic Press, New York, pp. 255–264.

Karpiak, S.E., Vilin, F. and Mahadik, S.P. (1984) Gangliosides accelerate rat neonatal learning and levels of cortical acetylcholinesterases. *Developmental Neuroscience* 6, 127–135.

Koketsu, M., Juneja, L.R., Kim, M., Ohta, M., Matsuura, F. and Yamamoto, T. (1993) Sialyloligosaccharides of delipidated egg yolk fraction. *Journal of Food Science* 58, 743–747.

Koketsu, M., Nakata, K., Juneja, L.R., Kim, M. and Yamamoto, T. (1995a) Learning performance of egg yolk sialyloligosaccharides fraction. *Oyotoshitsu Kagaku* (in Japanese) 9, 15–18.

Koketsu, M., Seko, A., Juneja, L.R., Kim, M., Kashimura, N. and Yamamoto, T. (1995b) An efficient preparation and structural characterization of sialylglycopeptides from protease treated egg yolk. *Journal of Carbohydrate Chemistry* 14, 833–841.

Koketsu, M., Nitoda, T., Juneja, L.R., Kim, M., Kashimura, N. and Yamamoto, T. (1995c) Sialylglycopeptides from egg yolk as an inhibitor of rotaviral infection. *Journal of Agricultural and Food Chemistry* 43, 858–861.

Koketsu, M., Enoki, Y., Juneja, L.R., Kim, M. and Yamamoto, T. (1996) Isolation of sialyloligosaccharides from egg yolk using enzymes and some biofunctional activities of the oligosaccharides isolated. *Oyo Toshitsu Kagaku* (in Japanese) 43, 283–287.

Matsuura, F. and Imaoka, A. (1988) Chromatographic separation of asparagine-linked oligosaccharides labeled with an ultraviolet absorbing compound, *p*-aminobenzoic acid ethyl ester. *Glycoconjugate Journal* 5, 13–26.

Matsuura, F., Ohta, M., Murakami, K., Hirano, K. and Sweeley, C.C. (1992) The combination of normal phase with reversed phase high performance liquid chromatography for the analysis of asparagine-linked neutral oligosaccharides labelled with *p*-aminobenzoic acid ethyl ester. *Biomedical Chromatography* 6, 77–83.

Morschhauser, J., Hoschutzky, H., Jann, K. and Hacker, J. (1990) Functional analysis of the sialic acid-binding adhesion SfaS of pathogenic *Escherichia coli* by site-specific mutagenesis. *Infection and Immunity* 58, 2133–2138.

Noel, J., Mansoor, A., Thaker, U., Hermann, J., Perronhenry, D. and Cubitt, W.D. (1994) Identification of adenoviruses in faeces from patients with diarrhoea at the hospitals for sick children, London, 1989–1992. *Journal of Medical Virology* 43, 84–90.

Ohta, M., Kobatake, M., Matsumura, A. and Matsuura, F. (1990) Separation of Asn-linked sialyloligosaccharides labeled with *p*-aminobenzoic acid ethyl ester by high performance liquid chromatography *Agricultural and Biological Chemistry* 54, 1045–1047.

Paulson, J.C., Rogers, G.N., Carroll, S.M., Higa, H.H., Pritchett, T., Milks, G. and Sabesan, S. (1984) Selection of influenza virus variants based on sialyloligosaccharide receptor specificity. *Pure and Applied Chemistry* 56, 797–805.

Phillips, M.L., Nudelman, E., Gaeta, F.C.A., Perez, M., Singhal, A.K., Hakomori, S. and Paulson, J.C. (1990) ELAM-1 mediates cell adhesion by recognition of a carbohydrate ligand, sialyl-lex. *Science* 250, 1130–1132.

Reutter, W., Kottgen, E., Bauer, C. and Gerok, W. (1982) Biological significance of sialic acid In: Schauer, R. (ed.), *Sialic Acid*. Springer-Verlag, New York, pp. 263–305.

Schultze, B. and Herrler, G. (1994) Recognition of cellular receptors by bovine coronavirus *Archives of Virology* (Suppl. 9), 451–459.

Seko, A., Koketsu, M., Nishizono, M., Enoki, Y., Ibrahim, H.R., Juneja, L.R., Kim, M. and Yamamoto, T. (1997) Occurrence of a sialylglycopeptide and free sialylglycans in hen's egg yolk. *Biochimica et Biophysica Acta* 1335, 23–32.

Smith, H., Gaastra, W., Kamerling, J.P., Vliegenthart, J.F.G. and de Graaf, F.K. (1984) Isolation and structural characterization of the equine erythrocyte receptor for enterotoxigenic *Escherichia coli* K99 fimbrial adhesion. *Infection and Immunity* 46, 578–584.

Suzuki, Y., Nakao, T., Ito, T., Watanabe, N., Toda, Y., Guiyun, X., Suzuki, T., Kobayashi, T., Kimura, Y., Yamada, A., Sugawara, K., Nishimura, H., Kitame, F., Nakamura, K., Deya, E., Kiso, M. and Hasegawa, A. (1992) Structural determination of gangliosides that bind to influenza A, B, and C viruses by an improved binding assay: strain-specific receptor epitopes in sialo-sugar chains. *Virology* 189, 121–131.

Svensson, L. (1992) Group C rotavirus requires sialic acid for erythrocyte and cell receptor binding. *Journal of Virology* 66, 5582–5585.

Tabassum, S., Shears, P. and Hart, C.A. (1994) Genomic characterization of rotavirus strains obtained from hospitalized children with diarrhoea in Bangladesh. *Journal of Medical Virology* 43, 50–56.

Vliegenthart, J.F.G., Dorland, L. and Van Halbeek, H. (1983) High-resolution, [1]H-nuclear magnetic resonance spectroscopy as a tool in the structural analysis of carbohydrates related to glycoproteins. *Advances in Carbohydrate Chemistry and Biochemistry* 41, 209–374.

Von Itzstein, M., Wu, W.Y., Kok, G.B., Pegg, M.S., Dyason, J.C., Jin, B., Phan, T.V., Smythe, M.L., White, H.F., Oliver, S.W., Colman, P.M., Varghese, J.N., Ryan, D.M., Woods, J.M., Bethell, R.C., Hotham, V.J., Cameron, J.M. and Penn, C.R. (1993) Rational design of potent sialidase-based inhibitors of influenza virus replication. *Nature* 363, 418–423.

Yamamoto, T., Juneja, L.R., Hattta, H. and Kim, M. (1997) *Hen Eggs: Their Basic and Applied Science*. CRC Press, Boca Raton, Florida.

Eggs as a Functional Food: Technology Update

19

C.M. Hasler

Functional Foods for Health Program, Department of Food Science and Human Nutrition, University of Illinois, Urbana, Illinois, USA

Eggs have not traditionally been regarded as a functional food primarily due to concerns about adverse effects on serum cholesterol levels. However, recent evidence indicates that individuals with normal cholesterol may consume up to four eggs per week as part of a moderate fat diet without significant adverse effects on blood lipids. More recently, however, research development efforts have focused on the production of value-added eggs through enhancing the level of ω-3 fatty acids and antioxidants. For example, 'Egg*stasy*® Eggs' (Century Acres Eggs, Port Washington, Wisconsin) have a reduced (25%) fat content in addition to being supplemented with vitamin E and antioxidants. 'EggsPlus' (Pilgrims's Pride) are enriched with 20% of the US Recommended Daily Allowance for vitamin E and contain the same level of ω-3 fatty acids as 3 ounces of salmon. 'NaturEggs' are also higher in ω-3 fatty acids and vitamin E in addition to being lower in saturated fat and cholesterol. These recent technological developments warrant a re-evaluation of eggs as a functional food.

Introduction

Functional foods, i.e. foods or food ingredients which may enhance health by providing a physiological benefit beyond the provision of basic nutrients (Institute of Medicine, 1994), are one of the most exciting trends in food technology today (Hasler, 1998). Food Processing Magazine's 1998 Top 100® R&D Survey ranks functional foods as the number one food category for the next 5 years (Meyer, 1998), up from its number three ranking in 1997 (Kevin, 1997). Numerous factors have contributed to the explosion of interest in functional foods, including: (i) extensive literature documenting the critical link between diet and optimal health; (ii) increasing consumer demand by ageing baby boomers for healthy products to augment a healthy lifestyle; (iii) staggering health care costs driven, in part, by diet-related diseases, advances in food technology and market opportunities; and (iv) recent regulatory developments (Hasler, 1996).

Eggs have not traditionally been regarded as a functional food, primarily due to concerns about adverse effects on serum cholesterol levels. It is well established that elevated total and low-density lipoprotein (LDL) cholesterols are the primary mutable risk factors for cardiovascular disease (CVD), which is the leading cause of death in the USA. An American dies of CVD every 33 s. In 1997, CVD was responsible for over 961,000 or 1 in every 2.4 deaths (American Heart Association, 1998). Estimated direct and indirect costs of CVD and stroke in 1998 are US$274 billion (American Heart Association, 1998). Approximately 96.8 million (51%) Americans have total cholesterol levels greater than 200 mg dl^{-1}; over the age of 55 years, these elevated cholesterol levels are seen in 70% of Americans. Data from the Lipid Research Clinics Coronary Primary Prevention Trial (1984) have demonstrated that there is a direct relationship between reduction in total cholesterol and the risk of coronary heart disease (CHD). For every 1% reduction in total cholesterol, risk of CHD is reduced by 2–4% (Holme, 1990). Recent studies show an increase in LDL cholesterol following cholesterol feeding in normolipidaemic subjects consuming a National Cholesterol Education Program (NCEP) Step I diet (Ginsberg *et al.*, 1995). Thus, because of the relatively high cholesterol content of egg yolks (215 mg), the NCEP Step I and II diets restrict egg intake to four and two weekly, respectively. This recommendation is supported by clinical studies in which egg consumption has been shown to increase total and LDL cholesterol levels.

Consumption of one egg per day in subjects with total cholesterol levels greater than 200 mg dl^{-1} ingesting a NCEP Step I diet resulted in a 9.2% increase in LDL cholesterol (Garber *et al.*, 1992). More recently, 161 free-living hypercholesterolaemic and combined hyperlipidaemic subjects (triglyceride concentrations < 75th percentile or ≥75 percentile, respectively) consumed two eggs per day or an egg substitute for 12 weeks in addition to an NCEP Step I diet. Egg-fed hypercholesterolaemic subjects experienced a significant increase in LDL and total cholesterols (Knopp *et al.*, 1997). Despite these findings, however, a meta-analysis of 27 studies showed that, when one or two eggs are added to a typical American diet (containing ~ 400 mg of cholesterol day^{-1}), little change would be expected in serum cholesterol (Hopkins, 1992). More recently, Ginsberg *et al.* (1994) demonstrated that individuals with normal cholesterol might consume up to four eggs per day as part of a moderate fat diet without significant adverse effects on blood lipid profile.

The negative image of eggs has resulted in a significant decline in per capita egg consumption over the last 31 years (Fig. 19.1) from its peak of 320 eggs per year in 1967 to 237 in 1996. However, good news for eggs came in the form of a 1997 meta-analysis by Howell *et al.* (1997), which demonstrated that only about 20% of any increase in blood total and LDL cholesterol can be attributed to dietary cholesterol such as would be provided by eggs. This review assessed data from 224 studies published between 1966 and 1994 involving 8143 subjects in 366 independent groups and included 878

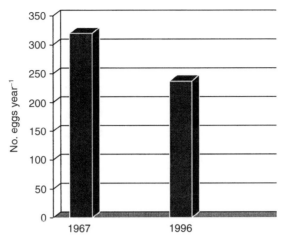

Fig. 19.1. According to the USDA, per capita egg consumption has declined from its peak of 320 eggs per year in 1967 to 237 eggs per year in 1996.

diet–blood lipid comparisons. This information prompted the American Egg Board to launch a national advertising campaign in 1997 headlined 'More Studies Say Eggs are OK' (Neff, 1998) to try and ease consumer apprehension about the potential adverse effects of egg consumption.

Clearly, sources of dietary cholesterol do not top the list of nutritional concerns for consumers today according to the 1997 Shopping for Health survey (Princeton Survey Research Associates, 1997). This sixth annual report from the Food Marketing Institute (FMI) and *Prevention* magazine involved a national survey of 1005 adults who have primary or equally shared responsibility for their household's food shopping with the objective of monitoring these shoppers' understanding and concern about key issues in nutrition and health. Not surprisingly, the fat content of a food remains the first item shoppers look for when reading nutrition labels, with 70% of consumers seeking this information. Cholesterol content ranks much lower, with only 11% of shoppers looking for this information and only 2% of them looking for it first (Table 19.1). An additional FMI trends survey of 2029 shoppers showed that cholesterol was less of a concern in 1997 than it was in 1996 (Abt Associates, Inc., 1997). Cholesterol was mentioned as a top nutritional concern by only 20% of shoppers in 1997, down from approximately 25% in 1996. No respondent indicated that they were eating fewer eggs to ensure that their diet was healthy.

Functional Eggs

One of the hallmarks of the functional foods movement is a paradigm shift away from 'removing negative ingredients' (e.g. cholesterol, fat and salt) to 'enhancement with positive ingredients' (e.g. antioxidant, vitamins and calcium). Although this has long been recognized in, for example, the fortified cereals market, nutritionally enhanced eggs is a relatively recent phenomenon (Hargis and Van Elswyk, 1993). The development of 'functional' eggs can be

Table 19.1. Only 11% of shoppers seek information about cholesterol levels on food labels according to Shopping for Health (1997).

		1997	
Information about:	1996 Total (%)	Total (%)	First mention (%)
Fat	80	70	51
Calories	51	33	10
Sodium	31	29	9
Ingredients (sugar, etc.)	14	21	6
Saturated fat	8	17	3
Vitamins	15	14	5
Cholesterol	11	11	2
Calories from fat	3	8	2
Preservatives/additives	6	8	2
Protein	7	6	2
Serving size	3	5	2
Fibre	3	2	—

accomplished by the nutritional manipulation of the diets of laying hens to include sources of n-3 fatty acids such as flaxseed and fish oil which promotes the incorporation of these components into the egg yolk (Van Elswyk, 1997). Consumption of one ω-3 enriched egg per day was recently shown to contribute substantially to the recommended daily intake of n-3 fatty acids (Farrell, 1998). A number of companies are now marketing eggs fortified with ω-3 fatty acids and vitamin E because of the health benefits associated with these compounds.

ω-3 (n-3) and ω-6 (n-6) fatty acids are the two essential classes of polyunsaturated fatty acids found in plants and animals. It has been suggested that the western-type diet is currently deficient in n-3 fatty acids, which is reflected in the current estimated n-3 : n-6 dietary ratio of 20 : 25–1, compared with the 1 : 1 ratio on which humans evolved (Simopoulos, 1991). The dramatic change in this ratio is due, in part, to increased meat consumption containing high amounts of pre-formed arachidonic acid (20 : 4n-6) and the recent emphasis on increasing the intake of polyunsaturated fatty acids at the expense of saturated fatty acids (Gerster, 1995). This has prompted researchers to examine the role of n-3 fatty acids in a number of disease states. The diseases of concern to us include hypertension (Toft *et al.*, 1995), rheumatic disorders (McCarthy and Kenny, 1992), renal disease (DeCaterina *et al.*, 1994), carcinogenesis (Gonzalez, 1995), stroke (Orencia *et al.*, 1996) and CVD (Schmidt, 1997), the latter having received the most attention.

Ingestion of large amounts of n-3 fatty acids from fish has not been shown unequivocally to reduce CVD risk in healthy men. However, consumption of 35 g or more of fish daily has been shown to reduce the risk of death from non-sudden myocardial infarction in the Chicago Western Electric Study (Daviglus *et al.*, 1997). As little as one serving of fish per week was associated with a significantly reduced risk of total cardiovascular mortality after 11 years in more than 20,000 US male physicians (Albert *et al.*, 1998), supporting the observation that these ω-3 fatty acids are important in CVD prevention.

Eggs enriched with ω-3 fatty acids first appeared on the market about 6 years ago, with the arrival in Canada of Dr. Sim's Designer Eggs, which are now marketed in Israel, Belgium and Japan (Henkes, 1998). Nearly one dozen Canadian companies have now developed ω-3 eggs (Henkes, 1998). In the USA, the biggest manufacturer of ω-3 eggs is Pilgrim's Pride (Dallas, Texas), the fourth largest poultry company in the USA. They have recently developed EggsPlus, a revolutionary fresh egg that provides an alternative to fish as a source of both ω-3 fatty acids and vitamin E (Anonymous, 1998a). By feeding laying hens a natural grain diet containing flaxseed, eggs are produced which contain six times more vitamin E (6 IU) than ordinary eggs (1 IU) and 1300 mg of essential fatty acids. These fatty acids consist of 1100 mg of ω-6 linoleic acid fatty acids, 100 mg of docosahexaenoic acid and 100 mg of ω-3 linolenic acid. Their educational material highlights 'A dozen reasons to eat EggsPlus' including the importance of ω-3 and ω-6 fatty acids in a balanced diet.

Vitamin E is well accepted as nature's most effective lipid-soluble, chain-breaking antioxidant (Packer, 1991). Because of this role, a great deal of research effort has been focused recently on the role of vitamin E in modulating the risk of CVD. It is well accepted that an elevated level of plasma LDL cholesterol is positively associated with CVD risk. However, it has only been within the last decade that the deleterious effects of oxidized LDL have been recognized. A wealth of accumulating evidence supports the role of vitamin E in CVD risk reduction. Vitamin E has been shown to inhibit LDL oxidation *in vitro* (Esterbauer *et al.*, 1989), and human studies have shown that oral supplementation with α-tocopherol renders LDL less susceptible to oxidation (Dieber-Rotheneder *et al.*, 1991). Two very large prospective studies of men (Rimm *et al.*, 1993) and women (Stampfer *et al.*, 1993) have recently shown that individuals taking vitamin E supplements had a 40% reduction in the incidence of CVD. The current US Recommended Daily Allowance (RDA) for vitamin E is 8–10 mg day^{-1}. However, results of large retrospective epidemiological studies indicate that the maximal reduction in CVD risk was attained when supplements of 100–250 IU day^{-1} (equivalent to 70–170 mg day^{-1}) had been taken for at least 2 years. Such a level of vitamin E intake may be difficult to obtain without also significantly increasing dietary fat intake, since major food sources of vitamin E are vegetable oils, polyunsaturated margarines, certain nuts and wheat germ. Thus, dietary supplementation may be necessary to achieve a reduction in CVD risk. Thus it is not surprising that vitamin E is the top nutritional supplement purchased by American consumers (Anonymous, 1998b).

In addition to Pilgrim's Pride, several other companies are attempting to capitalize on the interest in the proposed health benefits of vitamin E. Century Acres Eggs, Inc. (Port Washington, Wisconsin) has recently developed Egg-*stasy*® eggs which are enriched with vitamin E – 300% more than contained in a regular egg. Egg*stasy*® eggs are also reduced in cholesterol (180 mg of cholesterol), a 17% reduction in relation to regular eggs. BoneEE-Best Eggs (Lyn, Ontario) has also developed a reduced cholesterol egg (175 mg) containing 50% of the recommended dietary intake of vitamin E, and high ω-3 fatty acids (0.38 versus 0.05 g in a regular egg).

Priced at a premium (20–40% more than regular eggs), nutritionally enhanced eggs clearly fill a niche in the growing functional foods market. Eggs enhanced with ω-3 fatty acids and/or vitamin E clearly provide the message that 'eggs are no longer just eggs' (Henkes, 1998). More than that, however, functional eggs can be viewed as not only not bad for us, they may even be good for us!

Conclusion

Functional foods are the leading trend in the food industry today. This is being stimulated in part by changing consumer demographics and an intense interest in foods which can play a key role in contributing to a longer, healthier life (McMahon, 1998). Increasing numbers of companies are producing nutritionally enhanced products to cater to consumers eager to enhance their health and well being through foods (Brower, 1998). Companies are also attempting to capitalize on this lucrative market (Fig. 19.2) which has been estimated recently at US$28.9 billion (Decision Reports, 1998) with an estimated growth potential of 10–12% up to the year 2000 (Heasman and Mellentin, 1998). Eggs are experiencing a healthier image in the marketplace due to their excellent source of protein and a variety of other nutrients. Most recently, several companies have produced value-added eggs enriched with ω-3 fatty acids and antioxidant vitamins. This trend undoubtedly will continue as consumers seek new opportunities to enhance their health through diet and continuing research efforts unveil additional health benefits of these ingredients.

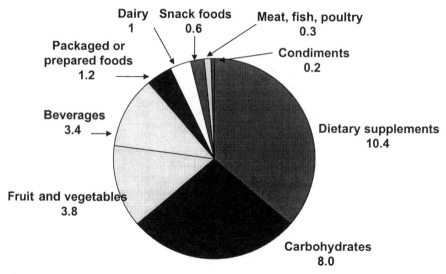

Fig. 19.2. The US retail market for functional foods presented as a segment of the total food category sales of US$457.2 billion according to Decision Resources (1998).

References

Abt Associates, Inc. (1997) *Trends in the United States. Consumer Attitudes and the Supermarket. Conducted for the Food Marketing Institute.* Washington, DC.

Albert, C.M., Hennekens, C.H., O'Donnell, C.J., Ajani, U.A., Carey, V.J., Willett, W.C., Ruskin, J.N. and Manson, J.E. (1998) Fish consumption and risk of sudden cardiac death. *Journal of the American Medical Association* 279, 23–28.

American Heart Association (1998) *Heart and Stroke Statistical Update.* American Heart Association, Dallas, Texas.

Anonymous (1998a) Pilgrim's Pride gains increasing recognition with EggsPlus. *Nutraceutical News* 1(2), 9.

Anonymous (1998b) St. John's wort, echinacea and ginkgo biloba now among ten most popular nutritional supplements. *Nutraceutical News* 1(8), 12.

Brower, V. (1998) Nutraceuticals: poised for a healthy slice of the healthcare market? *Nature Biotechnology* 16, 728–731.

Daviglus, M.L., Stamler, J., Orencia, A.J., Dyer, A.R., Liu, K., Greenland, P., Walsh, M., Morris, D. and Shekelle, R.B. (1997) Fish consumption and the 30-year risk of fatal myocardial infarction. *New England Journal of Medicine* 336, 1046–1053.

DeCaterina, R., Endres, S., Kristensen, S.D. and Schmidt, E.B. (1994) *n*-3 Fatty acids and renal diseases. *American Journal of Kidney Diseases* 24, 394–415.

Decision Reports. (1998) *Roadmaps to Market: Commercializing Functional Foods and Nutraceuticals.* Decision Resources, Inc., Waltham, Massachusetts.

Dieber-Rotheneder, M., Puhl, H., Waeg, G., Striegl, G. and Esterbauer, H. (1991) Effect of oral supplementation with D-α-tocopherol on the vitamin E content of human low density lipoproteins and resistance to oxidation. *Journal of Lipid Research* 32, 1325–1332.

Esterbauer, H., Striegl, G., Puhl, H., Oberreither, S., Rotheneder, M., el-Saadini, M. and Jurgens, G. (1989) The role of vitamin E and carotenoids in preventing oxidation of low density lipoproteins. *Annals of the New York Academy of Science* 570, 254–267.

Farrell, D.J. (1998) Enrichment of hen eggs with *n*-3 long-chain fatty acids and evaluation of enriched eggs in humans. *American Journal of Clinical Nutrition* 68, 538–544.

Garber, D.W., Henkin, Y., Osterlund, L.C., Darnell, B.E. and Segrest, J.P. (1992) Plasma lipoproteins in hyperlipidemic subjects eating iodine-enriched eggs. *Journal of the American College of Nutrition* 11, 294–303.

Gerster, H. (1995) The use of *n*-3 PUFAs (fish oil) in enteral nutrition. *International Journal of Vitamin and Nutrition Research* 65, 3–20.

Ginsberg, H.N., Karmally, W., Siddiqui, M., Holleran, S., Tall, A.R., Rumsey, S.C., Deckelbaum, R.J., Blaner, W.S. and Ramakrishnan, R. (1994) A dose–response study of the effects of dietary cholesterol on fasting and postprandial lipid and lipoprotein metabolism in healthy young men. *Arteriosclerosis and Thrombosis* 14, 576–586.

Ginsberg, H.N., Karmally, W., Siddiqui, M., Holleran, S., Tall, A.R., Rumsey, S.C., Deckelbaum, R.J., Blaner, W.S. and Ramakrishnan, R. (1995) Increases in dietary cholesterol are associated with modest increases in both LDL and HDL cholesterol in healthy young women. *Arteriosclerosis, Thrombosis and Vascular Biology* 15, 169–178.

Gonzalez, M.J. (1995) Fish oil, lipid peroxidation and mammary tumour growth. *Journal of the American College of Nutrition* 14, 325–335.

Hargis, P.S. and Van Elswyk, M.E. (1993) Manipulating the fatty acid composition of poultry meat and eggs for the health conscious consumer. *World's Poultry Science Journal* 49, 251–264.

Hasler, C.M. (1996) Functional foods: the western perspective. *Nutrition Reviews* 54, S6–S10.

Hasler, C.M. (1998) A new look at an ancient concept. *Chemistry & Industry* 2 February, 84–89.

Heasman, M. and Mellentin, J. (1998) *The Business of Healthy Eating. Global Trends, Developments and Strategies in Functional Foods and Nutraceuticals.* Financial Times Retail & Consumer, London.

Henkes, R. (1998) The rise of the omega-3 egg. *The Furrow* 27–28.

Holme, I. (1990) An analysis of randomized trials evaluating the effect of cholesterol reduction on total mortality and coronary heart disease. *Circulation* 82, 1916–1924.

Hopkins, P.N. (1992) Effects of dietary cholesterol on serum cholesterol: a meta-analysis and review. *American Journal of Clinical Nutrition* 55, 1060–1070.

Howell, W.H., McNamara, D.J., Tosca, M.A., Smith, B.T. and Gaines, J.A. (1997) Plasma lipid and lipoprotein responses to dietary fat and cholesterol – a meta-analysis. *American Journal of Clinical Nutrition* 65, 1747–1764.

Institute of Medicine, National Academy of Sciences (1994) Enhancing the food supply. In: Thomas, P.R. and Earl, R. (eds), *Opportunities in the Nutrition and Food Sciences.* National Academy Press, Washington, DC, pp. 98–142.

Kevin, K. (1997) The 1997 Top 100 R&D survey. *Food Processing* 58 (6), 65–70.

Knopp, R.H., Retzlaff, B.M., Walden, C.E., Dowdy, A.A., Tsunehara, C.H., Austin, M.A. and Nguyen, T. (1997) A double-blind, randomized, controlled trial of the effects of two eggs per day in moderately hypercholesterolemic and combined hyper-lipidemic subjects taught the NCEP Step I diet. *Journal of the American College of Nutrition* 16, 551–561.

Lipid Research Clinics Coronary Primary Prevention Trial Results (1984) *Journal of the American Medical Association* 251, 365–374.

McCarthy, G.M. and Kenny, D. (1992) Dietary fish oil and rheumatic diseases. *Seminars in Arthritis and Rheumatism* 21, 368–375.

McMahon, K.E. (1998) Consumers and key nutrition trends for 1998. *Nutrition Today* 33, 19–26.

Meyer, A. (1998) The 1998 Top 100® R&D Survey. *Food Processing* 59 (8), 32–40.

Neff, J. (1998) The great egg breakthrough. Will a healthy new image mean more ingredient use? *Food Processing* 59 (1), 25–27.

Orencia, A.J., Daviglus, M.L., Dyer, A.R., Shekelle, R.B. and Stamler, J. (1996) Fish consumption and stroke in men. 30-year findings of the Chicago Western Electric Study. *Stroke* 27, 204–209.

Packer, L. (1991) Protective role of vitamin E in biological systems. *American Journal of Clinical Nutrition* 53, 1050S–1055S.

Princeton Survey Research Associates (1997) *Shopping for Health. Balancing Convenience, Nutrition and Taste.* Food Marketing Institute, Washington, DC, and Prevention Magazine, Emmaus, PA.

Rimm, E.B., Stampfer, M.J., Ascherio, A., Giovannucci, E., Colditz, G.A. and Willett, W.C. (1993) Vitamin E consumption and the risk of coronary heart disease in men. *New England Journal of Medicine* 328, 1450–1455.

Schmidt, E.B. (1997) *n*-3 fatty acids and the risk of coronary heart disease. *Danish Medical Bulletin* 44, 1–22.

Simopoulos, A.P. (1991) Omega-3 fatty acids in health and disease and in growth and development. *American Journal of Clinical Nutrition* 54, 438–463.

Stampfer, M.J., Hennekens, C.H., Manson, J.E., Colditz, G.A., Rosner, B. and Willett, W.C. (1993) Vitamin E consumption and the risk of coronary disease in women. *New England Journal of Medicine* 328, 1444–1449.

Toft, I., Bonaa, K.H., Ingebretsen, O.E., Nordoy, A. and Jenssen, T. (1995) Effects of *n*-3 polyunsaturated fatty acids on glucose homeostasis and blood pressure in essential hypertension. A randomized, controlled trial. *Annals of International Medicine* 123, 911–918.

Van Elswyk, M.E. (1997) Comparison of *n*-3 fatty acid sources in laying hen rations for improvement of whole egg nutritional quality: a review. *British Journal of Nutrition* 78 (Suppl. 1), S61–S69.

Mechanical and Oxygen Barrier Properties of Transglutaminase Cross-linked Egg White Protein Films

20

L.T. Lim, Y. Mine, K. Montoya and M.A. Tung

*Department of Food Science, University of Guelph,
Guelph, Ontario, Canada*

A methodology for preparing biopolymer films from egg white proteins was developed in this study. Film formation was based on pre-heating egg white proteins at pH 10.5, followed by enzymatic polymerization of the proteins at 50°C, pH 8.2 using a Ca^{2+}-independent microbial transglutaminase. SDS–PAGE confirmed the cross-linking of protein and showed that the polymerization reaction increased with increasing pre-heating temperature (60–80°C) before the enzyme treatment. Films plasticized with a higher glycerol content possessed higher equilibrium moisture content, indicating higher film hydrophilicity. The tensile properties of the films were dependent on relative humidity (RH) and glycerol content. Oxygen permeabilities of the films were low under low RH conditions, but increased rapidly as RH increased. Films with reduced glycerol content possessed better oxygen barrier properties, but were more sensitive to RH variation.

Introduction

Combined consumer demands for high quality food products and the desire to reduce adverse environmental consequences of packaging have generated research interest in biodegradable films and coatings. The promise of such materials in food packaging applications arises from their capability to supplement and, possibly, to improve the performance of existing synthetic packaging polymers, with reduced environmental impacts (Krochta and Mulder-Johnston, 1997).

Several proteins have been used as base materials for preparing biodegradable films, including casein, milk whey proteins, maize zein, wheat gluten, soy protein, gelatin and others (Gontard *et al.*, 1992; Mahmoud and Savello, 1992; Avena-Bustillos and Krochta, 1993; Park and Chinnan, 1995; Gennadios *et al.*, 1996a; Arvanitoyannis *et al.*, 1997). In general, the barrier properties of protein films against oxygen and organic vapours are good under low relative humidity (RH) conditions, but weaken considerably as RH is elevated. Due to the inherent hydrophilic nature of proteins, biopolymer films derived from proteins are poor water vapour barriers.

In film preparation, plasticizers are often added to improve film flexibility and stretchability; however, such additives can weaken film barrier properties due to the greater segmental chain mobility of the polymer. Moreover, plasticizers used in biopolymer films are hydrophilic (mainly polyols), and would probably alter the water sensitivity of the plasticized polymer. Therefore, integrated studies involving evaluation of mechanical and barrier properties under various conditions of RH and plasticizer content are necessary in order to assess the end-use performance of biological polymer films.

Transglutaminase (TGase, protein–glutamine γ-glutamyltransferase, EC 2.3.2.13) is an enzyme capable of catalysing acyltransfer reactions, resulting in the formation of ε-(γ-glutaminyl)lysine intra- or intermolecular cross-links in proteins (Nielsen, 1995). Flexible proteins such as bovine caseins are good substrates for this cross-linking reaction (Nio *et al.*, 1985, 1986; Sakamoto *et al.*, 1994). However, globular proteins, such as β-lactoglobulin, α-lactalbumin and bovine serum albumin, are poor substrates due to their compact structures, which limit the accessibility of TGase to the target glutamine and lysine residues (Motoki and Nio, 1983; Mahmoud and Savello, 1992; Dickinson and Yamamoto, 1996; Matsumura *et al.*, 1996). The susceptibility of these globular proteins to TGase can be enhanced by partially unfolding the proteins using various techniques. Mahmoud and Savello (1992), Færgemand *et al.* (1997a) and Yildirim and Hettiarachchy (1997) used dithiothreitol (DTT) to disrupt intramolecular disulphide bonds to unfold globular whey proteins. Dickinson and Yamamoto (1996), Chanyongvorakul *et al.* (1997) and Færgemand *et al.* (1997b) demonstrated that milk proteins adsorbed and partially unfolded at oil–water interfaces were susceptible to cross-linking by the enzyme. Matsumura *et al.* (1996) induced a 'molten globule state', α-lactalbumin by depleting Ca^{2+} from the protein using ethylenediaminetetraacetic acid (EDTA), and showed that the TGase-catalysed cross-linking reaction was enhanced.

Egg yolk has a greater number of applications in the food industry as compared with egg white, leading to a surplus of egg albumen in the egg-breaking industry of North America (Gennadios *et al.*, 1996b). In an effort to develop further uses for this surplus product, we have chosen egg white as the base material for film preparation. Microbial Ca^{2+}-independent TGase has not been used for polymerizing egg white proteins in edible film applications to date, since it has been considered difficult to polymerize egg white proteins by TGase because of their compact structures.

The objectives of this study were: (i) to develop a methodology of utilizing hen egg white proteins to prepare biological polymer films using TGase as a cross-linking agent; (ii) to investigate the effects of plasticizer (glycerol) content and RH on the mechanical properties of the films; and (iii) to evaluate the RH and temperature effects on oxygen barrier properties of the films.

Materials and Methods

Materials

Egg white, separated from fresh hen eggs, was dialysed against deionized distilled water for 2 days at 4°C, freeze-dried and stored in a freezer until use. Commercial grade microbial Ca^{2+}-independent TGase powder was purchased from Ajinomoto Co. (Tokyo, Japan) and partially purified before use. The powder was dispersed in deionized distilled water and centrifuged at 70,000 **g** for 1 h using a Beckman L 8-M Ultracentrifuge (Beckman Instruments, Spinco Division, Palo Alto, California). The supernatant, containing 0.1% TGase, was used for polymerizing the egg white proteins. Glycerol, potassium acetate, potassium carbonate, sodium chloride, sodium nitrite, lithium chloride and potassium chloride were obtained from Fisher Scientific (Nepean, Ontario).

Film formation method

An aqueous solution of freeze-dried egg white powder (4.4%) was prepared and adjusted to pH 10.5 using 1 M NaOH. The resulting solution was heated at 80°C for 20 min in a thermostatted water bath, followed by the addition of glycerol (33–47%, glycerol/glycerol + protein). Undissolved aggregates were removed by filtration. Foams formed as a result of filtration were eliminated by applying and releasing a vacuum to the solution repeatedly until air bubbles disappeared. The egg white solution was then adjusted slowly to pH 8.2 using 0.1 M HCl before adding the enzyme (0.003%). Sodium azide was incorporated as a preservative (0.01%).

The film-forming solution was spread on a levelled glass plate fitted with a rim around the edge. The plate surface was 'polished' with a small quantity of high vacuum silicone lubricant (Dow Corning, Midland, Michigan) and then thoroughly wiped clean using ethanol. This treatment resulted in a glass surface that allowed the films to be easily peelable from the plate. The casting tray was covered with a lid to prevent drying and then incubated at 50°C for 8 h to form a layer of translucent gel. Due to the high RH of the headspace above the gel-forming solution, condensate droplets tended to form on the inner side of the lid and drip into the gelling solution, resulting in films with uneven surfaces. To overcome this problem, a fibreglass screen was fitted underneath the lid to trap the condensate droplets. Subsequent drying of the gel at the same temperature for 12–14 h with the lid removed resulted in a transparent, colourless film.

Electrophoretic analysis of polymerization

Sodium dodecyl sulphate–polyacrylamide gel electrophoresis (SDS–PAGE) was performed according to the method of Laemmli (1970) in a Mini-Protean II Electrophoresis Cell (Bio-Rad Laboratories, Hercules, California). Samples were run on 10% gels. Proteins were dissolved in sample buffer (100 mM Tris–HCl, pH 6.8) in the presence of β-mercaptoethanol, heated for 10 min at 95°C and loaded on to the gel at a concentration of 15 mg per well. Gels were run at a constant current (20 mA per slab gel) and stained with Coomassie brilliant blue R-250 in 10% acetic acid/30% methanol.

Moisture sorption

Moisture sorption isotherms of films containing 35 and 45% glycerol were determined gravimetrically under various RH conditions at 12.5, 25 and 35°C. Heating has been shown to induce changes in physical properties of protein films (Gennadios *et al.*, 1996a; Miller *et al.*, 1997). Therefore, in order to avoid any curing effect that may arise due to the heating process, film samples were cut into small pieces and dried at 30°C for 2 weeks in air-tight glass jars containing desiccant (Drierite, W.A. Hammond Drierite Co., Xenia, Ohio). The dried films were then equilibrated to various moisture contents in glass jars that were maintained at selected RH using appropriate saturated salt solutions (Table 20.1). Equilibrium moisture contents (EMC = gain in mass per dry mass × 100%) were determined when no further weight gain was observed in the samples.

Mechanical testing

Ultimate tensile strength (TS) and elongation at break (E) of the films were determined using an Instron Universal Tester (Instron Corp., Canton, Massachusetts) equipped with pneumatic-action grips. Samples were cut into 15 mm × 80 mm long strips and equilibrated in glass jars maintained under various RH conditions (22°C, Table 20.1) for 3 days before testing. Initial sample length and cross-head speed were 50 mm and 300 mm min^{-1}, respectively. Three thickness measurements were taken along each specimen with a micrometer (Mitutoyo Corp., Japan) and the mean values were taken for calculation. The typical film thickness was 0.10 ± 0.02 mm. TS was calculated from the force at failure divided by the original cross-sectional area of the unstressed sample (filmstrip width × thickness). E was derived from the sample elongation during testing (final stretched length at failure − original gauge length) compared with the original sample length and expressed as a

Table 20.1.   Equilibrium relative humidity values for selected saturated aqueous salt solutions at various temperatures.

Saturated solutions	Relative humidity (%)			
	12.5°C	22°C	25°C	35°C
LiCl	—	11.3	—	—
CH$_3$COOK	23.4	22.9	22.5	20.65
K$_2$CO$_3$	43.2	43.2	43.2	43.2
NaNO$_2$	67.0	65.0	64.4	62.3
NaCl	75.6	75.4	75.3	74.9
KCl	86.4	—	84.3	83.0

From: ASTM, 1985; Young, 1967.

percentage. The effects of glycerol content and RH on the mechanical properties of the egg white films were investigated using the response surface
methodology based on the Central Composite Rotatable Design as described
by Cochran and Cox (1992). The GLM procedure from SAS (SAS Institute,
1989) was used for the statistical analyses.

Oxygen permeability measurement

Oxygen transmission rate (OTR, ml m^{-2} day^{-1}) was determined using an
Ox-Tran permeability tester (Mocon Inc., Minneapolis, Minnesota). Films were
placed in the test cell, where one side (upstream) of the film was exposed to
oxygen and the other (downstream) to nitrogen carrier gas. A gas mixture of
0.5% (v/v) oxygen in nitrogen was used as the upstream gas to prevent
overloading the coulometric sensor. Since the flow rate was low (fixed at 10 ml
min^{-1}), the partial pressure difference (ΔP) across the films was essentially
0.005 atmosphere (0.51 kPa). Testing was performed over a range of RH (≈ 30
to $\approx 80\%$ RH) at three temperature levels (15, 25 and 35°C). Both up- and
downstream sides of the film were maintained at the same pre-determined RH.
Oxygen permeability coefficients (ml µm m^{-2} day^{-1} kPa^{-1}) were calculated by
multiplying the OTR by the film thickness and dividing by the ΔP.

Rheological measurement

The viscoelastic properties of the egg white protein solutions were investigated by dynamic oscillatory measurement using a Carri-Med CSL^2 500 rheometer (TA Instruments, New Castle, Delaware). The rheometer was equipped
with coaxial cylinder fixtures, consisting of a fixed outer cup and rotating bob.
Small deformation sinusoidal shear strains were applied to the samples in their
linear viscoelastic regimes (1% strain amplitude) at a constant frequency of
1 Hz. A constant temperature of 50°C was maintained by circulating a thermostatted fluid through the jacket surrounding the rheometer cup. In order to prevent evaporation of the gelling solution, the annular space above the exposed
egg white protein solution was covered with a thin layer of vegetable oil.

Results and Discussion

Cross-linking of proteins and film formation

At pH values far away from the pI and at low ionic strength, it is possible to
denature egg white proteins thermally without forming coagula due to the
electrostatic repulsion forces that hinder the formation of random aggregates
(Doi *et al.*, 1994). Under these conditions, the proteins are partially unfolded
and are more flexible than when in their native form (Mine *et al.*, 1990).
Proteins in this state are thought to be more susceptible to TGase attack
(Matsumura *et al.*, 1996). In Fig. 20.1, SDS–PAGE patterns of egg white
proteins are shown as functions of incubation time at various pre-heating
temperatures. In contrast to α-lactoglobulin, which has been shown to
be polymerizable by TGase under elevated pH conditions (pH 8.5–9.0;
Færgemand *et al.*, 1997a), evidence from the gel patterns showed that high pH

Pre-heating temperature (°C)

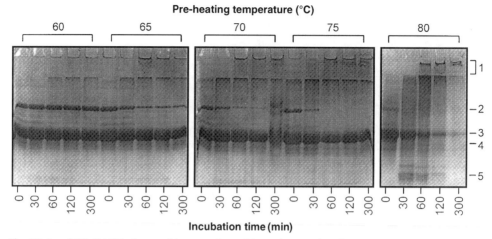

Incubation time (min)

Fig. 20.1. SDS–PAGE of egg white proteins subjected to pre-heating treatments at various temperatures. The protein bands 1, 2, 3, 4 and 5 (1, polymerized proteins; 2, ovotransferrin; 3, ovalbumin; 4, ovomucoid; 5, lysozyme).

alone would not induce sufficient conformational changes for the TGase cross-linking reaction to take place. As shown, only minimal amounts of aggregates were detected when samples were pre-heated at 60°C. As the pre-heating temperature was increased to 80°C, the aggregate bands progressively became more intensified. The formation of aggregates was accompanied by reductions in band intensities of the constituent proteins for the egg white, namely ovalbumin, ovomucoid, lysozyme and ovotransferrin. This provides evidence for the formation of higher molecular weight polymers through intermolecular cross-linking.

The cross-linking reaction was also supported by the oscillatory rheological testing, as reflected by the storage modulus (G') which is a measure of solution or gel elasticity. The protein solutions exhibited very low G' values due to a weak molecular interaction during the onset of TGase treatment, but progressively increased with incubation time and eventually levelled off to maximal G' values (Fig. 20.2). In addition, the rate of development of rigidity in the gels increased with increasing TGase concentrations. These observations suggested that solid-like three-dimensional networks were formed during the incubation treatment, as a consequence of the formation of ε-(γ-glutaminyl)-lysine cross-links in the proteins. Since the rate of gelation was dependent on the TGase concentration, the increase in gel elasticity would be attributable to the TGase-catalysed cross-linking reaction, rather than the incubation treatment effects.

Qualitatively, without the addition of TGase, egg white protein solutions remained in a liquid state even after prolonged periods of incubation. Subsequent drying of the solutions resulted in fragile films that cracked readily upon peeling from the casting tray. In contrast, films produced from protein solutions that went through the gelation process were strong and showed good integrity.

Moisture sorption behaviour

EMC values of egg white protein films were higher at low temperature, and increased rapidly as water activity (a_w) approached unity (Fig. 20.3). The exponential increase of EMC with increasing a_w indicated that water sorption

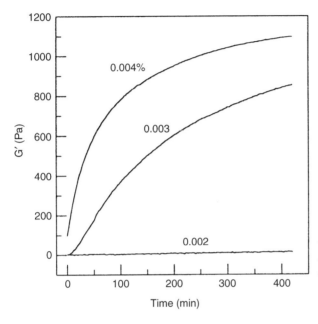

Fig. 20.2. Effects of TGase concentration on the development of elasticity in egg white protein solutions during gelation at 50°C.

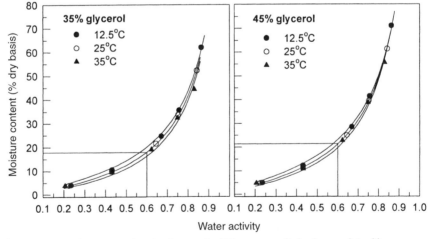

Fig. 20.3. Moisture sorption isotherms for TGase cross-linked egg white films, as affected by temperature and glycerol content. The solid lines were derived from the GAB equation (Equation 20.1). The estimated values of the GAB parameters for the 35% glycerol content films are $M_m = 12.8\%$, $C_0 = 0.00054$, $A_0 = 1.03$, $\Delta H_c = 19,000$ J mol^{-1}, $\Delta H_A = -210$ J mol^{-1}; and for the 45% glycerol film are $M_m = 14.6\%$, $C_0 = 0.0014$, $A_0 = 1.16$, $\Delta H_c = 16,700$ J mol^{-1}, $\Delta H_A = -477$ J mol^{-1}.

in the polymer did not follow Henry's law, i.e., the solubility of water in the polymer varied with the water partial pressure (Brown, 1992). The concomitant plasticization and swelling of the polymer matrix as the moisture content of the film increased, which resulted in the exposure of more binding sites for water sorption, may have caused the enhanced water loading at elevated a_w. The upward curvature of the isotherms may also suggest the formation of water clusters in the polymer matrix as water activities increased (Orofino *et al.*, 1969; Brown, 1980; Starkweather, 1980).

At any given a_w, EMC values were higher for higher glycerol content samples. Since an equal amount of protein was present in each film, the higher EMC observed can be attributed to the larger amount of glycerol incorporated into the polymer. The increased water loading of the films is hypothesized to be a result of the additional polar OH groups introduced by glycerol, resulting in films with higher hydrophilicity.

Due to the water-sensitive nature of the films, an accurate description of the water sorption data is important. The Guggenheim–Anderson–de Boer (GAB) equation, which has been shown to describe moisture sorption isotherms of many food products accurately, was used to model the isotherms (Tsami *et al.*, 1990; Kiranoudis *et al.*, 1993; Lim *et al.*, 1995):

$$M = \frac{M_m A C a_w}{(1 - A a_w)(1 - A a_w + A C a_w)}$$

(20.1)

where constants C and A are temperature dependent according to:

$$C = C_0 \exp\left(\frac{\Delta H_c}{RT}\right)$$

(20.2)

$$A = A_0 \exp\left(\frac{\Delta H_A}{RT}\right)$$

(20.3)

In these equations, M_m (%) is the monolayer moisture content, T is the absolute temperature (K) and R is the universal gas constant (8.314 J mol^{-1} K^{-1}). ΔH_C (J mol^{-1}) and ΔH_A (J mol^{-1}) are the difference in heat of adsorption for monolayer and free water, as compared with that of multilayer water, respectively. To reduce the uncertainties due to successive regressions, Equations 20.2 and 20.3 were substituted into Equation 20.1, and the resulting five-parameter equation was fitted to the sorption data using a non-linear regression procedure, PROC NLIN in SAS (SAS Institute, 1989). The derived GAB equations were plotted as solid lines in Fig. 20.3, showing the goodness of fit to the experimental data.

Based on the Clausius–Clapeyron equation, the net isosteric heat of sorption (ΔH_{st}) can be calculated according to Fennema (1985), Weisser (1985) and Kiranoudis *et al.* (1993). ΔH_{st} is defined as the total heat evolved during the sorption process at a fixed level of moisture content M minus the heat of condensation of free water.

$$\Delta H_{st} = -R\left(\frac{\delta(\ln a_w)}{\delta(1/T)}\right)_M$$

(20.4)

ΔH_{st} values, estimated from the derived GAB equations, are summarized in Fig. 20.4. As shown in the figure, the difference in affinity of water for both films was minimal, although the 35% glycerol samples tended to have slightly higher ΔH_{st} values. This suggested that water molecules may have interacted more strongly with the lower glycerol content films. At higher moisture content levels, it is noteworthy that ΔH_{st} values approached zero. Therefore, the net heat evolved during the sorption process was essentially that of the heat of condensation for free water, implying that a large fraction of water present at high RH was highly mobile.

Mechanical properties

The ultimate tensile strength (TS) represents the maximal tensile force per original cross-sectional area that the film could sustain before breaking, while the elongation at break (E) reflects the extensibility of the material. Relationships between TS and E and experimental factors are presented as three-dimensional response surface plots (Fig. 20.5). As shown, increasing glycerol content and RH strongly decreased the TS of the film, indicating that both water and glycerol were capable of plasticizing the cross-linked egg white protein films. TS was higher and more sensitive to RH variation when the plasticizer content of the film was low, but progressively became weaker and less sensitive to RH as the glycerol content was increased to higher levels. Note that above 70% RH, due to the extensive plasticization effect from the sorbed water, film samples were weak (TS < 2 MPa), with minimal change in TS regardless of the amount of glycerol used. The TS of the polymer is considered to arise from the interaction between polymer molecules at various active sites along the chains. Plasticizers reduce the number of such polymer–polymer

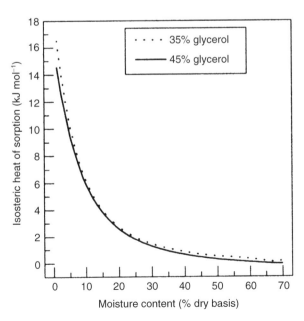

Fig. 20.4. Net isosteric heat of sorption for TGase cross-linked egg white protein films. At a fixed moisture content (*M*), water activity (*a$_w$*) values at various temperatures were estimated from the GAB equation (Equation 20.1).

(A)   (B)

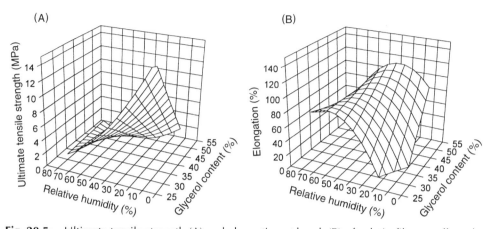

Fig. 20.5. Ultimate tensile strength (A) and elongation at break (B) of gelatin films as affected by relative humidity and glycerol content at 22°C.

interactions by solvating the polar active sites, resulting in polymers with lower cohesive energy densities and therefore weaker physical strength (Paton, 1972; Meier, 1990).

Plasticizers can also be envisaged as 'lubricants' which exist between the polymer chains, allowing the neighbouring molecules to slide past each other more readily, thus increasing the extensibility of the polymer. This effect can be seen in Fig. 20.5B; in general, films with a higher glycerol content possessed high E values. Below intermediate RH values, E increased strongly with increasing glycerol content. Maximal elongation, however, was observed near 50% RH. Above this RH, E dropped slightly and became less influenced by the change in glycerol content.

A stand-alone film should possess not only a reasonably high tensile strength, but also moderate elongation in order to impart flexibility. Although stronger films would be expected when lower amounts of glycerol are used (Fig. 20.5A), the corresponding films would possess very poor flexibility (Fig. 20.5B). Under these conditions, samples tended to crack or break when subjected to stress. In view of the water-sensitive nature of the films, RH conditions during the end-use application should be considered.

Oxygen permeability

As with many reported protein-based edible films (McHugh and Krochta, 1994; McHugh *et al.*, 1994; Gontard *et al.*, 1996; Krochta and Mulder-Johnston, 1997; Miller and Krochta, 1997), transport properties of O_2 in the TGase cross-linked egg white protein films were RH dependent (Fig. 20.6). O_2 permeability coefficients for both films increased rapidly with increasing RH (note that the plots are on logarithmic ordinates) and, in general, higher permeability values were observed for the 45% glycerol films. Moreover, changes in slope were observed near the 50% RH region, particularly for the 35% glycerol films (Fig. 20.6A). It is noteworthy that below about 50% RH, O_2 permeability was

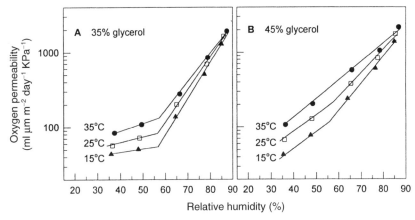

Fig. 20.6.   Oxygen permeability coefficients for TGase cross-linked egg white protein films with 35 and 45% glycerol content, as related to relative humidity and temperature (symbols represent means of two repeated tests).

less sensitive to RH variation for 35% glycerol films as compared with their higher glycerol counterpart. However, it increased more rapidly as RH increased beyond 50% RH, as evidenced by the greater slopes of the plots in contrast to the higher glycerol films. The permeability values eventually became similar for the two film compositions as RH approached saturation.

The increase in O_2 permeability could be related to the increase in diffusivity of the permeant, resulting from the structural plasticization of the protein matrix caused by the sorbed water. The water is believed to increase the free volume of the polymer system and cause a drop in the polymer glass transition temperature (T_g), the temperature above which the macromolecules would possess sufficient energy to allow vibrational motion and undergo a glassy-to-rubbery state transition (Tager, 1978). In activated diffusion, a permeation process is governed by two steps: the thermodynamic dissolution of a permeant in the matrix and the kinetic diffusion of permeant through the matrix, i.e. $P = DS$, where D and S are diffusion and solubility coefficients, respectively (Rogers, 1965; Robertson, 1993). The increase in polymer segmental movement due to the plasticization effects of water would increase the diffusivity of the permeant molecules. Also, as RH increases, the formation of larger water clusters may also favour the solubility of oxygen (Gavara and Hernandez, 1994; Gontard *et al.*, 1996), resulting in an overall increase in O_2 permeability.

The more prominent changes in slope of P versus RH plots for the lower glycerol samples strongly suggest that the permeation of O_2 below and above the 50% RH break point was governed by different mechanisms. According to the free volume theory, the magnitude of T_g depression would depend upon the volume fraction of the plasticizer in the polymer (Cowie, 1991). Below 50% RH, with the lower amounts of water sorbed, the polymer is assumed to exist in a glassy state, i.e. the test temperature $< T_g$. The limited segmental movements of the polymer would reduce the influence of RH upon the O_2 permeability. Accordingly, if the test temperature were elevated, the increased segmental motion would be expected to favour diffusion. This evidence can be seen in Fig. 20.6A, where the change in slope of permeability versus RH plot becomes less prominent when the temperature increases. With the same argument, it can be concluded that the less conspicuous changes in slope for the 45% glycerol samples were due to the existence of the polymer in the rubbery state ($T > T_g$), as a consequence of a more extensive plasticization effect due to the additional glycerol present.

The temperature dependence of permeability (P) can be described according to the classical Arrhenius equation

$$P = P_0 \, \exp - \frac{E_p}{RT}$$
20.5

where P_0 is the pre-exponential constant. E_p is the apparent activation energy for permeation which represents the summation of enthalpy of solution and activation energy of diffusion (Rogers, 1965; Robertson, 1993). As shown in Fig. 20.7, the activation energies estimated for 35% glycerol films were lower than for the 45% glycerol samples, especially in the low RH range. This implies that the O_2 permeability of the former was less sensitive to temperature changes. Over the low RH range, the increase in E_p as RH increased can be associated with the increasing molecular movements as temperature increased (Brown, 1992). As the polymer continued to gain moisture, the concomitant

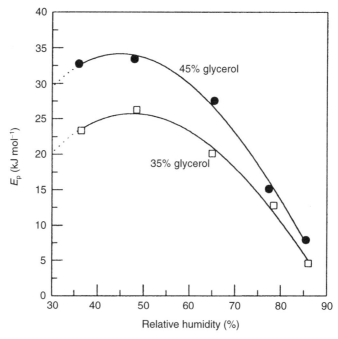

Fig. 20.7.   Apparent activation energy for oxygen permeation (E_p) for TGase cross-linked egg white protein films with 35% and 45% glycerol content, as affected by relative humidity (symbols represent means of two repeated tests).

large-scale molecular motion and swelling of the polymer matrix caused a diminished resistance to the relatively small O_2 molecules; thus, a further increase in temperature would have minimal effect on O_2 permeability (Costello and Koros, 1994).

Conclusions

High pH combined with heat treatments proved to be effective for enhancing the susceptibility of egg white proteins to the cross-linking reaction catalysed by TGase, and may be used in other globular proteins to achieve similar enzymatic polymerization. This method is more favourable than using DTT, which is not approved for use in food applications. Egg white films with a spectrum of mechanical and oxygen barrier properties can be obtained by varying the plasticizer content of the films. In view of the water-sensitive nature of the films, RH conditions during end-uses should be taken into consideration during film fabrication. For instance, when barrier properties are of prime interest and the RH conditions are anticipated to be relative high, low plasticizer content films should be used. In contrast, if mechanical properties are important and the RH conditions are expected to be low, a moderate amount of glycerol should be incorporated into the films.

Acknowledgements

This work was carried out with support from the Natural Sciences and Engineering Research Council of Canada and the George Weston Industrial Research Chair in Food Packaging Technology. The authors also gratefully acknowledge the Ontario Egg Producers' Marketing Board (Canada) for their financial support.

References

Arvanitoyannis, I., Psomiadou, E., Nakayama, A., Aiba, S. and Yamamoto, N. (1997) Edible films made from gelatin, soluble starch and polyols. Part 3. *Food Chemistry* 60, 593–604.

ASTM (1985) Standard practice for maintaining relative humidity by means of aqueous solutions. E 104-85. *Annual Book of American Standard Testing Methods*. ASTM, Philadelphia, Pennsylvania.

Avena-Bustillos, R.J. and Krochta, J.M. (1993) Water vapor permeability of caseinate-based edible films as affected by pH, calcium cross-linking and lipid content. *Journal of Food Science* 58, 904–907.

Brown, G.L. (1980) Clustering of water in polymers. In: Rowland, S.P. (ed.) *Water in Polymers. ACS Symposium Series*. American Chemical Society, Washington, DC, pp. 440–450.

Brown, W.E. (1992) *Plastics in Food Packaging: Properties, Design and Fabrication*. Marcel Dekker, New York, pp. 298–299, 323–324.

Chanyongvorakul, Y., Matsumura, Y., Sawa, A., Nio, N. and Mori, T. (1997) Polymerization of β-lactoglobulin and bovine serum albumin at oil–water interfaces in emulsion by transglutaminase. *Food Hydrocolloids* 11, 449–455.

Cochran, W.G. and Cox, G.M. (1992) *Experimental Designs*. John Wiley & Sons, New York, pp. 346–349.

Costello, L.M. and Koros, W. (1994) Effect of structure on the temperature dependence of gas transport and sorption in a series of polycarbonates. *Journal of Polymer Science, Part B* 32, 701–713.

Cowie, J.M.G. (1991) *Polymers: Chemistry and Physics of Modern Materials*, 2nd edn. Blackie Academic and Professional, Glasgow, UK.

Dickinson, E. and Yamamoto, Y. (1996) Rheology of milk protein gels and protein-stabilized emulsion gels cross-linked with transglutaminase. *Journal of Agricultural and Food Chemistry* 44, 1371–1377.

Doi, E., Tani, F., Murata, M., Koseki, T. and Kitabatake, N. (1994) Heat-induced transparent gels of globular proteins. In: Nishinari, K. and Doi, E. (eds), *Food Hydrocolloids: Structures, Properties and Functions*. Plenum Press, New York, pp. 317–325.

Færgemand, M., Otte, J. and Qvist, K.B. (1997a) Enzymatic cross-linking of whey proteins by a Ca^{2+}-independent microbial transglutaminase from *Streptomyces lydicus*. *Food Hydrocolloids* 11, 19–25.

Færgemand, M., Murray, B.S. and Dickinson, E. (1997b) Cross-linking of milk proteins with transglutaminase at the oil-water interface. *Journal of Agricultural and Food Chemistry* 45, 2514–2519.

Fennema, O.R. (1985) Water and ice. In: Fennema, O.R. (ed.), *Food Chemistry*. 2nd edn. Marcel Dekker, New York, pp. 23–67.

Gavara, R. and Hernandez, R.J. (1994) The effect of water on the transport of oxygen through nylon-6 films. *Journal of Polymer Science, Part B* 32, 2375–2382.

Gennadios, A., Ghorpade, V.M., Weller, C.L. and Hanna, M.A. (1996a) Heat curing of soy protein films. *Transactions of the American Society of Agricultural Engineers* 39, 575–579.

Gennadios, A., Hanna, M.A. and Weller, C.L. (1996b) Glycerine-plasticized egg albumen films. *INFORM* 7, 1074–1075.

Gontard, N., Guilbert, S. and Cuq, J. (1992) Edible wheat gluten films: influence of the main process variables on film properties using response surface methodology. *Journal of Food Science* 57, 190–196.

Gontard, N., Thibault, R., Cuq, B. and Guilbert, S. (1996) Influence of relative humidity and film composition on oxygen and carbon dioxide permeabilities of edible films. *Journal of Agricultural and Food Chemistry* 44, 1064–1069.

Kiranoudis, C.T., Maroulis, Z.B., Tsami, E. and Marinos Kouris, D. (1993) Equilibrium moisture content and heat of desorption of some vegetables. *Journal of Food Engineering* 20, 55–74.

Krochta, J.M. and Mulder-Johnston, C.D. (1997) Edible and biodegradable polymer films: challenges and opportunities. *Food Technology* 51, 61–74.

Laemmli, U.K. (1970) Cleavage of structural proteins during the assembly of the head of bacteriophage T4. *Nature* 222, 680–685.

Lim, L.-T.,Tang, J. and He, J. (1995) Moisture sorption characteristic of freeze dried blueberries. *Journal of Food Science* 60, 810–814.

Mahmoud, R. and Savello, P. (1992) Mechanical properties and water vapor transferability through whey protein films. *Journal of Dairy Science* 75, 942–946.

Matsumura, Y., Chanyongvorakul, Y., Kumazawa, Y., Ohtsuka, T. and Mori, T. (1996) Enhanced susceptibility to transglutaminase reaction of α-lactalbumin in the molten globule state. *Biochimica et Biophysica Acta* 1292, 69–76.

McHugh, T.H. and Krochta, J.M. (1994) Sorbitol- vs glycerol-plasticized whey protein edible films: integrated oxygen permeability and tensile property evaluation. *Journal of Agricultural and Food Chemistry* 42, 841–845.

McHugh, T.H., Aujard, J.F. and Krochta, J.M. (1994) Plasticized whey protein edible films: water vapor permeability properties. *Journal of Food Science* 59, 416–423.

Meier, L. (1990) Plasticizers. In: Gächter, R. and Müller, H. (eds), *Plastics Additives*, 8th edn. Hanser Publishers, New York, pp. 327–420.

Miller, K.S. and Krochta, J.M. (1997) Oxygen and aroma barrier properties of edible films: a review. *Trends in Food Science and Technology* 8, 228–237.

Miller, K.S., Chiang, M.T. and Krochta, J.M. (1997) Heat curing of whey protein films. *Journal of Food Science* 62, 1189–1193.

Mine, Y., Noutomi, T. and Haga, N. (1990) Thermally induced changes in egg white proteins. *Journal of Agricultural and Food Chemistry* 38, 2122–2125.

Motoki, M. and Nio, N. (1983) Cross-linking between different food proteins by transglutaminase. *Journal of Food Science* 48, 561–566.

Nielsen, P.M. (1995) Reactions and potential industrial applications of transglutaminase. Review of literature and patents. *Food Biotechnology* 9, 119–156.

Nio, N., Motoki, M. and Takinami, K. (1985) Gelation of casein and soybean globulins by transglutaminase. *Agricultural and Biological Chemistry* 49, 2283–2286.

Nio, N., Motoki, M. and Takinami, K. (1986) Gelation mechanism of protein solution by transglutaminase. *Agricultural and Biological Chemistry* 50, 851–855.

Orofino, T.A., Hopfenberg, H.B. and Stannett, V. (1969) Characterization of penetrant clustering in polymers. *Journal of Macromolecular Science and Physics, B3* 4, 777–788.

Park, H.J. and Chinnan, M.S. (1995) Gas and water vapor barrier properties of edible films from protein and cellulosic materials. *Journal of Food Engineering* 25, 497–507.

Paton, C. (1972) Theories of plasticizer action. In: Ritchie, P.D., Critchley, S.W. and Hill, A. (eds), *Plasticizers, Stabilizers and Fillers*. Iliffe Books Ltd, London, UK, pp. 39–49.

Robertson, G.L. (1993) *Food Packaging: Principles and Practice*. Marcel Dekker, New York.

Rogers, C.E. (1965) Solubility and diffusivity. In: Fox, D., Labes, M.M. and Arnold, W. (eds), *Physics and Chemistry of the Organic Solid State*. John Wiley and Sons, Inc., New York, pp. 509–635.

Sakamoto, H., Kumazawa, Y. and Motoki, M. (1994) Strength of protein gels prepared with microbial transglutaminase as related to reaction conditions. *Journal of Food Science* 59, 866–871.

SAS Institute Inc. (1989) *SAS/STAT User's Guide*, Version 6, 4th edn, *Vol. 2*. SAS Institute, Cary, North Carolina.

Starkweather, H.W., Jr (1980) Water in nylon. In: Rowland, S.P. (ed.), *Water in Polymers. ACS Symposium Series*. American Chemical Society, Washington, DC, pp. 433–440.

Tager, A. (1978) *Physical Chemistry of Polymers*. Mir Publishers, Moscow, Russia, pp. 559–560.

Tsami, E., Marinos Kouris, D. and Moroulis, Z.B. (1990) Water sorption isotherm of raisins, currants, figs, prunes and apricots. *Journal of Food Science* 55, 1594–1597.

Weisser, H. (1985) Influence of temperature on sorption equilibria. In: Simatos, D. and Multon, J.L. (eds), *Properties of Water In Foods*. Martinus Nijhoff Publishers, Dordrecht, The Netherlands, pp. 95–118.

Yildirim, M. and Hettiarachchy, N.S. (1997) Biopolymers produced by cross-linking soybean 11S globulin with whey proteins using transglutaminase. *Journal of Food Science* 62, 270–275.

Young, J.F. (1967) Humidity control in the laboratory using salt solutions – a review. *Journal of Applied Chemistry* 17, 241–245.

Lysozyme Polymer Formation and Functionality of Residuals after Lysozyme Extraction

21

J. Kijowski[1], G. Lesnierowski[1]
and A. Fabisz-Kijowska[2]

[1]Food Technology Department and [2]Department of Biochemistry and Biotechnology, Agricultural University of A. Cieszkowski, Poznan, Poland

Enzyme activity, purity (measured by electrophoresis, calorimetry and amino acid composition) and recovery of lysozyme were determined when separated from egg white using different extraction methods. Under the optimal conditions of a direct ultrafiltration technique, the recovery did not exceed 20%. More than 60% of the enzyme with an activity of approximately 12,500 U mg^{-1} and high purity was recovered by the crystallization technique. The highest enzyme activity of 24,000 U mg^{-1} and recovery of 87% was obtained using a weakly acidic ion-exchanger. From gel filtration and polyacrylamide gel electrophoresis, it was found that lysozyme thus prepared was highly homogeneous, but revealed polymeric forms of the enzyme. The quantity of dimeric and other polymeric forms was increased by the thermal denaturation of the monomer. The residual egg white after enzyme separation, which was desalted by ultrafiltration, demonstrated good foaming ability and sensory quality similar to that of native egg white.

Introduction

Lysozyme (EC 3.2.17, *N*-acetylmuramic-hydrolase), which was discovered by Fleming in 1922, is a bacteriolytic enzyme commonly found in nature. It is present in almost all secreted body fluids and tissues of humans and animals. It has also been isolated from some plants, bacteria and bacteriophages. A rich and easily available source of lysozyme is the egg white of birds. This enzyme constitutes approximately 3.5% of hen egg white (Osuga and Feeney, 1977).

The bacteriostatic and bactericidal properties of lysozyme have been used to preserve various food items (Yoshitake and Shinischiro, 1977; Cunningham *et al.*, 1991; Proctor and Cunningham, 1991; Kijowski and Lesnierowski, 1995), as well as in pharmacy, medicine and veterinary medicine (Kowalska, 1989; Cunningham *et al.*, 1991; Johnson, 1994; Kiczka, 1994).

Numerous methods are used in the laboratory to separate lysozyme from hen egg white, but only some of them have been used in industry. Alderton and Fevold (1946) developed a classical procedure of obtaining lysozyme, including direct crystallization from egg white. However, a disadvantage of this method is its slowness and inefficiency. Moreover, the functional properties of the remaining egg white deteriorate and thus limit its utilization in the food industry, primarily due to its salinity. Other methods for separating lysozyme include techniques based on adsorption of the enzyme. The most important methods are affinity chromatography (Bailon and Nishikawa, 1977; Weaver *et al.*, 1977; Fernandez-Sousa *et al.*, 1978; Yamada *et al.*, 1985) and ion-exchange chromatography (Ghielmetti and Trinchera, 1968; Ahvenaninen *et al.*, 1979; Banka *et al.*, 1993; Weaver and Carta, 1996).

Considering the physical and chemical properties of lysozyme, especially its low molecular weight, it is plausible to use membrane techniques, especially ultrafiltration (UF). However, detailed data on this method are scarce, and the only information available (Chiang *et al.*, 1993) indicates a limited recovery of lysozyme when separated from egg white and relatively low activity of the obtained enzymatic preparation using a wide range of permeability (10–300 kDa) for the membrane. Also, Durance (1994) reported a low efficiency of UF.

Lysozyme is one of the simplest ubiquitous enzymes. It has long been believed that lysozyme's antimicrobial action could only be attributed to its catalytic effect on certain Gram-positive bacteria, by splitting the bond between N-acetylmuramic acid and N-acetyl-glucosamine of peptidoglycan in the bacterial cell wall. Its structural, physiological (Blake *et al.*, 1965; Imoto *et al.*, 1972) and enzymatic characteristics (Joles and Joles, 1984; Muraki *et al.*, 1988) have been well explained.

In nature, lysozyme is found mainly as a monomer and, like many other natural compounds, might be even more active in dimeric or polymeric form. This enzyme has been reported to exist as a reversible dimer, which can be evoked by pH, concentration and/or temperature-dependent phase transition of the molecule (Sophianopoulos and Holde, 1964).

It has also been found that heat denaturation of lysozyme caused by increasing temperatures results in the progressive loss of enzymatic activity, while its antimicrobial action towards Gram-negative bacteria is greatly promoted (Ibrahim *et al.*, 1996a). Interestingly, lysozyme devoid of enzymatic activity (by heating at 80°C, pH 7.0) exhibited a strong bactericidal activity against not only Gram-positive but also Gram-negative bacteria, suggesting that this type of antibacterial action is independent of catalytic activity. Nowadays, lysozyme is recognized as a particularly interesting substance, which may exhibit a novel, but not completely defined antimicrobial action. Recent reports suggest that this unique antimicrobial action of unfolded lysozyme can be attributed to membrane binding and subsequent perturbation of its functions (Ibrahim *et al.*, 1996b).

It is now evident that, as well as lysozyme's bacteriolytic action, a dimeric form of lysozyme exhibits therapeutic, antiviral and anti-inflammatory properties. The studies conducted so far show that it induces the activity of phagocytizing cells, influences immunological processes by stimulating immunoglobin synthesis, promotes α-interferon synthesis and, most importantly, modulates tumour necrosis factor (TNF) generation (Kiczka, 1994).

The objectives of this chapter were to develop a method for obtaining lysozyme from hen egg white by direct UF and ion-exchange chromatography, and to isolate lysozyme using crystallization for comparison. It was also intended to investigate the formation of dimeric and multimeric forms of lysozyme when isolated from egg white. Furthermore, it was our aim to develop a method for desalting the egg white remaining after lysozyme separation, enabling its further use in food processing.

Materials and Methods

Egg white was separated from fresh hen eggs laid by Astra S laying hens at the experimental farm of the Poultry Research Division of the Department of Animal Husbandry, in Zakrzewo near Poznan.

Separation of lysozyme by direct ultrafiltration

After initial preparation of the material, i.e. breaking the eggs and separating the contents, as well as filtering and homogenizing the egg white, UF was carried out (ultrafiltration unit DDS 20-0.36 Lab, Union Filtration-Sanovo). Polysulphonate membranes with a cut-off of 20 (GR61PP), 30 (FS50PP), 50 (GR51PP) and 100 kDa (GR40PP) were used in the experiments. In order to optimize conditions, the UF process was performed with diluted egg white, where its amount in proportion to water ranged from 1 : 1 to 1 : 6. Different pH levels from 8.0 to 11.0 were used, as well as varying ionic strength of egg white solutions from 0.085 to 0.85.

The retentate (LU) obtained by UF was concentrated and desalted using the UF technique with 2 kDa cut-off membranes, and then was freeze-dried. Samples of natural egg white (EW) and egg white remaining after lysozyme separation (REW) were treated by the same processes.

Separation of lysozyme by ion-exchange

Ion-exchange resin E (Lesnierowski and Kijowski, 1996) with a large exchange capacity and high selectivity against lysozyme was used. Enzyme sorption was carried out in three ways: sonication (ultrasonic wave generator UM-20, Unitra-Unima, Olsztyn, Poland); shaking (wrist shaker, Burrel Co.); and stirring (SJR-1 rotating stirrer).

During lysozyme binding, its residual activity in egg white was determined. Sorption of lysozyme was complete after saturation of the ion-exchanger with enzyme when the lysozyme activity in the egg white sample no longer decreased. After completion of sorption, the residual egg white was decanted and the resin was rinsed exhaustively with distilled water. Following the removal of unbound proteins, lysozyme was eluted from the resin with several bed volumes of phosphate buffer. The eluted lysozyme (LCH) was dialysed and lyophilized. The samples of the natural hen egg white (EW) and the protein residue after enzyme separation (REW) were also lyophilized.

After completion of each lysozyme separation, the resin was regenerated by step-wise washing with HCl, then with NH_4OH, and finally submerged in phosphate buffer.

Separating lysozyme by crystallization

After 0.025% NaCl and crystalline lysozyme were added to egg white adjusted to pH 9.6, the enzyme was crystallized at 4–6°C. Subsequently, the mixture was centrifuged at 2500 g for 15 min. The precipitate containing mainly lysozyme was dissolved in dilute acetic acid at pH 5.0. The solution was centrifuged again to remove insoluble substances. The supernatant obtained was crystallized twice more under the same conditions, resulting in the purified lysozyme preparation (LC3). Samples of EW, REW and lysozyme preparations after the first (LC1), second (LC2) and the third crystallization (LC3) were lyophilized (lyophilizing cabinet GT3, Leybold-Heraeus). Freeze-dried samples were kept in airtight containers until analysed. REW containing NaCl was desalted by UF (ultrafiltration unit DDS 20-0.36 Lab). Polysulphonate membranes GR81PP (cut-off 6 kDa) and GR60PP (cut-off 25 kDa) were used. In order to remove NaCl in a fast, selective way, the diafiltration mode was used. The salt content, foaming ability and foam stability of the desalted egg white were determined. A model sample of confectionery, i.e. meringue, was evaluated.

Determination of physical and chemical characteristics of lysozyme

The enzymatic activity of lysozyme was determined by a spectrophotometric method using *Micrococcus lysodeikticus* (Shugar, 1952; Lesnierowski and Kijowski, 1995). A unit of biological activity (U) was calculated as the amount of enzyme which decreased the absorbance at 450 nm by 0.001 for a *M. lysodeikticus* suspension in 1 min at pH 6.24. Total protein content was measured by the Kjeldahl method (Kjeltec, type 1026, Tecator Co.) and the moisture content by drying to constant weight (Moisture Analyser, model MA30, Sartorius Co.).

To determine the amino acid composition, acid hydrolysis of samples was performed for 24 h in 6 M HCl. Amino acids were analysed using the automatic analyser AAA-T-339 (Mikrotechna). Chloride in the sample preparations was determined by the Mohr method, according to the Polish Standard (PN-73/A-82112).

Electrophoresis

SDS–PAGE was performed with the SE-600 apparatus (Hoefer Scientific Instruments) according to Laemmli (1970). The running gel and stacking gel with acrylamide concentrations of 12.5 and 5%, respectively, were used to separate proteins. The stained protein bands were measured using a densitometer model GS300 with computer software V3.02 (Hoefer Scientific Instruments).

To analyse monomers, dimers and higher polymers of lysozyme, electro-phoresis was performed on a 15% polyacrylamide gel under dissociating conditions with and without 2-mercaptoethanol, according to Laemmli, with some modifications; without 2-mercaptoethanol, covalent associations between protein molecules can occur. In the absence of the reducing agent, the intra- and inter-chain disulphide bonds of sample proteins remain intact (Garfin, 1990). Lydium-KLP (Nika Health Products), a veterinary medicine, was used as a standard of the dimeric form of lysozyme.

Calorimetry

Thermodynamic parameters were determined in a differential scanning calorimeter (DSC-7, Perkin-Elmer). Samples were moistened with deionized water (0.2 ml g^{-1}). The wetted samples of approximately 10 mg were placed in aluminium cups with a capacity of 20 μl, which were then made airtight with a Universal Press USP B013-9005 (Perkin-Elmer). After inserting the sealed cups into the calorimeter chamber, they were heated from 30 to 100°C at a rate of 5°C min^{-1}. An empty cup served as a reference. The enthalpy curve was moni-tored using a data processing system (1020 System Controller, Perkin-Elmer).

Column chromatography

Column chromatography was performed with porous polyacrylamide beads (Bio-Gel P-100, fractionation range 5000–100,000 Da, Bio-Rad). The columns were run at various pHs in the range 5.0–8.0 in 0.05 M phosphate (or citric acid/phosphate) buffer containing salt (NaCl) and/or non-ionic detergent (Triton X-100). The lysozyme substrate used was chitosan (deacetylated chitin, natural biodegradable polymer produced by Sea Fisheries Institute, Gdynia, Poland). The columns were calibrated with molecular size markers: bovine serum albumin (BSA), ovalbumin, cytochrome *c* and myoglobin. The effluent was monitored by measuring absorbance at 289 nm and the enzymatic activity (Lesnierowski and Kijowski, 1995).

Comparison of lysozyme separation

The efficiency of the lysozyme separation methods was compared on the basis of enzymatic activity, purity and recovery. Enzyme activity was expressed as U mg^{-1} of protein.

The extent of enzyme purification was expressed as the lysozyme activity compared with the activity of lysozyme in the original egg white. Separation recovery was expressed as a proportion of the amount of separated lysozyme relative to its content in the original egg white.

Functional properties of treated egg white

Foaming ability of egg white was determined according to the Polish Standard (PN-91/A86507). The method is based on the measurement of the percentage increase in the volume of egg white after the foam is prepared under standard conditions using a Hobart mixer. Foam stability was assessed by measuring the volume of egg white drip derived from the foam at 30 and 120 min after foaming.

Meringues were prepared from both egg white preparations (EW and REW) and were then subjected to sensory evaluation (Barylko-Pikielna, 1975). The evaluations were carried out by a team of 8–12 people who were given detailed instructions on the method of testing before each trial. The principle of evaluation was to determine the differences between meringues prepared with egg white remaining after lysozyme separation (REW) and a standard sample of meringues made from native egg white.

Statistical calculations

Computer software SPSS PC+ was used. The significance level was determined at $P = 0.05$, $n = 10$.

Results and Discussion

As a result of the experiments, lysozyme preparations were obtained using three methods: UF, chromatography and crystallization. Moreover, a method of UF to desalt the hen egg white remaining after enzyme separation was developed.

Lysozyme separation from egg white

Studies on UF for lysozyme isolation showed that the specific lysozyme activity in the separated enzyme preparations and its purity were dependent on the extent of dilution of the egg white, its pH and ionic strength. The results shown in Table 21.1 for UF conducted under optimal conditions indicate, however, low recoveries of the enzyme. A significant increase in the recovery was observed only when membranes with a high cut-off were used (Table 21.2). With an increase in the cut-off value, a considerably higher activity of the lysozyme preparations was observed (Table 21.2).

The increment in enzyme activity in the investigated range of cut-offs was not uniform, and the highest value ($\Delta = 4655$ U mg^{-1}) was observed for membranes of 20–30 kDa (Table 21.2). The results may indicate the possibile formation of lysozyme oligomers present in the filtered preparations, without excluding formation lysozyme complexes with other proteins of egg white.

Table 21.1. Effect of egg white preparation conditions on the characteristics of lysozyme obtained by direct ultrafiltration (LU).

Investigated parameter	Value	Activity (U mg^{-1})	Degree of enzyme purification	Percentage of recovered enzyme
Dilution	1 : 3	3240[a] ± 67	4.78[a] ± 0.03	2.03[a] ± 0.02
pH value	10.0	3558[b] ± 66	4.80[a] ± 0.03	2.25[b] ± 0.02
Ionic strength (mol)	0.85	7408[c] ± 73	9.75[b] ± 0.03	6.23[c] ± 0.03

[a,b,c]Mean values in columns denoted by varying letters differ significantly, $P \leq 0.05$.

The above suggestions were confirmed by the polyacrylamide gel electrophoresis analysis of proteins in the preparations obtained (Fig. 21.1). Lysozyme monomer has a molecular weight 14,300 Da appearing on the electrophoregram in all preparations. Using membranes with cut-offs of 30 and 50 kDa, additional bands appear, corresponding to lysozyme dimer (28 kDa) and trimer (43 kDa). With 100 kDa membranes, bands corresponding to higher molecular weight proteins are observed, probably as a result of contamination with ovalbumin (45 kDa) or conalbumin (75 kDa). This assumption was supported by the amino acid composition of all lysozyme preparations (Table 21.3). In the case of lysozyme separated by UF (LU), the amino acid composition is much more similar to that of egg white than that of other preparations (LC and LCH).

The best enzyme preparation in terms of quality was obtained by using ion-exchange chromatography (Table 21.4, Fig. 21.2). The enzyme activity of 23,000 U mg^{-1} was not only higher than those of lysozymes obtained by

Table 21.2. Properties of lysozyme separated by direct ultrafiltration with membranes of different cut-offs, at an NaCl concentration of 0.85 M and a pH of 10.0.

Membrane cut-off (kDa)	Activity (U mg^{-1})	Degree of enzyme purification	Percentage of recovered enzyme
20	2,589[a] ± 80	3.50[a] ± 0.04	1.15[a] ± 0.02
30	7,244[b] ± 114	7.97[b] ± 0.04	6.28[b] ± 0.03
50	9,470[c] ± 56	13.28[c] ± 0.03	9.85[c] ± 0.07
100	12,357[d] ± 48	16.95[d] ± 0.03	19.75[d] ± 0.16

[a-d]See Table 21.1.

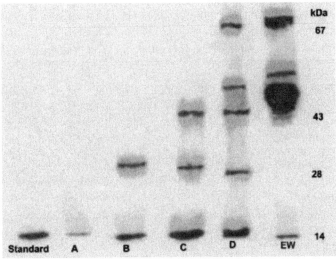

Fig. 21.1. SDS–PAGE analysis of lysome obtained by ultrafiltration. Lysozyme obtained with membranes with cut-offs of: A, 20 kDa; B, 30 kDa; C, 50 kDa; and D, 100 kDa.

Table 21.3.   Amino acid composition of lysozyme obtained by crystallization (LC), ultrafiltration (LU) and ion-exchange chromatography (LCH).

Amino acid	% of total amino acid				
	LC	LU	LCH	Standard	Egg white
Aspartic acid	15.79	10.47	15.41	15.57	10.22
Threonine	4.77	4.17	4.86	4.74	4.50
Serine	5.63	5.94	5.61	5.51	9.00
Glutamic acid	5.17	12.27	5.58	5.14	12.72
Proline	2.62	3.51	2.52	1.90	3.67
Cystine	8.36	6.46	8.85	6.56	2.68
Glycine	5.08	6.34	7.14	7.14	5.62
Alanine	6.21	5.40	6.09	6.11	9.08
Valine	3.61	5.66	3.86	3.90	6.80
Methionine	1.83	3.97	2.01	2.31	3.23
Isoleucine	3.92	4.24	3.90	3.98	4.42
Leucine	5.98	7.01	6.02	6.09	8.16
Tyrosine	3.47	3.89	3.65	3.46	2.69
Phenylalanine	2.98	4.82	2.97	3.39	4.53
Histidine	2.44	2.46	2.34	2.09	1.78
Lysine	6.19	5.69	5.89	5.54	6.72
Arginine	11.02	5.63	10.40	10.51	4.10

Table 21.4.   Properties of lysozyme separated on an ion-exchanger with the use of different techniques aiding sorption.

Sorption-aiding technique	Activity $(U\ mg^{-1})$	Degree of enzyme purification	Percentage of recovered enzyme
Sonication	$22{,}527^a \pm 135$	$26.8^a \pm 0.2$	$72.2^a \pm 0.3$
Shaking	$23{,}658^b \pm 133$	$28.2^b \pm 0.2$	$87.1^b \pm 0.4$
Stirring	$23{,}921^b \pm 138$	$28.5^b \pm 0.2$	$87.0^b \pm 0.3$

[a,b]See Table 21.1.

crystallization and UF, but also higher than that of the standard lysozyme produced by Park (21,253 U mg⁻¹). The highest degree of purification was obtained for the LCH preparation, which was even higher than the best sample obtained by crystallization (Fig. 21.3).

The results of electophoretic and calorimetric examinations (DSC) confirmed the high quality of the preparation obtained by chromatography (Fig. 21.4). As mentioned above, the results of the amino acid composition analysis of the preparations obtained using the different methods indicate that LCH is best in terms of quality and similar to the standard lysozyme (Table 21.3). Chromatography provided the highest recovery of the enzyme from egg white (Fig. 21.5) A total of 86% of lysozyme was recovered with this method, whereas the corresponding figures for crystallization and UF were 62 and only

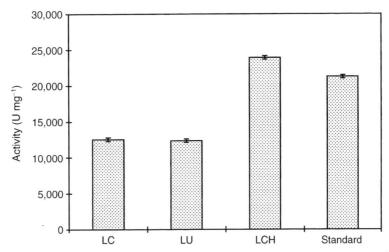

Fig. 21.2. Activity of lysozyme obtained by crystallization (LC), ultrafiltration (LU) and ion-exchange chromatography (LCH). The bars (I) denote the lowest significant difference at $P \leq 0.05$.

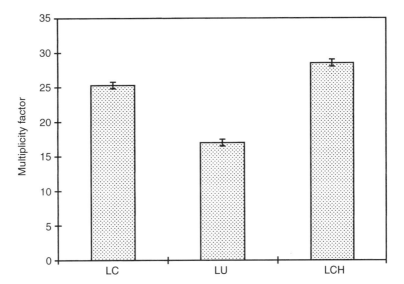

Fig. 21.3. Lysozyme purification obtained by crystallization (LC), ultrafiltration (LU) and ion-exchange chromatography (LCH). The bars (I) denote the lowest significant difference at $P \leq 0.05$.

19.8%, respectively. From these data, it can be concluded that ion-exchange is in all respects the best method. Moreover, the fact that no extra chemical compounds are required to be added to egg white during preparation simplifies the procedure.

Lysozyme obtained by crystallization from egg white was used to compare the quality with that of preparations obtained by direct UF and ionic-exchange

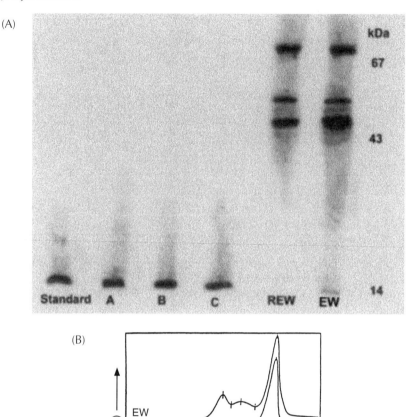

Fig. 21.4. (A) SDS–PAGE and (B) calorimetric (DSC) analysis of lysozyme obtained by ion-exchange chromatography. Lysozyme obtained by: A, sonication; B, shaking; and C, stirring.

chromatography, as well as that of the commercial standard. The results shown in Table 21.5 demonstrate the changes in quality of the enzyme preparations obtained after crystallizations. A significant increase in specific activity of lysozyme was observed, from 1650 U mg^{-1} after the first crystallization to

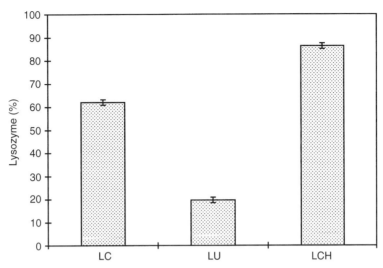

Fig. 21.5.   Recovery of lysozyme isolated from egg white by crystallization (LC), ultrafiltration (LU) and ion-exchange chromatography (LCH). The bars (I) denote the lowest significant difference at $P \leq 0.05$.

Table 21.5.   Properties of lysozyme obtained from egg white by crystallization.

Fraction	Activity (U mg^{-1})	Degree of enzyme purification	Percentage of recovered enzyme
LC1	1,639[a] ± 45	3.3[a] ± 0.2	66.5[c] ± 0.2
LC2	6,673[b] ± 67	13.5[b] ± 0.1	63.7[b] ± 0.2
LC3	12,535[c] ± 114	25.3[c] ± 0.2	62.1[a] ± 0.2

[a,b,c]See Table 21.1.

12,535 U mg^{-1} after the last crystallization. A considerable increase was also observed in the degree of enzyme purification (from 3.3 to 25.3). Electophoretic as well as calorimetric examinations (Fig. 21.6) again supported the increase in purity of the lysozyme preparations. In addition to high activity and purity of the enzyme preparations, a high efficiency of the process was also achieved. After crystallization for 96 h, a total of 66.5% of the enzyme included in the egg white was recovered.

Investigation of the molecular form of lysozyme

Gel filtration chromatography

In all experiments, different pHs were used for eluents (within the range of pH 5.0 of citric/phosphate to pH 8.0 of phosphate buffer) with and without salt (0.15 and 0.5 M NaCl), in the presence of the non-ionic detergent Triton X-100 (0.5 and 1%) or chitosan. Most (80–90%) of the lysozyme (LCH) was eluted from a Bio-Gel P100 column as a monomer, even when the pH deviated from pH 7.

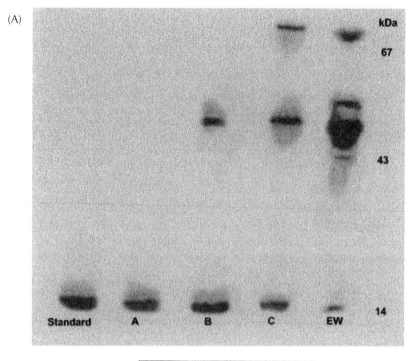

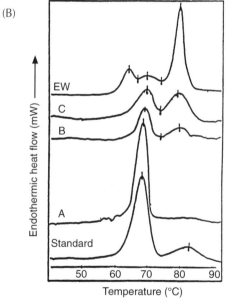

Fig. 21.6. (A) SDS–PAGE and (B) calorimetric (DSC) analysis of lysozyme obtained by crystallization. A, lysozyme after third crystallization; B, lysozyme after second crystallization; and C, lysozyme after first crystallization.

PAGE analysis

When the lysozyme preparation was heated at 80°C for 30 min, formation of dimers and higher polymers (trimers, tetramers, etc.) was observed (Fig. 21.7, lane 8). The thermal denaturation of preparations followed by electrophoretic analysis under denaturing and partly denaturing conditions (with or without 2-mercaptoethanol in the sample buffer) revealed that only the samples run without this denaturing agent showed a marked band for multimeric forms on the gel in addition to the monomeric form (Fig. 21.7, lanes 4, 6 and 8). However, in the samples run with 2-mercaptoethanol, no similar polymeric forms were clearly observed. No distinct changes in electrophoretic pattern were observed in the case of lysozyme dimer preparation tested in the same way as the lysozyme monomer (Fig. 21.7, lanes 3, 5 and 7).

In all experiments using different preparations of lysozyme, the formation of discrete polymeric forms was observed when a high concentration of

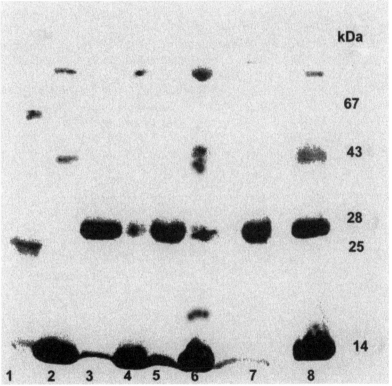

Fig. 21.7. SDS–PAGE electrophoretic pattern of lysozyme and Lydium (lysozyme dimer) run in denatured and partly denatured conditions (without 2-mercaptoethanol) on a 15% gel. Lane 1, molecular weight markers (BSA, chymotrypsinogen and lysozyme); lanes 2 and 3, lysozyme and Lydium denatured in the sample buffer with 2-mercaptoethanol; lanes 4 and 5, lysozyme and Lydium denatured without 2-mercaptoethanol; lanes 6 and 7, lysozyme and Lydium run without both denaturants; lane 8, lysozyme preparation heated for 30 min at 80°C at pH 7.0 and afterwards run on the gel without 2-mercaptoethanol.

protein was applied to the SDS–gel (Fig. 21.8A, lanes 2, 3 and 4; and B, lanes 2 and 3). These observations also strongly support the presence of polymeric forms of lysozyme in biological fluids, such as hen egg white. It is also evident that the reduction of the sulphydryl group prevents the polymerization.

It has been reported that denaturation of the molecule exposes two sulphydryl groups, which can form disulphide bridges with the adjacent molecule, thus forming polymers when oxidized (Ibrahim *et al.*, 1996a). In contrast, a commercially obtained preparation of veterinary medicine Lydium-KLP (lysozyme dimer) contains mostly the dimeric form with a minimal content of the monomeric form (Fig. 21.8B, lane 4).

Evaluation of egg white remaining after lysozyme separation (REW)

Economically, it is preferable to utilize all the egg white components remaining after lysozyme separation. In the case of crystallization for lysozyme separation, the main problem is the presence of high concentrations of salt, which limits the further utilization of REW. Therefore, an attempt was made to desalt REW using UF.

In addition to determination of the NaCl content before and after UF, foaming ability and foam stability were evaluated. A meringue baked with the desalted egg white was also evaluated for taste. The NaCl content decreased from 5.73% in the REW fraction to 1.18% in the DREW-6 fraction after diafiltration using 6 kDa cut-off membranes of type GR81PP (Table 21.6). A reduction of 83% of salt was achieved; however, the process was quite slow. To expedite the process, GR60PP membranes with a cut-off of 25 kDa were used. A more intensive desalting of 87% with 0.91% NaCl in the DREW-25

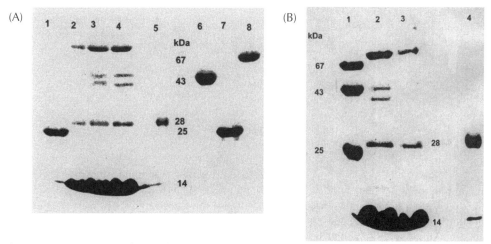

Fig. 21.8.   SDS–PAGE of a number of lysozyme preparations in a 15% gel. (A) Lanes 2, 3 and 4 represent increasing amounts of lysozyme preparation; lanes 1, 7,6 and 8, molecular weight markers (chymotrypsinogen, ovalbumin and BSA, respectively). In lane 5, the Lydium preparation was run (B) Lane 1, molecular weight markers (as above); lanes 2 and 3, lysozyme concentrated by trichloroacetic acid precipitation; lane 4, Lydium.

fraction was successful. This salt content of less than 1.0% did not affect the taste of meringue, achieving very high scores from the panel of tasters. The foaming ability of REW was high, being close to 400%, without a significant difference from that of the untreated control (Fig. 21.9).

Conclusion

A highly pure and active lysozyme preparation was obtained by ion-exchange chromatography of egg white. Although inefficient in terms of lysozyme separation, UF was useful in desalting the leftover egg white after lysozyme crystallization. Salting out crystallization resulted in a 60% recovery of lysozyme. However, the enzyme activity was not high (12,535 U mg^{-1}), and was similar to that of lysozyme produced by UF (12,357 U mg^{-1}).

Under the most favourable conditions of sorption with the ion-exchange resin, lysozyme activity was as high as 24,000 U mg^{-1}, with a good recovery of

Table 21.6. Sodium chloride content in liquid egg white remaining after lysozyme crystallization (REW fraction) and in desalted egg white (fractions DREW-6 and DREW-25).

Fraction	Sodium chloride content
REW	5.79[c] ± 0.11
DREW-6	1.18[b] ± 0.05
DREW-25	0.91[a] ± 0.05

[a,b,c]See Table 21.1.

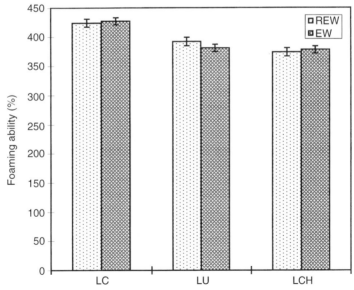

Fig. 21.9. Foaming ability of residual egg white (REW) in comparison with native egg white (EW) after separation of lysozyme by crystallization (LC), ultrafiltration (LU) and ion-exchange chromatography (LCH). The bars (I) denote the lowest significant difference at $P \le 0.05$.

87%. Since no additive was required, the remaining egg white maintained high quality even after processing.

The foaming properties of egg white remaining after lysozyme separation were not different from those of untreated egg white.

References

Ahvenaninen, R., Heikonen, M., Kreula, M., Linko, M. and Linko, P. (1979) Separation of lysozyme from egg white. *Food Process Engineering* 2, 301–310.

Alderton, G. and Fevold, H.L. (1946) Direct crystallization of lysozyme from egg white and some crystalline salts of lysozyme. *Journal of Biological Chemistry* 164, 1–5.

Bailon, P. and Nishikawa, A.H. (1977) Affinity purification methods. A novel and rapid isolation procedure for lysozyme. *Preparative Biochemistry* 7, 61–66.

Banka, L., Petrovic, S. and Becarevic, A. (1993) Lysozyme isolation from hen egg white on Fractogel TSK CM-650. *Lebensmittel Wissenschaft und Technologie* 26, 76–79.

Barylko-Pikielna, N. (1975) *An Outline of Sensory Analysis of Food (Zarys analizy Sensorycznej zywnosci).* Wydawnictwo Naukowo-Techniczne, Warszawa, s. 241–248.

Blake, C.C.F., Koeing, D.F., Mair, G.A., North, A.T.C., Phillips, D.C. and Sarma, V.R. (1965) Structure of hen egg-white lysozyme. *Nature* 206, 757–761.

Chiang, B.H., Su, C.K., Tsai, G.J. and Tsao, G.T. (1993) Egg white lysozyme purification by ultrafiltration and affinity chromatography. *Journal of Food Science* 58, 303–306.

Cunningham, F.E., Proctor, V.A. and Goetsch, S.J. (1991) Egg white lysozyme as a food preservative. *World's Poultry Science Journal* 47, 141–163.

Durance, T.D. (1994) Separation, purification, and thermal stability of lysozyme and avidin fom chicken egg white. In: Sim, J.S. and Nakai, S. (eds), *Egg Uses and Processing Technologies.* CAB International, Wallingford, UK, pp. 77–93.

Fernandez-Sousa, J.M., Perez-Castells, R. and Rodriguez, R.A. (1978) A simple one-step chromatographic procedure for the purification of lysozyme. *Biochimica et Biophysica Acta* 523, 430–434.

Garfin, D.E. (1990) One dimensional gel electrophoresis. *Methods in Enzymology* 182, 425–441.

Ghielmetti, G. and Trinchera, C. (1968) Process for the production of lysozyme. UK Patent. Nr. 1110466.

Ibrahim, H.R., Higashiguchi, S., Juneja, L.R., Kim, M. and Yamamoto,T. (1996a) A structural phase of heat-denatured lysozyme with novel antimicrobial action. *Journal of Agricultural and Food Chemistry* 44, 1416–1423.

Ibrahim, H.R., Higashiguchi, S., Koketsu, M., Juneja, L.R., Kim, M., Yamamoto,T., Sugimoto, Y. and Aoki, T. (1996b) Partially unfolded lysozyme at neutral pH agglutinates and kills Gram-negative and Gram-positive bacteria through membrane damage mechanism. *Journal of Agricultural and Food Chemistry* 44, 3799–3806.

Imoto, T., Johnson, L.N., North, A.C.T., Phillips, D.C. and Rupley, J.A. (1972) Vertebrate lysozymes. In: *The Enzymes.* Academic Press, New York, pp. 665–868.

Jolles, P. and Jolles, J. (1984) What is new in lysozyme research? *Molecular and Cellular Biochemistry* 63, 165–189.

Johnson, E.A. (1994) Egg white lysozyme as a preservative for use in foods. In: Sim, J.S. and Nakai, S. (eds), *Egg Uses and Processing Technologies.* CAB International, Wallingford, UK, pp. 177–191.

Kiczka, W. (1994) From lysozyme monomer to lysozyme dimer (review). *Zycie Weterynaryjne* 4A, 131–136.

Kijowski, J. and Lesnierowski, I,G. (1995) The use of lysozyme for food preservation and in medical diagnosis and pharmacology. *Biotechnologia* 2, 130–140.

Kowalska, M. (1989) Immunizing properties of lysozyme. *Medycyna Weterynaryjna* 45(6), 323–326.

Laemmli, U.K. (1970) Cleavage of structural proteins during the assembly of the head of bacteriophage T4. *Nature* 227, 680–685.

Lesnierowski, G. and Kijowski, J.M. (1995) Methods of enzymatic activity evaluation and quantitative estimation of hen egg-white lysozyme. *Przemysl Spozywczy* 12, 476–479.

Lesnierowski, G. and Kijowski, J. (1996) Application of ion-exchangers for separation of lysozyme from hen egg white. In: *Proceedings of the XXVI Research Conference of KTiChZ PAN*. Szczecin, pp. 124–125.

Muraki, M., Morikawa, M., Jigami, Y. and Tanaka, H. (1988) Engineering of human lysosyme as a polyelectrolyte by the alteration of molecular surface change. *Protein Engineering* 2, 49–54.

Osuga, D.T. and Feeney, R.E. (1977) Egg proteins, In: Whitaker, J.R. (ed.), *Food Proteins*. The AVI Publishing Company, Westport, Connecticut, pp. 209–221.

Polish Standard (1991) PN-91/A 86507. *Egg Products. Sampling and Testing Methods*. Polish Standard (1973) PN-73/A-82112. *Determination of Salt Content in Food*.

Proctor, V.A. and Cunningham, F.E. (1991) Activity of egg white lysozyme in various food systems. In: *Proceedings of the 4th European Symposium on The Quality of Eggs and Egg Products*. Doorwerth, The Netherlands, pp. 201–208.

Shugar, D. (1952) Measurement of lysozyme activity. *Biochimica et Biophysica Acta* 8, 302–309.

Sophianopoulos, A.J. and Holde, K.E. (1964) Physical studies of muramidase (lysozyme). II. pH-dependent dimerization. *Journal of Biological Chemistry* 239, 2516–2524.

Weaver, L.E., Jr and Carta, G. (1996) Protein adsorption on cation exchangers: comparison of macroporous and gel-composite media. *Biotechnology Progress* 12, 342–355.

Weaver, G.L., Kroger M. and Katz, F. (1977) Deaminated chitin affinity chromatography: a method for isolation, purification and concentration of lysozyme. *Journal of Food Science* 42, 1084–1087.

Yamada, H., Fukumura, T., Ito, Y. and Imoto, T. (1985) Chitin-coated celite as an affinity adsorbent for high-performance liquid chromatography of lysozyme. *Analytical Biochemistry* 146, 71–75.

Yoshitake, S. and Shinichiro, A. (1977) Use of egg white lysozyme in the food industry. *New Food Industry* 19, 7–22.

IgY Technologies

Control of Intestinal Diseases in Pigs by Feeding Specific Chicken Egg Antibodies

22

R.R. Marquardt

Department of Animal Science, University of Manitoba,
Winnipeg, Manitoba, Canada

The yolk of immunized chickens is a rich and inexpensive source of polyclonal antibodies. Relatively small amounts of highly conserved mammalian proteins are sufficient to induce a sustained immune response, with one egg yielding more than 100 mg of specific antibodies. Chicken egg yolk antibodies when administered orally can be used for passive immunization against infectious diarrhoeal diseases in animals. Therefore, these antibodies offer practical means of controlling certain intestinal disease caused by microorganisms such as enterotoxigenic *Escherichia coli* (ETEC) in domestic livestock, particularly the early weaned pig. In our laboratory, egg yolk antibodies obtained from hens immunized with fimbrial antigens from a local strain of ETEC K88+ were used in challenge studies of 3- and 14-day-old piglets. Piglets fed egg yolk with anti-ETEC antibodies only had transient diarrhoea, nearly all survived and all of the survivors had positive weight gains. In contrast, control piglets that were treated with egg yolk powder that did not contain the specific antibodies had severe diarrhoea, were dehydrated, lost weight and several died within 48 h. Antibody-treated pigs did not excrete K88+ ETEC whereas the challenged pigs did. Other researchers have reported similar results. Adhesion studies with specific ETEC K88+ receptors isolated from the mucus of piglets demonstrated that the chicken antibodies could prevent the binding of the ETEC to the receptors, supporting the observation that antibodies can block the effects of *E. coli*. These results demonstrated that small amounts of chicken egg yolk antibodies are highly effective at protecting piglets against the pathogenic effects of ETEC. The same treatment can be used to control other diseases in all classes of livestock and probably humans.

Introduction

It has been well recognized that diarrhoeal disease caused by enterotoxigenic *Escherichia coli* (ETEC) is by far the most common enteric colibacillosis encountered in neonatal pigs (Morris and Sujka, 1985; Yokayama *et al.*, 1992; Alexander, 1994; Hampson, 1994). It is also known that colonization of the small intestine of the pig by ETEC adhering to the epithelium accounts for most gastrointestinal disorders in both neonatal and post-weaning piglets (Yokoyama *et al.*, 1992; Alexander, 1994; Hampson, 1994). In a recent survey of pre-weaning disease, diarrhoea had the highest morbidity and represented 11% of the pre-weaning mortality, with ETEC being the primary and sole infectious cause (Alexander, 1994). A second disease, referred to as post-weaning *E. coli* diarrhoea (PWD), starts 3–10 days after weaning. This disease is a major cause of economic losses to the pig industry from both mortality and reduced growth rates, and is the most common cause of post-weaning mortality on many farms, killing 1.5–2% of pigs weaned (Hampson, 1994).

The strains of ETEC that are associated with intestinal colonization are those that express the K88, K99 and 987P fimbrial adhesins. These adhesins are located in the rod-like pili (fimbriae) that extend from the *E. coli* and are bound to specific receptors on the intestinal wall. Therefore, they provide a highly specific means of anchoring the *E. coli* to the host animal, a prerequisite for an infectious agent. Among the different ETEC, those expressing the K88+ fimbrial antigen are the most prevalent form of *E. coli* infection found worldwide wherever pigs are raised in high numbers (Rapacz and Hasler-Rapacz, 1986). It has been estimated that K88+ ETEC are responsible for 50% of the 10 million piglet deaths each year (Waters and Sellwood, 1982).

The problems associated with diarrhoea in neonatal and post-weaning pigs will become more serious in the future. A trend towards large, intensive herds is an important cause. The trend towards early weaning (at 14–21 days rather than 21–28 days of age) is another. In addition, the increased incidence of antibiotic resistance in microorganisms and the pressure by regulatory agents to ban or greatly reduce the use of antibiotics in feeds are also problems. This review presents an overview of means of controlling enteric diseases in piglets using therapeutic antibodies with emphasis on ETEC strain K88.

Early Weaning and Diarrhoeal Disease

Emphasis by the swine industry on increasing the number of pigs weaned per year favours a decreased weaning age. This has been the trend in swine production for many years. However, the early weaned pig has been typically characterized by poor growth performance (post-weaning 'lag' Fig. 22.1). The young pig, before weaning, receives sows milk that is highly palatable, readily digestible and has a high level of immunoglobulins in the colostrum. At weaning, the young pig is often fed a dry plant-based diet that has a high content of complex carbohydrates that is not utilized readily. Low digestibility of soybean proteins, a transient hypersensitive response to soybean meal and, possibly, the inability to resist enteric diseases may contribute to the poor growth of

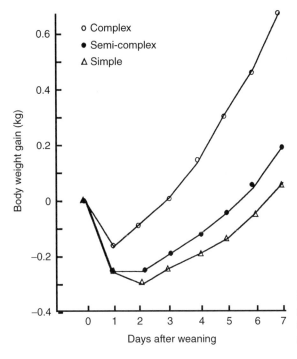

Fig. 22.1. Post-weaning growth rate of pigs weaned at 3 weeks of age, first week. (From Okai *et al.*, 1976.)

early weaned pigs. Weaning as early as 3 weeks of age has been accomplished for a number of years by the use of complex diets (Okai *et al.*, 1976). Such diets have minimized but have not prevented post-weaning lag at 3 weeks of age. An exciting recent development is the incorporation of spray-dried porcine protein (plasma protein), a by-product of blood obtained from pork slaughter plants, into the diet of early weaned pigs. Recently, many trials have been carried out with plasma protein (Table 22.1). These studies indicate that plasma protein consistently and dramatically improved feed intake and weight gain in young pigs, with the effect being most evident within a week of weaning. In addition, the scour score was reduced, suggesting that the plasma protein may have had a therapeutic effect possibly due to the presence of antibodies against intestinal pathogens. As can be seen, dramatic improvements in animal performance can be obtained compared with control treatments when spray-dried pig plasma is incorporated into the diet. A disadvantage of using spray-dried plasma is its relatively high cost and its unknown and variable level of antibodies. The rate of inclusion of this product has been from 3 to 10% of the total diet.

Need For and Possible Source of Therapeutic Antibodies

There is a need for an alternative control of intestinal disease to that obtained through the use of antibiotics. This is particularly important, as many organisms in recent years have developed resistance to antibiotics. This has potentially serious consequences not only for the animal industry, but also for

Table 22.1. A summary of recent experiments evaluating spray-dried porcine plasma as a protein source for weanling pigs. Length of test post-weaning was 2 weeks.

No.[a]	Experiment	Protein in control diet	Percentage improvement over pigs fed control diet[b]		
			ADG	ADF	F : G
1	Hansel et al. (1990)	Skim milk	+42	+37	−4
2	Gatnau et al. (1991)	Soybean meal	+102	+76	+12
3	Sohn et al. (1991)	Skim milk	+29	+24	+1
4	Gatnau et al. (1991)	Soybean meal	+82	+34	+60
5	Hansen et al. (1991)	Skim milk	+15	+28	−10
6	Gatnau et al. (1990)	Skim milk	+50	+54	+29
7	CS 1132	Skim milk	+22	+19	+3
8	CS 1098	Skim milk	+12	+9	+4
9	CS 1124	Skim milk	+15	+19	−2
10	Coffey and Cromwell (1995)	Skim milk	+40	+60	+12

[a]1–9 are taken from Maxwell (1992).
[b]ADG, average daily gain; ADF, average daily feed; and F : G, feed to gain ratio.
Pigs were weaned at 17 days of age and kept in a conventional nursery. Antimicrobial reagent was added to all diets.

humans. In a recent presentation, Dr Alexander Tomasz of the Rockerfeller University warned that 'we are on the verge of a medical disaster, that would return physicians to the pre-penicillin days when even seemingly small infections could turn lethal for lack of effect drugs' (Travis, 1994). This gruesome prediction, which would have been scoffed at a decade ago, stems from the remarkable ability of bacteria to develop resistance to almost any antibiotics that scientific research has thrown at them. Of particular concern is not only the appearance of organisms that are resistant to antibiotics, but also their ability to elaborate new toxins. The recent outbreaks of *E. coli* 0157:H7 infections in humans are humbling reminders of the ability of bacteria to adapt rapidly to new hosts, new conditions and new antibiotic counter-measures. One pathogen that is able to mutate rapidly is *E. coli*; as a result, many antibiotic-resistant strains have appeared. Therefore, there is a need to develop alternative strategies to control this organism in human and veterinary medicine, particularly in the swine industry. Also, the use of many antibiotics in the livestock industry has created increasing pressure for them to be banned since there is strong evidence to suggest that resistance in one pathogen (e.g. an animal pathogen) can be transmitted readily to another pathogen, such as a human pathogen.

Vaccination of the sow against specific strains of *E. coli* will result in the secretion of colostrum that will provide passive immunity to the nursing piglet against the injected pathogens. This protection, however, is transient, and all protection is lost shortly after weaning. Immunization of the piglet is also not practical, as colibacillosis will develop in the piglet sooner than they are able to develop immunity; as a result, immunization will not protect such pigs against the pathological effects of ETEC (Alexander, 1994; Hampson, 1994;

Isaacson, 1994). One highly attractive and effective alternative approach for the control of pathogens that infect the intestinal tract is to use therapeutic antibodies. These antibodies can be produced in any animal and can be administered orally to another animal to control a specific disease.

The advantage of using antibodies is that they will provide a long-term and sustainable means of controlling pathogens. Such a treatment would be highly effective, would not result in the development of resistant strains of microorganisms, would spare the use of antibiotics and could be relatively inexpensive to use. Antibodies can be obtained from several sources, including the colostrum of cows milk, blood of animals, transgenic plants or microorganisms and finally the yolk of the laying hen. Antibodies from the colostrum of the lactating animal, particularly dairy cattle, are impractical as colostrum is only produced over a short period of time. Antibodies obtained from spray-dried plasma proteins are probably highly effective (Table 22.1), but up to now no information has been published on the ability of this product to counteract different intestinal pathogens including *E. coli*.

There undoubtedly would be a large variation in the ability of plasma proteins from different sources to counteract specific pathogens. This is because the ability of plasma proteins to neutralize the effect of specific organisms would be dependent on the immunization and disease history of the pigs from which the blood was collected. Current technology for monoclonal antibody production is prohibitively expensive. Nevertheless, they have been shown to be highly effective in controlling certain diseases. The ultimate goal is to provide a library of antibodies with nearly endless specificity and without dependence on animals or their cells for their synthesis. These latter procedures, which will involve the production of antibodies in microorganisms or plants, are only being initiated and currently cannot be used for large-scale antibody production.

The Chicken as a Source of Therapeutic Antibodies

The egg yolk, however, is recognized as a rich source of specific antibodies (Gassmann *et al.*, 1990). These include the potential for producing more specific antibodies against mammalian antigens in birds compared with mammals because of the phylogenic distance between birds and mammals, the low cost of production, convenience and, what is becoming more important, compatibility with regulations for modern animal production. Chickens produce eggs non-invasively, and adjuvants do not cause severe responses, as occurs in mammals. It has also been shown that the production and maintenance of high levels of specific antibodies over long periods of time are possible in the laying hen. It is now possible to obtain antigen-specific antibodies from egg yolks of hyperimmunized hens. A hen lays 200–300 eggs per year, and one egg yolk contains approximately 150 mg of antibodies, an amount that has the potential to neutralize a large population of microorganisms. The yolk or the purified antibody (IgY) can be prepared by freeze-drying or spray-drying without loss of activity and can be fed directly to the young pig to provide protection against specific pathogens. In addition, the yolk is a source of highly digestible nutrients. These factors indicate that the egg of a chicken should be a good source of antibodies to control intestinal pathogens in pigs.

Passive Protective Effects of Chicken Egg Yolk Immunoglobulins against ETEC in Neonatal Pigs

An excellent study has been carried out by Yokoyama et al. (1992) on the use of chicken egg yolk antibodies to control E. coli-induced diarrhoea. The over-all procedure involved first the selection of toxigenic strains of E. coli (K88, K99 and 987P). This was followed by multiplication of the different strains in laboratory fermenters, and isolation and purification of the outer rod-like extensions containing the adhesins (the fimbriae). After injections of the fimbriae into laying hens, the antibodies (IgY) were isolated from the egg yolk and spray-dried when the antibody titre was high. Young pigs were infected with the different strains of E. coli with the appropriate antibody.

All piglets in their studies when challenged with the different strains of E. coli developed mild to severe diarrhoea within 12 h after infection. Treatment with antibodies having titres of 156 and 625 did not affect ($P > 0.05$) the incidence of diarrhoea on day 1 after the E. coli challenge. There was, however, a significant difference in faecal consistency score between the control piglets and the piglets treated with antibodies with the high titre (2500, $P < 0.01$). In general, the surviving pigs recovered by day 5, with the effects of the treatments on day 3 being intermediate to those obtained on days 1 and 5. More than 80% of the pigs died in the control group, while none of the pigs died when treated with antibodies containing titres of 625 or 2500 (Table 22.2).

The E. coli strains K88, K99 and 987P were isolated in cultures from rectal swabs of all piglets (Table 22.3). The results demonstrate that fewer piglets in the group receiving the antibodies excreted E. coli, and that the excretion of E. coli decreased with the amount of antibody given and with the duration of the experiment.

The data from these studies show that antibodies prepared from the yolk of eggs from hens immunized with fimbrial antigens of E. coli are protective in piglets against challenge with homologous ETEC strains. In all cases, they reduced the severity of diarrhoea and the incidence of mortality.

Studies at the University of Manitoba with E. coli K88+

In these studies, the protective effects of egg yolk antibodies obtained from hens immunized with antigens from a local strain (Manitoba, Canada) of K88+ piliated ETEC were evaluated in a 21-day-old piglet study in which ETEC diarrhoea was induced (Kim et al., 1996; Marquardt et al., 1999). Two types of antibodies were produced, one type from hens immunized with the attenuated whole organism and one type using the fimbriae of the ETEC. As can be seen from Table 22.4, the antibody titre was much greater when the fimbriae rather than the whole cells were used. Also purification of the anti-K88 fimbriae anti-bodies dramatically increased the titre. This latter step, however, is probably not necessary, as the antibody in the whole yolk would be as effective per unit of titre as the purified antibody. In addition, the yolk is highly nutritious.

Table 22.2. Clinical response of newborn piglets after challenge with ETEC K88+ and K99+ strains and treatment with antibody powder at various titres.

Strain	Antibody treatment (titre)	No. of piglets with diarrhoea/total (FC score)[a] on day:			No. dead/% total
		1	3	5	
K88	0	7/7 (3.0)	4/4 (2.8)	1/1 (2.0)	6/7 (86)
	156	6/7 (2.6)	3/5 (1.6)	0/5 (0.4)	2/7 (29)
	625	5/7 (2.1)	0/7 (0.0)	0/7 (0.0)	0/7 (0)
	2500	3/7 (1.3)	0/7 (0.1)	0/7 (0.0)	0/7 (0)
K99	0	4/4 (3.0)	0/0	0/0	4/4 (100)
	156	4/4 (3.0)	2/2 (3.0)	0/2 (0.0)	2/4 (50)
	625	4/4 (3.0)	4/4 (2.8)	1/4 (0.5)	0/4 (0)
	2500	3/4 (1.5)	0/4 (0.5)	0/4 (0.0)	0/4 (0)
987P	0	5/5 (3.0)	1/1 (3.0)	1/1 (3.0)	4/5 (80)
	156	5/5 (3.0)	2/3 (2.0)	2/3 (1.3)	2/5 (40)
	625	5/5 (3.0)	0/5 (0.4)	0/5 (0.0)	0/5 (0)
	2500	4/5 (2.0)	0/5 (0.0)	0/5 (0.0)	0/5 (0)

[a]The FC score is the mean faecal consistency score: 0, normal; 1, soft faeces; 2, mild diarrhoea; 3, severe diarrhoea.
Piglets were infected 4 h after birth and antibody was administered at onset of diarrhoea.
From: Yokoyama *et al.*, 1992.

In the animal feeding study, 21-day-old pigs were challenged with a high dose of the ETEC (10^{12} colony-forming units (c.f.u.)). One-half of the pigs (10) received the placebo (skim milk plus egg yolk antibodies from non-immunized hens) and one-half received the skim milk plus the antibody (IgY) from the immunized hens. The antibodies were administered to the piglets in the milk three times a day for 2 days. Control piglets that were treated with the placebo developed severe diarrhoea within 12 h and were dehydrated and lost weight within 48 h. Thirty per cent of the pigs died. In contrast, the pigs treated with antibody from the immunized hens exhibited no signs of diarrhoea 24 or 48 h after treatment, had a positive weight gain and none of the pigs died (Table 22.5). The results indicate that the 21-day-old piglets that received the antibodies from the hens immunized against ETEC were 100% protected against the deleterious effects of this organism.

Another study clearly demonstrated that purified antibodies from the yolk of the chicken against the fimbriae of *E. coli* K88+ were able to block the binding of *E. coli* K88+ to the mucosal receptor. The interaction of the antibodies with this strain of *E. coli* was fairly rapid, as maximum protection was provided within at least 15 min (Jin *et al.*, 1998). The effectiveness of the chicken egg yolk antibodies for inhibiting adhesion of ETEC was influenced by two factors: the dose of antibodies and the concentration of ETEC. Egg yolk antibodies when diluted 50- and 100-fold had a very strong inhibiting ability against *E. coli* K88 at a concentration of 10^9 c.f.u. ml^{-1} (adhesion was < 6%). However, a 100-fold dilution of the egg yolk antibodies was not able to inhibit the adhesion of *E. coli* to intestinal mucus when the concentration of *E. coli* K88 was 10^{10} c.f.u. ml^{-1}.

This study also demonstrated that antibodies were not able to displace *E. coli* K88+ once they were bound to the receptor. This indicates that the antibodies have a lower affinity for the receptor than that of K88+ fimbriae. However, that possibility may be unlikely since simultaneous exposure of the immobilized mucus to both antibodies and *E. coli* K88+ gave the same degree

Table 22.3. Rates of isolation of ETC K88+, K99+ and 987P+ strains from newborn piglets after challenge and treatment with antibody powder at various titres.

		Percentage of rectal swabs positive on day:		
Strain	Antibody treatment (titre)	1	3	5
K88	0	96	50	80
	156	79	43	34
	265	58	14	14
	2500	23	1	0
	Absorbed	95	60	60
K99	0	80	D[a]	D[a]
	156	96	43	0
	265	81	25	1
	2500	25	3	0
	Absorbed	90	80	
987P	0	92	40	40
	156	95	47	25
	265	94	18	0
	2500	21	0	0
	Absorbed	95	50	50

[a]All piglets died.
From: Yokoyama *et al.*, 1992.

Table 22.4. The protein concentration and antibody titre of egg yolk in different stages of the IgY isolation procedure.

	Concentration in yolk (mg ml^{-1})		
Stages	Protein (%)	IgY (%)	Antibody titre
Immunized with K88 antigen			
Egg yolk	446 (100)	18 (100)	8,600
Acidified yolk	98 (22)	16 (91)	29,000
Purified yolk	30 (7)	14 (81)	140,000
Immunized with whole cell			
Egg yolk	539 (100)	18 (100)	1,800
Acidified yolk	126 (24)	16 (90)	2,800
Purified yolk	32 (6)	15 (81)	12,000

From: Kim *et al.*, 1996.

Table 22.5.   Clinical response of 21-day-old pigs after challenge with a local strain of ETEC K88+ and treatment with yolk antibody powder.

Treatment	No. of pigs	No. of pigs with diarrhoea on:			Weight gain (g)	No. of dead
		Day 0	Day 1	Day 2		
		(FC score)[a]				
Control	10	3 (1.0)	8 (2.0)	4 (3.0)	−36.2	3
Ab treated	10	5 (1.6)	0 (0.0)	0 (0.5)	+90.6	0

[a]FC score: mean faecal consistency score; 0, normal; 1, soft faeces; 2, mild diarrhoea; 3, severe diarrhoea. Values in parentheses represent the mean faecal score.

All the piglets were challenged orally with K88+ ETEC twice (5 h interval) at a dose of 10^{12} c.f.u. of viable organisms per piglet on day 0. Piglets in the treatment group were treated with egg yolk antibody (50 mg of IgY), three times a day for two consecutive days after the first ETEC challenge. From: Kim *et al.*, 1996.

of inhibition of adhesion as that obtained when the organism was pre-incubated with egg yolk antibodies. Since the egg yolk antibodies did not remove previously bound *E. coli* K88+ from the mucus, prophylactic use of the egg yolk antibodies is suggested. However, as indicated in the previous sections, the therapeutic effects of egg yolk antibodies in the control of diarrhoea of piglets caused by *E. coli* K88 are well established (Yokoyama *et al.*, 1992; Kim *et al.*, 1996). On the basis of the study by Jin *et al.* (1998), it may be concluded that egg yolk antibodies inhibit adhesion of *E. coli* K88+ to piglet mucus. However, prolonged incubation of egg yolk antibodies did not further reduce the degree of adhesion of *E. coli* to mucus and egg yolk antibodies were unable to displace *E. coli* once they were attached to the mucus of the small intestine.

Summary and Conclusions

1.   ETEC strains K88, K99 and 987P are one of the main causes of diarrhoeal disease in piglets.

2.   ETEC are able to colonize the piglet as their rod-like extensions (fimbriae) which contain the adhesions (adhere to a surface of the intestine) recognize and bind to specific receptors on the intestinal wall of the pig. This is a prerequisite for infection.

3.   Diarrhoeal problems will become more severe in the future due to the reduced availability of different antibiotics, the reduced effectiveness of antibiotics caused by the development of ETEC that are resistant to antibiotics and the move towards earlier weaning.

4.   Early weaning of pigs has been characterized by poor growth performance (lag period), possibly due to intestinal infections.

5.   The reduced performance of pigs that are weaned early (i.e. 15–21 days of age) can be decreased greatly by the incorporation of spray-dried pig plasma into the diet. This effect may be attributed, in part, to the naturally occurring antibodies that are present in the plasma protein.

6. Antibodies for passive immunization of piglets can be obtained from several sources. Egg yolk antibodies have several advantages over those obtained from other sources.

7. Studies in Japan with chicken egg yolk antibodies against three common strains of *E. coli* demonstrated that they could provide passive protection against fatal enteric colibacillosis in the neonatal piglet.

8. Similar studies at the University of Manitoba also demonstrated that purified anti-K88 antibodies were highly effective at protecting 21-day-old piglets against the pathogenic effects of the organism.

9. Similar results would probably be obtained with the same disease in other animals or with other intestinal disease in pigs and in other animals.

10. These results demonstrate that the piglet can be passively protected against enterotoxigenic *E. coli*, an organism that can cause severe diarrhoea and death, by using a homologous antibody that has been produced in the laying hen and secreted into the yolk of the egg. The antibody treatments can be either therapeutic (given orally to infected piglets) or preventive (given in the feed for longer periods of time). Further research needs to be carried out to evaluate the economic and social benefits of this strategy for controlling enteric disease in animals.

11. Future research should be supported in view of the serious resistance problems that are becoming more evident. The possible banning of important antibiotics, the trend towards early weaning, the very dramatic improvements in animal performance and health obtained with antibodies and the fact that such treatments are sustainable and environmentally friendly should be taken into consideration.

References

Alexander, T.J.L. (1994) Neonatal diarrhoea in pigs. In: Gyles, C.L. (ed.), *Escherichia coli in Domestic Animals and Humans*. CAB International, Wallingford, UK, pp. 151–170.

Coffey, R.D. and Cromwell, G.L. (1995) The impact of environment and antimicrobial agents on the growth response of early-weaned pigs to spray-dried porcine plasma. *Journal of Animal Science* 73, 2532–2539.

Gassmann, M., Thömmes, P., Weiser, T. and Hübscher, U. (1990) Efficient production of chicken egg-yolk antibodies against a conserved mammalian protein. *Federation of the American Society of Experimental Biology Journal* 4, 2528–2532.

Hampson, D.J. (1994) Postweaning *Escherichia coli* diarrhoea in pigs. In: Gyles, G.L. (ed.), *Escherichia coli in Domestic Animals and Humans*. CAB International, Wallingford, UK, pp. 171–191.

Isaacson, R.E. (1994) Vaccines against *Escherichia coli* diseases. In: Gyles, C.L. (ed.), *Escherichia coli in Domestic Animals and Humans*. CAB International, Wallingford, UK, pp. 629–647.

Jin, L.Z., Baidoo, S.K., Marquardt, R.R. and Frohlich, A.A. (1998) *In vitro* inhibition of adhesion of enterotoxigenic *Escherichia coli* K88 to piglet mucus by egg-yolk antibodies. *FEMS Immunology and Medical Microbiology* 21, 313–321.

Kim, J.W., Marquardt, R.R., Baidoo, S.K. and Frohlich, A.A. (1996) The use of egg antibodies to counteract diarrheal diseases in piglets. *Journal of Animal Science* 74 (Suppl. 1), 195.

Marquardt, R.R., Jin, L.Z., Kim, J.-W., Fang, L., Frohlich, A.A. and Baidou, S.K. (1999) Passive protective effect of egg-yolk antibodies against enterotoxigenic *Escherichia coli* K88+ infection in neonatal and early-weaned piglets. *FEMS Immunology and Medical Microbiology* 23, 283–288.

Maxwell, C. (1992) Plasma proteins in early weaning pig diets. In: *Proceedings of the Arkansas Nutrition Conference*. Park Inn Fayetteville, Arkansas, pp. 64–85.

Morris, J.A. and Sojka, W.J. (1985) *Escherichia coli* as a pathogen in animals. In: Sussman, M. (ed.), *The Virulence of Escherichia coli*. Academic Press, New York, pp. 44–77.

Okai, D.B., Aherne, F.X. and Hardin, R.T. (1976) Effects of creep and starter composition on feed intake and performance of young pigs. *Canadian Journal of Animal Science* 56, 573–586.

Rapacz, J. and Hasler-Rapacz, J. (1986) Polymorphism and inheritance of swine small intestinal receptors mediating adhesion of three serological variants of *Escherichia coli* producing K99 plus antigen. *Animal Genetics* 17, 305–321.

Travis, J. (1994) Reviving the antibiotic miracle. *Science* 264, 360–362.

Waters, J.R. and Sellwood, R. (1982) Aspects of genetic resistance to K88 *E. coli* in pigs. In: *Proceedings of the 2nd World Congress on Genetics Applied to Livestock Production*. Madrid, p. 362.

Yokoyama, H., Peralta, R.C., Diaz, R., Sendo, S., Ikemori, Y. and Kodama, Y. (1992) Passive protective effect of chicken egg-yolk immunoglobulins against experimental enterotoxigenic *Escherichia coli* infection in neonatal pigs. *Infection and Immunity* 60, 998–107.

Preparation of Enteric-Coated Gelatin Capsules of IgY with Cellulose Acetate Phthalate

23

E.M. Akita and S. Nakai

Faculty of Agricultural Sciences, University of British Columbia, Vancouver, British Columbia, Canada

When IgY is administered orally, the antibody activity will be reduced substantially or destroyed completely by peptic digestion and the acidity of the stomach. The objective of this study was to prepare enteric-coated gelatin capsules of IgY and evaluate the effect of simulated gastric juice and pepsin on the stability of the macroencapsulated IgY. Gelatin capsules, containing IgG-specific IgY (150 mg per capsule), were coated with cellulose acetate hydrogen phthalate (CAP). Coating was done by dipping gelatin capsules in 20% CAP in acetone : 95% ethanol (9 : 1 v/v) followed by drying of the coated capsules. Dissolution studies were done by exposing both protected and unprotected IgY to simulated gastric conditions. The residual activity and stability of IgY were monitored by enzyme-linked immunosorbent assay and radial immunodiffusion. No residual activity of IgY was observed when unprotected IgY (control) or gelatin-encapsulated IgY were exposed to simulated gastric juice (0.08 N HCl containing 0.2% NaCl, pH 1.2). Enteric-coated capsules were completely stable against simulated gastric juice for over 3 h, but easily dissolved under alkaline conditions (0.01 M, pH 8.0) found in the small intestine. Enteric-coated gelatin capsules could, therefore, be an efficient way to deliver IgY orally.

Introduction

Evidence from both animal and clinical studies shows that oral administration of antibodies could be used to treat or prevent enteric infections of both viral (Bartz *et al.*, 1980; Ebina *et al.*, 1985; Brussow *et al.*, 1987) and bacterial (Mietens *et al.*, 1979; Tacket *et al.*, 1988; Yokoyama *et al.*, 1992) origin. Since oral administration requires a large amount of antibodies, a cheap source of antibodies is needed. Chicken egg yolk provides a cheap source of large

© CAB *International* 2000. *Egg Nutrition and Biotechnology*
(eds J.S. Sim, S. Nakai and W. Guenter)

amounts of easily purified antibodies. The additional advantages that it offers over conventional sources of antibodies include the convenience of collecting eggs instead of bleeding animals, which is compatible with modern animal welfare concerns.

The protective function of immunoglobulin Y (IgY) against enteric pathogens is attributed to its capacity to prevent colonization or neutralize toxins produced by the pathogen. The activity of IgY may be reduced or destroyed by peptic digestion and low pH (Shimizu *et al.*, 1988; Schmidt *et al.*, 1989). On the other hand, IgY was found to be fairly stable against the action of proteases found in the small intestines (Shimizu *et al.*, 1988). Since the primary site of the protective function of IgY is in the small intestines, orally administered IgY should be protected against peptic digestion and the acidity of the stomach.

Two approaches could be used to protect IgY against peptic digestion and acidity of the stomach. The first approach is to focus on the hostile environment, in this case, to neutralize the stomach acid before or during administration of the antibodies. Neutralization will also prevent peptic digestion since pepsin is inactivated at high pH. The second approach is to focus on the antibodies themselves. Antibodies can be protected chemically, by chemical modification, or physically, by encapsulation. Different types of coating materials have been used for encapsulation. Jackson and Lee (1991) have reviewed the materials used for coating, and the list includes gums (e.g. gum arabic), carbohydrates (e.g. starch), celluloses (e.g. cellulose acetate phthalate (CAP)), lipids (e.g. wax), inorganic materials (e.g. silicates) and proteins (e.g. gluten).

CAP has been used extensively for enteric coating (Maharaj *et al.*, 1984), probably because it is believed to be safe. Chronic toxicity studies carried out in rats and dogs showed no evidence of toxic effects in these animals; therefore, Hodge (1944) concluded that CAP seemed to be remarkably inert as a compound of the diet. CAP also has the interesting property of being insoluble in acid media $\leq$ pH 5.0, but soluble when the pH is $\geq$ 6.0 (Malm *et al.*, 1951). We therefore chose to protect IgY by encapsulation with CAP. The objective of this research was to prepare enteric-coated gelatin capsules of IgY and evaluate the effect of simulated gastric juice and pepsin on the stability of the macroencapsulated IgY.

Materials and Methods

Immunization of chickens

Bovine IgG (Jackson Immunoresearch, Baltimore, Maryland) at a protein concentration of 2.0 mg ml^{-1} was emulsified with an equal volume of complete Freund's adjuvant (Difco, Detroit, Michigan). A group of three laying hens (Rhode Island Red) were immunized intramuscularly with 1.0 ml of inoculum, injected into four sites (0.25 ml site^{-1}) in the pectoral muscle. Booster injections were given in a similar manner after 2, 4 and 6 weeks, and after 6 months using incomplete Freund's adjuvant. Eggs used for this study were collected 1–2 weeks after the third booster injection and stored at 4°C before use.

Purification of IgY

The water-soluble fraction (WSF) from egg yolk was prepared as described by Akita and Nakai (1992). IgY was purified from the WSF by ultrafiltration using a Harp™ hollow fibre ultrafiltration membrane cartridge (Supelco, Bellefonte, Pennsylvania) with a molecular weight cut-off of 100 kDa. The essential steps are as follows. NaCl was added to give a concentration of 1.5 M and the pH was adjusted to 9.0. The WSF was concentrated 10 times, followed by diafiltration with 1.5 M NaCl solution, pH 9.0. Elution of protein was monitored by absorbance at 280 nm. Diafiltration was stopped when a negligible amount of protein was eluted in the filtrate, i.e. after passing through eight volumes of 1.5 M NaCl, pH 9.0.

Coating of gelatin capsules with CAP

Empty gelatin capsules were purchased from a local pharmacy (Finladia Pharmacy, Vancouver, British Columbia) and were coated with CAP. Two concentrations of 10 and 20% CAP in acetone : 95% ethanol (9 : 1, v/v) were prepared. Gelatin capsules were coated by dipping in CAP solution, followed by air drying of coated capsules at room temperature for 12 h. Multiple coated capsules were prepared by repeating the dipping, drying, dipping cycle. To determine the efficacy of coating, coated capsules were incubated in 5 ml of (i) simulated gastric juice (SGJ) (0.08 N HCl containing 0.2% NaCl, pH 1.2; Maharaj *et al.*, 1984) or (ii) 0.01 M phosphate buffer (PB), pH 8.0, and time for complete dissolution of capsules was recorded.

Preparation of CAP-coated IgY-containing gelatin capsules

Gelatin capsules were filled with 150 mg of IgY. IgY-containing gelatin capsules were double-coated using 20% CAP solution.

Dissolution studies

One capsule was placed into a 50 ml beaker containing 20 ml of SGJ and incubated at 37°C with shaking at 200 r.p.m. in a water bath. The amount of protein released into the SGJ was monitored at predetermined times by measuring absorbance at 280 nm after centrifugation at 10,000 **g** for 5 min at 37°C. Aliquots of 100 µl of SGJ were taken after 1, 2 and 3 h digestions and added to 400 µl of 0.1 M phosphate buffer, and the activity and stability of IgY were determined by enzyme-linked immunosorbent assay (ELISA) and radial immunodiffusion (RID), respectively. After 3 h incubation with SGJ, undissolved capsules were blotted dry and transferred into 20 ml of PB, and incubated at 37°C with shaking at 200 r.p.m. The amount of protein released into PB was monitored at predetermined times by measuring absorbance at 280 nm. The activity and stability of IgY were measured by ELISA and RID, respectively.

Radial immunodiffusion

RID was carried out essentially as described by Mancini *et al.* (1965), with slight modifications. RID was done using a plate containing 2% rabbit anti-chicken IgG antisera (Sigma, St Louis, Missouri), 1% agarose A (70 mg, Pharmacia Biotech., Uppsala, Sweden) and 0.02% sodium azide in phosphate-buffered saline (PBS). Six µl of appropriately diluted samples and standards in the range 0.1–0.8 mg IgY ml^{-1} were added to 3 mm diameter wells. A standard curve was obtained by plotting the diameter squared of the precipitation rings after 18 h against log$_{10}$ concentration. The IgY concentration of unknown samples was determined by reference to this curve.

Competitive enzyme-linked immunosorbent assay

Competitive ELISA was performed as described by Akita and Nakai (1990), with modifications. Briefly, IgG (20 µg ml^{-1}; Jackson Immunoresearch, Baltimore, Maryland) was incubated for 30 min with an equal volume of increasing concentrations of IgY. Aliquots of 100 µl of this mixture were added to microtitre plates and incubated for 1 h. The microtitre plates had already been incubated for 1 h with 100 µl of 100 µg ml^{-1} IgY not exposed to SGJ, and washed. IgG was detected by addition of rabbit anti-bovine IgG alkaline phosphatase conjugate (Sigma, St Louis, Missouri) followed by substrate.

SDS–polyacrylamide gel electrophoresis

Sodium dodecyl sulphate–polyacrylamide gel electrophoresis (SDS–PAGE) was done under non-reducing conditions on a Pharmacia Phast System using 10–15% gradient PhastGel and Coomassie brilliant blue staining according to the manufacturer's recommendations (Pharmacia Biotech., Uppsala, Sweden) as described by Akita and Nakai (1992). Quantification of proteins on PhastGels was done with the Pharmacia Image Gel Analyser.

Results

Purification of IgY

Ultrafiltration of the WSF at pH 9.0 containing 1.5 M NaCl purified IgY extensively. Gram quantities of IgY were produced easily by this method, with a purity of over 93% as determined by SDS–PAGE, and recovery of over 90% as determined by RID.

Preparation of CAP-coated gelatin capsule

The amount of CAP deposited on gelatin capsules will determine its protective effect. Since the concentration of CAP in the coating solution and the number of coatings applied to capsules could control this amount, these factors were investigated.

Under the conditions of this experiment, optimum coating of gelatin was obtained by double-coating using 20% CAP (Table 23.1). Under these conditions, there was no dissolution of gelatin for at least 12 h in the presence of

SGJ, but capsules easily dissolved within 5 min in 0.1 M phosphate buffer which was used to simulate the alkaline conditions in the small intestine. This condition, i.e. double-coating of gelatin using 20% CAP, was therefore used to coat IgY-containing gelatin capsules for subsequent experiments.

Effect of SGJ on IgY-containing capsules

Since the uncoated gelatin capsules dissolved in SGJ within 5 min (Table 23.1), these were used as the control for the comparative studies. It was observed that IgY was precipitated when exposed to SGJ. Consequently, a low concentration of IgY (< 1 mg ml^{-1}) was obtained by absorbance at 280 nm from a solution which should have given about 7.0 mg ml^{-1} (Table 23.2). In this study, the activity of IgY is defined as its capacity to recognize IgG. The stability of IgY is defined as the capacity of anti-IgY antibodies to recognize IgY. Both the activity and stability of IgY were destroyed in the presence of SGJ.

Table 23.1.   Effect of multiple coating of CAP on solubilization of gelatin capsules in simulated gastric juice and phosphate buffer.

| | Time of dissolution | | | |
| | Simulated gastric juice | | 0.01 M phosphate buffer | |
No. of coats	10% CAP	20% CAP	10% CAP	20% CAP
0	< 5 min	< 5 min	< 5 min	< 5 min
1	< 5 min	> 2 h	5–10 min	5–10 min
2	< 5 min	> 12 h	5–10 min	5–10 min
3	10–15 min	> 12 h	5–10 min	5–10 min
4	10–15 min	> 12 h	ND	ND
5	10–15 min	> 12 h	ND	ND

ND, not determined.

Table 23.2.   Release of IgY (150 mg) into simulated gastric juice (20 ml) from CAP-coated and uncoated gelatin capsules as measured by absorbance at 280 nm.

| | Absorbance at 280 nm | | |
Time of incubation (min)	Gelatin capsule	Uncoated IgY-containing gelatin capsule	CAP-coated IgY-containing gelatin capsule
0	0	0	0
5	0.277	0.926	0.027
10	0.343	1.061	0.046
20	0.346	1.085	0.069
30	0.346	1.101	0.087
60	0.343	1.191	0.161
120	0.345	1.292	0.233
180	0.343	1.328	0.273

This was demonstrated by the fact that no residual activity of IgY was found after 1 h of incubation as measured by ELISA (Fig. 23.1), and failure of anti-IgY antibodies to recognize IgY as determined by RID (Table 23.3).

On the other hand, IgY was completely protected against SGJ when the IgY-containing gelatin capsules were coated with CAP, as demonstrated by the following observations.

1. CAP-coated capsules were not dissolved by SGJ as reflected by no protein being released into the SGJ for up to 3 h (Table 23.2).

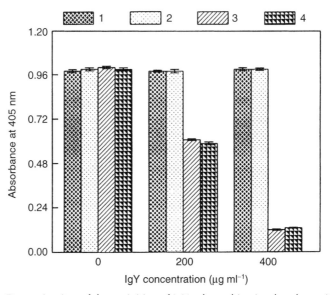

Fig. 23.1.   Determination of the activities of IgY released in simulated gastric juice or phosphate buffer by competitive ELISA. 1, uncoated gelatin capsules after incubation with simulated gastric juice; 2, CAP-coated gelatin capsules after incubation with simulated gastric juice; 3, CAP-coated gelatin capsules after incubation with phosphate buffer; and 4, Control – uncoated gelatin capsules not exposed to simulated gastric juice but solubilized in phosphate buffer.

Table 23.3.   Quantification by RID of IgY released into simulated gastric juice at different times of incubation.

Time of incubation (h)	Concentration of IgY (mg ml^{-1})		
	Control[a] gelatin capsule	Uncoated IgY-containing gelatin capsule	CAP-coated IgY-containing gelatin capsule
1	7.08	0	0
2	7.06	0	0
3	7.03	0	0

[a]Control refers to IgY-containing capsule not exposed to simulated gastric juice.

2. Similar activities of IgY were obtained for both CAP-coated IgY-containing capsules and control (IgY not exposed to SGJ) (Fig. 23.1).

3. A similar concentration of IgY, 7.0 mg ml^{-1}, was found for CAP-coated capsules and control (IgY not exposed to SGJ) as determined by RID (Tables 23.3 and 23.4).

4. Complete solubilization of IgY was obtained in PB after treatment with SGJ. Protein concentration was estimated to be 7.0 mg ml^{-1}, which was in good agreement with the concentration determined by RID (Table 23.4).

Similarly, complete protection was also observed when the CAP-coated IgY-containing gelatin capsules were incubated with SGJ in the presence of pepsin (140 µg protein ml^{-1} SGJ). Results are not shown.

Discussion

Since gram quantities of IgY were needed for this study, a method was used which allowed purification of large amounts of IgY. The major proteins in the WSF are livetins and low-density lipoproteins (McCully *et al.*, 1962). Since most of the contaminating proteins have a molecular weight between 36 and 70 kDa (Akita and Nakai, 1992), it should be possible to use ultrafiltration of the WSF to separate the contaminating proteins from IgY, which has a molecular weight of 180 kDa. However, direct ultrafiltration of the WSF (pH 5.0–5.2) using an ultrafiltration membrane with a molecular cut-off of 100 kDa failed to give IgY of high purity (Akita and Nakai, 1992). This could be attributed to possible association of the small molecular weight proteins with each other or with IgY during ultrafiltration. We reasoned that creating conditions which reduce their association would facilitate the separation. If this association is due to ionic interaction, increasing the pH, which gives net negative charges to the proteins, would reduce or eliminate co-polymerization or association of the proteins. It has also been reported that IgY undergoes reversible poly-merization to form dimers and trimers in the presence of 1.5 M NaCl (Hersh and Benedict, 1966). Consequently, we performed the ultrafiltration at high pH and high salt concentration. Our results show that ultrafiltration of IgY at pH 9.0 containing 1.5 M NaCl purifies IgY to a great extent.

Table 23.4. Release of IgY (150 mg) from CAP-coated gelatin capsules into 0.01 M phosphate buffer (20 ml) after 3 h incubation in simulated gastric juice. The concentration of IgY was measured by absorbance at 280 nm and RID.

Time of incubation (min)	Absorbance at 280 nm (mg ml^{-1})	RID (mg ml^{-1})
0	0	7.0
5	4.82	ND
10	6.00	ND
20	7.05	ND
30	7.04	7.0

ND, not determined.

Oral administration of bovine IgG was found to be effective in protecting adult humans against traveller's diarrhoea caused by enterotoxigenic *Escherichia coli* (Tacket *et al.*, 1988). However, Tacket *et al.* (1988) found the need to protect the antibodies against acidity of the stomach by incorporating antacid, magnesium and aluminium hydroxide in the antibody preparation which they administered to the volunteers. A possible problem with this approach is neutralization of the acidity in the stomach, which eliminates or reduces the effectiveness of this protective barrier of the body against pathogens.

A method, which has been used extensively to protect substances against a hostile environment is encapsulation. This process allows substances to be coated or entrapped within another substance. Encapsulation has been employed to protect IgY against the hostile acidic environment in the stomach. Shimizu *et al.* (1993) encapsulated IgY in liposomes by the dehydration/rehydration method. They reported that encapsulation reduced the loss of activity of IgY under acidic conditions. However, they found that encapsulation efficiency increased with increased levels of cholesterol. The use of higher levels of cholesterol as well as use of organic solvents may limit application of this method in food systems.

Other workers have used CAP to microencapsulate proteins (Maharaj *et al.*, 1984; Garcia *et al.*, 1989). Use of CAP allows preparation of enteric-coated microcapsules. Taking advantage of the unique properties of CAP, we designed a simple method to protect orally administered IgY. This approach involves incorporating IgY into gelatin capsules and coating the capsules with CAP.

One of the main advantages of this approach compared with most of the microencapsulation techniques using CAP is that no organic solvent comes into contact with IgY during the macroencapsulation. Furthermore, once a good barrier has been formed, complete protection of IgY is obtained, as demonstrated by this work, since IgY will not come into contact with the acidic conditions in the stomach.

On the other hand, it has been reported that 30–50% of liposome-entrapped β-galactosidase was adsorbed on the outer surface of the vesicles, and that the surface enzymes completely lost their activity when exposed to acidic conditions. This could, in part, explain the observation by Shimizu *et al.* (1993) that entrapment of IgY in liposomes led to only partial protection of IgY under acidic conditions. Garcia *et al.* (1989) also reported that invertase retained approximately 40% of its activity after 1 h incubation with gastric juice when microencapsulated in acetylphthalyl cellulose membrane by the double emulsification method. The macroencapsulation method described in this work could, therefore, provide an efficient method for oral administration of IgY since it provided complete protection. This is corroborated by the work of Hodge *et al.* (1944) who found in their clinical studies that, *in vivo*, capsules coated with CAP resisted the action of gastric juice for long periods, and in the majority of cases the CAP-coated capsules were found intact and outside the stomach. Obviously, if the purpose is to fortify foods, e.g. infant formula, with IgY, microencapsulation techniques may have to be employed.

Coating of IgY-containing gelatin capsules could easily be done with existing technology. For example, fluidized bed coating or the Wurster process commonly used in the pharmaceutical industry could be used (Arshady, 1993). In this case, the IgY-containing gelatin capsules will be fluidized, coated with CAP by spraying upon the surface of the gelatin capsules and allowed to dry. This could provide a rapid, large-scale production of uniformly coated IgY-containing gelatin capsules.

In conclusion, CAP was used successfully to coat IgY-containing gelatin capsules. The activity of the unprotected IgY was destroyed completely by simulated gastric juice. On the other hand, CAP-coated capsules were completely protected against simulated gastric juice for over 3 h in both the presence and absence of pepsin, but dissolved easily under alkaline conditions (0.01 M, pH 8.0). Enteric-coated gelatin capsules could, therefore, be an efficient vehicle for the oral delivery of IgY.

References

Akita, E.M. and Nakai, S. (1990) Lipophilization of β-lactoglobulin: effect on allergenicity and digestibility. *Journal of Food Science* 55, 718–723.

Akita, E.M. and Nakai, S. (1992) Isolation and purification of immunoglobulins from egg yolk. *Journal of Food Science* 57, 629–634.

Arshady, R. (1993) Microcapsules for food. *Journal of Microencapsulation* 10, 413–435.

Bartz, C.R., Conklin, R.H., Tunstall, C.B., and Steele, J.H. (1980) Prevention of murine rotavirus infection with chicken egg immunoglobulin. *Journal of Infectious Diseases* 142, 439–441.

Brussow, H., Hilpert, H., Walther, I., Sidoti, J., Mietens, C. and Bachmann, P. (1987) Bovine milk immunoglobulins for passive immunity to infantile rotavirus gastroenteritis. *Journal of Clinical Microbiology* 25, 982–986.

Ebina, T., Sato, A., Umezu, K., Ishida, N., Ohyama, S., Oizumi, A., Aikawa, K., Katagiri, S., Katsushima, N., Imai, A., Kitaoka, S., Suzuki, H. and Konno, T. (1985) Prevention of rotavirus infection by oral administration of cow colostrum containing antihuman rotavirus antibody. *Medical Microbiology and Immunology* 174, 177–185.

Garcia, I., Aisina, R.B., Ancheta, O. and Pascual, C. (1989) Action of gastric juice on microencapsulated invertase. *Enzyme Microbiology and Technology* 11, 247–251.

Hersh, R.T. and Benedict, A.A. (1966) Aggregation of chicken γ G immunoglobulin in 1.5 M sodium chloride. *Biochimica et Biophysica Acta* 115, 242–244.

Hodge, H.C. (1944) The chronic toxicity of cellulose acetate phthalate in rats and dogs. *Journal of Pharmacology and Experimental Therapeutics* 80, 250–255.

Hodge, H.C., Forsyth, H.H., Jr and Ramsey, G.H. (1944) Clinical tests of cellulose acetate phthalate as an enteric coating. *Journal of Pharmacology and Experimental Therapeutics* 80, 241–249.

Jackson, L.S. and Lee, K. (1991) Microencapsulation and the food industry. *Lebensmittel, Wissenschaft und Technologie* 24, 289–297.

Maharaj, I., Nairn, J.G. and Campbell, J.B. (1984) Simple rapid method for the preparation of enteric-coated microspheres. *Journal of Pharmaceutical Sciences* 73, 39–42.

Malm, C.J., Emerson, J. and Hiatt, G.D. (1951) Cellulose acetate phthalate as an enteric coating material. *Journal of the American Pharmaceutical Association* 40, 520–525.

Mancini, G., Carbonora, A.O. and Heremans J.F. (1965) Immunochemical quantification of antigen by single radial immunodiffusion. *Immunochemistry* 2, 235–254.

McCully, K.A., Mok, C.C. and Common, R.H. (1962) Paper electrophoresis characterization of proteins and lipoproteins of hen's yolk. *Canadian Journal of Biochemistry and Physiology* 40, 937–952.

Mietens, C., Keinhorst, H., Hilpert, H., Gerber, H., Amster, H. and Pahud, J.J. (1979) Treatmen of infantile *E. coli* gastroenteritis with specific bovine anti-*E. coli* milk immunoglobulins. *European Journal of Paediatrics* 132, 239–252.

Schmidt, P., Hafner, A., Reubel, G.H., Wanke, R., Franke, V., Losch, U. and Dahme, E. (1989) Production of antibodies to canine distemper virus in chicken eggs for immunochemistry. *Journal of Veterinarian Medicine, Series B* 36, 661–668.

Shimizu, M., Fitzsimmons, R.C. and Nakai, S. (1988) Anti-*E. coli* immunoglobulin Y isolated from egg yolk of immunized chicken as a potential food ingredient. *Journal of Food Science* 53, 1360–1366.

Shimizu, M., Miwa, Y., Hashimoto, K. and Goto, A. (1993) Encapsulation of chicken egg yolk immunoglobulin G (IgY) by liposomes. *Bioscience, Biotechnology and Biochemistry* 57, 1445–1449.

Tacket, C.O., Losonsky, G., Link, H., Hoang, Y., Guerry, P., Hilpert, H., and Levine, M.M. (1988) Protection by milk immunoglobulin concentrate against oral challenge with enterotoxigenic *E. coli*. *New England Journal of Medicine* 318, 1240–1243.

Yokoyama, H., Peralta, R.C., Diaz, R., Sendo, S., Ikemori, Y. and Kodama, Y. (1992) Passive protective effect of chicken egg-yolk immunoglobulins against experimental enterotoxigenic *Escherichia coli* infection in neonatal pigs. *Infection and Immunity* 60, 998–1007.

Preparation of Antigen-Specific IgY for Food Application

24

H.H. Sunwoo[1], X. Li[1], E.N. Lee[1], Y.K. Kim[2]
and J.S. Sim[1]

[1]Department of Agricultural, Food and Nutritional
Science, University of Alberta, Edmonton, Alberta,
Canada; [2]National Livestock Research Institute,
RDA, Korea

Serum antibodies of hyperimmunized hens are transferred and accumulated efficiently in the egg yolk. Egg yolk contains 8–20 mg of immunoglobulins (IgY) ml^{-1} or 136–340 mg yolk^{-1}. By immunizing hens with specific antigens and collecting IgY from egg yolk, the IgY has been applied extensively for many diagnostic, prophylactic and therapeutic uses. However, there is no quick assay technique available for routine estimation of the specific IgY concentration in the freshly laid egg. By using bovine serum albumin (BSA; 1 mg ml^{-1}) in complete Freund's adjuvant, specific antibodies were incubated in twenty 35-week-old chickens of both Single Comb White Leghorn (SCWL) and Rhode Island Red (RIR) strains. Chickens were boosted once with the same amount of BSA in incomplete Freund's adjuvant at 2 weeks after the first injection. During the period of the experiment, the quantitative enzyme-linked immunosorbent assay (ELISA) showed that the concentration of total IgY was 6.89 ± 0.45 and 6.69 ± 0.36 mg ml^{-1} in the egg yolk of SCWL and RIR hens, respectively. The concentration of specific anti-BSA IgY at 54 days of immunization was 894.86 ± 62.72 and 746.18 ± 66.94 µg ml^{-1} in the egg yolk of SCWL and RIR hens, respectively. The proportion of specific anti-BSA IgY in total IgY on days 14 and 54 of immunization was 2.7 and 12.1% in SCWL hens and 2.0% and 11.4% in RIR hens, respectively. We suggest that the quantitative ELISA technique can be a simple and fast method in this study.

Introduction

Avian sera contain three principal classes of immunoglobulins, i.e. IgA, IgG (also called IgY) and IgM. These proteins can bind to specific antigens such as bacteria, viruses, carcinogens and toxins, and can neutralize the harmful effects of the antigens. It is known that the major serum antibody, IgY, in chickens is transferred across the follicular epithelium of the ovary and accumulated in the yolk during oogenesis in a manner similar to the placental transfer of IgG in mammals (Rose and Orlans, 1981). Other antibody isotypes, IgA and IgM, are also transferred to the egg white in limited amounts.

Chickens have been immunized with various antigens including bovine serum albumin (BSA) (Ermeling *et al.*, 1992; Li *et al.*, 1998a), human serum albumin (Rose and Orlans, 1981; Losch *et al.*, 1986), α-subunit of insulin receptor (Song *et al.*, 1985), proteoglycan (Li *et al.*, 1998b), lipopolysaccharide (LPS) (Sunwoo *et al.*, 1996), viruses (Bar-Joseph and Malkinson, 1980; Polson and Wechman, 1980; Gardner and Kaye, 1982) and bacteria (Shimizu *et al.*, 1988). The laying hens immunized with various antigens produce antigen-specific IgY. In terms of physicochemical characterization of IgY, it differs from mammalian IgG in molecular size, isoelectric point, susceptibility to proteolysis and attachment to mammalian complement (Hassl *et al.*, 1987; Hatta *et al.*, 1988; Otani *et al.*, 1991).

Production of IgY in hen's egg yolk is an efficient economical method to raise polyclonal antibodies, in that bleeding of hens is not necessary and purification of IgY is relatively simple (Akita and Nakai, 1992). The potential application of IgY may increase its use as a preventive medicine, biological or diagnostic agent, and functional food supplement, as well as oral immuno-supplementation for prophylaxis. The IgYs extracted from egg yolk also have a great potential for the isolation/purification of other bioactive compounds or pathogens, and for immunoassay, because of their excellent specificity.

Recently, IgY has been used as a biological tool for cancer therapy and as a biochemical tool for protein characterization. Hens were immunized with an antigen of P110 protein, which was purified from human stomach cancer MGC-803 cells. The purified IgY could recognize gastrointestinal cancer cells. The conjugation of antibodies and drugs may be an important agent for cancer treatment (Yang *et al.*, 1997). As a biochemical reagent, IgY is useful for characterizing the high molecular weight mucin-like glycoprotein-A (HMGP-A) of human milk (Shimizu *et al.*, 1995).

Chicken IgY has been explored extensively by a number of researchers for prophylaxis and therapy of infectious diseases in order to enhance immunity after oral administration. Using a small animal model, the effect of IgY has been investigated on the passive protection of suckling mice against the human rotavirus strain causing gastroenteritis represented by diarrhoea. Oral administration of IgY prevented the infection due to rotavirus in mice (Bartz *et al.*, 1980) and the infection due to the human group A rotavirus MO strain (G serotype 3) in 5-day-old BALB/c mice (Ebina, 1996). Yokoyama *et al.* (1992) also reported the protection of neonatal pigs from diarrhoea by orally administering IgY raised against enterotoxigenic *Escherichia coli*. Similarly, feeding vaccinated cow's colostrum prevented diarrhoea in infants due to *E. coli* infection (Brussow *et al.*, 1987), rotavirus (Ebina *et al.*, 1985) and traveller's diarrhoea (Tacket *et al.*, 1988). The production of antiviral or antibacterial antibodies (rotavirus, *E. coli*, echinococcoses and many others) and their utilization may enhance immunity by oral administration to humans.

Passive immunization involving the delivery of antibodies specific to pathogens of infectious diseases to the host has been an attractive approach to establish protective immunity against a variety of microbial pathogens. The effect of passive immunization with IgY against the Marek's disease virus (MDV) was examined in White Leghorn chickens and was found to delay the development of MDV lesions (Kermani-Arab *et al.*, 1976). *Streptococcus mutans* is the principal aetiological agent of dental caries in humans. The IgY obtained from hens immunized with *S. mutans* inhibited the adherence of dental plaque of humans. Otake *et al.* (1991) reported the effect of IgY on dental caries caused by bacteria using rats as experimental animals fed a diet containing *S. mutans*-specific IgY. Hatta *et al.* (1997) reported the effectiveness of IgY with specificity for *S. mutans* in preventing the colonization of streptococci in the oral cavity of humans.

The objective of this Chapter was to review the production and application of antigen-specific IgY. In addition, there is limited information available on the determination of the specific IgY concentration, instead of the titre, showing the antibody activity in egg yolk, even though purified IgY has been applied broadly to the areas of diagnosis, prophylaxis, therapy and food supplements. In the present study, the specific IgY concentration was determined by the quantitative enzyme-linked immunosorbent assay (ELISA) technique.

Production and Application of IgY from Egg Yolk

Immune response against bovine serum albumin (BSA)

Ten laying chickens (35-week-old Single Comb White Leghorn; SCWL) were immunized with BSA emulsifed with complete Freund's adjuvant for the first injection. Each hen was injected intramuscularly with BSA at four different sites of breast muscle. A booster injection was given intramuscularly 2 weeks after the first injection with the same dose emulsified with Freund's incomplete adjuvant. Blood samples were collected from a wing vein every week after the initial injection. Eggs were collected daily and stored at 4°C until analysed.

The activity of anti-BSA antibody was determined by ELISA in the egg yolk from laying hens as shown in Fig. 24.1. The antibody activity in serum increased rapidly and reached a plateau on day 14. The antibody activity in egg yolk was very weak on day 7, rapidly increased on day 14, and gradually increased thereafter to reach the peak on day 56.

Effects of egg and yolk weights on IgY production

The percentage hen-day production in chickens and their egg and yolk weights during the experimental periods are shown in Fig. 24.2. The percentage hen-day production was approximately twice as high in the SCWL than in the Rhode Island Red (RIR) hens, and both egg and yolk weights were 1.3 times greater in the SCWL than in the RIR hens.

The ratio of yolk weight to egg white was similar in the two strains of chickens. The content of total IgY in the egg yolk was relatively constant (average 0.6%) among the chickens regardless of the strain, egg weight or egg production per day during the experimental period. However, the total content of IgY in the yolk was approximately 1.3 times greater, and the total IgY

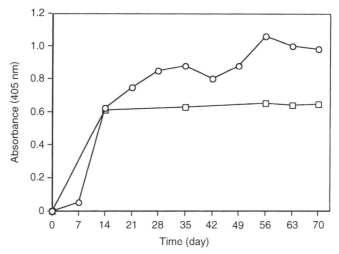

Fig. 24.1. Changes of antibody activities in serum and egg yolk during the immunization period. Antibody activities in sera (□) and egg yolk (○) (both at 1 : 1000 dilution) from chickens were measured by ELISA, and were expressed as ELISA absorbance at 405 nm.

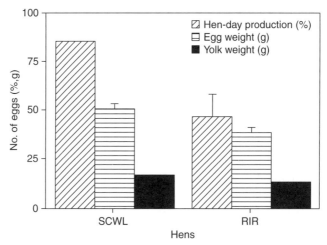

Fig. 24.2. Laying performance of Single Comb White Leghorn (SCWL) and Rhode Island Red (RIR) hens during the immunization period.

produced during the 18-week experimental period was three times greater in the SCWL than in the RIR hens (Fig. 24.3). Therefore, the egg yolk weight and the percentage hen-day production are considered to be important factors for the efficient production of IgY.

IgY against proteoglycan

Chickens as antibody producers have obvious advantages over mammals in that IgY can react strongly against antigens of mammalian origin because of

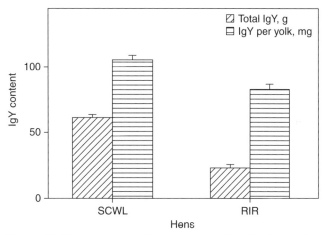

Fig. 24.3.   The total IgY and average IgY content in yolk of Single Comb White Leghorn (SCWL) and Rhode Island Red (RIR) hens during the immunization period.

the phylogenetic distance between avian and mammalian systems. Decorin, a member of the proteoglycan family consisting of a dermatan sulphate chain and a protein core, is known to be a relatively weak immunogen in mammalian species. The molecule is found in extracellular matrix of skin and cartilage, with the important physiological function of maintaining the integrity of tissues. The present study was undertaken to examine the IgY production in egg yolk against decorin extracted from bovine skin.

Three 35-week-old SCWL hens were immunized by intramuscular injection with 1 mg of decorin antigens emulsified in Freund's complete adjuvant. The IgY activities against bovine decorin were determined by ELISA by incubating water-soluble fractions in plates pre-coated with antigens. The IgY activities measured by ELISA increased 7 days after immunization, rapidly increased and remained relatively constant after 35 days. The result indicated that the decorin was highly antigenic to chickens. To determine whether the IgY produced is specific to the protein core or to the dermatan sulphate chains, an ELISA inhibition assay was carried out to assess the antigenicities of the fragments remaining after enzymatic digestion using papain and chondroitinase ABC (Fig. 24.4). Digestion of decorin with papain to cleave its protein core caused a complete loss of antigenicity, while chondroitinase ABC treatment to cleave its dermatan sulphate chain showed no appreciable effect. This indicates that the epitopes recognized by the anti-decorin IgY are located in the protein core and not in the dermatan sulphate chain.

Thus, chickens are efficient producers of antibodies specific to the protein core of bovine decorin. We also suggest that the anti-decorin IgY prepared in our laboratory could be useful in the study of the biochemical roles of proteoglycans.

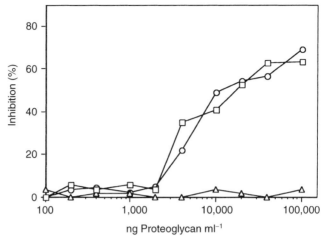

Fig. 24.4. Inhibition of binding of IgY to bovine decorin. The antigenicity of decorin digested with papain (□) and with chondroitinase ABC (o) was compared with that of untreated decorin (Δ).

IgY against *Salmonella*

Salmonella food poisoning has increased dramatically in Europe and North America and has remained the third most common cause of human Salmonellosis. For example, poultry has been implicated in outbreaks of Salmonellosis resulting in a serious threat to public health and to the marketing of poultry products. It has been recognized that chickens are common hosts to *Salmonella* as a foodborne bacterium. If ingested in large numbers, humans can be infected, resulting in nausea, vomiting, abdominal cramps, diarrhoea, fever and headache. Fear of *Salmonella* poisoning is widespread in the public's perception associated with poultry meat and eggs, and efforts have been made by the regulatory agencies and meat industries to control and prevent further outbreaks.

Twelve 40-week-old White Leghorn hens were immunized with lipopoly-saccharide (LPS) antigens from *S. typhimurium*. The immune response of laying hens resulted in the production of antibodies specific to LPS, a major constituent of the outer membrane of Gram-negative bacteria. It was shown that immunization of chickens with LPS antigens led to a strong immunogenic reaction, producing a large amount of LPS-specific IgY (Sunwoo *et al.*, 1996). We also found that the activity of antibodies against a LPS fraction containing lipid-A was higher than that of those against a LPS fraction lacking lipid-A. The results indicated that IgY specific for the LPS fraction might be useful in the prevention of *Salmonella* adhesion and diseases.

Measuring antibody activities in egg yolk by ELISA monitored the immune response of laying hens to LPS antigens from *Salmonella*. The level of anti-LPS IgY activity increased after a booster injection (Fig. 24.5).

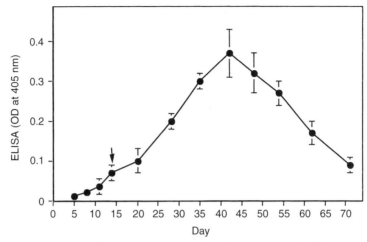

Fig. 24.5.   ELISA value of anti-LPS (*Salmonella typhimurium*) antibody activity in egg yolk. The activity is expressed as ELISA absorbance at 405 nm for egg yolk at a 1 : 1000 dilution. Vertical bars indicate the standard deviation. The arrow indicates the booster injection of LPS from *S. typhimurium*.

Microstatic and prophylactic use of IgY

IgY can be applied to prevent the growth of various pathogenic bacteria such as *E. coli* and *Salmonella* using specific polyclonal antibodies, which can effectively neutralize or reduce the proliferation of bacteria in meat products and prevent the ever increasing threat of food poisoning incidents. In this respect, we are investigating the biological effect of IgY on the inhibition of bacterial growth. The pathogenic bacterium contacting IgY may lose its mobility and reduce its colony-forming abilities. The research requires three stages of experimentation for: (i) immunizing actively laying chickens and harvesting anti-bacterial IgY-loaded eggs; (ii) isolating and purifying high titre IgY from fresh egg yolk; and (iii) testing bacteriostatic potency on bacteria in culture media.

Porcine enterotoxigenic *E. coli* (ETEC) causes diarrhoeal disease in piglets. To achieve this, ETEC colonizes the small intestine by adhering to the epithelium. Pili of porcine ETEC known to be associated with intestinal colonization are 987P, K88 and K99.

IgY of hens immunized with a porcine ETEC 987P was isolated by a water-soluble extract method (Akita and Nakai, 1992). The activity of IgY against ETEC was measured by ELISA absorbance at 405 nm (data not shown). The result indicated that the water-soluble IgY reacted specifically with the ETEC.

To examine the inhibitory effects of the IgY on growth of porcine ETEC 987P, the bacteria (1.2×10^7 c.f.u. ml^{-1} E-media broth) were cultured with the specific IgY or control IgY at IgY concentrations of 0.625–40 mg ml^{-1} at 37°C for 1–6 h in tryptic soy broth (TSB). The growth curve was plotted by measuring the turbidity at 550 nm of bacteria in culture. Inhibition of bacterial growth was observed at IgY concentrations of 5 and 10 mg ml^{-1} (Fig. 24.6).

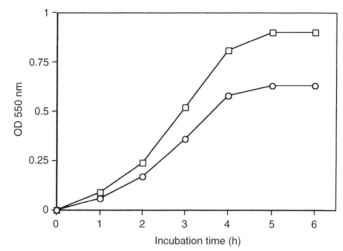

Fig. 24.6. The effect of anti-ETEC IgY on the growth of porcine ETEC 987P strain. ETEC (1.2×10^7 c.f.u. ml^{-1}) in TSB was incubated with 5 mg ml^{-1} of anti-ETEC IgY ($\square$) and 5 mg ml^{-1} of control IgY ($\circ$) at 37°C, and the turbidity of the culture was measured at OD 550 nm at 1, 2, 3, 4, 5 and 6 h after culture. The results are expressed as the mean $\pm$ SE value of triplicate measurements.

Thus, anti-ETEC IgY could be useful for the inhibition of bacterial growth by blocking the attachment of bacteria to the intestinal epithelium.

In addition, IgY can be stored in egg yolk and harvested in large quantities from daily eggs. Thus, IgY plays an increasingly important role as an alternative to mammalian polyclonal antibodies. It can be used widely in biomedical research, and for diagnosis, prophylaxis and therapy of diseases. Purified IgY has been tested by an array of various assays and diagnostic techniques.

Quantitative ELISA Technique

The concentration of IgY in the egg yolk is higher than that of IgG in the hen's serum (Rose *et al.*, 1974; Sunwoo *et al.*, 1996). Production of IgY in hen's egg yolk is obviously more economical compared with collecting antiserum from immunized animals (e.g. rabbit and sheep). One egg contains 100–200 mg of IgY (Leslie and Clem, 1969), suggesting that more than 30 g of IgY can be obtained from one immunized hen per year. However, there is little information about the specific IgY concentration. Thus, we conducted a study on the concentration of specific antibody instead of the antibody titre.

Immunization

Twenty 35-week-old chickens of both SCWL and RIR strains were immunized by intramuscular injection (four different sites; 0.25 ml per site of breast muscle) with BSA (1 mg ml^{-1}) in Freund's complete adjuvant. Booster shots of BSA with an equal volume of Freund's incomplete adjuvant were given 2 weeks after the initial challenge. Eggs were collected every day and stored at

4°C until used. All chickens were cared for in accordance with the Canadian Council on Animal Care guidelines of animal welfare (1993).

Quantitative ELISA for measurement of anti-BSA-specific IgG concentrations and standard IgG

Wells in a plate were coated with 100 µl of rabbit anti-chicken IgG and BSA at a concentration of 10.0 or 2.0 µg ml^{-1} in coating buffer, respectively. Plates were incubated at 4°C for 24 h and washed three times with PBS–Tween. Wells were blocked with 150 µl of 0.5% gelatin. Aliquots of 150 µl of serial 1 : 2 dilutions of water-soluble fractions (WSF) from egg yolks prepared by the method of Akita and Nakai (1992) were applied in triplicate to the wells coated with BSA. Whole molecule chicken IgG (standard IgG; Sigma), 150 µl of serial 1 : 2 dilutions (10–0.078 µg ml^{-1}) in triplicate, were applied to the wells coated with rabbit anti-chicken IgG to prepare a standard curve (Tirawanchai *et al.*, 1991).

In addition, WSF were added to the wells to measure the content of total IgY. Plates were incubated at 37°C for 2 h and washed with PBS–Tween and then incubated with 150 µl of rabbit anti-chicken IgG conjugated with horseradish peroxidase (1 : 1000 in PBS–Tween). After incubation at 37°C for 1 h, plates were washed three times with PBS–Tween, followed by addition of 100 µl of freshly prepared substrate solution, 2,2-azino-bis (3-ethylbenzthiazoline-6-sulphonic acid) in 0.05 M phosphate citrate buffer (pH 5.0). The optical density at 405 nm was converted to µg of specific IgY ml^{-1} of egg yolk by using the standard curve determined by the titration between affinity-purified rabbit anti-chicken IgG and purified chicken IgG.

Results

During the immunization period, samples were collected on days 0, 14, 39, 54 and 70. Concentrations of total immunoglobulins and of immunoglobulin specific to BSA in egg yolk were measured by a quantitative ELISA. The quantitative ELISA showed that the contents of total antibody in egg yolks from SCWL and RIR hens were similar, 6.69 ± 0.36 and 6.89 ± 0.45 mg ml^{-1}, respectively. The result showed that the strain, egg weight and egg production did not affect the total content of IgY.

There was no difference in the antibody activity in the egg yolk (absorbance at 405 nm) between the two strains of chickens during the experimental period. The average level of specific antibody in egg yolks of both strains increased from 44 to 711 µg ml^{-1} during the experimental period of 10 weeks. However, the concentration of specific anti-BSA IgY at 54 days of immunization was significantly different ($P > 0.05$), 894.86 ± 62.72 and 746.18 ± 66.94 µg ml^{-1} in the egg yolk of SCWL and RIR hens, respectively (Fig. 24.7).

The proportions of specific anti-BSA IgY in total immunoglobulins on days 14 and 54 of immunization were 2.7 and 12.1% in SCWL and 2.0 and 11.4% in RIR hens, respectively (Fig. 24.8).

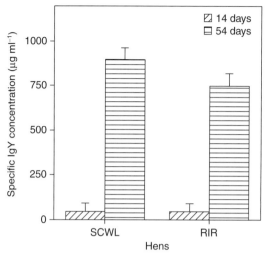

Fig. 24.7. Specific IgY concentration (μg ml^{-1}) in the egg yolk of SCWL and RIR hens at 14 and 54 days of immunization.

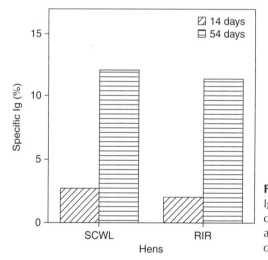

Fig. 24.8. Percentage of specific IgY in relation to the total IgY content in the egg yolk of SCWL and RIR hens at days 14 and 54 of immunization.

Based on the present study, we suggest that the quantitative ELISA technique can be used to determine the specific IgY concentration. This may be especially important when quantities of antibody need to be known for industrial uses or when a mixture of antibodies against various antigens is used as a food additive.

Acknowledgements

We thank the staff of the University of Alberta Poultry Research Centre for their assistance of feeding chickens and collecting eggs. This research was supported by NLRI, international cooperative research grant from Korea.

References

Akita, E.M. and Nakai, S. (1992) Immunoglobulins from egg yolk: isolation and purification. *Journal of Food Science* 57, 629–634.

Bar-Joseph, M. and Malkinson, M. (1980) Hen egg yolk as a source of antiviral antibodies in the enzyme-linked immunosorbent assay (ELISA): a comparison of two plant viruses. *Journal of Virological Methods* 1, 179–183.

Bartz, C.R., Conklin, R.H., Tunstall, C.B. and Steele, J.H. (1980) Prevention of murine rotavirus infection with chicken egg immunoglobulin. *Journal of Infectious Diseases* 142, 439–444.

Brussow, H., Hilpert, H., Walther, I., Sidoti, J., Mietens, C. and Bachmann, P. (1987) Bovine milk immunoglobulins for passive immunity to infantile rotavirus gastroenteritis. *Journal of Clinical Microbiology* 25, 982–986.

Ebina, T. (1996) Prophylaxis of rotavirus gastroenteritis using immunoglobulin. *Archives of Virology* (Suppl. 12), 217–223.

Ebina, T., Sato, A., Umezu, K., Ishida, N., Ohyama, S., Oizumi, A., Aikawa, K., Katagiri, S., Katsushima, N., Imai, A., Kitaoka, S., Suzuki, H. and Kanno, T. (1985) Prevention of rotavirus infection by oral administration of cow colostrum containing antihuman rotavirus antibody. *Medical Microbiology and Immunology* 174, 177–185.

Ermeling, B.L., Steffen, E.K., Fish, R.E. and Hook, R.R. (1992) Evaluation of subcutaneous chambers as an alternative to conventional methods of antibody production in chickens. *Laboratory Animal Science* 42, 402–407.

Gardner, P.S. and Kaye, S. (1982) Egg globulins in rapid virus diagnosis. *Journal of Virological Methods* 4, 257–262.

Hassl, A., Aspock, H. and Flamm, H. (1987) Comparative studies on the purity and specificity of yolk immunoglobulin Y isolated from eggs laid by hens immunized with *Toxoplasma gondii* antigen. *Zentralblatt für Bakteriologie, Mikrobiologie und Hygiene* A267, 247–253.

Hatta, H., Sim, J.S. and Nakai, S. (1988) Separation of phospholipids from egg yolk and recovery of water-soluble proteins. *Journal of Food Science* 53, 425–427.

Hatta, H., Tsuda, K., Ozeki, M., Kim, M., Yamamoto, T., Otake, S., Hirasawa, M., Katz, J., Childers, N.K. and Michalek, S.M. (1997) Passive immunization against dental plaque formation in humans: effect of a mouth rinse containing egg yolk antibodies (IgY) specific to *Streptococcus mutans*. *Caries Research* 31(4), 268–274.

Kermani-Arab, V., Moll, T., Cho, B.R., Davis, W.C. and Lu, Y.S. (1976) Effects of IgY antibody on the development of Marek's disease. *Avian Diseases* 20, 32–41.

Leslie, G.A. and Clem, W.L. (1969) Phylogeny of immunoglobulin structure and function: immunoglobulins of the chicken. *Journal of Experimental Medicine* 130, 1337–1352.

Li, X., Nakano, T., Sunwoo, H.H., Paek, B.H., Chae, H.S. and Sim, J.S. (1998a) Effects of egg and yolk weights on yolk antibody (IgY) production in laying chickens. *Poultry Science* 77, 266–270.

Li, X., Nakano, T., Chae, H.S., Sunwoo, H.H. and Sim, J.S. (1998b) Production of chicken egg yolk antibody (IgY) against bovine proteoglycan. *Canadian Journal of Animal Science* 78, 287–291.

Losch, Y., Schranner, I., Wanke, R. and Jurgens, L. (1986) The chicken egg, an antibody source. *Journal of Veterinarian Medicine* B33, 609–619.

Otake, S., Nishihara, Y., Makimura, M., Hatta, H., Kim, M., Yamamoto, T. and Hirasawa, M. (1991) Protection of rats against dental carries by passive immunization with hen-egg-yolk antibody (IgY). *Journal of Dental Research* 70, 162–166.

Otani, H., Matsumoto, K., Saeki, A. and Hosono, A. (1991) Comparative studies on properties of hen egg yolk IgY and rabbit serum IgG antibodies. *Lebensmittel, Wissenschaft und Technologie* 24, 152–158.

Polson, A. and Wechmar, M.B.V. (1980) Isolation of viral IgY antibodies from yolks of immunized hens. *Immunological Communications* 9, 475–493.

Rose, M.E. and Orlans, E. (1981) Immunoglobulins in the egg, embryo and young chick. *Developmental and Comparative Immunology* 5, 15–20, 371–375.

Rose, M.E., Orlans, E. and Buttress, N. (1974) Immunoglobulin classes in the hen's egg: their segregation in yolk and white. *European Journal of Immunology* 4, 521–523.

Shimizu, M., Fitzsimmons, R.C. and Nakai, S. (1988) Anti-*E. coli* immunoglobulin Y isolated from egg yolk of immunized chickens as a potential food ingredient. *Journal of Food Science* 53, 1360–1366.

Shimizu, M., Watanabe, A. and Tanaka, A. (1995) Detection of high-molecular weight mucin-like glycoprotein-A (HMGP-A) of human milk by chicken egg yolk antibody. *Bioscience, Biotechnology and Biochemistry* 59, 138–139.

Song, C.S., Yu, J.H., Bai, D.H., Hester, P.Y. and Kim, K.H. (1985) Antibodies to the α-subunit of insulin receptor from eggs of immunized hens. *Journal of Immunology* 135, 3354–3359.

Sunwoo, H.H., Nakano, T., Dixon, W.T. and Sim, J.S. (1996) Immune responses in chickens against lipopolysaccharide of *Escherichia coli* and *Salmonella typhimurium*. *Poultry Science* 75, 342–345.

Tacket, C.O., Losonsky, G., Link, H., Hoang, Y., Guerry, P., Hilpert, H. and Levine, M.M. (1988) Protection by milk immunoglobulin concentrate against oral challenge with enterotoxigenic *E. coli*. *New England Journal of Medicine* 318, 1240–1243.

Tirawanchai, N., Winger, L.A., Nicholas, J. and Sinden, R.E. (1991) Analysis of immunity induced by the affinity-purified 21-kilodalton zygote-ookinete surface antigen of *Plasmodium berghei*. *Infection and Immunity* 59, 36–44.

Yang, H., Jin, Z., Yu, Q., Yang, T., Wang, H. and Liu, L. (1997) The selective recognition of IgY for digestive system cancers. *Chinese Journal of Biotechnology* 13, 85–90.

Yokoyama, H., Peralta, R.C., Diaz, R., Sendo, S., Ikemori, Y. and Kodama, Y. (1992) Passive protective effect of chicken egg yolk immunoglobulins against experimental enterotoxigenic *Escherichia coli* infection in neonatal piglets. *Infection and Immunity* 60, 998–1007.

Applications of Egg Immunoglobulins in Immunoaffinity Chromatography

25

E.C.Y. Li-Chan

Faculty of Agricultural Sciences, University of British Columbia, Vancouver, British Columbia, Canada

High titres of specific antibodies can be obtained in egg yolk immunoglobulins (IgY) by immunization of laying hens against target antigens. For prophylactic or therapeutic applications, IgY may be used directly in the form of yolk powder or as a water-soluble fraction. However, applications involving IgY for diagnostic assays or immunoaffinity purification of bioactive molecules require isolation of specific antibody fractions from the crude immunoglobulins. In all of these cases, the effects of various conditions and processes on the structural properties and antibody activity of IgY must be considered.

Yolk IgY has been reported to be less stable than mammalian IgG under low pH and elevated temperature conditions, such as may be encountered in the gastric tract or during immunoaffinity chromatography. Recent results indicate that IgY is stable even after 2 h at pH 2.8, provided the temperature is at or below about 25°C. Incorporation of protective agents such as sucrose or trehalose during acidic pH elution can prevent the denaturation of IgY, which has been observed as an increase in surface hydrophobicity monitored by fluorescence probes. High ionic strength (e.g. 1.5 M NaCl) and processes of concentration, such as ultrafiltration or freeze-drying, promote aggregation, insolubilization and subsequent reduction in antibody activity of IgY molecules. To avoid these changes, ion-exchange chromatography may be recommended as an alternative process for concentration, and antibody preparations may be stored as frozen solutions or freeze-dried only under low ionic strength conditions.

Using these optimal conditions to maintain structural and antibody stability, immunoaffinity columns bearing immobilized yolk antibodies have been applied successfully for simple one-step isolation of value-added proteins such as lactoferrin and immunoglobulins from colostrum, milk or cheese whey.

Introduction

Specific antibodies play a critical role in therapy, diagnostic assays and purification of bioactive molecules. For many of these applications, the immunoglobulins from egg yolk (IgY) can be a valuable source of antibodies, especially when obtained from eggs of hens which have been immunized against target antigens. The advantages of IgY include the potential to produce and maintain high levels of specific antibodies, as well as the ease of collecting these antibodies from eggs rather than from sera, which facilitates compliance with animal welfare considerations (Rose *et al.*, 1974; Larsson *et al.*, 1993; Hatta *et al.*, 1997). The evolutionary distance between avian and mammalian species means that highly conserved mammalian antigens such as insulin are more likely to be immunogenic and elicit production of specific antibodies in hens than in other animals such as rabbits (Hatta *et al.*, 1997). Furthermore, IgY does not fix mammalian complement or react with rheumatoid factor, and has a lower likelihood of producing significant clinical side effects such as serum sickness and anaphylactic shock, which can occur upon administration of mammalian serum proteins (Thalley and Carroll, 1990; Larsson *et al.*, 1993). For this reason, rattlesnake and scorpion antivenoms purified from chicken eggs were proposed to be pharmaceutically safer and more economical to produce than the current horse antivenom products (Thalley and Carroll, 1990).

Despite growing interest in research applications, however, purified IgY preparations have yet to be adopted as the antibody of choice compared with other sources such as monoclonal antibodies or mammalian polyclonal antibodies. This hesitation in using egg immunoglobulins may arise from the lack of information on the optimal conditions ensuring high specific activity and stability of IgY. The critical parameters required for more widespread acceptance of IgY include the following: (i) protocols for production of high titres of specific antibodies by immunization with antigen; (ii) ease of isolation of specific antibodies; (iii) stability of antibodies to conditions of use (e.g. immunoaffinity chromatography, passage through the gastrointestinal tract); and (iv) long-term storage of the antibody (e.g. frozen or lyophilized preparations).

The objective of this chapter is to highlight some recent research from our laboratory, to establish the potential of IgY as an economically viable and technically reliable technology through a systematic investigation of processes affecting IgY structure and stability, and to establish guidelines for antibody purification, concentration and immunoaffinity chromatography. The effects of various conditions (e.g. pH, temperature, ionic strength and eluting medium) or processes (e.g. freezing, freeze-drying, concentration or immunoaffinity separation) on the structural properties and antibody activity of IgY will be discussed. Application of this knowledge to simple and economical separation of bioactive and functional proteins from food and food industry waste streams will be illustrated by the isolation of value-added protein products from bovine milk, colostrum and cheese whey.

Production and Isolation of IgY

Typical immunization protocols for yolk antibody production

To obtain high titres of specific antibodies against a target antigen, immunization of laying hens with the antigen is required. Typically, the initial immunization is performed by injection of the antigen (0.5–1 mg ml^{-1} emulsion
containing Freund's complete adjuvant) into the pectoralis muscle. Two to four
boosters of the antigen in incomplete adjuvant are usually required to maintain
production of high titres of specific antibodies, which appear at 5–6 weeks
after the initial immunization and continue for up to a year. It is important to
note that vaccination of laying hens to protect them against various pathogenic
microorganisms is already a common practice, which is well accepted by
poultry farmers as well as the consuming public.

Figure 25.1 shows the profile of production of specific antibodies against
bovine serum IgG$_1$ and IgG$_2$ subclasses and the IgG isolated from cheddar
cheese whey (CCW). Approximately 3–4 g of IgY could be obtained per laying hen each month. This corresponds to an annual yield of 40–50 g IgY per
hen, which is about 30 times greater than the IgG produced in the serum of an
immunized rabbit (Hatta *et al.*, 1997). Depending on the immunogenicity of
the antigen, the percentage of specific antibody in IgY preparations has been
reported by Hatta *et al.* (1997) to range from 5 (anti-insulin antibody) to 28%
(anti-mouse IgG antibody). Using bovine IgG and lactoferrin as antigens,

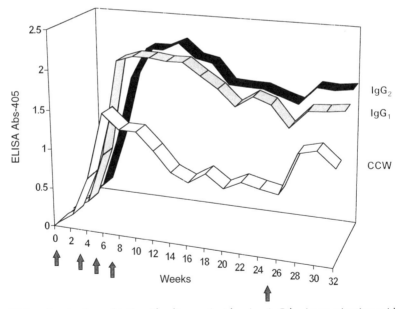

Fig. 25.1. Production of IgY antibodies against bovine IgG by immunization with
pure bovine serum IgG$_1$, IgG$_2$ or IgG from cheddar cheese whey (CCW). The production of IgG-specific antibodies was monitored by absorbance at 405 nm in ELISA as
a function of time in weeks after first immunization. The arrows indicate the first
immunization at 0 week and the subsequent boosters at 3, 5, 7 and 25 weeks.

approximately 10–15% of the total IgY were specific antibodies (Akita and Li-Chan, 1998; Li-Chan *et al.*, 1998), and one-third of the anti-IgG-specific yolk antibodies were subclass-specific antibodies (Akita and Li-Chan, 1998).

Isolation of IgY and specific antibodies

Whole egg or yolk powder containing IgY antibodies may be used as a food or feed ingredient without further processing. However, for most applications, some purification of the IgY fraction is desirable. The first step in this purification involves separation of water-soluble proteins including IgY from the water-insoluble lipid and lipoproteins. As reviewed in several recent reports (Akita and Nakai, 1993a; Svendsen *et al.*, 1995; Hatta *et al.*, 1997), many methods have been investigated for this purpose, including ultracentrifugation, extraction with organic solvents and precipitation of lipoproteins with polyethyleneglycol, sodium dextran sulphate, polyacryl acid resins or food-grade gums such as alginate, carrageenan and xanthan gum.

We have established a simple water dilution method involving 10-fold dilution of yolk with water at pH 5.2, yielding a clear supernatant or water-soluble fraction containing IgY (15% purity, protein basis), which can be recovered by centrifugation or simple decanting (Fichtali *et al.*, 1992; Akita and Nakai, 1993a). This water-soluble fraction can be used as a lipid-free ingredient for feeding, or as the starting material for further isolation of IgY or its specific antibodies.

Further fractionation of the proteins in the water-soluble fraction using ammonium or sodium sulphate precipitation yields IgY preparations with greater than 80% purity; these products can, in turn, be purified further by gel permeation chromatography or ultrafiltration to yield IgY with 96–99% purity (Akita and Nakai, 1993a). A simple separation of IgY from the water-soluble fraction based on ultrafiltration and intended for practical industrial application has also been reported recently (Kim and Nakai, 1998).

For immunoaffinity applications, isolation of antibodies specific to the target antigen is required. Purified IgY preparations have commonly been used as the starting material for this purpose. However, as shown in Table 25.1, the yields of specific antibodies against lactoferrin which could be obtained by immunoaffinity chromatographic purification was approximately 11% of the total immunoglobulin fraction, whether the latter was in the form of a purified IgY preparation or the crude, water-soluble fraction. In other words, the recovery of specific IgY_{Lf} antibodies was not affected by the purity of the starting sample, and it may be concluded that specific antibodies can be isolated directly from the water-soluble fraction, without the need for preliminary purification of an immunoglobulin fraction.

Stability of IgY Antibody Preparations

Structural basis for differences in stability between IgY and mammalian IgG

Leslie and Clem (1969) proposed that the predominant serum Ig of chicken should be called IgY rather than IgG. This distinction is not a trivial one limited

Table 25.1.   Comparison of yields of lactoferrin-specific antibodies (IgY$_{Lf}$) isolated from purified yolk immunoglobulins (IgY) or water-soluble fraction (WSF).

Starting sample	IgY applied (mg)	IgY$_{Lf}$ eluted (mg)	% specific IgY$_{Lf}$ antibody[a]
IgY[b]	40–185	5.0–17.0	10.6 ± 1.5 ($n = 4$)
WSF[c]	135–200	14.7–24.3	10.7 ± 1.1 ($n = 5$)

[a] % Specific antibody = (IgY$_{Lf}$/IgY) × 100%. Values are mean ± standard deviation, for the number of replicates shown in parentheses. The original data are from Li-Chan *et al.* (1998).
[b] Purified IgY (Taiyo Kagaku Company, Mie, Japan).
[c] Water-soluble fraction from yolk, containing 1 mg of IgY ml^{-1}.
IgY solution or water-soluble fraction was applied to immobilized lactoferrin columns. After washing unbound fractions with phosphate-buffered saline, the bound IgY$_{Lf}$ was eluted using either Actisep™ elution medium (for IgY) or pH 2.8 glycine buffer (for WSF), as described in Li-Chan *et al.* (1998).

to nomenclature, as it is now clear that chicken immunoglobulins, whether in the serum or in the yolk, are structurally and functionally distinct from IgG. The heavy chain of the IgG molecule contains three constant regions (C$_{\gamma 1 - \gamma 3}$) as well as a characteristically mammalian feature – the hinge region. In contrast, the heavy chain of IgY contains four constant regions (C$_{\upsilon 1 - \upsilon 4}$) and no hinge region. Differences in localization and content of disulphide bonds and of carbohydrate moieties have also been reported (Hatta *et al.*, 1997).

These differences do not appear to affect antigen-binding properties, as IgY are capable of binding to antigen strongly and with the expected valence of 2.0 (Warr *et al.*, 1995). However, greater susceptibility of IgY than mammalian IgG to conformational change in response to environmental conditions such as pH and temperature as well as to proteolysis has been attributed to these differences in their structure (Otani *et al.*, 1991; Shimizu *et al.*, 1992). The absence of a hinge region has also been suggested to be the basis for the limited segmental flexibility and functional diversity of IgY, as well as the inability to exhibit efficient precipitation and agglutination reactions under certain conditions (Warr *et al.*, 1995). It has been suggested that the absence of a hinge region results in close alignment of the two Fab arms. Conditions which facilitate precipitation, e.g. high salt concentrations or low pH, presumably result in conformational changes that release the Fab arms, permitting functional independence of the binding sites and subsequent cross-linking.

Stability to acidic pH conditions

Various studies have reported the application of IgY for prophylactic use in disease prevention or therapy (e.g. Bartz *et al.*, 1980; Yolken *et al.*, 1988; Ebina *et al.*, 1990; Yokoyama *et al.*, 1992; Imbrechts *et al.*, 1997; Koroki *et al.*, 1997). However, the effectiveness of IgY for such applications may be limited to infant or neonatal mammals. The lower stability of IgY in comparison with mammalian antibodies such as IgG would probably result in its inactivation under the acidic conditions found in the mature gastric tract of older children and adults. Since the Fab' fragment of IgY was reported to be stable against further pepsin digestion at pH above 4.2 (Akita and Nakai, 1993b), it has been suggested that IgY could be effective in infants under 6 months old whose gastric tracts are still immature.

Otani *et al.* (1991) reported less than 5% loss in activity after 1 h incubation at pH 4.0, while Schmidt *et al.* (1989) reported over 60% loss of activity under the same incubation conditions. No residual activity was observed at pH 2.0 in either of those studies (Schmidt *et al.*, 1989; Otani *et al.*, 1991). In contrast, the neutralization activities of IgY and Fab' fragments against the heat-labile toxin of enterotoxigenic *E. coli* (ETEC) strain H10407 were partially retained even after incubation for 4 h at pH 2 and 37°C (Akita *et al.*, 1998). Similarly, Hatta *et al.* (1993) indicated that the activity of IgY against anti-human rotavirus (Mo strain) determined by enzyme-linked immunosorbent assay (ELISA) was considerably decreased after incubation at pH 3.0 for 4 h, whereas about 70% of the initial activity was measured when the antibody activity was determined as neutralization titres. It was suggested that conformational changes in IgY exposed to acidic conditions may result in inability of the secondary antibody in the ELISA protocol to recognize the IgY molecule; however, these changes may not be severe enough to destroy completely the functional activity of the IgY molecule as an antibody.

Stability to conditions of immunoaffinity chromatography

Little if any information has been published on the stability of yolk antibodies in immunoadsorption or immunoaffinity applications. Denaturation of antibodies, whether from yolk or other sources, can result not only from immobilization but also from the harsh elution protocols commonly required to dissociate the antigen–antibody complex (Yarmush *et al.*, 1992). The most commonly used protocol involves elution under acidic pH conditions. Alternative eluents which have been suggested include highly alkaline conditions (Kuronen *et al.*, 1997) and high concentrations of guanidine hydrochloride (Otani *et al.*, 1991) and magnesium chloride, especially in conjunction with ethylene glycol (Tsang and Wilkins, 1991). However, potential changes in structure and recovery of specific antibody activity of yolk antibodies subjected to these conditions have not been reported previously.

A modified ELISA technique known as ELISA-elution assay was used to screen the effects of a large number of eluent conditions on their effectiveness in dissociating IgY antibody–antigen complexes during immunoaffinity processes (Kummer and Li-Chan, 1998). In addition, the potential denaturing effects of the eluents were also assessed on the basis of retention of recognition by antibodies specific for IgY or IgG. The results indicated that acidic pH buffers (pH 2.30–3.25), a commercially available eluent claimed to be non-denaturing (Actisep™) and high concentrations of magnesium chloride (4 M MgCl$_2$), all dissociated the IgY–IgG complexes successfully. However, some denaturation was apparent in the presence of MgCl$_2$ and, to a lesser extent, Actisep™. The ELISA-elution assay did not indicate any denaturation of IgY or IgG after exposure to three successive 20-min incubation periods with acidic pH eluents at ambient temperature, followed by neutralization in phosphate-buffered saline.

Other studies have shown various changes in IgY after exposure to acidic pH or to high concentrations of guanidine hydrochloride, by measuring its intrinsic fluorescence emission spectra, surface hydrophobicity and antigen-binding activity (Chansarkar, 1998). Figure 25.2 (solid bars) shows the effects of pH (7.0, 4.0 and 2.8) and temperature (4, 25 and 37°C) during a 2 h incubation period, on the surface hydrophobicity measured by a fluorescence probe (1,8-anilinonaphthalene sulphonate; ANS) and antigen-binding activity measured by ELISA. Acidic pH treatment resulted in dramatic increases in the

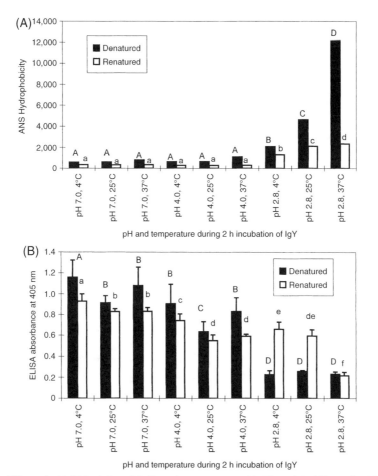

Fig. 25.2. Effect of pH (7.0, 4.0 and 2.8) and temperature (4, 25 and 37°C) on the (A) ANS hydrophobicity (%$^{-1}$) and (B) lactoferrin-binding activity (absorbance at 405 nm in ELISA) of IgY. Solid bars denote 'denatured' IgY after a 2 h incubation under the different pH and temperature conditions, while open bars denote 'renatured' IgY analysed after exhaustive dialysis against citrate phosphate-buffered saline at pH 7. Bars with different letters within each data set (upper case letters for solid bars, lower case letters for open bars) are significantly different ($P < 0.05$).

surface hydrophobicity as well as decreases in antigen-binding activity, especially for IgY incubated at pH 2.8 and 37°C.

In order to assess the possibility that these changes in IgY could be reversed upon neutralization, the treated samples were dialysed exhaustively against pH 7 buffer, and these 'renatured' samples were evaluated by the ANS probe and ELISA methods. As shown in Fig. 25.2 (open bars), the changes were partially reversed for IgY samples incubated at pH 4 as well as those incubated at pH 2.8 and 4 or 25°C. However, for IgY samples which had been incubated at pH 2.8 and 37°C, there was no recovery of antigen-binding activity after dialysis at neutral pH, although there were some conformational changes suggested by a lowering of the surface hydrophobicity.

Similar trends were observed for guanidine hydrochloride treatment (Chansarkar, 1998; data not shown). Increases in surface hydrophobicity and decreases in antigen-binding activity, which were only partially reversed by exhaustive dialysis, were observed after exposure to guanidine hydrochloride concentrations greater than 3 M. These results demonstrate that some irreversible structural changes, involving the epitopes responsible for antigen binding and exposure of hydrophobic groups, result from exposure to acidic pH (2.8). This phenomenon is true especially at higher temperature (37°C), or high (≥ 3 M) concentrations of guanidine hydrochloride.

Figure 25.3 shows the effects of elution with glycine–HCl buffer at pH 2.8 during immunoaffinity chromatography on the surface hydrophobicity of IgY antibodies measured by the ANS probe method. Although the antibodies were neutralized immediately upon elution, a dramatic increase in hydrophobicity was observed, which suggests structural changes leading to greater exposure of hydrophobic groups to the molecular surface. These changes were only partially reversible. After storage at neutral pH for a week, the hydrophobicity of eluted antibodies decreased, but was still significantly greater than the hydrophobicity of the starting IgY preparations at neutral pH, at both low and high ionic strength. In contrast, when elution was performed at pH 2.8 but in the presence of the stabilizing disaccharide trehalose, the hydrophobicity of the eluted antibodies was only slightly greater than that of the starting IgY preparations. Similar protective effects of sucrose and invert sugar have been reported by Shimizu *et al.* (1994), but only at very high (50%) concentrations of sugar. Trehalose is a more effective stabilizer at low concentrations and has the added advantage that it is highly soluble, non-reducing, non-hygroscopic and one of the most chemically unreactive sugars (Draber *et al.*, 1995).

Stability to concentration and lyophilization processes

An essential consideration in antibody technology is the preparation of products having adequate storage properties. This may include storage of liquid aliquots in the frozen state or at 2–4°C with added preservatives to retard microbial growth, or storage of dried products. However, concentration, lyophilization and other processes used to prepare these products have been reported to result in denaturation of antibodies (McCue *et al.*, 1988; Rousell and McCue, 1991; Draber *et al.*, 1995). Destabilization of IgY may be related to

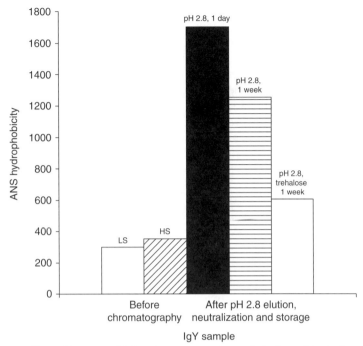

Fig. 25.3.   Effect of immunoaffinity chromatography and elution with glycine–HCl buffer at pH 2.8 on the ANS hydrophobicity (%$^{-1}$) of IgY. Yolk antibodies against lactoferrin were isolated using immunoaffinity chromatography as described by Li-Chan *et al.* (1998). Specific antibodies were eluted using glycine–HCl buffer at pH 2.8 in the absence or presence of 15% trehalose, neutralized to pH 7 immediately after elution, then analysed after 1 day or 1 week at 4°C. The hydrophobicity of eluted antibodies was compared with that of the starting IgY samples in citrate phosphate buffer at pH 7 and low or high ionic strength (LS = 0.14 M NaCl; HS = 1.5 M NaCl).

aggregation of IgY with increasing ionic strength (Hersch and Benedict, 1966; Kubo and Benedict, 1969). The combination of low pH (2) and high ionic strength (1.4 M NaCl) resulted in complete destruction of the neutralization activity of IgY against ETEC labile toxin, but some activity was retained for Fab' fragments under those conditions (Akita *et al.*, 1998). In this regard, IgY is not unique. Purified IgG has been reported to self-associate readily in solution at physiological pH and, as early as 1945, formulation of IgG with saline was recognized as being inadvisable, due to the resulting turbidity, aggregation, thermal instability and loss of antibody titres (Rousell and McCue, 1991). Milder processing and addition of excipients such as glycine, maltose or proteins such as albumin have therefore been suggested for commercial Ig products.

For the preparation of liquid concentrates of purified IgY or specific antibody preparations, membrane processes such as ultrafiltration or dialysis may be used. However, we have observed that these processes promote aggregation and precipitation of IgY, especially in the case of the affinity-purified specific antibodies. Losses of between 40 and 70% were reported to result from insolubilization when IgY was concentrated by ultrafiltration or when dialysed samples were subsequently lyophilized and reconstitution was attempted (Akita and Li-Chan, 1998). An alternative method was therefore developed to concentrate IgY, by anion-exchange chromatography of dilute solutions at pH 8.6 and final ionic strength of 0.025–0.050 M. A concentrated IgY fraction could be recovered by elution with 0.15 M phosphate buffer at pH 7 and containing 0.5 M NaCl (Akita and Li-Chan, 1998).

In some cases, freeze-dried products may be recommended to minimize risk from bacterial growth (Rousell and McCue, 1991). Since freeze-drying is a low temperature process, in comparison with spray-drying, it is usually considered to be less destructive. However, proteins may suffer loss of activity during freeze-drying as a result of conformational changes, aggregation or adsorption (Skrabanja et al., 1994). Careful attention should be paid to process and formulation details which may lead to freezing and drying stresses (Pikal, 1994).

The effects of freezing and freeze-drying under different conditions on the solubility (Fig. 25.4) and antigen-binding activity (Fig. 25.5) of IgY have been studied recently (Chansarkar, 1998). IgY solutions (sets A and B, at 30 and 1 mg ml^{-1}, respectively) were prepared in pH 7 citrate phosphate buffer containing either 0.14 or 1.5 M NaCl (low salt or LS, and high salt or HS, respectively). Solutions were frozen at either –8 or –80°C for a week, then one set of each was freeze-dried (FD). Samples which were frozen or freeze-dried at the high protein concentration of 30 mg ml^{-1} showed a drastic loss of solubility when analysed directly at that concentration, especially for samples containing high salt (Fig. 25.4, set A, solid bars). However, with the exception of the freeze-dried sample prepared under conditions of high salt and –80°C freezing (HS-80FD), this insolubilization was reversible, since solubility was recovered by diluting the samples to 1 mg ml^{-1} before analysis (Fig. 25.4, set A*, shaded bars). Samples which were frozen and freeze-dried at the lower concentration of 1 mg ml^{-1} (Fig. 25.4, set B, open bars) showed slight insolubilization, with greater loss after freeze-drying.

With the exception of the samples frozen at –8°C (LS –8 and HS –8, Fig. 25.5), all frozen and freeze-dried samples showed some loss of antigen-binding activity as determined by ELISA, compared with unfrozen controls stored at 4°C (LS 4°C and HS 4°C in Fig. 25.5). The greatest losses in antibody activity were observed for freeze-dried IgY samples prepared after freezing at 1 mg ml^{-1} concentration.

Application of IgY in Immunoaffinity Chromatography

Over the last decade, the number of protein products produced by biotechnology has grown tremendously, generating a demand for simple and mild processes which can isolate products with high purity, activity and stability (Yarmush et al., 1992; Skrabanja et al., 1994). Immunoaffinity chromatography is a process for the isolation and purification of target molecules, using immobilized specific antibodies directed against the target molecule or antigen. Due to the specific nature of the antibody–antigen interaction, immunoaffinity

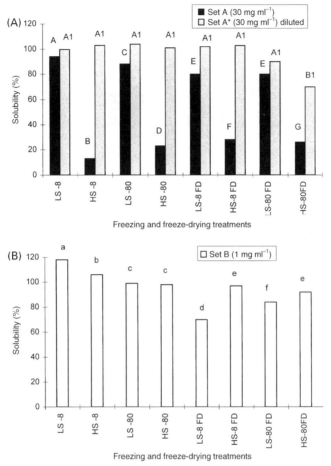

Fig. 25.4.   Effect of freezing (−8 or −80°C) and freeze-drying (FD) on the solubility (%) of IgY. Solutions of IgY were prepared in citrate phosphate buffer at pH 7 and low or high ionic strength (LS = 0.14 M NaCl; HS = 1.5 M NaCl). Solid bars (A) and open bars (B) denote IgY solutions prepared at 30 and 1 mg ml^{-1}, respectively. Solubility for samples frozen or freeze-dried at 30 mg ml^{-1} was measured without dilution (set A) or after dilution to 1 mg ml^{-1} (set A*). Bars with different letters within each data set (upper case letters for set A, upper case letters followed by the number 1 for set A*, lower case letters for set B) are significantly different ($P < 0.05$).

chromatography offers the possibility of simple, one-step purification of a single protein species from complex starting materials. However, in spite of this potential, a more widespread process scale use has been limited by the high cost of the technique and parameters related to production of antibody and efficiency of immobilization (Yarmush *et al.*, 1992). The relative ease of production of sizeable quantities and titres of specific antibodies in yolk suggests that IgY has good potential for replacing other sources of polyclonal antibodies or monoclonal antibodies currently used in immunoaffinity chromatography.

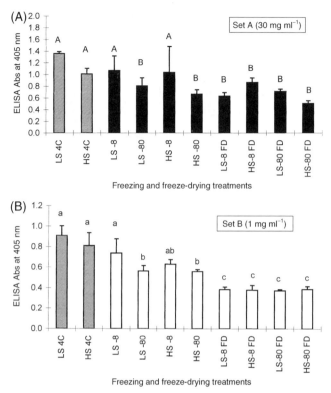

Fig. 25.5. Effect of freezing (–8 or –80°C) and freeze-drying (FD) on the lactoferrin-binding activity (absorbance at 405 nm in ELISA) of IgY. Solutions of IgY were prepared in citrate phosphate buffer at pH 7 and low or high ionic strength (LS = 0.14 M NaCl; HS = 1.5 M NaCl). Solid bars (A) and open bars (B) denote IgY solutions prepared at 30 and 1 mg ml^{-1}, respectively. All samples, including control samples stored at 4°C (LS 4C and HS 4C), were diluted to the same protein concentration of 1 μg ml^{-1} for ELISA. Bars with different letters within each data set (upper case letters for set A, lower case letters for set B) are significantly different ($P < 0.05$).

In our laboratory, we have immobilized yolk antibodies for the purpose of immunoaffinity isolation of value-added proteins from dairy products (Akita and Li-Chan, 1998; Kim and Li-Chan, 1998; Li-Chan *et al.*, 1998). The simplicity and specificity of the immunoaffinity process are illustrated in the flow chart (Fig. 25.6) and typical elution profile for preparation of purified IgG$_1$ from cow's milk using a column bearing immobilized anti-IgG$_1$ yolk antibodies (Fig. 25.7). This approach has been used successfully for simple one-step isolation of lactoferrin (Li-Chan *et al.*, 1998) and immunoglobulins from colostrum, milk or cheese whey (Akita and Li-Chan, 1998; Li-Chan and Kim, 1998). The purity of the recovered proteins was 99% as determined by radial immunodiffusion. Separation of immunoglobulin subclasses usually involves time-consuming multiple step processes. The specificity of the immunoaffinity technique using immobilized yolk antibodies prepared against each subclass was demonstrated by double immunodiffusion analysis results, showing subclass specificity and lack of cross-reactivity in the products obtained (Akita and Li-Chan, 1998).

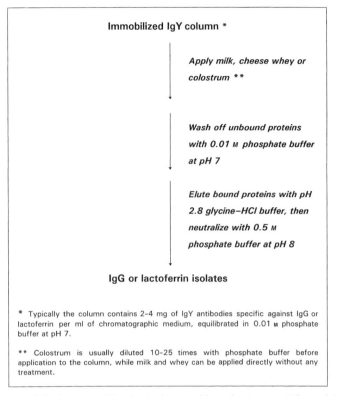

Immobilized IgY column *

> *Apply milk, cheese whey or colostrum ***

> *Wash off unbound proteins with 0.01 M phosphate buffer at pH 7*

> *Elute bound proteins with pH 2.8 glycine–HCl buffer, then neutralize with 0.5 M phosphate buffer at pH 8*

IgG or lactoferrin isolates

* Typically the column contains 2–4 mg of IgY antibodies specific against IgG or lactoferrin per ml of chromatographic medium, equilibrated in 0.01 M phosphate buffer at pH 7.

** Colostrum is usually diluted 10–25 times with phosphate buffer before application to the column, while milk and whey can be applied directly without any treatment.

Fig. 25.6.   Simplified protocol for the isolation of lactoferrin or IgG from dairy products by immunoaffinity chromatography on immobilized yolk antibodies. Details of the procedures are described in Akita and Li-Chan (1998), Li-Chan *et al.* (1998) and Kim and Li-Chan (1998).

The efficiency of immobilization, antigen-binding capacity, useful life and re-usability of immunoadsorbents are important parameters in assessing the feasibility of immunoaffinity chromatography (Yarmush *et al.*, 1992). Using different immobilization chemistries, including monoaldehyde, hydrazide and periodate activation-based chemistries, coupling efficiency of 90% or greater and antigen-binding capacity ranging from 50 to 100% (mol antigen bound per mol of immobilized IgY) have been achieved for immobilized IgY columns. The columns are re-usable, and have been used in our laboratory for more than 50 cycles without significant decreases in binding capacity. To extend the use of such columns, we have also established the feasibility of preparing immunoaffinity columns in which biotinylated IgY is held by strong non-covalent interaction on columns bearing immobilized avidin (Kim and Li-Chan, 1998). When the antibody activity has been reduced by prolonged use, these columns may be regenerated by dissociating the avidin–biotinylated IgY complex using guanidine hydrochloride and acidic pH, and active immunoadsorbents prepared by the application of fresh preparations of biotinylated IgY (Kim *et al.*, 1999).

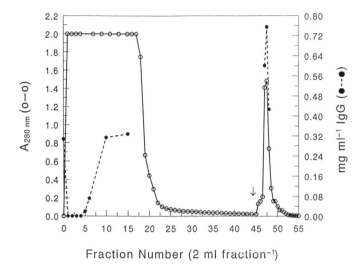

Fraction Number (2 ml fraction⁻¹)

Fig. 25.7. Typical elution profile for isolation of IgG_1 from cow's milk. Raw skimmed milk (30 ml) was applied to the immunoaffinity column (3 mg of anti-IgG_1 IgY immobilized on 3 ml of periodate-oxidized Sepharose CL6B). Unbound proteins were washed off with 0.01 M phosphate buffer at pH 7. The bound fraction containing IgG_1 was eluted using 0.05 M glycine–HCl buffer at pH 2.8 (indicated by the arrow), and immediately neutralized with 0.1 volume of 0.5 M phosphate buffer at pH 8. Fractions were monitored for proteins using absorbance at 280 nm and for IgG_1 concentration using radial immunodiffusion assay.

Conclusions

The yolk of hens' eggs is a valuable source of specific antibodies, which can be used in prophylactic or therapeutic treatment to confer passive immunity, in diagnostic assays as the primary or secondary antibody, and in downstream processing through one-step immunoaffinity chromatographic purification of value-added products. In all of these applications, the yolk IgY immunoglobulins must be in the form of functional antibodies which interact specifically with the target antigens. The particular conditions of production, isolation, storage and utilization of IgY must, therefore, be controlled carefully to ensure structural stability and activity of these specific antibodies. As more basic information on the function and stability of the IgY molecule becomes available, the potential for widespread applications of immunoglobulins from egg yolk will be realized.

Acknowledgements

The research expertise and technical assistance of E.M. Akita, N. Chansarkar, H. Kim, A. Kummer and S.S. Ler are gratefully acknowledged. This work was supported by research grants from the Natural Sciences and Engineering Research Council of Canada and the Dairy Farmers of Canada.

References

Akita, E.M. and Li-Chan, E.C.Y. (1998) Isolation of bovine immunoglobulin G subclasses from milk, colostrum and whey using immobilized egg yolk antibodies. *Journal of Dairy Science* 81, 54–63.

Akita, E.M. and Nakai, S. (1993a) Comparison of four purification methods for the production of immunoglobulins from eggs laid by hens immunised with an enterotoxigenic *E. coli* strain. *Journal of Immunological Methods* 160, 207–214.

Akita, E.M. and Nakai, S. (1993b) Production of Fab′ fragments from chicken egg yolk immunoglobulin Y (IgY). *Journal of Immunological Methods* 162, 155–164.

Akita, E.M., Li-Chan, E.C.Y. and Nakai, S. (1998) Neutralization of enterotoxigenic *Escherichia coli* heat labile toxin by chicken egg yolk immunoglobulin (IgY) and its antigen binding fragments. *Food and Agricultural Immunology* 10, 161–172.

Bartz, C.R., Conklin, R.H., Tunstall, C.B. and Steele, J.H. (1980) Prevention of murine rotavirus infection with chicken egg immunoglobulin. *Journal of Infectious Diseases* 152, 439–441.

Chansarkar, N.L. (1998) Studies on structural stability of hen's egg yolk immunoglobulin (IgY). MSc Thesis, The University of British Columbia, Vancouver, British Columbia, Canada.

Draber, P., Drabevora, E. and Novakova, M. (1995) Stability of monoclonal M antibodies freeze-dried in the presence of trehalose. *Journal of Immunological Methods* 181, 37–43.

Ebina, T., Tsukuda, K., Umezu, K., Nose, M., Tsuda, K., Hatta, H., Kim, M. and Yamamoto, T. (1990) Gastroenteritis in suckling mice caused by human rotavirus can be prevented with egg yolk immunoglobulin (IgY) and treated with a protein-bound polysaccharide preparation (PSK). *Microbiology and Immunology* 34, 617–629.

Fichtali, J., Charter, E.A., Lo, K.V. and Nakai, S. (1992) Separation of egg yolk immunoglobulins using an automated liquid chromatography system. *Biotechnology and Bioengineering* 40, 1388–1394.

Hatta, H., Tsuda, K., Akachi, S., Kim, M., Yamamoto, T. and Ebina, T. (1993) Oral passive immunization effect of antihuman rotavirus IgY and its behavior against proteolytic enzymes. *Bioscience, Biotechnology and Biochemistry* 57, 1077–1081.

Hatta, H., Ozeki, M. and Tsuda, K. (1997) Egg yolk antibody IgY and its application. In: Yamamoto, T., Juneja, L.R., Hatta, H. and Kim, M. (eds), *Hen Eggs. Their Basic and Applied Science*. CRC Press Inc., Boca Raton, Florida, pp. 151–178.

Hersch, R.T. and Benedict, A.A. (1966) Aggregation of chicken γG immunoglobulin in 1.5 M sodium chloride. *Biochimica et Biophysica Acta* 115, 242–244.

Imbrechts, H., Deprez, P., Van Driessehe, E. and Pohl, P. (1997) Chicken egg yolk antibodies against F18ab fimbriae of *Escherichia coli* inhibit shedding of F18 positive *E. coli* by experimentally infected pigs. *Veterinary Microbiology* 54, 329–341.

Kim, H. and Li-Chan, E.C.Y. (1998) Separation of immunoglobulin G from cheddar cheese whey by avidin–biotinylated IgY chromatography. *Journal of Food Science* 63, 429–434.

Kim, H. and Nakai, S. (1998) Simple separation of immunoglobulin from egg yolk by ultrafiltration. *Journal of Food Science* 63, 485–490.

Kim, H., Durance, T.D. and Li-Chan, E.C.Y. (1999) Reusability of avidin-biotinylated immunoglobulin Y columns in immunoaffinity chromatography. *Analytical Biochemistry* 268, 383–397.

Kubo, R.T. and Benedict, A.A. (1969) Comparison of various avian and mammalian IgG immunoglobulins for salt induced aggregation. *Journal of Immunology* 103, 1022–1028.

Kummer, A. and Li-Chan, E.C.Y. (1998) Application of an ELISA-elution assay as a screening tool for dissociation of yolk antibody–antigen complexes. *Journal of Immunological Methods* 211, 125–137.

Kuroki, M., Ohta, M., Ikemori, Y., Icatlo, F.C., Jr, Kobayashi, C., Yokoyama, H. and Kodama, Y. (1997) Field evaluation of chicken egg yolk immunoglobulins specific for bovine rotavirus in neonatal calves. *Archives of Virology* 142, 843–851.

Kuronen, I., Kokko, H., Mononen, I. and Parviainen, M. (1997) Hen egg yolk antibodies purified by antigen affinity under highly alkaline conditions provide new tools for diagnostics. Human intact parathyrin as a model antigen. *European Journal of Clinical Chemistry and Clinical Biochemistry* 35, 435–440.

Larsson, A., Balow, R., Lindahl, T.L. and Forsberg, P. (1993) Chicken antibodies: taking advantage of evolution; a review. *Poultry Science* 72, 1807–1812.

Leslie, G.A. and Clem, L.W. (1969) Phylogeny of immunoglobulin structure and function – III. Immunoglobulins of chicken. *Journal of Experimental Medicine* 130, 1337–1352.

Li-Chan, E.C.Y., Ler, S.S., Kummer, A. and Akita, E.M. (1998) Isolation of lactoferrin by immunoaffinity chromatography using yolk antibodies. *Journal of Food Biochemistry* 22, 179–195.

McCue, J.P., Sasagawa, P.K. and Hein, R.H. (1988) Changes induced in antibodies by isolation methods. *Biotechnology and Applied Biochemistry* 10, 63–71.

Otani, H., Matsumoto, K., Saeki, A. and Hosono, A. (1991) Comparative studies on properties of hen egg yolk IgY and rabbit serum IgG antibodies. *Lebensmittel Wissenschaft und Technologie* 24, 152–158.

Pikal, M.J. (1994) Freeze-drying of proteins. Process, formulation and stability. In: Cleland, F.L. and Langer, R. (eds), *Formulation and Delivery of Proteins and Peptides*. ACS Symposium Series 567, American Chemical Society, Washington, DC, pp. 120–133.

Rose, M.E., Orlans, E. and Buttress, N. (1974) Immunoglobulin classes in the hen's egg: their segregation in yolk and white. *European Journal of Immunology* 4, 521–523.

Rousell, R.H. and McCue, J.P. (1991) Antibody purification from plasma. In: Harris, J.R. (ed.), *Blood Separation and Plasma Fractionation*. Wiley-Liss, New York, pp. 307–340.

Schmidt, P., Hafner, A., Reubel, G.H., Wanke, R., Franke, V., Losch, U. and Dahme, E. (1989) Production of antibodies to canine distemper virus in chicken eggs for immunochemistry. *Journal of Veterinary Medicine* B36, 661–668.

Shimizu, M., Nagashima, H., Sano, K., Hashimoto, K., Ozeki, M., Tsuda, K. and Hatta, H. (1992) Molecular stability of chicken and rabbit immunoglobulin G. *Bioscience, Biotechnology and Biochemistry* 56, 270–274.

Shimizu, M., Nagashima, H., Hashimoto, K. and Suzuki, T. (1994) Egg yolk antibody (IgY) stability in aqueous solution with high sugar concentrations. *Journal of Food Science* 59, 763–765, 772.

Skrabanja, A.T.P., De Meere, A.L.J., De Ruiter, R.A. and Van Den Oetelaar, P.J.M. (1994) Lyophilization of biotechnology products. *PDA Journal of Pharmaceutical Science and Technology* 48, 311–317.

Svendsen, L., Crowley, A., Østegaard, L.H., Stodulski, G. and Hau, J. (1995) Development and comparison of purification strategies for chicken antibodies from egg yolk. *Laboratory Animal Science* 45, 89–93.

Thalley, B.S. and Carroll, S.B. (1990) Rattlesnake and scorpion antivenoms from the egg yolks of immunized hens. *Bio/Technology* 8, 934–938.

Tsang, V.C.W. and Wilkins, P.P. (1991) Optimum dissociating conditions for immuno-affinity and preferential isolation of antibodies with high specific activity. *Journal of Immunological Methods* 138, 291–299.

Warr, G.W., Magor, K.E. and Higgins, D.A. (1995) IgY: clues to the origins of modern antibodies. *Immunology Today* 16, 392–398.

Yarmush, M.L., Antonse, K.P., Sundaram, S. and Yarmush, D.M. (1992) Immuno-adsorption: strategies for antigen elution and production of reusable adsorbents. *Biotechnology Progress* 8, 168–178.

Yokoyama, H., Peralta, R.C., Diaz, R., Sendo, S., Ikemori, Y. and Kodama, Y. (1992) Passive protective effect of chicken egg immunoglobulins against experimental enterotoxigenic *Escherichia coli* infection in neonatal piglets. *Infection and Immunity* 60, 998–1007.

Yolken, R.H., Leister, F., Wee, S.B., Miskuff, R. and Vonderfecht, S. (1988) Antibodies to rotaviruses in chickens' eggs: a potential source of antiviral immunoglobulins suitable for human consumption. *Pediatrics* 81, 291–295.

Prevention of *Yersinia ruckeri* Infection in Rainbow Trout with Hen's Egg Yolk Immunoglobulin

26

Y. Mine[1], S.B. Lee[1] and R.M.W. Stevenson[2]
[1]*Department of Food Science and* [2]*Department of Microbiology, University of Guelph, Guelph, Ontario, Canada*

Anti-*Yersinia ruckeri* immunoglobulin (IgY) was inducted to hen's egg yolk immunized with formalin-killed whole cells and its lipopolysaccharide (LPS) of serovar 1 and serovar 2. The IgY was specific for their homologous LPS in Western immunoblots, even though their purified LPS had a poor immunogenicity. The antibody microencapsulation was prepared successfully using a microbial transglutaminase to protect against acid pepsin digestion in gastroenteritic juice in the fish. The encapsulated IgY was stable for at least 2 h in the rainbow trout stomach. Feeding specific anti-serovar 1 *Y. ruckeri* IgY to fish either before or after immersion infection produced marginal reductions in mortalities and in intestine infection. The same IgY passively protected rainbow trout against infection when administered by intraperitoneal infection 4 h before an immersion challenge.

Introduction

Antibodies have been investigated as a tool for immunoassay and also as passive immunotherapy for infectious diseases. In passive immunization, a relatively large amount of antibody is required because of oral administration. Hen's egg yolk antibody (IgY) has attracted considerable attention because the feasibility of cost-effective, large-scale production has favoured the use of egg yolk. The efficacy of this approach has been shown in human and veterinary medicine, for rotavirus-induced diarrhoea in humans (Yolken *et al.*, 1988), *Escherichia coli* infections in pigs (Hoblet *et al.*, 1986; Yokoyama *et al.*, 1992; Imbrechts *et al.*, 1997) and rabbits (O'Farrelly *et al.*, 1992), and *Streptococcus mutans*-induced dental caries (Hamada *et al.*, 1991). In aquatic species, IgY against *Edwardsiella tarda* was administered orally to provide passive immunization of the Japanese eel *Anguilla japonica* Temminck and Schlegel

© CAB *International* 2000. *Egg Nutrition and Biotechnology*
(eds J.S. Sim, S. Nakai and W. Guenter)

(Gutierrez *et al.*, 1993; Hatta *et al.*, 1993). In those studies, the challenge dose of live *E. tarda* was mixed into a paste of yolk powder containing 20% IgY and sterilized eel diet, and administered by cannulation into the stomach of each eel. These studies illustrated that IgY antibodies could provide a barrier against *E. tarda* infections establishing through the gastrointestinal tract. Mixing the IgY and bacteria together would optimize the protective effect but, in practical aquaculture, it would be difficult to anticipate precisely when a pathogen might infect fish, and the cost of continuous feeding of IgY to prevent initial infection would be prohibitive except for very small fish.

Nevertheless, we were interested in determining whether oral application of IgY could protect rainbow trout (*Oncorhynchus mykiss*) against infection with *Yersinia ruckeri*, the causative agent of enteric redmouth disease and a systemic bacterial septicaemia of salmonid fishes (Stevenson and Airdrie, 1984). *Y. ruckeri* can be isolated from the intestinal lining of fish (Busch and Lingg, 1974), and Evelyn (1996) has suggested that this bacterium may be resistant enough to use the gastrointestinal tract as one of its routes of infection. The objective of this study was to determine if egg yolk IgY raised against *Y. ruckeri* could be effective against infections in salmonid fish. The first aim of the present work was to determine if IgY antibodies raised against the fish pathogen *Y. ruckeri* could discriminate between two serological varieties of this pathogen. Subsequently, the IgY was used in attempts to determine if infections could be reduced, particularly when administered orally.

Materials and Methods

Immunization of hens

Yersinia ruckeri strains RS1154 (serovar 1) and RS 1153 (serovar 2) were fish-passaged strains from the Fish Health Laboratory collection, Department of Microbiology, University of Guelph. They were grown in tryptic soy broth (Difco, Detroit, Michigan) at 18°C for 48 h in flasks with shaking. The cultures were treated with 0.3% formalin for 24 h, tested for viability and then collected by centrifugation (10,000 **g**, 10 min). Lipopolysaccharide (LPS) of *Y. ruckeri* was isolated by the phenol–hot water extraction method of Westphal and Jann (1965). A group of White Leghorn hens, 23–26 weeks old, were immunized with antigen consisting of 1 mg ml^{-1} of freeze-dried *Y. ruckeri* cells or 1 mg ml^{-1} of LPS, emulsified with an equal volume of Freund's complete adjuvant (Sigma, St Louis, Missouri).

Enzyme-linked immunosorbent assay (ELISA)

The ELISA was performed to evaluate the specific IgY activity. The 96-well microplate was coated with *Y. ruckeri* whole cell suspension (10^8 well^{-1}) or LPS (10 µg ml^{-1}) solution and blocked with 2.0% bovine serum albumin (BSA). Alkaline phosphatase-conjugated rabbit anti-chicken IgG (Sigma) and *p*-nitrophenylphosphate were used as the second antibody and the substrate, respectively.

Electrophoresis and immunoblotting

Sodium dodecyl sulphate–polyacrylamide gel electrophoresis (SDS–PAGE) was carried out according to Laemmli (1970) using a 10% acrylamide gel. The protein was stained with a mixture of Coomassie brilliant blue R-250 (Sigma). Western blotting was carried out according to the method of Johnstone and Thorpe (1996) using a nitrocellulose membrane.

IgY microencapsulation

The mixture of gelatin, starch and anti-*Y. ruckeri* IgY was incubated with a microbial transglutaminase (Ajinomoto Co., Tokyo, Japan) at 37°C for 2 h. The treated sample was dried in an oven (40°C) overnight and ground using a laboratory mill. The resulting IgY pellet contained 12.5 mg of specific anti-*Y. ruckeri* IgY in each 100 mg pellet. The IgY itself was also polymerized by the enzyme as a control.

Effects of proteolytic enzymes and digestion on IgY activity

Pepsin from porcine stomach mucosa (Sigma) was added at a ratio of 1 : 80 to 10 mg ml^{-1} of anti-*Y. ruckeri* IgY solution and the microencapsulated IgY. The mixtures were incubated at 37°C at pH 2.0. After the enzyme reaction, the residual antibody activity was measured by ELISA. To examine the effects of the activity of gastric secretions and enteric digestive enzymes of the rainbow trout on the antibody, anti-*Y. ruckeri* IgY was administered into the stomach of anaesthetized 150 g rainbow trout by cannulation. The stomach as well as front and back sections of the intestine were sampled from each fish at 0, 2, 4 and 6 h after administration of IgY. Samples were put into 10 ml of cold phosphate-buffered saline (PBS: 10 mM phosphate, 0.15 M NaCl, pH 7.2) and homogenized. The suspension was centrifuged at 10,000 **g** for 10 min, and then the supernatant was filtered through a 0.45 μm pore size membrane filter and IgY activity measured by ELISA.

Fish experiments

For intraperitoneal (i.p.) challenges, anaesthetized rainbow trout of 270–300 g were injected with a 1 : 1 mixture of viable *Y. ruckeri* RS1154 (3.5×10^7 c.f.u. ml^{-1}) and anti-*Y. ruckeri* RS1154 IgY, at a final concentration of either 4 or 40 mg per fish. After injection, fish were monitored for distress at frequent intervals, to 4 days post-challenge. Fish were then killed, necropsied and tested for the presence of *Y. ruckeri* in the kidney and intestine. For immersion challenges, groups of 4–5 rainbow trout (5 g) were assigned to 700 ml experimental tanks to provide a biomass of approximately 4% (w/v) in each tank. The immersion challenge in 1.8×10^8 c.f.u. ml^{-1} of *Y. ruckeri* was given 4 h after the injection. In the first feeding trial, each tank of fish was fed 400 mg of commercial rainbow trout diet mixed either with 400 mg of IgY pellet, or with 400 mg of a control pellet lacking IgY. After 2 h, fish were exposed to 2×10^8 c.f.u. ml^{-1} of *Y. ruckeri*. In the second feeding trial, each tank of fish was fed 400 mg of feed and 400 mg of IgY pellet, given either as a pre-feed (once before challenge), a post-feed (once after challenge) or as a multiple feed (four times after challenge). Control tanks received 400 mg of the control pellet lacking IgY. These fish were exposed to 4.1×10^8 c.f.u. ml^{-1} of viable *Y. ruckeri*.

Results and Discussion

Antibody production

Figure 26.1 shows the immune response of hens against *Y. ruckeri*. After 30–40 days of first immunization, antibodies to whole cells of both serovars of *Y. ruckeri* were found at high titres in egg yolks. The maximum ELISA value against serovar 1 strain RS 1154 was twice as high as that for serovar 2 strain RS 1153, for equivalent concentrations of ELISA test antigens. Hens immunized with purified LPS of either serovar showed a very poor antibody response. This differs from the general experience with raising antisera in rabbits or fish, where serovar 2 responses are usually higher (Raymond, 1991). After salting out by 50% ammonium sulphate, the purified IgY from egg yolk was determined to be about 80% pure, based on SDS–PAGE. A 10 mg ml^{-1} solution of freeze-dried IgY had an agglutinating titre of 1 : 32 for anti-*Y. ruckeri* RS 1154 IgY and 1 : 16 for the anti-*Y. ruckeri* RS 1153 IgY (data are not shown). In Western immunoblotting, some cross-reactions were observed between the two strains of *Y. ruckeri* (Fig. 26.2). At least three of the immunodominant

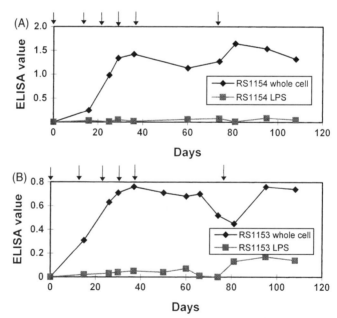

Fig. 26.1. Antibody response in the egg yolk from hens injected with antigens of *Y. reckeri*. Antibody level in a 1000-fold dilution of egg yolk water-soluble fraction was measured by ELISA using the whole cell antigens or LPS antigens. Arrows indicate days of injection. (A) Serovar 1, *Y. ruckeri* (RS1154) IgY, (B) serovar 2, *Y. ruckeri* LPS (RS1153).

(A)

1   2

(B)

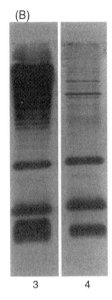

3   4

Fig. 26.2. Western immuno-blotting of lipopolysaccharide (LPS) of *Y. ruckeri* using the IgY raised against whole cells of (A) serovar 1 strain RS1154 and (B) serovar 2 RS1153. Lanes 1 and 4, LPS of RS1154; lanes 2 and 3, LPS of RS1153.

bands which appeared with anti-*Y. ruckeri* IgY were also present when control IgY prepared from eggs of non-immunized hens was used, or with anti-*Escherichia coli* IgY (data not shown).

The anti-*Y. ruckeri* RS 1153 IgY also reacted well with some other bands in the RS 1154 preparation (Fig. 26.2A), which also appear in some immunoblots with anti-*E. coli* IgY and anti-*Y. ruckeri* RS 1154 IgY (data not shown). The LPS of serovars 1 and 2 strains of *Y. ruckeri* were recognized by their homologous anti-whole cell IgY preparations, but they did not cross-react with each other. The IgY against serovar 2 IgY reacted distinctly against its whole LPS (Fig. 26.2A) while the anti-serovar 1 IgY reacted mainly with higher molecular weight LPS (Fig. 26.2B). Neither serovar 1 nor serovar 2 LPS reacted when immunoblotted with control IgY or anti-*E.coli* IgY.

Stability of IgY

Figure 26.3 shows the antibody stability in rainbow trout stomach after feeding. The activity of anti-sevovar 1 *Y. ruckeri* IgY decreased rapidly after 2 h exposure in the stomach and was completely lost after 5 h of oral administration. In parallel measurements, the pH of the rainbow trout stomach following the feeding decreased rapidly from an initial pH of 4.5–5.0 to pH 2.6–3.0 after 30 min, then increased again after 3 h. It was reported that the ELISA value of anti-*E. tarda* IgY activity in eel digestive tracts was found to be maintained for 6 h after oral administration (Gutierrez *et al.*, 1993). Their results are contradictory to our results during fish digestion. Changes in pH of the eel stomach were not given in their report. It was shown that acidity in the eel stomach increased after food intake (Mackay, 1929). It has been shown that it reached pH 2.0 in the stomach of *Tilapia* a few hours after daily feeding (Moriarty, 1973). Shimizu *et al.* (1989) also reported that the activity of IgY specific to

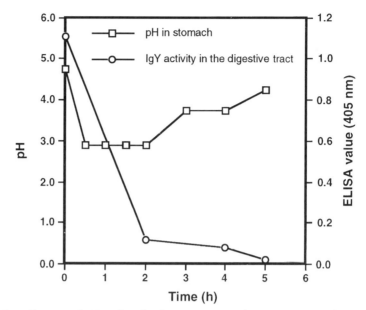

Fig. 26.3. Changes of pH and antibody activity in rainbow trout stomach after feeding. Data are the average of duplicate measurements. The stability of anti-*Y. ruckeri* (RS1154) IgY in the digestive tracts of rainbow trout after oral administration of IgY was measured by ELISA using the whole cells as an antigen.

E. coli examined by competitive ELISA was sensitive to pepsin at low pHs (pH > 4.0).

In our study, it is obvious that anti-*Y. ruckeri* IgY administered orally to rainbow trout reached the small intestine with severe damage by gastric enzymes and low pH. If the IgY is introduced into the small intestine without a significant loss of activity caused by gastric enzymes and pH, antibodies can reach the intestine of rainbow trout after oral administration. Therefore, it is important to protect the IgY from degradation in the presence of gastric enzyme and low pH for at least 2 h. We used a new method of IgY microencapsulation employing a microbial transglutaminase. The IgY polymer was significantly more susceptible to pepsin digestion than was the IgY pellet preparation (microencapsulation) (Fig. 26.4). The polymerized IgY appears to break down after pepsin digestion for 1 h. In contrast, the IgY pellet activity was stable after a 2 h pepsin digestion, and no cleavage of the IgY was observed in SDS–PAGE (Fig. 31.4B, lane 5). The agglutination titre of the IgY pellet was 1 : 16.

Passive protection of fish

Groups of rainbow trout, weighing about 5 g, which had been fed anti-*Y. ruckeri* IgY 2 h prior to an immersion challenge with *Y. ruckeri* RS 1154 had lower mortalities after 8 days compared with fish fed with normal food before the challenge. The group fed IgY appeared to have a lower number of infected fish after 8 days, based on organ and intestine culture. In a subsequent trial of

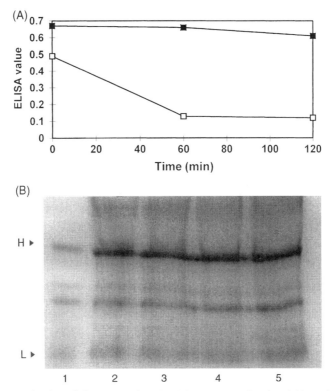

Fig. 26.4. Antibody stability (A) and SDS-PAGE patterns (B) of anti-*Y. ruckeri* IgY following digestion with pepsin at 1 : 80 ratio (w/w) for 2 h at 37°C. (A) Anti-*Y. ruckeri* activity of IgY polymer (□) and IgY pellet (■) by ELISA. (B) SDS–PAGE patterns of the IgY pellet following pepsin digestion. Lane 1, IgY solution, heavy chain (H), light chain (L); lane 2, IgY pellet, lanes 3–5, IgY pellet with pepsin digestion at pH 2.0 for 0.5 (lane 3), 1 (lane 4) and 2 h (lane 5), respectively.

the feeding procedures in triplicate of the groups, the IgY-fed fish showed lower mortalities than groups receiving normal feed (Table 26.1). The numbers of IgY-fed fish carrying *Y. ruckeri* in intestine samples appeared lower than the normal-feed controls, regardless of whether the feeding was given before or after the challenge. The groups fed IgY three times post-infection gave inconsistent results. Two groups of sampled fish, one in each of these treatments, showed no *Y. ruckeri* in individual intestinal samples, nor in a pool of kidney tissues. While fish used in the trials above were actively feeding on the IgY mixtures, the doses taken up by the fish were uncertain, because of uneven feeding and some discrimination between particles in the feed.

Table 26.2 shows the passive immunization of anti-*Y. ruckeri* IgY against immersion challenge. Four days after a challenge dose of 10^7 c.f.u. of *Y. ruckeri* was injected i.p. into three rainbow trout (~285 g), all fish had *Y. ruckeri* associated with the intestinal tract tissue, but none in the kidney tissue by direct streak. If the dose was mixed with either 4 or 40 mg of the IgY preparation immediately prior to injection, only one fish in each group had *Y.*

Table 26.1. Effects of anti-*Y. ruckeri* IgY pellet feeding on prevention of *Y. ruckeri* infection of kidney and intestine after immersion challenge.

Treatment	IgY pellet[a] IgY	Additive	Mortality[b]	No. of fish in each group infected with *Y. ruckeri* in intestine	No. of group that have *Y. ruckeri* in a kidney pool[c]
No challenge normal feed	—	—	0/5	0	0/1
Challenge normal feed	—	—	6/15	T1 5/5	
				T2 5/5	3/3
				T3 5/5	
Challenge pre-fed IgY pellet	+	+	1/15	T1 2/5	
				T2 2/5	3/3
				T3 2/4	
Challenge post-fed IgY pellet	+	+	2/15	T1 2/3	
				T2 2/5	3/3
				T3 2/5	
Challenge multiple fed IgY pellet	+	+	2/14[d]	T1 1/3	
				T2 0/5	2/3
				T3 3/4	

[a]IgY pellet was mixed with IgY, gelatin and starch, and polymerized with TGase for 2 h. The 400 mg IgY pellet contained the 50 mg of anti-*Y. ruckeri* (RS1154) IgY. Additive was polymerized with gelatin and starch with TGase for 2 h.
[b]No. of dead fish/no. of tested group fish.
[c]Kidney pool: groups were divided into T1, T2 and T3, each group having five fish. The kidney pool was collected from 3–5 fish kidneys. The kidneys from dead fish were not included in the kidney pool.
[d]One fish which died 1 day post-challenge before first feeding of IgY was not included in the total.

ruckeri after 4 days, indicating some direct passive immunization effect of IgY but not carrier material. When groups of 5 g fish were passively immunized by i.p. injection with IgY and subsequently immersion challenged, no *Y. ruckeri* was found in the intestine or kidney after 7 days, while fish groups injected with a non-specific IgY or saline had the bacteria in both kidney and intestinal tissue. Therefore, the i.p. injection of anti-*Y. ruckeri* at a dose of 4 mg is effective against an immersion challenge of *Y. ruckeri* of 10^8 c.f.u. ml^{-1}.

Many pathogens of fish have been reported to spread by infection through the intestinal mucosa. The natural oral feeding of specific IgY against fish pathogens with feed will be an alternative to the method using antibiotics and chemotherapy for prevention of fish diseases in fish farms. Moreover, the oral feeding of active IgY would be a novel approach for preventing viral infection diseases of fish because no medicine has been reported to be effective.

Acknowledgement

This work was supported by Ontario Egg Producers' Marketing Board, Ontario, Canada.

Table 26.2. Effects of rainbow trout by passive immunization[a] of anti-*Y. ruckeri* IgY against immersion challenge[b].

Treatment	c.f.u. g^{-1} in group[c] Intestine	Kidney	No. of infected *Y. ruckeri* in group[d] Intestine	Kidney	No. of fish	*Y. ruckeri* positive Intestine	Kidney
Challenge high dose specific IgY	5.6×10^4	0	0/5	0/5	1 2 3 4 5	– – – – –	– – – – –
Challenge low dose specific IgY	7.2×10^3	0	0/5	0/5	1 2 3 4 5	– – – – –	– – – – –
Challenge non-specific IgY	7.4×10^6	6.2×10^7	4/5	4/5	1 2 3 4 5	– + + + +	– + + + +
Challenge saline	3.6×10^5	3.8×10^6	3/5	3/5	1 2 3 4 5	– – + + +	– – + + +

[a]Passive immunization: fish were injected with 0.1 ml of anti-*Y. ruckeri* (RS1154) IgY (high dose: 20 mg, low dose: 4 mg) and non-specific IgY (4 mg).
[b]Immersion challenge with viable *Y. ruckeri* (1.8×10^8 c.f.u. ml^{-1}).
[c]c.f.u. g^{-1} of group in intestine and kidney on 7 days after immersion challenge.
[d]No. of *Y. ruckeri* positive/no. tested fish.

References

Busch, R.A. and Lingg, A.J. (1974) Establishment of an asymptomatic carrier state infection of enteric redmouth disease in rainbow trout (*Salmo gairdneri*). *Journal of Fishery Research and Education in Canada* 32, 2429–2432.

Evelyn, T.P.T. (1996) Infection and disease. In: Iwama, G. and Nakanishi, T. (eds), *The Fish Immune System: Organism, Pathogen and Environment*. Academic Press, San Diego, California, pp. 339–362.

Gutierrez, M.A., Miyazaki, T., Hatta, H. and Kim, M. (1993) Protective properties of egg yolk IgY containing anti-*Edwardsiella tarda* antibody against paracolo disease in the Japanese eel, *Anguilla japonica* Temminck & Schlegel. *Journal of Fish Diseases* 16, 113–122.

Hamada, S., Horikoshi, T., Minami, T., Kawabata, S., Hiraoka, J., Fujiwara, T. and Ooshima, T. (1991) Oral passive immunization against dental caries in rats by use of hen egg yolk antibodies specific for cell-associated glucosyltransferase of *Streptococcus mutans. Infection and Immunity* 59, 4161–4167

Hatta, H., Tsuda, K., Akachi, S., Kim, M., Yamamoto, T. and Ebina, T. (1993) Oral passive immunization effect of anti-human rotavirus IgY and its behavior against proteolytic enzyme. *Bioscience, Biotechnology and Biochemistry* 57, 1077–1081.

Hoblet, K.H., Kohler, E.M., Saif, L.J., Theil, K.W. and Ingalls, W.L. (1986) Study of porcine postweaning diarrhea involving K88(–) hemolytic *Escherichia coli, American Journal of Veterinary Research* 47, 1910–1912.

Imbrechts, H., Deprez, P., Van Driessche, E. and Pohl, P. (1997) Chicken egg yolk antibodies against F18ab fimbriae of *Escherichia coli* inhibit shedding of F18 positive *E. coli* by experimentally infected pigs. *Veterinary Microbiology* 54, 329–341.

Johnstone, A. and Thorpe, R. (1996) Specific detection of antigens separated by polyacrylamide gel electrophoresis. In: Johnstone, A. and Thorpe, R. (eds), *Immunochemistry in Practice*. 3rd edn. Blackwell Science, Cambridge, Massachusetts, pp. 211–228.

Laemmli, U.K. (1970) Cleavage of structural proteins during the assembly of the head of bacteriophage T4. *Nature* 227, 680–685.

Mackay, M.E. (1929) The digestive system of eel-pout *Zoarces anguillaris. Biological Bulletin, Marine Biological Laboratory, Woods Hole* 56, 8–23.

Moriarty, D.J.W. (1973) The physiology of digestion of blue-green algae in the cichlid fish *Tilapia nilotica. Journal of Zoology* 171, 25–39.

O'Farrelly, C., Branton, D. and Wanke, C.A. (1992) Oral ingestion of egg yolk immunoglobulin from hens immunized with an enterotoxigenic *Escherichia coli* strain prevents diarrhea in rabbits challenged with the same strain. *Infection and Immunity* 60, 2593–2597.

Raymond, B.T. (1991) Immune responses in fish to *Yersinia ruckeri*. MSc Thesis, University of Guelph, Ontario, Canada.

Shimizu, M., Fitzsimmons, C.R. and Nakai, S. (1989) Serum and egg antibody response in chicken to *Escherichia coli. Agricultural and Biological Chemistry* 53, 3233–3288.

Stevenson, R.M.W. and Airdrie, D.W. (1984) Serological variation among *Yersinia ruckeri* strains. *Journal of Fish Diseases* 7, 247–254.

Westphal, O. and Jann, K. (1965) Bacterial lipopolysaccharides. *Methods in Carbohydrate Chemistry* 5, 83–91.

Yokoyama, H., Peralta, R.C., Diaz, R., Sendo, S., Ikemori, Y. and Kodama, Y. (1992) Passive protective effect of chicken egg yolk immunoglobulins against experimental enterotoxigenic *Escherichia coli* infection in neonatal piglets. *Infection and Immunity* 60, 998–1007.

Yolken, R.H., Leister, S., Wee, S.B., Miskuff, R. and Vonderiecht, S. (1988) Antibodies to rotaviruses in chickens' eggs: a potential source of antiviral immunoglobulins suitable for human consumption. *Pediatrics* 81, 291–295.

Using Egg Antibodies to Treat Diseases

27

M. Coleman
MAC Associates, Columbus, Ohio, USA

The human immunodeficiency virus (HIV) is a time bomb ready to explode within 7–10 years into a full blown case of acquired immune deficiency syndrome (AIDS). Frequently, AIDS, transplant, burn, cancer patients and other immune-suppressed individuals die from infections of pathogens which almost every person has in their normal gut flora. Specially produced eggs can replace the immunity lost by these diseases, while in many cases they may ameliorate the effects of the diseases themselves. Antibodies are different from antibiotics. They work by chelating antigens, thereby not allowing resistance to develop. Chickens are one of the best antibody producers in the world. They lay a 'golden egg' filled with antibodies almost every day.

This study was performed to determine if feeding antibodies could reduce the somatic cell count (SCC). The SCC was measured every 3 days for 3 weeks pre-trial (125 cows). Cows with an SCC of 250,000–750,000 were treated with egg antibodies raised against *Staphylococcus aureus* and *Streptococcus agilata* at 0 (control), 50, 100 and 200 p.p.m. in their feed. Complete blood counts and milk samples were taken every third day for 9 weeks. Milk (a.m. and p.m.) was tested for volume, fat, protein, solids not fats (SNF) and SCC. Cultures were taken from the teats of cows exhibiting > 1,000,000 SCC and from the teats of all cows 6 weeks post-trial. Microorganisms were compared in 492/481 cows with a high SCC (> 1,000,000) before and after the experiment. Treated cows were protected from *Staphylococcus/Streptococcus*, but not from other mastitis-causing agents. SCCs were decreased (–44% $P < 0.05$) for at least 3 weeks post-trial (control +72%). Milk (p.m.) production (+9%), protein (+9%) and SNF (+2%) content increased ($P < 0.05$). *Staphylococcus/Streptococcus* were found in 56 and 57% respectively of the high SCC cows before and after this experiment, but no treated cows exhibiting high SCC cultured positive for *Staphylococcus* or *Steptococcus*. There were no significant differences in complete blood counts. This suggests that orally fed antibodies can be effective in tissues remote from the intestines.

Introduction

Current egg antibody patents (USA)

The use of egg antibodies (IgY) to prevent or treat disease is a novel and exciting application of egg technology. There are two types of patents for using IgY to treat diseases. The first involves antibody–organism binding on the surface of an anatomical structure. Stolle (1988) and Tokoro (1992) received patents for such surface activity. Both cited as an example the use of egg antibodies against *Streptococcus mutans* to prevent dental carries in rats. However, preceding these patents, a group of investigators in Germany published experiments from 1986 to 1991 also showing the use of antibodies to treat surface infections causing intestinal disorders (Losch *et al.*, 1986; Kuhlmann *et al.*, 1988; Schmidt *et al.*, 1989; Wiedemann *et al.*, 1990, 1991; Jungling *et al.*, 1991). The second type of patent demonstrates that orally ingested egg antibody can treat systemic disorders effectively. Coleman (1996) fed egg antibodies to produce benefits beyond the lumen of the gut. Antibody was raised against bacteria that cause mastitis in dairy cows. When the IgY was fed, the infecting organisms in the teats were reduced or cleared. Both of these patents use specific egg yolk antibodies without separation. Polson (1982, 1985) patented methods to separate the antibody from the egg. It is cheaper to use the whole egg, and the amount of antibody is higher since antibody is lost during each step of any separation process.

Antibodies and antibiotics are confused by laymen

An antibiotic works by altering the growth chemistry of the pathogen against which it is used. If the level of antibiotic is not high enough (for example, when patients do not take all of their medication) or if patients are on long-term antibiotic treatment, then the pathogen has a chance to mutate or change chemistry so that the antibiotic is no longer effective. This is known as resistance. There are now many bacteria that are resistant to commonly used antibiotics. It is clear that antibiotics have been overused.

The very young, very old, the immunosuppressed and chronically ill have an increased incidence of infection. These 'at risk' populations are growing. Thus, there is a need for an inexpensive, safe and innovative therapy that does not have these problems.

A similar situation exists in cattle. As the inbreeding of dairy herds becomes more intense, the hybrid vigour and resistance to infection has declined. This has made cows more susceptible to infectious diseases. Somatic cell count (SCC) is a descriptive term in the dairy industry referring to the number of white blood cells (pus) found in milk. Inbred cattle have a higher than normal SCC. Further, past overuse of antibiotic treatment predisposes the bacteria invading their teats to resistance. The farmer, in this case, may have to cull that animal to keep other animals from getting the resistant strain of bacteria. This practice, though necessary, is costly. Another problem is that if all of the cows in the herd have a slightly elevated SCC, the farmer cannot receive the premium price paid for low SCC milk. After some antibiotic treatments, there is a long period of withdrawal since the antibiotics and their metabolites show up in the milk for some time after stopping treatment and would potentiate resistance problems throughout the milk-consuming population. This further increases the cost of milk production since the milk from those cows cannot be sold.

An antibody works in an entirely different way. The antibody is 'programmed' by the immune system to carry a very specific attraction for some part of the pathogen such as their pillae (appendages). The pillus is an adhesion 'arm' used by the pathogen to attach to a receptor site of the host. The antibody 'captures' the antigen by forming an irreversible bond between the antigen (a pillus in this example) and antibody. Now the pathogen is blocked from attaching to the host receptor, which is a necessary first step to cause disease. This antibody–antigen complex allows the body to dispose of the pathogen harmlessly by a series of immune events. The ability to neutralize the bacteria in this way depends to some extent upon the number of sites or epitopes that match between the bacteria and the antibody.

There are two major types of antibodies – monoclonal and polyclonal. The monoclonal antibody is usually genetically engineered at great cost and has only one binding site. The polyclonal antibody is natural and has multiple pathogen-binding sites, i.e., it binds to several epitopes that are different from each other and are located at different sites on the surface of the pathogen. The bond is formed where specific sites between the antigen and antibody match. The more binding sites that match, the more likely it will be that an antibody will 'capture' the antigen. If the antibody covers the pathogen's adhesans, then the pathogens can no longer attach to the patient. If they cannot adhere, they cannot cause disease. The pathogens cannot mutate against the antibody because they are captured, not altered. Whereas antibiotics are excreted as potentially toxic residues to create environmental problems, an antibody only affects those organisms to which it is targeted. The antibody is then digested and produces no residue. The antibody will attack neither the host nor the beneficial bacteria residing in the body. Excitingly, we have discovered that egg yolk antibody can be eaten and is still effective. No injections, side effects or possibility of overdosing or toxic residues occur with antibodies. As this technology develops, antibodies may be the treatment of the future, potentially replacing antibiotics.

Commercialization of antibodies

There are several commercial antibody companies in the US and European Union (EU) market place. Anitox/Diamond V and DCV Biologicals are using the Stolle/Tokoro patent, while Farnam, Immunosmarte, For Your Health and Hokovit are utilizing the Coleman patent. All of the commercially available IgY antibodies are polyclonal. Although it is too early for a conclusive opinion, these antibody treatments have been shown to provide a safer, more efficient and less expensive method than antibiotics for managing disease-causing pathogens.

Since most opportunistic organisms that cause the progressive deterioration of the immune-suppressed patient can be found in the 'barnyard' environment, it would appear to be advantageous to have these patients consume colostrum or egg yolks containing antibodies against those organisms. Both cows (Tzipori *et al.*, 1986) and chickens can be 'trained' by vaccination to produce the antibodies that are needed to protect an individual with a failing immune system. In addition, bovine and avian antibodies have the important advantage of being somewhat protected from inactivation by digestion, unlike, for example, monoclonal antibodies (Chmel, 1990) or egg antibodies that have been chemically separated from the yolk granules (Schmidt *et al.*, 1989).

The chicken is an optimum animal to produce antibodies. The cow or other mammals produce colostrum at parturition. At other times, the amount of antibody in milk is minimal. Techniques to obtain bovine antibodies at times other than parturition involve desanguination. The chicken has the same immune organs as the mammals plus the hadrian gland in the naso/tracheal region to 'sample' what the chicken pecks and the bursa in the cloacal region to sample what she sits on. This multiorgan configuration allows a stronger response to antigens or disease-causing organisms in the environment and thus greater production of antibodies. Specific antibodies titres can be achieved at a level of 1×10^{15} U ml^{-1}.

To test the hypothesis that egg antibody can treat pathogens remote from the intestines, an experiment was conducted evaluating the treatment of mastitis via oral administration of eggs with antibodies raised against specific mastitis-causing organisms.

Immune system overview

The immune system has two major divisions: the innate (provides physical barriers, e.g. skin, body fluids and gastric juices) and the specific, which involves organs (thymus, spleen, intestines and Peyer's patches) and blood cells such as lymphocytes and phagocytes.

Physical barriers form the first line of defence. Tears produced by the lachrymal apparatus help wash away microorganisms. Tears contain an enzyme (lysozyme) that can destroy bacteria. The mouth also contains lysozyme in the saliva. The nose hairs help prevent entry of microorganisms on dust particles. The sneeze reflex assists this process. Mucus secreted by cells lining the throat, windpipe and bronchi trap microorganisms, which are then swept away by cilia (hairs on cells in the lining). The cough reflex also helps to expel microbes. Stomach acid destroys the vast majority of microorganisms swallowed. The intestines contain harmless bacteria (commensals) that compete with and therefore control adhesion of harmful organisms to the mucosa. These commensals are frequently compromised by antibiotic treatment, but not by antibody treatment. The genitourinary system includes the vagina and urethra that also contain commensals and are protected by mucus. Spermine in semen may also exert some antimicrobial action. Intact skin provides an effective barrier against most microorganisms. Skin sebaceous glands secrete chemicals that are highly toxic to many bacteria.

Breast-feeding after parturition provides the first antibodies for the infant. These antibodies are formed actively by the mother against specific micro-organisms in her environment and are transferred to the baby in her breast milk as colostrum. The chicken provides specific antibodies, similar to colostrum, that place antibody in the egg yolk to protect the newly hatched chick from its environment until the chick can form its own specific antibodies. These events are examples of specific immunity, which can be passed to off-spring (or others) by ingesting the antibody, which is called passive immunity.

Most of the organs associated with specific or passive immunity, such as the adenoids and tonsils, become obsolete by puberty. The major organ there-after is the gut-associated lymphoid tissue (GALT). The major components of GALT are the Peyer's patches. Several thousands line the small intestines. These patches are collections of lymphocytes that identify proteins or epitopes on the surface of organisms isolated from the gut lumen. The most effective antibodies are those produced against adhesans such as the pillae mentioned earlier. A gut lining receptor is usually a glycoprotein but can be a glycolipid or a peptide called an integrin. Lectans are a class of proteins on the infecting organism that can rapidly combine selectively and reversibly with these recep-tors. T-lymphocytes within the Peyer's patches pass the epitope information to B-lymphocytes. The B-lymphocytes, in turn, migrate into the circulating blood where they become plasma cells.

Plasma cells travel throughout the bloodstream and concentrate in the lamina propria or the layer under all moist surfaces of the body. From there, they produce that specific antibody to coat these moist surfaces and to prevent adhesion by the offending organisms. If a pathogenic organism cannot adhere to the tissue surface, it cannot proliferate and cause infection. Circulating antibodies perform this function in cells remote from the intestine, but IgG activates complement which calls white cells to get involved. Neither IgY nor IgA activate complement. They simply block adhesion, prevent disease and set the organism up for harmless elimination.

If the above system fails and an organism adheres to the tissue surface, mediators of inflammation, e.g. tumour necrosis factor (TNF), interleukins 1, 6 and 8 (IL-1, -6 and -8), etc., are released. These mediators then initiate the production of such other mediators as prostaglandins, leukotrienes and thromboxines. The resultant 'cascade' is associated with the metabolic and physiological changes of illness. A now inflamed and therefore compromised incompetent intestine allows translocation of disease-associated factors, such as organisms to leak from the intestinal lumen into the systemic circulation, to cause a systemic response to illness at sites remote from the intestinal lumen.

Treatment of Immune-suppressed Patients with Antibodies

Many people think that immune-suppressed patients mostly include human immunodeficiency virus (HIV)-infected individuals. This is not true. Patients also comprising this group are cancer therapy, transplant and burn patients, those in intensive care units, the malnourished and others. Even those with rheumatoid arthritis, inflammatory bowel disease and Crones disease are at risk.

In certain of the aforementioned categories of immune-suppressed individuals, antibody production can return to normal if the patient does not succumb to the primary disease or opportunistic infections. With HIV infection, however, recovery of immune competence cannot occur. Perhaps a reason for this is that a favoured site for HIV to concentrate is the lamina propria of the intestine. It may be noteworthy that the lamina propria is the layer just below the mucosa or surface and is the location where plasma cells concentrate to produce IgA to neutralize the adhesans and lectans of potential pathogens. If they can bind to the mucosa, they cause inflammation, leaky gut and diarrhoea.

Advantages of egg antibodies over others available

The advantages of egg yolk antibodies over bovine or monoclonal antibodies are many. Chicken antibodies do not react with mammalian complement (Benson *et al.*, 1991), iron receptors, protein A or protein G. Yolk antibodies administered in their natural form exhibit great acid and heat resistance (Losch *et al.*, 1986). Antibodies are naturally protected by the yolk granules (Schmidt *et al.*, 1989) or, if chemically removed and treated with a gelatin covering (Akita and Nakai, Chapter 23), are particularly resistant to pH, gastric and pancreatic enzymes. Monoclonal antibodies do not have the same protection as polyclonal antibodies (Zanetti *et al.*, 1991). IgY is less expensive than bovine or monoclonal antibodies. A US commercial egg antibody company has been given GRAS (generally regarded as safe) status from both the USDA and FDA for the antibodies they produce. With GRAS status, approval of individual products by the FDA for use of egg antibody in human patients is relatively unencumbered. After all, millions of people are eating eggs every day. All eggs contain some antibodies, and more at hyperimmunized levels.

The net effect of treating the immune-suppressed patients with egg antibodies is to prevent a virus, fungus, protozoan or bacterium from adhering to its receptor on the cell, replicating, and translocating into the patient's portal system to cause systemic disease. HIV, for instance, incubates in the lamina propria using TNF-α (an inflammatory mediator) as a signal to the viral genome to start replication (Rodgers and Kagnoff, 1988; Alverdy *et al.*, 1992). Therefore, production of antibody to neutralize the HIV's gp120/v3 loop adhesion and the inflammatory mediator TNF-α may help slow the disease. Neutralization of opportunistic organisms in the gut is also helpful in that their adhesion to the mucosa causes inflammation and TNF-α release. Further, there are proteins essential to the life cycle of HIV that do not mutate. HIV protease is an example. Blocking such 'fixed' targets is a fruitful endeavour based on the early success of protease inhibitors. By blocking these 'fixed' targets with an antibody instead of an antibiotic, resistance will not occur as is happening now.

Normally the gut surface is protected by IgA, an antibody secreted by plasma cells onto the surface of the mucosa. An average of 13 g of IgA is produced daily, making this the most prolifically manufactured protein in the body. The immune-suppressed patient lacks the ability to produce adequate IgA, consequently he or she is unable to protect himself or herself against disease-causing organisms usually carried harmlessly in the intestine. Using egg antibody as surrogate, secretory IgA is an option that has been produced successfully in our laboratory. The IgY would act as surrogate secretory IgA providing the protection that has been disabled by HIV. This three-prong approach for acquired immune deficiency syndrome (AIDS) patients (i.e. use IgY to gum up HIV 'fixed targets' of replication and suppression of TNF-α plus surrogate secretory IgA) is just one example of the potential power of the egg antibody concept to treat human disease.

Cost of AIDS

There was US$150,000–US$200,000 spent in 1997 to supply health care for each victim of AIDS. An average of US$2000 per month is spent by the US health care system. Since health and life insurance companies will not insure any person who is HIV positive, the above-mentioned costs eventually come from the US taxpayer. In 1997, US$38,900,000,000 was spent by the US taxpayers for AIDS patients. Every 13 min, another person in the USA is infected with HIV and the costs add up. The latest UN study indicates that 30 million people worldwide were infected with AIDS. Of these, 21 million were in Africa where they cannot afford the new 'cocktail', which has shown promise in the USA AIDS is hitting Africa so fiercely that it now rivals the great epidemics of history – even the Black Death of the Middle Ages that killed 20 million people, or one-quarter of Europe's population, in 4 years. A more cost-effective therapy will have to be produced to help developing countries. The three-prong treatment effect mentioned above could prove very cost effective and may become the novel therapy being sought to treat millions of people worldwide.

It is estimated that in the USA alone, more than 130,000 deaths in 1997 were associated with bacteraemia. A large proportion of these resulted from microorganisms that normally reside in the gut. Even organisms that are usually considered non-pathogenic may establish local infections and secondary bacteraemias in HIV (Beachey, 1981). Disabling gastrointestinal symptoms are prominent in both patients with established AIDS and patients with earlier stages of HIV infection.

To recap, there are three areas of potential benefit of IgY in HIV treatment: (i) by attacking fixed targets in the life cycle; or (ii) by inhibiting mediators necessary for HIV to replicate such as TNF-α; and (iii) by providing the necessary immune support (surrogate secretory IgA) to the gut to prevent adhesion of opportunistic organisms.

Attacking fixed targets

Many epitopes on the HIV particle have been genetically engineered. Monoclonal antibodies have been used with poor prolonged efficacy. The problem with producing monoclonal antibodies against these epitopes is that they are so specific and the HIV particle is changing. If IgY is used, a polyclonal antibody can be produced which will target several sites, thus increasing the chance for binding the HIV particle at multiple locations and allowing the immune system to get rid of it harmlessly. Antibody has also been raised against HIV protease. It can be raised against reverse transcriptase and 6–8 other molecules in the life cycle of HIV that do not mutate frequently.

TNF-α response to disease

TNF-α has also been identified as an important factor in causing deterioration of the brain and nervous system, pulmonary function, loss of appetite and further deterioration of the intestine, leading to further opportunistic organism adhesion, diarrhoea and malabsorption. The ensuing malnutrition itself is known to depress production of antibody and lymphocyte count. Also, the lymphocyte count drops acutely in response to any infection, particularly in response to TNF-α. In addition to the destruction of lymphocytes by the virus, the systemic effect of an increasing rate of recurrent infections by opportunistic organisms will suppress the lymphocyte count further. It is the gut's involvement in the inflammatory process that causes the patient to lose his or her appetite and develop malabsorption, leading to AIDS wasting. Thus, the patient suffers from a triple indemnity, i.e. suppressed lymphocyte count from the virus, leading to a suppressed lymphocyte count from infection, which is then potentiated by malnutrition. This is the mechanism whereby HIV-infected patients develop AIDS, then waste and die. The virus itself does not cause the wasted appearance, nor is the individual's body being consumed by the virus. Rather, the above chain of events leading to chronic intestine-associated infection, malnutrition and death causes the wasted appearance.

IgY has been raised against TNF-α in our laboratory. It was shown to delay mortality in mice 24–48 h after oral administration of the antibody by gavage and simultaneous intraperitoneal administration of lipopolysaccharide (LPS) LD100 (Fig. 27.1). If effective, this nutraceutical or biologic would represent an

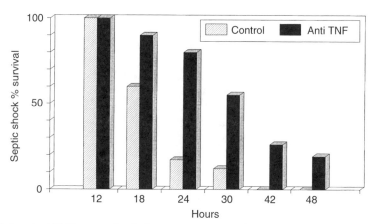

Fig. 27.1. Anti TNF egg antibody in mouse. IgY raised against TNF-α delays mortality in mice 24–48 h after oral administration of the antibody.

inexpensive treatment with side effects limited to that of eating an egg to down-regulate exuberant TNF-α.

IgY as surrogate secretory IgA

Plasma cells, which produce and secrete IgA, are destroyed in HIV infection either directly or as a result of destruction of lymphocytes. Although the virus cannot be eradicated, IgY taken orally on a daily basis can control the negative effects of reduced immunity to opportunistic infections to some extent. Infection by these opportunistic organisms stimulates the production of inflammatory mediators, as described above. Principal among them is TNF-α. In addition to being a major stimulator of metabolic and physiological changes associated with illness, TNF-α turns on replication of HIV. Thus, there exists a kind of symbiotic relationship between systemic infection and TNF-α that results in progression of the HIV-infected patient toward AIDS. Secretory IgA must be supported to break this cycle.

Patients who are HIV positive do not die from the virus *per se*. Rather, they eventually die from the effect of the virus on the immune system. Recurrent and progressive opportunistic infections set into motion a spiral that ultimately leads to the demise of the patient. Central to this downward clinical course is the failure of gut immunity as well as systemic immunity. Gastrointestinal organisms are not pathogenic because they are neutralized by an individual's defence system. They only cause disease when these natural defences fail. When gastrointestinal organisms overcome innate and specific immunity and adhere to the mucosa, they multiply and are associated with local production of inflammatory mediators. These factors translocate across the intestinal lining to cause systemic disease. When patients die of advanced AIDS, they are usually malnourished. The opportunistic infections from which they suffer are not diseases they 'caught' but rather diseases from potentially pathogenic organisms they have carried in their gastrointestinal tracts for most of their lives but can no longer defend against. By hyperimmunizing hens against opportunistic organisms, IgY can be used to replace failing secretory IgA and protect the mucosa from adhesion of enteric pathogens, thus preventing the above scenario.

Enteric infections are major causes of problems in all immune-suppressed patients. Also, viral infections of the gastrointestinal tract constitute a major health problem during the first years of a child's life. Prolonged infections occur in patients and render them immunocompromised by congenital diseases or malnutrition. In children with impaired T-cell function, for example, rotavirus infection is an especially serious problem (Yolken *et al.*, 1990). To demonstrate the validity of the surrogate secretory IgA concept, specific egg antibodies have been used to provide both nutritional and medical treatment for these populations, with low cost, high reliability and safety. Diarrhoeal diseases due to rotavirus in neonatal animals, such as piglets, have been treated successfully with IgY (Yokoyama *et al.*, 1992).

A wide range of infectious pathogens is encountered in both patients with established AIDS and patients in the earlier stages of HIV infection. Viruses include cytomegalovirus (CMV), herpes simplex virus (HSV) and papovavirus, of which CMV is by far the most devastating. CMV infection may simultaneously or sequentially involve the entire gastrointestinal tract, and the virus is extremely invasive and serious, producing systemic and localized symptoms, which include dysphagia, odynophagia, vomiting, abdominal pain, nausea, diarrhoea with or without blood and mucus, episodes of megacolon and localized peritonitis, biliary obstruction, dementia and blindness. Surrogate secretory IgA is needed to protect against CMV.

Bacterial pathogens include the various forms of tuberculosis, *Mycobacterium avium intracellulare* (MAI), *E. coli*, *Haemophilus*, *Neisseria gonorrhoeae*, *Salmonella typhimurium*, *Campylobacter jejuni*, *Shigella flexneri* and *S. cholera*. Patients with AIDS are especially susceptible to infection by *S. typhimurium*, which may result in life-threatening diarrhoea and recurrent systemic bacteraemia resistant to antibacterial therapy. IgY can be made against all of these. MAI is the most common cause of disseminated bacterial infection of patients with AIDS. In normal or non-immunocompromised hosts, disease due to this organism is rare, and clinical manifestations, if any, are primarily pulmonary. In AIDS patients, MAI typically causes a widespread infection with involvement of the bone marrow, spleen, lungs, lymph nodes, intestinal tract, brain and adrenal glands.

Protozoa which threaten 'at risk' patients include *Isospora*, *Pneumocystis carinii*, *Toxoplasma*, *Entamoeba histolytica*, *Giardia lamblia* and *G. coccidia*. Symptoms of *Paracytoxis* infection in immunocompetent individuals are usually of short duration, with intestinal involvement resulting in moderate to severe diarrhoea and possible weight loss. In 'at risk' individuals, however, infections can become persistent and life threatening. In a small percentage of AIDS patients, parasites are invasive and can produce a syndrome of overwhelming chronic and large volume diarrhoea, abdominal pain, hypovolaemia, electrolyte disturbances and nutritional deficiency. The Coleman patent has demonstrated the systemic efficacy of IgY. IgY may be useful to treat other systemic diseases as above.

Fungi that cause problems in 'at risk' patients include *Candida albicans*, *Cryptococcus* and *Histoplasma*. Persistent oral candidiasis is seen in a large percentage of AIDS patients and is usually thought to herald the onset of 'end-stage' AIDS as it invades, progressing to fungal septicaemia and death. We currently are testing the efficacy of anti-candida IgY to treat systemic disease.

Neutralizing antibody against a variety of pathogens, e.g. rotavirus, cholera, enterotoxigenic *E. coli*, *Streptococcus mutans*, *Salmonella*, *N. gonorrhoeae*, HIV, TNF-α, IL-1, IL-6, endotoxin, spider and snake venom, etc., has been produced in various ways and reported in the scientific literature. Methods of production include genetically engineered bacteria, monoclonal hybridomas and hyperimmunization of chickens and cows. Such antibodies have been shown to neutralize the targeted pathogens *in vitro* and *in vivo* in the intestine at the pathogen or mucosal interface. IgY can be used most effectively to neutralize these pathogens whether in the lumen or in the circulation, to keep the disease from becoming systemic. The author has produced IgY against more than one specific organism or antigen at a time in a single egg. These multiorganism hyperimmune IgY eggs could be cost effective and safe for any immune-compromised patient.

Types of specific immunity

There are two types of immunity – active and passive immunity. Specific immunity always involves antibodies. In passive immunity, antibodies are passed and provide immediate, but short-lived protection against specific diseases. Most neonates receive passive immunity from their mother either as colostrum (IgA) in mammals or as egg yolks (IgY) in reptiles and birds. Chicken egg yolks have been tested and shown to contain up to 200 different antibodies in the yolk. Every foreign protein or microorganism that the chicken has been exposed to, whether by vaccination or by natural exposure, will be processed and antibodies raised against it. These antibodies are then placed in the egg yolk at differing titres depending upon the degree of exposure.

Blood taken from a person or, rarely, an animal previously exposed to a specific microorganism contains antibodies against that organism. The extract of blood containing antibodies can be injected into the person to be protected. This is also a form of passive immunity. The most common treatment is with γ-globulin taken by tourists travelling to certain world locations where hepatitis is endemic. This procedure, however, can be dangerous since, if the subject is not desensitized, the next injection could create anaphylactic shock and possibly death. If a mammal is desensitized to the foreign protein in egg, even IgY can be injected also (Stolle, 1987). As mentioned, chicken antibodies do not fix complement. It has been hypothesized that when eggs are eaten, the major portion of the heavy and light chains of the antibody is digested. Specific peptides of the hypervariable segments are absorbed intact or nearly intact, circulate and bind to their receptor targets. These peptides are relatively short and are not antigenic. Whatever the mechanism of action, passive immunity is apparently created and the positive effects have been documented for up to 6 weeks after discontinuing the antibody in the feed of dairy cows.

Active immunization primes the body to make its own antibodies and confers life-long immunity. The biggest pitfall for active immunization is that those who need protection the most may have a compromised immune system. Therefore, they would not be able to mount their own immunity efficiently. Vaccines are injected containing organisms, which are killed or modified. The immune system (if it is functioning) is provoked into making antibodies against these modified microorganisms. During this process, the immune system retains a 'memory' of the organism. If the real microorganism then enters, antibodies are produced rapidly in large numbers to halt the infection. This is called the anamnestic response.

IgA is the most abundant protein in the body, protecting all moist surfaces from adhesion by organisms in the environment that are ingested in the gut. If the patient/animal is immunocompromised, we as an industry could make a miracle egg for these patients, to mimic the secretory IgA. This surrogate secretory IgA would protect the host.

How does the antibody get into the bloodstream?

Egg antibodies themselves do not get into the bloodstream. We are not sure of the exact mechanism of action of the IgY when orally administered. The major antibody complex is digested. The hypervariable regions are made up of very small peptides with 9–11 amino acids (Sharon and Lis, 1993). We do not believe that these peptides are digested much further, but are taken up and carried throughout the bloodstream to affect treatment by binding systemically to the specific antigens against which they were raised. In any case, we know for a fact that orally ingested IgY can be used to treat conditions remote from the intestines. Many researchers have shown that antibodies are digested. The most common way to detect egg antibody is by enzyme-linked immunosorbent assay (ELISA) using the 'Y' portion of the antibody. We have not been able to find the 'Y' portion of the antibody in any blood fluids or other parts of the body when orally administered. We can only speculate as to how elements of IgY rendering passive immunity reach their target. The lining of the gut is made up of microvilli. These microvilli have an extensive supply of blood vessels to aid in the digestion and absorption of nutrients. The lymphatic system also has blind end vessels called lacteals that also absorb the small peptides that are between 9 and 11 amino acid in length. In whatever manner, the antibodies are broken down but the active moieties are absorbed and circulated.

Other opportunities for egg antibodies

The American Heart Association has created doubts about the consumption of eggs in the minds of consumers. The *Salmonella enteritidis* scare of 1985 created more doubts for physicians. Some hospitals even withheld eggs from their sickest patients to protect them from *S. enteritidis*. In the future, it is hoped that hospitals, as well as day care centres, colleges, prisons, geriatric units, community living facilities, institutions and cruise ships, will use the hyperimmunized egg as protection against this disease. In 1998, one out of four people can expect to spend at least 1 year in an extended care facility or sheltered accommodation during their lifetime (Kemper *et al.*, 1991), while one in 11 people can expect to spend at least 5 years in extended care. Currently 12.8% of the population is over 65 years, while in 2040 when the maximum number of 'baby boomers' reach retirement age, this percentage will be 20.7% of the total US population (Treas, 1995). Intensive housing of individuals presents more chance of contracting disease and a greater risk of food-related maladies. The use of a food-based deterrent such as egg antibodies can serve two purposes in these and similar populations, i.e. nutrition and disease control.

Refugees from wars or natural disasters frequently have water quality problems due to squalid housing conditions. Eggs containing specific antibodies for cholera, typhoid or yellow fever can be held in dry storage. The dried product can be stored for 2 or more years. During a crisis, feeding these eggs can provide nutrition while also providing protection for those individuals housed in the makeshift conditions. Egg antibodies for water-related diseases could be immediately available and effective where often vaccines are not as easily dispensed and take time to render immunity.

Egg yolk antibodies can also be used against snake venoms; an estimated 1.7 million people are bitten or stung by venomous snakes, scorpions, jelly fish or spiders each year, 40,000–50,000 fatally (Bucherl, 1968; Habermehl, 1981). The most widely accepted treatment of envenomation is the use of specific antivenoms to neutralize the toxic, potentially lethal effects of venoms. Thalley and Carroll (1990) described how egg yolk antibodies could be used for this purpose. To minimize the burden of foreign protein administered, they 'affinity-purified' venom-specific chicken immunoglobulin using efficient and relatively gentle procedures (S. Carroll, 1989, patent pending). Chicken antivenoms are easier to produce and, when affinity-purified, have a higher bioactivity than antivenoms raised in horses. These qualities may make this system a safer, more convenient alternative to current commercial methods of antivenom production.

Egg yolk antibodies have been used for diagnostic purposes for many years (Fertel *et al.*, 1981). In most cases, the antibodies must be separated from the yolk granules. There are numerous companies producing purified egg yolk antibodies on a small scale for their internal use and for others. These purified antibodies sell for around US$500 g^{-1}. Each hen can produce approximately 5 g of highly purified individual antibody per month.

Oral Antibody Treatment with Systemic Effects

Egg antibodies to lower SCC levels in dairy cows

Mastitis is an extremely important veterinary disease. In 1992, mastitis infections cost the American Dairy Association members U$200,000,000. As mentioned in the introduction, the somatic cell count (SCC) is a measure of pus found in the milk of dairy cows. A higher than normal SCC indicates infection in the animal. High SCCs in cow's milk result in a loss of approximately 200,000 lbs of milk per cow a year. This is equivalent to a financial cost of approximately US$1000 per cow. There are 9,750,000 cows in the USA. Only 10% of the dairy cows in the USA attain the highest ranking on SCC (< 100,000). A dairyman receives US$0.50 cwt^{-1} of milk more when they get the highest ranking on SCC. The environment (weather) can have an effect on SCC. One important example is the floods in the Upper Midwest in summer 1993. A 6-week experiment was conducted during which dairy cows in a well-managed herd were given a fresh egg as a top dress on their feed once a day. Group I fed eggs containing antibodies raised against *Staphylococcus aureus* and *Streptococcus agilata* were considered the treatment group, while group II received 'generic' eggs collected from hens in the same house but not hyperimmunized, used as egg control. Group III consisted of a 'non-egg' general control group fed wet soybean meal at the same protein concentration as a top dress. Those cows receiving the hyperimmune antibody had 25% lower SCCs than those on the 'generic egg product'. Group III control animals increased their SCCs by 25% during the same period.

In Minnesota at that time, where this research was conducted, 20 out of 26 dairies did not pass the SCC standards for two testing periods in a row (June and July). The SCC is not monitored in August. Normally the month of August is the best month of the year for milk production, therefore the DHIP (dairy herd improvement plan) does not monitor SCCs for that month. If they had been monitored, it is highly probable that the results would have continued dropping due to the quality of the grazing areas. If the SCC value was high for 3 months in a row it would have meant an automatic revocation of the sale of that milk for any purpose. The financial losses would have been enormous.

Another experiment was done to gain information about dosing. It was not going to be practical or economical to feed an egg a day per cow. The next field experiment was conducted in the Upper Midwest from December 1993 to March 1994. Active mastitis cases before and after this experiment were monitored. The causative bacteria were noted. *S. aureus* and *S. agilata* made up the majority of the symptomatic cases. Wild-types of those bacteria were collected from the vets in the area and used for antigen production. In order to show that the effect was specific for the antibody and not the yolk itself, other types of bacteria known to be causative agents were not used for antigen production, only the two major disease-causing bacteria. Mastitis caused by bacteria other than *S. aureus* and *S. agilata* was expected during the experiment. One hundred and twenty five dairy cows were checked routinely for SCC three times in 14 days. Those cows exhibiting an SCC of 400,000–600,000 were divided randomly into four groups. Those animals out of this range received no yolk treatment and will be referred to hereafter as the 'general control' group. Each of the cows in the experimental groups was given 200 p.p.m. of yolk powder (as calculated on a total feed basis) daily at the rates shown in Table 27.1.

The cows were in commercial dairies and were visited frequently by the vet in charge of the experiment. The dairy was small by US standards and had individual stalls for milking and feeding. The yolk products were mixed with dry milk as a filler so that each cow received a 10 g portion as a top dress once a day. Blood and milk samples were taken from the experimental groups every 5 days for 3 weeks during the baseline period, every 5 days for 3 weeks during the treatment period and every 5 days for 3 weeks during the post-treatment period. The 'general control' groups were sampled for SCC only on a DHIP basis during this same period. Complete blood counts (CBC) were determined for each sampling. Morning and evening milks were collected for each period.

Table 27.1. Description of break down of egg yolk administration for testing effects of *Staphylococcus aureus* and *Streptococcus agilata* antibodies on the quality and quantity of milk in dairy cows. Each cow in the experimental groups received 200 g tonne^{-1} of egg yolk powder. The only differences in the groups were the proportion of hyperimmune yolk.

Description	Experimental yolk	Generic yolk
Antibody control	0	200
50 p.p.m.	50	150
100 p.p.m.	100	100
200 p.p.m.	200	0
General control	0	0

Protein, solids not fat (SNF), volumes and SCC were determined for each milk sample. If a cow exhibited more than a 1,000,000 SCC, the teats were cultured for bacteria. All cows were tested 6 weeks after the end of the experiment to determine latent bacteria in the teats. Those cows which received anti-*Staphylococcus* and anti-*Streptococcus* antibodies were deleted from the data bank if the bacteria exhibited in a hot mastitis situation and were not the organism for which the hyperimmune antibody was given. Data were analysed by Student *t*-test, with each cow used as its own control.

There were no significant differences in any blood parameters. The 'general control' group increased in SCC approximately 25%, as did other dairy herds in the region during the testing period. There was a significant ($P < 0.01$) decrease in SCC for all of the experimental group compared with the 'general control'. Within the treatment groups, there was a significant decrease ($P < 0.01$) in SCC related to the increased use of specific anti-*Staphylococcus*/anti-*Streptococcus* antibody. There was no significant difference in morning milk, but the volume of evening milk was higher in those cows receiving anti-*Staphylococcus*/anti-*Streptococcus* yolk (Fig. 27.2). A linear relationship developed between concentration of hyperimmunized yolk and increased milk volumes. There was a significant interaction between levels of anti-*Staphylococcus*/anti-*Streptococcus* yolk for protein (Fig. 27.3). There was a significant ($P < 0.01$) increase in SNF with increased dosing of anti-*Staphylococcus*/anti-*Streptococcus* antibody (Fig. 27.4) in the treated cows.

During 9 weeks of monitoring, there was extreme and variable weather. It was the coldest winter on record for the Upper Midwest. In fact, it was so cold that the teat dip applications had to be discontinued. Therefore, all dairies in the region had elevated SCCs over the time period of this experiment. This was true of the 'general control' also, but those cows receiving even the generic egg actually decreased in SCC during the experiment.

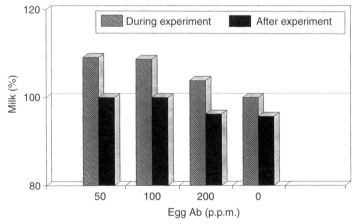

Fig. 27.2. Evening milk volume increased with anti-*Staphylococcus*/anti-*Streptococcus* IgY treatment. Normal reduction of milk production was reduced with IgY.

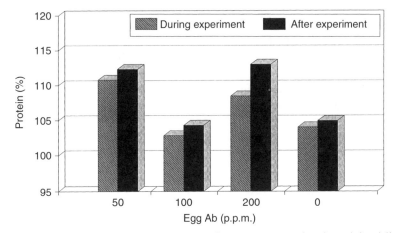

Fig. 27.3.   There was a significant interaction between protein levels and the different doses of anti-*Staphylococcus*/anti-*Streptococcus* IgY treatment.

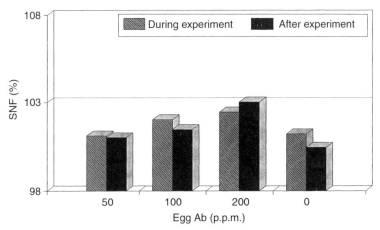

Fig. 27.4.   There was a significant increase in SNF with increasing dosing of anti-*Staphylococcus*/anti-*Streptococcus* IgY.

The cows which exhibited an SCC of 1,000,000 had a variety of bacterial infections during the experiment. None of the anti-*Staphylococcus*/anti-*Streptococcus* antibody cows had *Staphylococcus* or *Streptococcus* mastitis. Table 27.2 shows the types of mastitis found before and after this experiment as well as a summary of all of the positive samples taken 6 weeks after the experiment ended.

There was a lingering effect of fed antibodies dependent upon the level of anti-*Staphylococcus*/anti-*Streptococcus* antibody used. Even 3 weeks after the last experimental antibody dose, the 200 p.p.m. antibody group held a 43% reduction in SCC compared with their own controls prior to the experiment (Fig. 27.5). This is highly significant. The SCCs of dairy cows usually increase as lactation progresses. The weather problems precipitated significant

Table 27.2. Comparison of known causes of mastitis in 1992 with chronic mastitis in field trial 3/94.

Type of organism	Winter 1993 Total samples: 492		Summer 1993 Total samples: 481		Average summer versus winter 1993	Field trial 3/94 Total samples: 43	
	n	%	*n*	%	%	*n*	%
Staphylococcus aureus	109	22.15	145	30.15	26.15	9	20.93
Streptococcus agilata	45	9.15	76	15.80	12.48	6	13.95
Streptococcus species	274	55.69	205	42.62	49.16	38	88.37
Staphylococcus species	283	57.52	255	53.01	55.27	33	76.74
Pure	72	14.63	49	10.19	12.41	1	2.33
Coliform bacillus	42	8.54	29	6.03	7.29	9	20.93
Serratia	1	0.20			0.10		
Klebsiella	2	0.41			0.21		
Non-coliform bacillus	32	6.50	30	6.24	6.37	8	18.60
Pseudomonas			5	1.04	0.52		
Corynebacteria	1	0.20			0.10		
Yeast	1	0.20			0.10		
Contaminated sample	15	3.05			1.53		
Pure bacillus	1	0.20			0.10	4	9.30
No growth	10	2.03			1.02		
Total (%)[a]		180.47		165.08	172.81		251.15

[a]Percentages equal more than 100% due to mixed cultures.

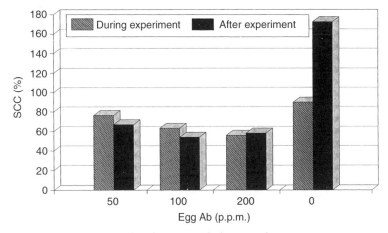

Fig. 27.5. Dairy cows treated with anti-*Staphylococcus*/anti-*Streptococcus* IgY continued to maintain lower SCC counts even 3 weeks after treatment ended.

increases in all of the regional dairies, but the experimental cows maintained the lowered SCC for at least 3 weeks after treatment. This could mean that ingested IgY active moieties circulated for at least 3 weeks. This compares with i.v. administered antibody treatment which has been shown to be circulating for 6 weeks. Comparing the 'general control' with the experimental control, there was more than a 50% reduction in SCC with the 'generic egg' treatment. This was similar to the results found in experiments conducted in the previous summer. This decreased SCC represents a significant increase in profits for the farmer at very low costs for treatment.

Potential Use of IgY to Treat Intestinal Disease

Many papers have been published on the use of chicken egg antibodies for treatment of gut-related disease. The first paper in an early German series showed temperature and acid degradation resistance of the egg antibody as long as the antibody was not removed from the whole egg carrier (Losch *et al.*, 1986). The second demonstrated the resistance to digestion of the egg antibody as long as it was protected either by natural occurrence in the yolk or protected after removal from the yolk (Schmidt *et al.*, 1989). The third studied *in vivo* adhesion in piglets. The authors showed that egg whites protected the antibody from digestion in the jejunum. They also showed that pelleting destroyed some of the activity of the egg antibodies. Boiling eggs for 4 min reduced the activity compared with eggs kept at 70°C (Wiedemann *et al.*, 1990). Further, egg antibodies can survive to the end of the gastrointestinal tract as long as they are protected by whole egg components. Their latest papers reported the protective effects of egg yolk antibodies *in vitro* (Jongling *et al.*, 1991), with Wiedemann *et al.* (1991) publishing field studies using IgY for protection in piglets. This author commercially produced and successfully treated shipping fever (scours) in dairy cows in 1985.

Many authors have since published papers about the protection of yolk antibodies raised against various agents for neonatal mammals (Ikemori *et al.*, 1992). Using egg antibodies to treat human rotaviruses was proposed as early as 1986 (Yolken *et al.*, 1990). The NIH supported this work. The list goes on, and the potential is great. Again, why have we, as an industry, not done more to exploit the potential of egg antibody to prevent or treat animal or human diseases?

References

Alverdy, J., Aoys, E., Weiss-Carrington, P. and Burke, D. (1992) The effect of glutamine-enriched TPN on gut immune cellularity. *Journal of Surgical Research* 52, 34–38.

Beachey, E. (1981) Bacterial adherence: adhesin–receptor interactions mediating the attachment of a bacteria to mucosal surfaces. *Journal of Infectious Diseases* 143, 325–345.

Benson, H., Brumfield, H. and Pomeroy, B. (1991) Requirement of avian C1 for fixation of guinea pig complement by avian antibody–antigen complexes. *Journal of Immunology* 87, 616–622.

Bernhisel-Broadbent, J., Yolken, R. and Sampson, H. (1991) Allergenicity of oral administered immunoglobulin preparations in food-allergic children. *Pediatrics* 87, 208–214.

Bucherl, W. (1968) *Venomous Animals and Their Venoms.* Academic Press, New York.

Carroll, S. (1989) Patent pending.

Chmel, H. (1990) Role of monoclonal antibody therapy in the treatment of infectious disease. *American Journal of Hospital Pharmacy* 47, s11–s15.

Coleman, M. (1996) Oral administration of chicken yolk immunoglobulins to lower somatic cell count in the milk of lactating ruminants. US patent #5585098.

Fertel, R., Yetiv, J., Coleman, M., Schwarz, R., Greenwald, J. and Bianchine, J. (1981) *Biochemical and Biophysical Research Communications* 102, 1028–1033.

Habermehl, G. (1981) *Venomous Animals and Their Toxins.* Springer-Verlag, Berlin.

Ikemori, Y., Kuroki, M., Peralta, R., Yokoyama, H. and Kodama, Y. (1982) Protection of neonatal calves against fatal enteric colibacillosis by administration of egg yolk powder from hens imunized with K99-piliated enterotoxigenic *Escherichia coli. American Journal of Veterinary Research* 53, 2005–2008.

Jungling, A., Wiedemann, V., Kuhlmann, R., Erhard, M., Schmidt, P. and Losch, U. (1991) Chicken egg antibodies for prophylaxis and therapy of infectious intestinal diseases: *in vitro* studies on protective effects against adhesion of enterotoxogenic *Escherichia coli* to isolated enterocytes. *Journal of Veterinary Medicine* 38, 373–381.

Kemper, P., Spillman and Murtough (1991) *Inquiry* 28, 333–334.

Kuhlmann, R., Wiedemann, V., Schmidt, P., Wanke, R., Linckh, E. and Losch, U. (1988) Chicken egg antibodies for prophylaxis and therapy of infectious intestinal diseases: immunization and antibody determination. *Journal of Veterinary Medicine* 35, 610–616.

Losch, U., Schranner, I., Wanke, R. and Jurgens, L. (1986) The chicken egg, an antibody source. *Journal of Veterinary Medicine* 33, 609–619.

Polson, A. (1982) Recovering purified antibodies from egg yolk. US patent #4357272.

Polson, A. (1985) Manufacture and use of fowl egg antibodies. US patent # 4550019.

Rodgers, A. and Kagnoff, M. (1988) AIDS syndrome and disease of the gastrointestinal tract, immunology and allergic clinics of NA 8 : 3. *Gut and Intestinal Immunology* 451–467.

Schmidt, P., Wiedemann, V., Kuhlmann, R., Wanke, R., Linckh, E. and Losch, U. (1989) Chicken egg antibodies for prophylaxis and therapy of infectious intestinal diseases: *in vitro* studies on gastric and enteric digestion of egg yolk antibodies specific against pathogenic *Escherichia coli* strains. *Journal of Veterinary Medicine* 36, 619–628.

Sharon, N. and Lis, H. (1993) Carbohydrates in cell recognition. *Scientific American* January, 82–89.

Stolle, R. (1988) Method of passive immunization of mammals using avian antibody. US patent # 4478018.

Thalley, B. and Carroll, S. (1990) Rattlesnake and scorpion antivenoms from the egg yolks of immunized hens. *Biotechnology* 8, 934–938.

Tokoro, H. (1992) The specific antibody containing substance from eggs and method of production and use there of. US patent # 5080895.

Treas, J. (1995) Population Reference Bureau, *Older Americans in 1990's and Beyond.* US Bureau of Census Vol. 50: 2 May 1995.

Tzipori, S., Roberton, D. and Chapman, C. (1986) Remission of diarrhea due to cryptosporidiosis in an immunodeficient child treated with hyperimmune bovine colostrum. *British Medical Journal* 293, 1276–1277.

Ungar, B., Ward, D., Fayer, R. and Quinn, C. (1990) Cessation of cryptosporidium-associated diarrhea in an acquired immunodeficiency syndrome patient after treatment with hyperimmune bovine colostrum. *Gastroenterology* 98, 486–489.

Wiedemann, V., Linckh, E., Kuhlmann, R., Schmidt, P. and Losch, U. (1990) Chicken egg antibodies for prophylaxis and therapy of infectious intestinal diseases: *in vivo* tenacity test in piglets with artificial jejunal fistula. *Journal of Veterinary Medicine* 37, 163–172.

Wiedemann, V., Linckh, E., Kuhlmann, R., Schmidt, P. and Losch, U. (1991) Chicken egg antibodies for prophylaxis and therapy of infectious intestinal diseases: *in vivo* studies on protective effects against *Escherichia coli* diarrhea in pigs. *Journal of Veterinary Medicine* 38, 283–291.

Yokoyama, H., Peralta, R., Diaz, R., Sendo, S., Ikemore, Y. and Kodama, Y. (1992) Passive protective effect of chicken egg yolk immunoglobulins against experimental enterotoxigenic *Escherichia coli* infection in neonatal piglets. *Infection and Immunity* 60, 998–1007.

Yolken, F., Leister, S., Wee, R., Miskuff, S. and Vodnerfecht, S. (1990) Immunoglobulins and other modalities for the prevention and treatment of enteric viral infections. *Journal of Clinical Immunology* 10, 80S–86S.

Zanetti, G., Galauser M. and Baumgartner, J. (1991) Use of immunoglobulins in prevention and treatment of infection in critically ill patients: review and critique. *Reviews of Infectious Diseases* 13, 985–992.

Prevention of Chronic *Pseudomonas aeruginosa* Colonization by Gargling with Specific Antibodies: a Preliminary Report

28

D. Carlander[1], H. Kollberg[2], P.E. Wejåker[1] and A. Larsson[1]

[1]*Department of Medicine and* [2]*Department of Paediatrics, Cystic Fibrosis Centre, University Hospital, Uppsala, Sweden*

Chronic colonization with *Pseudomonas aeruginosa* in the airways is the principal cause of high morbidity and mortality of patients with cystic fibrosis (CF). At Uppsala, of 27 CF patients (median age 22.5 years), 13 (48%) were found to be colonized chronically with *P. aeruginosa*. Specific antibodies against *P. aeruginosa* were produced by repeated immunizations of hens with killed *P. aeruginosa*. Ten patients, each of whom had had their first *P. aeruginosa*-positive sputum culture, immediately received antibiotic treatment with 3 weeks of oral ciprofloxacin and inhalation of antibiotics. During this course, patients started to gargle daily for 2 min and thereafter swallow the specific antibody solution. They then gargled continuously every day. We have carried out more than 12 months of treatment on three patients (39, 14 and 12 months) and all ten patients have had at least 4 months of treatment. During this time, only three positive cultures were found. One of these cultures was found in one patient who had decided to interrupt the treatment, and two cultures were due to problems with delivery of the solution to the patients. No positive cultures were found when the patients received the treatment. Our results are comparable with the results reported from Copenhagen where 14 CF patients have been treated in the same way with antibiotics. These CF patients were observed for up to 27 months. During this time, there were 49 sputum cultures positive for *P. aeruginosa* out of 214. The result of this first oral antibody trial suggests that treatment with antibodies from eggs against *P. aeruginosa* have a prophylactic and therapeutic effect.

Introduction

Chronic colonization with *Pseudomonas aeruginosa* in the airways is the principal cause of high morbidity and mortality of patients with cystic fibrosis (CF) (Shale and Elborn, 1996). Once *P. aeruginosa* has been found in sputum of CF patients, it is very difficult to eliminate. Temporary eradication can be achieved by vigorous antibiotic treatment in the very early phases; however, the bacteria return very soon.

The basic defect in CF is a mutation in the cystic fibrosis transmembrane conductance regulator (CFTR) gene on chromosome 7 (Rommens *et al.*, 1989), which results in the faulty transport of sodium and chloride and causes the body to produce abnormally thick mucus. This abnormal mucus clogs the lungs and leads to respiratory infections. Although several agents may be responsible for respiratory infections in patients with CF (e.g. *Staphylococcus aureus, Haemophilus influenzae* and *Burkholderia cepacia*), chronic *P. aeruginosa* infections ultimately occur in virtually all patients. The purpose of this study was to see if treatment with specific egg yolk antibodies against *P. aeruginosa* can prevent chronic colonization with *P. aeruginosa* in CF patients.

Methods

Specific antibodies against *P. aeruginosa* were produced by repeated immunizations of hens with killed *P. aeruginosa*. Eggs from at least ten animals were pooled to reduce batch to batch variations. The antibodies were purified from the egg yolk by a water dilution method (Akita and Nakai, 1998). After purification, the antibodies were frozen at −20°C in 70 ml aliquots in plastic bottles. The antibodies were mailed to the patients in a frozen condition. The antibody preparations were tested for their specific activity by immunodot-blot against *P. aeruginosa* bacteria.

Patients, who each had had their first *P. aeruginosa*-positive sputum culture, immediately received antibiotic treatment with 3 weeks oral ciprofloxacin and inhalation of antibiotics. During this course, the patients started to gargle daily with the antibody preparation in the evening for 2 min and then swallow it.

Results

Three patients received long-term treatment of 39, 14 and 12 months, respectively, and another seven patients had 4 months of treatment. During this time, only three positive cultures were found. One positive culture resulted after problems with the delivery of mail and the patient did not gargle for a week. Another positive culture occurred when one of the patients moved to a new apartment and due to this had a short interruption in the gargling, and the third positive culture was from a patient who decided herself not to gargle regularly. These three patients who had positive cultures received another antibiotic treatment which was identical to the one they received when they were included in the study. They became *P. aeruginosa* negative again and are now gargling regularly. No positive cultures have been found when the patients have had the treatment.

Our results can initially be compared with results reported from previous studies where 14 CF patients were treated with the same antibiotic therapy after each *P. aeruginosa*-positive culture (Table 28.1). These CF patients were

Table 28.1.   Comparison between Uppsala study and previous studies.

	Uppsala study	Previous studies
Median age in months (range)	94.5 (22–287)	103 (36–228)
Male/female	3/7	6/8
After 4 months	0%	98%
Positive sputum cultures/total number of tested cultures	3/88 (3.4%)[a]	49/214 (22.8%)[b]
Number of chronic infections after 7 months	0/3 (0%)	2/14 (14%)

[a]All positive cultures found after interruption of treatment.
[b]After 27 months.

observed for up to 27 months. During this time, there were 49 sputum cultures positive for *P. aeruginosa* out of 214 (Valerius *et al.*, 1991).

Discussion

Hens which have been immunized with specific bacteria produce specific antibodies against these bacteria. These antibodies are transported to the egg yolk in large quantities from the blood of laying hens during gestation. Egg yolk antibodies are an inexpensive way of producing large amounts of specific antibodies. These antibodies also have biochemical properties that make them attractive for peroral immunotherapy: they do not activate the human complement system (Larsson *et al.*, 1992) or human Fc receptors (Lindahl *et al.*, 1992), which are well-known cell activators and mediators of inflammation. Eggs are also a normal dietary component and there is, except for persons with egg allergy, practically no risk of toxic side effects of IgY. Peroral administrations of specific antibodies from egg yolk have been used to treat bacterial infections in animals (Hamada *et al.*, 1991; Yokoyama *et al.*, 1992) and to prevent dental plaque formation in humans (Hatta *et al.*, 1997).

This is the first trial to prevent infections in the respiratory tract of humans with orally administered antibodies. The result strongly indicates that treatment with antibodies from eggs against *P. aeruginosa* has a prophylactic effect against chronic *P. aeruginosa* colonization in the lungs. During the last 3 years, since we have had access to specific *P. aeruginosa* antibodies derived from eggs, there have not been any new patients with chronic *P. aeruginosa* infection at the Uppsala CF centre.

References

Akita, E.M. and Nakai, S. (1998) Isolation and purification of immunoglobulins from egg yolk. *Journal of Food Science* 57, 629–634.

Hamada, S., Horikoshi, T., Minami, T., Kawabata, S., Hiraoka, J., Fujiwara, T. and Ooshima, T. (1991) Oral passive immunization against dental caries in rats by use of hen egg yolk antibodies specific for cell-associated glucosyltransferase of *Streptococcus mutans*. *Infection and Immunity* 59, 4161–4167.

Hatta, H., Tsuda, K., Ozeki, M., Kim, M., Yamamoto, T., Otake, S., Hirasawa, M., Katz, J., Childers, N.K. and Michalek, S.M. (1997) Passive immunization against dental plaque formation in humans: effect of a mouth rinse containing egg yolk antibodies (IgY) specific to *Streptococcus mutans*. *Caries Research* 31, 268–274.

Larsson, A., Wejaker, P.E., Forsberg, P.O. and Lindahl, T. (1992) Chicken antibodies: a tool to avoid interference by complement activation in ELISA. *Journal of Immunological Methods* 156, 79–83.

Lindahl, T.L., Festin, R. and Larsson, A. (1992) Studies of fibrinogen binding to platelets by flow cytometry: an improved method for studies of platelet activation. *Thrombosis and Haemostasis* 68, 221–225.

Rommens, J.M., Iannuzzi, M.C., Kerem, B., Drumm, M.L., Melmer, G., Dean, M., Rozmahel, R., Cole, J.L., Kennedy, D. and Hidaka, N. (1989) Identification of the cystic fibrosis gene: chromosome walking and jumping. *Science* 245, 1059–1065.

Shale, D.J. and Elborn, J.S. (1996) *Lung Injury in Cystic Fibrosis*. BMJ Publishing Group, London, pp. 62–78.

Valerius, N.H., Koch, C. and Hoiby, N. (1991) Prevention of chronic *Pseudomonas aeruginosa* colonisation in cystic fibrosis by early treatment. *Lancet* 338, 725–726.

Yokoyama, H., Peralta, R.C., Diaz, R., Sendo, S., Ikemori, Y. and Kodama, Y. (1992) Passive protective effect of chicken egg yolk immunoglobulins against experimental enterotoxigenic *Escherichia coli* infection in neonatal piglets. *Infection and Immunity* 60, 998–1007.

Food Safety

Re-evaluation of Liquid Egg Pasteurization Technology: Newly Emerging and Industrial Applications, Theory and Practice

29

G.W. Froning[1], D.L. Peters[1] and S.S. Sumner[2]

[1]*Department of Food Science and Technology, University of Nebraska, Lincoln, Nebraska, USA;* [2]*Department of Food Science, Virginia Tech University, Blacksburg, Virginia, USA*

Pasteurization guidelines for liquid egg products in the USA were established in the 1960s. Considerable basic research at that time measured the heat resistance of *Salmonella* in eggs. These guidelines have served the egg industry well since there have been no known *Salmonella* outbreaks from pasteurized eggs in the USA. Nevertheless, with changes in the egg industry during the last 30 years, there is a need to re-evaluate present pasteurization methods. Eggs are now marketed earlier and more frequently. Eggs are produced in integrated operations in which they are refrigerated on the farm and transported to the plant at least three or four times a week. Since *Salmonella* is more heat resistant at lower pH and fresher eggs have lower albumen pH, pasteurization guidelines may be affected. *Salmonella enteritidis* is now an important consideration since it is more heat resistant. Heat resistance of *Salmonella* in salted or sugared yolk egg products also needs further emphasis in establishing the adequacy of pasteurization.

Introduction

The present recommended pasteurization guidelines for liquid egg products in the USA were developed in the 1960s and published by the USDA in 1969 (Table 29.1). Several studies in the 1960s provided basic data on heat resistance of *Salmonella* in egg white, which were appropriate to the egg processing industry at that time (Anellis *et al.*, 1954; Osborne *et al.*, 1954; Kline *et al.*, 1965a,b; Cotterill, 1968; Garibaldi *et al.*, 1969). Osborne *et al.* (1954) noted that recommended pasteurization guidelines must be selected carefully in order to avoid adverse affects on functional properties of eggs. Garibaldi *et al.* (1969) studied the heat resistance of *Salmonella typhimurium* TM-1 (Table 29.1). Cotterill (1968) and Garibaldi *et al.* (1969) indicated that the pasteurization process should be adjusted according to the pH of the egg white. Palumbo

Table 29.1.   Pasteurization temperatures.

Product	Relative heat resistance[a]	Temperatures for pasteurization in 3.5 min (°C)
Whole eggs	1.00	60
Yolks, plain	1.38	61.1
Yolks, sugared	10.00	63.3
Yolks, salted	11.00	63.3
Whites, pH 7	0.63	60
Whites, pH 9	0.14	56.7

[a]Garibaldi *et al.*, 1969.
From: USDA, 1969.

et al. (1996) further observed greater heat resistance of *Salmonella* in egg white at low pH values.

With changes in the egg industry during the last 25–30 years, there is a need to re-evaluate present pasteurization methods. Eggs are now marketed more rapidly and probably are fresher than those processed in the 1960s. The USDA pasteurization handbook (1969) reported that most of the commercially produced egg white at that time had a pH of around 8.9–9.1. Eggs are now produced primarily in integrated operations in which eggs are refrigerated at the farm and transported to the egg-processing plant at least 3–4 times a week. Consequently, the pH of the albumen may be substantially lower. This means that *Salmonella* would be more resistant at this lower pH. Another important consideration is the increased concern of *Salmonella enteritidis* infections. Humphrey (1994) and Palumbo *et al.* (1995) observed that *S. enteritidis* is somewhat more heat resistant than other commonly reported strains.

Palumbo *et al.* (1996) recently reported on the thermal resistance of *Salmonella* spp. (six strain mixture of *S. enteritidis, S. typhimurium* and *S. senftenberg* (not 775W)) in liquid egg white using a submerged 9 ml vial at different temperatures (55.5, 56.6 and 57°C) and varied pH values. The *D* value at pH 7.8 and a temperature of 56.6°C was 3.60 min, while the *D* value at pH 9.3 and a temperature of 56.6°C was 1.08 min. This study provides new updated data related to new pasteurization guidelines. The heat resistance of salmonellae is increased by long periods of exposure to salt or sugar before pasteurization (Garibaldi *et al.*, 1969; Baird-Parker *et al.*, 1970; Goepfert *et al.*, 1970; Ng *et al.*, 1979; Sumner *et al.*, 1991). Therefore, higher pasteurization temperatures are needed to eliminate *Salmonella* from salted or sugared egg products (Palumbo *et al.*, 1995). Cotterill and Glauert (1971) found that the heat resistance of salmonellae is increased by long exposure in egg yolk containing 10% salt or sugar, with the maximum heat resistance after 4 days storage at 6°C. In addition to salt or sugar considerations, several different blends of egg products are marketed today. These products may include different combinations of yolk and white, as well as other ingredients (e.g. carbohydrates, dried milk solids, salt, sugar, etc.).

Methodology has been greatly improved through the years. Methods to determine thermal destruction of *Salmonella* in the 1960s often used test tubes, which required long come-up times to reach the desired end-point temperatures. Schuman *et al.* (1997) observed marked differences in *D* values when using sealed capillary tubes as compared with capped test tubes.

This study, which is funded by the United Egg Association, was designed to provide accurate thermal resistance data using capillary tubes, which provide an instantaneous come-up time. The investigation includes a range of temperatures and pHs. *D*, *Z* and *F* values are determined.

Methods

Egg preparation

Fresh shell eggs were obtained from the University poultry farm. Preparation varied according to product type. To obtain egg whites with pH values of 7.8 and 8.2, fresh eggs were used. For pH values of 8.8 and 9.3, the shell eggs were held for 1 and 2 weeks, respectively. Prior to separation of the white from the yolk, the shells were disinfected with a 200 p.p.m. chlorine solution. The whites were separated from the yolk aseptically and blended for 2 min using a Waring blender attached to a variable speed rheostat set at 20 r.p.m. and 120 V. This kept the white from foaming. The pH was measured with a Ross pH electrode on an Orion SA720 pH meter (Orion Research, Boston, Massachusetts). The pH was adjusted immediately after inoculation for all pH levels. The desired pH was achieved using 1 M HC1 or 1 M NaOH.

Organisms and culture conditions

Five cultures were used in an inoculum cocktail: *S. enteritidis* (phage type 4 and 13), *S. typhimurium* TM-1, *S. blockley* and *S. heidelberg*. These cultures were kept frozen in brain–heart infusion broth (BHI, Difco Laboratories, Detroit, Michigan) with 10% glycerol, at −70°C. Two tubes of each individual culture were grown separately to stationary phase in 10 ml of BHI (35°C for 24 h). For all pH levels, each tube was centrifuged and washed twice with 10 ml of triple strength peptone that had been adjusted to a pH close to the final desired pH and resuspended in 5 ml of egg white. This cocktail was mixed thoroughly and kept on ice and the final pH adjusted immediately. The count obtained from these egg white cocktails ranged from 1×10^7 to 1×10^9 c.f.u. ml^{-1}.

Count reduction method

Capillary tubes were used to minimize long come-up times, since they have a small diameter (0.8–1.1 mm×90 mm, Kimble No. 34502). Suspensions of the egg white cocktail were distributed in 0.05 ml aliquots to sterile capillary tubes using a syringe. Capillary tubes were cut to eliminate the large head space and sealed with hot wax. The tubes were placed in a 3.5×0.5 in screen material which was tied onto individual glass rods with heavy thread in preparation for immersion in a heated circulating water bath (four tubes, four time intervals for each of four set temperatures). The heat treatments were done on the same day to avoid the pH problems (see below). Temperature data were collected with thermocouples and verified by a calibrating thermometer. Data from the thermocouples were recorded continuously. All tubes for a single temperature were immersed at the same time (16 tubes). At the end of each time interval, a rod containing the four replicates was removed and the tubes immersed immediately in an ice water bath for 5 min, followed by transfer to hypochlorite (200 p.p.m.) at room temperature for 2 min.

Tubes were removed from the hypochlorite, rinsed in sterile water and crushed aseptically into 5 ml of buffered peptone (BP) containing 0.5% yeast extract and 0.5% sodium cholate for enrichment of heat-injured *Salmonella*. Serial dilutions were made and plated on xylose lysine tergitol 4 (XLT4) agar. Plates and BP enrichment tubes were incubated at 35°C for 24–48 h. All BP tubes were streaked onto XLT4 agar. Initial populations in the capillary tubes were verified by recovery and enumeration from sealed, unheated, control tubes of products identical to the heated menstrum with *Salmonella*.

When using 2 days to run the test, the pH values seemed to be different on the day on which the tubes were filled and the day on which the heat treatments were run because the pH was hard to control for very long. Due to these variations in pH, the 1-day test arose, and every attempt was made to ensure that the egg whites stayed cool and the peptone used to wash the cells was at a pH close to that desired for the end pH. The heating treatments were run as quickly as possible after the capillary tubes were filled and sealed to eliminate the variations in pH. Since the pH7.8 and 8.2 tests had been run using the 2-day method, they were re-done using the 1-day method to ensure that all results were obtained using the same method.

Determination of thermal death time

Plate counts from three capillary tubes for each pull-out time were averaged to determine count reductions for each temperature. The count reductions for each temperature were plotted to determine D values. The D values were then calculated for the three trials at each temperature using the equation below.

$$D = t/(\log N_0 - \log N) \qquad 29.1$$

A phantom thermal death time (TDT) curve (semi-logarithmic plot of D value versus temperature) was drawn by linear regression and the slope of the curve used to calculate a Z value using the equation below. Correlation coefficients are included with the data to test linearity.

$$Z = (T_2 - T_1)/(\log D_{T1} - \log D_{T2}) \qquad 29.2$$

Measuring Thermal Destruction

Heat resistance of pathogens (*Salmonella*) is measured by inoculating various culture cocktails into egg samples (yolk, whole egg or white) and introducing the sample into a test tube or capillary tubes. After heating at various temperatures in a water bath, decimal reduction times (D values) can be calculated. D values are defined as the time required to kill 90% of the viable cells at a specified temperature. The temperature change required to transverse one log cycle is defined as the Z value. Determination of these values provides the necessary data for the required times and temperatures for effective pasteurization.

Many researchers have used a capped test tube method. This method may require a longer come-up time than that obtained using sealed capillary tubes, which may affect the calculated D values. Schuman *et al.* (1997) compared heat resistance of *Aeromonas hydrophila* using capped test tubes or sealed capillary tubes (Table 29.2). Cells heated in test tubes exhibited non-linear (tailing) survivor curves and the D values were higher than those obtained using the capillary method.

Egg White Pasteurization

Pasteurization of liquid egg white has been a problem due to heat sensitivity of albumen proteins. If pasteurization temperatures are too high, functional properties may be greatly impaired. When heating without chemicals, 57°C is the recommended pasteurization temperature (USDA, 1969).

The heat resistance of *Salmonella* in egg white at lower pH values has been a concern. Several studies have investigated this aspect. Osborne *et al.* (1954) used *Salmonella senftenberg* 775W, which is very heat resistant, to study this aspect. Many scientists today feel that *S. senftenberg* 775W is not a realistic strain to use since it is not found in egg products. Osborne *et al.* (1954), however, noted that this strain was much more heat resistant in egg white at a pH below 7.0. Cotterill (1968) reported that pasteurization of egg white at higher pH values permits the use of lower pasteurization temperatures and also reduces the chance of survival if the product becomes recontaminated. Equivalent pasteurization temperatures for egg white at different pHs are: 60°C with Al^{3+} at pH 7.0; 57.8°C at pH 8.7; or 56.2°C at pH 9.1. Garibaldi *et al.* (1969) studied the heat resistance of *S. typhimurium* TM-1 in egg white at various pH values, and found the following results: Egg white (pH 7.0) pasteurized at pH 7.3 and stabilized with Al^{3+} at 60°C, D value = 0.20; Egg white (pH 9.2) pasteurized at 60°C, D value = 0.55. Recently Palumbo *et al.* (1996) observed that D values for *Salmonella* were substantially lower when the albumen pH was 8.8 or higher (Table 29.3). On the other hand, *Listeria D* values were substantially reduced at lower pH values, which creates a problem. Hopefully, antibacterial factors (e.g. lysozyme and conalbumin) will control *Listeria*. Results in our laboratory show similar trends with respect to pH and D values (Table 29.4). These lower D values corroborate the results of

Table 29.2.   Thermal resistance (D values) of *Aeromonas hydrophila* in liquid whole egg as affected by methodology.

Pasteurization temperature (°C)	Sealed capillary tube (min)	Capped test tube (min)
48	8.55	14.28
51	2.86	4.05

From: Schuman *et al.*, 1997.

Schuman *et al.* (1997) when using sealed capillary tubes. Calculated 9*D* values provide an indicator of pasteurization guidelines. With respect to pH and its relationship to *D* values, it may be advisable to look at the effect of storage on the egg white pH. Several scientists have reported work related to this aspect (Froning and Swanson, 1961; Schwall *et al.*, 1961; Heath, 1977). Their studies generally indicate that egg white will reach a pH of 8.8–8.9 after about 72 h at storage temperatures of 7.2–12.7°C (Table 29.5).

One method of pasteurization commonly used in the industry is the utilization of hydrogen peroxide as a bactericidal agent. Armour and Company (Lloyd and Harriman, 1957) published a patent on a process using a combination of heat and hydrogen peroxide to pasteurize egg white. Liquid egg white is heated to 52–53°C and held at that temperature for 1.5 min. At this time, 0.075–0.10% hydrogen peroxide is injected and heating is continued for an additional 2.0 min. After cooling, catalase is added to remove the residual

Table 29.3. Liquid egg white *D* values for *Salmonella* and *Listeria monocytogenes* at 56.6°C and different pH values.

pH	*D* values (*Salmonella*) (min)	*D* values (*Listeria*) (min)
7.8	3.60	10.4
8.2	2.14	16.5
8.8	1.59	20.3
9.3	1.08	20.9

From: Palumbo *et al.*, 1996.

Table 29.4. Calculated *D* and *Z* values of egg white pasteurized at 56.7 and different pH values.

pH	*D* value (min)	9*D*	*Z* value (°C)
7.8	0.86	7.77	3.14
8.2	0.67	6.03	3.09
8.9	0.22	1.95	4.34
9.3	0.15	1.38	5.08

Table 29.5. Changes in pH during storage.

No. of hours	7.2–12.7°C[a]	12.7°C[b]	22°C[c]
0	7.90	7.80	8.00
4		8.04	
8		8.04	
24	8.50	8.50	8.65
48		8.75	
72	8.80		9.10
96			
168	9.00		9.30

[a]Schwall *et al.*, 1961; [b]Froning and Swanson, 1961; [c]Heath, 1977.

hydrogen peroxide. This method has proven to be a reliable approach for pasteurization of egg white in the egg industry.

Ballas Egg Products developed a vacuum method for pasteurizing egg white (USDA, 1969). The system consists of a high temperature short time pasteurizer equipped with a vacuum chamber. A vacuum of 17–20 in is applied prior to heat treatment to remove residual air, which allows for a lower pasteurization temperature. The egg white is then heated to 57°C for 3.5 min. If egg white is adjusted to pH 7.0 with a food-grade acid (e.g. lactic acid) and a metal salt added, egg white proteins are stabilized so that higher pasteurization temperatures of 60–62°C for 3.5–4 min can be used (Lineweaver and Cunningham, 1966). The heat stability of ovalbumin, lysozyme, ovomucoid and ovomucin is increased. Conalbumin is not stabilized at these lower pH values unless iron or aluminium salts are added. Metallic ions form a complex with conalbumin, which is more heat stable. Aluminium sulphate is used since it will not cause discoloration of the egg albumen. Thus, this pasteurization method involves adjustment of the albumen pH to 6.8–7.0 with lactic acid and the addition of aluminium sulphate. The stabilized albumen is then pasteurized at 60°C for 3.5 min. Several firms initially adopted this pasteurization method, but problems arose in moving up to plant scale.

In the late 1940s and early 1950s, heat treatment of egg white solids to destroy *Salmonella* was proposed (Ayres and Slosberg, 1949; Banwart and Ayres, 1956). These studies indicated that storing dried egg white solids at elevated temperatures from 50 to 70°C eliminated *Salmonella* without impairing functional properties. The rate of *Salmonella* destruction is dependent on both temperature and moisture content. Generally, the industry has found that a temperature of 52–54°C for 7–10 days with a powder containing 6% moisture is effective.

Bergquist (1961) patented a 'hot room' treatment, which produced a dried albumen with a lower bacterial load. This process involved desugarization followed by low temperature pasteurization of the liquid albumen and 'hot room' treatment of the dried albumen solids.

- Product (glucose-free and spray-dried to 6% moisture) packed
- Hot room 50–70°C for 7–10 days
- Must test *Salmonella* negative.

The 'hot room' pasteurization of dried albumen solids is widely used by the industry today. Product pasteurized by this method must be indicated to be salmonellae negative prior to shipment.

Pasteurization of Egg Yolk and Whole Egg

Since egg yolk has a lower pH and a higher content of solids, *Salmonella* is more heat resistant. Thus, yolk must be pasteurized at a higher temperature than either egg white or whole egg. *D* values (*Salmonella*) for plain yolk are shown below.

- 0 days storage pasteurized at 57°C = 3.50 (Cotterill and Glauert, 1971)
- 4 days storage pasteurized at 57°C = 2.50 (Cotterill and Glauert, 1971)

- 0 days storage pasteurized at 60°C = 0.40 (Garibaldi *et al.*, 1969)
- 0 days storage pasteurized at 61.1°C = 0.57 (Palumbo *et al.*, 1995)
- 0 days storage pasteurized at 63.3°C = 0.20 (Palumbo *et al.*, 1995).

Salt or sugar further increases the heat resistance of *Salmonella* and influences the flow characteristics of egg yolk products. Cotterill and Glauert (1969) found that the thermal resistance of *S. oranienburg* varied with time of exposure in salted yolk. They attributed this change to the high osmotic effect of salt. Cotterill and Glauert (1971) further noted that storage of 10% salted yolk increased *D* values up to 4 days at 61°C, after which they decreased. Palumbo *et al.* (1995) reported high *D* values even at 0 h which is somewhat different from the results reported by Cotterill and Glauert (1971) (see below).

- 0 days storage pasteurized at 61°C = 6.00 (Cotterill and Glauert, 1971)
- 4 days storage pasteurized at 61°C = 11.50 (Cotterill and Glauert, 1971)
- 0 days storage pasteurized at 63.3°C = 11.50 (Palumbo *et al.*, 1995)
- 0 days storage pasteurized at 64.4°C = 6.44 (Palumbo *et al.*, 1995)
- 0 days storage pasteurized at 65.5°C = 3.85 (Palumbo *et al.*, 1995)
- 0 days storage pasteurized at 66.7°C = 2.07 (Palumbo *et al.*, 1995).

Cotterill and Glauert (1971) observed a further increase in *D* values for *S. oranienburg*, when inoculated into tryptic soy broth with 4% salt at 61.0°C pasteurization temperature. The initial *D* value was 0.80 and, after 3 days storage at 25°C, it had risen to 1.38. Cotterill and Glauert (1971) recommended alternatives for salted yolk. They suggested either pasteurizing immediately after blending the salt or pasteurizing yolk followed by addition of salt. Generally, *D* values of *Salmonella* in 10% sugared yolk are not increased by storage (see below).

- 0 days storage pasteurized at 57°C = 7.00 (Cotterill and Glauert, 1971)
- 4 days storage at 6°C pasteurized at 57°C = 4.50 (Cotterill and Glauert, 1971)
- 0 days storage pasteurized at 61.1°C = 0.74 (Palumbo *et al.*, 1995)
- 0 days storage pasteurized at 63.3°C = 0.72 (Palumbo *et al.*, 1995)
- 0 days storage pasteurized at 64.4°C = 0.20 (Palumbo *et al.*, 1995).

As previously noted in Table 29.1, whole egg is pasteurized at 60°C for 3.5 min in the USA. The UK requires pasteurization of whole eggs at 64.4°C for 2.5 min, which results in some loss of functional properties. Recently, there has been increased interest in extended shelf-life liquid whole egg. Liquid whole egg is a highly convenient product for use by the food service industry.

North Carolina State University has patented an extended shelf-life process called ultrapasteurization. Six patents have been issued, with Michael Foods Inc. having exclusive rights (Swartzel *et al.*, 1989, 1990a,b,c, 1991a,b; Swartzel and Ball, 1991). This method uses continuous flow high temperature (63.7–72.0°C), short time (2.7–192 s) pasteurization followed by aseptic packaging. The result is a shelf-life of up to 16 weeks at 4°C.

1. The highly non-Newtonian properties of liquid whole egg at elevated temperatures do not permit the construction of a simple formula to predict its flow behaviour in a pasteurization system. The authors claimed that high shear rates would allow higher temperatures and/or exposure times for pasteurization.

2. The authors indicate that increased turbulence in the pasteurization process is an important aspect of this new technology.

3. They claimed that the percentage soluble protein loss as a function of time and temperature could be used as a limiting factor in processing.

4. Another aspect of their claims includes the application of the equivalent-point method of thermal evaluation. This method defines the thermal treatment with one time temperature independent of activation energy.

Plant Pasteurization Equipment

Today, great advances have been made in pasteurization equipment and technology with the introduction of the HTST System (heating, cooling, regeneration), the flow diversion value and the fact that most equipment can be cleaned *in situ*. Physical properties of egg products are an important consideration. Flow characteristics and holding times can be influenced by viscosity. A very viscous product may exhibit laminar flow. Thus, times based on the fastest moving particle become important. The most desired flow would be turbulent flow. With these factors in mind, it is important to determine the desired holding times in the individual plant pasteurization equipment.

New Technologies

Several non-thermal technologies have been reported e.g. electroheating (Reznick and Knipper, 1994), high-intensity pulsed electric fields (Qin *et al.*, 1995), high hydrostatic pressure (Mertens and Knorr, 1992) and irradiation. Reznik and Knipper (1994) with Papetti's patented electroheating pasteurization technology used high-frequency radio waves in combination with heat (60°C for 3.5 min) to produce an extended shelf-life whole egg product. They used a radio frequency of 200 kHz, and obtained USDA approval for the process. Ponce *et al.* (1998) utilized hydrostatic pressure at 450 MPa at 20°C for 15 min to obtain a 5-log reduction of *Listeria innocua*. Microbial inactivation increased at advancing pressure. At high pressures, temperature was of less importance.

Qin *et al.* (1995) reviewed the application of high-intensity pulsed electric fluids. They mixed liquid whole egg with 0.15% citric acid and treated this with high-intensity pulses. Shelf life was reported to be 4 weeks, with no apparent adverse effects on physical and chemical properties.

Irradiation has been studied extensively with respect to liquid egg products. Recent studies using an electron beam linear accelerator (Wong *et al.*, 1996; Huang *et al.*, 1997) have emphasized pasteurization dosages with some success. Wong *et al.* (1996) pasteurized egg white at 2.5–3.3 kGy and observed no adverse effect on angel cake volume. The egg white was packed in polyethylene bags at 3.5 cm, and irradiated at 2.5–3.3 kGy using a linear accelerator, then stored for up to 90 days at 4°C (Table 29.6). Huang *et al.* (1997) subjected liquid egg yolk to linear beam irradiation at 2.5 kGy dosage (Table 29.7). Irradiated liquid egg yolk exhibited emulsifying capacity, which

Table 29.6.   Volume of angel cake prepared from irradiated or thermally pasteurized (57°C for 3.5 min) liquid egg white.

	Angel cake volume (cm³)	
Time (days)	Irradiated	Thermally pasteurized
1	423	410
7	386	375
14	387	301
21	295	287

From: Wong *et al.*, 1996.

Table 29.7.   Effect of electron beam irradiation (2.3–3.0 kGy) on emulsion capacity of egg yolk.

	Emulsion capacity (g oil per g yolk)	
Storage days	Unpasteurized	Irradiated
0	3.93	4.89
1	4.49	5.49
7	4.18	4.47
15	4.21	4.54

From: Huang *et al.*, 1997.

appeared to be superior to that of unpasteurized eggs. Use of electron accelerator technology to irradiate eggs has the advantage of greater plant safety. The accelerator can be shut off when not in use. The disadvantage of electron beam technology is the poor penetration capability.

Summary

Several promising breakthroughs in egg pasteurization are coming to the forefront. Possible combinations of new technologies with heat pasteurization may hold promise. Any changes must ensure products with good functional and sensory attributes. The continuing work on re-evaluation of present pasteurization methods is important and should provide the continuing marketing of safe egg products.

References

Anellis, A., Lubas, J. and Rayman, M.A. (1954) Heat resistance in liquid eggs of some strains of the genus *Salmonella. Food Research* 19, 377–395.

Ayres, J.C. and Slosberg, H.M. (1949) Destruction of *Salmonella* in egg albumen. *Food Technology* 3, 180–183.

Baird-Parker, A.C., Boothroyd, M. and Jones, E. (1970) The effect of water activity on the heat resistance of heat sensitive and heat resistant strains of salmonellae. *Journal of Applied Bacteriology* 33, 515.

Banwart, G.J. and Ayres, J.C. (1956) The effect of high temperature storage on the content of *Salmonella* and on the functional properties of egg white. *Food Technology* 10, 68–73.

Bergquist, D.H. (1961) Method of producing egg albumen solids with low bacteria count. US Patent 2,982,663.

Cotterill, O.J. (1968) Equivalent pasteurization temperatures to kill Salmonellae in liquid egg white of various pH values. *Poultry Science* 47, 354–365.

Cotterill, O.J. and Glauert, J. (1969) Thermal resistance of Salmonellae in egg yolk products containing sugar or salt. *Poultry Science* 58, 1156–1166.

Cotterill, O.J. and Glauert, J. (1971) Thermal resistance of Salmonellae in egg yolk containing 10% sugar or salt after storage at various temperatures. *Poultry Science* 50, 109–115.

Froning, G.W. and Swanson, M.H. (1962) Oiled versus unoiled eggs for short storage periods. 1. The effect of time and method of oiling. *Poultry Science* 41, 1880–1886.

Garibaldi, J.A., Straka, R.P. and Ijichi, K. (1969) Heat resistance of *Salmonella* in various egg products. *Applied Microbiology* 17, 491–496.

Goepfert, J.M., Iskander, I.K. and Amundson, C.H. (1970) Relation of the heat resistance of *Salmonellae* to the water activity of the environment. *Applied Microbiology* 19, 429–433.

Heath, J.L. (1977) Chemical and related osmotic changes in egg albumen during storage. *Poultry Science* 56, 822–828.

Huang, S., Herald, T.J. and Mueller, D.D. (1997) Effect of election beam irradiation on physical, physiochemical and functional properties of liquid egg yolk during frozen storage. *Poultry Science* 76, 1607–1615.

Humphrey, T.J. (1994) Contamination of egg-shell and contents with *Salmonella enteritidis*: a review. *International Journal of Food Microbiology* 21, 31–40.

Kline, L., Sughihara, T.F. and Ijichi, K. (1965a) Further studies on heat pasteurization of raw liquid egg white. *Food Technology* 20, 1604–1606.

Kline, L., Sughihara, T.F., Bean, M.L. and Ijichi, K. (1965b) Heat pasteurization of raw liquid egg white. *Food Technology* 19, 1709–1718.

Lineweaver, H. and Cunningham, F.E. (1966) Heat pasteurization of natural and modified egg white. US Patent 3, 251, 697.

Lloyd, W.E. and Harriman, L.A. (1957) Method of treating egg whites. US Patent 2,776, 214.

Mertens, B. and Knorr, D. (1992) Developments of nonthermal processes for food preservation. *Food Technology* 46(5), 124–133.

Ng, H., Garibaldi, J.A., Ijichi, K. and Mihara, K.L. (1979) Pasteurization of salted whole egg inoculated with 24 *Arizona* or *Salmonella*. *Applied Environmental Microbiology* 37, 1091–1095.

Osborne, W.W., Straka, R.P. and Lineweaver, H. (1954) Heat resistance of strains of *Salmonella* in liquid whole egg, egg yolk and egg white. *Food Research* 19, 451–463.

Palumbo, M.S., Beers, S.M., Bhaduri, S. and Palumbo, S.A. (1995) Thermal resistance of *Salmonella* spp. and *Listeria monocytogenes* in liquid egg yolk and egg yolk products. *Journal of Food Protection* 58, 960–966.

Palumbo, M.S., Beers, S.M., Bhaduri, S. and Palumbo, S.A. (1996) Thermal resistance of *Listeria monocytogenes* and *Salmonella* spp. in liquid egg white. *Journal of Food Protection* 59, 1182–1186.

Ponce, E., Pla, R., Mor-Mur, M., Gervilla, R. and Guamis, B. (1998) Inactivation of *Listeria innocua* inoculated in whole egg by high hydrostatic pressure. *Journal of Food Protection* 61, 119–122.

Qin, B., Pothakamury, U.R., Vega, H., Martin, O., Barbosa-Canovas, G.V. and Swanson, B.G. (1995) Food pasteurization using high-intensity pulsed electric fields. *Food Technology* 49(12), 55–60.

Reznik, D. and Knipper, A. (1994) Method of electroheating liquid egg and product thereof. US Patent 5,290,538.

Schuman, J.D., Sheldon, B.W. and Foegeding, P.M. (1997) Thermal resistance of *Aeromonas hydrophila* in liquid whole egg. *Journal of Food Protection* 60, 231–236.

Schwall, D.V., Gardner, F.A. and Parnell, E.D. (1961) Effects of oil treating on shell egg quality during short-term refrigerated storage. *Poultry Science* 40, 583–588.

Sumner, S.S., Sandros, T.M., Harmon, M.C., Scott, V.N. and Bernard, D.T. (1991) Heat resistance of *Salmonella typhimurium* and *Listeria monocytogenes* in sucrose solutions of various water activities. *Journal of Food Science* 56, 1741–1743.

Swartzel, K.R. and Ball, H.R., Jr (1991) Method for pasteurization liquid whole egg products. US Patent 5,019,407.

Swartzel, K.R., Ball, H.R., Jr and Hamid-Samimi, M.H. (1989) Method for the ultra-pasteurization of liquid whole egg products. US Patent 4,808,425.

Swartzel, K.R., Ball, H.R., Jr and Hamid-Samimi, M.H. (1990a) Method for the ultra-pasteurization of liquid whole egg products. US Patent 4,957,759.

Swartzel, K.R., Ball, H.R., Jr and Liebrecht, J.W. (1990b) Ultrapasteurization of liquid whole egg products with direct heat. US Patent 4,957,760.

Swartzel, K.R., Ball, H.R., Jr and Hamid-Samimi, M.H. (1991a) Method for the ultra-pasteurization of liquid whole egg. US Patent 4,994,291.

Swartzel, K.R., Ball, H.R., Jr and Hamid-Samimi, M.H. (1991b) Method for the ultra-pasteurization of liquid whole egg products. U.S. Patent 5,019,408.

USDA Agricultural Research Services (1969) *Egg Pasteurization Manual.*

Wong, Y.C., Herald, T.J. and Hachmeister, K.A. (1996) Comparison between irradiated and thermally pasteurized liquid egg white on functional, physical and microbiological properties. *Poultry Science* 75, 803–806.

Food Pasteurization Using High-intensity Pulsed Electric Fields: Promising New Technology for Non-thermal Pasteurization for Eggs

30

L. Ma[1], F.J. Chang[2], M.M. Góngora-Nieto[2],
G.V. Barbosa-Cánovas[2] and B.G. Swanson[3]
[1]*Douglas, Georgia, USA;* [2]*Department of Biological
Systems Engineering and* [3]*Department of Food Science
and Human Nutrition, Washington State University,
Pullman, Washington, USA*

Liquid whole egg (LWE) inoculated with *Escherichia coli* was treated by pulsed electric fields using two different processing modes, step-wise or continuous circulation. In both modes, the LWE was exposed to a 38 or 48 kV cm^{-1} pulsed electric field (PEF) and up to 187 pulses using a pulsing rate of 3 Hz in all experiments while the bulk temperature was maintained below 40°C. The inactivation of *E. coli* was a function of the number of pulses and processing mode. More than a seven log (7D) reduction of viable *E. coli* in LWE was obtained with the step-wise processing mode when 50 pulses of 48 kV cm^{-1} PEF intensity were used, while more than a 6D reduction of viable *E. coli* in LWE was achieved after 93 pulses with the continuous circulation processing mode. After 50 pulses at a PEF intensity of 38 kV cm^{-1} with the step-wise processing mode, more than a 5D reduction of viable *E. coli* in LWE was attained and more than a 6D reduction after 114 pulses with the continuous circulation processing mode. The microorganism inactivation satisfied Hülsheger's model following first order kinetics.

Introduction

In recent years, knowledge of human health in relation to diet, changing demography and economic prosperity has significantly influenced new product development and advances in food technology (Selman, 1992). As consumers demand more fresh-tasting products, reduced thermal inputs during food preservation are sought (Mertens and Knorr, 1992). High-intensity pulsed electric field (PEF) treatment is an attractive alternative for food preservation. Ohmic heating uses electricity to generate heat or electrical methods that

© CAB *International* 2000. *Egg Nutrition and Biotechnology*
(eds J.S. Sim, S. Nakai and W. Guenter)

rely on the electrolytic generation of oxidizing agents. High intensity pulsed electric fields inactivate microorganisms with very little heating of the medium (Knorr *et al.*, 1994).

Inactivation of microorganisms exposed to PEFs is related to electro-mechanical instability of the cell membrane (Coster and Zimmermann, 1975; Jacob *et al.*, 1981). One effect of an electric field on microorganisms is an increase in membrane permeability due to membrane compression and poration. The inactivation of microorganisms is achieved because of the osmotic imbalance across the cell membrane induced by the poration, which causes swelling and membrane rupture.

Inactivation of microorganisms by PEF treatments depends on parameters such as electric field intensity, number of pulses, pulse duration, physical and chemical characteristics of food, and the microorganisms (Hülsheger *et al.*, 1981; Jacob *et al.*, 1981; Grahl *et al.*, 1992; Zhang *et al.*, 1994a,b,c, 1995; Pothakamury *et al.*, 1995a,b; Vega-Mercado *et al.*, 1996a; Qin *et al.*, 1998).

Escherichia coli, a Gram-negative facultative anaerobic microorganism, is often an indicator of faecal contamination in food products. This micro-organism is found in soil and water, on plants, in the intestinal tract of animals, and in animal products and prepared foods handled by people. These organisms are also recovered from improperly sanitized working surfaces in processing plants (Banwart, 1989).

Eggs are among the most complete foods available to humans and are relatively inexpensive (Ronsivalli and Vieira, 1992). Though the contents of freshly laid eggs generally are sterile, the shell surface contains many bacteria. Liquid or raw beaten eggs may be contaminated during processing with micro-organisms such as *E. coli* because of improper handling and unsanitary condi-tions (Vanderzant and Splittstoesser, 1992). Regulatory agencies in the USA and several other countries require pasteurization of commercial egg products removed from the shells. Pasteurization of whole eggs requires heating to 60–62°C for 3.5–4 min (Potter and Hotchkiss, 1995). Successful pasteurization is based on a critical time–temperature relationship where a lower than speci-fied temperature decreases the efficiency of pasteurization and overheating may result in coagulation of the egg and formation of a film on the heat exchanger surface (Powrie and Nakai, 1985; Banwart, 1989). Limitations in the use of thermal treatments for the pasteurization of liquid whole egg (LWE) make it necessary to consider a non-thermal procedure to inactivate micro-organisms in egg products.

The objective of this research was to achieve the optimum PEF process conditions for the inactivation of *E. coli* suspended in LWE when exposed to a different intensity of PEFs. The conditions under study were step-wise and continuous recirculation treatment schemes, and increasing number of pulses.

Materials and Methods

Preparation of LWE

Fresh eggs from a local supermarket were inspected for integrity of the shell, rinsed with distilled water before breaking the shell, and the contents of selected eggs removed and stored in a sterile beaker until 4.0 l of LWE was collected. The LWE were beaten for 10 min. Between the second and third minute of mixing, 10 ml of 60% (w/v) citric acid were added. The homogeneous LWE was filtered twice with a metallic kitchen sieve.

Microbial inoculation and plate counts

The frozen cultures of *E. coli* (ATCC 11775) were thawed at room temperature for 5 min and centrifuged at 4000 *g* at 5°C for 5 min. The supernatant was decanted and the cell pellet inoculated and mixed in 4 l of beaten egg for 20 min before being subjected to any experimental procedure.

The viable counts in inoculated LWE before and after PEF treatments were assayed by counting the colony-forming units per ml (c.f.u. ml^{-1}) on tryptic soy agar (Difco) with an overlay of violet red bile agar. The plates were incubated at 37°C for 24 h as described by Vanderzant and Splittstoesser (1992). Dilutions for the viable count were carried out to achieve a number of colonies on the agar plates between 25 and 250 c.f.u. ml^{-1}; the mean of two plates was reported for each dilution.

Electrical characteristics of LWE

The conductivity of LWE was measured with a conductivity meter (Hydac, Cambridge Scientific Instruments, Cambridge, Maryland). The effective resistance, *R*, of LWE in the treatment chamber was then determined using the following relationship (Zhang *et al.*, 1995):

$$R = \frac{d}{A\sigma}$$

30.1

where *d*, *A* and σ are the gap between electrodes (0.6 cm), effective electrode area (38.9 cm^2) and conductivity of foods (0.64 Siemens m^{-1}), respectively.

Pulsed electric field treatments

A continuous treatment chamber (Fig. 30.1) consisting of a concentric electrode and a stainless steel body with 28 ml capacity and 0.6 cm gap was used. This applies the high intensity PEF treatments with a constant flow rate of 500 ml min^{-1} using a peristaltic pump (Masterflex Model 7564-00, Cole Palmer Instrument Co., Chicago, Illinois). The pulsing rate was set at 3 Hz, and the input voltages used were 35 or 40 kV (Table 30.1).

Two different types of PEF treatments were conducted to inactivate *E. coli* in LWE. They were: (i) continuous circulation treatments (Fig. 30.2) using 1 litre of LWE inoculated with *E. coli* (samples were collected at 0, 10, 30, 46, 70, 93, 116, 140, 163 and 187 pulses); and (ii) a step-wise treatment consisting of five consecutive treatments of 10 pulses per step (Fig. 30.3). The LWE was collected and cooled to 15°C after each treatment of 10 pulses followed by a complete disassembly and thorough cleaning of the treatment chamber and fittings using chlorine (> 200 p.p.m.) and sterilized water. Each time, the system was conditioned, and the LWE from the previous step was re-treated.

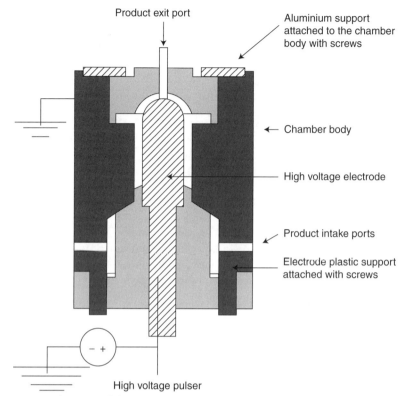

Fig. 30.1.   Schematic of the PEF continuous treatment chamber.

Table 30.1.   Treatment conditions for liquid egg exposed to PEF.

Parameters	Setting 1		Setting 2	
	Step-wise	Continuous circulation	Step-wise	Continuous circulation
Capacitance (μF)	0.5	0.5	0.5	0.5
Input voltage (kV)	40	40	35	35
Input flow rate (l min^{-1})	0.5	0.5	0.5	0.5
Input pulse rate (Hz)	3	3	3	3
Peak voltage (kV)	29	29	23	23
Electric field intensity (kV cm^{-1})	48	48	38	38
Pulse energy (J)	210	210	132	132
Maximum temperature (°C)	41	41	36	36

The electric field intensity was determined with an oscilloscope (Hewlett Packard 54520A, Colorado Spring, Colorado) when the electric field was generated using a pilot plant size pulser manufactured by Physics International (San Leandro, California). The temperature of the treated LWE was measured

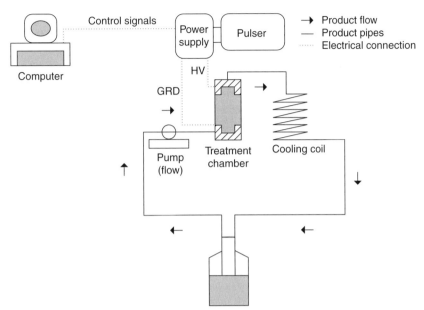

Fig. 30.2. Continuous circulation PEF operation.

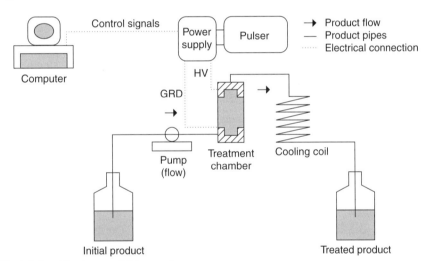

Fig. 30.3. Single pass PEF operation.

at the exit of the treatment chamber using a digital thermometer (John Fluke Mfg. Co., Everett, Washington).

Thermal treatment of *E. coli* in LWE

Aliquots of 200 ml of LWE were conditioned in water baths, where the temperature was set at 40, 45, 50, 55 or 60°C before inoculating with *E. coli*. Samples of LWE inoculated with *E. coli* were then collected at 0, 5, 10, 20 or 30 min intervals. The viable counts in inoculated LWE were assayed by counting the c.f.u. ml^{-1} on tryptic soy agar overlaid with violet red bile agar.

Results and Discussion

High intensity PEF (48 kV cm^{-1}) in a continuous flow system inactivates *E. coli* inoculated in LWE with more than a seven log (7D) reduction after 50 pulses with the step-wise process mode and more than a 6D reduction after 93 pulses with the continuous circulation process (Fig. 30.4). There is limited information about inactivation of *E. coli* in foods such as LWE by PEF. In this study, it is found that the step-wise processing mode is more effective in inactivating *E. coli* than the continuous circulation processing mode. For instance, to achieve a 6D reduction of viable *E. coli* in LWE, the continuous circulation processing mode needs more than 86 pulses, while the step-wise processing mode needs 32 pulses. Zhang *et al.* (1994b) observed a 6D reduction in *E. coli* suspended in potato dextrose agar and exposed to 64 pulses of 40 kV cm^{-1} at 15°C, and a 9D reduction using 70 kV cm^{-1} and *E. coli* suspended in simulated milk ultrafiltrate (SMUF) (Zhang *et al.*, 1994a). Grahl *et al.* (1992) nearly reached 5D by exposing *E. coli* suspended in sodium alginate to an electric field of 14 kV cm^{-1} with five pulses of 2 μs.

The thermal effect of *E. coli* (ATCC11775) is presented in Fig. 30.5. The optimum growth temperature for *E. coli* is 37°C. The thermal effect study (Fig. 30.5) demonstrated that the *E. coli* strain (ATCC11775) was very stable at temperatures below 50°C. When the temperature was higher than 55°C, the thermal inactivation became significant (Fig. 30.5). The temperature profile of LWE (Fig. 30.4) showed that the peak temperature during the PEF processing was below 40°C under both step-wise and continuous circulation processing modes, thereby demonstrating that the inactivation of *E. coli* in the LWE was due to the pulsing effect.

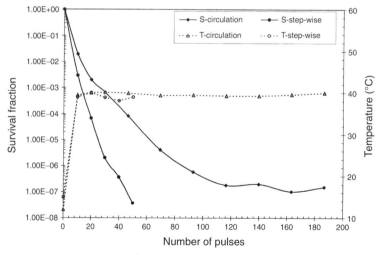

Fig. 30.4. Inactivation of *E. coli* in LWE at 48 kV cm^{-1} of pulsed electric fields.

The overall inactivation for PEF at 38 kV cm^{-1} was less intensive than that at 48 kV cm^{-1}. At a PEF intensity of 38 kV cm^{-1} after 50 pulses with the step-wise processing mode, more than a 5D reduction of viable *E. coli* in LWE was achieved, while more than a 6D reduction of viable *E. coli* in LWE was achieved after 114 pulses with the continuous circulation processing mode (Fig. 30.6). These results are similar to those shown in Fig. 30.4, where a step-wise process is more effective than the continuous circulation process mode at a PEF intensity of 48 kV cm^{-1}. As an example of this effect, to achieve a reduction of 6D of viable *E. coli* in LWE, the continuous circulation processing mode needs more than 86 pulses, while the step-wise processing mode needs 32 pulses.

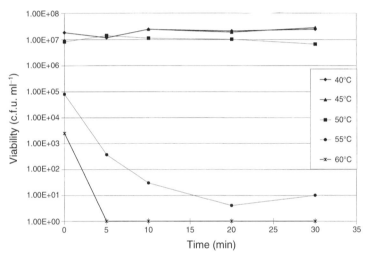

Fig. 30.5.   Thermal effect of *E. coli* in LWE at various temperatures.

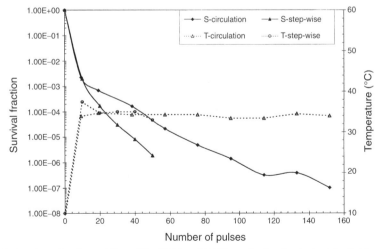

Fig. 30.6.   Inactivation of *E. coli* in LWE at 38 kV cm^{-1} of pulsed electric fields.

The temperature profile showed that the peak temperature during the PEF processing was below 36°C under both step-wise and continuous process modes. Compared with the thermal effect of *E. coli* (Fig. 30.5), it is demonstrated that inactivation of *E. coli* by PEF in the LWE was due to a pulsing effect.

It may be concluded that at both PEF intensities (38 and 48 kV cm^{-1}), the step-wise processing mode is more effective than the continuous circulation processing mode. Calculating the obtained survival rates as a function of a common parameter *t* provides a mathematical approach for the comparison of the results in Figs 30.4 and 30.6. The parameter *t*, called treatment time, is defined as a product of the time constant and the pulse number, *n*:

$$t = n\tau = nRC \qquad\qquad 30.2$$

The survival rate results as function of *t* are drawn in Figs 30.7 and 30.8 based on the following equation (Hülsheger *et al.*, 1981):

$$\ln(s) = -b \ln(t/t_c) \qquad\qquad 30.3$$

where *s*, *b* and t_c are survival fraction, regression coefficient and extrapolated critical value of *t* for 100% survival, respectively.

The related statistical parameters are listed in Table 30.2, indicating that the differences between the obtained function of *t* are significant. In a log–log plot of survival fraction of *E. coli* versus processing time, the parameter *b* is the slope. The greater the value of *b*, the shorter is the processing time required, thus resulting in more effective processing. It is noteworthy that the higher the PEF intensity, the greater the *b* value, implying faster processing at a greater intensity of PEF. It should also be noted that the value of the parameter *b* for step-wise processing is greater than for the continuous circulation process at both 38 and 48 kV cm^{-1}. Therefore, the step-wise processing mode is more effective than the continuous circulation process.

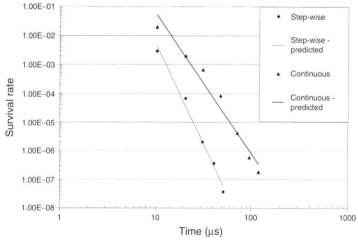

Fig. 30.7. Survival rates of *E. coli* as a function of treatment time at a PEF intensity of 48 kV cm^{-1}.

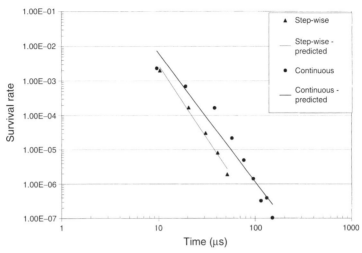

Fig. 30.8. Survival rates of *E. coli* as a function of treatment time at a PEF intensity of 38 kV cm⁻¹.

Table 30.2. Parameters from regression analysis of experiments with various processing modes.

Processing mode[a]	48S	48C	38S	38C	48S	48C	38S	38C
			b				t_c (µs)	
Parameter value	6.961	4.870	4.225	3.730	4.709	5.607	2.486	2.563
SE	0.4232	0.3998	0.2582	0.3373	0.5235	1.007	0.3713	0.7495
CV%	0.0608	0.0821	0.0611	0.0904	0.1112	0.1795	0.1494	0.2924
r^2	0.9036	0.8611	0.9459	0.9251	0.9036	0.8611	0.9459	0.9251

[a]48S, PEF intensity of 48 kV cm⁻¹ with step-wise processing; 48C, PEF intensity of 48 kV cm⁻¹ with continuous circulation processing; 38S, PEF intensity of 38 kV cm⁻¹ with step-wise processing; 38C, PEF intensity of 38 kV cm⁻¹ with continuous circulation processing.

Considering the amount of energy applied to the LWE, the energy input may be calculated by the following equation (Zhang *et al.*, 1995):

$$E = \frac{V_0^2 Cn}{2v} = \frac{V_0^2 t}{2Rv}$$

30.4

where C, V_0, R, n and v are the capacitance (µF), the measured potential across the treatment chamber (kV), resistance of LWE (Ω), number of pulses applied and effective volume of the treatment chamber (m³), respectively.

Figure 30.9 demonstrates that the inactivation of *E. coli* in LWE is a function of the energy consumed and the processing modes. The comparisons of different processing modes and PEF intensities in this study demonstrate that the step-wise processing mode was more energy efficient than the continuous processing mode. Grahl *et al.* (1992) reported that to achieve a microbial survival rate of 10⁻⁴, an optimum energy density of 297 kJ l⁻¹ at a field strength of 25 kV cm⁻¹ is required. In our study, upon inactivation of 6D of viable

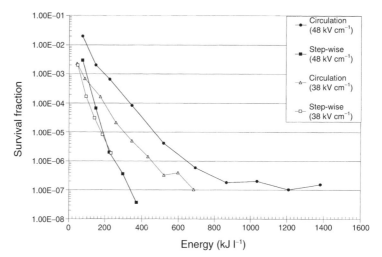

Fig. 30.9.   Inactivation of *E. coli* as a function of PEF input energy.

E. coli, the required energy is 250 kJ l⁻¹ for the step-wise processing mode, whereas it is 640 kJ l⁻¹ for the continuous circulating process mode at PEF intensity 48 kV cm⁻¹.

Conclusions

PEF treatment inactivated *E. coli* in LWE. The bacterial inactivation rate was a function of intensity of the PEFs and the processing mode. The step-wise processing mode was more effective than the continuous circulation processing mode. PEF treatment at either 38 or 48 kV cm⁻¹ and at a temperature lower than 40°C inactivated the bacteria with no risk of protein coagulation. The inactivation of *E. coli* reported here demonstrates the feasibility of PEF as a non-thermal process for LWE.

References

Banwart, G.J. (1989) *Basic Food Microbiology*. AVI, Van Nostrand Reinhold, New York.

Coster, H.G.L. and Zimmermann, U. (1975) The mechanisms of electrical breakdown in the membrane of *Valonia utricularis*. *Journal of Membrane Biology* 22, 73–90.

Grahl, T., Sitzmann, W. and Markl, H. (1992) Killing of microorganisms in fluid media by high voltage pulses. In: *Proceedings of the DECHEMA Biotechnology Conference*. Hamburg, Series, 5B, pp. 675–678.

Hülsheger, H., Potel, J. and Niemann, E.G. (1981) Killing of bacteria with electric pulses of high field strength. *Radiation and Environmental Biophysics* 20, 53–65.

Hülsheger, H., Potel, J. and Niemann, E.G. (1983) Electric field effects on bacteria and yeast cells. *Radiation and Environmental Biophysics* 22, 149–162.

Jacob, H.E., Foster, W. and Berg, H. (1981) Microbial implication of electric field effects. II. Inactivation of yeast cells and repair of their cell envelope. *Zeitschrift für Allgemeine Mikrobiologie* 21, 225–233.

Knorr, D., Geulen, M., Grahl, T. and Sitzmann, W. (1994) Food application of high electric field pulses. *Trends in Food Science and Technology* 5, 70–75.

Mertens, B. and Knorr, D. (1992). Developments of nonthermal processes for food preservation. *Food Technology* 46(5), 124–133.

Pothakamury, U.R., Monsalve-González, A., Barbosa-Cánovas, G.V. and Swanson, B.G. (1995a) Inactivation of *Escherichia coli* and *Staphylococcus aureus* in model foods by pulsed electric field technology. *Food Research International* 28, 167–171.

Pothakamury, U.R., Monsalve-González, A., Barbosa-Cánovas, G.V. and Swanson, B.G. (1995b) High voltage pulsed electric field inactivation of *Bacillus subtilis* and *Lactobacillus delbrueckii*. *Revista Española de Ciencia Tecnologia de Alimentos* 35, 101–107.

Potter, N.N. and Hotchkiss, J.H. (1995) Meat, poultry and eggs. In: Potter, N.N. (ed.), *Food Science*. 5th edn. Chapman and Hall, New York, pp. 316–344.

Powrie, W.D. and Nakai, S. (1985) Characteristics of edible fluids of animal origin: eggs. In: Fennema, O.R. (ed.), *Food Chemistry*. Marcel Dekker Inc., New York, pp. 829–856.

Qin, B.L., Barbosa-Cánovas, G.V., Swanson, B.G., Pedrow, P.D. and Olsen, R.G. (1998) Inactivating microorganisms using a pulsed electric field continuous treatment system. *IEEE Transactions in Industry Applications* 34, 43–50.

Ronsivalli, L.J. and Vieira, E.R. (1992) Poultry and eggs. In: Ronsivalli, L.J. and Vieira, E.R. (eds), *Elementary Food Science*. AVI, Van Nostrand Reinhold, New York, pp. 228–239.

Selman, J. (1992) New technologies for the food industry. *Food Science and Technology Today* 6(4), 205–209.

Vanderzant, C. and Splittstoesser, D.F. (1992) *Compendium of Methods for the Microbiological Examination of Foods*. 3rd edn. American Public Health Association, Washington, DC.

Vega-Mercado, H., Martín-Belloso, O., Chang, F.J., Barbosa-Cánovas, G.V. and Swanson, B.G. (1996) Inactivation of *E. coli* and *B. subtilis* suspended in pea soup using pulsed electric fields. *Journal of Food Processing and Preservation* 20, 501–510.

Zhang, Q., Chang, F.J., Barbosa-Canovas, G.V. and Swanson, B.G. (1994a) Inactivation of *E. coli* for food pasteurization by high intensity short duration pulsed electric fields. *Journal of Food Processing and Preservation* 17, 469–478.

Zhang, Q., Chang, F.J., Barbosa-Canovas, G.V. and Swanson, B.G. (1994b) Inactivation of microorganisms in a semisolid model food using high voltage pulsed electric fields. *Food Science and Technology (LWT)* 27(6), 538–543.

Zhang, Q., Monsalve-González, A., Barbosa-Canovas, G.V. and Swanson, B.G. (1994c) Inactivation of *E. coli* and *S. cerevisiae* by pulsed electric fields under controlled temperature conditions. *Transactions of the American Society of Agricultural Engineers* 37, 581–587.

Zhang, Q., Barbosa-Cánovas, G.V. and Swanson, B.G. (1995) Engineering aspects of pulsed electric field pasteurization. *Journal of Food Engineering* 25, 261–281.

Processing and Cooling Shell Eggs to Enhance Safety and Quality

31

P.A. Curtis

Department of Food Science, North Carolina State University, Raleigh, North Carolina, USA

Recent research has shown that *Salmonella enteritidis* proliferation declines with temperature, and at 7.2°C the organism stops replicating. In addition, when *S. enteritidis* is exposed to these lower temperatures during storage, it is killed more easily during cooking. Current shell egg processing technology limits the ability of processors to lower the internal egg temperature in very short periods of time. This has hindered the federal rule-making process in instigating a temperature requirement of 7.2°C.

How rapidly do eggs cool? This is a question that has been asked and answered over time; however, each time the answer is different depending on the environment to which the eggs are exposed. Research has shown that eggs held at 10°C cooled individually at the rate of 22.2°C h^{-1}. When they were placed in baskets, the cooling rate decreased to 3.6°C h^{-1} and in cases to 0.72°C h^{-1}. Three survey studies have been conducted which examined the temperature of eggs as they were washed and graded, stacked for shipment, packaged in different packaging materials and shipped in refrigerated transport vehicles.

Overview

Eggs have changed over the years. They have become larger and rounder in shape and more susceptible to bacterial penetration. However, processing technology and regulations have not changed with the eggs. For example, egg washing research indicates that washing eggs in water cooler than the egg will produce a negative pressure, which will pull water and bacteria into the egg. Most of this research was done in the 1950s and 1960s and used immersion washers.

Lorenz and Starr (1952) examined shell egg bacterial loads in spray- and immersion-washed eggs as well as the effects of wash water temperature. They found that eggs which were spray washed had less spoilage than eggs that were immersion washed. Brant and Starr (1962) used immersion washing times of 1 and 3 min in their study. They determined that the water temperature should be at least 6°C higher than the egg temperature in order to reduce spoilage. They also found that cooler eggs showed lower bacterial counts.

Current commercial egg-processing plants are very different from those described above. Current processing methods spray-wash eggs for approximately 1 min before they are blown dry and packaged for shipment. Thus, while the pressure gradient theory may hold true when eggs are immersed in water, it may not apply to modern spray-washing methods of processing in which eggs are never immersed. In addition, processed eggs are held in storage for much shorter periods of time than was the case 30–40 years ago. Nevertheless, improper processing can affect the physical and microbiological quality of table eggs (Frazier, 1967; Moats, 1979).

Washing eggs in water at 45–50°C causes an increase in internal egg temperature (Anderson *et al.*, 1992). Because eggs are packaged in cartons that are placed in cases and then stacked on pallets immediately after commercial processing, egg cooling is highly inefficient. Shell eggs placed in coolers at 12°C take more than 219 h to reach that ambient temperature. Therefore, it is impossible for them to reach the 5°C internal temperature described in the *Food Code* (US Department of Health and Human Services, 1993). Thus, present processing and packaging methods may prolong the time that eggs are held at temperatures which are optimal for bacterial growth (Anderson *et al.*, 1992). Kim *et al.* (1989) concluded that the chances of recovery of *Salmonella enteritidis* can be increased 10^6-fold or more by holding the eggs at temperatures of 21 or 27°C for more than 20 days.

Anderson (1993) studied the effects of the washing and grading process on the temperature of shell eggs. He reported a surface temperature of 41°C as eggs exited from 43°C wash water. Hillerman (1955) reported that wash water kept at 46.1°C increased egg temperature by 0.22°C s^{-1}. Lucore *et al.* (1997) studied the effect of washing eggs at low temperatures. They found that egg wash water temperature is not inversely related to internal contamination rates of eggs in spray-wash situations. In fact, their results indicate that cold water washing is one way to enhance egg cooling.

Holley and Proulx (1986) evaluated the effect of wash water pH at moderate temperatures to prevent the survival of *Salmonella*. They found that *Salmonella* was able to grow at 38 and 42°C when the wash water pH was less than or equal to 9.5. *Salmonella* have been reported to show increased sensitivity to heat at more alkaline pHs (Anellis *et al.*, 1954; Cotterill, 1968). Alkaline cleaning formations give an initial pH in the wash water near 11, and wash water pH during operation is usually in the range of 10–11, which is unfavourable for growth of most bacteria (Moats, 1978). Kinner and Moats (1981) found that at pH 10 and 11, bacterial counts always decreased regardless of water temperature. They also reported that bacterial counts decreased at 50 and 55°C regardless of pH. Laird *et al.* (1991) indicated that current processing practices are not sufficient to prevent the potential contamination of washed eggs with

Listeria monocytogenes. Their study has shown that *Listeria* is readily isolated from the washing environment, including the wash water.

Several studies have shown that a pH above 10 is necessary to control bacteria. However, many shell egg processors have no idea as to the pH in their wash water. Those who do, often have difficulty in monitoring pH. With recycling wash water, overflow losses and added water, pH is not always maintained constant. Generally, detergent, which controls pH, is dispensed based on the concentrations necessary to clean the eggshell with minimal thought given to maintaining a constant pH. Dual wash tanks are also becoming more popular. Depending on how dual tank wash systems are connected and how the detergent is added, the pH of water in each of the tanks can be very different.

Salmonella enteritidis outbreaks have focused attention on the microbial load contained on or within shell eggs. There are two possible routes of contamination of intact chicken eggs which have been considered. The first is direct contamination of yolk or albumen originating from a *Salmonella* infection of the reproductive organs before the eggs are covered by the shell (Hopper and Mawer, 1988; Lister, 1988; Bygrave and Gallagher, 1989; Shivaprasad *et al.*, 1990). The second is transmission of *Salmonella* through the shell (Sparks and Board, 1985; Gast and Beard, 1990; Barrow and Lovell, 1991; Humphrey *et al.*, 1991). Stokes *et al.* (1956) reported that there is a much higher incidence of *Salmonella* on or in the shells of eggs than is found internally. They also found that at an appropriate temperature, *Salmonella* in the shell could penetrate the protective shell membranes and multiply to enormous numbers within the egg. They reported that storing eggs at low temperatures inhibited *Salmonella* growth. Miyamota *et al.* (1998) reported that *Salmonella* readily penetrated the shell of freshly laid eggs, but that this penetration was suppressed by cooling the eggs before they were exposed to *Salmonella*. Humphrey *et al.* (1989) have reported that *S. enteritidis* PT4 grows in the yolks of eggs stored at room temperature and achieves populations that permit survival of a variety of forms of cooking. The organism cannot grow, however, in eggs stored at 8°C or below, and storage at this temperature significantly increased the heat sensitivity of *S. enteritidis* PT4 (Humphrey, 1990). Figure 31.1 shows the growth rate of *S. enteritidis* at different temperatures (Rhorer, 1991).

Current shell egg processing technology limits the processor's ability to lower the internal egg temperature in very short periods of time. This has hindered the federal rule-making process in instigating a temperature requirement.

How rapidly do eggs cool? This is a question that has been asked and answered over time. However, each time the answer is different depending on the environment to which the eggs are exposed. Research has shown that eggs held at 10°C cooled individually at the rate of 22.2°C h^{-1}. When they were placed in baskets, the cooling rate decreased to 3.6°C h^{-1} and in cases to 0.7°C h^{-1} (Funk, 1935).

Three surveys have been conducted which examined the temperature of eggs as they were washed and graded, stacked for shipment, packaged in different packaging materials and shipped in refrigerated transport vehicles. Anderson (1993) conducted an egg cooling study using an infrared video

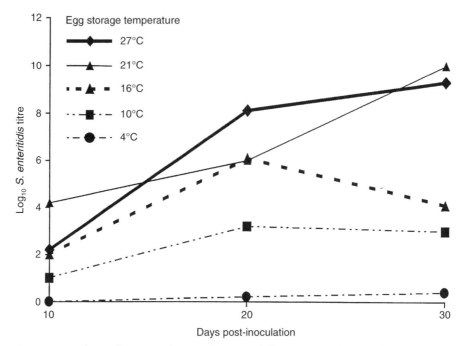

Fig. 31.1. *Salmonella enteritidis* growth in eggs following inoculation (Rhorer, 1991).

camera/recorder. Using this tool, they were able to measure the egg surface temperatures as eggs passed through processing equipment in an off-line facility. Prior to washing and before the eggs were packed, internal egg temperatures were verified using a probe thermometer. The findings showed that internal egg temperatures were within 1.1°C of the surface temperature. Initial egg temperatures ranged from 16.7 to 20°C when the eggs were brought into the packing room from the pre-processing coolers and placed on the unloader. Five minutes after the eggs were processed, their surface temperature was 24.4–26.7°C, a 6.7–7.7°C rise in temperature. Immediately following washing and grading, the eggs were packaged in 30 egg fibre flats in 30 dozen cases then stacked on a pallet consisting of 900 dozen (30 cases). Pallets were then placed in a post-processing cooler (13°C). Thermocouples placed in eggs in the centre of the pallet showed that these eggs required in excess of 219 h to reach ambient temperature. This was due to the total mass of eggs, the insulative value of the packaging materials and the distance from circulating air (Fig. 31.2). Eggs near the outside of the pallet equalized in less than 72 h.

In a Georgia egg cooling study, cooling profiles of shell eggs in individual foam cartons, flats in baskets and flats in cardboard cases (which were grouped singly or in 900 dozen pallets) were examined (Czarick and Savage, 1992). The cooling patterns found were similar to those found in the North Carolina study in that cooling was faster at the outer surfaces and the warmest eggs were at the centre of the pallet. Eggs packaged in wire or plastic baskets cooled at a much faster rate, 0.6°C h^{-1} versus 0.6–0.3°C for cardboard cases

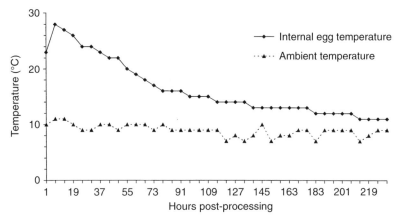

Fig. 31.2. Heat loss pattern in a 30-case pallet (Anderson *et al.*, 1992).

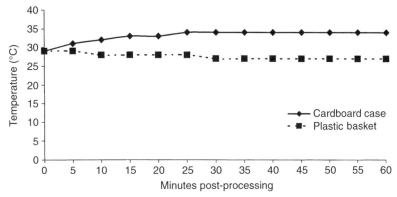

Fig. 31.3. Initial egg temperatures in cases and plastic baskets (Czarick and Savage, 1992).

(Fig. 31.3). This means that eggs in cardboard cases stacked in pallets would require 5 days to reach ambient temperature. The primary difference in cooling rates is most likely due to the increased contact with air that the baskets afforded. The styrofoam cartons retarded the cooling rates of eggs when placed in cardboard boxes due to the decreased air movement and the insulative value of the carton.

Damron *et al.* (1994) conducted an egg transport truck survey. Thirty temperature probes were used in each truck to collect temperatures from front to back, top to bottom, and side to side with a comparison with the ambient temperature. The average temperature of the trailers during the warehouse deliveries was 8°C. The trailers were considered 'in compliance' if temperatures were 8°C or below. When the temperatures were examined as a percentage of time below 8°C, the front of the trailer fell below this average 20–24% of the time, while the back of the trailer fell below 66% of the time (Fig. 31.4). The sides were always cooler than the middle. However, the average temperatures of the top and bottom were not different.

Two research groups have looked at ways to cool shell eggs rapidly. The University of California has taken the concept of forced air-cooling used to cool fresh fruit and vegetables and applied it to shell eggs. Figure 31.5 shows the airflow pattern. This process will require some cooler modification and double handling of packaged eggs. However, the process can reduce the cooling time to 2–6 h. It could be even more efficient if egg packaging (cartons and cases) were redesigned to allow more airflow across the eggs.

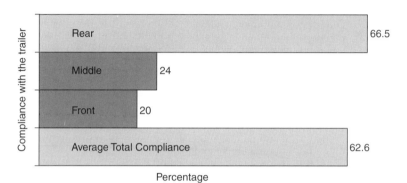

Fig. 31.4.   Temperature distribution in warehouse delivery trailers as a percentage of time in compliance (Damron *et al.*, 1994).

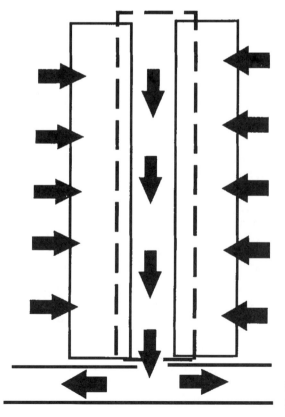

Fig. 31.5.   Forced air flow pattern.

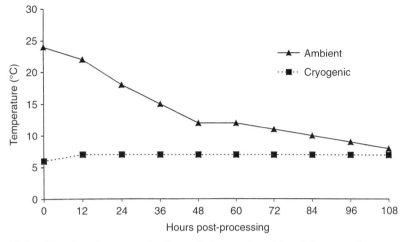

Fig. 31.6.   Heat loss in cryogenically cooled eggs placed in a 30-case pallet.

North Carolina State University has developed a rapid cooling technique using cryogenic gas (Curtis *et al.*, 1995). The eggs are cooled after they are washed, but prior to closing the carton. The eggs are cooled by passing them through a cooling tunnel containing a cryogenic gas. The cooling curves for the cryogenic and traditional cooling are shown in Fig. 31.6. Depending on the temperature of the cooling tunnel, the internal temperature of the egg can reach 7°C in 15 min–24 h. This technique did not cause an increased number of cracked eggs or draw microorganisms inside the shell.

References

Anderson, K.E. (1993) Refrigeration and removal of heat from eggs. *World's Poultry Science Journal* 49, 40–43.

Anderson, K.E., Jones, F.T. and Curtis, P.A. (1992) Heat loss from commercially packed eggs in post-processing coolers. *North Carolina Cooperative Extension Service Special Report*. Vol. 1, ER-1, April, North Carolina State University, Raleigh, North Carolina.

Anellis, A., Lubas, J. and Rayman, M.M. (1954) Heat resistance in liquid eggs of some strains of the genus *Salmonella*. *Food Research* 19, 377–395.

Barrow, P.A. and Lovell, M.A. (1991) Experimental infection of egg-laying hens with *Salmonella enteritidis* phage type 4. *Avian Pathology* 20, 335–348.

Brant, A.W. and Starr, P.B. (1962) Some physical factors related to egg spoilage. *Poultry Science* 73, 64.

Bygrave, A.C. and Gallagher, J. (1989) Transmission of *Salmonella enteritidis* in poultry. *Veterinary Record* 124, 571.

Cotterill, O.J. (1968) Equivalent pasteurization temperatures to kill *Salmonella* in liquid egg white at various pH levels. *Poultry Science* 47, 354–365.

Curtis, P.A., Anderson, K.E., and Jones, F.T. (1995) Cryogenic gas for rapid cooling of commercially processed shell eggs before packaging. *Journal of Food Protection* 58, 389–394.

Czarick, M. and Savage, S. (1992) Egg cooling characteristics in commercial egg coolers. *Journal of Applied Poultry Research* 1, 258–270.

Damron, B.L., Douglas, G.R. and Jacobs, R.D. (1994) Temperature patterns in commercial egg transport vehicles. *Journal of Applied Poultry Research* 3, 193–198.

Frazier, W.C. (1967) *Food Microbiology*, 2nd edn. McGraw-Hill Book Co., New York, pp. 39–41.

Funk, E.M. (1935) The cooling of eggs. *Missouri Agricultural Experiment Station Bulletin* Number 350.

Gast, R.K. and Beard, C.W. (1990) Production of *Salmonella enteritidis*-contaminated eggs by experimentally infected hens. *Avian Diseases* 34, 438–446.

Hillerman, J.P. (1955) Quick cooling for better eggs. *Pacific Poultryman*, 18–20.

Holley, R.A. and Proulx, M. (1986) Use of egg washwater pH to prevent survival of *Salmonella* at moderate temperatures. *Poultry Science* 65, 1517–1520.

Hopper, S.A. and Mawer, S. (1988) *Salmonella enteritidis* in a commercial layer flock. *Veterinary Record* 123, 351.

Humphrey, T.J. (1990) Heat resistance in *Salmonella enteritidis* phage type 4: the influence of storage temperatures before heating. *Journal of Applied Bacteriology* 69, 493–497.

Humphrey, T.J., Greenwood, M., Gilbert, R.J., Chapman, P.A. and Rowe, B. (1989) The survival of *Salmonellas* in shell eggs cooked under simulated domestic conditions. *Epidemiology and Infection* 103, 35–45.

Humphrey, T.J., Chart, H., Baskerville, A. and Rowe, B. (1991) The influence of age on the response of SPF hens to infection with *Salmonella enteritidis* PT4. *Epidemiology and Infection* 106, 33–43.

Kim, C.J., Emery, D.A., Rinke, H., Nagaraja, K.V. and Halvorson, D.A. (1989) Effect of time and temperature on growth of *Salmonella enteritidis* in experimentally inoculated eggs. *Avian Diseases* 33, 735–742.

Kinner, J.A. and Moats, W.A. (1981) Effect of temperature, pH and detergent on survival of bacteria associated with shell eggs. *Poultry Science* 60, 761–767.

Laird, J.M., Barlett, F.M. and McKellar, R.C. (1991) Survival of *Listeria monocytogenes* in egg washwater. *Journal of Food Microbiology* 12, 115–122.

Lister, S.A. (1988) *Salmonella enteritidis* infection in broilers and broiler breeders. *Veterinary Record* 123, 350.

Lorenz, F.W. and Starr, P.B. (1952) Spoilage of washed eggs: 1. Effect of spray versus static water under different washing temperatures. *Poultry Science* 31, 204–213.

Lucore, L.A., Jones, F.T., Anderson, K.E. and Curtis, P.A. (1997) Internal and external bacterial counts from shells of eggs washed in a commercial-type processor at various wash-water temperatures. *Journal of Food Protection* 60(11), 1324–1328.

Miyamoto, T., Horie, T., Baba, E., Sasai, K., Fukata, T. and Arakawa, A. (1998) *Salmonella* penetration through egg-shell associated with freshness of laid eggs and refrigeration. *Journal of Food Protection* 61, 350–353.

Moats, W.A. (1978) Egg washing – a review. *Journal of Food Protection* 41, 919–925.

Moats, W.A. (1979) The effect of washing eggs under commercial conditions on bacterial loads on egg shells. *Poultry Science* 58, 1228–1233.

Rhorer, A.R. (1991) What every producer should know about refrigeration. *Egg Industry* 97, 16–25.

Shivaprasad, H.L., Timoney, J.F., Morales, S., Lucio, B. and Baker, R.C. (1990) Pathogenesis of *Salmonella enteritidis* infection in laying chickens. I. Studies on egg transmission, clinical signs, fecal shedding and serologic responses. *Avian Diseases* 34, 548–557.

Sparks, N.H.C. and Board, R.G. (1985) Bacterial penetration of recently oviposited shell of hen's eggs. *Australian Veterinary Journal* 62, 169–170.

Stokes, J.L., Osborne, W.W. and Bayne, H.G. (1956) Penetration and growth of *Salmonella* in shell eggs. *Food Research* 221, 510–518.

U.S. Department of Health and Human Services, Public Health Service, Food and Drug Administration (1993) Food Code. US Government Printing Office, Washington, DC.

Effects of Cryogenic Cooling of Shell Eggs on Interior Quality and Microbiological Integrity

32

D.R. Jones[1], J.B. Tharrington[1], P.A. Curtis[1],
K.E. Anderson[2] and F.T. Jones[3]
[1]Department of Food Science and [2]Department of Poultry
Science, North Carolina State University, Raleigh, USA;
[3]Department of Poultry Science, University of Arkansas,
Fayetteville, Arkansas, USA

A prototype cooling tunnel designed by Prxair, Inc. was placed in a commercial egg-processing facility. Processed eggs were cooled rapidly with liquid nitrogen (LN), gaseous nitrogen (GN) or gaseous carbon dioxide (GC). Traditional eggs were considered those which were packaged in cases directly from the processing line. Two replicates of each treatment were processed during two separate test periods and held in refrigerated storage for testing. Samples from each treatment replicate were selected randomly and measured 4 days a week over an 8–10 week period. These measurements included: Haugh units, egg grading, yolk membrane strength and bacterial counts of the contents.

The vitelline membrane of cryogenically cooled eggs required significantly higher breaking forces. Rapid cooling of eggs increased the average Haugh unit value and these eggs maintained a higher value over an extended period of time. Data indicated that rapidly cooling eggs significantly reduced the bacterial growth seen in shell eggs post-processing and during an extended storage period. As expected, Haugh unit values and yolk membrane breaking force decreased progressively over the storage period. Egg quality also decreased in that the percentage of loss eggs increased over time. Cryogenically cooled eggs maintained an overall higher interior egg quality over time compared with those cooled by the traditional treatment. The GN- and GC-cooled eggs maintained a higher interior quality level than the LN-treated eggs.

Introduction

Food safety has become a very hot topic during the past few years. Government regulations are beginning to be put into place and committees have been formed to help ensure the quality of the US food supply. Eggs have always been a concern for their possible connection with food-borne disease. The widespread use of antibiotics and the decreased exposure to some organisms have caused our population to become susceptible. Therefore, consumers want some sense of assurance that they are purchasing and using 'safe' eggs.

Shell egg processors have always been concerned with egg quality. The bottom line has always been to produce the best quality egg for the least cost. Consumers are now also demanding higher quality in the products they purchase. The market has begun to shift so that cheapest is not always considered best.

Shell egg producers are limited, at times, to the area which they can service. Short shelf lives have somewhat limited the ability of producers to conquer foreign markets. A process which could possibly increase the available storage time for shell eggs could help to combat this problem.

Cryogenically cooling eggs during processing could help to meet all of these concerns. Previously, it has been recorded that days are required for packaged eggs to reach an internal temperature of 45°F (Anderson *et al.*, 1992). This delay could lead to increased microbial growth and decreased interior quality. By rapidly cooling the eggs before they are placed in the carton, some of these negative effects could be eliminated. Furthermore, these changes could lead to an increased shelf life.

Materials and Methods

This study was conducted in a commercial egg-processing facility. Eggs were processed, using the commercial equipment, over two separate periods. After being washed and placed in cartons, the eggs were either passed through a cooling tunnel or directly packaged in cases. The eggs in the cooling tunnel were exposed to gaseous nitrogen (GN), liquid nitrogen (LN) or gaseous carbon dioxide (GC) before being placed in cases. Traditionally cooled (TC) eggs were considered those eggs which were washed and processed but did not receive a cooling treatment. Two replicates were run of each treatment during a period. Each treatment group was stacked in a pallet and stored in a commercial cooler. A temperature probe with a data logger was placed in the centre egg of a case from each replicate. This case of eggs was placed in a pallet simulator (Curtis *et al.*, 1995) and cooling curves were constructed from these data.

The eggs were stored at 7°C and tested for 8–10 weeks. Testing occurred on 4 days each week. The eggs were tested for interior quality (Haugh unit), vitelline membrane strength and microbial counts, and were graded. Haugh unit measurements were conducted utilizing the procedure outlined by Haugh (1937). The measurements were performed with the aid of the Technical Services and Supplies QCD Instrument Range. Fifteen egg samples were tested from each replicate 4 days a week. Compression measurements were made using the TA.XT2 Texture Analyzer (Texture Technologies, Scarsdale, New York) with a 5 kg capacity and 0.1 g sensitivity. Ten eggs from each replicate were tested 4 days a week. A 1 mm rounded end, stainless steel probe was used to apply pressure to the yolk vitelline membrane until membrane rupture occurred. Membrane breaking strength was reported as g of force required for rupture.

The egg contents were sampled aseptically and stomached. A 1.3 ml sample was plated on tryptic agar and incubated at 37°C for 24 h. Sweating was accomplished by placing cooled eggs in an incubator at 38°C and 90% humidity for 2.5 h. Professional egg graders from the North Carolina Department of Agriculture conducted egg grading. Fifty egg samples from each replicate were graded each day. The exception was the week of the run when 100 egg samples were graded. The graders checked for loss and chex eggs as described by the USDA Egg-Grading Manual (1990).

Data were analysed utilizing the general linear regression procedure of SAS (1989). Means were separated by least square means.

Results and Discussion

The combined average temperature profiles are shown in Fig. 32.1. From this figure, it can be seen that the GN treatment fell below 50°F more quickely than any other treatments. This drop actually occurred during the first 15 min after packaging. The GC treatment fell below 50°F within 24 h of packaging. The LN and TC treatments both required more than 4 days to fall below 50°F. The average GC temperature was much cooler than those maintained by other treatments.

The treatments which were cryogenically cooled, required a greater force to rupture the vitelline membrane. The TC eggs therefore appear to have weaker yolk membranes, which could lead to a greater amount of yolk leakage into the albumen. This leakage could result in a higher percentage of loss

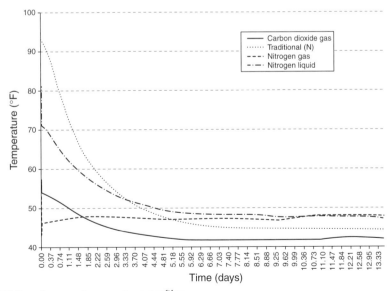

Fig. 32.1. Average temperature profiles.

eggs. A weakened vitelline membrane causes the yolk to be potentially more susceptible to microbial penetration.

The effect of treatment and age on average Haugh unit values is illustrated in Fig. 32.2. From this figure, it can be seen that the GN and GC treatments maintained AA grades 1–3 weeks longer than the TC and LN treatments. The GC eggs maintained AA quality until 8 weeks of storage.

Within the nitrogen treatments, GN had a significantly ($P < 0.001$) higher percentage of chex eggs (10.52%). There was also a greater percentage of loss eggs in the GN treatment. This increased percentage was due primarily to the increased incidence of stuck yolks in this treatment. A significant ($P < 0.05$) difference was also found to exist between GC and TC eggs in the percentage of chex eggs (6.81 and 5.52%, respectively). Although this difference does exist, both levels are lower than the 7% allowed by US Department of Agriculture. There were no differences in the amounts of loss eggs between the GC and TC treatments.

There were no differences found in total microbial counts among the treatments up to 6 weeks of storage (Fig. 32.3). After 6 weeks, the GC and GN treatments maintained the lowest microbial loads. Cracked eggs had higher bacterial counts than intact eggs. However, cryogenically treated cracked eggs had lower counts than TC cracked eggs. When comparing the overall microbial counts between traditional and cryogenically treated eggs, there were no differences found.

Conclusion

Shell eggs can be cooled effectively via cryogenics commercially for 2–2.5 cents per dozen. This cost does not include the savings from reduced refrigeration requirements. Gaseous nitrogen and carbon dioxide provide effective rapid cooling of shell eggs. Carbon dioxide treatment leads to a longer shelf

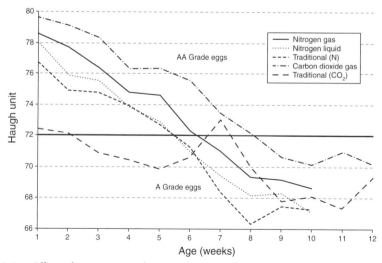

Fig. 32.2.   Effect of treatment and age on Haugh unit values.

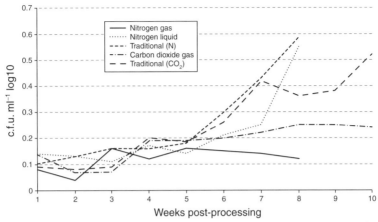

Fig. 32.3.   Effect of post-processing storage on microbial counts in contents of eggs using cryogenic cooling.

life, a lower percentage of loss eggs and an increased average Haugh unit value. Sweating does not increase internal bacterial load.

References

Anderson, K.E., Jones, F.T. and Curtis, P.A. (1992) Heat loss from commercially packed eggs in post-processing coolers. *Commercial Egg Special Report*. Vol. 1 ER-1 April, North Carolina State University, Raleigh, North Carolina.

Curtis, P.A., Anderson, K.E. and Jones, F.T. (1995) Cryogenic gas for rapid cooling of commercially processed shell eggs before packaging. *Journal of Food Protection* 58, 389–394.

US Department of Agriculture, Agricultural Marketing Division (1990) Egg-Grade Manual. *Agriculture Handbook* No. 75.

Haugh, R.R. (1937) The Haugh unit for measuring egg quality. *US Egg Poultry Magazine* 43, 552–555, 572–573.

SAS Institute (1989) *A User's Guide to SAS®, 1989*. Sparks Press, Inc., Cary, North Carolina.

Behaviour of *Salmonella enteritidis* in Industrial Egg White: Egg Naturally Contains Factors Inhibitory to *Salmonella* Growth

33

F. Baron, S. Fauvel and M. Gautier

Laboratoire de Technologie Alimentaire, Ecole Nationale Supérieure Agronomique, Rennes, France

This study was designed to investigate the growth potential of *Salmonella enteritidis* in liquid egg white, to examine the mechanism of egg white resistance to *Salmonella* growth and to evaluate the consequences of egg white processing. When *Salmonella* was inoculated in sterile egg white collected manually, we observed low and variable growth. To investigate whether a lack of nutrients or the presence of inhibitory factors could explain this low development, the growth of *Salmonella* in egg white filtrate was examined. To determine the role of the different egg white proteins, the effect of each protein added to the filtrate was evaluated, and supplementation with the corresponding ligands of three binding proteins was also investigated. Our study showed that ovotransferrin, or iron deficiency resulting from its binding to ovotransferrin, was the major mechanism implicated in the inhibition of the growth of *S. enteritidis* in egg white. To evaluate the influence of processing, industrial egg whites were taken from four egg-breaking factories and inoculated with *S. enteritidis*. Our study shows the importance of yolk contamination (poor separation of yolk and white during breaking) on *Salmonella* growth. We observed rapid growth of *Salmonella* in egg white reconstituted from powder. Protein denaturation, especially that of ovotransferrin, during powder pasteurization after drying (75°C for 15 days) enhanced the *Salmonella* growth in egg white reconstituted from powder. The major role played by ovotransferrin in inhibiting *Salmonella* growth was again demonstrated.

Introduction

Eggs and egg products are considered to be the major sources of confirmed *Salmonella* toxi-infection in France (Lepoutre *et al.*, 1994). Furthermore, the consumption of liquid egg products has increased. These products are used in the fabrication of various foodstuffs (sausages, sauces, cakes, pasta) and it is essential that they be considered safe, especially when they are used in the preparation of an uncooked food product (Montjoie, 1993). Heat treatment of liquid egg white (55–57°C for 2–6 min) decreases the risk of contamination by *Salmonella* spp. However, this heat treatment is mild enough to prevent destruction of the thermally fragile egg white and does not cause total destruction of *S. enteritidis*. Egg white is not a suitable medium for bacterial growth, as reported in many studies. Several factors have been proposed to explain the inability of egg white to support bacterial growth. These factors are high pH, heterogeneous structure and viscosity (Yadav and Vadehra, 1977), lack of free water required for the dissolution of nutrients (Nath and Baker, 1973) or the presence of inhibitory proteins such as lysozyme (Hartsell, 1949), proteinase inhibitors and binding proteins (Stevens, 1991).

The objectives of this study were to investigate the behaviour of *S. enteritidis* in liquid egg white and to indicate the factors involved in liquid egg white resistance to *Salmonella* growth. Due to the fact that egg products are used in the fabrication of various food products, egg-breaking factories have proposed investigating the effects of different technological treatments that could modify egg white composition, thereby affecting its ability to prevent *Salmonella* growth. Therefore, we have tried to evaluate the consequences of factory egg breaking and the effect of egg white processing on *Salmonella* growth.

Materials and Methods

Egg white collected manually

Eggs between 3 and 10 days old from Isabrown hens were obtained from a local supermarket. The eggshell surfaces were sterilized with 70% alcohol and the residual alcohol was removed by flaming the shell. The egg white was then collected aseptically in a sterile beaker by cracking the shell on the side of the beaker. The sterility of the egg white was confirmed as follows: 1 ml of egg white was poured into a Petri dish with tryptone soy agar (TSA, Biomerieux, Marcy-l'Etoile, France) and incubated overnight at 37°C. The pH of the egg white was measured using a pH meter WTW type pH95 (Weilheim, Germany). The egg white was then transferred into flasks (20 ml per flask) prior to inoculation with *S. enteritidis*. Experiments were carried out with raw egg white as well as egg white after addition of yolk (collected manually aseptically) at levels of 0.5–1% (v/v).

Filtrate of egg white

To test the influence of egg white protein, we removed the protein from egg white using an ultrafiltration unit (Amicon, Beverly, Massachusetts) equipped with an ultrafiltration cartridge with a cut-off of 10,000 Da. Filtrate was then sterilized by filtration (Nalgene® filter unit, pore size < 0.2 µm, Osi, Elancourt, France).

Glucose content in the filtrate was determined using an enzymatic test (Boehringer-Mannheim, Germany) and the quantity of iron was measured with an atomic adsorption spectrometer (Varian, Les Ulysses, France). The azote fraction (total nitrogen) was determined using the Kjeldahl method (Tecator auto 1035, Perstop Analytical, Bezons, France). Filtrate was chromatographed by high-performance liquid chromatography (Spectra-Physics Analytical, Fremont, USA) using a C4 column (C4 Vydac 214TP, Touzard et Matignon, Vitry sur Seine, France) by eluting with an acetonitrile gradient (25–100% in 30 min). The flow rate was 0.8 ml min^{-1} and the detection wavelength was 280 nm. Protein content was estimated using egg white as a reference. The sterility of the filtrate was assessed as follows: 1 ml was poured into a Petri dish with TSA and incubated overnight at 37°C. Filtrates in flasks (20 ml per flask) were then inoculated with *S. enteritidis*.

The inhibitory effect of egg white protein

To test the inhibitory potency of egg white protein, growth was assessed in filtrate supplemented with increasing concentrations of egg white, ranging from 0.5 to 10% (v/v). To test the inhibitory potency of egg white protein, the effect of adding each protein (ovalbumin, lysozyme, ovomucoid, ovoinhibitor, cystatin, ovotransferrin, flavoprotein (riboflavin-binding protein) and avidin) on the growth of *S. enteritidis* in the filtrate was compared. All egg white proteins, obtained from Sigma Chemical Co. (Saint Quentin Fallavier, France), were dissolved in filtrate. Protein concentrations in the final flasks (ovalbumin 5.4 g l^{-1}; lyzozyme 0.35 g l^{-1}; ovomucoid 1.1 g l^{-1}; ovoinhibitor 0.15 g l^{-1}; cystatin 0.005 g l^{-1}; ovotransferrin 1.3 g l^{-1}; flavoprotein 0.08 g l^{-1}; avidin 0.005 g l^{-1}) were 10% of the theoretical concentration found in egg white for each protein. Each solution was sterilized by filtration (Nalgene® filter unit, Osi) before inoculation of flasks (20 ml per flask).

To assess the overall effect of biotin, riboflavin and iron deficiency resulting from their binding to avidin, flavoprotein and ovotransferrin, respectively, we supplemented filtrate with 10% egg white and aliquots of filtered sterilized solutions of biotin, riboflavin and ammonium ferric citrate obtained from Sigma Chemical Co. Supplementation with biotin, riboflavin and iron was performed at levels up to 10 times more than those required for avidin, flavoprotein and ovotransferrin, respectively, for theoretical saturation. The final concentrations added were: biotin 0.07, riboflavin 0.9 and iron 2.9 mg l^{-1} of egg white. After all compounds were dissolved in the filtrate, the solutions of a total volume of 1 ml were transferred to flasks containing 20 ml of egg white.

Study in factory-separated (industrial) egg white

Industrial liquid egg whites (raw liquid, salted egg white and sugared egg white) from four egg-breaking factories were taken into flasks and inoculated with a mutant of *S. enteritidis*. After the pH was measured, the endogenous flora were enumerated. Frozen egg white was thawed for 24 h at 4°C and powder was reconstituted to make 12.5% with sterile distilled water, before inoculation.

The quantity of iron in egg white and in powder was measured with an atomic adsorption spectrometer (Varian, Les Ulysses, France) after digestion with nitric acid.

The denaturation of protein in egg white and powder was investigated using hydrophobicity measurements. The nitrogen content (to convert to protein content) was determined using the Kjeldahl method (Tecator auto 1035, Perstop Analytical, Bezons, France). After egg white reconstitution from powder and adjustment to the same nitrogen content, ANS hydrophobicity was measured according to Yamamoto et al. (1996). ANS (8-anilino-1-naphthalenesulphonic acid) was purchased from Sigma Chemical Co. Egg white was diluted 100 times with 0.01 M sodium phosphate buffer (pH 7.0). A 20 µl aliquot of ANS (8 mM in a 0.02 M sodium phosphate buffer at pH 7.0) was added to 4 ml of egg white solution. The relative fluorescence intensity was measured using a Perkin-Elmer LS50B spectro-fluorometer at excitation and emission wavelengths of 390 and 470 nm, respectively.

Cultures and growth conditions

The strain of S. enteritidis used for experiments in sterile media was isolated from egg white and identified by Sylvine Fremy (Centre National d'Etudes Vétérinaires et Alimentaires, Paris, France).

In experiments using industrial egg white, we used a double mutant (antibiotic-resistant) of this wild-type strain to select our strain from egg white endogenous flora during enumeration. This antibiotic-resistant strain was selected using a combination of two methods described by Blackburn and Davies (1994) and Catalano and Knabel (1994). The wild-type strain was inoculated into 100 ml of tryptic soy broth (TSB, Biomerieux) and incubated at 37°C for 24 h, and 100 ml of TSB containing 100 µg ml^{-1} nalidixic acid was added to the incubated culture, which was then incubated at 37°C for a further 24 h. After incubation, 0.1 ml of culture was spread on the surface of a TSA plate containing 100 µg ml^{-1} nalidixic acid which was then incubated at 37°C for 24 h. One nalidixic acid-resistant isolated colony was grown in 100 ml of TSB containing 100 µg ml^{-1} nalidixic acid. After incubation, 100 ml of TSB containing 500 µg ml^{-1} streptomycin was added to the incubated culture, which was then incubated for a further 24 h. A 0.1 ml aliquot of the culture was spread on the surface of a TSA plate containing both 100 µg ml^{-1} nalidixic acid and 500 µg ml^{-1} streptomycin. We obtained a spontaneous mutant resistant to both antibiotics. This antibiotic-resistant strain was tested in TSB, in filtrate and in egg white to ensure that the mutant would behave as the wild-type S. enteritidis culture under similar conditions.

All cultures (wild-type and mutant) were conserved in cryobeads (AES Co., Combourg, France) at −18°C and propagated at 37°C for 18–24 h in TSB or in TSB containing antibiotics before use. Serial 10-fold dilutions of the 18–24 h culture were prepared in the filtrate and then inoculated at a concentration of 2% into each flask. The purpose of this operation was to obtain a final inoculum of about 10^3 S. enteritidis cells ml^{-1} in the flask, without the addition of any nutrients or salts. Each flask was inoculated individually with the same culture of *Salmonella* to obtain an inoculum of about 10^3 c.f.u. ml^{-1}. After inoculation, flasks of media were maintained in a 30°C bath.

Enumeration of *Salmonella*

After the desired incubation time, five or ten flasks per medium and per day were removed and examined for *Salmonella* cell counts. To count the number of *S. enteritidis* cells present in egg white, it was necessary first to homogenize each flask of inoculated egg white. Enumeration in filtrate or in egg white protein solutions did not require this procedure. Serial 10-fold dilutions in peptone water were made from homogenized egg white, filtrate or solutions. Then, 1 ml sample of each dilution were plated in TSA (for the wild-type strain) or in TSA containing 100 μg ml^{-1} nalidixic acid and 500 μg ml^{-1} strepto-mycin (for the mutant strain). After incubation at 37°C for 24–28 h, the colony-forming units (c.f.u.) were counted.

Results and Discussion

Growth of *S. enteritidis* in egg white

We observed a slow growth of *S. enteritidis* in egg white, in comparison with that in optimum medium (TSB) at 30°C: cell counts rose by two log during 4–6 days of incubation (Fig. 33.1). This observation suggests that certain factors present limit the growth of *Salmonella* in egg white. In addition, compared with TSB, the results in egg white showed a variation between flasks after 4 and 5 days of incubation. This variability did not disappear with homogeniza-tion and shaking of egg white. Our results corroborate the results of the major-ity of authors who have concluded that bacterial growth (Nath and Baker, 1973) and *Salmonella* growth (Yadav and Vadhera, 1977; Ruzickova, 1994) is restricted in egg white. Although we observed in some flasks a three log increase in the number of *Salmonella* cells after 4 days incubation, we concluded that *S. enteritidis* growth in egg white was still relatively slow.

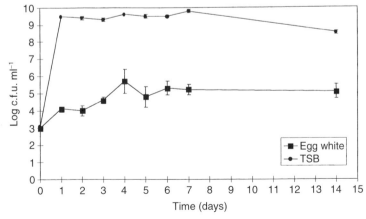

Fig. 33.1.   Growth of *S. enteritidis* in egg white and in tryptic soy broth (TSB) at 30°C. Initial inoculum: 10^3 cells ml^{-1}.

Some authors suggested that either lack of free water and nutrients (Nath and Baker, 1973), unavailability of some nutrients due to sequestering agents, or the presence of an inhibitory factor could explain the inability of egg white to support bacterial growth. Sequestering agents involved are ovotransferrin (Valenti *et al.*, 1983) and vitamin-binding protein (Stevens, 1991). Also, possible inhibitory factors proposed are lysosyme (Hartsell, 1949) and proteinase inhibitors (Stevens, 1991).

Growth of *S. enteritidis* in egg white filtrate

Filtrate of egg white may be considered as egg white without protein (Table 33.1). Figure 33.2 shows the growth of one strain of *S. enteritidis* in TSB, filtrate, egg white and in filtrate with 10% egg white added. Comparison of *Salmonella* grown in filtrate and TSB showed that growth in filtrate occurred. These results show clearly that filtrate is a good medium for *Salmonella* growth: it contains a sufficient carbon source, iron and probably also free amino acids, vitamins, salts and oligoelements. After 15 days of subculturing at 30°C, every 2 days, in the filtrate, *S. enteritidis* continued its rapid growth (data not shown). We observed that only 10% egg white is sufficient to decrease the

Table 33.1. Composition and pH of egg white filtrate.

Composition	Egg white	Filtrate of egg white
pH	9.3	9.3
Glucose (g l⁻¹)	4–5[a]	4
Azote fraction (g l⁻¹)		0.08
Iron	trace[a]	trace
Ovalbumin (g l⁻¹)	54[a]	0.024
Ovotransferrin (g l⁻¹)	13[a]	0.001
Lysozyme (g l⁻¹)	3.5[a]	0.009

[a]Theoretical composition (Sauveur, 1988).

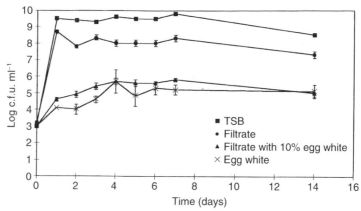

Fig. 33.2.   Growth of *S. enteritidis* in filtrate with 10% egg white, in egg white, in filtrate and in TSB at 30°C. Initial inoculum: 10³ cells ml⁻¹.

growth of *S. enteritidis* in filtrate to the same level as the growth observed in egg white. We observed that the growth of *S. enteritidis* in filtrate with 10% egg white added was more homogeneous than the growth of this bacteria in egg white. These results suggest that egg white proteins are implicated in the mechanisms of resistance to *Salmonella* growth.

Studies on the influence of egg white proteins

Addition of egg white protein to filtrate

Studies in filtrate with the addition of egg white protein showed the inhibitory potency of each protein (Fig. 33.3). The amount of each protein added was 10% of the theoretical concentration found in egg white, but we observed that only 10% egg white was sufficient to decrease the growth in filtrate to the same level as that observed in raw egg white. We observed that only ovotransferrin decreased the growth in filtrate. The level of growth in filtrate with ovotransferrin after 1 day of culture was three log less than that observed in filtrate and one log more than the growth observed in filtrate with 10% egg white. It is possible that the ovotransferrin obtained from Sigma had a lower affinity for Fe^{3+} than the ovotransferrin that is present in raw egg white. In view of these results, only ovotransferrin seemed to have an inhibitory effect.

Supplementation

Supplementation with biotin and riboflavin had no significant effect (data not shown), but addition of iron (at a concentration of up to ten times that required for ovotransferrin saturation) reversed the inhibitory effect of egg white (Fig. 33.4). This result suggests that ovotransferrin, or iron deficiency resulting from its binding to ovotransferrin, is implicated in the inhibition of the growth of *S. enteritidis* observed in egg white.

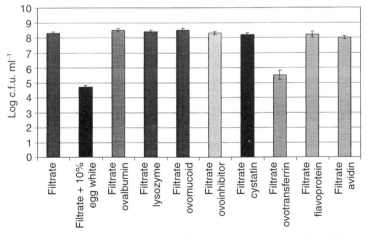

Fig. 33.3.   Effect of egg white proteins on the growth of *S. enteritidis* in filtrate after 1 day of incubation at 30°C (initial inoculum: 10^3 cells ml^{-1}, protein concentrations were 10% of the theoretical concentrations found in egg white).

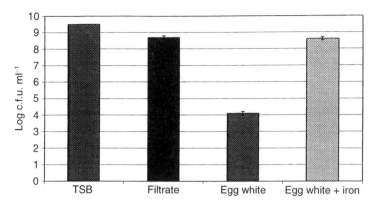

Fig. 33.4. Effect of iron suplementation of egg white on the *Salmonella* growth after 1 day of incubation at 30°C (initial inoculum : 10^3 cells ml^{-1}, iron was added to obtain an ovotransferrin saturation of 110%).

The iron content of egg white was generally reported to be insufficient to allow ovotransferrin saturation (Sauveur, 1988): there was no free iron present in egg white and addition of ovotransferrin had no effect (data not shown). Ovotransferrin is reported to form stable complexes with metal ions, especially with two atoms of ferric iron (Azari and Baugh, 1967). Iron is a nutrient that is probably universally required by living cells. The ubiquitous presence of cytochromes and non-haem iron in the respiratory chains of aerobic and facultative anaerobic species provides a central role for this element in the energy metabolism of microorganisms (Neilands, 1981). The fast growth observed in filtrate suggests that the iron present in the filtrate may be due to iron contamination during ultrafiltration. This contamination could not be estimated because of the very low iron content of filtrate, close to the detection limits of the atomic adsorption spectrometer.

It has been shown repeatedly that the bacteriostatic action of egg albumen against Gram-negative bacteria in general is reduced by the addition of iron in amounts sufficient to saturate ovotransferrin (Sauter and Petersen, 1969; Lock and Board, 1992). Garibaldi (1970) showed that the major role in preventing growth of Gram-negative spoilage bacteria in egg white was played by ovotransferrin rather than high pH or ovomucoid. This author showed clearly that the importance of the different inhibitory factors on growth varied with the bacteria tested and with the experimental conditions. The present study is the first extensive study that shows why *Salmonella* was inhibited in egg white because the effect of each factor was tested in filtrate, a medium without protein but close in nature to egg white (same pH, glucose content, etc.). This study showed that *S. enteritidis* grows slowly (with an increase of two log and three log in some flasks) in egg white, even in iron-deficient conditions. It has been shown that some microorganisms excrete iron-binding compounds when grown on media containing insufficient iron to meet their needs (Garibaldi, 1970). These compounds, called siderophores, have a high affinity for ferric iron and allow bacteria to avail themselves of iron that is bound by ovotransferrin. Studies reported that the majority of *Salmonella* species isolated from various environments excreted siderophores (Visca *et al.*, 1991). All strains tested in our laboratory excrete siderophores (data not shown).

This study has demonstrated the major role played by ovotransferrin and iron deficiency in the inhibition of *S. enteritidis* in egg white, but further experiments should be carried out to clarify the factors responsible for the variability of growth observed. We believe that distribution of iron–ovotransferrin complex, inaccessibility due to viscosity and molecular dimension and the loss of mobility (loss of flagella due to high pH) could explain this great variability.

In view of the importance of iron availability for *Salmonella* growth, we examined the consequences of factory egg white processing.

Studies on factory-separated (industrial) egg white

We have studied the growth of *S. enteritidis* in industrial egg white from four egg-breaking factories. The growth in industrial egg white was comparable between factories (Fig. 33.5) and with growth observed in egg white collected in the laboratory, except for one egg-breaking factory. The egg white from this factory seemed to be contaminated with a large amount of yolk, and the *Salmonella* growth was rapid.

The level of *Salmonella* growth observed suggests that egg white collected manually in the laboratory is a good model for studying *Salmonella* behaviour in liquid egg white. Thus, we decided to test the influence of the addition of yolk to egg white on *Salmonella* growth. The addition of yolk to egg white in the laboratory (from 0.5 to 1%) enhanced the growth of *Salmonella* in egg white (Fig. 33.6).

The level of growth observed in egg white collected in the factory was comparable with the level observed in egg white collected in the laboratory, with the addition of 0.7% yolk. We can conclude that the high level of growth observed in egg white from factory number three was probably related to high yolk contamination due to poor separation of white and yolk during breaking.

The better growth observed in egg white with addition of yolk demonstrates that yolk provides some nutrients necessary for *Salmonella* growth. We believe that this observation is related to the iron provided by the yolk. Ovotransferrin is not saturated in egg white, which contains only a trace of

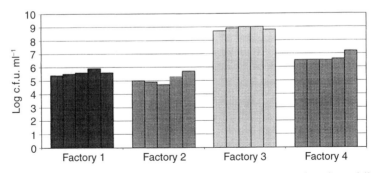

Fig. 33.5. Comparison of *S. enteritidis* growth in industrial egg white from different egg-breaking plants after 1 day of incubation at 30°C (initial inoculum: 10^3 cells ml^{-1}).

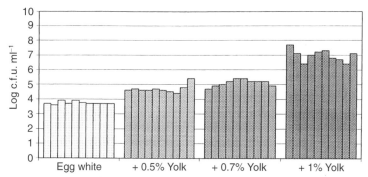

Fig. 33.6. Comparison of *S. enteritidis* growth in egg white and in egg white with yolk after 1 day of incubation at 30°C. Egg white was collected in the laboratory and yolk was added to white (from 0.5 to 1%, v/v), initial inoculum: 10^3 cells ml^{-1}.

iron. However, the yolk contains 10 mg of iron per 100 g of yolk (Sauveur, 1988). The addition of 0.7% yolk to egg white saturates the egg white ovotransferrin at about 37%. Addition of ferric citrate to egg white at a concentration required for different degrees of ovotransferrin saturation (data not shown) allows us to conclude that the enhanced growth observed with the addition of yolk is related to the iron provided by the yolk: iron availability is essential for *Salmonella* growth. *Salmonella* growth in industrial egg white was comparable with the growth observed in egg white collected in the laboratory, except when it was contaminated by yolk. The resistance of industrial egg white to *Salmonella* growth is directly correlated with iron deficiency of egg white. In view of these observations, the quality of eggs for breaking (age) and the operator vigilance during breaking seem very important with respect to egg product contamination by *S. enteritidis*.

To complete our study, we tried to evaluate the effect of technological treatment such as drying, freezing or the addition of ingredients (salt or saccharose).

Effect of egg white technological treatments on resistance to *Salmonella* growth

We have compared the *Salmonella* growth after 4 days of incubation at 30°C in: (i) egg white collected in the laboratory; (ii) industrial frozen egg white (frozen at –40°C, conserved at –15°C and thawed for 24 h at 4°C); (iii) egg white with 30% saccharose; (iv) egg white with 10% salt; and (v) egg white powder (egg white dried in the factory and reconstituted with sterile distilled water in the laboratory).

We show in Fig. 33.7 that the freezing process or the addition of 30% saccharose had no effect on *Salmonella* growth. On the other hand, this figure shows a marked effect of the addition of salt and of the drying process. Salt addition enhanced egg white resistance to *Salmonella* growth: we observed no culturable cells after 4 days of incubation in egg white with 10% salt. We believe that the effect of salt was probably related to low water availability, high viscosity and high osmotic pressure in egg white.

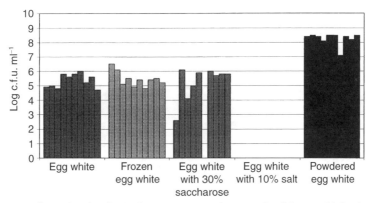

Fig. 33.7.   Effect of technological treatments on the growth of *S. enteritidis* after 4 days of incubation at 30°C. Initial inoculum was 10^3 cells ml^{-1}.

Concerning the effect of drying, we observed rapid growth in egg white reconstituted from powder: *Salmonella* cell counts rose from 10^3 to 10^8 cells ml^{-1} of egg white during the first day of incubation. This rapid growth was observed in powder from all the egg-breaking factories investigated.

In view of the mechanism of egg white resistance and the major role played by iron availability and by ovotransferrin, we investigated several hypotheses to explain this rapid growth: iron provided during the drying process and/or denaturation of protein, especially ovotransferrin.

Estimation of the amounts of iron in egg white and in egg white reconstituted from powder using atomic adsorption showed no important contamination of iron in egg white from powder. During the drying process, iron could be provided at different stages. It could be provided during reconstitution: water required for the reconstitution of egg white from powder could contain sufficient amounts of iron to allow bacterial growth. Reconstitution with water without iron (removed by fixation onto ovotransferrin and ultrafiltration at 10,000 Da, Ultrafree, Amicon, Beverley, Massachusetts) always shows rapid *Salmonella* growth, so this hypothesis could not explain the rapid growth observed. Iron could be provided during egg breaking: yolk contamination could enhance *Salmonella* growth, but industrial liquid egg white employed in the drying process usually comes from eggs broken in the same manner as the 'fresh liquid egg white'.

Removal of sugar (glucose) before drying could also provide iron. In France, sugar is removed from egg white by yeast fermentation (utilization of glucose oxidase is prohibited): we can suppose that lysed yeast after fermentation provided sufficient iron for *Salmonella* growth. An experiment into *Salmonella* growth was carried out on egg white where sugar was removed by yeast fermentation and on egg white where sugar was removed by enzymatic reaction (glucose oxidase). The two types of industrial egg white permitted rapid *Salmonella* growth, so we cannot conclude that iron was provided by yeast fermentation. Nevertheless, iron could be also provided by stainless steel equipment used during the drying process. The release of iron

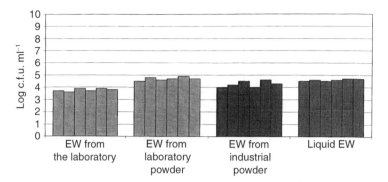

Fig. 33.8. Comparison of the *Salmonella* growth in industrial and laboratory egg white (EW) and in egg white reconstituted from industrial or laboratory powder (powder just after drying without pasteurization). Initial inoculum was 10^3 cells ml^{-1}.

from stainless steel equipment was possible but it does not seem probable because there is no indication that iron was released during drying more than during breaking or other operations. Therefore, in view of this observation, we tried to evaluate protein denaturation in the powder.

To evaluate the effect of protein denaturation on *Salmonella* growth and to determine at what stage this denaturation could occur, we compared the *Salmonella* growth in: (i) liquid egg white collected in the laboratory; (ii) egg white reconstituted from powder freeze-dried in the laboratory; (iii) liquid egg white collected in the factory; and (iv) egg white reconstituted from industrial powder after the drying process just before pasteurization (Fig. 33.8).

The results show low growth in industrial powder (without pasteurization) and relatively comparable with growth in liquid egg white and in egg white from laboratory powder. These observations seem to confirm that iron possibly provided during processing was not implicated in the rapid growth observed in egg white from powder. On the other hand, the results show clearly that drying had no effect on *Salmonella* growth.

To verify the influence of powder pasteurization on *Salmonella* growth, we compared the growth in egg white from powder collected after drying and powder after drying and laboratory pasteurization for 4, 7 and 15 days in an incubator at 75°C. Powder pasteurization enhanced *Salmonella* growth: cell counts rose by four log between egg white from powder before pasteurization and the same powder pasteurized for 15 days.

To confirm that the influence of pasteurization on *Salmonella* growth was due to egg white protein denaturation, we evaluated the total protein denaturation of powder after 0, 4, 7 and 15 days of pasteurization by measuring the surface hydophobicity by fluorescence (Fig. 33.9).

The results show clearly that powder pasteurization denatures the egg white protein. The drying process does not denature protein as much as pasteurization. We can observe that an increase in *Salmonella* growth was correlated directly with an increase in denaturation (correlation coefficient: 0.9).

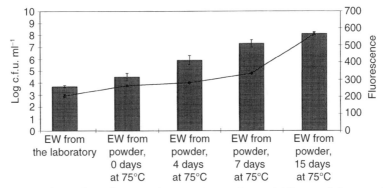

Fig. 33.9. Relationship of protein denaturation to *S. enteritidis* growth in egg white (EW), and in egg white reconstituted from powder pasteurized at 75°C for 0, 4, 7 and 15 days. Initial inoculum was 10^3 cells ml^{-1}, the protein denaturation was estimated by measurement of the surface hydrophobicity by fluorescence.

Ovotransferrin is the most heat-labile protein in egg white. At pH 9, the thermal denaturation of a purified and desalted ovotransferrin occurred at 60°C, and this temperature decreases at a lower pH (Hegg, 1978). We believe that the increase in *Salmonella* growth was related to protein denaturation and probably especially to ovotransferrin denaturation. To determine if ovotransferrin denaturation could occur during pasteurization and if this denaturation was especially implicated in the increase in *Salmonella* growth, other studies will be carried out on pasteurized ovalbumin and ovotransferrin powder.

Consequently, in the factory, powder pasteurization is carried out in order to decrease the endogeneous flora of egg white, but this pasteurization may decrease the natural ability of egg white to resist *Salmonella* growth and may be dangerous in view of post-processing contamination.

In conclusion, this study shows the major role played by ovotransferrin and iron deficiency in *Salmonella* growth in egg white. The importance of this iron deficiency in the egg white resistance mechanism was illustrated by evaluating the consequences of egg white processing. An operation which could provide iron, denature ovotransferrin or modify iron accessibility could probably enhance *Salmonella* growth in egg white (e.g. contamination by yolk that provides iron, or pasteurization that denatures protein).

In view of these results, it will be important to investigate the effect of other technological treatments on ovotransferrin. At present, work is being carried out to test the effect of pasteurization of liquid egg white on protein and on *Salmonella* growth. Other studies have been carried out to evaluate the consequences of nutritional stress (iron deficiency) on *Salmonella* physiology, resistance to different stresses and virulence.

Acknowledgements

We thank Stéphanie Barolo, Fréderique Duval, Stéphanie Humbert, Emmanuelle Delecault, Christèle Guichet and Caroline Robles for their assistance.

References

Azari, P. and Baugh, R.F. (1967) A simple procedure for preparation of large quatities of pure ovotransferrin. *Archives in Biochemistry and Biophysics* 118, 138–144.

Blackburn, C.deW. and Davies, A.R. (1994) Development of antibiotic resistant strains for enumeration of food borne pathogenic bacteria in stored foods. *International Journal of Food Technology* 24, 125–136.

Catalano, C.R. and Knabel, J.S. (1994) Destruction of *Salmonella enteritidis* by high pH and rapid chilling during simulated commercial egg processing. *Journal of Food Protection* 57, 592–595.

Garibaldi, J.A. (1970) Role of microbial iron transport compounds in the bacteria spoilage of eggs. *Applied Microbiology* 20, 558–560.

Hartsell, S.E. (1949) The newer knowledge of lysozyme and bacteria. *Proceedings of Industrial Academic Science* 75, 44–53.

Hegg, P.O. (1978) Thermal aggregation and denaturation of egg white proteins. A model study of food protein behaviour. Doctoral dissertation. University of Lund.

Lepoutre, A., Salomon, J., Charley, C. and Le Querrc, F. (1994) Les toxi-infections alimentaires collectives en 1993. *Bulletin Epidémiologique Hebdomadaire* 52, 245–248.

Lock, J.L. and Board, R.G. (1992) Persistence of contamination of hen's egg albumen *in vitro* with *Salmonella* serotypes. *Epidemiology and Infection* 108, 389–396.

Montjoie, Y. (1993) Ovoproduits: sur un marché en croissance, la qualité est la première des exigeances. *L'Aviculteur* 540, 56–59.

Nath, K.R. and Baker, C. (1973) Factors affecting the growth of *Pseudomonas fluorescens* in liquid egg white. *Applied Microbiology* 25, 442–446.

Neilands, J.B. (1981) Iron absorption and transport in microorganisms. *Annual Review of Nutrition* 1, 27–46.

Ruzickova, V. (1994) Growth and survival of *Salmonella enteritidis* in selected egg foods. *Veterinary Medicine* 39, 187–195.

Sauter, E.A. and Petersen, G.F. (1969) The effect of egg shell quality on penetration by *Pseudomonas fluorescens*. *Poultry Science* 48, 1525–1528

Sauveur, B. (1988) Structure, composition et valeur nutritionelle de l'oeuf. In: Institut National de la Recherche Agronomique (ed.), *Reproduction des Volailles et Production d'Oeufs*. Durand, Luisant, France, Ch. 13.

Stevens, L. (1991) Mini-review, egg white proteins. *Comparative Biochemical Physiology* 100B(1), 1–9.

Valenti, P., Antonini, G., Von Hunolstein, C., Visca, P., Orsi, N. and Antonini, E. (1983) Studies on the antimicrobial activity of ovotransferrin. *International Journal of Tissues Reaction* 5(1), 97–105.

Visca, P., Filetici, E., Anastoasio, M.P., Vetriani, C., Fantasia, M. and Orsi, N. (1991) Siderophore production by *Salmonella* species isolated from different sources. *FEMS Microbiology Letters* 63, 225–231.

Yadav, N.K. and Vadehra, D.V. (1977) Mechanism of egg white resistance to bacterial growth. *Journal of Food Science* 42, 97–99.

Yamamoto, Y., Kato, E. and Ando, A. (1996) Increased antioxidative activity of ovalbumin by heat treating in an emulsion of linoleic acid. *Bioscience, Biotechnology and Biochemistry* 60(9), 1430–1433.

Salmonella enteritidis in Eggs and Egg Products: Assessing and Understanding the Risks and Responses

34

R.K. Gast

US Department of Agriculture, Agricultural Research Service, Southeast Poultry Research Laboratory, Athens, Georgia, USA

Efforts to reduce the incidence of egg-transmitted *Salmonella enteritidis* infection have included both pre-harvest and post-harvest elements. Principal control points in such endeavours have included identifying and controlling the sources of introduction of *S. enteritidis* into flocks of laying chickens, preventing the transmission of *S. enteritidis* within and between flocks, and developing and applying improved technologies for processing, storing and preparing eggs and egg products. Perhaps because diverse environmental sources (especially rodents) perpetuate a cycle of continuing re-introduction of *S. enteritidis* into poultry flocks, controlling *S. enteritidis* at the production flock level has so far proven to be more challenging than was initially anticipated. Furthermore, as egg contamination occurs very infrequently, tangible progress is difficult to document. Surveys of the incidence of *S. enteritidis* in unpasteurized liquid egg samples and in the intestinal tracts of spent laying hens, conducted by the US Department of Agriculture, indicated an increased incidence of *S. enteritidis* recovery from 1991 to 1995. Recently, many egg producers have adopted voluntary quality assurance programmes. Common features of such programmes include using chicks certified as uninfected, implementing effective pest control plans, thorough cleaning and disinfection of facilities between flocks, heightened biosecurity measures, and prompt and diligent washing and refrigeration of eggs. In some programmes, flocks are tested to verify the effectiveness of control measures. In combination with intensified efforts to ensure that eggs will be handled, prepared and consumed safely, participation in quality assurance programmes may offer the most cost-effective opportunity for achieving long-term reductions in the incidence of egg-transmitted illness due to *S. enteritidis*.

Eggs, *Salmonella* and Human Illness

Although diverse bacterial genera are found routinely on the exterior shell surfaces of eggs, and egg contents provide nutrients that can support extensive growth by a wide variety of bacterial pathogens, human disease outbreaks attributed to eggs have most often involved members of the genus *Salmonella*. For example, all egg-associated disease outbreaks in the USA between 1988 and 1992 were attributed to *Salmonella* (Bean *et al.*, 1996). Until the late 1960s, eggs were a fairly frequent source of human salmonellosis. Such outbreaks were caused by a wide range of *Salmonella* serotypes and typically were related to the use of cracked or dirty eggs or improperly processed egg products. The institution in 1970 of more stringent regulations to ensure adequate pasteurization of liquid eggs and to prevent the sale of cracked and dirty table eggs dramatically reduced the frequency of transmission of *Salmonella* by eggs. However, an international increase in the incidence of human *S. enteritidis* infections began to receive significant publicity in the late 1980s (St. Louis *et al.*, 1988). Associated with the consumption of internally contaminated clean and intact eggs, this new problem has again focused the attention of government, industry and consumers on the microbiology of eggs and egg products (Tauxe, 1997).

S. enteritidis in People and Chickens

During the past two decades, *S. enteritidis* has become an increasingly significant public health issue in many nations. Accounting for only about 5% of all human *Salmonella* isolates reported to the Centers for Disease Control in 1976, *S. enteritidis* isolates represented more than 25% of the total in the USA by the mid 1990s – more than any other single serotype (Hogue *et al.*, 1998). Similar trends have been reported in other nations (Rodrigue *et al.*, 1990; Gomez *et al.*, 1997). Although the number of *S. enteritidis* outbreaks in the USA has declined from an annual high of 77 in 1989, at least 44 outbreaks have occurred in each subsequent year. Eggs have been implicated as the source of *S. enteritidis* transmission more often than any other food vehicle (eggs are responsible for > 80% of outbreaks with an identifiable source). However, a specific source of infection has not been determined for the majority of *S. enteritidis* outbreaks (Mishu *et al.*, 1994). The potential complexity of the epidemiology of *S. enteritidis* was illustrated by the results of an investigation of a Californian egg-laying flock. Although this flock was found to be infected with phage type 4 *S. enteritidis*, it was also located downstream from a human sewage treatment plant that was releasing this same phage type of *S. enteritidis* in its effluent (Kinde *et al.*, 1996a).

The contamination of eggs is a direct consequence of some distinctive characteristics of *S. enteritidis* infections in laying chickens. Like most other *Salmonella* species, *S. enteritidis* can establish a persistent colonization of the intestinal tracts of chickens and is released back into the poultry house environment via faecal shedding (Gast and Beard, 1990a). Horizontal transmission can lead to widespread distribution of infection throughout flocks (Nakamura *et al.*, 1994, 1997). Most *S. enteritidis* strains are also highly invasive, even in mature chickens, and can disseminate to a wide range of internal tissue sites (Gast and Beard, 1990b). Systemically infected laying hens sometimes continue to harbour *S. enteritidis* for many months, and can deposit the pathogen inside eggs before oviposition (Gast and Beard, 1990a; Keller *et al.*, 1995). In a study in the UK, a diversity of *Salmonella* serotypes was found on egg shells, but only *S. enteritidis* was found within eggs (Humphrey *et al.*, 1991). This suggests that most internal contamination of eggs with *S. enteritidis* may occur independently of shell contamination. Experimental infection studies have indicated that orally inoculated hens can lay eggs with *S. enteritidis* contamination of either the yolk or albumen (Gast, 1994; Humphrey, 1994). Contaminants present on the shell can be also transferred to the edible egg contents during the breaking process.

Characteristics and Consequences of *S. enteritidis* Contamination of Eggs

Although some experimental infection studies have produced relatively high frequencies of egg contamination (Gast and Beard, 1990a), the incidence of *S. enteritidis* contamination of eggs laid by commercial flocks has generally been observed to be quite low, even from flocks known to be infected. In a field study in Pennsylvania (Schlosser *et al.*, 1995), *S. enteritidis* was found in the laying house environments of about 50% of surveyed commercial laying flocks. Only about 2.75 in 10,000 eggs from the environmentally positive flocks in this study were found to contain *S. enteritidis*. In a study of a Californian laying flock infected with phage type 4 *S. enteritidis*, the incidence of egg contamination was only about 2.28 per 10,000 (Kinde *et al.*, 1996b). Accordingly, the overall incidence of internal contamination of eggs with *S. enteritidis* is likely to be 0.01% or lower in all flocks in the USA.

Moreover, most contaminated eggs apparently contain rather small numbers of *S. enteritidis* cells. A study in the UK determined that about 95% of contaminated eggs contained fewer than ten *S. enteritidis* cells (Humphrey *et al.*, 1991). Even in eggs from hens experimentally infected with very large oral doses of *S. enteritidis*, a relatively low number of contaminants have been detected (Gast and Beard, 1992). In this latter study, even after eggs were held for 7 days at room temperature, the magnitude of the expansion in the numbers of *S. enteritidis* cells present was fairly modest. Data from the UK have likewise suggested that dangerous increases in the numbers of *S. enteritidis* contaminants in eggs may not generally occur until after the second week of storage at ambient temperatures (Humphrey and Whitehead, 1993). This type of evidence indirectly corroborates the hypothesis that most *S. enteritidis* contamination of eggs occurs in the albumen rather than inside the yolk. Deposition of bacteria within the nutrient-rich yolk should lead to rapid and dramatic multiplication, whereas the albumen contains diverse inhibitory factors that restrict microbial growth (Baron *et al.*, 1997). In a study of eggs from experimentally infected hens, *S. enteritidis* could be isolated by sampling albumen or entire yolks (including the vitelline membranes), but not by sampling only the interior contents of yolks (Gast and Beard, 1990a).

Efforts to detect *S. enteritidis* in egg contents are made significantly more difficult by both the low incidence of contamination and the generally low level of bacterial cells present. An acceptably high probability of detecting an extremely low incidence of *S. enteritidis* contamination can normally only be achieved by sampling a very large number of eggs. To keep sample sizes within manageable boundaries, this is usually achieved by pooling together the contents of 10–30 eggs for bacteriological culturing. However, studies using experimentally contaminated eggs have indicated that small numbers of *S. enteritidis* can be readily detected in egg pools only when those pools are first incubated for one or more days to allow the small initial bacterial population to expand within the larger volume of the pool (Gast, 1993a,b,c). Nutrient supplementation of these incubating egg pools can enhance microbial multiplication further to allow for more rapid detection of *S. enteritidis* by standard culturing methods (Gast and Holt, 1995a,b, 1998).

The infrequent nature of egg contamination by *S. enteritidis* has also contributed to some distinctive epidemiological trends for human disease outbreaks. Because freshly laid eggs do not often contain definitively dangerous numbers of *S. enteritidis* cells, most outbreaks have involved temperature abuse that facilitates bacterial multiplication. Cross-contamination involving additional kitchen surfaces and foods, and cooking methods inadequate to destroy all bacteria present can also be the causes of the outbreaks (Lin *et al.*, 1988; Boyce *et al.*, 1996). Such improper practices have especially severe consequences in commercial or institutional kitchens that serve large numbers of people. Only a relatively small percentage of *S. enteritidis* outbreaks have been reported to occur in private homes. Nearly 60% of *S. enteritidis* outbreaks in the USA between 1985 and 1991 were associated with restaurants or similar establishments (Mishu *et al.*, 1994).

Controlling *S. enteritidis*

The typically low incidence and level of *S. enteritidis* contamination of eggs also influences the prospects for success of the various approaches in preventing human illness caused by this pathogen. Efforts to decrease the frequency of egg-transmitted *S. enteritidis* infection have been focused both on reducing the incidence of *S. enteritidis* in commercial egg-laying flocks and on developing methods for safely processing, storing and preparing eggs and egg-containing foods. Because the frequency of egg contamination associated with commercial flocks is already very low, attacking the problem by controlling *S. enteritidis* infections in laying flocks is likely to yield tangible results far more slowly than can be accomplished by concentrating on how eggs are handled and cooked. Opportunities for effective action at this latter level include optimizing egg wash water temperature and replacement rates, the use of eggshell sanitizers, improved refrigeration technologies and wider application of pasteurization and pasteurized products. Nevertheless, because the preponderance of resources committed to *S. enteritidis* control to date have been focused on flocks of egg-laying chickens, the remainder of the present discussion will be devoted to this arena.

Opportunities for Controlling *S. enteritidis* in Egg-laying Flocks

Potential 'critical control points' for reducing the incidence of *S. enteritidis* infections in commercial egg-producing chickens (thereby also the incidence of production of contaminated eggs) can be assigned to two principal categories. The first category involves issues related to eliminating the sources and reservoirs of *S. enteritidis* in poultry flocks and facilities. Important sources and reservoirs of *S. enteritidis* in laying flocks include the replacement chicks themselves (as a result of vertical transmission of the pathogen from breeder flocks and horizontal transmission in the hatchery), the poultry house environment, rodents and other pests, and feed. A large-scale field study of commercial flocks in Pennsylvania (Schlosser *et al.*, 1995) determined that the presence of *S. enteritidis* in the laying house environment was strongly correlated with the likelihood that a flock would produce contaminated eggs. This study also reported that cleaning and disinfection could only successfully remove *S. enteritidis* contamination from about 50% of environmentally positive houses. These researchers further noted that environmentally positive poultry houses often had heavy mouse infestations (these mice were often infected with the same phage type of *S. enteritidis* found in the environment, chickens and eggs). Rodent control was the only management practice that these investigators found to correlate strongly with a diminished probability of finding *S. enteritidis* in the house environment.

The second category of opportunities for controlling *S. enteritidis* in laying flocks involves issues related to pathogen transmission within and between flocks. Such transmission can be mediated or influenced by direct contact between birds, vectors (both biological and physical), fomites (the various materials and surfaces within houses), air movement and factors that affect the susceptibility of chickens to infection. Airborne movement of contaminated dust and aerosols can result in the dissemination of *S. enteritidis* between groups of chickens not in direct contact with each other (Gast *et al.*, 1998; Holt *et al.*, 1998). Recent research has provided some useful insight about methods designed to reduce the susceptibility of chickens to *S. enteritidis*. Vaccination of pullets or hens (using either killed or live vaccine preparations) can significantly reduce the undesirable consequences of exposure to *S. enteritidis*, including faecal shedding, organ invasion and egg contamination (Gast *et al.*, 1992, 1993; Cooper *et al.*, 1994). However, vaccination does not generally provide an impenetrable barrier against infection and is particularly vulnerable in the face of very high challenge doses of *S. enteritidis*. Colonization control, by prophylactic administration of bacterial cultures that competitively exclude *Salmonella* from the intestinal tract, has been quite useful in immature broiler chickens that have not yet acquired their own protective gut flora. However, it is of questionable relevance for protecting mature laying hens against environmentally acquired *S. enteritidis*. Another important susceptibility issue has been highlighted by research showing that the forced moulting of laying hens by feed deprivation can increase the frequency, transmission and severity of *S. enteritidis* infections (Holt, 1993, 1995; Macri *et al.*, 1997).

Regulatory Efforts to Control *S. enteritidis* in Poultry

From 1990 until 1995, the US Department of Agriculture administered a trace-back testing programme in an effort to eradicate *S. enteritidis* in commercial laying flocks (USDA, 1991; Hogue *et al.*, 1998). When eggs were implicated as the source of a human *S. enteritidis* outbreak, and when the laying flock that produced those eggs could be identified, a two-tiered testing strategy was employed. First, environmental samples were collected from the implicated houses and tested for the presence of *S. enteritidis*. If any environmental samples were positive, internal tissues from selected hens were then removed and cultured to detect *S. enteritidis*. Positive results in this second tier of testing led to restrictions on releasing eggs into the table egg market (thus forcing the managers of such flocks to choose between diverting their eggs for pasteurization and depopulating the affected laying houses). Producers were not indemnified or compensated for any costs or losses in income that resulted from the application of this trace-back programme.

During the life span of the trace-back programme, 304 *S. enteritidis* outbreaks occurred, eggs were implicated in 96 of these, and these eggs could be traced to 38 laying flocks. As a consequence of trace-back testing, 31 flocks were restricted, nearly 9 million layers were voluntarily depopulated, and more than 1 billion eggs were diverted for pasteurization. However, during this same time period, the overall incidence of *S. enteritidis* in poultry and eggs apparently continued to rise. National surveys performed by USDA indicated that the overall frequency at which *S. enteritidis* was found in faecal samples from spent laying hens (collected at slaughter plants) increased from 27% in 1991 to 45% in 1995 (Ebel *et al.*, 1992, 1993; Hogue *et al.*, 1997). Similar USDA national surveys of the presence of *S. enteritidis* in samples of unpasteurized liquid eggs (collected at breaking plants) showed an overall increase from 13% in 1991 to 19% in 1995 (Ebel *et al.*, 1992, 1993; Hogue *et al.*, 1997). The evident failure of the reactive trace-back approach may have been due to its inability to keep pace with an evolving problem. A strategy based on eliminating a presumably small number of infected flocks was ultimately ineffective in resisting the continuous re-introduction of *S. enteritidis* into poultry flocks from diverse environmental sources.

Quality Assurance and Risk Reduction for Controlling *S. enteritidis* in Poultry

In recent years, voluntary microbial quality assurance programmes have been developed and implemented by many of the egg-producing states to reduce the likelihood that contaminated eggs will be laid by their flocks. Common risk reduction features of such programmes include using only chicks from source flocks certified as uninfected, implementing effective plans for controlling pests (especially rodents), thorough cleaning and disinfection of facilities between flocks, heightened biosecurity measures, and prompt and diligent washing and refrigeration of eggs. In some quality assurance programmes, environmental samples and eggs are tested for *S. enteritidis*, and participating producers are required to divert eggs from positive flocks for pasteurization

(Hogue *et al.*, 1998). Because of the potential negative economic consequences of the testing/diversion strategy for controlling *S. enteritidis*, flock testing requirements are unpopular with many egg producers. However, another long-term role for testing is often ignored in this debate.

Testing results provide essential verification of the effectiveness of control programmes and their components, thereby ensuring that the commitment of resources to risk reduction efforts is cost effective. In this context, the principal purpose of testing (and the corresponding target for remedial action when test results are positive) might eventually become to evaluate the efficacy of quality assurance programmes rather than to assess the risk posed by individual flocks or their eggs. Thorough knowledge of the likely sources and reservoirs of *S. enteritidis* infections in laying flocks should help increase confidence in the usefulness of particular risk reduction practices. Eventually, it may thus be possible to streamline testing objectives to focus on simply identifying flocks in which the risk reduction strategy in use has somehow failed. Easily automated screening methods such as testing for egg yolk antibodies may offer rapid and affordable alternatives for identifying flocks that have been exposed to *S. enteritidis* (Gast and Beard, 1991; Gast *et al.*, 1997a,b).

Conclusions

Because of the relatively low incidence and level of *S. enteritidis* contamination of eggs, ensuring that eggs are processed, handled and prepared safely will probably provide the best short-term protection for consumers. Nevertheless, long-term goals of reducing the production of eggs contaminated by *S. enteritidis* are also likely to be attainable by patient and persistent application of risk reduction programmes of verified effectiveness. In 1992, before initiation of their state's egg quality assurance programme, 38% of 47 surveyed commercial laying flocks in Pennsylvania were environmentally positive. After 3 years of participation in this plan, *S. enteritidis* was found in the environments of only 12% of these same flocks (White *et al.*, 1997).

References

Baron, F., Gautier, M. and Brule, G. (1997) Factors involved in the inhibition of growth of *Salmonella enteritidis* in liquid egg white. *Journal of Food Protection* 60, 1318–1323.

Bean, N.H., Goulding, J.S., Lao, C. and Angulo, F.J. (1996) Surveillance for foodborne-disease outbreaks – United States, 1988–1992. *Morbid, Mortal, Weekly Report* 45, 1–55.

Boyce, T.G., Koo, D., Swerdlow, D.L., Gomez, T.M., Serrano, B., Nickey, L.N., Hickman-Brenner, F.W., Malcolm, G.B. and Griffin. P.M. (1996) Recurrent outbreak of *Salmonella enteritidis* infections in a Texas restaurant: phage type 4 arrives in the United States. *Epidemiology and Infection* 117, 29–34.

Cooper, G.L., Venables, L.M., Woodward, M.J. and Hormaeche, C.E. (1994) Vaccination of chickens with strain CVL30, a genetically defined *Salmonella enteritidis aroA* live oral vaccine candidate. *Infection and Immunity* 62, 4747–4754.

Ebel, E.D., David, M.J. and Mason, J. (1992) Occurrence of *Salmonella enteritidis* in the US commercial egg industry: report on a national spent hen survey. *Avian Diseases* 36, 646–654.

Ebel, E.D., Mason, J., Thomas, L.A., Ferris, K.E., Beckman, M.G., Cummins, D.R., Scroeder-Tucker, L., Sutherlin, W.D., Glasshoff, R.L. and Smithhisler, N.M. (1993) Occurrence of *Salmonella enteritidis* in unpasteurized liquid egg in the United States. *Avian Diseases* 37, 135–142.

Gast, R.K. (1993a) Recovery of *Salmonella enteritidis* from inoculated pools of egg contents. *Journal of Food Protection* 56, 21–24.

Gast, R.K. (1993b) Detection of *Salmonella enteritidis* in experimentally infected laying hens by culturing pools of egg contents. *Poultry Science* 72, 267–274.

Gast, R.K. (1993c) Evaluation of direct plating for detecting *Salmonella enteritidis* in pools of egg contents. *Poultry Science* 72, 1611–1614.

Gast, R.K. (1994) Understanding *Salmonella enteritidis* in laying chickens: the contributions of experimental infections. *International Journal of Food Microbiology* 21, 107–116.

Gast, R.K. and Beard, C.W. (1990a) Production of *Salmonella enteritidis*-contaminated eggs by experimentally infected hens. *Avian Diseases* 34, 438–446.

Gast, R.K. and Beard, C.W. (1990b) Isolation of *Salmonella enteritidis* from internal organs of experimentally infected hens. *Avian Diseases* 34, 991–993.

Gast, R.K. and Beard, C.W. (1991) Detection of *Salmonella* serogroup D-specific antibodies in the yolks of eggs laid by hens infected with *Salmonella enteritidis*. *Poultry Science* 70, 1273–1276.

Gast, R.K. and Beard, C.W. (1992) Detection and enumeration of *Salmonella enteritidis* in fresh and stored eggs laid by experimentally infected hens. *Journal of Food Protection* 55, 152–156.

Gast, R.K. and Holt, P.S. (1995a) Iron supplementation to enhance the recovery of *Salmonella enteritidis* from pools of egg contents. *Journal of Food Protection* 58, 268–272.

Gast, R.K. and Holt, P.S. (1995b) Differences in the multiplication of *Salmonella enteritidis* strains in liquid whole egg: implications for detecting contaminated eggs from commercial laying flocks. *Poultry Science* 74, 893–897.

Gast, R.K. and Holt, P.S. (1998) Supplementing pools of egg contents with concentrated enrichment media to improve rapid detection of *Salmonella enteritidis*. *Journal of Food Protection* 61, 107–109.

Gast, R.K., Stone, H.D., Holt, P.S. and Beard, C.W. (1992) Evaluation of the efficacy of an oil-emulsion bacterin for protecting chickens against *Salmonella enteritidis*. *Avian Diseases* 36, 992–999.

Gast, R.K., Stone, H.D. and Holt, P.S. (1993) Evaluation of the efficacy of oil-emulsion bacterins for reducing fecal shedding of *Salmonella enteritidis* by laying hens. *Avian Diseases* 37, 1085–1091.

Gast, R.K., Porter, R.E., Jr and Holt, P.S. (1997a) Applying tests for specific yolk antibodies to predict contamination by *Salmonella enteritidis* in eggs from experimentally infected laying hens. *Avian Diseases* 41, 195–202.

Gast, R.K., Porter, R.E., Jr and Holt, P.S. (1997b) Assessing the sensitivity of egg yolk antibody testing for detecting *Salmonella enteritidis* infections in laying hens. *Poultry Science* 76, 798–801.

Gast, R.K., Mitchell, B.W. and Holt, P.S. (1998) Airborne transmission of *Salmonella enteritidis* infection between groups of chicks in controlled-environment isolation cabinets. *Avian Diseases* 42, 315–320.

Gomez, T.M., Motarjemi, Y., Miyagawa, S., Käferstein, F.K. and Stöhr, K. (1997) Food-borne salmonellosis. *World Health Statistics Quarterly* 50, 81–89.

Hogue, A.T., Ebel, E.D., Thomas, L.A., Schlosser, W., Bufano, N. and Ferris, K. (1997) Surveys of *Salmonella enteritidis* in unpasteurized liquid egg and spent hens at slaughter. *Journal of Food Protection* 60, 1194–1200.

Hogue, A., White, P., Guard-Petter, J., Schlosser, W., Gast, R., Ebel, E., Farrar, I., Gomez, T., Madden, J., Madison, M., McNamara, A.M., Morales, R., Parham, D., Sparling, P., Sutherlin, W. and Swerdlow, D. (1998) Epidemiology and control of egg-associated *Salmonella enteritidis* in the United States of America. *Revue Scientifique et Technique, Office International des Épizooties* 16, 542–553.

Holt, P.S. (1993) Effect of induced molting on the susceptibility of white leghorn hens to a *Salmonella enteritidis* infection. *Avian Diseases* 37, 412–417.

Holt, P.S. (1995) Horizontal transmission of *Salmonella enteritidis* in molted and unmolted laying chickens. *Avian Diseases* 39, 239–249.

Holt, P.S., Mitchell, B.W. and Gast, R.K. (1998) Airborne horizontal transmission of *Salmonella enteritidis* in molted laying chickens. *Avian Diseases* 42, 45–52.

Humphrey, T.J. (1994) Contamination of egg shell and contents with *Salmonella enteritidis*: a review. *International Journal of Food Microbiology* 21, 31–40.

Humphrey, T.J. and Whitehead, A. (1993) Egg age and the growth of *Salmonella enteritidis* in egg contents. *Epidemiology and Infection* 111, 209–291.

Humphrey, T.J., Whitehead, A., Gawler, A.H.L., Henley, A. and Rowe, B. (1991) Numbers of *Salmonella enteritidis* in the contents of naturally contaminated hens' eggs. *Epidemiology and Infection* 106, 489–496.

Keller, L.H., Benson, C.E., Krotec, K. and Eckroade, R.J. (1995) *Salmonella enteritidis* colonization of the reproductive tract and forming and freshly laid eggs of chickens. *Infection and Immunity* 63, 2443–2449.

Kinde, H., Read, D.H., Ardans, A., Breitmeyer, R.E., Willoughby, D., Little, H.E., Kerr, D., Gireesh, R. and Nagaraja, K.V. (1996a) Sewage effluent: likely source of *Salmonella enteritidis*, phage type 4 infection in a commercial chicken layer flock in southern California. *Avian Diseases* 40, 672–676.

Kinde, H., Read, D.H., Chin, R.P., Bickford, A.A., Walker, R.L., Ardans, A., Breitmeyer, R.E., Willoughby, D., Little, H.E., Kerr, D. and Gardner, I.A. (1996b) *Salmonella enteritidis*, phage type 4 infection in a commercial layer flock in Southern California: bacteriological and epidemiologic findings. *Avian Diseases* 40, 665–671.

Lin, F.-Y.C., Morris, J.G., Jr, Trump, D., Tilghman, D., Wood, P.K., Jackman, N., Israel, E. and Libonati, J.P. (1988) Investigation of an outbreak of *Salmonella enteritidis* gastroenteritis associated with consumption of eggs in a restaurant chain in Maryland. *American Journal of Epidemiology* 128, 839–844.

Macri, N.P., Porter, R.E. and Holt, P.S. (1997) The effects of induced molting on the severity of acute intestinal inflammation caused by *Salmonella enteritidis*. *Avian Diseases* 41, 117–124.

Mishu, B., Koehler, J., Lee, L.A., Rodrigue, D., Brenner, F.H., Blake, P. and Tauxe, R.V. (1994) Outbreaks of *Salmonella enteritidis* infections in the United States, 1985–1991. *Journal of Infectious Disease* 169, 547–552.

Nakamura, M., Nagamine, N., Takahashi, T., Suzuki, S., Kijima, M., Tamura, Y. and Sato, S. (1994) Horizontal transmission of *Salmonella enteritidis* and effect of stress on shedding in laying hens. *Avian Diseases* 38, 282–288.

Nakamura, M., Takagi, M., Takashi, T., Suzuki, S., Sato, S. and Takehara, K. (1997) The effect of the flow of air on horizontal transmission of *Salmonella enteritidis* in chickens. *Avian Diseases* 41, 354–360.

Rodrigue, D.C., Tauxe, R.V. and Rowe, B. (1990) International increase in *Salmonella enteritidis*: a new pandemic? *Epidemiology and Infection* 105, 21–27.

Schlosser, W., Henzler, D., Mason, J., Hurd, S., Trock, S., Sischo, W., Kradel, D. and Hogue, A. (1995) *Salmonella enteritidis Pilot Project Progress Report*. US Government Printing, Washington, DC.

St. Louis, M.E., Morse, D.L., Potter, M.E., DeMelfi, T.M., Guzewich, J.J., Tauxe, R.V. and Blake, P.A. (1988) The emergence of Grade A eggs as a major source of *Salmonella enteritidis* infections. New implications for the control of salmonellosis. *Journal of the American Medical Association* 259, 2103–2107.

Tauxe, R.V. (1997) Emerging foodborne diseases: an evolving public health challenge. *Dairy, Food Environmental Sanitation* 17, 788–795.

US Department of Agriculture (1991) Rules and regulations: chickens affected by *Salmonella enteritidis*. *Federal Register* 56, 3730–3743.

White, P.L., Schlosser, W., Benson, C.E., Maddox, C. and Hogue, A. (1997) Environmental survey by manure drag sampling for *Salmonella enteritidis* in chicken layer houses. *Journal of Food Protection* 60, 1189–1193.

Egg and Serum Cholesterol as Influenced by Mannan Oligosaccharide and Aflatoxin

35

V.G. Stanley[1] and A.E. Sefton[2]

[1]Prairie View A&M University, Prairie View, Texas, USA;
[2]Alltech Inc., Guelph, Ontario, Canada

Mannan oligosaccharide has been shown to counteract many of the negative effects of aflatoxin in poultry. As liver size increases in the presence of aflatoxin, it was of interest to look at the combined effects of mannan oligosaccharide (Bio-Mos, Alltech) and aflatoxin. Sixty 18-month-old laying hens were assigned randomly to a 2×2 factorial experiment (aflatoxin (0 or 3 p.p.m.) and Bio-Mos (0 or 0.1% of the 17% crude protein layer ration)). Aflatoxin increased egg and serum total cholesterol, while Bio-Mos lowered egg and blood total cholesterol as compared with the control. Bio-Mos counteracted the effect of aflatoxin on egg total cholesterol, but not serum total cholesterol. Similarly, aflatoxin increased serum low-density lipoprotein (LDL) cholesterol, while Bio-Mos reduced serum LDL cholesterol. Bio-Mos was unable to counteract the effect of aflatoxin on serum LDL cholesterol. Bio-Mos reduced total egg cholesterol by 22% in the presence of aflatoxin and by 11% in the absence of aflatoxin.

Introduction

The initial observation of Stanley *et al.* (1993) that yeast culture counteracts the negative effects of aflatoxin has been confirmed and expanded by several other groups. Devegowda *et al.* (1994) confirmed that *Saccharomyces cervisiae* reduced liver enlargement in the presence of aflatoxin and showed immune system benefits. Savage and Zakrzewska (1996) and Savage *et al.* (1997) reported that yeast-based mannan oligosaccharide enhanced poult performance as well as increasing immunoglobulin production. Cotter and Weinner (1997) showed yeast-based mannan oligosaccharide to modulate the immune system.

It was therefore of interest to determine the effect of this product on the serum and egg cholesterol levels.

© CAB *International* 2000. *Egg Nutrition and Biotechnology*
(eds J.S. Sim, S. Nakai and W. Guenter)

Experimental Method

Sixty 18-month-old commercial laying hens at 60% production were fed diets containing aflatoxin (0 or 3 p.p.m.), and Bio-Mos (Alltech, Inc., Nicholasville, Kentucky) (0 and 0.1%) using a 2×2 factorial design in order to examine the effects on egg and serum cholesterol. They were fed a 17% crude protein, 2800 kcal kg^{-1} maize/soy layer ration for a 1 week adjustment period. The experimental rations were based on the same formula, but dietary treatments were introduced for the 5-week experimental period. Eggs were collected daily and analysed for cholesterol. Complete egg cholesterol data were available only for the first 4 weeks. At the end of the experimental period, hens were weighed and blood samples collected for serum analysis. Livers were extracted and analysed for cholesterol and total protein.

Results and Discussion

Bio-Mos tended to reduce the serum and egg cholesterol level over the treatment period (Figs 35.1 and 35.2), while aflatoxin increased both serum and egg cholesterol. Bio-Mos in the presence of aflatoxin was able to reduce egg cholesterol but not serum cholesterol. This was true whether the comparison was made with the negative control or the aflatoxin treatment. It is of interest that the serum low-density lipoprotein (LDL) cholesterol changes are in the same direction as are the changes in total serum cholesterol.

Based on these findings, egg producers need to avoid as much as possible the use of aflatoxin-contaminated feeds, especially when producing low cholesterol eggs. The use of Bio-Mos would be of benefit in the production of low cholesterol eggs in both the presence and absence of aflatoxin.

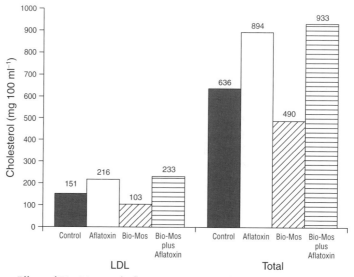

Fig. 35.1.   Effect of Bio-Mos and aflatoxin on serum cholesterol levels.

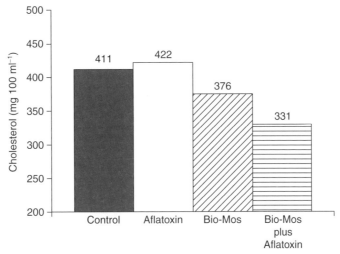

Fig. 35.2.   Effect of Bio-Mos and aflatoxin on average egg cholesterol levels.

References

Cotter, P.F. and Weinner, J. (1997) Bio-Mos modulates the phytohemagglutinin wattle reaction in commercial pullets. *Poultry Science* 76 (Suppl. 1), 111.

Devegowda, G., Aravind, B.I.R., Rajendra, K.M., Morton, G., Baburathna, A. and Sudarshan, C. (1994) A biological approach to counteract aflatoxicosis in broiler chickens and ducklings by the use of *Saccharomyces cerevisiae* cultures in the feed. In: Lyons, T.P. and Jacques, K.A. (eds), *Biotechnology in the Feed Industry, Proceedings of Alltech's 10th Annual Symposium.* Nottingham University Press, Nottingham, UK, pp. 235–245.

Savage, T.F. and Zakrzewska, E.I. (1996) Performance of male turkeys to 8 weeks of age when fed an oligosaccharide derived from yeast cells. *Poultry Science* 74 (Suppl. 1), 53.

Savage, T.F., Zakrzewska E.I. and Andreasen, J.R. (1997) The effects of feeding mannan oligosaccharide supplemented diets to poults on performance and morphology of the small intestine. *Poultry Science* 76 (Suppl. 1), 139.

Stanley, V.G., Woldesenbet, R.O.S., Hutchinson, D.H. and Kubena, L.F. (1993) The use of *Saccharomyces cervisiae* to suppress the effects of aflatoxicosis in broiler chicks. *Poultry Science* 72, 1867–1872.

Shell Eggs

Eggshell Proteins and Shell Strength: Molecular Biology of Eggshell Matrix Proteins and Industry Applications

36

M.T. Hincke[1], M. St Maurice[1], Y. Nys[2],
J. Gautron[2], M. Panheleux[2], C.P.W. Tsang[3],
M.M. Bain[4], S.E. Solomon[4] and M.D. McKee[5]

[1]*Department of Cellular and Molecular Medicine, Faculty of Medicine, University of Ottawa, Ottawa, Ontario, Canada;* [2]*INRA, Station de Recherches Avicoles, Nouzilly, France;* [3]*Agriculture Canada, Central Experimental Farm, Ottawa, Canada;* [4]*Glasgow University Veterinary School, Poultry Research Group, Glasgow, UK;* [5]*Faculty of Dentistry, McGill University, Montreal, Quebec, Canada*

The chicken eggshell is a composite biomaterial in which the soluble and insoluble protein components (termed matrix proteins) pervade the mineral phase, and are thought to modify significantly the mechanical and structural properties of the resulting material. Eggshell formation is spatially and temporally controlled; there is a specific sequence to the appearance of eggshell matrix proteins in the uterine fluid, which corresponds to the initiation, growth and terminal phases of shell formation. Matrix proteins exhibit distinct localization patterns in the mammillary and palisade layers of the shell. Certain of these matrix proteins are eggshell specific (i.e. ovocleidin-17), while others are also found in egg white (ovalbumin, lysozyme and ovotransferrin), or in bone (osteopontin and serum albumin). We have demonstrated that ovocleidin-17 and ovalbumin are conserved in eggshell from a number of avian species, suggesting that they play a fundamental role in the process of eggshell formation. Consistent with this hypothesis is our observation that the level of ovocleidin-17 protein in mammillary knobs is inversely correlated with shell quality. It is of great interest to purify eggshell matrix proteins that modify calcium carbonate precipitation and therefore may influence eggshell mineralization. A partially purified protein fraction containing osteopontin was found to inhibit calcium carbonate precipitation strongly, suggesting that this protein, as well as others that remain to be characterized, regulate calcium carbonate precipitation during eggshell formation. The goal of our studies is to obtain insight into the process of eggshell mineralization. This information will assist the egg-producing industry in developing solutions to the problem of eggshell breakage and downgraded eggs (cracks).

Introduction

Background

In spite of a great deal of basic research into calcium metabolism and eggshell formation, the problem of weak or poor quality eggshell remains a significant factor in the egg-producing industry. The incidence of eggshell breakage and downgraded eggs (cracks) remains elevated despite improvements in shell quality by manipulation of nutritional, environmental and genetic factors. Furthermore, a decrease in eggshell quality is observed as hens approach the end of the laying period. Estimates of total losses due to breakage range from 7–8% (Hamilton, 1982) to 13–20% (Roland, 1988). Canada C eggs (cracks) represented about 2.5% of all eggs that were graded in Canada in 1994, i.e. 143 million eggs (Todd, 1996). Such eggs are considered to be hazardous because their contents are exposed to bacterial pathogens, and they may be used in products that are not thoroughly cooked. It has been estimated that about 10,500 cases of salmonellosis occur each year in Canada due to consumption of Canada C eggs or products made with these eggs (Todd, 1996). A better knowledge of the process of eggshell mineralization will help in developing solutions to these problems.

Eggshell structure

The mineralized portion of the avian eggshell is subdivided into an outer palisade layer and an inner mammillary knob layer. The mammillary knobs are an array of rounded cones on the inner surface of the mineralized shell, to the tips of which the fibrous shell membranes are attached and penetrate (Parsons, 1982; Hamilton, 1986; Burley and Vadehra, 1989; Dennis *et al.*, 1996). The palisade layer of mineral extends about 200 μm from the bases of the mammillary knobs towards the surface of the shell. This layer is formed mainly by calcium carbonate with the (001) plane of the calcite crystals parallel to the surface of the shell (i.e. the *c*-axis of the crystals is perpendicular to the surface) (Silyn-Roberts and Sharp, 1986). The palisade layer terminates in a vertical prismatic layer that is covered by the cuticle. The eggshell is 94% calcite, 4% organic components (proteins), and contains a variety of other elements, of which magnesium (0.4%) and phosphorus (0.4%) are the most elevated. The phosphorus is concentrated in the superficial layer of the shell, where spherical aggregates of fine needles of hydroxyapatite are found in the inner cuticle layer (Dennis *et al.*, 1996). Complex mixtures of glycoproteins, proteoglycans and mucopolysaccharides are differentially distributed between the mammillary and palisade layers (Baker and Balch, 1962; Abatangelo *et al.*, 1978; Parsons, 1982; Eckert *et al.*, 1986; Arias *et al.*, 1992; Hincke *et al.*, 1992; Fernandez *et al.*, 1997). X-ray studies of the avian shell suggest that the matrix content is positively correlated with shell strength (Silyn-Roberts and Sharp, 1986; Simkiss and Wilbur, 1989).

Eggshell formation

The egg sequentially acquires the shell as it passes through different regions of the oviduct. The protein components of the egg white are secreted in the magnum, and then the cells of the white isthmus secrete the shell membranes. When the egg reaches the distal part of the isthmus (red isthmus), the mammillary knobs begin to form at discrete nucleation sites upon the surface of the outer shell membrane. The epithelial cells found here secrete the organic material of the mammillary cores (Wyburn *et al.*, 1973). The egg then passes into the shell gland (uterus), where it remains for 18–20 h during mineralization of the eggshell. The initiation of mineralization at the sites of origin of the individual mammillary knobs has given rise to the hypothesis that these are epitactic centres that initiate calcification (Creger *et al.*, 1976; Stemberger *et al.*, 1977). This proposal would account for the observed correlation between shell quality and the uniformity, density and shape of mammillary knobs (reviewed in Parsons, 1982; Hamilton, 1986; Bain, 1992). Using morphological criteria, investigators have defined different subregions of the mammillary knobs, to which various functional properties have been attributed (reviewed in Dieckert *et al.*, 1989; Dennis *et al.*, 1996).

Role of uterine fluid in eggshell formation

The uterine fluid contains high levels of ionized calcium and bicarbonate, such that calcium carbonate is present at 50–60 times its solubility product (Nys *et al.*, 1989). This supersaturated solution also contains a rich variety of proteins that we have demonstrated are the precursors of the matrix proteins that become incorporated into the eggshell. The protein components of the uterine fluid vary according to the stage of shell formation (Gautron *et al.*, 1997a), suggesting that they have specialized functions at different phases of mineralization. Uterine fluid sampled at precise stages of shell formation contains protein activity that strongly influences the precipitation of calcium carbonate; this activity is highest in uterine fluid collected during the growth and terminal phase of shell formation (Gautron *et al.*, 1996, 1997a). Crystallization studies with dialysed uterine fluid reveal that the proteins also exert a dramatic effect upon the size and morphology of calcite crystals grown *in vitro*. Such modifications of crystal growth are also seen with total extracts of eggshell matrix protein following decalcification (Gautron *et al.*, 1996). These effects must be due to interactions between calcium carbonate and matrix proteins that are relevant to eggshell formation.

Eggshell Matrix Proteins

The protein components of biomineralized structures (matrix proteins) influence the properties of the final structure of calcium phosphate (hydroxylapatite) or calcium carbonate (calcite) by modulating crystal nucleation and growth (Mann, 1988; Lowenstam and Weiner, 1989; Addadi and Weiner, 1992). These mechanisms are not well understood, but may involve inhibition of crystal growth on specific crystallographic faces, due to specific interactions between binding sites on organic molecules and calcium carbonate (Krampitz and Graser, 1988; Weiner and Addadi, 1991; Mann *et al.*, 1993). This view is based on experiments with simple organic molecules, and with mixtures of proteins from decalcified molluscan shell (Addadi *et al.*, 1987; Mann *et al.*, 1988; Addadi and Weiner, 1992). The view is supported by studies demonstrating that different preparations of molluscan shell matrix proteins can reproducibly specify either the calcite or aragonite crystal forms of calcium carbonate (Falini *et al.*, 1996).

Our work over the past number of years has led to the identification of a number of the matrix proteins that are found in the eggshell of the domestic hen (Table 36.1), while a large number remain to be characterized. This has been done by purifying soluble matrix proteins after eggshell decalcification using chromatographic methods and gel electrophoresis, coupled with comparative analysis of the protein components of the uterine fluid at different stages of shell calcification. Microsequencing to obtain N-terminal amino acid sequences allows unambiguous identification of certain proteins (i.e. egg white proteins, osteopontin and serum albumin). In other cases, database searching reveals that certain proteins are as yet unknown. For example, our sequencing data for ovocleidin-17 (OC-17) (50 residues of N-terminal sequence and 24 residues of internal sequence) reveals that there is no strong homology with any protein in the NIH database.

OC-17 was the first matrix protein which we purified because our early work showed that it is the most abundant protein component of the soluble eggshell extract after decalcification (Hincke *et al.*, 1993, 1995). Our studies of the purified protein indicate that it aggregates at physiological pH and ionic strength, and readily precipitates. In addition, it co-purifies with osteopontin during preparative procedures. Immunohistochemistry reveals that OC-17 is present in the mammillary knobs and also throughout the palisade layer. Immunolocalization by electron microscopy demonstrates that within the palisade layer it is associated with 'sheets' of flocculent organic matrix (Fig. 36.1). Our current hypothesis is that OC-17 is a self-assembling protein scaffold that interacts with other matrix proteins in order to form a three-dimensional organic lattice that modulates calcite crystal growth.

The non-collagenous bone protein osteopontin is also present in the eggshell matrix (Pines *et al.*, 1996; Panheleux *et al.*, 1997). Osteopontin is expressed in the uterine epithelium in a circadian fashion, and is only found during the period of eggshell calcification (Pines *et al.*, 1996). This protein is thought to play a fundamental role in bone formation where it probably acts

Table 36.1. Summary of identified eggshell matrix proteins.

	Type of matrix protein	
1.	Eggshell specific	Ovocleidin-17
2.	Bone proteins	Osteopontin, serum albumin
3.	Egg white proteins	Ovalbumin, ovotransferrin, lysozyme
4.	Proteoglycans	Keratan sulphate, dermatan sulphate

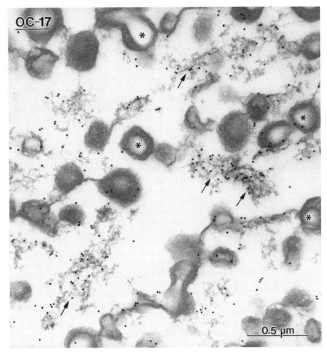

Fig. 36.1. Ultrastructural localization of OC-17 in the palisade layer by transmission electron microscopy. Post-embedding colloidal gold immunocytochemistry was performed as previously described (McKee and Nanci, 1995) to localize OC-17 in the organic matrix of eggshell from White Leghorn birds. In the palisade region, immuno-labelling is associated predominantly with sheets of flocculent organic matrix (arrows) intermingling with numerous vesicular structures (*).

as an inhibitor of calcium phosphate accretion by regulating crystal growth. In eggshell, it is not localized with the hydroxyapatite crystallites of the inner cuticle layer, but co-localizes in the palisade layer together with OC-17 immunoreactivity (McKee *et al.*, 1997a,b).

In addition to novel eggshell-specific proteins and osteopontin, a number of previously identified proteins are also present in the eggshell matrix. Certain egg white proteins (ovalbumin, ovotransferrin and lysozyme) are localized by immunofluorescence to the mammillary knobs where they are intramineral (Hincke, 1995; Hincke *et al.*, 1996; Gautron *et al.*, 1997; Panheleux *et al.*, 1997). Intense lysozyme and ovotransferrin immunoreactivity is additionally seen at the level of the shell membranes by immunofluorescence, which is not the case for ovalbumin. However, ultrastructural localization reveals that substantial ovalbumin immunoreactivity is present in the shell membrane, but only in the cores of the fibres and not in the mantle (Fig. 36.2). Reverse transcription–polymerase chain reaction (RT–PCR) data using ovalbumin-, lysozyme- and ovotransferrin-specific primers indicate that their messages are expressed in the white and red isthmus where the protein precursors of the shell membranes and mammillary cores are synthesized and secreted, respectively

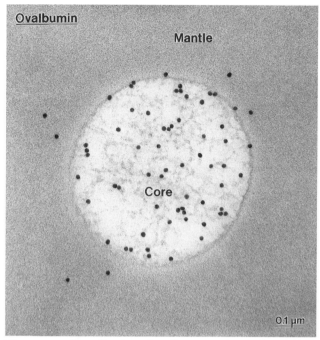

Fig. 36.2.   Ultrastructural localization of ovalbumin in the shell membranes. Immunocytochemical colloidal gold labelling for ovalbumin shows its incorporation into the core of the shell membrane fibres.

(i.e. lysozyme, Fig. 36.3). This evidence suggests that the egg white proteins detected in these structures are *not* a non-specific contamination by the luminal material secreted by the magnum. These proteins may represent a microbial defence mechanism, or exert a specific effect upon mineralization and shell formation. These possibilities are currently under investigation.

Cross-species comparison of eggshell matrix components reveals that some of these proteins (i.e. OC-17 and ovalbumin) are conserved in eggshell from a number of avian species, suggesting that they play a fundamental role in the process of eggshell formation (Panheleux *et al.*, 1999).

Correlation of eggshell matrix proteins with shell quality

We have used OC-17-specific antibodies to explore a possible correlation between shell quality and levels of matrix proteins in eggshell. This approach, performed at the University of Glasgow, involved immunogold labelling at the electron microscopic level, and counting the number of gold particles per unit area that are found in different zones. Shell quality was assessed in a semi-quantitative manner, following plasma etching to remove organic material, according to the incidence of each of 12 structural variants associated with the mammillary layer (Bain, 1992). The overall ultrastructural integrity of the shell is expressed in terms of a total score which comprises: (i) the summation of each of the individual scores assigned to structural variants such as

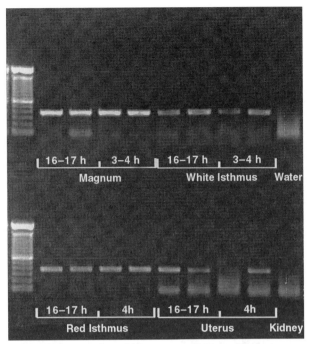

Fig. 36.3.   RT–PCR demonstration of lysozyme mRNA in different segments of the oviduct. Lysozyme-specific 17-mer primers were designed selectively to amplify nucleotides 102–483 of the chicken lysozyme coding sequence. RNA was extracted from oviduct tissues harvested at different stages of eggshell calcification (two birds/stage) (RNA InstaPure, Eurogentech). Reverse transcription was performed using random priming and Superscript II, RNase H reverse transcriptase (Life Technologies). Thermocycling using *Taq* polymerase was performed for 30 cycles (magnum, red isthmus and white isthmus) or 40 cycles (uterus, kidney and water control).

mammillary density, confluence, capping and fusion; and (ii) the presence of aragonite and the type of physical interaction with the shell membranes. These are weighted in terms of whether a high or low incidence of that particular feature contributes to or detracts from the shell's performance under load. The higher the score, the poorer the shell in terms of its ultrastructure. In this way, shell structure (morphology) and quality were correlated with protein localization in adjacent pieces of shell.

This study revealed that the amount of OC-17 localized in the mammillary knobs was inversely correlated with shell quality (Fig. 36.4), i.e. reduced levels of OC-17 and improvements in shell quality are significantly correlated in the mammillary region ($P < 0.05$). On the other hand, there was no correlation between shell quality and levels of OC-17 in the palisade layer.

Expression Cloning of Eggshell Matrix Proteins

We have prepared a vector-ligated, directional complementory DNA (cDNA) library using the Stratagene ZAP-cDNA synthesis kit and mRNA prepared from pooled uterine tissue (four hens) harvested at the midpoint of eggshell

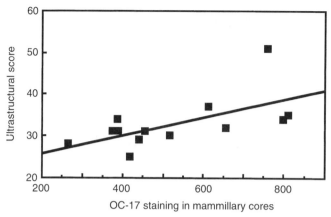

Fig. 36.4. Correlation of OC-17 in the mammillary knobs with shell quality. Immunogold localization of OC-17 in decalcified eggshell from CFAR White Leghorn strain 1 (five eggs), strain 3 (four eggs) and strain 4 (four eggs) was performed after embedding in LR White and sectioning. Grids were incubated with polyclonal anti-OC-17 (1 : 250) (three grids), diluted normal rabbit serum (three grids) or immuno-buffer (three grids); and then with gold-conjugated secondary antibody (particle size 10 nm, 1 : 60). Gold particles were counted automatically using image analysis software, and the numbers summarized and compared at three sites (mammillary layer, mid palisade and upper palisade region). Analysis of shell ultrastructure was carried out using the standard methodology and scoring system (Bain, 1992). Data from eggshell of all three strains are grouped in this figure.

calcification. Expression screening of this library with polyclonal antibodies led to the isolation of a number of plasmids containing inserts of differing 5′ length and an overall open reading frame of 2340 bp. We have tentatively denoted this cDNA as OCQ. Northern blotting with OCQ cDNA reveals that the 2.4 kb message is strongly expressed in shell gland mucosa during the middle of eggshell calcification, and absent in magnum (Fig. 36.5). Similar results are seen by RT–PCR utilizing OCQ-specific primers, also indicating that OCQ is not expressed in red isthmus or in white isthmus, but is uterine specific (not shown). When RNA extracts from shell gland of two CFAR strains of laying hens (strain 1 = superior quality, strain 8R = inferior quality) were compared by Northern blotting with an OCQ probe, higher expression levels were found in mRNA derived from the strain which had been selected to lay poorer eggshell quality (Fig. 36.5). Recently we have sequenced full-length OCQ cDNA, and determined that it codes for a 116 kDa dermatan sulphate proteoglycan OC-116 (Hincke *et al.*, 1999).

Bioassays to Study the Mechanisms of Eggshell Formation

Significant efforts have been expended to devise sensitive and specific assays in order to purify relevant proteins from uterine fluid and from eggshell matrix extracts. A pH stat assay can be used to monitor the proton production that accompanies calcium carbonate precipitation, based upon the inhibition that

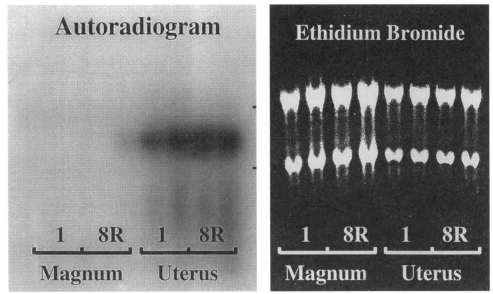

Fig. 36.5. Northern blot with OCQ probe. Total RNA was extracted from oviduct tissues harvested at the midpoint of eggshell calcification from four White Leghorn hens (CFAR strains 1 and 8R), and transferred to nylon hybridization membrane following agarose gel electrophoresis. A restriction enzyme fragment from OCQ cDNA was radiolabelled by random priming. The positions of the ethidium bromide-stained 18S and 28S RNA species are indicated with black horizontal bars.

soluble shell extracts (molluscan or eggshell) exert upon a metastable solution of calcium chloride and sodium bicarbonate (Gautron *et al.*, 1996; Wheeler *et al.*, 1981). The solubility product of calcium carbonate is exceeded in these solutions, and there is normally a rapid precipitation of this insoluble salt, which corresponds to certain aspects of mineral deposition during eggshell formation. Inhibition of calcium carbonate precipitation by partially purified eggshell or uterine fluid proteins is thought to reflect the interaction of protein(s) with either the nucleation or growth phase of calcite crystallization.

The pH stat apparatus is set to titrate the acidifying solution during calcium carbonate precipitation, and the time course of base addition allows the kinetics of the reaction to be determined (Hincke and St Maurice, 1999). Figure 36.6 demonstrates a control reaction, in the absence of added protein, in which a characteristic lag time, maximum rate and extent of precipitation are observed. Each of these parameters was affected by compounds that inhibited calcium precipitation. For example, Fig. 36.7 reveals the highly inhibitory effect of a synthetic, negatively charged compound, poly-L-aspartate. Inhibitory activity was detected in eggshell matrix proteins extracted from decalcified shell and subjected to chromatography on DEAE–Sephacel (Fig. 36.8). The active fractions exhibited a dose-dependent inhibition of the precipitation of calcium carbonate (Fig. 36.9). Western blotting studies of the active fractions indicate that osteopontin immunoreactive bands co-purify

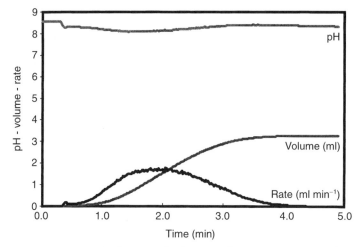

Fig. 36.6. pH stat – control. The rate of calcium carbonate precipitation from a solution containing 20 mM NaHCO$_3$, pH 8.5, 130 mM NaCl, 10 mM CaCl$_2$ was determined by quantifying the rate of addition of 50.0 mM NaOH in order to maintain the pH at a pre-set 8.3, using a Radiometer PHM 290 pH stat controller. The sharp initial decline in the pH trace indicates the time of addition of CaCl$_2$ and the start of the reaction. The temperature was maintained at 40°C throughout this process.

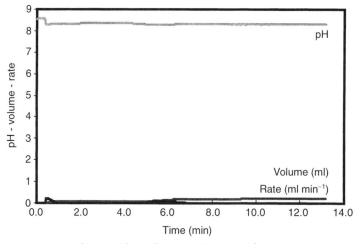

Fig. 36.7. pH stat – poly ASP. The influence of 10 µg ml^{-1} poly-L-aspartic acid (Sigma P-6762, average mol. wt 28,800 Da) upon the rate of calcium carbonate precipitation from a solution containing 20 mM NaHCO$_3$, pH 8.5, 130 mM NaCl, 10 mM CaCl$_2$ was investigated under the same conditions as in Fig. 36.6.

with the inhibitory activity through certain ion-exchange chromatographies (CM–Sephacel and DEAE–Sephacel) (not shown). Therefore, osteopontin must be considered as one candidate molecule in the regulation of eggshell mineralization.

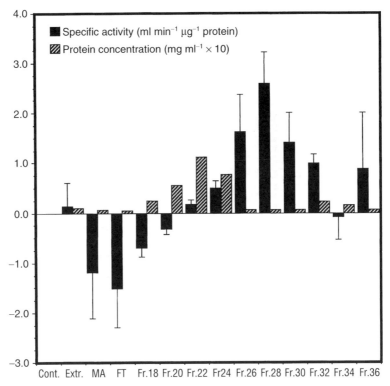

Fig. 36.8.   pH stat – purification of inhibitory activity in eggshell matrix. Activity that inhibited the rate of calcium carbonate precipitation was partially purified by DEAE – Sephacel ion-exchange chromatography. The activity corresponds to the maximum rate of calcium carbonate precipitation under each condition. Specific activity = [activity (no protein) – activity (dialysed protein sample)]/total protein (µg). Each point is the mean of duplicate determinations. Protein concentration was measured as previously (Hincke, 1995). The samples are indicated as follows: Extr. (total soluble extract from decalcified eggshell); MA (material applied to DEAE–Sephacel column); FT (void volume material which did not bind to DEAE–Sephacel); Frac. 18–Frac. 36 (fractions eluted by a gradient of increasing NaCl concentration).

Conclusions

The process of eggshell formation is complex and fascinating. In contrast to other biominerals, the fabrication of the hen eggshell is a rapid and daily event that occurs in an acellular milieu. Five grams of mineral is deposited within a 20-h period. The mechanisms that underlie this autoassembly are not completely understood; our data suggest that the matrix protein components of the eggshell are an integral element in this process. We have identified a number of eggshell matrix proteins that have the potential to be biochemical markers for shell quality, in that their levels in eggshell may be correlated with shell quality (specific gravity, shell thickness, breaking strength) due to their influence on mineralization. These proteins are likely to interact with each

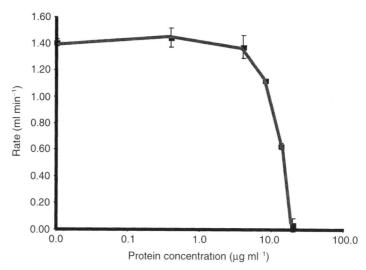

Fig. 36.9.   pH stat – dose response for partially purified inhibitory activity. Fraction 28 (Fig. 36.8) was lyophilized, redissolved and dialysed against the test buffer. Different dilutions were assayed for inhibition of calcium carbonate precipitation, and the maximum rate of base addition is presented (average of duplicate determinations). An IC_{50} of about 5 µg ml^{-1} was calculated from this curve.

other and to influence the process of eggshell formation in a multifactorial manner. Further studies to determine the relationship between specific matrix proteins and shell quality are currently underway. In addition, cloning the genes which code for matrix proteins will lead to an understanding of the hormonal control of their expression, and eventually to manipulation of protein levels to influence shell quality. This research will provide insights into the mechanism of eggshell formation that will be of benefit to industrial breeding programmes in their ongoing programmes to improve eggshell quality.

Acknowledgements

Supported by NSERC and the Ontario Egg Producers Marketing Board (M.T.H.) and the MRC of Canada (M.D.M.).

References

Abatangelo, G., Daga-Gordini, D., Castellani, I. and Cortivo, R. (1978) Some observations on the calcium ion binding to the eggshell matrix. *Calcified Tissue Research* 26, 247–252.

Addadi, L. and Weiner, S. (1992) Control and design principles in biological mineralization. *Angewande Chemie (English Edition)* 31, 153–169.

Addadi, L., Moradian, J., Shay, E., Maroudas, N.G. and Weiner, S. (1987) A chemical model for the cooperation of sulfates and carboxylates in calcite crystal nucleation: relevance to biomineralization. *Proceedings of the National Academy of Sciences of the United States of America* 84, 2732–2736.

Arias, J.L., Carrino, D.A., Fernandez, M.S., Rodriguez, J.P., Dennis, J.E. and Caplan, A.I. (1992) Partial biochemical and immunochemical characterization of avian eggshell extracellular matrices. *Archives of Biochemistry and Biophysics* 298, 293–302.

Bain, M.M. (1992) Eggshell strength: a relationship between the mechanism of failure and the ultrastructural organization of the mammillary layer. *British Poultry Science* 33, 303–319.

Baker, J.R. and Balch, D.A. (1962) A study of the organic material of the hen's-egg shell. *Biochemical Journal* 82, 352–361.

Burley, R.W. and Vadehra, D.V. (1989) *The Avian Egg, Chemistry and Biology.* John Wiley and Sons, Toronto.

Creger, C.R., Phillips, H. and Scott, J.T. (1976) Formation of an eggshell. *Poultry Science* 55, 1717–1723.

Dennis, J.E., Xiao, S.-Q., Agarwal, M., Fink, D.J., Heuer, A.H. and Caplan, A.I. (1996) Microstructure of matrix and mineral components of eggshells from white leghorn chickens (*Gallus gallus*). *Journal of Morphology* 228, 287–306.

Dieckert, J.W., Dieckert, M.C. and Creger, C.R. (1989) Calcium reserve assembly: a basic structural unit of the calcium reserve system of the hen egg shell. *Poultry Science* 68, 1569–1584.

Eckert, J., Glock, H., Schade, R., Krampitz, G., Enbergs, H. and Petersen, J. (1986) Synthesis of a precursor polypeptide of egg shell matrix in the liver of laying hen. *Journal of Animal Physiology and Animal Nutrition* 56, 258–267.

Falini, G., Albeck, S., Weiner, S. and Addadi, L. (1996) Control of aragonite or calcite polymorphism by mollusk shell macromolecules. *Science* 271, 67–69.

Fernandez, M.S., Araya, M. and Arias, J.L. (1997) Eggshells are shaped by a precise spatio-temporal arrangement of sequentially deposited macromolecules. *Matrix Biology* 16, 13–20.

Gautron, J., Bain, M., Solomon, S. and Nys, Y. (1996) Soluble matrix of hen's eggshell extracts changes *in vitro* the rate of calcium carbonate precipitation and crystal morphology. *British Poultry Science* 37, 853–866.

Gautron, J., Hincke, M.T. and Nys, Y. (1997a) Precursors of matrix proteins in the uterine fluid change with stages of eggshell formation in hens. *Connective Tissue Research* 36, 195–210.

Gautron, J., Hincke, M.T., Dominguez-Vera, J.M., Garcia-Ruiz, J.M. and Nys, Y. (1997b) Ovotransferrin and lysozyme are constituents of the hen eggshell matrix. In: *Seventh European Symposium on the Quality of Eggs and Egg Products.* Poznan, Poland, pp.172–181.

Hamilton, R.M.G. (1982) Methods and factors that affect the measurement of egg shell quality. *Poultry Science* 61, 2022–2039.

Hamilton, R.M.G. (1986) The microstructure of the hens egg-shell – a short review. *Food Microstructure* 5, 99–110.

Hincke, M.T. (1995) Ovalbumin is a component of the chicken eggshell matrix. *Connective Tissue Research* 31, 227–233.

Hincke, M.T. and St Maurice, M. (1999) Phosphorylation-dependent modulation of calcium carbonate precipitation by chicken eggshell matrix proteins. In: *6th International Conference on the Chemistry and Biology of Mineralized Tissues.* Vittel, France (in press).

Hincke, M.T., Bernard, A.-M., Lee, E.R., Tsang, C.P.W. and Narbaitz, R. (1992) Soluble protein constituents of the domestic fowl's eggshell. *British Poultry Science* 33, 505–516.

Hincke, M.T., Tsang, C.P.W., Courtney, M. and Narbaitz, R. (1993) Soluble matrix proteins of the chicken eggshell: characterization and immunochemistry. In: *Fifth*

European Symposium on the Quality of Eggs and Egg Products. Tours, France pp. 127–133.

Hincke, M.T., Tsang, C.P.W., Courtney, M., Hill, V. and Narbaitz, R. (1995) Purification and characterization of a soluble matrix protein of the chicken eggshell (ovocleidin 17). *Calcified Tissue International* 56, 578–583.

Hincke, M.T., Nys, Y., Gautron, J. and McKee, M.D. (1996) Protein components of the chicken eggshell matrix. *Molecular Biology of the Cell* 7, 584.

Hincke, M.T., Gautron, J., Tsang, C.P.W., McKee, M.D. and Nys, Y. (1999) Molecular cloning and ultrastructural localization of the core protein of an eggshell matrix proteoglycan, Oxocleidin-116. *Journal of Biological Chemistry* (in press).

Krampitz, G. and Graser, G. (1988) Molecular mechanisms of biomineralization in the formation of calcified shells. *Angewande Chemie* (*English Edition*) 27, 1145–1156.

Lowenstam, H.A. and Weiner, S. (1989) *On Biomineralization.* Oxford University Press, New York.

Mann, S. (1988) Molecular recognition in biomineralization. *Nature* 332, 119–124.

Mann, S., Heywood, B.R., Rajam, S. and Birchall, J.D. (1988) Controlled crystallization of $CaCO_3$ under stearic acid monolayers. *Nature* 334, 692–695.

Mann, S., Archibald, D.D., Didymus, J.M., Douglas, T., Heywood, B.R., Meldrum, F.C. and Reeves, N.G. (1993) Crystallization at inorganic– organic interfaces: biominerals and biomimetic synthesis. *Science* 261, 1286–1292.

McKee, M.D. and Nanci, A. (1995) Post-embedding colloidal-gold immunocyto-chemistry of non-collagenous extracellular matrix proteins in mineralized tissues. *Microscopic Research Techniques* 31, 44–62.

McKee, M.D., Nanci, A. and Hincke, M.T. (1997a) The avian eggshell as a model to study the role of noncollagenous proteins in calcification. In: *Proceedings of the 3rd Canadian Connective Tissue Conference.* Queen's University, Kingston, Spring 1997, p. 19.

McKee, M.D., Nanci, A. and Hincke, M.T. (1997b) Noncollagenous matrix components of the avian eggshell and their association *in situ* with sites of calcium carbonate mineralization. *Journal of Bone Mineral Research* 12, 5301.

Nys, Y., Zawadzki, J., Gautron, J. and Mills, A.D. (1989) Whitening of brown-shelled eggs: mineral composition of uterine fluid and rate of protoporphyrin deposition. *Poultry Science* 70, 1236–1245.

Panheleux, M., Bain, M., Fernandez, M., Morales, I., Gautron, J., Arias, J., Solomon, S., Hincke, M. and Nys, Y. (1999) Organic matrix composition and ultrastructure of eggshell: a comparative study. *British Poultry Science* 40, 240–252.

Parsons, A.H. (1982) Structure of the eggshell. *Poultry Science* 61, 2013–2021.

Pines, M., Knopov, V. and Bar, A. (1996) Involvement of osteopontin in egg shell formation in the laying chicken. *Matrix Biology* 14, 765–771.

Roland, D.A., Sr (1988) Research note: egg shell problems: estimates of incidence and economic impact. *Poultry Science* 67, 1801–1803.

Silyn-Roberts, H. and Sharp, R.M. (1986) Crystal growth and the role of the organic network in eggshell mineralization. *Proceedings of the Royal Society of London, Series B* 227, 303–324.

Simkiss, K. and Wilbur, K.M. (1989) *Biomineralization, Cell Biology and Mineral Deposition.* Academic Press, San Diego.

Stemberger, B.H., Mueller, W.J. and Leach, R.M. (1977) Microscopic study of the initial stages of eggshell calcification. *Poultry Science* 56, 537–543.

Todd, E.C.D. (1996) Risk assessment of use of cracked eggs in Canada. *International Journal of Food Microbiology* 30, 125–143.

Weiner, S. and Addadi, L. (1991) Acidic macromolecules of mineralized tissues: the controllers of crystal formation. *Trends in Biochemical Science* 16, 252–256.

Wheeler, A.P., George, J.W. and Evans, C.A. (1981) Control of calcium carbonate nucleation and crystal growth by soluble matrix of oyster shell. *Science* 212, 1397–1399.

Wyburn, G.M., Johnston, H.S., Draper, M.H. and Davidson, M.F. (1973) The ultrastructure of the shell forming region of the oviduct and the development of the shell of *Gallus domesticus*. *Quarterly Journal of Experimental Physiology* 58, 143–151.

Econometric Feeding and Management of Commercial Leghorns: Optimizing Profits Using New Technology

37

D.A. Roland, Sr[1], M.M. Bryant[1], J.X. Zhang[1],
D.A. Roland, Jr[1] and J. Self[2]

[1]Poultry Science Department, Auburn University, Auburn,
Alabama, USA; [2]Cal-Maine Foods Inc., Jackson,
Mississippi, USA

During the past 40 years, significant improvements in efficiency and profits have been made. However, none of the significant advances allowed producers to alter nutrient intake as feed and egg prices change (the two most important factors influencing profits). As a result, producers had no way of using egg and feed prices in establishing feeding programmes. Nutrient requirements were determined based only on performance and fixed costs.

The purpose of this chapter is to demonstrate that in order to maximize profits, producers must let egg, protein and energy prices dictate nutrient requirements. Because egg and feed prices change, there can be no fixed nutrient requirements (total sulphur amino acids; TSAA). We will demonstrate that in order to maximize profits, producers must least cost nutrient requirements prior to using least cost feed formulation programmes to obtain formulas which will meet those requirements. Data will be presented which demonstrate why and how producers must alter TSAA and energy intake as protein and energy cost and price spread in egg prices change to maximize profits. Producers who understand and use the concept presented in the 'Econometric Feeding and Management Programme of Commercial Leghorns' will have an economic advantage (up to 2 cents dozen^{-1} or more) over those who do not.

Introduction

Approximately 15 years ago, we realized that there was something basically wrong with the way in which commercial leghorns were fed. The price of eggs and feed, the two major factors influencing profits, along with environmental temperature, which controls feed intake, had little or no influence on nutrient

© CAB International 2000. Egg Nutrition and Biotechnology
(eds J.S. Sim, S. Nakai and W. Guenter)

463

levels used. Producers simply fed the same least cost formulas month after month based on feed intake to ensure hens received their fixed requirements.

The purpose of this chapter is to demonstrate why there can be no fixed total sulphur amino acid (TSAA) requirements and to explain why producers must let egg and feed prices dictate nutrient requirements in order to maximize profits. All nutrient (TSAA) requirement specifications previously published in Breeder Management Guides, NRC, referred journal publications or in any book are fixed requirements based on performance which may or may not give maximum profits. 'Econometric Feeding and Management of Commercial Leghorns' has been developed which allows the integration of economics and environmental control into nutritional programmes. It does this by automatically re-calculating protein, TSAA and energy requirements as the price of eggs and feed change. This allows producers to alter TSAA and energy intake as market conditions dictate, increasing profits up to 2 cents dozen^{-1} or more. By simply understanding the relationship of energy to protein price, product price and environmental temperature along with having the correct tools and data, it is easy for producers to optimize profits by letting egg and feed prices dictate nutrient levels fed.

Overview of the Procedure Used in Determining Nutrient Requirement

To understand the relationship of energy and protein price to feeding and management programmes, it is important to review how nutrient requirements are established. To determine nutrient requirements, nutritionists feed graded levels of nutrients from deficient to excessive (Fig. 37.1). Sharp increases in performance (production, feed efficiency, egg weight, etc.) can be observed

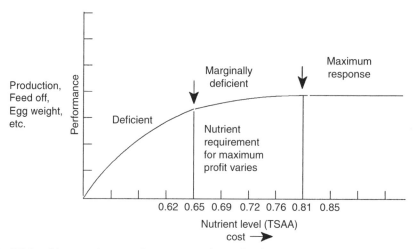

Fig. 37.1. How nutrient requirements are determined. In many instances, maximum response gives maximum profits. In many instances it does not. If price of feed and product income were constant, we could select one diet that always gives maximum return.

with increasing nutrient levels as long as the animal is deficient. As the nutrient level becomes marginally deficient, the increase in performance response decreases until a maximum response is obtained. Once the nutritionist determines a nutrient requirement for maximum response or near maximum response, those fixed requirements may be used for years.

It is important to know those nutrient requirements for which the maximum response remains constant. However, nutrient requirements for maximum profits vary. For example, the price of energy has a major influence on the TSAA requirement for maximum profits. As the price of energy (maize) varies, the nutrient requirement for maximum profits shifts. Sometimes, a diet containing 0.65% TSAA is required, and other times a diet containing 0.81% is required even when hens are the same age.

Influence of Energy (Maize) Price on Nutrient Requirement for Maximum Profits

For each dollar increase per bushel of maize, feed price increases by approximately US$21 tonne^{-1} (Table 37.1). However, it should be understood that the absolute price of feed does not influence the nutrient requirement for maximum profits. This is where many producers may get into trouble. They may reason, as the price of feed has increased, I must feed a diet less dense (less expensive) to reduce losses. Reasoning such as this may or may not be correct.

For example, as nutrient density is increased from 0.65 to 0.81% TSAA (levels typically fed), feed cost increases with each unit increase in nutrient density (Fig. 37.1). The price of energy (maize) has a major influence on the extent of the increase. Depending upon the price of energy, the 0.81% TSAA diet giving maximum response may cost US$30 tonne^{-1} more than the diet containing 0.65% or it may cost only US$3 tonne^{-1} more. The spread in price (US$30 versus US$3) along with the improved performance (increased product value) obtained from feeding a more dense diet determines the nutrient requirement for maximum profits.

As the price of maize increases from US$2 to US$6 bushel^{-1}, the cost of the 0.81% TSAA diet increases from US$116 to US$201 tonne^{-1}. However, the cost of increasing TSAA levels (making the diet denser) becomes less (Table 37.2).

Table 37.1. Influence of increasing maize price (US$ bushel^{-1}) on feed cost of an 18% protein layer feed.

Maize (US$ bushel^{-1})	Feed cost (US$ tonne^{-1})	US$ tonne^{-1} increase
2	116.17	
3	137.32	21.15
4	158.36	42.19
5	179.51	63.34
6	200.43	84.26

Increase in maize price (US$1 bushel^{-1}) = US$21.15 tonne^{-1} increase in feed cost.

Table 37.2.   Feed cost (US tonne^{-1}) as influenced by maize price and TSAA level.

TSAA (%)	US$2 bushel^{-1} maize US$200 tonne^{-1} SBOM	US$4 bushel^{-1} maize US$200 tonne^{-1} SBOM	US$6 bushel^{-1} maize US$200 tonne^{-1} SBOM
0.81	116	158	201
0.76	112	156	200
0.72	108	154	199
0.69	105	152	198
0.65	102	150	197

Diets formulated based on lysine.

With US$2 bushel^{-1} maize, it costs US$4 for each 0.04 unit increase in TSAA level or US$14 tonne^{-1} to increase nutrient density from 0.65 to 0.81% TSAA. With US$4 bushel^{-1} maize, it costs only US$8 and only US$4 for US$6 bushel^{-1} maize.

Therefore, as the price of maize (energy) increases and it costs less to feed a more dense diet (more TSAA), the nutrient requirement for maximum profits will shift toward the requirement needed for maximum response. Unless producers continually recognize how maize (energy) price influences the spread and know the value of the product lost or gained when nutrient density is changed, they could either not shift diets or even shift diets fed in the wrong direction and increase the adverse effect of high-priced maize.

Influence of Maize Price in Relation to Soybean Oil Meal (Protein) Price on Nutrient Requirement for Maximum Profits

There are many factors in addition to maize price which influence nutrient requirements. Therefore, the decision on how to shift nutrient requirements to continually maximize profits are usually not as easy to determine as in the example just presented. For example, the cost of protein in relation to energy also has a significant influence on the cost of increasing TSAA levels. The effect of increasing protein price on price spread is exactly opposite to the effect of increasing maize price. As the cost of maize increases, the spread becomes less (US$14 versus US$4, Table 37.2).

However, as the cost of soybean oil meal (SBOM) increases, the spread becomes greater (Table 37.3). For example, if SBOM price increases from US$200 to US$400 tonne^{-1}, the cost of increasing TSAA levels from 0.65 to 0.81% doubles from US$14 to US$28. Remember that the animal response to increasing TSAA levels (value of product gained or loss) is the same regardless of feed price. Therefore, as protein price increases, the cost of increasing TSAA levels increases and the nutrient requirement for maximum profits tends to shift further from the requirement for maximum performance.

Egg price or spread in egg price due to size also has a major influence on nutrient requirements for maximum profit. For example, if there is a large spread between medium and large or large and extra-large, etc., more protein is required to maximize profits than when there is a small spread.

Table 37.3.   Feed cost (US$ tonne⁻¹) as influenced by SBOM price and TSAA level.

TSAA (%)	US$2 bushel⁻¹ maize US$200 tonne⁻¹ SBOM	US$2 bushel⁻¹ maize US$400 tonne⁻¹ SBOM
0.81	116.17	170.16
0.76	112.38	162.70
0.72	108.20	154.82
0.69	104.84	148.50
0.65	101.66	142.36

Diets formulated based on lysine.

Once a producer understands how feed and egg prices influence nutrient requirements, only two things are needed to integrate economics and environmental control into an existing feeding and management programme. First, the producer must know what nutrient level (TSAA and energy) gives maximum response and how much performance is lost using graded levels of TSAA below that level at different environmental temperatures. Second, the producer needs a software program that will calculate which TSAA level gives maximum profits using current feed and egg prices.

Although using the program is simple, developing the program was time consuming and complex. It took 7 years, 30–40 research trials and over half a million dollars. A mandate of the concept was that it had to be simple to use and fit directly into existing programmes.

The nutrient levels we chose to use were those ranging from 0.65 to 0.81% TSAA. These are levels found to be best for Hy-Line W_{36} hens. They could be different for another strain. For example, with another strain, maximum response may be obtained with 0.72% TSAA not 0.81%. The TSAA levels shown here when fed based on feed intake (0.17–0.21 lb per hen day⁻¹) will supply 620 mg of TSAA per hen day⁻¹. All diets are formulated based on lysine, to supply 83% as much lysine as TSAA. In addition to those levels, many other levels were also fed to confirm that we were in fact using the best levels.

All experiments were conducted in computerized, environmentally controlled houses in which average feed intake was approximately 82–90 g h⁻¹ day⁻¹ depending upon temperature and hen age. With environment control, we control feed intake not the bird. All hens are moulted at 65 weeks. You may moult at a different age or not moult; it does not matter. There are nine parts to the Econometric Feeding and Management Programme. The parts are phases 1, 2 and 3 for first cycle hens, phases 1, 2 and 3 for second cycle hens, and phases 1, 2 and 3 for third cycle hens. Again, collecting all the data necessary for the programme was time consuming because it takes 3 years for a complete cycle. In addition to collecting data for W_{36} hens, we also collected data for another strain, which ate more feed and laid heavier eggs.

We repeated some phases as many as five times. After all data were obtained, all fixed costs along with egg and feed prices for each location (complex) are entered into a software program which automatically calculates the diet and temperature required for maximum profits. The data presented are for first cycle phase 1 hens only. The concept for all phases is the same.

Influence of Increase in Maize Price on Nutrient (TSAA) Requirement for Maximum Profits

With US$2 bushel^{-1} maize, it costs US$4 tonne^{-1} of feed to increase nutrient (TSAA) density by 0.04 units (Table 37.4). With US$6 bushel^{-1} maize, it costs only one dollar for each 0.04 unit increase in TSAA level (Table 37.4). Because of this, the TSAA requirement for maximum profits is 0.72% with US$2 bushel^{-1} maize. With US$6 bushel^{-1} maize, the TSAA requirement is 0.81%. If a producer were feeding the 0.72% TSAA diet and maize price increased and no change in nutrient level from 0.72 to 0.81% was made, the producer would lose an additional 0.7 cent dozen^{-1} (13.0 versus 13.7 cents dozen^{-1}). The nutrient requirements for maximum profits shift from 0.72 to 0.81% as maize price increases because, with high priced maize, it costs much less to increase the TSAA level. For US$6 bushel^{-1} maize, it costs only US$2 to increase the TSAA level from 0.72 to 0.81 (US$199 versus US$201) whereas the cost is US$8 for US$2 bushel^{-1} maize (US$108 versus US$116).

Influence of Maize and SBOM Price and Environmental Temperature on TSAA Requirement for Maximum Profits

The previous example demonstrated how maize price influences the TSAA requirement for maximum profits. The following example will demonstrate how maize price, SBOM price and environmental temperature influence the TSAA requirement for maximum profits.

With US$4 bushel^{-1} maize and US$200 tonne^{-1} SBOM, the TSAA requirement for maximum profits at 78°F is 0.81% (Table 37.5). With US$2 bushel^{-1} maize and US $400 tonne^{-1} SBOM at 78°F, the requirement is 0.72%. If a producer were feeding the diet containing 0.81% TSAA with US $4 bushel^{-1} maize and did not change to 0.72% as maize decreased and SBOM increased, he would lose an additional 1.2 cents dozen^{-1} (19.1 versus 17.9 cents dozen^{-1}), approximately a quarter of a million dollars per million hens year^{-1}. Notice

Table 37.4. Influence of maize price on TSAA requirements for maximum profits (cents dozen^{-1} eggs).

Maize (price per bushel)		TSAA (%)				
		0.81	0.76	0.72	0.69	0.65
US$2	Profits	25.4	25.4	25.6	23.9	23.9
	Feed cost[a]	116	112	108	105	102
US$6	Profits	13.7	13.4	13.0	11.3	10.7
	Feed cost[a]	201	200	199	198	197

10 cents spread between medium and large; 98 cents large egg price.
[a]Dollars tonne^{-1}.

Table 37.5. Influence of maize and SBOM price and environmental temperature on profits (cents dozen^{-1}).

Ingredient price	Temperature (°F)	TSAA (%)				
		0.81	0.76	0.72	0.69	0.65
US$4 maize[a] (US$200 SBOM)[b]	78	19.6	19.4	19.3	17.6	17.3
	68	19.2	20.0	20.3	19.4	19.5
Feed price[b]		158	156	153	151	150
US$2 maize[a] (US$400 SBOM)[b]	78	17.9	18.5	19.1	18.0	18.3
	68	17.4	19.0	20.1	19.9	20.6
Feed price[b]		170	163	155	148	142

10 cents spread between medium and large; 98 cents large egg price.
[a]Dollars bushel^{-1}; [b]dollars tonne^{-1}.

also the influence that environmental temperature has on profits and TSAA requirements. With US$4 bushel^{-1} maize and a temperature of 78°F, the TSAA requirement is 0.81%. However, with US$2 bushel^{-1} maize, US$400 tonne^{-1} SBOM and a temperature of 68°F, the TSAA requirement for maximum profits is 0.65%. If maize price decreased and a producer continued to feed the 0.81% TSAA (making no change), he would lose 3.2 cents dozen^{-1} (17.4 versus 20.6 cents dozen^{-1}) or approximately three-quarters of a million dollars per million hens year^{-1}. That would be the equivalent to a producer paying US$3.75 bushel^{-1} for maize when he could buy the same maize for US$3.00 bushel^{-1}.

The TSAA requirement varies due to different ingredient prices. For example, with US$4 bushel^{-1} maize and US$200 tonne^{-1} SBOM, the 0.81% TSAA diet costs only US$8 more than the 0.65% TSAA diet (US$150 versus US$158). However, with US$2 bushel^{-1} maize and US$400 tonne^{-1} SBOM, the 0.81% diet costs US$28 more than the 0.65% TSAA diet (US$142 versus US$170). The change in performance (value of product gain or loss) as dietary nutrient density is changed is not influenced by feed cost. Therefore, the requirement for maximum profits is 0.81% for the US$4 and 0.65% for US$2 bushel^{-1} maize. Producers who understand this concept and apply it will have a significant edge over those who do not.

Influence of Price Spread due to Egg Size on TSAA Requirements for Maximum Profits

The next example will demonstrate how price spread between medium and large eggs or large and other sizes influences the protein (TSAA) requirement for maximum profits. Hen performance (egg size and production) is not influenced by the price of eggs or feed. However, prices of eggs and feed are two primary factors controlling profits. Therefore, to optimize profits, different levels of methionine + cysteine (M + C) must be fed as prices of eggs and feed change.

To calculate how nutrient requirements change, we determine the point where the cost of feeding more protein to increase egg size or production becomes greater than the increased income resulting from the additional protein. For example in phase 1 first cycle hens (Table 37.6), when the price spread between medium and large eggs is 15 cents dozen^{-1}, increasing egg size by feeding more M + C (0.81 versus 0.65%) increases egg income by 5.3 cents (33.9–39.2 cents). The corresponding increase in feed cost is only 2.1 cents dozen^{-1} (16.4–18.5 cents). Profits are maximized at 2.7 cents dozen^{-1} with at least 721 mg M + C per hen day^{-1}.

When the spread is 3 cents dozen^{-1} (Table 37.6) increasing egg size by feeding more M + C increases egg income by only 1.5 cents dozen^{-1} (51.0–52.5 cents). However, the increase in feed cost is still 2.1 cents dozen^{-1} (16.4–18.5 cents). When the spread is 3 cents dozen^{-1}, profits are maximized with 548 mg not 721 mg M + C per hen day^{-1}.

Feeding more protein (M + C) increases egg size by the same amount regardless of the spread between medium and large and other sizes. As the spread increases, the value of the increase in egg size becomes greater, which causes the protein requirement for maximum profits to increase. Nutrient requirements for maximum egg size remain constant, but nutrient requirements for maximum profit vary. As the value of eggs changes due to price spreads, we alter egg size and/or control the increase in egg size by manipulating protein (M + C) intake through dietary means and energy intake using environmental control.

Influence of Energy Cost on Method of Formulation Required for Maximum Profits

As you know, not all nutritionists agree on the same nutrient requirement. Energy and protein prices determine the TSAA requirement for maximum profits using any fixed nutrient requirement. Energy cost also determines the method of formulation required for maximum profits.

Table 37.6. Influence of price spread between medium and large eggs on the TSAA requirement for maximum profits (cents dozen^{-1} eggs).

Price spread (cents dozen^{-1})		TSAA (%)				
		0.81	0.76	0.72	0.69	0.65
15	Egg income	39.2	37.9	34.6	34.6	33.9
	Feed cost	18.5	17.7	17.5	16.6	16.4
	Profit	2.7	2.2	2.4	0.0	0.5
	TSAA (mg hen^{-1} day^{-1})	721	661	638	598	566
3	Egg income	52.5	52.1	51.2	51.2	51.0
	Feed cost	18.5	17.7	17.5	16.6	16.4
	Profit	16.0	16.4	16.6	16.7	16.6
	TSAA (mg hen^{-1} day^{-1})	721	661	638	598	566

For example, some nutritionists believe diets formulated based on protein with increased levels of energy (1300 ME kcal lb^{-1} or more) and protein are needed to optimize performance and profits (Table 37.7). The Hy-Line Management guides and some other breeder management guides recommend this method of formulation. When this method is used, protein and methionine or M + C ratios are held constant as feed intake changes. Many hens are fed these diets.

Other nutritionists believe formulating diets (based on lysine) which contain more moderate protein levels and energy levels near 1280 ME kcal lb^{-1} will allow for maximum profits (Table 37.8). Nutritionists using this method maintain constant ratios of lysine and M + C as feed intake changes. The differences between the methods are 3.2% protein and 31 calories.

We conducted first and second complete cycle (2-year) trials using both methods of formulation with two strains of hens. We discovered that hens fed diets formulated based on protein (more protein) and energy produced heavier and more eggs. However, what determines the most profitable method of feeding is the difference in feed cost between the two methods. With US$2 maize (low priced maize) and US$400 SBOM, the difference in feed cost between the two methods is US$35 tonne^{-1}. With that much difference in feed

Table 37.7. Nutrient and cost comparison between diets formulated based on lysine versus protein.

Feeding method	TSAA (%)	Protein (%)	Methionine (%)	ME (kcal lb^{-1})	US$2[a] maize US$400[b] SBOM
Protein	0.86	22.0	0.51	1300	213.00
	0.77	19.8	0.46	1305	190.34
	0.66	17.9	0.40	1316	171.84
Lysine	0.81	18.0	0.51	1274	170.16
	0.76	16.6	0.45	1277	162.70
	0.65	15.5	0.40	1278	142.36
Average difference	0.04	3.2	0	31	35

[a]Dollars bushel^{-1}; [b]dollars tonne^{-1}.

Table 37.8. Nutrient and cost comparison between diets formulated based on lysine versus protein.

Feeding method	TSAA (%)	Protein (%)	Methionine (%)	ME (kcal lb^{-1})	US$4[a] maize US$200[b] SBOM
Lysine	0.81	18.0	0.51	1274	170
	0.72	16.6	0.45	1277	164
	0.65	15.5	0.40	1278	159
Protein	0.81	22.0	0.51	1300	158
	0.72	19.8	0.46	1305	154
	0.65	17.9	0.40	1316	150
Average difference	0.04	3.0	0	31	10

[a]Dollars bushel^{-1}; [b]dollars tonne^{-1}.

cost, the value of increased performance (production and egg weight) will not offset the increased cost. Depending upon product value, producers feeding based on lysine may make significantly more than producers feeding based on protein. With typical feed cost, that is the case. However, with US$4 bushel^{-1} maize (high priced maize) and US$200 tonne^{-1} SBOM, the difference in cost between the two methods of feeding is only US$10 tonne^{-1} (Table 37.8). With these prices, it may be more economical to feed diets formulated based on protein. One of the most important benefits of integrating economics with nutrition is that it allows producers to know which method of formulation (lysine versus protein) allows maximum profits.

Ingredient prices dictate almost every aspect of our feeding and management programmes. They even dictate which breed or strain of animal we should use for maximum profits. For example, with low priced maize, the spread between formulating for hens eating 0.20 lbs per hen day^{-1} and those eating 0.23 lbs hen per day may be US$14 tonne^{-1}. Under these conditions, the strain producing bigger eggs and eating more of a less expensive (dense) feed may make more even though feed efficiency is worse. However, as maize price increases and the spread decreases, the strain eating less of a more dense feed and laying smaller eggs may make more. Therefore, price of maize (energy) along with product price can easily dictate which strain of bird is the most profitable. The integration of economics with nutrition helps producers confirm if they are using the best strain or not.

In the past, due to lack of technology and data necessary to develop computer programs to handle the infinite number of possibilities for ingredient prices, product prices, environmental temperature, spread in prices, etc, we have simply based requirements on average feed and product prices. Without the availability of an 'Econometric Feed and Management Software' such as that developed at Auburn, requirements have to be based on average feed and egg prices. Many producers are already making some adjustments with feeding programmes as prices change; however, many do not. Producers who understand the Econometric Feeding and Management concept presented and put forth the necessary effort to apply the concept, will have a significant economic advantage over those who do not.

We must recognize that feed and egg prices vary throughout the world, therefore, each producer has to determine requirements using his own egg and feed prices. The time when you could look in a management guide or ask some nutritionist to give you a fixed requirement that you can use constantly is gone, if you want to maximize profits continually. The extremely volatile nature of the grain market emphasizes the importance of letting feed and egg prices dictate nutrient levels fed.

Effect of Feeding Organic Selenium in Diets of Laying Hens on Egg Selenium Content

38

A.H. Cantor, M.L. Straw, M.J. Ford,
A.J. Pescatore and M.K. Dunlap
Department of Animal Sciences, University of Kentucky,
Lexington, Kentucky, USA

The effect of supplementing layer diets with selenized yeast (SY) (Sel-Plex 50, Alltech Inc.) or sodium selenite (SS) as sources of selenium (Se) on transfer of Se to the egg was studied. All hens were fed a low Se diet for a 4-week pre-treatment period. Then hens were fed the low Se diet without supplementation (C), with 0.3 mg kg^{-1} of Se added from SS, or with 0.3 mg kg^{-1} of Se added from SY. Analysis of the diets indicated that they contained 0.04, 0.28 and 0.31 mg of Se kg^{-1} (as fed, respectively). At no time did feed intake or body weights differ. The average egg Se concentration (wet basis) was 0.04 mg kg^{-1} at week 0. Egg Se levels were 0.05, 0.18 and 0.24 mg kg^{-1} after 3 weeks, and 0.06, 0.20 and 0.24 mg kg^{-1} after 6 weeks for C, SS and SY, respectively. At both 3 and 6 weeks, SY eggs had significantly higher ($P > 0.05$) Se than SS eggs. These data indicate that more Se is transferred to the eggs when Se is supplemented in the organic than the inorganic form.

Objective

The objective of this study was to compare the resulting levels of selenium (Se) in the edible portion of eggs due to the use of an organic source of Se, selenized yeast (SY) (Sel-Plex 50, Alltech Inc., Nicholasville, Kentucky) and an inorganic source, sodium selenite (SS), when both provided 0.3 mg of Se kg^{-1} diet for laying hens.

Materials and Methods

Hens

A total of 144 laying hens of a commercial white shell producing strain (H & N 'Nick Chick'), 61 weeks of age, were used in this study. The initial rate of egg production (hen–day production) was 82%. Eight replicate groups of six hens were assigned to each of three dietary treatments.

Housing and management

Hens were housed two per cage (25 cm wide, 41 cm deep) in an environmentally controlled room. Temperature was maintained between 20 and 29°C. Light was provided at 16 h light–8 h dark at approximately 10 lux. Trough-type feeders that supplied three adjacent cages were used to provide feed on an *ad libitum* basis. Water was also supplied on an *ad libitum* basis using automatic drinking cups. The water in the area of the research facility used is known to have an extremely low concentration of Se.

Diets

A practical basal layer diet was formulated with maize and soybean meal as the main ingredients (Table 38.1). The maize and soybean meal used were from lots that were locally available in the state of Kentucky (i.e. not selected for Se content). The diet was fed with no Se supplement or with a supplement of 0.3 mg of Se kg^{-1} diet provided by SS or SY. The yeast contained approximately 1000 mg of Se kg^{-1}, while the commercial SS supplement contained 200 mg of Se kg^{-1} in a limestone carrier.

All hens were fed the unsupplemented diet (C) during a 4-week pre-treatment period in order to obtain a uniformly low concentration of Se in the eggs. The hens were then fed the three diets for a period of 6 weeks.

Egg sampling

Eggs were sampled for Se analysis at the end of the pre-treatment period and after 3 and 6 weeks of feeding the experimental diets. Eggs with shell abnormalities (cracks, thin shells, etc.) were excluded because excessive moisture loss during storage and handling of these abnormal eggs can result in false values upon nutrient analysis. Four eggs per replicate group were weighed on each sampling date. The contents of the four eggs were then pooled and the air-dried shells were weighed. Following gentle homogenization of the pooled egg contents, aliquots (*c.* 1 g) were taken for Se analysis.

Selenium analysis

Feed and egg samples were analysed for Se using the fluorometric procedure of Olson *et al.* (1975) as modified by Cantor and Tarino (1982). After finely grinding representative samples of each diet, an aliquot of *c.* 1 g (as-fed basis) was taken for Se analysis. Analyses on feed were conducted in triplicate, while analyses of liquid egg contents were conducted in duplicate.

Statistical analyses

Experimental data were subjected to analysis of variance. Means were separated by the test of least significant difference (LSD) when a significant

Table 38.1. Composition of the basal diet[a].

Ingredient	%
Maize	66.15
Soybean meal, 48% protein	20.70
Dehydrated lucerne meal	2.00
Blended animal–vegetable fat	1.00
Iodized salt	0.40
Dicalcium phosphate (18.7% P, 22% Ca)	1.20
Limestone (38% Ca)	5.40
Oyster shell	3.00
Vitamin–mineral mix[b]	0.10
DL-methionine, 99%	0.05
Total	100.00

[a]Calculated nutrient content: 2825 kcal AME_n; 16.0% protein, 3.5% Ca, 0.33% available P, 0.32% Met, 0.60% Met + Cys, 0.80% Lys, 0.18% Na.
[b]Commercial poultry vitamin-trace mineral mix with no added Se.

Table 38.2. Effect of supplemental Se as selenized yeast (SY, Sel-Plex 50) and sodium selenite (SS) in laying hen diets on feed intake, egg production, egg Se concentration and Se content[a].

	Diet			
	Basal	Sodium selenite[b]	Selenized yeast[b]	SEM
Daily feed intake (g hen^{-1})	116	120	118	1.5
Hen–day egg production (%)	86.6	83.2	83.1	2.2
Egg Se concentration[c], 3 weeks (mg kg^{-1})	0.047	0.182	0.235	0.004
Egg Se concentration[c], 6 weeks (mg kg^{-1})	0.059	0.197	0.235	0.006
Egg Se content[c], 3 weeks (μg)	2.57	9.89	13.0	0.22
Egg Se content[c], 6 weeks (μg)	3.28	10.9	13.5	0.42

[a]Each diet was fed to eight replicate groups of six hens.
[b]Provided 0.3 mg added Se kg^{-1}.
[c]Average of one pooled sample of four eggs per replicate.

value of F was obtained in the analysis of variance. A probability (P) level of < 0.05 was required for statements of significance.

Results and Discussion

Dietary treatments did not significantly affect the rate of egg production nor the average daily feed intake during the 6-week trial (Table 38.2). The analyses of the diets used for the C, SS and SY treatments indicated that they contained 0.04, 0.28 and 0.31 mg Se kg^{-1}, respectively. Thus, the calculated daily intake of Se was 5, 34 and 36 μg per hen for the C, SS and SY treatments, respectively.

Both Se supplements significantly elevated egg Se concentrations after 3 and 6 weeks of feeding (Table 38.2). At both sampling times, the concentration of Se in eggs was significantly higher for hens fed the SY diet compared with the SS diet. In eggs sampled after 3 and 6 weeks, the Se concentration was 29% and 19% higher, respectively, for the hens supplemented with the organic form of Se compared with values for those given selenite. Based on the weights of sampled eggs, total Se in eggs from hens fed the unsupplemented diet was approximately 3 µg, while the respective values for hens fed the SS and SY diets were 10–11 µg and 13–13.5 µg.

The results from this study show that organic Se, in the form of selenized yeast, was more effective in increasing egg Se levels than inorganic Se. Egg Se concentrations in eggs produced by hens fed the SY diets were similar to those of eggs from hens fed high Se soybean meal (unpublished results). However, transporting high Se oilseed meals or grains to areas where local crops typically have low Se concentrations is not normally economically feasible due to the costs involved. Thus, providing organic Se in the form of selenized yeast is an attractive alternative.

Using organic Se to elevate egg Se beyond levels that can be obtained with sodium selenite can have several useful applications. Firstly, in the production of table eggs, it can be employed to produce a nutritionally enhanced 'designer' egg. Consumption of eggs with elevated Se could make a substantial contribution toward the recommended daily dietary allowances of 55–75 µg Se for adult humans (Food and Nutrition Board, National Research Council, 1989). Secondly, in the production of hatching eggs, elevated egg Se could be useful in improving the Se status of the embryo during incubation and the newly hatched chick.

References

Cantor, A.H. and Tarino, J.Z. (1982) Comparative effects of inorganic and organic dietary sources of selenium upon selenium levels and selenium-dependent glutathione peroxidase activity in blood of young turkeys. *Journal of Nutrition* 112, 2187–2196.

Food and Nutrition Board, National Research Council (1989) *Recommended Dietary Allowances*, 10th edn National Academy Press, Washington, DC.

Olson, O.E., Palmer, I.S. and Carey, E.E. (1975) Modification of the official method for selenium in plants. *Journal of the Association of Official Analytical Chemists* 58, 117–121.

Influence of Eggshell 49 on Shell Quality of Hens Grouped According to Shell Quality

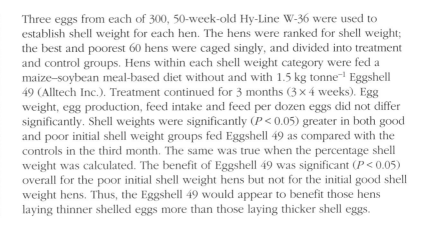

39

R.D. Miles[1] and C.W. Comer[2]

[1]University of Florida, Gainesville, Florida, USA;
[2]Alltech Inc., Guelph, Ontario, Canada

Three eggs from each of 300, 50-week-old Hy-Line W-36 were used to establish shell weight for each hen. The hens were ranked for shell weight; the best and poorest 60 hens were caged singly, and divided into treatment and control groups. Hens within each shell weight category were fed a maize–soybean meal-based diet without and with 1.5 kg tonne^{-1} Eggshell 49 (Alltech Inc.). Treatment continued for 3 months (3×4 weeks). Egg weight, egg production, feed intake and feed per dozen eggs did not differ significantly. Shell weights were significantly ($P < 0.05$) greater in both good and poor initial shell weight groups fed Eggshell 49 as compared with the controls in the third month. The same was true when the percentage shell weight was calculated. The benefit of Eggshell 49 was significant ($P < 0.05$) overall for the poor initial shell weight hens but not for the initial good shell weight hens. Thus, the Eggshell 49 would appear to benefit those hens laying thinner shelled eggs more than those laying thicker shell eggs.

Objective

In any flock of laying hens, there are some hens that will benefit more than others from dietary treatments and products. The following experiment was designed to determine whether the response to Eggshell 49 was different in hens producing eggs with high eggshell weight from that of hens producing eggs of low shell weight.

Materials and Methods

Hyline W-36 layers at 50 weeks of age were used in the study. Prior to the initiation of the study, eggs were collected individually from 300 laying hens for 3 days or until three eggs from each hen were collected, and an average eggshell weight for each hen was calculated. The hens were ranked by shell weight, and the 60 hens with the highest eggshell weight and the 60 hens with the lowest eggshell weight were used in the experiment.

Each group of 60 hens was divided into two groups consisting of 30 individually caged hens. Replications of each experimental treatment consisted of six pens of five individually caged hens all eating from a common feeder. One group of 30 hens with good egg shell weight was fed the unsupplemented maize–soybean meal basal diet and the other group of 30 individually caged hens with good eggshell weights was fed the same diet supplemented with Eggshell 49 at 1.5 kg tonne^{-1}. The same procedure was followed with the hens in the poor eggshell quality group. The maize–soybean meal diet was formulated to contain the recommended nutrient concentrations for hens of this age according to the breeder's guide.

The experimental diets were fed for three consecutive 28-day periods. Total egg production and feed consumed for each 28-day period were determined. Every seventh day of the experimental period, all eggs laid were collected, weighed, and eggshell weight was determined. Feed conversion (kg dozen^{-1}) was calculated.

Results

Egg and shell weights

Average egg weight was 65 g and did not differ with treatment. Birds with high shell weight had egg weights which were higher than those for hens in the low shell weight group (67 versus 63 g, respectively; Table 39.1). Overall, hens fed Eggshell 49 deposited significantly ($P < 0.05$) more shell on the egg than those hens not receiving Eggshell 49 (5.57 versus 5.43 g, respectively; Table 39.2).

Eggshell 49 did not significantly improve shell weights for the birds within the high shell weight group; however, there was a continuous numerical trend for the hens in the high shell weight group to deposit more shell on the egg. A significant increase in the amount of shell deposited on the egg resulted from feeding Eggshell 49 to those hens that had low shell weight. These hens

Table 39.1. Monthly mean egg weight for commercial laying hens producing good or poor shell weight and fed control (C) or diets supplemented with Eggshell 49 (ES 49).

Shell weight	Diet	Mean egg weight (g)				
		Initial	1	2	3	Total
Good	C	65.80	66.91	67.72	66.77	67.18
	ES 49	66.86	66.68	67.28	66.98	67.00
Poor	C	62.01	63.69	63.28	63.60	63.52
	ES 49	62.64	63.08	63.40	63.48	63.32
Total	C	63.82	65.33	65.50	65.30	65.35
	ES 49	64.88	64.88	65.36	65.26	65.16

No significant ($P > 0.05$) differences observed between diets in shell quality.

Table 39.2. Monthly mean egg shell weight for commerical laying hens producing good or poor shell weight and fed control diets (C) or diets supplemented with Eggshell 49 (ES 49).

Shell weight	Diet	Mean egg shell weight (g)				
		Initial	1	2	3	Total
Good	C	5.88[a]	5.96[a]	5.95[a]	5.47[a]	5.80[a]
	ES 49	5.88[a]	5.99[a]	5.98[a]	5.72[a]	5.90[a]
Poor	C	4.96[a]	5.24[a]	5.11[a]	4.87[b]	5.06[b]
	ES 49	5.09[a]	5.36[a]	5.21[a]	5.16[a]	5.23[a]
Total	C	5.40[a]	5.60[a]	5.53[a]	5.17[b]	5.43[b]
	ES 49	5.41[a]	5.68[a]	5.60[a]	5.44[a]	5.57[a]

Significant ($P < 0.05$) differences observed between diets in shell quality where letters differ.

deposited approximately 170 mg more shell on the egg when fed Eggshell 49 (5.23 versus 5.06 g, respectively; $P < 0.05$).

Overall, no significant differences were observed in percentage shell during the first two periods of 28 days of the study. However, during each week of the study, the percentage shell was higher for those hens fed Eggshell 49 within each shell quality group. Significant ($P < 0.05$) differences in percentage shell began to appear during the last 28-day period between the control and Eggshell 49-fed hens within each shell quality group. At the end of the study, hens within each shell quality group receiving Eggshell 49 had a higher percentage shell than the hens not fed Eggshell 49 (Table 39.3). This increase in percentage shell was significant ($P < 0.05$) in the hens laying low weight eggshells (8.28 versus 7.98%, respectively). Thus, Eggshell 49 benefited the hens in the low eggshell weight group more than the hens in the high eggshell weight group.

Egg production, monthly feed consumption and monthly feed conversion

Neither feed conversion, egg production nor monthly feed consumption were significantly affected; however, there was a numerical improvement in feed conversion throughout the entire experimental period favouring the birds that were fed Eggshell 49 within each eggshell quality group (Tables 39.4 and 39.5).

Conclusions

In this study, using hens that had been housed and managed under the best of conditions, Eggshell 49 resulted in a significant increase in the amount of shell deposited on the egg in the hens laying low shell weight eggs. This was also true for the percentage shell on the egg. This response was noted to occur mostly at the end of the study during the third 28-day period. It is unfortunate that this study could not be continued beyond this period when the beneficial response in eggshell quality due to Eggshell 49 was beginning to become increasingly significant. The results of this study indicate that Eggshell 49 has

Table 39.3. Monthly mean percentage egg shell weight for commerical laying hens producing good and poor shell weight and fed control diets (C) or diets supplemented with Eggshell 49 (ES 49).

Shell weight	Diet	Mean egg shell weight (%)				
		Initial	1	2	3	Total
Good	C	8.97[a]	8.93[a]	8.82[a]	8.21[b]	8.65[a]
	ES 49	8.82[a]	9.00[a]	8.90[a]	8.57[a]	8.81[a]
Poor	C	8.02[a]	8.24[a]	8.09[a]	7.65[b]	7.98[b]
	ES 49	8.14[a]	8.51[a]	8.24[a]	8.15[a]	8.28[a]
Total	C	8.47[a]	8.59[a]	8.46[a]	7.93[b]	8.31[b]
	ES 49	8.50[a]	8.76[a]	8.57[a]	8.36[a]	8.55[a]

Significant ($P < 0.05$) differences observed between diets in shell weight where letters differ.

Table 39.4. Monthly mean egg production for commercial laying hens producing good and poor shell weight and fed control (C) or diets supplemented with Eggshell 49 (ES 49).

Shell weight	Diet	Monthly egg production (%)		
		1	2	3
Good	C	79.8	77.4	75.6
	ES 49	82.3	83.3	78.7
Poor	C	80.8	81.8	80.6
	ES 49	82.7	83.2	80.4
Total	C	80.3	79.6	78.1
	ES 49	82.5	83.3	79.5

No significant ($P > 0.05$) differences observed between diets in shell quality.

Table 39.5. Monthly mean feed consumption and feed conversion for commercial laying hens producing good and poor shell weight and fed control (C) or diets supplemented with Eggshell 49 (ES 49).

Shell weight	Diet	Monthly mean feed consumption (kg)			Monthly mean feed conversion (kg feed dozen eggs^{-1})		
		1	2	3	1	2	3
Good	C	14.99	15.48	14.16	1.62	1.73	1.62
	ES 49	14.70	14.90	13.59	1.54	1.54	1.48
Poor	C	13.66	14.15	13.44	1.45	1.49	1.43
	ES 49	14.03	13.93	13.18	1.46	1.44	1.41
Total	C	14.33	14.81	13.80	1.53	1.61	1.53
	ES 49	14.37	14.42	13.38	1.50	1.49	1.44

No significant ($P > 0.05$) differences observed between diets in shell weight.

the ability to promote more deposition of shell on the egg, especially in the hens within a flock that are not laying eggs with the best shell quality. These are the hens within the flock that need the most help with respect to improving their eggshell quality.

Index